BRIEF TABLE OF INTEGRALS

D1284938

1. $\displaystyle\int u^n \, du = \frac{u^{n+1}}{n+1} + C, \, n \neq -1$

2. $\displaystyle\int \frac{1}{u} \, du = \ln|u| + C$

3. $\displaystyle\int e^u \, du = e^u + C$

4. $\displaystyle\int a^u \, du = \frac{1}{\ln a} a^u + C$

5. $\displaystyle\int \sin u \, du = -\cos u + C$

6. $\displaystyle\int \cos u \, du = \sin u + C$

7. $\displaystyle\int \sec^2 u \, du = \tan u + C$

8. $\displaystyle\int \csc^2 u \, du = -\cot u + C$

9. $\displaystyle\int \sec u \tan u \, du = \sec u + C$

10. $\displaystyle\int \csc u \cot u \, du = -\csc u + C$

11. $\displaystyle\int \tan u \, du = -\ln|\cos u| + C$

12. $\displaystyle\int \cot u \, du = \ln|\sin u| + C$

13. $\displaystyle\int \sec u \, du = \ln|\sec u + \tan u| + C$

14. $\displaystyle\int \csc u \, du = \ln|\csc u - \cot u| + C$

15. $\displaystyle\int u \sin u \, du = \sin u - u \cos u + C$

16. $\displaystyle\int u \cos u \, du = \cos u + u \sin u + C$

17. $\displaystyle\int \sin^2 u \, du = \tfrac{1}{2}u - \tfrac{1}{4}\sin 2u + C$

18. $\displaystyle\int \cos^2 u \, du = \tfrac{1}{2}u + \tfrac{1}{4}\sin 2u + C$

19. $\displaystyle\int \tan^2 u \, du = \tan u - u + C$

20. $\displaystyle\int \cot^2 u \, du = -\cot u - u + C$

21. $\displaystyle\int \sin^3 u \, du = -\tfrac{1}{3}\left(2 + \sin^2 u\right)\cos u + C$

22. $\displaystyle\int \cos^3 u \, du = \tfrac{1}{3}\left(2 + \cos^2 u\right)\sin u + C$

23. $\displaystyle\int \tan^3 u \, du = \tfrac{1}{2}\tan^2 u + \ln|\cos u| + C$

24. $\displaystyle\int \cot^3 u \, du = -\tfrac{1}{2}\cot^2 u - \ln|\sin u| + C$

25. $\displaystyle\int \sec^3 u \, du = \tfrac{1}{2}\sec u \tan u + \tfrac{1}{2}\ln|\sec u + \tan u| + C$

26. $\displaystyle\int \csc^3 u \, du = -\tfrac{1}{2}\csc u \cot u + \tfrac{1}{2}\ln|\csc u - \cot u| + C$

27. $\displaystyle\int \sin au \cos bu \, du = \frac{\sin(a-b)u}{2(a-b)} - \frac{\sin(a+b)u}{2(a+b)} + C$

28. $\displaystyle\int \cos au \cos bu \, du = \frac{\sin(a-b)u}{2(a-b)} + \frac{\sin(a+b)u}{2(a+b)} + C$

29. $\displaystyle\int e^{au} \sin bu \, du = \frac{e^{au}}{a^2 + b^2}\left(a \sin bu - b \cos bu\right) + C$

30. $\displaystyle\int e^{au} \cos bu \, du = \frac{e^{au}}{a^2 + b^2}\left(a \cos bu + b \sin bu\right) + C$

31. $\displaystyle\int \sinh u \, du = \cosh u + C$

32. $\displaystyle\int \cosh u \, du = \sinh u + C$

33. $\displaystyle\int \operatorname{sech}^2 u \, du = \tanh u + C$

34. $\displaystyle\int \operatorname{csch}^2 u \, du = -\coth u + C$

35. $\displaystyle\int \tanh u \, du = \ln(\cosh u) + C$

36. $\displaystyle\int \coth u \, du = \ln|\sinh u| + C$

37. $\displaystyle\int \ln u \, du = u \ln u - u + C$

38. $\displaystyle\int u \ln u \, du = \tfrac{1}{2}u^2 \ln u - \tfrac{1}{4}u^2 + C$

39. $\displaystyle\int \frac{1}{\sqrt{a^2 - u^2}} \, du = \sin^{-1}\frac{u}{a} + C$

40. $\displaystyle\int \frac{1}{\sqrt{a^2 + u^2}} \, du = \ln\left|u + \sqrt{a^2 + u^2}\right| + C$

41. $\displaystyle\int \sqrt{a^2 - u^2} \, du = \frac{u}{2}\sqrt{a^2 - u^2} + \frac{a^2}{2}\sin^{-1}\frac{u}{a} + C$

42. $\displaystyle\int \sqrt{a^2 + u^2} \, du = \frac{u}{2}\sqrt{a^2 + u^2} + \frac{a^2}{2}\ln\left|u + \sqrt{a^2 + u^2}\right| + C$

43. $\displaystyle\int \frac{1}{a^2 + u^2} \, du = \frac{1}{a}\tan^{-1}\frac{u}{a} + C$

44. $\displaystyle\int \frac{1}{a^2 - u^2} \, du = \frac{1}{2a}\ln\left|\frac{a+u}{a-u}\right| + C$

Note: Some techniques of integration, such as integration by parts and partial fractions, are reviewed in the *Student Resource and Solutions Manual* that accompanies this text.

DE TOOLS CORRELATION GUIDE

The DE Tools are a suite of simulations that provide an interactive, visual exploration of the concepts presented in this text. Visit academic.cengage.com/math/zill to find out more or contact your local sales representative to ask about options for bundling the DE Tools with this textbook.

TEXT TOOLS	PROJECT TOOLS
Chapter 1 **Interval of Definition** Illustrates the concept of the interval of definition of a solution of a differential equation. **Chapter 2** **Direction Field** Supports visual exploration of the relationship between direction fields and solutions of first-order ODEs of the form $dy/dx = f(x, y)$. **Phase Line** Lets you view the phase line, the solution graphs, and the graph of the differential equation for several first-order differential equations. **Euler Method** Supports visual and numerical comparison of the Euler Method and the Runge-Kutta Method of approximating solutions to the first order ODE, $dy/dx = f(x, y)$. **Chapter 3** **Growth and Decay** Visual exploration of exponential growth and decay for the first order ODE, $dx/dt = rx$, or its solution $x(t)$. **Mixture** By allowing you to vary input-output rates and input concentration, this tool lets you see how the amount of salt changes when two brine solutions are mixed together in a large tank. **_LR_ Circuit** Qualitative exploration of the behavior of a model of a series circuit containing an inductor and a resistor model as parameters are varied. **Predator-Prey** Illustrates solution curves for the Lotka-Volterra predator-prey model. **Chapter 5** **Spring/Mass** Supports graphical exploration of the effects of parameter changes on the motion of the spring/mass system: $mx'' + \beta x' + kx = F_0 \sin(\gamma t)$. **Chapter 7** **Linear Double Pendulum** Visual exploration of a double pendulum. **Chapter 8** **Linear Phase Portrait** Lets you generate phase portraits and solution curves for systems $\mathbf{X}' = \mathbf{AX}$ of two first-order DEs with constant coefficients. You see how the phase portrait depends on the eigenvalues of the coefficient matrix **A**. **Chapter 9** **Numerical Methods** Visual and numerical comparison of the Euler Method, the Improved Euler Method, and the Runge-Kutta Method of approximating solutions to systems of two differential equations.	**Chapter 1** **Project: Deception Pass** Supports visual exploration of the effect of the tide and channel width on the velocity of water moving through Deception Pass. **Chapter 2** **Project: Logistic Harvest** Exploration of logistic population growth with either constant or proportional harvesting. **Chapter 3** **Project: Swimming** Determine the relationship between the speed of a river and the speed of a person swimming across the river. **Chapter 4** **Project: Bungee Jumping** Explore the forces acting on a bungee jumper as you change the weight of the jumper and the elasticity of the bungee cord. **Chapter 5** **Project: Tacoma Bridge** Exploration of the rising and falling of the roadbed of a bridge. **Chapter 6** **Project: Tamarisk** Exploration of the series solution for the growth of tamarisk in a desert canyon. **Chapter 7** **Project: Newton's Law of Cooling** Use the mathematical model for Newton's law of cooling to determine the rate at which a body warms or cools to find the time the "Mayfair Diner Murder" took place and the time the body was moved from the kitchen to the refrigerator. **Chapter 8** **Project: Earthquake** Visual exploration of the displacements of the floors of a three-story building in an earthquake. **Chapter 9** **Project: Hammer** Exploration of a pendulum model using different numerical methods, time step sizes, and initial conditions. The projects referenced above can be found at academic.cengage.com/math/zill.

A First Course in Differential Equations

Special 9th edition with Complete Solutions

Dennis G. Zill

CENGAGE
Learning™

Australia • Brazil • Japan • Korea • Mexico • Singapore • Spain • United Kingdom • United States

CENGAGE
Learning™

A First Course in Differential Equations: Special 9th edition with Complete Solutions

Dennis G. Zill

Executive Editors:
 Maureen Staudt
 Michael Stranz

Senior Project Development Manager:
 Linda DeStefano

Marketing Specialist:
 Sara Mercurio
 Lindsay Shapiro

Senior Production / Manufacturing Manager:
 Donna M. Brown

PreMedia Supervisor:
 Joel Brennecke

Rights & Permissions Specialist:
 Kalina Hintz
 Todd Osborne

Cover Image:
 Getty Images*

* Unless otherwise noted, all cover images used by Custom Solutions, a part of Cengage Learning, have been supplied courtesy of Getty Images with the exception of the Earthview cover image, which has been supplied by the National Aeronautics and Space Administration (NASA).

© 2009 Cengage Learning

ALL RIGHTS RESERVED. No part of this work covered by the copyright herein may be reproduced, transmitted, stored or used in any form or by any means graphic, electronic, or mechanical, including but not limited to photocopying, recording, scanning, digitizing, taping, Web distribution, information networks, or information storage and retrieval systems, except as permitted under Section 107 or 108 of the 1976 United States Copyright Act, without the prior written permission of the publisher.

For product information and technology assistance, contact us at
Cengage Learning Customer & Sales Support, 1-800-354-9706

For permission to use material from this text or product,
submit all requests online at **cengage.com/permissions**
Further permissions questions can be emailed to
permissionrequest@cengage.com

ISBN-13: 978-1-4240-7052-7

ISBN-10: 1-4240-7052-X

Cengage Learning
5191 Natorp Boulevard
Mason, Ohio 45040
USA

Cengage Learning is a leading provider of customized learning solutions with office locations around the globe, including Singapore, the United Kingdom, Australia, Mexico, Brazil, and Japan. Locate your local office at:
international.cengage.com/region

Cengage Learning products are represented in Canada by Nelson Education, Ltd.

For your lifelong learning solutions, visit **www.cengage.com/custom**

Visit our corporate website at **www.cengage.com**

Printed in the United States of America

Table of Contents

1 INTRODUCTION TO DIFFERENTIAL EQUATIONS

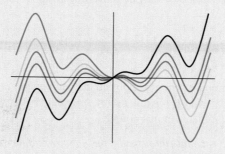

The words *differential* and *equations* certainly suggest solving some kind of equation that contains derivatives y', y'', ... Analogous to a course in algebra and trigonometry, in which a good amount of time is spent solving equations such as $x^2 + 5x + 4 = 0$ for the unknown number x, in this course *one* of our tasks will be to solve differential equations such as $y'' + 2y' + y = 0$ for an unknown function $y = \phi(x)$.

The preceding paragraph tells something, but not the complete story, about the course you are about to begin. As the course unfolds, you will see that there is more to the study of differential equations than just mastering methods that someone has devised to solve them.

But first things first. In order to read, study, and be conversant in a specialized subject, you have to learn the terminology of that discipline. This is the thrust of the first two sections of this chapter. In the last section we briefly examine the link between differential equations and the real world. Practical questions such as *How fast does a disease spread? How fast does a population change?* involve rates of change or derivatives. As so the mathematical description—or mathematical model—of experiments, observations, or theories may be a differential equation.

1.1   DEFINITIONS AND TERMINOLOGY

REVIEW MATERIAL

- Definition of the derivative
- Rules of differentiation
- Derivative as a rate of change
- First derivative and increasing/decreasing
- Second derivative and concavity

INTRODUCTION   The derivative dy/dx of a function $y = \phi(x)$ is itself another function $\phi'(x)$ found by an appropriate rule. The function $y = e^{0.1x^2}$ is differentiable on the interval $(-\infty, \infty)$, and by the Chain Rule its derivative is $dy/dx = 0.2xe^{0.1x^2}$. If we replace $e^{0.1x^2}$ on the right-hand side of the last equation by the symbol y, the derivative becomes

$$\frac{dy}{dx} = 0.2xy. \tag{1}$$

Now imagine that a friend of yours simply hands you equation (1)—you have no idea how it was constructed—and asks, *What is the function represented by the symbol y?* You are now face to face with one of the basic problems in this course:

How do you solve such an equation for the unknown function $y = \phi(x)$?

A DEFINITION   The equation that we made up in (1) is called a **differential equation.** Before proceeding any further, let us consider a more precise definition of this concept.

DEFINITION 1.1.1   Differential Equation

An equation containing the derivatives of one or more dependent variables, with respect to one or more independent variables, is said to be a **differential equation (DE).**

To talk about them, we shall classify differential equations by **type, order,** and **linearity.**

CLASSIFICATION BY TYPE   If an equation contains only ordinary derivatives of one or more dependent variables with respect to a single independent variable it is said to be an **ordinary differential equation (ODE).** For example,

A DE can contain more
than one dependent variable
↓   ↓

$$\frac{dy}{dx} + 5y = e^x, \qquad \frac{d^2y}{dx^2} - \frac{dy}{dx} + 6y = 0, \qquad \text{and} \qquad \frac{dx}{dt} + \frac{dy}{dt} = 2x + y \tag{2}$$

are ordinary differential equations. An equation involving partial derivatives of one or more dependent variables of two or more independent variables is called a

partial differential equation (PDE). For example,

$$\frac{\partial^2 u}{\partial x^2} + \frac{\partial^2 u}{\partial y^2} = 0, \qquad \frac{\partial^2 u}{\partial x^2} = \frac{\partial^2 u}{\partial t^2} - 2\frac{\partial u}{\partial t}, \qquad \text{and} \qquad \frac{\partial u}{\partial y} = -\frac{\partial v}{\partial x} \qquad (3)$$

are partial differential equations.[*]

Throughout this text ordinary derivatives will be written by using either the **Leibniz notation** dy/dx, d^2y/dx^2, d^3y/dx^3, ... or the **prime notation** y', y'', y''', ... By using the latter notation, the first two differential equations in (2) can be written a little more compactly as $y' + 5y = e^x$ and $y'' - y' + 6y = 0$. Actually, the prime notation is used to denote only the first three derivatives; the fourth derivative is written $y^{(4)}$ instead of y''''. In general, the nth derivative of y is written d^ny/dx^n or $y^{(n)}$. Although less convenient to write and to typeset, the Leibniz notation has an advantage over the prime notation in that it clearly displays both the dependent and independent variables. For example, in the equation

$$\frac{d^2x}{dt^2} + 16x = 0$$

unknown function or dependent variable

independent variable

it is immediately seen that the symbol x now represents a dependent variable, whereas the independent variable is t. You should also be aware that in physical sciences and engineering, Newton's **dot notation** (derogatively referred to by some as the "flyspeck" notation) is sometimes used to denote derivatives with respect to time t. Thus the differential equation $d^2s/dt^2 = -32$ becomes $\ddot{s} = -32$. Partial derivatives are often denoted by a **subscript notation** indicating the independent variables. For example, with the subscript notation the second equation in (3) becomes $u_{xx} = u_{tt} - 2u_t$.

CLASSIFICATION BY ORDER The **order of a differential equation** (either ODE or PDE) is the order of the highest derivative in the equation. For example,

second order   first order

$$\frac{d^2y}{dx^2} + 5\left(\frac{dy}{dx}\right)^3 - 4y = e^x$$

is a second-order ordinary differential equation. First-order ordinary differential equations are occasionally written in differential form $M(x, y)\,dx + N(x, y)\,dy = 0$. For example, if we assume that y denotes the dependent variable in $(y - x)\,dx + 4x\,dy = 0$, then $y' = dy/dx$, so by dividing by the differential dx, we get the alternative form $4xy' + y = x$. See the *Remarks* at the end of this section.

In symbols we can express an nth-order ordinary differential equation in one dependent variable by the general form

$$F(x, y, y', \ldots, y^{(n)}) = 0, \qquad (4)$$

where F is a real-valued function of $n + 2$ variables: $x, y, y', \ldots, y^{(n)}$. For both practical and theoretical reasons we shall also make the assumption hereafter that it is possible to solve an ordinary differential equation in the form (4) uniquely for the

---

[*]Except for this introductory section, only ordinary differential equations are considered in *A First Course in Differential Equations with Modeling Applications,* Ninth Edition. In that text the word *equation* and the abbreviation DE refer only to ODEs. Partial differential equations or PDEs are considered in the expanded volume *Differential Equations with Boundary-Value Problems,* Seventh Edition.

highest derivative $y^{(n)}$ in terms of the remaining $n + 1$ variables. The differential equation

$$\frac{d^n y}{dx^n} = f(x, y, y', \ldots, y^{(n-1)}),\tag{5}$$

where f is a real-valued continuous function, is referred to as the **normal form** of (4). Thus when it suits our purposes, we shall use the normal forms

$$\frac{dy}{dx} = f(x, y)\qquad\text{and}\qquad\frac{d^2 y}{dx^2} = f(x, y, y')$$

to represent general first- and second-order ordinary differential equations. For example, the normal form of the first-order equation $4xy' + y = x$ is $y' = (x - y)/4x$; the normal form of the second-order equation $y'' - y' + 6y = 0$ is $y'' = y' - 6y$. See the *Remarks*.

CLASSIFICATION BY LINEARITY An nth-order ordinary differential equation (4) is said to be **linear** if F is linear in $y, y', \ldots, y^{(n)}$. This means that an nth-order ODE is linear when (4) is $a_n(x)y^{(n)} + a_{n-1}(x)y^{(n-1)} + \cdots + a_1(x)y' + a_0(x)y - g(x) = 0$ or

$$a_n(x)\frac{d^n y}{dx^n} + a_{n-1}(x)\frac{d^{n-1} y}{dx^{n-1}} + \cdots + a_1(x)\frac{dy}{dx} + a_0(x)y = g(x).\tag{6}$$

Two important special cases of (6) are linear first-order ($n = 1$) and linear second-order ($n = 2$) DEs:

$$a_1(x)\frac{dy}{dx} + a_0(x)y = g(x)\qquad\text{and}\qquad a_2(x)\frac{d^2 y}{dx^2} + a_1(x)\frac{dy}{dx} + a_0(x)y = g(x).\tag{7}$$

In the additive combination on the left-hand side of equation (6) we see that the characteristic two properties of a linear ODE are as follows:

- The dependent variable y and all its derivatives $y', y'', \ldots, y^{(n)}$ are of the first degree, that is, the power of each term involving y is 1.
- The coefficients $a_0, a_1, \ldots, a_n$ of $y, y', \ldots, y^{(n)}$ depend at most on the independent variable x.

The equations

$$(y - x)dx + 4x\,dy = 0,\qquad y'' - 2y' + y = 0,\qquad\text{and}\qquad \frac{d^3 y}{dx^3} + x\frac{dy}{dx} - 5y = e^x$$

are, in turn, linear first-, second-, and third-order ordinary differential equations. We have just demonstrated that the first equation is linear in the variable y by writing it in the alternative form $4xy' + y = x$. A **nonlinear** ordinary differential equation is simply one that is not linear. Nonlinear functions of the dependent variable or its derivatives, such as $\sin y$ or $e^{y'}$, cannot appear in a linear equation. Therefore

$$\underset{\substack{\text{nonlinear term:}\\\text{coefficient depends on }y}}{(1 - y)y' + 2y = e^x,}\qquad \underset{\substack{\text{nonlinear term:}\\\text{nonlinear function of }y}}{\frac{d^2 y}{dx^2} + \sin y = 0,}\qquad\text{and}\qquad \underset{\substack{\text{nonlinear term:}\\\text{power not 1}}}{\frac{d^4 y}{dx^4} + y^2 = 0}$$

are examples of nonlinear first-, second-, and fourth-order ordinary differential equations, respectively.

SOLUTIONS As was stated before, one of the goals in this course is to solve, or find solutions of, differential equations. In the next definition we consider the concept of a solution of an ordinary differential equation.

> **DEFINITION 1.1.2**   **Solution of an ODE**
>
> Any function ϕ, defined on an interval I and possessing at least n derivatives that are continuous on I, which when substituted into an nth-order ordinary differential equation reduces the equation to an identity, is said to be a **solution** of the equation on the interval.

In other words, a solution of an nth-order ordinary differential equation (4) is a function ϕ that possesses at least n derivatives and for which

$$F(x, \phi(x), \phi'(x), \ldots, \phi^{(n)}(x)) = 0 \qquad \text{for all } x \text{ in } I.$$

We say that ϕ *satisfies* the differential equation on I. For our purposes we shall also assume that a solution ϕ is a real-valued function. In our introductory discussion we saw that $y = e^{0.1x^2}$ is a solution of $dy/dx = 0.2xy$ on the interval $(-\infty, \infty)$.

Occasionally, it will be convenient to denote a solution by the alternative symbol $y(x)$.

INTERVAL OF DEFINITION   You cannot think *solution* of an ordinary differential equation without simultaneously thinking *interval*. The interval I in Definition 1.1.2 is variously called the **interval of definition,** the **interval of existence,** the **interval of validity,** or the **domain of the solution** and can be an open interval (a, b), a closed interval $[a, b]$, an infinite interval (a, ∞), and so on.

EXAMPLE 1   Verification of a Solution

Verify that the indicated function is a solution of the given differential equation on the interval $(-\infty, \infty)$.

(a) $dy/dx = xy^{1/2}; \quad y = \frac{1}{16}x^4$ **(b)** $y'' - 2y' + y = 0; \quad y = xe^x$

SOLUTION   One way of verifying that the given function is a solution is to see, after substituting, whether each side of the equation is the same for every x in the interval.

(a) From

$$\text{left-hand side:} \qquad \frac{dy}{dx} = \frac{1}{16}(4 \cdot x^3) = \frac{1}{4}x^3,$$

$$\text{right-hand side:} \qquad xy^{1/2} = x \cdot \left(\frac{1}{16}x^4\right)^{1/2} = x \cdot \left(\frac{1}{4}x^2\right) = \frac{1}{4}x^3,$$

we see that each side of the equation is the same for every real number x. Note that $y^{1/2} = \frac{1}{4}x^2$ is, by definition, the nonnegative square root of $\frac{1}{16}x^4$.

(b) From the derivatives $y' = xe^x + e^x$ and $y'' = xe^x + 2e^x$ we have, for every real number x,

$$\text{left-hand side:} \qquad y'' - 2y' + y = (xe^x + 2e^x) - 2(xe^x + e^x) + xe^x = 0,$$

$$\text{right-hand side:} \qquad 0. \qquad\qquad\qquad ■$$

Note, too, that in Example 1 each differential equation possesses the constant solution $y = 0$, $-\infty < x < \infty$. A solution of a differential equation that is identically zero on an interval I is said to be a **trivial solution.**

SOLUTION CURVE   The graph of a solution ϕ of an ODE is called a **solution curve.** Since ϕ is a differentiable function, it is continuous on its interval I of definition. Thus there may be a difference between the graph of the *function* ϕ and the graph of the *solution* ϕ. Put another way, the domain of the function ϕ need not be the same as the interval I of definition (or domain) of the solution ϕ. Example 2 illustrates the difference.

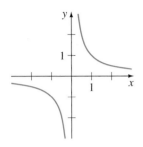

(a) function $y = 1/x$, $x \neq 0$

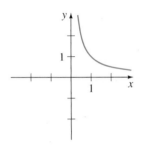

(b) solution $y = 1/x$, $(0, \infty)$

FIGURE 1.1.1 The function $y = 1/x$ is not the same as the solution $y = 1/x$

EXAMPLE 2 Function versus Solution

The domain of $y = 1/x$, considered simply as a *function*, is the set of all real numbers x except 0. When we graph $y = 1/x$, we plot points in the xy-plane corresponding to a judicious sampling of numbers taken from its domain. The rational function $y = 1/x$ is discontinuous at 0, and its graph, in a neighborhood of the origin, is given in Figure 1.1.1(a). The function $y = 1/x$ is not differentiable at $x = 0$, since the y-axis (whose equation is $x = 0$) is a vertical asymptote of the graph.

   Now $y = 1/x$ is also a solution of the linear first-order differential equation $xy' + y = 0$. (Verify.) But when we say that $y = 1/x$ is a *solution* of this DE, we mean that it is a function defined on an interval I on which it is differentiable and satisfies the equation. In other words, $y = 1/x$ is a solution of the DE on *any* interval that does not contain 0, such as $(-3, -1)$, $\left(\frac{1}{2}, 10\right)$, $(-\infty, 0)$, or $(0, \infty)$. Because the solution curves defined by $y = 1/x$ for $-3 < x < -1$ and $\frac{1}{2} < x < 10$ are simply segments, or pieces, of the solution curves defined by $y = 1/x$ for $-\infty < x < 0$ and $0 < x < \infty$, respectively, it makes sense to take the interval I to be as large as possible. Thus we take I to be either $(-\infty, 0)$ or $(0, \infty)$. The solution curve on $(0, \infty)$ is shown in Figure 1.1.1(b). ■

EXPLICIT AND IMPLICIT SOLUTIONS You should be familiar with the terms *explicit functions* and *implicit functions* from your study of calculus. A solution in which the dependent variable is expressed solely in terms of the independent variable and constants is said to be an **explicit solution.** For our purposes, let us think of an explicit solution as an explicit formula $y = \phi(x)$ that we can manipulate, evaluate, and differentiate using the standard rules. We have just seen in the last two examples that $y = \frac{1}{16}x^4$, $y = xe^x$, and $y = 1/x$ are, in turn, explicit solutions of $dy/dx = xy^{1/2}$, $y'' - 2y' + y = 0$, and $xy' + y = 0$. Moreover, the trivial solution $y = 0$ is an explicit solution of all three equations. When we get down to the business of actually solving some ordinary differential equations, you will see that methods of solution do not always lead directly to an explicit solution $y = \phi(x)$. This is particularly true when we attempt to solve nonlinear first-order differential equations. Often we have to be content with a relation or expression $G(x, y) = 0$ that defines a solution ϕ implicitly.

DEFINITION 1.1.3 Implicit Solution of an ODE

A relation $G(x, y) = 0$ is said to be an **implicit solution** of an ordinary differential equation (4) on an interval I, provided that there exists at least one function ϕ that satisfies the relation as well as the differential equation on I.

   It is beyond the scope of this course to investigate the conditions under which a relation $G(x, y) = 0$ defines a differentiable function ϕ. So we shall assume that if the formal implementation of a method of solution leads to a relation $G(x, y) = 0$, then there exists at least one function ϕ that satisfies both the relation (that is, $G(x, \phi(x)) = 0$) and the differential equation on an interval I. If the implicit solution $G(x, y) = 0$ is fairly simple, we may be able to solve for y in terms of x and obtain one or more explicit solutions. See the *Remarks*.

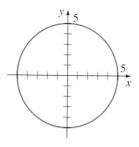

(a) implicit solution

$$x^2 + y^2 = 25$$

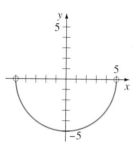

(b) explicit solution

$$y_1 = \sqrt{25 - x^2}, \ -5 < x < 5$$

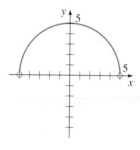

(c) explicit solution

$$y_2 = -\sqrt{25 - x^2}, \ -5 < x < 5$$

FIGURE 1.1.2 An implicit solution and two explicit solutions of $y' = -x/y$

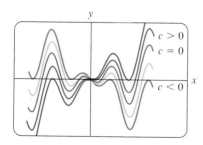

FIGURE 1.1.3 Some solutions of $xy' - y = x^2 \sin x$

EXAMPLE 3   Verification of an Implicit Solution

The relation $x^2 + y^2 = 25$ is an implicit solution of the differential equation

$$\frac{dy}{dx} = -\frac{x}{y} \tag{8}$$

on the open interval $(-5, 5)$. By implicit differentiation we obtain

$$\frac{d}{dx}x^2 + \frac{d}{dx}y^2 = \frac{d}{dx}25 \quad \text{or} \quad 2x + 2y\frac{dy}{dx} = 0.$$

Solving the last equation for the symbol dy/dx gives (8). Moreover, solving $x^2 + y^2 = 25$ for y in terms of x yields $y = \pm\sqrt{25 - x^2}$. The two functions $y = \phi_1(x) = \sqrt{25 - x^2}$ and $y = \phi_2(x) = -\sqrt{25 - x^2}$ satisfy the relation (that is, $x^2 + \phi_1^2 = 25$ and $x^2 + \phi_2^2 = 25$) and are explicit solutions defined on the interval $(-5, 5)$. The solution curves given in Figures 1.1.2(b) and 1.1.2(c) are segments of the graph of the implicit solution in Figure 1.1.2(a). ∎

Any relation of the form $x^2 + y^2 - c = 0$ *formally* satisfies (8) for any constant c. However, it is understood that the relation should always make sense in the real number system; thus, for example, if $c = -25$, we cannot say that $x^2 + y^2 + 25 = 0$ is an implicit solution of the equation. (Why not?)

Because the distinction between an explicit solution and an implicit solution should be intuitively clear, we will not belabor the issue by always saying, "Here is an explicit (implicit) solution."

FAMILIES OF SOLUTIONS   The study of differential equations is similar to that of integral calculus. In some texts a solution ϕ is sometimes referred to as an **integral** of the equation, and its graph is called an **integral curve.** When evaluating an antiderivative or indefinite integral in calculus, we use a single constant c of integration. Analogously, when solving a first-order differential equation $F(x, y, y') = 0$, we *usually* obtain a solution containing a single arbitrary constant or parameter c. A solution containing an arbitrary constant represents a set $G(x, y, c) = 0$ of solutions called a **one-parameter family of solutions.** When solving an nth-order differential equation $F(x, y, y', \ldots, y^{(n)}) = 0$, we seek an **$n$-parameter family of solutions** $G(x, y, c_1, c_2, \ldots, c_n) = 0$. This means that *a single differential equation can possess an infinite number of solutions* corresponding to the unlimited number of choices for the parameter(s). A solution of a differential equation that is free of arbitrary parameters is called a **particular solution.** For example, the one-parameter family $y = cx - x \cos x$ is an explicit solution of the linear first-order equation $xy' - y = x^2 \sin x$ on the interval $(-\infty, \infty)$. (Verify.) Figure 1.1.3, obtained by using graphing software, shows the graphs of some of the solutions in this family. The solution $y = -x \cos x$, the blue curve in the figure, is a particular solution corresponding to $c = 0$. Similarly, on the interval $(-\infty, \infty)$, $y = c_1e^x + c_2xe^x$ is a two-parameter family of solutions of the linear second-order equation $y'' - 2y' + y = 0$ in Example 1. (Verify.) Some particular solutions of the equation are the trivial solution $y = 0$ ($c_1 = c_2 = 0$), $y = xe^x$ ($c_1 = 0$, $c_2 = 1$), $y = 5e^x - 2xe^x$ ($c_1 = 5$, $c_2 = -2$), and so on.

Sometimes a differential equation possesses a solution that is not a member of a family of solutions of the equation—that is, a solution that cannot be obtained by specializing *any* of the parameters in the family of solutions. Such an extra solution is called a **singular solution.** For example, we have seen that $y = \frac{1}{16}x^4$ and $y = 0$ are solutions of the differential equation $dy/dx = xy^{1/2}$ on $(-\infty, \infty)$. In Section 2.2 we shall demonstrate, by actually solving it, that the differential equation $dy/dx = xy^{1/2}$ possesses the one-parameter family of solutions $y = \left(\frac{1}{4}x^2 + c\right)^2$. When $c = 0$, the resulting particular solution is $y = \frac{1}{16}x^4$. But notice that the trivial solution $y = 0$ is a singular solution, since it is not a member of the family $y = \left(\frac{1}{4}x^2 + c\right)^2$; there is no way of assigning a value to the constant c to obtain $y = 0$.

In all the preceding examples we used x and y to denote the independent and dependent variables, respectively. But you should become accustomed to seeing and working with other symbols to denote these variables. For example, we could denote the independent variable by t and the dependent variable by x.

EXAMPLE 4 Using Different Symbols

The functions $x = c_1 \cos 4t$ and $x = c_2 \sin 4t$, where c_1 and c_2 are arbitrary constants or parameters, are both solutions of the linear differential equation

$$x'' + 16x = 0.$$

For $x = c_1 \cos 4t$ the first two derivatives with respect to t are $x' = -4c_1 \sin 4t$ and $x'' = -16c_1 \cos 4t$. Substituting x'' and x then gives

$$x'' + 16x = -16c_1 \cos 4t + 16(c_1 \cos 4t) = 0.$$

In like manner, for $x = c_2 \sin 4t$ we have $x'' = -16c_2 \sin 4t$, and so

$$x'' + 16x = -16c_2 \sin 4t + 16(c_2 \sin 4t) = 0.$$

Finally, it is straightforward to verify that the linear combination of solutions, or the two-parameter family $x = c_1 \cos 4t + c_2 \sin 4t$, is also a solution of the differential equation. ■

The next example shows that a solution of a differential equation can be a piecewise-defined function.

EXAMPLE 5 A Piecewise-Defined Solution

You should verify that the one-parameter family $y = cx^4$ is a one-parameter family of solutions of the differential equation $xy' - 4y = 0$ on the inverval $(-\infty, \infty)$. See Figure 1.1.4(a). The piecewise-defined differentiable function

$$y = \begin{cases} -x^4, & x < 0 \\ x^4, & x \geq 0 \end{cases}$$

is a particular solution of the equation but cannot be obtained from the family $y = cx^4$ by a single choice of c; the solution is constructed from the family by choosing $c = -1$ for $x < 0$ and $c = 1$ for $x \geq 0$. See Figure 1.1.4(b). ■

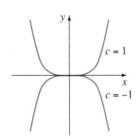

(a) two explicit solutions

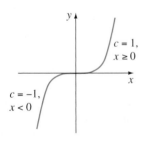

(b) piecewise-defined solution

FIGURE 1.1.4 Some solutions of $xy' - 4y = 0$

SYSTEMS OF DIFFERENTIAL EQUATIONS Up to this point we have been discussing single differential equations containing one unknown function. But often in theory, as well as in many applications, we must deal with systems of differential equations. A **system of ordinary differential equations** is two or more equations involving the derivatives of two or more unknown functions of a single independent variable. For example, if x and y denote dependent variables and t denotes the independent variable, then a system of two first-order differential equations is given by

$$\frac{dx}{dt} = f(t, x, y)$$

$$\frac{dy}{dt} = g(t, x, y). \tag{9}$$

A **solution** of a system such as (9) is a pair of differentiable functions $x = \phi_1(t)$, $y = \phi_2(t)$, defined on a common interval I, that satisfy each equation of the system on this interval.

REMARKS

(*i*) A few last words about implicit solutions of differential equations are in order. In Example 3 we were able to solve the relation $x^2 + y^2 = 25$ for y in terms of x to get two explicit solutions, $\phi_1(x) = \sqrt{25 - x^2}$ and $\phi_2(x) = -\sqrt{25 - x^2}$, of the differential equation (8). But don't read too much into this one example. Unless it is easy or important or you are instructed to, there is usually no need to try to solve an implicit solution $G(x, y) = 0$ for y explicitly in terms of x. Also do not misinterpret the second sentence following Definition 1.1.3. An implicit solution $G(x, y) = 0$ can define a perfectly good differentiable function ϕ that is a solution of a DE, yet we might not be able to solve $G(x, y) = 0$ using analytical methods such as algebra. The solution curve of ϕ may be a segment or piece of the graph of $G(x, y) = 0$. See Problems 45 and 46 in Exercises 1.1. Also, read the discussion following Example 4 in Section 2.2.

(*ii*) Although the concept of a solution has been emphasized in this section, you should also be aware that a DE does not necessarily have to possess a solution. See Problem 39 in Exercises 1.1. The question of whether a solution exists will be touched on in the next section.

(*iii*) It might not be apparent whether a first-order ODE written in differential form $M(x, y)dx + N(x, y)dy = 0$ is linear or nonlinear because there is nothing in this form that tells us which symbol denotes the dependent variable. See Problems 9 and 10 in Exercises 1.1.

(*iv*) It might not seem like a big deal to assume that $F(x, y, y', \ldots, y^{(n)}) = 0$ can be solved for $y^{(n)}$, but one should be a little bit careful here. There are exceptions, and there certainly are some problems connected with this assumption. See Problems 52 and 53 in Exercises 1.1.

(*v*) You may run across the term *closed form solutions* in DE texts or in lectures in courses in differential equations. Translated, this phrase usually refers to explicit solutions that are expressible in terms of *elementary* (or familiar) *functions:* finite combinations of integer powers of x, roots, exponential and logarithmic functions, and trigonometric and inverse trigonometric functions.

(*vi*) If *every* solution of an nth-order ODE $F(x, y, y', \ldots, y^{(n)}) = 0$ on an interval I can be obtained from an n-parameter family $G(x, y, c_1, c_2, \ldots, c_n) = 0$ by appropriate choices of the parameters c_i, $i = 1, 2, \ldots, n$, we then say that the family is the **general solution** of the DE. In solving linear ODEs, we shall impose relatively simple restrictions on the coefficients of the equation; with these restrictions one can be assured that not only does a solution exist on an interval but also that a family of solutions yields all possible solutions. Nonlinear ODEs, with the exception of some first-order equations, are usually difficult or impossible to solve in terms of elementary functions. Furthermore, if we happen to obtain a family of solutions for a nonlinear equation, it is not obvious whether this family contains all solutions. On a practical level, then, the designation "general solution" is applied only to linear ODEs. Don't be concerned about this concept at this point, but store the words "general solution" in the back of your mind—we will come back to this notion in Section 2.3 and again in Chapter 4.

EXERCISES 1.1

Answers to selected odd-numbered problems begin on page ANS-1.

In Problems 1–8 state the order of the given ordinary differential equation. Determine whether the equation is linear or nonlinear by matching it with (6).

1. $(1 - x)y'' - 4xy' + 5y = \cos x$

2. $x\dfrac{d^3y}{dx^3} - \left(\dfrac{dy}{dx}\right)^4 + y = 0$

3. $t^5 y^{(4)} - t^3 y'' + 6y = 0$

4. $\dfrac{d^2u}{dr^2} + \dfrac{du}{dr} + u = \cos(r + u)$

5. $\dfrac{d^2y}{dx^2} = \sqrt{1 + \left(\dfrac{dy}{dx}\right)^2}$

6. $\dfrac{d^2R}{dt^2} = -\dfrac{k}{R^2}$

7. $(\sin \theta)y''' - (\cos \theta)y' = 2$

8. $\ddot{x} - \left(1 - \dfrac{\dot{x}^2}{3}\right)\dot{x} + x = 0$

In Problems 9 and 10 determine whether the given first-order differential equation is linear in the indicated dependent variable by matching it with the first differential equation given in (7).

9. $(y^2 - 1)\, dx + x\, dy = 0$; in y; in x

10. $u\, dv + (v + uv - ue^u)\, du = 0$; in v; in u

In Problems 11–14 verify that the indicated function is an explicit solution of the given differential equation. Assume an appropriate interval I of definition for each solution.

11. $2y' + y = 0$; $y = e^{-x/2}$

12. $\dfrac{dy}{dt} + 20y = 24$; $y = \dfrac{6}{5} - \dfrac{6}{5}e^{-20t}$

13. $y'' - 6y' + 13y = 0$; $y = e^{3x}\cos 2x$

14. $y'' + y = \tan x$; $y = -(\cos x)\ln(\sec x + \tan x)$

In Problems 15–18 verify that the indicated function $y = \phi(x)$ is an explicit solution of the given first-order differential equation. Proceed as in Example 2, by considering ϕ simply as a *function*, give its domain. Then by considering ϕ as a *solution* of the differential equation, give at least one interval I of definition.

15. $(y - x)y' = y - x + 8$; $y = x + 4\sqrt{x + 2}$

16. $y' = 25 + y^2$; $y = 5\tan 5x$

17. $y' = 2xy^2$; $y = 1/(4 - x^2)$

18. $2y' = y^3\cos x$; $y = (1 - \sin x)^{-1/2}$

In Problems 19 and 20 verify that the indicated expression is an implicit solution of the given first-order differential equation. Find at least one explicit solution $y = \phi(x)$ in each case. Use a graphing utility to obtain the graph of an explicit solution. Give an interval I of definition of each solution ϕ.

19. $\dfrac{dX}{dt} = (X - 1)(1 - 2X)$; $\ln\left(\dfrac{2X - 1}{X - 1}\right) = t$

20. $2xy\, dx + (x^2 - y)\, dy = 0$; $-2x^2y + y^2 = 1$

In Problems 21–24 verify that the indicated family of functions is a solution of the given differential equation. Assume an appropriate interval I of definition for each solution.

21. $\dfrac{dP}{dt} = P(1 - P)$; $P = \dfrac{c_1 e^t}{1 + c_1 e^t}$

22. $\dfrac{dy}{dx} + 2xy = 1$; $y = e^{-x^2}\displaystyle\int_0^x e^{t^2}\, dt + c_1 e^{-x^2}$

23. $\dfrac{d^2y}{dx^2} - 4\dfrac{dy}{dx} + 4y = 0$; $y = c_1 e^{2x} + c_2 xe^{2x}$

24. $x^3\dfrac{d^3y}{dx^3} + 2x^2\dfrac{d^2y}{dx^2} - x\dfrac{dy}{dx} + y = 12x^2$;

$y = c_1 x^{-1} + c_2 x + c_3 x \ln x + 4x^2$

25. Verify that the piecewise-defined function

$$y = \begin{cases} -x^2, & x < 0 \\ x^2, & x \geq 0 \end{cases}$$

is a solution of the differential equation $xy' - 2y = 0$ on $(-\infty, \infty)$.

26. In Example 3 we saw that $y = \phi_1(x) = \sqrt{25 - x^2}$ and $y = \phi_2(x) = -\sqrt{25 - x^2}$ are solutions of $dy/dx = -x/y$ on the interval $(-5, 5)$. Explain why the piecewise-defined function

$$y = \begin{cases} \sqrt{25 - x^2}, & -5 < x < 0 \\ -\sqrt{25 - x^2}, & 0 \leq x < 5 \end{cases}$$

is *not* a solution of the differential equation on the interval $(-5, 5)$.

In Problems 27–30 find values of m so that the function $y = e^{mx}$ is a solution of the given differential equation.

27. $y' + 2y = 0$

28. $5y' = 2y$

29. $y'' - 5y' + 6y = 0$

30. $2y'' + 7y' - 4y = 0$

In Problems 31 and 32 find values of m so that the function $y = x^m$ is a solution of the given differential equation.

31. $xy'' + 2y' = 0$

32. $x^2y'' - 7xy' + 15y = 0$

In Problems 33–36 use the concept that $y = c$, $-\infty < x < \infty$, is a constant function if and only if $y' = 0$ to determine whether the given differential equation possesses constant solutions.

33. $3xy' + 5y = 10$

34. $y' = y^2 + 2y - 3$

35. $(y - 1)y' = 1$

36. $y'' + 4y' + 6y = 10$

In Problems 37 and 38 verify that the indicated pair of functions is a solution of the given system of differential equations on the interval $(-\infty, \infty)$.

37. $\dfrac{dx}{dt} = x + 3y$

$\dfrac{dy}{dt} = 5x + 3y;$

$x = e^{-2t} + 3e^{6t},$

$y = -e^{-2t} + 5e^{6t}$

38. $\dfrac{d^2x}{dt^2} = 4y + e^t$

$\dfrac{d^2y}{dt^2} = 4x - e^t;$

$x = \cos 2t + \sin 2t + \tfrac{1}{5} e^t,$

$y = -\cos 2t - \sin 2t - \tfrac{1}{5} e^t$

Discussion Problems

39. Make up a differential equation that does not possess any real solutions.

40. Make up a differential equation that you feel confident possesses only the trivial solution $y = 0$. Explain your reasoning.

41. What function do you know from calculus is such that its first derivative is itself? Its first derivative is a constant multiple k of itself? Write each answer in the form of a first-order differential equation with a solution.

42. What function (or functions) do you know from calculus is such that its second derivative is itself? Its second derivative is the negative of itself? Write each answer in the form of a second-order differential equation with a solution.

43. Given that $y = \sin x$ is an explicit solution of the first-order differential equation $\dfrac{dy}{dx} = \sqrt{1 - y^2}$. Find an interval I of definition. [*Hint: I* is *not* the interval $(-\infty, \infty)$.]

44. Discuss why it makes intuitive sense to presume that the linear differential equation $y'' + 2y' + 4y = 5 \sin t$ has a solution of the form $y = A \sin t + B \cos t$, where A and B are constants. Then find specific constants A and B so that $y = A \sin t + B \cos t$ is a particular solution of the DE.

In Problems 45 and 46 the given figure represents the graph of an implicit solution $G(x, y) = 0$ of a differential equation $dy/dx = f(x, y)$. In each case the relation $G(x, y) = 0$ implicitly defines several solutions of the DE. Carefully reproduce each figure on a piece of paper. Use different colored pencils to mark off segments, or pieces, on each graph that correspond to graphs of solutions. Keep in mind that a solution ϕ must be a function and differentiable. Use the solution curve to estimate an interval I of definition of each solution ϕ.

45.

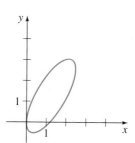

FIGURE 1.1.5 Graph for Problem 45

46.

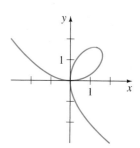

FIGURE 1.1.6 Graph for Problem 46

47. The graphs of members of the one-parameter family $x^3 + y^3 = 3cxy$ are called **folia of Descartes.** Verify that this family is an implicit solution of the first-order differential equation

$$\frac{dy}{dx} = \frac{y(y^3 - 2x^3)}{x(2y^3 - x^3)}.$$

48. The graph in Figure 1.1.6 is the member of the family of folia in Problem 47 corresponding to $c = 1$. Discuss: How can the DE in Problem 47 help in finding points on the graph of $x^3 + y^3 = 3xy$ where the tangent line is vertical? How does knowing where a tangent line is vertical help in determining an interval I of definition of a solution ϕ of the DE? Carry out your ideas, and compare with your estimates of the intervals in Problem 46.

49. In Example 3 the largest interval I over which the explicit solutions $y = \phi_1(x)$ and $y = \phi_2(x)$ are defined is the open interval $(-5, 5)$. Why can't the interval I of definition be the closed interval $[-5, 5]$?

50. In Problem 21 a one-parameter family of solutions of the DE $P' = P(1 - P)$ is given. Does any solution curve pass through the point $(0, 3)$? Through the point $(0, 1)$?

51. Discuss, and illustrate with examples, how to solve differential equations of the forms $dy/dx = f(x)$ and $d^2y/dx^2 = f(x)$.

52. The differential equation $x(y')^2 - 4y' - 12x^3 = 0$ has the form given in (4). Determine whether the equation can be put into the normal form $dy/dx = f(x, y)$.

53. The normal form (5) of an nth-order differential equation is equivalent to (4) whenever both forms have exactly the same solutions. Make up a first-order differential equation for which $F(x, y, y') = 0$ is not equivalent to the normal form $dy/dx = f(x, y)$.

54. Find a linear second-order differential equation $F(x, y, y', y'') = 0$ for which $y = c_1x + c_2x^2$ is a two-parameter family of solutions. Make sure that your equation is free of the arbitrary parameters c_1 and c_2.

Qualitative information about a solution $y = \phi(x)$ of a differential equation can often be obtained from the equation itself. Before working Problems 55–58, recall the geometric significance of the derivatives dy/dx and d^2y/dx^2.

55. Consider the differential equation $dy/dx = e^{-x^2}$.

(a) Explain why a solution of the DE must be an increasing function on any interval of the x-axis.

(b) What are $\lim\limits_{x \to -\infty} dy/dx$ and $\lim\limits_{x \to \infty} dy/dx$? What does this suggest about a solution curve as $x \to \pm\infty$?

(c) Determine an interval over which a solution curve is concave down and an interval over which the curve is concave up.

(d) Sketch the graph of a solution $y = \phi(x)$ of the differential equation whose shape is suggested by parts (a)–(c).

56. Consider the differential equation $dy/dx = 5 - y$.

(a) Either by inspection or by the method suggested in Problems 33–36, find a constant solution of the DE.

(b) Using only the differential equation, find intervals on the y-axis on which a nonconstant solution $y = \phi(x)$ is increasing. Find intervals on the y-axis on which $y = \phi(x)$ is decreasing.

57. Consider the differential equation $dy/dx = y(a - by)$, where a and b are positive constants.

(a) Either by inspection or by the method suggested in Problems 33–36, find two constant solutions of the DE.

(b) Using only the differential equation, find intervals on the y-axis on which a nonconstant solution $y = \phi(x)$ is increasing. Find intervals on which $y = \phi(x)$ is decreasing.

(c) Using only the differential equation, explain why $y = a/2b$ is the y-coordinate of a point of inflection of the graph of a nonconstant solution $y = \phi(x)$.

(d) On the same coordinate axes, sketch the graphs of the two constant solutions found in part (a). These constant solutions partition the xy-plane into three regions. In each region, sketch the graph of a nonconstant solution $y = \phi(x)$ whose shape is suggested by the results in parts (b) and (c).

58. Consider the differential equation $y' = y^2 + 4$.

(a) Explain why there exist no constant solutions of the DE.

(b) Describe the graph of a solution $y = \phi(x)$. For example, can a solution curve have any relative extrema?

(c) Explain why $y = 0$ is the y-coordinate of a point of inflection of a solution curve.

(d) Sketch the graph of a solution $y = \phi(x)$ of the differential equation whose shape is suggested by parts (a)–(c).

Computer Lab Assignments

In Problems 59 and 60 use a CAS to compute all derivatives and to carry out the simplifications needed to verify that the indicated function is a particular solution of the given differential equation.

59. $y^{(4)} - 20y''' + 158y'' - 580y' + 841y = 0$; $y = xe^{5x}\cos 2x$

60. $x^3y''' + 2x^2y'' + 20xy' - 78y = 0$; $y = 20\dfrac{\cos(5\ln x)}{x} - 3\dfrac{\sin(5\ln x)}{x}$

1.2	INITIAL-VALUE PROBLEMS

REVIEW MATERIAL

- Normal form of a DE
- Solution of a DE
- Family of solutions

INTRODUCTION We are often interested in problems in which we seek a solution $y(x)$ of a differential equation so that $y(x)$ satisfies prescribed side conditions—that is, conditions imposed on the unknown $y(x)$ or its derivatives. On some interval I containing x_0 the problem

$$\text{Solve:} \qquad \frac{d^n y}{dx^n} = f\left(x, y, y', \ldots, y^{(n-1)}\right)$$

$$\text{Subject to:} \qquad y(x_0) = y_0, y'(x_0) = y_1, \ldots, y^{(n-1)}(x_0) = y_{n-1},$$

(1)

where $y_0, y_1, \ldots, y_{n-1}$ are arbitrarily specified real constants, is called an **initial-value problem (IVP).** The values of $y(x)$ and its first $n-1$ derivatives at a single point x_0, $y(x_0) = y_0$, $y'(x_0) = y_1, \ldots, y^{(n-1)}(x_0) = y_{n-1}$, are called **initial conditions.**

FIRST- AND SECOND-ORDER IVPS The problem given in (1) is also called an *n*th-order initial-value problem. For example,

$$\text{Solve:} \qquad \frac{dy}{dx} = f(x, y)$$

$$\text{Subject to:} \qquad y(x_0) = y_0$$

(2)

and

$$\text{Solve:} \qquad \frac{d^2 y}{dx^2} = f(x, y, y')$$

$$\text{Subject to:} \qquad y(x_0) = y_0, y'(x_0) = y_1$$

(3)

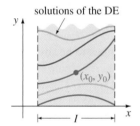

FIGURE 1.2.1 Solution of first-order IVP

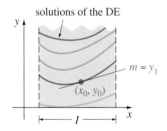

FIGURE 1.2.2 Solution of second-order IVP

are **first-** and **second-order** initial-value problems, respectively. These two problems are easy to interpret in geometric terms. For (2) we are seeking a solution $y(x)$ of the differential equation $y' = f(x, y)$ on an interval I containing x_0 so that its graph passes through the specified point (x_0, y_0). A solution curve is shown in blue in Figure 1.2.1. For (3) we want to find a solution $y(x)$ of the differential equation $y'' = f(x, y, y')$ on an interval I containing x_0 so that its graph not only passes through (x_0, y_0) but the slope of the curve at this point is the number y_1. A solution curve is shown in blue in Figure 1.2.2. The words *initial conditions* derive from physical systems where the independent variable is time t and where $y(t_0) = y_0$ and $y'(t_0) = y_1$ represent the position and velocity, respectively, of an object at some beginning, or initial, time t_0.

Solving an *n*th-order initial-value problem such as (1) frequently entails first finding an *n*-parameter family of solutions of the given differential equation and then using the n initial conditions at x_0 to determine numerical values of the n constants in the family. The resulting particular solution is defined on some interval I containing the initial point x_0.

EXAMPLE 1 Two First-Order IVPs

In Problem 41 in Exercises 1.1 you were asked to deduce that $y = ce^x$ is a one-parameter family of solutions of the simple first-order equation $y' = y$. All the solutions in this family are defined on the interval $(-\infty, \infty)$. If we impose an initial condition, say, $y(0) = 3$, then substituting $x = 0$, $y = 3$ in the family determines the

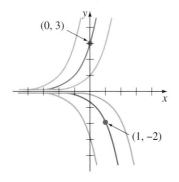

FIGURE 1.2.3 Solutions of two IVPs

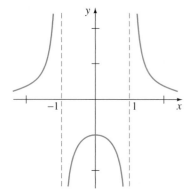

(a) function defined for all x except $x = \pm 1$

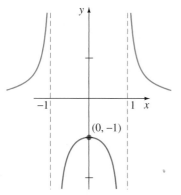

(b) solution defined on interval containing $x = 0$

FIGURE 1.2.4 Graphs of function and solution of IVP in Example 2

constant $3 = ce^0 = c$. Thus $y = 3e^x$ is a solution of the IVP

$$y' = y, \quad y(0) = 3.$$

Now if we demand that a solution curve pass through the point $(1, -2)$ rather than $(0, 3)$, then $y(1) = -2$ will yield $-2 = ce$ or $c = -2e^{-1}$. In this case $y = -2e^{x-1}$ is a solution of the IVP

$$y' = y, \quad y(1) = -2.$$

The two solution curves are shown in dark blue and dark red in Figure 1.2.3. ∎

The next example illustrates another first-order initial-value problem. In this example notice how the interval I of definition of the solution $y(x)$ depends on the initial condition $y(x_0) = y_0$.

EXAMPLE 2 Interval *I* of Definition of a Solution

In Problem 6 of Exercises 2.2 you will be asked to show that a one-parameter family of solutions of the first-order differential equation $y' + 2xy^2 = 0$ is $y = 1/(x^2 + c)$. If we impose the initial condition $y(0) = -1$, then substituting $x = 0$ and $y = -1$ into the family of solutions gives $-1 = 1/c$ or $c = -1$. Thus $y = 1/(x^2 - 1)$. We now emphasize the following three distinctions:

- Considered as a *function*, the domain of $y = 1/(x^2 - 1)$ is the set of real numbers x for which $y(x)$ is defined; this is the set of all real numbers except $x = -1$ and $x = 1$. See Figure 1.2.4(a).
- Considered as a *solution of the differential equation* $y' + 2xy^2 = 0$, the interval I of definition of $y = 1/(x^2 - 1)$ could be taken to be any interval over which $y(x)$ is defined and differentiable. As can be seen in Figure 1.2.4(a), the largest intervals on which $y = 1/(x^2 - 1)$ is a solution are $(-\infty, -1)$, $(-1, 1)$, and $(1, \infty)$.
- Considered as a *solution of the initial-value problem* $y' + 2xy^2 = 0$, $y(0) = -1$, the interval I of definition of $y = 1/(x^2 - 1)$ could be taken to be any interval over which $y(x)$ is defined, differentiable, *and* contains the initial point $x = 0$; the largest interval for which this is true is $(-1, 1)$. See the red curve in Figure 1.2.4(b). ∎

See Problems 3–6 in Exercises 1.2 for a continuation of Example 2.

EXAMPLE 3 Second-Order IVP

In Example 4 of Section 1.1 we saw that $x = c_1 \cos 4t + c_2 \sin 4t$ is a two-parameter family of solutions of $x'' + 16x = 0$. Find a solution of the initial-value problem

$$x'' + 16x = 0, \quad x\left(\frac{\pi}{2}\right) = -2, \quad x'\left(\frac{\pi}{2}\right) = 1. \tag{4}$$

SOLUTION We first apply $x(\pi/2) = -2$ to the given family of solutions: $c_1 \cos 2\pi + c_2 \sin 2\pi = -2$. Since $\cos 2\pi = 1$ and $\sin 2\pi = 0$, we find that $c_1 = -2$. We next apply $x'(\pi/2) = 1$ to the one-parameter family $x(t) = -2 \cos 4t + c_2 \sin 4t$. Differentiating and then setting $t = \pi/2$ and $x' = 1$ gives $8 \sin 2\pi + 4c_2 \cos 2\pi = 1$, from which we see that $c_2 = \frac{1}{4}$. Hence $x = -2 \cos 4t + \frac{1}{4} \sin 4t$ is a solution of (4). ∎

EXISTENCE AND UNIQUENESS Two fundamental questions arise in considering an initial-value problem:

Does a solution of the problem exist?
If a solution exists, is it unique?

For the first-order initial-value problem (2) we ask:

Existence $\begin{cases} \textit{Does the differential equation } dy/dx = f(x, y) \textit{ possess solutions?} \\ \textit{Do any of the solution curves pass through the point } (x_0, y_0)? \end{cases}$

Uniqueness $\begin{cases} \textit{When can we be certain that there is precisely one solution curve} \\ \textit{passing through the point } (x_0, y_0)? \end{cases}$

Note that in Examples 1 and 3 the phrase "*a* solution" is used rather than "*the* solution" of the problem. The indefinite article "a" is used deliberately to suggest the possibility that other solutions may exist. At this point it has not been demonstrated that there is a single solution of each problem. The next example illustrates an initial-value problem with two solutions.

EXAMPLE 4   An IVP Can Have Several Solutions

Each of the functions $y = 0$ and $y = \frac{1}{16}x^4$ satisfies the differential equation $dy/dx = xy^{1/2}$ and the initial condition $y(0) = 0$, so the initial-value problem

$$\frac{dy}{dx} = xy^{1/2}, \quad y(0) = 0$$

has at least two solutions. As illustrated in Figure 1.2.5, the graphs of both functions pass through the same point $(0, 0)$. ∎

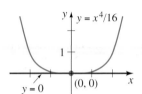

FIGURE 1.2.5   Two solutions of the same IVP

Within the safe confines of a formal course in differential equations one can be fairly confident that *most* differential equations will have solutions and that solutions of initial-value problems will *probably* be unique. Real life, however, is not so idyllic. Therefore it is desirable to know in advance of trying to solve an initial-value problem whether a solution exists and, when it does, whether it is the only solution of the problem. Since we are going to consider first-order differential equations in the next two chapters, we state here without proof a straightforward theorem that gives conditions that are sufficient to guarantee the existence and uniqueness of a solution of a first-order initial-value problem of the form given in (2). We shall wait until Chapter 4 to address the question of existence and uniqueness of a second-order initial-value problem.

THEOREM 1.2.1   Existence of a Unique Solution

Let R be a rectangular region in the xy-plane defined by $a \le x \le b, c \le y \le d$ that contains the point (x_0, y_0) in its interior. If $f(x, y)$ and $\partial f/\partial y$ are continuous on R, then there exists some interval I_0: $(x_0 - h, x_0 + h)$, $h > 0$, contained in $[a, b]$, and a unique function $y(x)$, defined on I_0, that is a solution of the initial-value problem (2).

The foregoing result is one of the most popular existence and uniqueness theorems for first-order differential equations because the criteria of continuity of $f(x, y)$ and $\partial f/\partial y$ are relatively easy to check. The geometry of Theorem 1.2.1 is illustrated in Figure 1.2.6.

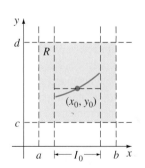

FIGURE 1.2.6   Rectangular region R

EXAMPLE 5   Example 4 Revisited

We saw in Example 4 that the differential equation $dy/dx = xy^{1/2}$ possesses at least two solutions whose graphs pass through $(0, 0)$. Inspection of the functions

$$f(x, y) = xy^{1/2} \qquad \text{and} \qquad \frac{\partial f}{\partial y} = \frac{x}{2y^{1/2}}$$

shows that they are continuous in the upper half-plane defined by $y > 0$. Hence Theorem 1.2.1 enables us to conclude that through any point (x_0, y_0), $y_0 > 0$ in the upper half-plane there is some interval centered at x_0 on which the given differential equation has a unique solution. Thus, for example, even without solving it, we know that there exists some interval centered at 2 on which the initial-value problem $dy/dx = xy^{1/2}$, $y(2) = 1$ has a unique solution. ∎

In Example 1, Theorem 1.2.1 guarantees that there are no other solutions of the initial-value problems $y' = y$, $y(0) = 3$ and $y' = y$, $y(1) = -2$ other than $y = 3e^x$ and $y = -2e^{x-1}$, respectively. This follows from the fact that $f(x, y) = y$ and $\partial f/\partial y = 1$ are continuous throughout the entire xy-plane. It can be further shown that the interval I on which each solution is defined is $(-\infty, \infty)$.

INTERVAL OF EXISTENCE/UNIQUENESS Suppose $y(x)$ represents a solution of the initial-value problem (2). The following three sets on the real x-axis may not be the same: the domain of the function $y(x)$, the interval I over which the solution $y(x)$ is defined or exists, and the interval I_0 of existence *and* uniqueness. Example 2 of Section 1.1 illustrated the difference between the domain of a function and the interval I of definition. Now suppose (x_0, y_0) is a point in the interior of the rectangular region R in Theorem 1.2.1. It turns out that the continuity of the function $f(x, y)$ on R by itself is sufficient to guarantee the existence of at least one solution of $dy/dx = f(x, y)$, $y(x_0) = y_0$, defined on some interval I. The interval I of definition for this initial-value problem is usually taken to be the largest interval containing x_0 over which the solution $y(x)$ is defined and differentiable. The interval I depends on both $f(x, y)$ and the initial condition $y(x_0) = y_0$. See Problems 31–34 in Exercises 1.2. The extra condition of continuity of the first partial derivative $\partial f/\partial y$ on R enables us to say that not only does a solution exist on some interval I_0 containing x_0, but it is the *only* solution satisfying $y(x_0) = y_0$. However, Theorem 1.2.1 does not give any indication of the sizes of intervals I and I_0; *the interval I of definition need not be as wide as the region R, and the interval I_0 of existence and uniqueness may not be as large as I.* The number $h > 0$ that defines the interval I_0: $(x_0 - h, x_0 + h)$ could be very small, so it is best to think that the solution $y(x)$ is *unique in a local sense*—that is, a solution defined near the point (x_0, y_0). See Problem 44 in Exercises 1.2.

REMARKS

(*i*) The conditions in Theorem 1.2.1 are sufficient but not necessary. This means that when $f(x, y)$ and $\partial f/\partial y$ are continuous on a rectangular region R, it must always follow that a solution of (2) exists and is unique whenever (x_0, y_0) is a point interior to R. However, if the conditions stated in the hypothesis of Theorem 1.2.1 do not hold, then anything could happen: Problem (2) *may* still have a solution and this solution *may* be unique, or (2) may have several solutions, or it may have no solution at all. A rereading of Example 5 reveals that the hypotheses of Theorem 1.2.1 do not hold on the line $y = 0$ for the differential equation $dy/dx = xy^{1/2}$, so it is not surprising, as we saw in Example 4 of this section, that there are two solutions defined on a common interval $-h < x < h$ satisfying $y(0) = 0$. On the other hand, the hypotheses of Theorem 1.2.1 do not hold on the line $y = 1$ for the differential equation $dy/dx = |y - 1|$. Nevertheless it can be proved that the solution of the initial-value problem $dy/dx = |y - 1|$, $y(0) = 1$, is unique. Can you guess this solution?

(*ii*) You are encouraged to read, think about, work, and then keep in mind Problem 43 in Exercises 1.2.

EXERCISES 1.2

Answers to selected odd-numbered problems begin on page ANS-1.

In Problems 1 and 2, $y = 1/(1 + c_1 e^{-x})$ is a one-parameter family of solutions of the first-order DE $y' = y - y^2$. Find a solution of the first-order IVP consisting of this differential equation and the given initial condition.

1. $y(0) = -\frac{1}{3}$

2. $y(-1) = 2$

In Problems 3–6, $y = 1/(x^2 + c)$ is a one-parameter family of solutions of the first-order DE $y' + 2xy^2 = 0$. Find a solution of the first-order IVP consisting of this differential equation and the given initial condition. Give the largest interval I over which the solution is defined.

3. $y(2) = \frac{1}{3}$

4. $y(-2) = \frac{1}{2}$

5. $y(0) = 1$

6. $y\left(\frac{1}{2}\right) = -4$

In Problems 7–10, $x = c_1 \cos t + c_2 \sin t$ is a two-parameter family of solutions of the second-order DE $x'' + x = 0$. Find a solution of the second-order IVP consisting of this differential equation and the given initial conditions.

7. $x(0) = -1, \quad x'(0) = 8$

8. $x(\pi/2) = 0, \quad x'(\pi/2) = 1$

9. $x(\pi/6) = \frac{1}{2}, \quad x'(\pi/6) = 0$

10. $x(\pi/4) = \sqrt{2}, \quad x'(\pi/4) = 2\sqrt{2}$

In Problems 11–14, $y = c_1 e^x + c_2 e^{-x}$ is a two-parameter family of solutions of the second-order DE $y'' - y = 0$. Find a solution of the second-order IVP consisting of this differential equation and the given initial conditions.

11. $y(0) = 1, \quad y'(0) = 2$

12. $y(1) = 0, \quad y'(1) = e$

13. $y(-1) = 5, \quad y'(-1) = -5$

14. $y(0) = 0, \quad y'(0) = 0$

In Problems 15 and 16 determine by inspection at least two solutions of the given first-order IVP.

15. $y' = 3y^{2/3}, \quad y(0) = 0$

16. $xy' = 2y, \quad y(0) = 0$

In Problems 17–24 determine a region of the xy-plane for which the given differential equation would have a unique solution whose graph passes through a point (x_0, y_0) in the region.

17. $\dfrac{dy}{dx} = y^{2/3}$

18. $\dfrac{dy}{dx} = \sqrt{xy}$

19. $x\dfrac{dy}{dx} = y$

20. $\dfrac{dy}{dx} - y = x$

21. $(4 - y^2)y' = x^2$

22. $(1 + y^3)y' = x^2$

23. $(x^2 + y^2)y' = y^2$

24. $(y - x)y' = y + x$

In Problems 25–28 determine whether Theorem 1.2.1 guarantees that the differential equation $y' = \sqrt{y^2 - 9}$ possesses a unique solution through the given point.

25. $(1, 4)$

26. $(5, 3)$

27. $(2, -3)$

28. $(-1, 1)$

29. (a) By inspection find a one-parameter family of solutions of the differential equation $xy' = y$. Verify that each member of the family is a solution of the initial-value problem $xy' = y, y(0) = 0$.

(b) Explain part (a) by determining a region R in the xy-plane for which the differential equation $xy' = y$ would have a unique solution through a point (x_0, y_0) in R.

(c) Verify that the piecewise-defined function

$$y = \begin{cases} 0, & x < 0 \\ x, & x \geq 0 \end{cases}$$

satisfies the condition $y(0) = 0$. Determine whether this function is also a solution of the initial-value problem in part (a).

30. (a) Verify that $y = \tan(x + c)$ is a one-parameter family of solutions of the differential equation $y' = 1 + y^2$.

(b) Since $f(x, y) = 1 + y^2$ and $\partial f/\partial y = 2y$ are continuous everywhere, the region R in Theorem 1.2.1 can be taken to be the entire xy-plane. Use the family of solutions in part (a) to find an explicit solution of the first-order initial-value problem $y' = 1 + y^2$, $y(0) = 0$. Even though $x_0 = 0$ is in the interval $(-2, 2)$, explain why the solution is not defined on this interval.

(c) Determine the largest interval I of definition for the solution of the initial-value problem in part (b).

31. (a) Verify that $y = -1/(x + c)$ is a one-parameter family of solutions of the differential equation $y' = y^2$.

(b) Since $f(x, y) = y^2$ and $\partial f/\partial y = 2y$ are continuous everywhere, the region R in Theorem 1.2.1 can be taken to be the entire xy-plane. Find a solution from the family in part (a) that satisfies $y(0) = 1$. Then find a solution from the family in part (a) that satisfies $y(0) = -1$. Determine the largest interval I of definition for the solution of each initial-value problem.

(c) Determine the largest interval I of definition for the solution of the first-order initial-value problem $y' = y^2$, $y(0) = 0$. [*Hint:* The solution is not a member of the family of solutions in part (a).]

32. (a) Show that a solution from the family in part (a) of Problem 31 that satisfies $y' = y^2$, $y(1) = 1$, is $y = 1/(2 - x)$.

(b) Then show that a solution from the family in part (a) of Problem 31 that satisfies $y' = y^2$, $y(3) = -1$, is $y = 1/(2 - x)$.

(c) Are the solutions in parts (a) and (b) the same?

33. (a) Verify that $3x^2 - y^2 = c$ is a one-parameter family of solutions of the differential equation $y\, dy/dx = 3x$.

(b) By hand, sketch the graph of the implicit solution $3x^2 - y^2 = 3$. Find all explicit solutions $y = \phi(x)$ of the DE in part (a) defined by this relation. Give the interval I of definition of each explicit solution.

(c) The point $(-2, 3)$ is on the graph of $3x^2 - y^2 = 3$, but which of the explicit solutions in part (b) satisfies $y(-2) = 3$?

34. (a) Use the family of solutions in part (a) of Problem 33 to find an implicit solution of the initial-value problem $y\, dy/dx = 3x$, $y(2) = -4$. Then, by hand, sketch the graph of the explicit solution of this problem and give its interval I of definition.

(b) Are there any explicit solutions of $y\, dy/dx = 3x$ that pass through the origin?

In Problems 35–38 the graph of a member of a family of solutions of a second-order differential equation $d^2y/dx^2 = f(x, y, y')$ is given. Match the solution curve with at least one pair of the following initial conditions.

(a) $y(1) = 1$, $y'(1) = -2$

(b) $y(-1) = 0$, $y'(-1) = -4$

(c) $y(1) = 1$, $y'(1) = 2$

(d) $y(0) = -1$, $y'(0) = 2$

(e) $y(0) = -1$, $y'(0) = 0$

(f) $y(0) = -4$, $y'(0) = -2$

35.

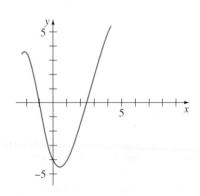

FIGURE 1.2.7 Graph for Problem 35

36.

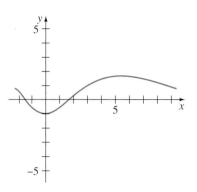

FIGURE 1.2.8 Graph for Problem 36

37.

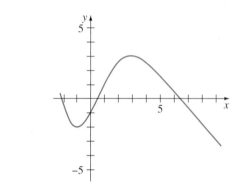

FIGURE 1.2.9 Graph for Problem 37

38.

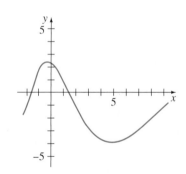

FIGURE 1.2.10 Graph for Problem 38

Discussion Problems

In Problems 39 and 40 use Problem 51 in Exercises 1.1 and (2) and (3) of this section.

39. Find a function $y = f(x)$ whose graph at each point (x, y) has the slope given by $8e^{2x} + 6x$ and has the y-intercept $(0, 9)$.

40. Find a function $y = f(x)$ whose second derivative is $y'' = 12x - 2$ at each point (x, y) on its graph and $y = -x + 5$ is tangent to the graph at the point corresponding to $x = 1$.

41. Consider the initial-value problem $y' = x - 2y$, $y(0) = \frac{1}{2}$. Determine which of the two curves shown in Figure 1.2.11 is the only plausible solution curve. Explain your reasoning.

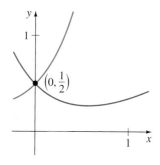

FIGURE 1.2.11 Graphs for Problem 41

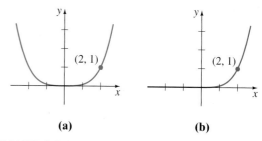

(a)   **(b)**

FIGURE 1.2.12 Two solutions of the IVP in Problem 44

42. Determine a plausible value of x_0 for which the graph of the solution of the initial-value problem $y' + 2y = 3x - 6$, $y(x_0) = 0$ is tangent to the x-axis at $(x_0, 0)$. Explain your reasoning.

43. Suppose that the first-order differential equation $dy/dx = f(x, y)$ possesses a one-parameter family of solutions and that $f(x, y)$ satisfies the hypotheses of Theorem 1.2.1 in some rectangular region R of the xy-plane. Explain why two different solution curves cannot intersect or be tangent to each other at a point (x_0, y_0) in R.

44. The functions $y(x) = \frac{1}{16}x^4$, $-\infty < x < \infty$ and

$$y(x) = \begin{cases} 0, & x < 0 \\ \frac{1}{16}x^4, & x \geq 0 \end{cases}$$

have the same domain but are clearly different. See Figures 1.2.12(a) and 1.2.12(b), respectively. Show that both functions are solutions of the initial-value problem

$dy/dx = xy^{1/2}$, $y(2) = 1$ on the interval $(-\infty, \infty)$. Resolve the apparent contradiction between this fact and the last sentence in Example 5.

Mathematical Model

45. Population Growth Beginning in the next section we will see that differential equations can be used to describe or *model* many different physical systems. In this problem suppose that a model of the growing population of a small community is given by the initial-value problem

$$\frac{dP}{dt} = 0.15P(t) + 20, \quad P(0) = 100,$$

where P is the number of individuals in the community and time t is measured in years. How fast—that is, at what *rate*—is the population increasing at $t = 0$? How fast is the population increasing when the population is 500?

1.3	**DIFFERENTIAL EQUATIONS AS MATHEMATICAL MODELS**

REVIEW MATERIAL

- Units of measurement for weight, mass, and density
- Newton's second law of motion
- Hooke's law
- Kirchhoff's laws
- Archimedes' principle

INTRODUCTION In this section we introduce the notion of a differential equation as a mathematical model and discuss some specific models in biology, chemistry, and physics. Once we have studied some methods for solving DEs in Chapters 2 and 4, we return to, and solve, some of these models in Chapters 3 and 5.

MATHEMATICAL MODELS It is often desirable to describe the behavior of some real-life system or phenomenon, whether physical, sociological, or even economic, in mathematical terms. The mathematical description of a system of phenomenon is called a **mathematical model** and is constructed with certain goals in mind. For example, we may wish to understand the mechanisms of a certain ecosystem by studying the growth of animal populations in that system, or we may wish to date fossils by analyzing the decay of a radioactive substance either in the fossil or in the stratum in which it was discovered.

Construction of a mathematical model of a system starts with

(*i*) identification of the variables that are responsible for changing the system. We may choose not to incorporate all these variables into the model at first. In this step we are specifying the **level of resolution** of the model.

Next

(*ii*) we make a set of reasonable assumptions, or hypotheses, about the system we are trying to describe. These assumptions will also include any empirical laws that may be applicable to the system.

For some purposes it may be perfectly within reason to be content with low-resolution models. For example, you may already be aware that in beginning physics courses, the retarding force of air friction is sometimes ignored in modeling the motion of a body falling near the surface of the Earth, but if you are a scientist whose job it is to accurately predict the flight path of a long-range projectile, you have to take into account air resistance and other factors such as the curvature of the Earth.

Since the assumptions made about a system frequently involve *a rate of change* of one or more of the variables, the mathematical depiction of all these assumptions may be one or more equations involving *derivatives*. In other words, the mathematical model may be a differential equation or a system of differential equations.

Once we have formulated a mathematical model that is either a differential equation or a system of differential equations, we are faced with the not insignificant problem of trying to solve it. *If* we can solve it, then we deem the model to be reasonable if its solution is consistent with either experimental data or known facts about the behavior of the system. But if the predictions produced by the solution are poor, we can either increase the level of resolution of the model or make alternative assumptions about the mechanisms for change in the system. The steps of the modeling process are then repeated, as shown in the following diagram:

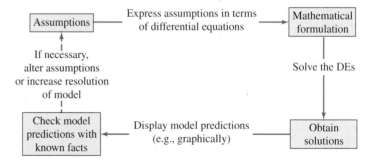

Of course, by increasing the resolution, we add to the complexity of the mathematical model and increase the likelihood that we cannot obtain an explicit solution.

A mathematical model of a physical system will often involve the variable time *t*. A solution of the model then gives the **state of the system;** in other words, the values of the dependent variable (or variables) for appropriate values of *t* describe the system in the past, present, and future.

POPULATION DYNAMICS   One of the earliest attempts to model human **population growth** by means of mathematics was by the English economist Thomas Malthus in 1798. Basically, the idea behind the Malthusian model is the assumption that the rate at which the population of a country grows at a certain time is proportional[*] to the total population of the country at that time. In other words, the more people there are at time *t*, the more there are going to be in the future. In mathematical terms, if *P(t)* denotes the

---

[*]If two quantities *u* and *v* are proportional, we write $u \propto v$. This means that one quantity is a constant multiple of the other: $u = kv$.

total population at time t, then this assumption can be expressed as

$$\frac{dP}{dt} \propto P \qquad \text{or} \qquad \frac{dP}{dt} = kP, \tag{1}$$

where k is a constant of proportionality. This simple model, which fails to take into account many factors that can influence human populations to either grow or decline (immigration and emigration, for example), nevertheless turned out to be fairly accurate in predicting the population of the United States during the years 1790–1860. Populations that grow at a rate described by (1) are rare; nevertheless, (1) is still used to model *growth of small populations over short intervals of time* (bacteria growing in a petri dish, for example).

RADIOACTIVE DECAY   The nucleus of an atom consists of combinations of protons and neutrons. Many of these combinations of protons and neutrons are unstable— that is, the atoms decay or transmute into atoms of another substance. Such nuclei are said to be radioactive. For example, over time the highly radioactive radium, Ra-226, transmutes into the radioactive gas radon, Rn-222. To model the phenomenon of **radioactive decay,** it is assumed that the rate dA/dt at which the nuclei of a substance decay is proportional to the amount (more precisely, the number of nuclei) $A(t)$ of the substance remaining at time t:

$$\frac{dA}{dt} \propto A \qquad \text{or} \qquad \frac{dA}{dt} = kA. \tag{2}$$

Of course, equations (1) and (2) are exactly the same; the difference is only in the interpretation of the symbols and the constants of proportionality. For growth, as we expect in (1), $k > 0$, and for decay, as in (2), $k < 0$.

The model (1) for growth can also be seen as the equation $dS/dt = rS$, which describes the growth of capital S when an annual rate of interest r is compounded continuously. The model (2) for decay also occurs in biological applications such as determining the half-life of a drug—the time that it takes for 50% of a drug to be eliminated from a body by excretion or metabolism. In chemistry the decay model (2) appears in the mathematical description of a first-order chemical reaction. The point is this:

> *A single differential equation can serve as a mathematical model for many different phenomena.*

Mathematical models are often accompanied by certain side conditions. For example, in (1) and (2) we would expect to know, in turn, the initial population P_0 and the initial amount of radioactive substance A_0 on hand. If the initial point in time is taken to be $t = 0$, then we know that $P(0) = P_0$ and $A(0) = A_0$. In other words, a mathematical model can consist of either an initial-value problem or, as we shall see later on in Section 5.2, a boundary-value problem.

NEWTON'S LAW OF COOLING/WARMING   According to Newton's empirical law of cooling/warming, the rate at which the temperature of a body changes is proportional to the difference between the temperature of the body and the temperature of the surrounding medium, the so-called ambient temperature. If $T(t)$ represents the temperature of a body at time t, T_m the temperature of the surrounding medium, and dT/dt the rate at which the temperature of the body changes, then Newton's law of cooling/warming translates into the mathematical statement

$$\frac{dT}{dt} \propto T - T_m \qquad \text{or} \qquad \frac{dT}{dt} = k(T - T_m), \tag{3}$$

where k is a constant of proportionality. In either case, cooling or warming, if T_m is a constant, it stands to reason that $k < 0$.

SPREAD OF A DISEASE A contagious disease—for example, a flu virus—is spread throughout a community by people coming into contact with other people. Let $x(t)$ denote the number of people who have contracted the disease and $y(t)$ denote the number of people who have not yet been exposed. It seems reasonable to assume that the rate dx/dt at which the disease spreads is proportional to the number of encounters, or *interactions*, between these two groups of people. If we assume that the number of interactions is jointly proportional to $x(t)$ and $y(t)$—that is, proportional to the product xy—then

$$\frac{dx}{dt} = kxy, \tag{4}$$

where k is the usual constant of proportionality. Suppose a small community has a fixed population of n people. If one infected person is introduced into this community, then it could be argued that $x(t)$ and $y(t)$ are related by $x + y = n + 1$. Using this last equation to eliminate y in (4) gives us the model

$$\frac{dx}{dt} = kx(n + 1 - x). \tag{5}$$

An obvious initial condition accompanying equation (5) is $x(0) = 1$.

CHEMICAL REACTIONS The disintegration of a radioactive substance, governed by the differential equation (1), is said to be a **first-order reaction.** In chemistry a few reactions follow this same empirical law: If the molecules of substance A decompose into smaller molecules, it is a natural assumption that the rate at which this decomposition takes place is proportional to the amount of the first substance that has not undergone conversion; that is, if $X(t)$ is the amount of substance A remaining at any time, then $dX/dt = kX$, where k is a negative constant since X is decreasing. An example of a first-order chemical reaction is the conversion of t-butyl chloride, $(CH_3)_3CCl$, into t-butyl alcohol, $(CH_3)_3COH$:

$$(CH_3)_3CCl + NaOH \rightarrow (CH_3)_3COH + NaCl.$$

Only the concentration of the t-butyl chloride controls the rate of reaction. But in the reaction

$$CH_3Cl + NaOH \rightarrow CH_3OH + NaCl$$

one molecule of sodium hydroxide, $NaOH$, is consumed for every molecule of methyl chloride, CH_3Cl, thus forming one molecule of methyl alcohol, CH_3OH, and one molecule of sodium chloride, $NaCl$. In this case the rate at which the reaction proceeds is proportional to the product of the remaining concentrations of CH_3Cl and $NaOH$. To describe this second reaction in general, let us suppose *one* molecule of a substance A combines with *one* molecule of a substance B to form *one* molecule of a substance C. If X denotes the amount of chemical C formed at time t and if α and β are, in turn, the amounts of the two chemicals A and B at $t = 0$ (the initial amounts), then the instantaneous amounts of A and B not converted to chemical C are $\alpha - X$ and $\beta - X$, respectively. Hence the rate of formation of C is given by

$$\frac{dX}{dt} = k(\alpha - X)(\beta - X), \tag{6}$$

where k is a constant of proportionality. A reaction whose model is equation (6) is said to be a **second-order reaction.**

MIXTURES The mixing of two salt solutions of differing concentrations gives rise to a first-order differential equation for the amount of salt contained in the mixture. Let us suppose that a large mixing tank initially holds 300 gallons of brine (that is, water in which a certain number of pounds of salt has been dissolved). Another

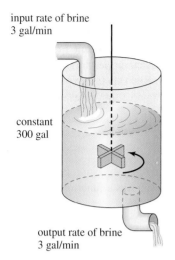

input rate of brine
3 gal/min

constant
300 gal

output rate of brine
3 gal/min

FIGURE 1.3.1 Mixing tank

brine solution is pumped into the large tank at a rate of 3 gallons per minute; the concentration of the salt in this inflow is 2 pounds per gallon. When the solution in the tank is well stirred, it is pumped out at the same rate as the entering solution. See Figure 1.3.1. If $A(t)$ denotes the amount of salt (measured in pounds) in the tank at time t, then the rate at which $A(t)$ changes is a net rate:

$$\frac{dA}{dt} = \left(\begin{array}{c}\textit{input rate}\\ \textit{of salt}\end{array}\right) - \left(\begin{array}{c}\textit{output rate}\\ \textit{of salt}\end{array}\right) = R_{in} - R_{out}. \qquad (7)$$

The input rate R_{in} at which salt enters the tank is the product of the inflow concentration of salt and the inflow rate of fluid. Note that R_{in} is measured in pounds per minute:

$$R_{in} = \underset{\substack{\uparrow \\ \text{concentration}\\ \text{of salt}\\ \text{in inflow}}}{(2 \text{ lb/gal})} \cdot \underset{\substack{\uparrow \\ \text{input rate}\\ \text{of brine}}}{(3 \text{ gal/min})} = \underset{\substack{\uparrow \\ \text{input rate}\\ \text{of salt}}}{(6 \text{ lb/min})}.$$

Now, since the solution is being pumped out of the tank at the same rate that it is pumped in, the number of gallons of brine in the tank at time t is a constant 300 gallons. Hence the concentration of the salt in the tank as well as in the outflow is $c(t) = A(t)/300$ lb/gal, so the output rate R_{out} of salt is

$$R_{out} = \underset{\substack{\uparrow \\ \text{concentration}\\ \text{of salt}\\ \text{in outflow}}}{\left(\frac{A(t)}{300} \text{ lb/gal}\right)} \cdot \underset{\substack{\uparrow \\ \text{output rate}\\ \text{of brine}}}{(3 \text{ gal/min})} = \underset{\substack{\uparrow \\ \text{output rate}\\ \text{of salt}}}{\frac{A(t)}{100} \text{ lb/min}}.$$

The net rate (7) then becomes

$$\frac{dA}{dt} = 6 - \frac{A}{100} \qquad \text{or} \qquad \frac{dA}{dt} + \frac{1}{100}A = 6. \qquad (8)$$

If r_{in} and r_{out} denote general input and output rates of the brine solutions,* then there are three possibilities: $r_{in} = r_{out}$, $r_{in} > r_{out}$, and $r_{in} < r_{out}$. In the analysis leading to (8) we have assumed that $r_{in} = r_{out}$. In the latter two cases the number of gallons of brine in the tank is either increasing ($r_{in} > r_{out}$) or decreasing ($r_{in} < r_{out}$) at the net rate $r_{in} - r_{out}$. See Problems 10–12 in Exercises 1.3.

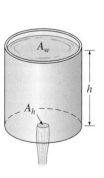

FIGURE 1.3.2 Draining tank

DRAINING A TANK In hydrodynamics **Torricelli's law** states that the speed v of efflux of water though a sharp-edged hole at the bottom of a tank filled to a depth h is the same as the speed that a body (in this case a drop of water) would acquire in falling freely from a height h—that is, $v = \sqrt{2gh}$, where g is the acceleration due to gravity. This last expression comes from equating the kinetic energy $\frac{1}{2}mv^2$ with the potential energy mgh and solving for v. Suppose a tank filled with water is allowed to drain through a hole under the influence of gravity. We would like to find the depth h of water remaining in the tank at time t. Consider the tank shown in Figure 1.3.2. If the area of the hole is A_h (in ft²) and the speed of the water leaving the tank is $v = \sqrt{2gh}$ (in ft/s), then the volume of water leaving the tank per second is $A_h \sqrt{2gh}$ (in ft³/s). Thus if $V(t)$ denotes the volume of water in the tank at time t, then

$$\frac{dV}{dt} = -A_h \sqrt{2gh}, \qquad (9)$$

---

*Don't confuse these symbols with R_{in} and R_{out}, which are input and output rates of *salt*.

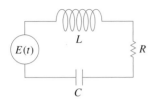

(a) *LRC*-series circuit

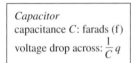

Inductor
inductance *L*: henries (h)
voltage drop across: $L\dfrac{di}{dt}$

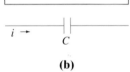

$i \rightarrow$ *L*

Resistor
resistance *R*: ohms (Ω)
voltage drop across: iR

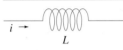

$i \rightarrow$ *R*

Capacitor
capacitance *C*: farads (f)
voltage drop across: $\dfrac{1}{C}q$

$i \rightarrow$ *C*

(b)

FIGURE 1.3.3 Symbols, units, and voltages. Current $i(t)$ and charge $q(t)$ are measured in amperes (A) and coulombs (C), respectively

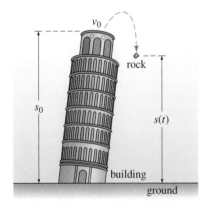

FIGURE 1.3.4 Position of rock measured from ground level

where the minus sign indicates that *V* is decreasing. Note here that we are ignoring the possibility of friction at the hole that might cause a reduction of the rate of flow there. Now if the tank is such that the volume of water in it at time *t* can be written $V(t) = A_w h$, where A_w (in ft^2) is the *constant* area of the upper surface of the water (see Figure 1.3.2), then $dV/dt = A_w\, dh/dt$. Substituting this last expression into (9) gives us the desired differential equation for the height of the water at time *t*:

$$\frac{dh}{dt} = -\frac{A_h}{A_w}\sqrt{2gh}. \qquad (10)$$

It is interesting to note that (10) remains valid even when A_w is not constant. In this case we must express the upper surface area of the water as a function of *h*—that is, $A_w = A(h)$. See Problem 14 in Exercises 1.3.

SERIES CIRCUITS Consider the single-loop series circuit shown in Figure 1.3.3(a), containing an inductor, resistor, and capacitor. The current in a circuit after a switch is closed is denoted by $i(t)$; the charge on a capacitor at time *t* is denoted by $q(t)$. The letters *L*, *R*, and *C* are known as inductance, resistance, and capacitance, respectively, and are generally constants. Now according to **Kirchhoff's second law,** the impressed voltage $E(t)$ on a closed loop must equal the sum of the voltage drops in the loop. Figure 1.3.3(b) shows the symbols and the formulas for the respective voltage drops across an inductor, a capacitor, and a resistor. Since current $i(t)$ is related to charge $q(t)$ on the capacitor by $i = dq/dt$, adding the three voltages

$$\underset{\text{inductor}}{L\frac{di}{dt} = L\frac{d^2q}{dt^2},} \qquad \underset{\text{resistor}}{iR = R\frac{dq}{dt},} \qquad \text{and} \qquad \underset{\text{capacitor}}{\frac{1}{C}q}$$

and equating the sum to the impressed voltage yields a second-order differential equation

$$L\frac{d^2q}{dt^2} + R\frac{dq}{dt} + \frac{1}{C}q = E(t). \qquad (11)$$

We will examine a differential equation analogous to (11) in great detail in Section 5.1.

FALLING BODIES To construct a mathematical model of the motion of a body moving in a force field, one often starts with Newton's second law of motion. Recall from elementary physics that **Newton's first law of motion** states that a body either will remain at rest or will continue to move with a constant velocity unless acted on by an external force. In each case this is equivalent to saying that when the sum of the forces $F = \sum F_k$—that is, the *net* or resultant force—acting on the body is zero, then the acceleration *a* of the body is zero. **Newton's second law of motion** indicates that when the net force acting on a body is not zero, then the net force is proportional to its acceleration *a* or, more precisely, $F = ma$, where *m* is the mass of the body.

Now suppose a rock is tossed upward from the roof of a building as illustrated in Figure 1.3.4. What is the position $s(t)$ of the rock relative to the ground at time *t*? The acceleration of the rock is the second derivative d^2s/dt^2. If we assume that the upward direction is positive and that no force acts on the rock other than the force of gravity, then Newton's second law gives

$$m\frac{d^2s}{dt^2} = -mg \qquad \text{or} \qquad \frac{d^2s}{dt^2} = -g. \qquad (12)$$

In other words, the net force is simply the weight $F = F_1 = -W$ of the rock near the surface of the Earth. Recall that the magnitude of the weight is $W = mg$, where *m* is the mass of the body and g is the acceleration due to gravity. The minus sign in (12) is used because the weight of the rock is a force directed downward, which is opposite to the positive direction. If the height of the building is s_0 and the initial velocity of the rock is v_0, then s is determined from the second-order initial-value problem

$$\frac{d^2s}{dt^2} = -g, \quad s(0) = s_0, \quad s'(0) = v_0. \tag{13}$$

Although we have not been stressing solutions of the equations we have constructed, note that (13) can be solved by integrating the constant $-g$ twice with respect to t. The initial conditions determine the two constants of integration. From elementary physics you might recognize the solution of (13) as the formula $s(t) = -\frac{1}{2}gt^2 + v_0t + s_0$.

FALLING BODIES AND AIR RESISTANCE Before Galileo's famous experiment from the leaning tower of Pisa, it was generally believed that heavier objects in free fall, such as a cannonball, fell with a greater acceleration than lighter objects, such as a feather. Obviously, a cannonball and a feather when dropped simultaneously from the same height *do* fall at different rates, but it is not because a cannonball is heavier. The difference in rates is due to air resistance. The resistive force of air was ignored in the model given in (13). Under some circumstances a falling body of mass m, such as a feather with low density and irregular shape, encounters air resistance proportional to its instantaneous velocity v. If we take, in this circumstance, the positive direction to be oriented downward, then the net force acting on the mass is given by $F = F_1 + F_2 = mg - kv$, where the weight $F_1 = mg$ of the body is force acting in the positive direction and air resistance $F_2 = -kv$ is a force, called **viscous damping,** acting in the opposite or upward direction. See Figure 1.3.5. Now since v is related to acceleration a by $a = dv/dt$, Newton's second law becomes $F = ma = m\, dv/dt$. By equating the net force to this form of Newton's second law, we obtain a first-order differential equation for the velocity $v(t)$ of the body at time t,

$$m\frac{dv}{dt} = mg - kv. \tag{14}$$

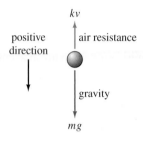

FIGURE 1.3.5 Falling body of mass m

Here k is a positive constant of proportionality. If $s(t)$ is the distance the body falls in time t from its initial point of release, then $v = ds/dt$ and $a = dv/dt = d^2s/dt^2$. In terms of s, (14) is a second-order differential equation

$$m\frac{d^2s}{dt^2} = mg - k\frac{ds}{dt} \quad \text{or} \quad m\frac{d^2s}{dt^2} + k\frac{ds}{dt} = mg. \tag{15}$$

SUSPENDED CABLES Suppose a flexible cable, wire, or heavy rope is suspended between two vertical supports. Physical examples of this could be one of the two cables supporting the roadbed of a suspension bridge as shown in Figure 1.3.6(a) or a long telephone wire strung between two posts as shown in Figure 1.3.6(b). Our goal is to construct a mathematical model that describes the shape that such a cable assumes.

(a) suspension bridge cable

(b) telephone wires

FIGURE 1.3.6 Cables suspended between vertical supports

To begin, let's agree to examine only a portion or element of the cable between its lowest point P_1 and any arbitrary point P_2. As drawn in blue in Figure 1.3.7, this element of the cable is the curve in a rectangular coordinate system with y-axis chosen to pass through the lowest point P_1 on the curve and the x-axis chosen a units below P_1. Three forces are acting on the cable: the tensions $\mathbf{T}_1$ and $\mathbf{T}_2$ in the cable that are tangent to the cable at P_1 and P_2, respectively, and the portion $\mathbf{W}$ of the total vertical load between the points P_1 and P_2. Let $T_1 = |\mathbf{T}_1|$, $T_2 = |\mathbf{T}_2|$, and $W = |\mathbf{W}|$ denote the magnitudes of these vectors. Now the tension $\mathbf{T}_2$ resolves into horizontal and vertical components (scalar quantities) $T_2 \cos \theta$ and $T_2 \sin \theta$.

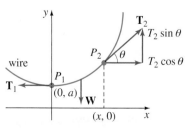

FIGURE 1.3.7 Element of cable

Because of static equilibrium we can write

$$T_1 = T_2 \cos \theta \qquad \text{and} \qquad W = T_2 \sin \theta.$$

By dividing the last equation by the first, we eliminate T_2 and get $\tan \theta = W/T_1$. But because $dy/dx = \tan \theta$, we arrive at

$$\frac{dy}{dx} = \frac{W}{T_1}. \tag{16}$$

This simple first-order differential equation serves as a model for both the shape of a flexible wire such as a telephone wire hanging under its own weight and the shape of the cables that support the roadbed of a suspension bridge. We will come back to equation (16) in Exercises 2.2 and Section 5.3.

WHAT LIES AHEAD Throughout this text you will see three different types of approaches to, or analyses of, differential equations. Over the centuries differential equations would often spring from the efforts of a scientist or engineer to describe some physical phenomenon or to translate an empirical or experimental law into mathematical terms. As a consequence a scientist, engineer, or mathematician would often spend many years of his or her life trying to find the solutions of a DE. With a solution in hand, the study of its properties then followed. This quest for solutions is called by some the *analytical approach* to differential equations. Once they realized that explicit solutions are at best difficult to obtain and at worst impossible to obtain, mathematicians learned that a differential equation itself could be a font of valuable information. It is possible, in some instances, to glean directly from the differential equation answers to questions such as *Does the DE actually have solutions? If a solution of the DE exists and satisfies an initial condition, is it the only such solution? What are some of the properties of the unknown solutions? What can we say about the geometry of the solution curves?* Such an approach is *qualitative analysis.* Finally, if a differential equation cannot be solved by analytical methods, yet we can prove that a solution exists, the next logical query is *Can we somehow approximate the values of an unknown solution?* Here we enter the realm of *numerical analysis.* An affirmative answer to the last question stems from the fact that a differential equation can be used as a cornerstone for constructing very accurate approximation algorithms. In Chapter 2 we start with qualitative considerations of first-order ODEs, then examine analytical stratagems for solving some special first-order equations, and conclude with an introduction to an elementary numerical method. See Figure 1.3.8.

(a) analytical   (b) qualitative   (c) numerical

FIGURE 1.3.8   Different approaches to the study of differential equations

REMARKS

Each example in this section has described a dynamical system—a system that changes or evolves with the flow of time t. Since the study of dynamical systems is a branch of mathematics currently in vogue, we shall occasionally relate the terminology of that field to the discussion at hand.

In more precise terms, a **dynamical system** consists of a set of time-dependent variables, called **state variables,** together with a rule that enables us to determine (without ambiguity) the state of the system (this may be a past, present, or future state) in terms of a state prescribed at some time t_0. Dynamical systems are classified as either discrete-time systems or continuous-time systems. In this course we shall be concerned only with continuous-time systems — systems in which *all* variables are defined over a continuous range of time. The rule, or mathematical model, in a continuous-time dynamical system is a differential equation or a system of differential equations. The **state of the system** at a time t is the value of the state variables at that time; the specified state of the system at a time t_0 is simply the initial conditions that accompany the mathematical model. The solution of the initial-value problem is referred to as the **response of the system.** For example, in the case of radioactive decay, the rule is $dA/dt = kA$. Now if the quantity of a radioactive substance at some time t_0 is known, say $A(t_0) = A_0$, then by solving the rule we find that the response of the system for $t \geq t_0$ is $A(t) = A_0 e^{(t-t_0)}$ (see Section 3.1). The response $A(t)$ is the single state variable for this system. In the case of the rock tossed from the roof of a building, the response of the system—the solution of the differential equation $d^2s/dt^2 = -g$, subject to the initial state $s(0) = s_0$, $s'(0) = v_0$, is the function $s(t) = -\frac{1}{2}gt^2 + v_0 t + s_0, 0 \leq t \leq T$, where T represents the time when the rock hits the ground. The state variables are $s(t)$ and $s'(t)$, which are the vertical position of the rock above ground and its velocity at time t, respectively. The acceleration $s''(t)$ is *not* a state variable, since we have to know only any initial position and initial velocity at a time t_0 to uniquely determine the rock's position $s(t)$ and velocity $s'(t) = v(t)$ for any time in the interval $t_0 \leq t \leq T$. The acceleration $s''(t) = a(t)$ is, of course, given by the differential equation $s''(t) = -g, 0 < t < T$.

One last point: Not every system studied in this text is a dynamical system. We shall also examine some static systems in which the model is a differential equation.

EXERCISES 1.3

Answers to selected odd-numbered problems begin on page ANS-1.

Population Dynamics

1. Under the same assumptions that underlie the model in (1), determine a differential equation for the population $P(t)$ of a country when individuals are allowed to immigrate into the country at a constant rate $r > 0$. What is the differential equation for the population $P(t)$ of the country when individuals are allowed to emigrate from the country at a constant rate $r > 0$?

2. The population model given in (1) fails to take death into consideration; the growth rate equals the birth rate. In another model of a changing population of a community it is assumed that the rate at which the population changes is a *net* rate—that is, the difference between the rate of births and the rate of deaths in the community. Determine a model for the population $P(t)$ if both the birth rate and the death rate are proportional to the population present at time t.

3. Using the concept of net rate introduced in Problem 2, determine a model for a population $P(t)$ if the birth rate is proportional to the population present at time t but the death rate is proportional to the square of the population present at time t.

4. Modify the model in Problem 3 for net rate at which the population $P(t)$ of a certain kind of fish changes by also assuming that the fish are harvested at a constant rate $h > 0$.

Newton's Law of Cooling/Warming

5. A cup of coffee cools according to Newton's law of cooling (3). Use data from the graph of the temperature $T(t)$ in Figure 1.3.9 to estimate the constants T_m, T_0, and k in a model of the form of a first-order initial-value problem: $dT/dt = k(T - T_m)$, $T(0) = T_0$.

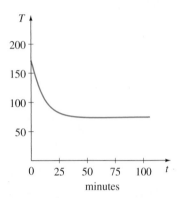

FIGURE 1.3.9 Cooling curve in Problem 5

6. The ambient temperature T_m in (3) could be a function of time t. Suppose that in an artificially controlled environment, $T_m(t)$ is periodic with a 24-hour period, as illustrated in Figure 1.3.10. Devise a mathematical model for the temperature $T(t)$ of a body within this environment.

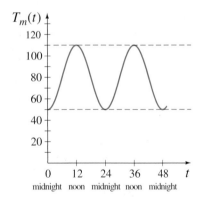

FIGURE 1.3.10 Ambient temperature in Problem 6

Spread of a Disease/Technology

7. Suppose a student carrying a flu virus returns to an isolated college campus of 1000 students. Determine a differential equation for the number of people $x(t)$ who have contracted the flu if the rate at which the disease spreads is proportional to the number of interactions between the number of students who have the flu and the number of students who have not yet been exposed to it.

8. At a time denoted as $t = 0$ a technological innovation is introduced into a community that has a fixed population of n people. Determine a differential equation for the number of people $x(t)$ who have adopted the innovation at time t if it is assumed that the rate at which the innovations spread through the community is jointly proportional to the number of people who have adopted it and the number of people who have not adopted it.

Mixtures

9. Suppose that a large mixing tank initially holds 300 gallons of water in which 50 pounds of salt have been dissolved. Pure water is pumped into the tank at a rate of 3 gal/min, and when the solution is well stirred, it is then pumped out at the same rate. Determine a differential equation for the amount of salt $A(t)$ in the tank at time t. What is $A(0)$?

10. Suppose that a large mixing tank initially holds 300 gallons of water is which 50 pounds of salt have been dissolved. Another brine solution is pumped into the tank at a rate of 3 gal/min, and when the solution is well stirred, it is then pumped out at a *slower* rate of 2 gal/min. If the concentration of the solution entering is 2 lb/gal, determine a differential equation for the amount of salt $A(t)$ in the tank at time t.

11. What is the differential equation in Problem 10, if the well-stirred solution is pumped out at a *faster* rate of 3.5 gal/min?

12. Generalize the model given in equation (8) on page 23 by assuming that the large tank initially contains N_0 number of gallons of brine, r_{in} and r_{out} are the input and output rates of the brine, respectively (measured in gallons per minute), c_{in} is the concentration of the salt in the inflow, $c(t)$ the concentration of the salt in the tank as well as in the outflow at time t (measured in pounds of salt per gallon), and $A(t)$ is the amount of salt in the tank at time t.

Draining a Tank

13. Suppose water is leaking from a tank through a circular hole of area A_h at its bottom. When water leaks through a hole, friction and contraction of the stream near the hole reduce the volume of water leaving the tank per second to $cA_h\sqrt{2gh}$, where c ($0 < c < 1$) is an empirical constant. Determine a differential equation for the height h of water at time t for the cubical tank shown in Figure 1.3.11. The radius of the hole is 2 in., and $g = 32$ ft/s^2.

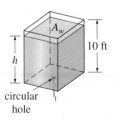

FIGURE 1.3.11 Cubical tank in Problem 13

14. The right-circular conical tank shown in Figure 1.3.12 loses water out of a circular hole at its bottom. Determine a differential equation for the height of the water h at time t. The radius of the hole is 2 in., $g = 32$ ft/s², and the friction/contraction factor introduced in Problem 13 is $c = 0.6$.

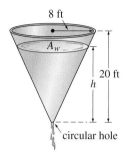

FIGURE 1.3.12 Conical tank in Problem 14

Series Circuits

15. A series circuit contains a resistor and an inductor as shown in Figure 1.3.13. Determine a differential equation for the current $i(t)$ if the resistance is R, the inductance is L, and the impressed voltage is $E(t)$.

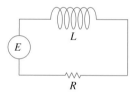

FIGURE 1.3.13 *LR* series circuit in Problem 15

16. A series circuit contains a resistor and a capacitor as shown in Figure 1.3.14. Determine a differential equation for the charge $q(t)$ on the capacitor if the resistance is R, the capacitance is C, and the impressed voltage is $E(t)$.

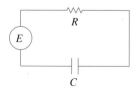

FIGURE 1.3.14 *RC* series circuit in Problem 16

Falling Bodies and Air Resistance

17. For high-speed motion through the air—such as the skydiver shown in Figure 1.3.15, falling before the parachute is opened—air resistance is closer to a power of the instantaneous velocity $v(t)$. Determine a differential equation for the velocity $v(t)$ of a falling body of mass m if air resistance is proportional to the square of the instantaneous velocity.

FIGURE 1.3.15 Air resistance proportional to square of velocity in Problem 17

Newton's Second Law and Archimedes' Principle

18. A cylindrical barrel s feet in diameter of weight w lb is floating in water as shown in Figure 1.3.16(a). After an initial depression the barrel exhibits an up-and-down bobbing motion along a vertical line. Using Figure 1.3.16(b), determine a differential equation for the vertical displacement $y(t)$ if the origin is taken to be on the vertical axis at the surface of the water when the barrel is at rest. Use **Archimedes' principle:** Buoyancy, or upward force of the water on the barrel, is equal to the weight of the water displaced. Assume that the downward direction is positive, that the weight density of water is 62.4 lb/ft³, and that there is no resistance between the barrel and the water.

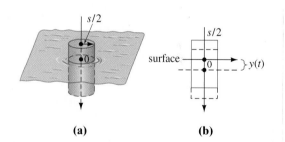

FIGURE 1.3.16 Bobbing motion of floating barrel in Problem 18

Newton's Second Law and Hooke's Law

19. After a mass m is attached to a spring, it stretches it s units and then hangs at rest in the equilibrium position as shown in Figure 1.3.17(b). After the spring/mass

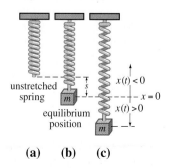

FIGURE 1.3.17 Spring/mass system in Problem 19

system has been set in motion, let $x(t)$ denote the directed distance of the mass beyond the equilibrium position. As indicated in Figure 1.3.17(c), assume that the downward direction is positive, that the motion takes place in a vertical straight line through the center of gravity of the mass, and that the only forces acting on the system are the weight of the mass and the restoring force of the stretched spring. Use **Hooke's law:** The restoring force of a spring is proportional to its total elongation. Determine a differential equation for the displacement $x(t)$ at time t.

20. In Problem 19, what is a differential equation for the displacement $x(t)$ if the motion takes place in a medium that imparts a damping force on the spring/mass system that is proportional to the instantaneous velocity of the mass and acts in a direction opposite to that of motion?

Newton's Second Law and the Law of Universal Gravitation

21. By **Newton's universal law of gravitation** the free-fall acceleration a of a body, such as the satellite shown in Figure 1.3.18, falling a great distance to the surface is *not* the constant g. Rather, the acceleration a is inversely proportional to the square of the distance from the center of the Earth, $a = k/r^2$, where k is the constant of proportionality. Use the fact that at the surface of the Earth $r = R$ and $a = g$ to determine k. If the positive direction is upward, use Newton's second law and his universal law of gravitation to find a differential equation for the distance r.

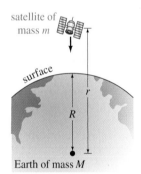

FIGURE 1.3.18 Satellite in Problem 21

22. Suppose a hole is drilled through the center of the Earth and a bowling ball of mass m is dropped into the hole, as shown in Figure 1.3.19. Construct a mathematical model that describes the motion of the ball. At time t let r denote the distance from the center of the Earth to the mass m, M denote the mass of the Earth, M_r denote the mass of that portion of the Earth within a sphere of radius r, and δ denote the constant density of the Earth.

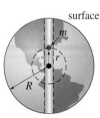

FIGURE 1.3.19 Hole through Earth in Problem 22

Additional Mathematical Models

23. **Learning Theory** In the theory of learning, the rate at which a subject is memorized is assumed to be proportional to the amount that is left to be memorized. Suppose M denotes the total amount of a subject to be memorized and $A(t)$ is the amount memorized in time t. Determine a differential equation for the amount $A(t)$.

24. **Forgetfulness** In Problem 23 assume that the rate at which material is *forgotten* is proportional to the amount memorized in time t. Determine a differential equation for the amount $A(t)$ when forgetfulness is taken into account.

25. **Infusion of a Drug** A drug is infused into a patient's bloodstream at a constant rate of r grams per second. Simultaneously, the drug is removed at a rate proportional to the amount $x(t)$ of the drug present at time t. Determine a differential equation for the amount $x(t)$.

26. **Tractrix** A person P, starting at the origin, moves in the direction of the positive x-axis, pulling a weight along the curve C, called a **tractrix**, as shown in Figure 1.3.20. The weight, initially located on the y-axis at $(0, s)$, is pulled by a rope of constant length s, which is kept taut throughout the motion. Determine a differential equation for the path C of motion. Assume that the rope is always tangent to C.

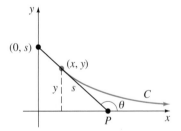

FIGURE 1.3.20 Tractrix curve in Problem 26

27. **Reflecting Surface** Assume that when the plane curve C shown in Figure 1.3.21 is revolved about the x-axis, it generates a surface of revolution with the property that all light rays L parallel to the x-axis striking the surface are reflected to a single point O (the origin). Use the fact that the angle of incidence is equal to the angle of reflection to determine a differential equation that

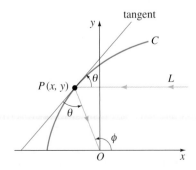

FIGURE 1.3.21 Reflecting surface in Problem 27

describes the shape of the curve C. Such a curve C is important in applications ranging from construction of telescopes to satellite antennas, automobile headlights, and solar collectors. [*Hint*: Inspection of the figure shows that we can write $\phi = 2\theta$. Why? Now use an appropriate trigonometric identity.]

Discussion Problems

28. Reread Problem 41 in Exercises 1.1 and then give an explicit solution $P(t)$ for equation (1). Find a one-parameter family of solutions of (1).

29. Reread the sentence following equation (3) and assume that T_m is a positive constant. Discuss why we would expect $k < 0$ in (3) in both cases of cooling and warming. You might start by interpreting, say, $T(t) > T_m$ in a graphical manner.

30. Reread the discussion leading up to equation (8). If we assume that initially the tank holds, say, 50 lb of salt, it stands to reason that because salt is being added to the tank continuously for $t > 0$, $A(t)$ should be an increasing function. Discuss how you might determine from the DE, without actually solving it, the number of pounds of salt in the tank after a long period of time.

31. Population Model The differential equation $\dfrac{dP}{dt} = (k \cos t)P$, where k is a positive constant, is a model of human population $P(t)$ of a certain community. Discuss an interpretation for the solution of this equation. In other words, what kind of population do you think the differential equation describes?

32. Rotating Fluid As shown in Figure 1.3.22(a), a right-circular cylinder partially filled with fluid is rotated with a constant angular velocity ω about a vertical y-axis through its center. The rotating fluid forms a surface of revolution S. To identify S, we first establish a coordinate system consisting of a vertical plane determined by the y-axis and an x-axis drawn perpendicular to the y-axis such that the point of intersection of the axes (the origin) is located at the lowest point on the surface S. We then seek a function $y = f(x)$ that represents the curve C of intersection of the surface S and the vertical coordinate plane. Let the point $P(x, y)$ denote the position of a particle of the rotating fluid of mass m in the coordinate plane. See Figure 1.3.22(b).

(a) At P there is a reaction force of magnitude F due to the other particles of the fluid which is normal to the surface S. By Newton's second law the magnitude of the net force acting on the particle is $m\omega^2 x$. What is this force? Use Figure 1.3.22(b) to discuss the nature and origin of the equations

$$F \cos \theta = mg, \qquad F \sin \theta = m\omega^2 x.$$

(b) Use part (a) to find a first-order differential equation that defines the function $y = f(x)$.

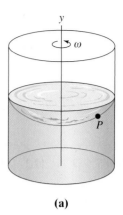

(a)

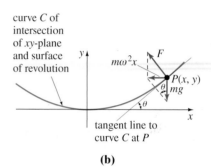

(b)

FIGURE 1.3.22 Rotating fluid in Problem 32

33. Falling Body In Problem 21, suppose $r = R + s$, where s is the distance from the surface of the Earth to the falling body. What does the differential equation obtained in Problem 21 become when s is very small in comparison to R? [*Hint*: Think binomial series for

$$(R + s)^{-2} = R^{-2}(1 + s/R)^{-2}.]$$

34. Raindrops Keep Falling In meteorology the term *virga* refers to falling raindrops or ice particles that evaporate before they reach the ground. Assume that a typical raindrop is spherical. Starting at some time, which we can designate as $t = 0$, the raindrop of radius r_0 falls from rest from a cloud and begins to evaporate.

(a) If it is assumed that a raindrop evaporates in such a manner that its shape remains spherical, then it also makes sense to assume that the rate at which the raindrop evaporates—that is, the rate at which it loses mass—is proportional to its surface area. Show that this latter assumption implies that the rate at which the radius r of the raindrop decreases is a constant. Find $r(t)$. [*Hint*: See Problem 51 in Exercises 1.1.]

(b) If the positive direction is downward, construct a mathematical model for the velocity v of the falling raindrop at time t. Ignore air resistance. [*Hint*: When the mass m of an object is changing with time, Newton's second law becomes $F = \dfrac{d}{dt}(mv)$, where F is the net force acting on the body and mv is its momentum.]

35. Let It Snow The "snowplow problem" is a classic and appears in many differential equations texts but was probably made famous by Ralph Palmer Agnew:

> *"One day it started snowing at a heavy and steady rate. A snowplow started out at noon, going 2 miles the first hour and 1 mile the second hour. What time did it start snowing?"*

Find the text *Differential Equations,* Ralph Palmer Agnew, McGraw-Hill Book Co., and then discuss the construction and solution of the mathematical model.

36. Reread this section and classify each mathematical model as linear or nonlinear.

CHAPTER 1 IN REVIEW

Answers to selected odd-numbered problems begin on page ANS-1.

In Problems 1 and 2 fill in the blank and then write this result as a linear first-order differential equation that is free of the symbol c_1 and has the form $dy/dx = f(x, y)$. The symbol c_1 represents a constant.

1. $\dfrac{d}{dx} c_1 e^{10x} =$ _____

2. $\dfrac{d}{dx} (5 + c_1 e^{-2x}) =$ _____

In Problems 3 and 4 fill in the blank and then write this result as a linear second-order differential equation that is free of the symbols c_1 and c_2 and has the form $F(y, y'') = 0$. The symbols c_1, c_2, and k represent constants.

3. $\dfrac{d^2}{dx^2} (c_1 \cos kx + c_2 \sin kx) =$ _____

4. $\dfrac{d^2}{dx^2} (c_1 \cosh kx + c_2 \sinh kx) =$ _____

In Problems 5 and 6 compute y' and y'' and then combine these derivatives with y as a linear second-order differential equation that is free of the symbols c_1 and c_2 and has the form $F(y, y', y'') = 0$. The symbols c_1 and c_2 represent constants.

5. $y = c_1 e^x + c_2 x e^x$
6. $y = c_1 e^x \cos x + c_2 e^x \sin x$

In Problems 7–12 match each of the given differential equations with one or more of these solutions:

(a) $y = 0$, **(b)** $y = 2$, **(c)** $y = 2x$, **(d)** $y = 2x^2$.

7. $xy' = 2y$
8. $y' = 2$
9. $y' = 2y - 4$
10. $xy' = y$
11. $y'' + 9y = 18$
12. $xy'' - y' = 0$

In Problems 13 and 14 determine by inspection at least one solution of the given differential equation.

13. $y'' = y'$
14. $y' = y(y - 3)$

In Problems 15 and 16 interpret each statement as a differential equation.

15. On the graph of $y = \phi(x)$ the slope of the tangent line at a point $P(x, y)$ is the square of the distance from $P(x, y)$ to the origin.

16. On the graph of $y = \phi(x)$ the rate at which the slope changes with respect to x at a point $P(x, y)$ is the negative of the slope of the tangent line at $P(x, y)$.

17. (a) Give the domain of the function $y = x^{2/3}$.

(b) Give the largest interval I of definition over which $y = x^{2/3}$ is solution of the differential equation $3xy' - 2y = 0$.

18. (a) Verify that the one-parameter family $y^2 - 2y = x^2 - x + c$ is an implicit solution of the differential equation $(2y - 2)y' = 2x - 1$.

(b) Find a member of the one-parameter family in part (a) that satisfies the initial condition $y(0) = 1$.

(c) Use your result in part (b) to find an explicit *function* $y = \phi(x)$ that satisfies $y(0) = 1$. Give the domain of the function ϕ. Is $y = \phi(x)$ a *solution* of the initial-value problem? If so, give its interval I of definition; if not, explain.

19. Given that $y = x - 2/x$ is a solution of the DE $xy' + y = 2x$. Find x_0 and the largest interval I for which $y(x)$ is a solution of the first-order IVP $xy' + y = 2x, y(x_0) = 1$.

20. Suppose that $y(x)$ denotes a solution of the first-order IVP $y' = x^2 + y^2, y(1) = -1$ and that $y(x)$ possesses at least a second derivative at $x = 1$. In some neighborhood of $x = 1$ use the DE to determine whether $y(x)$ is increasing or decreasing and whether the graph $y(x)$ is concave up or concave down.

21. A differential equation may possess more than one family of solutions.

(a) Plot different members of the families $y = \phi_1(x) = x^2 + c_1$ and $y = \phi_2(x) = -x^2 + c_2$.

(b) Verify that $y = \phi_1(x)$ and $y = \phi_2(x)$ are two solutions of the nonlinear first-order differential equation $(y')^2 = 4x^2$.

(c) Construct a piecewise-defined function that is a solution of the nonlinear DE in part (b) but is not a member of either family of solutions in part (a).

22. What is the slope of the tangent line to the graph of a solution of $y' = 6\sqrt{y} + 5x^3$ that passes through $(-1, 4)$?

In Problems 23–26 verify that the indicated function is a particular solution of the given differential equation. Give an interval of definition I for each solution.

23. $y'' + y = 2 \cos x - 2 \sin x; \quad y = x \sin x + x \cos x$

24. $y'' + y = \sec x; \quad y = x \sin x + (\cos x)\ln(\cos x)$

25. $x^2y'' + xy' + y = 0;\quad y = \sin(\ln x)$

26. $x^2y'' + xy' + y = \sec(\ln x)$;
$y = \cos(\ln x)\ln(\cos(\ln x)) + (\ln x)\sin(\ln x)$

In Problems 27–30, $y = c_1e^{3x} + c_2e^{-x} - 2x$ is a two-parameter family of the second-order DE $y'' - 2y' - 3y = 6x + 4$. Find a solution of the second-order IVP consisting of this differential equation and the given initial conditions.

27. $y(0) = 0, y'(0) = 0$ **28.** $y(0) = 1, y'(0) = -3$

29. $y(1) = 4, y'(1) = -2$ **30.** $y(-1) = 0, y'(-1) = 1$

31. The graph of a solution of a second-order initial-value problem $d^2y/dx^2 = f(x, y, y')$, $y(2) = y_0$, $y'(2) = y_1$, is given in Figure 1.R.1. Use the graph to estimate the values of y_0 and y_1.

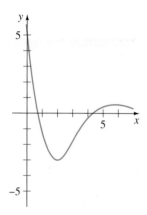

FIGURE 1.R.1   Graph for Problem 31

32. A tank in the form of a right-circular cylinder of radius 2 feet and height 10 feet is standing on end. If the tank is initially full of water and water leaks from a circular hole of radius $\frac{1}{2}$ inch at its bottom, determine a differential equation for the height h of the water at time t. Ignore friction and contraction of water at the hole.

33. The number of field mice in a certain pasture is given by the function $200 - 10t$, where time t is measured in years. Determine a differential equation governing a population of owls that feed on the mice if the rate at which the owl population grows is proportional to the difference between the number of owls at time t and number of field mice at time t.

34. Suppose that $dA/dt = -0.0004332\,A(t)$ represents a mathematical model for the radioactive decay of radium-226, where $A(t)$ is the amount of radium (measured in grams) remaining at time t (measured in years). How much of the radium sample remains at the time t when the sample is decaying at a rate of 0.002 gram per year?

2 FIRST-ORDER DIFFERENTIAL EQUATIONS

The history of mathematics is rife with stories of people who devoted much of their lives to solving equations—algebraic equations at first and then eventually differential equations. In Sections 2.2–2.5 we will study some of the more important analytical methods for solving first-order DEs. However, before we start solving anything, you should be aware of two facts: It is possible for a differential equation to have no solutions, and a differential equation can possess a solution yet there might not exist any analytical method for finding it. In Sections 2.1 and 2.6 we do not solve any DEs but show how to glean information directly from the equation itself. In Section 2.1 we see how the DE yields qualitative information about graphs that enables us to sketch renditions of solutions curves. In Section 2.6 we use the differential equation to construct a numerical procedure for approximating solutions.

SOLUTION CURVES WITHOUT A SOLUTION

REVIEW MATERIAL

- The first derivative as slope of a tangent line
- The algebraic sign of the first derivative indicates increasing or decreasing

INTRODUCTION   Let us imagine for the moment that we have in front of us a first-order differential equation $dy/dx = f(x, y)$, and let us further imagine that we can neither find nor invent a method for solving it analytically. This is not as bad a predicament as one might think, since the differential equation itself can sometimes "tell" us specifics about how its solutions "behave."
   We begin our study of first-order differential equations with two ways of analyzing a DE qualitatively. Both these ways enable us to determine, in an approximate sense, what a solution curve must look like without actually solving the equation.

2.1.1   DIRECTION FIELDS

SOME FUNDAMENTAL QUESTIONS   We saw in Section 1.2 that whenever $f(x, y)$ and $\partial f/\partial y$ satisfy certain continuity conditions, qualitative questions about existence and uniqueness of solutions can be answered. In this section we shall see that other qualitative questions about properties of solutions—How does a solution behave near a certain point? How does a solution behave as $x \rightarrow \infty$?—can often be answered when the function f depends solely on the variable y. We begin, however, with a simple concept from calculus:

A derivative dy/dx of a differentiable function $y = y(x)$ gives slopes of tangent lines at points on its graph.

SLOPE   Because a solution $y = y(x)$ of a first-order differential equation

$$\frac{dy}{dx} = f(x, y) \tag{1}$$

is necessarily a differentiable function on its interval I of definition, it must also be continuous on I. Thus the corresponding solution curve on I must have no breaks and must possess a tangent line at each point $(x, y(x))$. The function f in the normal form (1) is called the **slope function** or **rate function.** The slope of the tangent line at $(x, y(x))$ on a solution curve is the value of the first derivative dy/dx at this point, and we know from (1) that this is the value of the slope function $f(x, y(x))$. Now suppose that (x, y) represents any point in a region of the xy-plane over which the function f is defined. The value $f(x, y)$ that the function f assigns to the point represents the slope of a line or, as we shall envision it, a line segment called a **lineal element.** For example, consider the equation $dy/dx = 0.2xy$, where $f(x, y) = 0.2xy$. At, say, the point $(2, 3)$ the slope of a lineal element is $f(2, 3) = 0.2(2)(3) = 1.2$. Figure 2.1.1(a) shows a line segment with slope 1.2 passing though $(2, 3)$. As shown in Figure 2.1.1(b), *if* a solution curve also passes through the point $(2, 3)$, it does so tangent to this line segment; in other words, the lineal element is a miniature tangent line at that point.

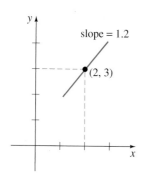

(a) lineal element at a point

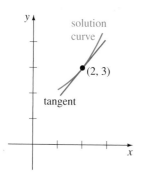

(b) lineal element is tangent to solution curve that passes through the point

FIGURE 2.1.1   A solution curve is tangent to lineal element at $(2, 3)$

DIRECTION FIELD   If we systematically evaluate f over a rectangular grid of points in the xy-plane and draw a line element at each point (x, y) of the grid with slope $f(x, y)$, then the collection of all these line elements is called a **direction field** or a **slope field** of the differential equation $dy/dx = f(x, y)$. Visually, the direction field suggests the appearance or shape of a family of solution curves of the differential equation, and consequently, it may be possible to see at a glance certain qualitative aspects of the solutions—regions in the plane, for example, in which a

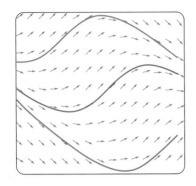

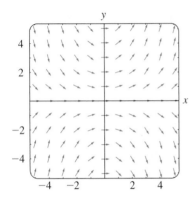

FIGURE 2.1.2 Solution curves following flow of a direction field

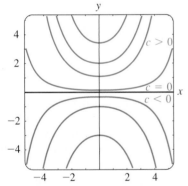

(a) direction field for $dy/dx = 0.2xy$

(b) some solution curves in the family $y = ce^{0.1x^2}$

FIGURE 2.1.3 Direction field and solution curves

solution exhibits an unusual behavior. A single solution curve that passes through a direction field must follow the flow pattern of the field; it is tangent to a line element when it intersects a point in the grid. Figure 2.1.2 shows a computer-generated direction field of the differential equation $dy/dx = \sin(x + y)$ over a region of the xy-plane. Note how the three solution curves shown in color follow the flow of the field.

EXAMPLE 1 Direction Field

The direction field for the differential equation $dy/dx = 0.2xy$ shown in Figure 2.1.3(a) was obtained by using computer software in which a 5×5 grid of points (mh, nh), m and n integers, was defined by letting $-5 \le m \le 5$, $-5 \le n \le 5$, and $h = 1$. Notice in Figure 2.1.3(a) that at any point along the x-axis $(y = 0)$ and the y-axis $(x = 0)$, the slopes are $f(x, 0) = 0$ and $f(0, y) = 0$, respectively, so the lineal elements are horizontal. Moreover, observe in the first quadrant that for a fixed value of x the values of $f(x, y) = 0.2xy$ increase as y increases; similarly, for a fixed y the values of $f(x, y) = 0.2xy$ increase as x increases. This means that as both x and y increase, the lineal elements almost become vertical and have positive slope ($f(x, y) = 0.2xy > 0$ for $x > 0$, $y > 0$). In the second quadrant, $|f(x, y)|$ increases as $|x|$ and y increase, so the lineal elements again become almost vertical but this time have negative slope ($f(x, y) = 0.2xy < 0$ for $x < 0$, $y > 0$). Reading from left to right, imagine a solution curve that starts at a point in the second quadrant, moves steeply downward, becomes flat as it passes through the y-axis, and then, as it enters the first quadrant, moves steeply upward—in other words, its shape would be concave upward and similar to a horseshoe. From this it could be surmised that $y \to \infty$ as $x \to \pm\infty$. Now in the third and fourth quadrants, since $f(x, y) = 0.2xy > 0$ and $f(x, y) = 0.2xy < 0$, respectively, the situation is reversed: A solution curve increases and then decreases as we move from left to right. We saw in (1) of Section 1.1 that $y = e^{0.1x^2}$ is an explicit solution of the differential equation $dy/dx = 0.2xy$; you should verify that a one-parameter family of solutions of the same equation is given by $y = ce^{0.1x^2}$. For purposes of comparison with Figure 2.1.3(a) some representative graphs of members of this family are shown in Figure 2.1.3(b). ∎

EXAMPLE 2 Direction Field

Use a direction field to sketch an approximate solution curve for the initial-value problem $dy/dx = \sin y$, $y(0) = -\frac{3}{2}$.

SOLUTION Before proceeding, recall that from the continuity of $f(x, y) = \sin y$ and $\partial f/\partial y = \cos y$, Theorem 1.2.1 guarantees the existence of a unique solution curve passing through any specified point (x_0, y_0) in the plane. Now we set our computer software again for a 5×5 rectangular region and specify (because of the initial condition) points in that region with vertical and horizontal separation of $\frac{1}{2}$ unit—that is, at points (mh, nh), $h = \frac{1}{2}$, m and n integers such that $-10 \le m \le 10$, $-10 \le n \le 10$. The result is shown in Figure 2.1.4. Because the right-hand side of $dy/dx = \sin y$ is 0 at $y = 0$, and at $y = -\pi$, the lineal elements are horizontal at all points whose second coordinates are $y = 0$ or $y = -\pi$. It makes sense then that a solution curve passing through the initial point $(0, -\frac{3}{2})$ has the shape shown in the figure. ∎

INCREASING/DECREASING Interpretation of the derivative dy/dx as a function that gives slope plays the key role in the construction of a direction field. Another telling property of the first derivative will be used next, namely, if $dy/dx > 0$ (or $dy/dx < 0$) for all x in an interval I, then a differentiable function $y = y(x)$ is increasing (or decreasing) on I.

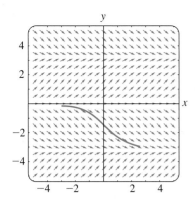

FIGURE 2.1.4 Direction field for Example 2

REMARKS

Sketching a direction field by hand is straightforward but time consuming; it is probably one of those tasks about which an argument can be made for doing it once or twice in a lifetime, but it is overall most efficiently carried out by means of computer software. Before calculators, PCs, and software the **method of isoclines** was used to facilitate sketching a direction field by hand. For the DE $dy/dx = f(x, y)$, any member of the family of curves $f(x, y) = c$, c a constant, is called an **isocline.** Lineal elements drawn through points on a specific isocline, say, $f(x, y) = c_1$ all have the same slope c_1. In Problem 15 in Exercises 2.1 you have your two opportunities to sketch a direction field by hand.

2.1.2 AUTONOMOUS FIRST-ORDER DEs

AUTONOMOUS FIRST-ORDER DEs In Section 1.1 we divided the class of ordinary differential equations into two types: linear and nonlinear. We now consider briefly another kind of classification of ordinary differential equations, a classification that is of particular importance in the qualitative investigation of differential equations. An ordinary differential equation in which the independent variable does not appear explicitly is said to be **autonomous.** If the symbol x denotes the independent variable, then an autonomous first-order differential equation can be written as $f(y, y') = 0$ or in normal form as

$$\frac{dy}{dx} = f(y). \tag{2}$$

We shall assume throughout that the function f in (2) and its derivative f' are continuous functions of y on some interval I. The first-order equations

$$\overset{f(y)}{\underset{\downarrow}{}} \qquad\qquad \overset{f(x, y)}{\underset{\downarrow}{}}$$

$$\frac{dy}{dx} = 1 + y^2 \qquad \text{and} \qquad \frac{dy}{dx} = 0.2xy$$

are autonomous and nonautonomous, respectively.

Many differential equations encountered in applications or equations that are models of physical laws that do not change over time are autonomous. As we have already seen in Section 1.3, in an applied context, symbols other than y and x are routinely used to represent the dependent and independent variables. For example, if t represents time then inspection of

$$\frac{dA}{dt} = kA, \qquad \frac{dx}{dt} = kx(n + 1 - x), \qquad \frac{dT}{dt} = k(T - T_m), \qquad \frac{dA}{dt} = 6 - \frac{1}{100}A,$$

where k, n, and T_m are constants, shows that each equation is time independent. Indeed, *all* of the first-order differential equations introduced in Section 1.3 are time independent and so are autonomous.

CRITICAL POINTS The zeros of the function f in (2) are of special importance. We say that a real number c is a **critical point** of the autonomous differential equation (2) if it is a zero of f—that is, $f(c) = 0$. A critical point is also called an **equilibrium point** or **stationary point.** Now observe that if we substitute the constant function $y(x) = c$ into (2), then both sides of the equation are zero. This means:

> If c is a critical point of (2), then $y(x) = c$ is a constant solution of the autonomous differential equation.

A constant solution $y(x) = c$ of (2) is called an **equilibrium solution;** equilibria are the *only* constant solutions of (2).

As was already mentioned, we can tell when a nonconstant solution $y = y(x)$ of (2) is increasing or decreasing by determining the algebraic sign of the derivative dy/dx; in the case of (2) we do this by identifying intervals on the y-axis over which the function $f(y)$ is positive or negative.

EXAMPLE 3   An Autonomous DE

The differential equation

$$\frac{dP}{dt} = P(a - bP),$$

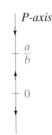

FIGURE 2.1.5   Phase portrait of $dP/dt = P(a - bP)$

where a and b are positive constants, has the normal form $dP/dt = f(P)$, which is (2) with t and P playing the parts of x and y, respectively, and hence is autonomous. From $f(P) = P(a - bP) = 0$ we see that 0 and a/b are critical points of the equation, so the equilibrium solutions are $P(t) = 0$ and $P(t) = a/b$. By putting the critical points on a vertical line, we divide the line into three intervals defined by $-\infty < P < 0$, $0 < P < a/b$, $a/b < P < \infty$. The arrows on the line shown in Figure 2.1.5 indicate the algebraic sign of $f(P) = P(a - bP)$ on these intervals and whether a nonconstant solution $P(t)$ is increasing or decreasing on an interval. The following table explains the figure.

Interval	Sign of $f(P)$	$P(t)$	Arrow
$(-\infty, 0)$	minus	decreasing	points down
$(0, a/b)$	plus	increasing	points up
$(a/b, \infty)$	minus	decreasing	points down

Figure 2.1.5 is called a **one-dimensional phase portrait**, or simply **phase portrait**, of the differential equation $dP/dt = P(a - bP)$. The vertical line is called a **phase line**.

SOLUTION CURVES   Without solving an autonomous differential equation, we can usually say a great deal about its solution curves. Since the function f in (2) is independent of the variable x, we may consider f defined for $-\infty < x < \infty$ or for $0 \leq x < \infty$. Also, since f and its derivative f' are continuous functions of y on some interval I of the y-axis, the fundamental results of Theorem 1.2.1 hold in some horizontal strip or region R in the xy-plane corresponding to I, and so through any point (x_0, y_0) in R there passes only one solution curve of (2). See Figure 2.1.6(a). For the sake of discussion, let us suppose that (2) possesses exactly two critical points c_1 and c_2 and that $c_1 < c_2$. The graphs of the equilibrium solutions $y(x) = c_1$ and $y(x) = c_2$ are horizontal lines, and these lines partition the region R into three subregions R_1, R_2, and R_3, as illustrated in Figure 2.1.6(b). Without proof here are some conclusions that we can draw about a nonconstant solution $y(x)$ of (2):

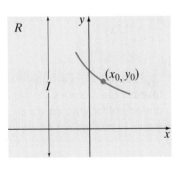

(a) region R

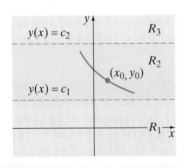

(b) subregions R_1, R_2, and R_3 of R

FIGURE 2.1.6   Lines $y(x) = c_1$ and $y(x) = c_2$ partition R into three horizontal subregions

- If (x_0, y_0) is in a subregion R_i, $i = 1, 2, 3$, and $y(x)$ is a solution whose graph passes through this point, then $y(x)$ remains in the subregion R_i for all x. As illustrated in Figure 2.1.6(b), the solution $y(x)$ in R_2 is bounded below by c_1 and above by c_2, that is, $c_1 < y(x) < c_2$ for all x. The solution curve stays within R_2 for all x because the graph of a nonconstant solution of (2) cannot cross the graph of either equilibrium solution $y(x) = c_1$ or $y(x) = c_2$. See Problem 33 in Exercises 2.1.

- By continuity of f we must then have either $f(y) > 0$ or $f(y) < 0$ for all x in a subregion R_i, $i = 1, 2, 3$. In other words, $f(y)$ cannot change signs in a subregion. See Problem 33 in Exercises 2.1.

- Since $dy/dx = f(y(x))$ is either positive or negative in a subregion R_i, $i = 1$, 2, 3, a solution $y(x)$ is strictly monotonic — that is, $y(x)$ is either increasing or decreasing in the subregion R_i. Therefore $y(x)$ cannot be oscillatory, nor can it have a relative extremum (maximum or minimum). See Problem 33 in Exercises 2.1.

- If $y(x)$ is *bounded above* by a critical point c_1 (as in subregion R_1 where $y(x) < c_1$ for all x), then the graph of $y(x)$ must approach the graph of the equilibrium solution $y(x) = c_1$ either as $x \to \infty$ or as $x \to -\infty$. If $y(x)$ is *bounded* — that is, bounded above and below by two consecutive critical points (as in subregion R_2 where $c_1 < y(x) < c_2$ for all x) — then the graph of $y(x)$ must approach the graphs of the equilibrium solutions $y(x) = c_1$ and $y(x) = c_2$, one as $x \to \infty$ and the other as $x \to -\infty$. If $y(x)$ is *bounded below* by a critical point (as in subregion R_3 where $c_2 < y(x)$ for all x), then the graph of $y(x)$ must approach the graph of the equilibrium solution $y(x) = c_2$ either as $x \to \infty$ or as $x \to -\infty$. See Problem 34 in Exercises 2.1.

With the foregoing facts in mind, let us reexamine the differential equation in Example 3.

EXAMPLE 4   Example 3 Revisited

The three intervals determined on the P-axis or phase line by the critical points $P = 0$ and $P = a/b$ now correspond in the tP-plane to three subregions defined by:

$$R_1: -\infty < P < 0, \qquad R_2: 0 < P < a/b, \qquad \text{and} \qquad R_3: a/b < P < \infty,$$

where $-\infty < t < \infty$. The phase portrait in Figure 2.1.7 tells us that $P(t)$ is decreasing in R_1, increasing in R_2, and decreasing in R_3. If $P(0) = P_0$ is an initial value, then in R_1, R_2, and R_3 we have, respectively, the following:

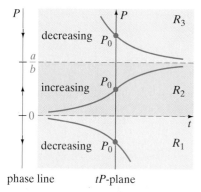

P decreasing P_0 P R_3

$\frac{a}{b}$

increasing P_0 R_2

0 t

decreasing P_0 R_1

phase line tP-plane

FIGURE 2.1.7 Phase portrait and solution curves in each of the three subregions

(i)   For $P_0 < 0$, $P(t)$ is bounded above. Since $P(t)$ is decreasing, $P(t)$ decreases without bound for increasing t, and so $P(t) \to 0$ as $t \to -\infty$. This means that the negative t-axis, the graph of the equilibrium solution $P(t) = 0$, is a horizontal asymptote for a solution curve.

(ii)   For $0 < P_0 < a/b$, $P(t)$ is bounded. Since $P(t)$ is increasing, $P(t) \to a/b$ as $t \to \infty$ and $P(t) \to 0$ as $t \to -\infty$. The graphs of the two equilibrium solutions, $P(t) = 0$ and $P(t) = a/b$, are horizontal lines that are horizontal asymptotes for any solution curve starting in this subregion.

(iii)   For $P_0 > a/b$, $P(t)$ is bounded below. Since $P(t)$ is decreasing, $P(t) \to a/b$ as $t \to \infty$. The graph of the equilibrium solution $P(t) = a/b$ is a horizontal asymptote for a solution curve.

In Figure 2.1.7 the phase line is the P-axis in the tP-plane. For clarity the original phase line from Figure 2.1.5 is reproduced to the left of the plane in which the subregions R_1, R_2, and R_3 are shaded. The graphs of the equilibrium solutions $P(t) = a/b$ and $P(t) = 0$ (the t-axis) are shown in the figure as blue dashed lines; the solid graphs represent typical graphs of $P(t)$ illustrating the three cases just discussed. ∎

In a subregion such as R_1 in Example 4, where $P(t)$ is decreasing and unbounded below, we must necessarily have $P(t) \to -\infty$. Do *not* interpret this last statement to mean $P(t) \to -\infty$ as $t \to \infty$; we could have $P(t) \to -\infty$ as $t \to T$, where $T > 0$ is a finite number that depends on the initial condition $P(t_0) = P_0$. Thinking in dynamic terms, $P(t)$ could "blow up" in finite time; thinking graphically, $P(t)$ could have a vertical asymptote at $t = T > 0$. A similar remark holds for the subregion R_3.

The differential equation $dy/dx = \sin y$ in Example 2 is autonomous and has an infinite number of critical points, since $\sin y = 0$ at $y = n\pi$, n an integer. Moreover, we now know that because the solution $y(x)$ that passes through $(0, -\frac{3}{2})$ is bounded above and below by two consecutive critical points $(-\pi < y(x) < 0)$ and is decreasing ($\sin y < 0$ for $-\pi < y < 0$), the graph of $y(x)$ must approach the graphs of the equilibrium solutions as horizontal asymptotes: $y(x) \to -\pi$ as $x \to \infty$ and $y(x) \to 0$ as $x \to -\infty$.

EXAMPLE 5 **Solution Curves of an Autonomous DE**

The autonomous equation $dy/dx = (y - 1)^2$ possesses the single critical point 1. From the phase portrait in Figure 2.1.8(a) we conclude that a solution $y(x)$ is an increasing function in the subregions defined by $-\infty < y < 1$ and $1 < y < \infty$, where $-\infty < x < \infty$. For an initial condition $y(0) = y_0 < 1$, a solution $y(x)$ is increasing and bounded above by 1, and so $y(x) \to 1$ as $x \to \infty$; for $y(0) = y_0 > 1$ a solution $y(x)$ is increasing and unbounded.

Now $y(x) = 1 - 1/(x + c)$ is a one-parameter family of solutions of the differential equation. (See Problem 4 in Exercises 2.2) A given initial condition determines a value for c. For the initial conditions, say, $y(0) = -1 < 1$ and $y(0) = 2 > 1$, we find, in turn, that $y(x) = 1 - 1/(x + \frac{1}{2})$, and $y(x) = 1 - 1/(x - 1)$. As shown in Figures 2.1.8(b) and 2.1.8(c), the graph of each of these rational functions possesses

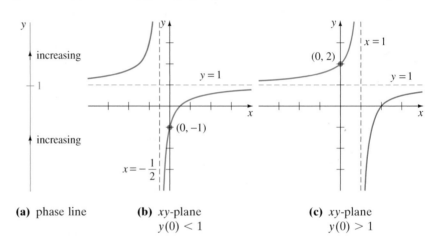

(a) phase line   **(b)** xy-plane   **(c)** xy-plane
$y(0) < 1$ $y(0) > 1$

FIGURE 2.1.8 Behavior of solutions near $y = 1$

a vertical asymptote. But bear in mind that the solutions of the IVPs

$$\frac{dy}{dx} = (y - 1)^2, \quad y(0) = -1 \quad \text{and} \quad \frac{dy}{dx} = (y - 1)^2, \quad y(0) = 2$$

are defined on special intervals. They are, respectively,

$$y(x) = 1 - \frac{1}{x + \frac{1}{2}}, \quad -\frac{1}{2} < x < \infty \quad \text{and} \quad y(x) = 1 - \frac{1}{x - 1}, \quad -\infty < x < 1.$$

The solution curves are the portions of the graphs in Figures 2.1.8(b) and 2.1.8(c) shown in blue. As predicted by the phase portrait, for the solution curve in Figure 2.1.8(b), $y(x) \to 1$ as $x \to \infty$; for the solution curve in Figure 2.1.8(c), $y(x) \to \infty$ as $x \to 1$ from the left. ∎

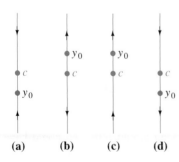

(a)   **(b)**   **(c)**   **(d)**

FIGURE 2.1.9 Critical point c is an attractor in (a), a repeller in (b), and semi-stable in (c) and (d).

ATTRACTORS AND REPELLERS Suppose that $y(x)$ is a nonconstant solution of the autonomous differential equation given in (1) and that c is a critical point of the DE. There are basically three types of behavior that $y(x)$ can exhibit near c. In Figure 2.1.9 we have placed c on four vertical phase lines. When both arrowheads on either side of the dot labeled c point *toward* c, as in Figure 2.1.9(a), all solutions $y(x)$ of (1) that start from an initial point (x_0, y_0) sufficiently near c exhibit the asymptotic behavior $\lim_{x \to \infty} y(x) = c$. For this reason the critical point c is said to be

asymptotically stable. Using a physical analogy, a solution that starts near c is like a charged particle that, over time, is drawn to a particle of opposite charge, and so c is also referred to as an **attractor.** When both arrowheads on either side of the dot labeled c point *away* from c, as in Figure 2.1.9(b), all solutions $y(x)$ of (1) that start from an initial point (x_0, y_0) move away from c as x increases. In this case the critical point c is said to be **unstable.** An unstable critical point is also called a **repeller,** for obvious reasons. The critical point c illustrated in Figures 2.1.9(c) and 2.1.9(d) is neither an attractor nor a repeller. But since c exhibits characteristics of both an attractor and a repeller—that is, a solution starting from an initial point (x_0, y_0) sufficiently near c is attracted to c from one side and repelled from the other side—we say that the critical point c is **semi-stable.** In Example 3 the critical point a/b is asymptotically stable (an attractor) and the critical point 0 is unstable (a repeller). The critical point 1 in Example 5 is semi-stable.

AUTONOMOUS DEs AND DIRECTION FIELDS   If a first-order differential equation is autonomous, then we see from the right-hand side of its normal form $dy/dx = f(y)$ that slopes of lineal elements through points in the rectangular grid used to construct a direction field for the DE depend solely on the y-coordinate of the points. Put another way, lineal elements passing through points on any *horizontal* line must all have the same slope; slopes of lineal elements along any *vertical* line will, of course, vary. These facts are apparent from inspection of the horizontal gold strip and vertical blue strip in Figure 2.1.10. The figure exhibits a direction field for the autonomous equation $dy/dx = 2y - 2$. With these facts in mind, reexamine Figure 2.1.4.

slopes of lineal elements on a vertical line vary

slopes of lineal elements on a horizontal line are all the same

FIGURE 2.1.10   Direction field for an autonomous DE

EXERCISES 2.1

Answers to selected odd-numbered problems begin on page ANS-1.

2.1.1   DIRECTION FIELDS

In Problems 1–4 reproduce the given computer-generated direction field. Then sketch, by hand, an approximate solution curve that passes through each of the indicated points. Use different colored pencils for each solution curve.

1. $\dfrac{dy}{dx} = x^2 - y^2$

(a) $y(-2) = 1$ (b) $y(3) = 0$
(c) $y(0) = 2$ (d) $y(0) = 0$

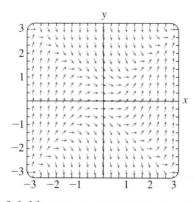

FIGURE 2.1.11   Direction field for Problem 1

2. $\dfrac{dy}{dx} = e^{-0.01xy^2}$

(a) $y(-6) = 0$ (b) $y(0) = 1$
(c) $y(0) = -4$ (d) $y(8) = -4$

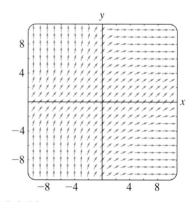

FIGURE 2.1.12   Direction field for Problem 2

3. $\dfrac{dy}{dx} = 1 - xy$

(a) $y(0) = 0$ (b) $y(-1) = 0$
(c) $y(2) = 2$ (d) $y(0) = -4$

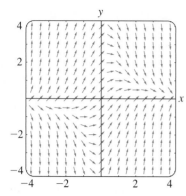

FIGURE 2.1.13 Direction field for Problem 3

4. $\dfrac{dy}{dx} = (\sin x) \cos y$

  (a) $y(0) = 1$ **(b)** $y(1) = 0$

  (c) $y(3) = 3$ **(d)** $y(0) = -\dfrac{5}{2}$

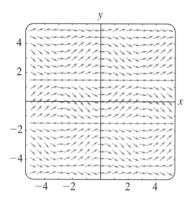

FIGURE 2.1.14 Direction field for Problem 4

In Problems 5–12 use computer software to obtain a direction field for the given differential equation. By hand, sketch an approximate solution curve passing through each of the given points.

5. $y' = x$

  (a) $y(0) = 0$

  (b) $y(0) = -3$

6. $y' = x + y$

  (a) $y(-2) = 2$

  (b) $y(1) = -3$

7. $y\dfrac{dy}{dx} = -x$

  (a) $y(1) = 1$

  (b) $y(0) = 4$

8. $\dfrac{dy}{dx} = \dfrac{1}{y}$

  (a) $y(0) = 1$

  (b) $y(-2) = -1$

9. $\dfrac{dy}{dx} = 0.2x^2 + y$

  (a) $y(0) = \dfrac{1}{2}$

  (b) $y(2) = -1$

10. $\dfrac{dy}{dx} = xe^y$

  (a) $y(0) = -2$

  (b) $y(1) = 2.5$

11. $y' = y - \cos\dfrac{\pi}{2}x$

  (a) $y(2) = 2$

  (b) $y(-1) = 0$

12. $\dfrac{dy}{dx} = 1 - \dfrac{y}{x}$

  (a) $y\!\left(-\dfrac{1}{2}\right) = 2$

  (b) $y\!\left(\dfrac{3}{2}\right) = 0$

In Problems 13 and 14 the given figure represents the graph of $f(y)$ and $f(x)$, respectively. By hand, sketch a direction field over an appropriate grid for $dy/dx = f(y)$ (Problem 13) and then for $dy/dx = f(x)$ (Problem 14).

13.

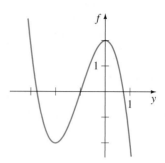

FIGURE 2.1.15 Graph for Problem 13

14.

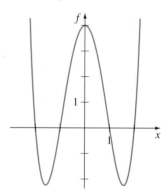

FIGURE 2.1.16 Graph for Problem 14

15. In parts (a) and (b) sketch **isoclines** $f(x, y) = c$ (see the *Remarks* on page 37) for the given differential equation using the indicated values of c. Construct a direction field over a grid by carefully drawing lineal elements with the appropriate slope at chosen points on each isocline. In each case, use this rough direction field to sketch an approximate solution curve for the IVP consisting of the DE and the initial condition $y(0) = 1$.

  (a) $dy/dx = x + y$; c an integer satisfying $-5 \le c \le 5$

  (b) $dy/dx = x^2 + y^2$; $c = \dfrac{1}{4}$, $c = 1$, $c = \dfrac{9}{4}$, $c = 4$

Discussion Problems

16. (a) Consider the direction field of the differential equation $dy/dx = x(y - 4)^2 - 2$, but do not use technology to obtain it. Describe the slopes of the lineal elements on the lines $x = 0$, $y = 3$, $y = 4$, and $y = 5$.

  (b) Consider the IVP $dy/dx = x(y - 4)^2 - 2$, $y(0) = y_0$, where $y_0 < 4$. Can a solution $y(x) \to \infty$ as $x \to \infty$? Based on the information in part (a), discuss.

17. For a first-order DE $dy/dx = f(x, y)$ a curve in the plane defined by $f(x, y) = 0$ is called a **nullcline** of the equation, since a lineal element at a point on the curve has zero slope. Use computer software to obtain a direction field over a rectangular grid of points for $dy/dx = x^2 - 2y$, and then superimpose the graph of the nullcline $y = \frac{1}{2}x^2$ over the direction field. Discuss the behavior of solution curves in regions of the plane defined by $y < \frac{1}{2}x^2$ and by $y > \frac{1}{2}x^2$. Sketch some approximate solution curves. Try to generalize your observations.

18. (a) Identify the nullclines (see Problem 17) in Problems 1, 3, and 4. With a colored pencil, circle any lineal elements in Figures 2.1.11, 2.1.13, and 2.1.14 that you think may be a lineal element at a point on a nullcline.

  (b) What are the nullclines of an autonomous first-order DE?

2.1.2 AUTONOMOUS FIRST-ORDER DEs

19. Consider the autonomous first-order differential equation $dy/dx = y - y^3$ and the initial condition $y(0) = y_0$. By hand, sketch the graph of a typical solution $y(x)$ when y_0 has the given values.

  (a) $y_0 > 1$ **(b)** $0 < y_0 < 1$
  (c) $-1 < y_0 < 0$ **(d)** $y_0 < -1$

20. Consider the autonomous first-order differential equation $dy/dx = y^2 - y^4$ and the initial condition $y(0) = y_0$. By hand, sketch the graph of a typical solution $y(x)$ when y_0 has the given values.

  (a) $y_0 > 1$ **(b)** $0 < y_0 < 1$
  (c) $-1 < y_0 < 0$ **(d)** $y_0 < -1$

In Problems 21–28 find the critical points and phase portrait of the given autonomous first-order differential equation. Classify each critical point as asymptotically stable, unstable, or semi-stable. By hand, sketch typical solution curves in the regions in the xy-plane determined by the graphs of the equilibrium solutions.

21. $\dfrac{dy}{dx} = y^2 - 3y$ **22.** $\dfrac{dy}{dx} = y^2 - y^3$

23. $\dfrac{dy}{dx} = (y - 2)^4$ **24.** $\dfrac{dy}{dx} = 10 + 3y - y^2$

25. $\dfrac{dy}{dx} = y^2(4 - y^2)$ **26.** $\dfrac{dy}{dx} = y(2 - y)(4 - y)$

27. $\dfrac{dy}{dx} = y \ln(y + 2)$ **28.** $\dfrac{dy}{dx} = \dfrac{ye^y - 9y}{e^y}$

In Problems 29 and 30 consider the autonomous differential equation $dy/dx = f(y)$, where the graph of f is given. Use the graph to locate the critical points of each differential equation. Sketch a phase portrait of each differential equation. By hand, sketch typical solution curves in the subregions in the xy-plane determined by the graphs of the equilibrium solutions.

29.

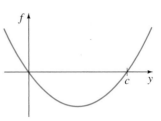

FIGURE 2.1.17   Graph for Problem 29

30.

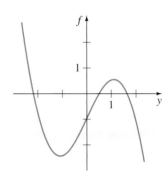

FIGURE 2.1.18   Graph for Problem 30

Discussion Problems

31. Consider the autonomous DE $dy/dx = (2/\pi)y - \sin y$. Determine the critical points of the equation. Discuss a way of obtaining a phase portrait of the equation. Classify the critical points as asymptotically stable, unstable, or semi-stable.

32. A critical point c of an autonomous first-order DE is said to be **isolated** if there exists some open interval that contains c but no other critical point. Can there exist an autonomous DE of the form given in (1) for which *every* critical point is nonisolated? Discuss; do not think profound thoughts.

33. Suppose that $y(x)$ is a nonconstant solution of the autonomous equation $dy/dx = f(y)$ and that c is a critical point of the DE. Discuss. Why can't the graph of $y(x)$ cross the graph of the equilibrium solution $y = c$? Why can't $f(y)$ change signs in one of the subregions discussed on page 38? Why can't $y(x)$ be oscillatory or have a relative extremum (maximum or minimum)?

34. Suppose that $y(x)$ is a solution of the autonomous equation $dy/dx = f(y)$ and is bounded above and below by two consecutive critical points $c_1 < c_2$, as in subregion R_2 of Figure 2.1.6(b). If $f(y) > 0$ in the region, then $\lim_{x \to \infty} y(x) = c_2$. Discuss why there cannot exist a number $L < c_2$ such that $\lim_{x \to \infty} y(x) = L$. As part of your discussion, consider what happens to $y'(x)$ as $x \to \infty$.

35. Using the autonomous equation (1), discuss how it is possible to obtain information about the location of points of inflection of a solution curve.

36. Consider the autonomous DE $dy/dx = y^2 - y - 6$. Use your ideas from Problem 35 to find intervals on the y-axis for which solution curves are concave up and intervals for which solution curves are concave down. Discuss why *each* solution curve of an initial-value problem of the form $dy/dx = y^2 - y - 6$, $y(0) = y_0$, where $-2 < y_0 < 3$, has a point of inflection with the same y-coordinate. What is that y-coordinate? Carefully sketch the solution curve for which $y(0) = -1$. Repeat for $y(2) = 2$.

37. Suppose the autonomous DE in (1) has no critical points. Discuss the behavior of the solutions.

Mathematical Models

38. Population Model The differential equation in Example 3 is a well-known population model. Suppose the DE is changed to

$$\frac{dP}{dt} = P(aP - b),$$

where a and b are positive constants. Discuss what happens to the population P as time t increases.

39. Population Model Another population model is given by

$$\frac{dP}{dt} = kP - h,$$

where h and k are positive constants. For what initial values $P(0) = P_0$ does this model predict that the population will go extinct?

40. Terminal Velocity In Section 1.3 we saw that the autonomous differential equation

$$m\frac{dv}{dt} = mg - kv,$$

where k is a positive constant and g is the acceleration due to gravity, is a model for the velocity v of a body of mass m that is falling under the influence of gravity. Because the term $-kv$ represents air resistance, the velocity of a body falling from a great height does not increase without bound as time t increases. Use a phase portrait of the differential equation to find the limiting, or terminal, velocity of the body. Explain your reasoning.

41. Suppose the model in Problem 40 is modified so that air resistance is proportional to v^2, that is,

$$m\frac{dv}{dt} = mg - kv^2.$$

See Problem 17 in Exercises 1.3. Use a phase portrait to find the terminal velocity of the body. Explain your reasoning.

42. Chemical Reactions When certain kinds of chemicals are combined, the rate at which the new compound is formed is modeled by the autonomous differential equation

$$\frac{dX}{dt} = k(\alpha - X)(\beta - X),$$

where $k > 0$ is a constant of proportionality and $\beta > \alpha > 0$. Here $X(t)$ denotes the number of grams of the new compound formed in time t.

(a) Use a phase portrait of the differential equation to predict the behavior of $X(t)$ as $t \to \infty$.

(b) Consider the case when $\alpha = \beta$. Use a phase portrait of the differential equation to predict the behavior of $X(t)$ as $t \to \infty$ when $X(0) < \alpha$. When $X(0) > \alpha$.

(c) Verify that an explicit solution of the DE in the case when $k = 1$ and $\alpha = \beta$ is $X(t) = \alpha - 1/(t + c)$. Find a solution that satisfies $X(0) = \alpha/2$. Then find a solution that satisfies $X(0) = 2\alpha$. Graph these two solutions. Does the behavior of the solutions as $t \to \infty$ agree with your answers to part (b)?

| 2.2 | SEPARABLE VARIABLES |

REVIEW MATERIAL

- Basic integration formulas (See inside front cover)
- Techniques of integration: integration by parts and partial fraction decomposition
- See also the *Student Resource and Solutions Manual*.

INTRODUCTION We begin our study of how to solve differential equations with the simplest of all differential equations: first-order equations with separable variables. Because the method in this section and many techniques for solving differential equations involve integration, you are urged to refresh your memory on important formulas (such as $\int du/u$) and techniques (such as integration by parts) by consulting a calculus text.

SOLUTION BY INTEGRATION Consider the first-order differential equation $dy/dx = f(x, y)$. When f does not depend on the variable y, that is, $f(x, y) = g(x)$, the differential equation

$$\frac{dy}{dx} = g(x) \qquad (1)$$

can be solved by integration. If $g(x)$ is a continuous function, then integrating both sides of (1) gives $y = \int g(x)\,dx = G(x) + c$, where $G(x)$ is an antiderivative (indefinite integral) of $g(x)$. For example, if $dy/dx = 1 + e^{2x}$, then its solution is $y = \int(1 + e^{2x})\,dx$ or $y = x + \frac{1}{2}e^{2x} + c$.

A DEFINITION Equation (1), as well as its method of solution, is just a special case when the function f in the normal form $dy/dx = f(x, y)$ can be factored into a function of x times a function of y.

DEFINITION 2.2.1 **Separable Equation**

A first-order differential equation of the form

$$\frac{dy}{dx} = g(x)h(y)$$

is said to be **separable** or to have **separable variables.**

For example, the equations

$$\frac{dy}{dx} = y^2 x e^{3x+4y} \qquad \text{and} \qquad \frac{dy}{dx} = y + \sin x$$

are separable and nonseparable, respectively. In the first equation we can factor $f(x, y) = y^2 x e^{3x+4y}$ as

$$f(x, y) = y^2 x e^{3x+4y} = \underset{\downarrow}{(x e^{3x})}\underset{\downarrow}{(y^2 e^{4y})},$$

$$\overset{g(x)\quad h(y)}{}$$

but in the second equation there is no way of expressing $y + \sin x$ as a product of a function of x times a function of y.

Observe that by dividing by the function $h(y)$, we can write a separable equation $dy/dx = g(x)h(y)$ as

$$p(y)\frac{dy}{dx} = g(x), \qquad (2)$$

where, for convenience, we have denoted $1/h(y)$ by $p(y)$. From this last form we can see immediately that (2) reduces to (1) when $h(y) = 1$.

Now if $y = \phi(x)$ represents a solution of (2), we must have $p(\phi(x))\phi'(x) = g(x)$, and therefore

$$\int p(\phi(x))\phi'(x)\,dx = \int g(x)\,dx. \qquad (3)$$

But $dy = \phi'(x)\,dx$, and so (3) is the same as

$$\int p(y)\,dy = \int g(x)\,dx \qquad \text{or} \qquad H(y) = G(x) + c, \qquad (4)$$

where $H(y)$ and $G(x)$ are antiderivatives of $p(y) = 1/h(y)$ and $g(x)$, respectively.

METHOD OF SOLUTION Equation (4) indicates the procedure for solving separable equations. A one-parameter family of solutions, usually given implicitly, is obtained by integrating both sides of $p(y)\, dy = g(x)\, dx$.

NOTE There is no need to use two constants in the integration of a separable equation, because if we write $H(y) + c_1 = G(x) + c_2$, then the difference $c_2 - c_1$ can be replaced by a single constant c, as in (4). In many instances throughout the chapters that follow, we will relabel constants in a manner convenient to a given equation. For example, multiples of constants or combinations of constants can sometimes be replaced by a single constant.

EXAMPLE 1 Solving a Separable DE

Solve $(1 + x)\, dy - y\, dx = 0$.

SOLUTION Dividing by $(1 + x)y$, we can write $dy/y = dx/(1 + x)$, from which it follows that

$$\int \frac{dy}{y} = \int \frac{dx}{1 + x}$$

$$\ln|y| = \ln|1 + x| + c_1$$

$$y = e^{\ln|1+x|+c_1} = e^{\ln|1+x|} \cdot e^{c_1} \quad \leftarrow \text{laws of exponents}$$

$$= |1 + x|\, e^{c_1}$$

$$= \pm e^{c_1}(1 + x). \qquad \leftarrow \begin{cases} |1 + x| = 1 + x, & x \geq -1 \\ |1 + x| = -(1 + x), & x < -1 \end{cases}$$

Relabeling $\pm e^{c_1}$ as c then gives $y = c(1 + x)$.

ALTERNATIVE SOLUTION Because each integral results in a logarithm, a judicious choice for the constant of integration is $\ln|c|$ rather than c. Rewriting the second line of the solution as $\ln|y| = \ln|1 + x| + \ln|c|$ enables us to combine the terms on the right-hand side by the properties of logarithms. From $\ln|y| = \ln|c(1 + x)|$ we immediately get $y = c(1 + x)$. Even if the indefinite integrals are not *all* logarithms, it may still be advantageous to use $\ln|c|$. However, no firm rule can be given. ∎

In Section 1.1 we saw that a solution curve may be only a segment or an arc of the graph of an implicit solution $G(x, y) = 0$.

EXAMPLE 2 Solution Curve

Solve the initial-value problem $\dfrac{dy}{dx} = -\dfrac{x}{y}$, $y(4) = -3$.

SOLUTION Rewriting the equation as $y\, dy = -x\, dx$, we get

$$\int y\, dy = -\int x\, dx \qquad \text{and} \qquad \frac{y^2}{2} = -\frac{x^2}{2} + c_1.$$

We can write the result of the integration as $x^2 + y^2 = c^2$ by replacing the constant $2c_1$ by c^2. This solution of the differential equation represents a family of concentric circles centered at the origin.

Now when $x = 4$, $y = -3$, so $16 + 9 = 25 = c^2$. Thus the initial-value problem determines the circle $x^2 + y^2 = 25$ with radius 5. Because of its simplicity we can solve this implicit solution for an explicit solution that satisfies the initial condition.

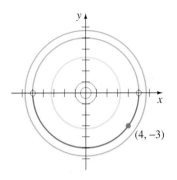

FIGURE 2.2.1 Solution curve for the IVP in Example 2

We saw this solution as $y = \phi_2(x)$ or $y = -\sqrt{25 - x^2}$, $-5 < x < 5$ in Example 3 of Section 1.1. A solution curve is the graph of a differentiable function. In this case the solution curve is the lower semicircle, shown in dark blue in Figure 2.2.1 containing the point $(4, -3)$. ∎

LOSING A SOLUTION Some care should be exercised in separating variables, since the variable divisors could be zero at a point. Specifically, if r is a zero of the function $h(y)$, then substituting $y = r$ into $dy/dx = g(x)h(y)$ makes both sides zero; in other words, $y = r$ is a constant solution of the differential equation. But after variables are separated, the left-hand side of $\dfrac{dy}{h(y)} = g(x)\,dx$ is undefined at r. As a consequence, $y = r$ might not show up in the family of solutions that are obtained after integration and simplification. Recall that such a solution is called a singular solution.

EXAMPLE 3   Losing a Solution

Solve $\dfrac{dy}{dx} = y^2 - 4$.

SOLUTION We put the equation in the form

$$\frac{dy}{y^2 - 4} = dx \qquad \text{or} \qquad \left[\frac{\frac{1}{4}}{y - 2} - \frac{\frac{1}{4}}{y + 2}\right] dy = dx. \tag{5}$$

The second equation in (5) is the result of using partial fractions on the left-hand side of the first equation. Integrating and using the laws of logarithms gives

$$\frac{1}{4} \ln|y - 2| - \frac{1}{4} \ln|y + 2| = x + c_1$$

$$\text{or} \qquad \ln\left|\frac{y - 2}{y + 2}\right| = 4x + c_2 \qquad \text{or} \qquad \frac{y - 2}{y + 2} = \pm e^{4x + c_2}.$$

Here we have replaced $4c_1$ by c_2. Finally, after replacing $\pm e^{c_2}$ by c and solving the last equation for y, we get the one-parameter family of solutions

$$y = 2\frac{1 + ce^{4x}}{1 - ce^{4x}}. \tag{6}$$

Now if we factor the right-hand side of the differential equation as $dy/dx = (y - 2)(y + 2)$, we know from the discussion of critical points in Section 2.1 that $y = 2$ and $y = -2$ are two constant (equilibrium) solutions. The solution $y = 2$ is a member of the family of solutions defined by (6) corresponding to the value $c = 0$. However, $y = -2$ is a singular solution; it cannot be obtained from (6) for any choice of the parameter c. This latter solution was lost early on in the solution process. Inspection of (5) clearly indicates that we must preclude $y = \pm 2$ in these steps. ∎

EXAMPLE 4   An Initial-Value Problem

Solve $(e^{2y} - y)\cos x \dfrac{dy}{dx} = e^y \sin 2x$, $y(0) = 0$.

SOLUTION Dividing the equation by $e^y \cos x$ gives

$$\frac{e^{2y} - y}{e^y} dy = \frac{\sin 2x}{\cos x} dx.$$

Before integrating, we use termwise division on the left-hand side and the trigonometric identity $\sin 2x = 2 \sin x \cos x$ on the right-hand side. Then

integration by parts $\rightarrow$ $$\int (e^y - ye^{-y}) \, dy = 2 \int \sin x \, dx$$

yields $$e^y + ye^{-y} + e^{-y} = -2 \cos x + c. \tag{7}$$

The initial condition $y = 0$ when $x = 0$ implies $c = 4$. Thus a solution of the initial-value problem is

$$e^y + ye^{-y} + e^{-y} = 4 - 2 \cos x. \tag{8} \quad \blacksquare$$

USE OF COMPUTERS The *Remarks* at the end of Section 1.1 mentioned that it may be difficult to use an implicit solution $G(x, y) = 0$ to find an explicit solution $y = \phi(x)$. Equation (8) shows that the task of solving for y in terms of x may present more problems than just the drudgery of symbol pushing—sometimes it simply cannot be done! Implicit solutions such as (8) are somewhat frustrating; neither the graph of the equation nor an interval over which a solution satisfying $y(0) = 0$ is defined is apparent. The problem of "seeing" what an implicit solution looks like can be overcome in some cases by means of technology. One way[*] of proceeding is to use the contour plot application of a computer algebra system (CAS). Recall from multivariate calculus that for a function of two variables $z = G(x, y)$ the *two-dimensional* curves defined by $G(x, y) = c$, where c is constant, are called the *level curves* of the function. With the aid of a CAS, some of the level curves of the function $G(x, y) = e^y + ye^{-y} + e^{-y} + 2 \cos x$ have been reproduced in Figure 2.2.2. The family of solutions defined by (7) is the level curves $G(x, y) = c$. Figure 2.2.3 illustrates the level curve $G(x, y) = 4$, which is the particular solution (8), in blue color. The other curve in Figure 2.2.3 is the level curve $G(x, y) = 2$, which is the member of the family $G(x, y) = c$ that satisfies $y(\pi/2) = 0$.

If an initial condition leads to a particular solution by yielding a specific value of the parameter c in a family of solutions for a first-order differential equation, there is a natural inclination for most students (and instructors) to relax and be content. However, a solution of an initial-value problem might not be unique. We saw in Example 4 of Section 1.2 that the initial-value problem

$$\frac{dy}{dx} = xy^{1/2}, \quad y(0) = 0 \tag{9}$$

has at least two solutions, $y = 0$ and $y = \frac{1}{16}x^4$. We are now in a position to solve the equation. Separating variables and integrating $y^{-1/2} \, dy = x \, dx$ gives

$$2y^{1/2} = \frac{x^2}{2} + c_1 \quad \text{or} \quad y = \left(\frac{x^2}{4} + c\right)^2.$$

When $x = 0$, then $y = 0$, so necessarily, $c = 0$. Therefore $y = \frac{1}{16}x^4$. The trivial solution $y = 0$ was lost by dividing by $y^{1/2}$. In addition, the initial-value problem (9) possesses infinitely many more solutions, since for any choice of the parameter $a \geq 0$ the

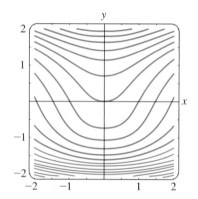

FIGURE 2.2.2 Level curves $G(x, y) = c$, where $G(x, y) = e^y + ye^{-y} + e^{-y} + 2 \cos x$

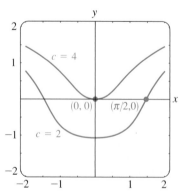

FIGURE 2.2.3 Level curves $c = 2$ and $c = 4$

---

[*]In Section 2.6 we will discuss several other ways of proceeding that are based on the concept of a numerical solver.

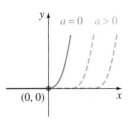

FIGURE 2.2.4 Piecewise-defined solutions of (9)

piecewise-defined function

$$y = \begin{cases} 0, & x < a \\ \frac{1}{16}(x^2 - a^2)^2, & x \geq a \end{cases}$$

satisfies both the differential equation and the initial condition. See Figure 2.2.4.

SOLUTIONS DEFINED BY INTEGRALS If g is a function continuous on an open interval I containing a, then for every x in I,

$$\frac{d}{dx}\int_a^x g(t)\, dt = g(x).$$

You might recall that the foregoing result is one of the two forms of the fundamental theorem of calculus. In other words, $\int_a^x g(t)\, dt$ is an antiderivative of the function g. There are times when this form is convenient in solving DEs. For example, if g is continuous on an interval I containing x_0 and x, then a solution of the simple initial-value problem $dy/dx = g(x)$, $y(x_0) = y_0$, that is defined on I is given by

$$y(x) = y_0 + \int_{x_0}^x g(t)\, dt$$

You should verify that $y(x)$ defined in this manner satisfies the initial condition. Since an antiderivative of a continuous function g cannot always be expressed in terms of elementary functions, this might be the best we can do in obtaining an explicit solution of an IVP. The next example illustrates this idea.

EXAMPLE 5 **An Initial-Value Problem**

Solve $\dfrac{dy}{dx} = e^{-x^2}$, $y(3) = 5$.

SOLUTION The function $g(x) = e^{-x^2}$ is continuous on $(-\infty, \infty)$, but its antiderivative is not an elementary function. Using t as dummy variable of integration, we can write

$$\int_3^x \frac{dy}{dt}\, dt = \int_3^x e^{-t^2}\, dt$$

$$y(t)\Big]_3^x = \int_3^x e^{-t^2}\, dt$$

$$y(x) - y(3) = \int_3^x e^{-t^2}\, dt$$

$$y(x) = y(3) + \int_3^x e^{-t^2}\, dt.$$

Using the initial condition $y(3) = 5$, we obtain the solution

$$y(x) = 5 + \int_3^x e^{-t^2}\, dt. \qquad \blacksquare$$

The procedure demonstrated in Example 5 works equally well on separable equations $dy/dx = g(x)f(y)$ where, say, $f(y)$ possesses an elementary antiderivative but $g(x)$ does not possess an elementary antiderivative. See Problems 29 and 30 in Exercises 2.2.

REMARKS

(i) As we have just seen in Example 5, some simple functions do not possess an antiderivative that is an elementary function. Integrals of these kinds of functions are called **nonelementary**. For example, $\int_3^x e^{-t^2}\,dt$ and $\int \sin x^2\,dx$ are nonelementary integrals. We will run into this concept again in Section 2.3.

(ii) In some of the preceding examples we saw that the constant in the one-parameter family of solutions for a first-order differential equation can be relabeled when convenient. Also, it can easily happen that two individuals solving the same equation correctly arrive at dissimilar expressions for their answers. For example, by separation of variables we can show that one-parameter families of solutions for the DE $(1 + y^2)\,dx + (1 + x^2)\,dy = 0$ are

$$\arctan x + \arctan y = c \qquad \text{or} \qquad \frac{x + y}{1 - xy} = c.$$

As you work your way through the next several sections, bear in mind that families of solutions may be equivalent in the sense that one family may be obtained from another by either relabeling the constant or applying algebra and trigonometry. See Problems 27 and 28 in Exercises 2.2.

EXERCISES 2.2

Answers to selected odd-numbered problems begin on page ANS-1.

In Problems 1–22 solve the given differential equation by separation of variables.

1. $\dfrac{dy}{dx} = \sin 5x$

2. $\dfrac{dy}{dx} = (x + 1)^2$

3. $dx + e^{3x}dy = 0$

4. $dy - (y - 1)^2 dx = 0$

5. $x\dfrac{dy}{dx} = 4y$

6. $\dfrac{dy}{dx} + 2xy^2 = 0$

7. $\dfrac{dy}{dx} = e^{3x + 2y}$

8. $e^x y \dfrac{dy}{dx} = e^{-y} + e^{-2x - y}$

9. $y \ln x \dfrac{dx}{dy} = \left(\dfrac{y + 1}{x}\right)^2$

10. $\dfrac{dy}{dx} = \left(\dfrac{2y + 3}{4x + 5}\right)^2$

11. $\csc y\,dx + \sec^2 x\,dy = 0$

12. $\sin 3x\,dx + 2y \cos^3 3x\,dy = 0$

13. $(e^y + 1)^2 e^{-y}\,dx + (e^x + 1)^3 e^{-x}\,dy = 0$

14. $x(1 + y^2)^{1/2}\,dx = y(1 + x^2)^{1/2}\,dy$

15. $\dfrac{dS}{dr} = kS$

16. $\dfrac{dQ}{dt} = k(Q - 70)$

17. $\dfrac{dP}{dt} = P - P^2$

18. $\dfrac{dN}{dt} + N = Nte^{t+2}$

19. $\dfrac{dy}{dx} = \dfrac{xy + 3x - y - 3}{xy - 2x + 4y - 8}$

20. $\dfrac{dy}{dx} = \dfrac{xy + 2y - x - 2}{xy - 3y + x - 3}$

21. $\dfrac{dy}{dx} = x\sqrt{1 - y^2}$

22. $(e^x + e^{-x})\dfrac{dy}{dx} = y^2$

In Problems 23–28 find an explicit solution of the given initial-value problem.

23. $\dfrac{dx}{dt} = 4(x^2 + 1), \quad x(\pi/4) = 1$

24. $\dfrac{dy}{dx} = \dfrac{y^2 - 1}{x^2 - 1}, \quad y(2) = 2$

25. $x^2 \dfrac{dy}{dx} = y - xy, \quad y(-1) = -1$

26. $\dfrac{dy}{dt} + 2y = 1, \quad y(0) = \tfrac{5}{2}$

27. $\sqrt{1 - y^2}\,dx - \sqrt{1 - x^2}\,dy = 0, \quad y(0) = \dfrac{\sqrt{3}}{2}$

28. $(1 + x^4)\,dy + x(1 + 4y^2)\,dx = 0, \quad y(1) = 0$

In Problems 29 and 30 proceed as in Example 5 and find an explicit solution of the given initial-value problem.

29. $\dfrac{dy}{dx} = ye^{-x^2}, \quad y(4) = 1$

30. $\dfrac{dy}{dx} = y^2 \sin x^2, \quad y(-2) = \tfrac{1}{3}$

31. (a) Find a solution of the initial-value problem consisting of the differential equation in Example 3 and the initial conditions $y(0) = 2$, $y(0) = -2$, and $y\left(\tfrac{1}{4}\right) = 1$.

(b) Find the solution of the differential equation in Example 4 when $\ln c_1$ is used as the constant of integration on the *left-hand* side in the solution and $4 \ln c_1$ is replaced by $\ln c$. Then solve the same initial-value problems in part (a).

32. Find a solution of $x \dfrac{dy}{dx} = y^2 - y$ that passes through the indicated points.

(a) $(0, 1)$ **(b)** $(0, 0)$ **(c)** $\left(\frac{1}{2}, \frac{1}{2}\right)$ **(d)** $\left(2, \frac{1}{4}\right)$

33. Find a singular solution of Problem 21. Of Problem 22.

34. Show that an implicit solution of

$$2x \sin^2 y \, dx - (x^2 + 10) \cos y \, dy = 0$$

is given by $\ln(x^2 + 10) + \csc y = c$. Find the constant solutions, if any, that were lost in the solution of the differential equation.

Often a radical change in the form of the solution of a differential equation corresponds to a very small change in either the initial condition or the equation itself. In Problems 35–38 find an explicit solution of the given initial-value problem. Use a graphing utility to plot the graph of each solution. Compare each solution curve in a neighborhood of $(0, 1)$.

35. $\dfrac{dy}{dx} = (y - 1)^2, \quad y(0) = 1$

36. $\dfrac{dy}{dx} = (y - 1)^2, \quad y(0) = 1.01$

37. $\dfrac{dy}{dx} = (y - 1)^2 + 0.01, \quad y(0) = 1$

38. $\dfrac{dy}{dx} = (y - 1)^2 - 0.01, \quad y(0) = 1$

39. Every autonomous first-order equation $dy/dx = f(y)$ is separable. Find explicit solutions $y_1(x)$, $y_2(x)$, $y_3(x)$, and $y_4(x)$ of the differential equation $dy/dx = y - y^3$ that satisfy, in turn, the initial conditions $y_1(0) = 2$, $y_2(0) = \frac{1}{2}$, $y_3(0) = -\frac{1}{2}$, and $y_4(0) = -2$. Use a graphing utility to plot the graphs of each solution. Compare these graphs with those predicted in Problem 19 of Exercises 2.1. Give the exact interval of definition for each solution.

40. (a) The autonomous first-order differential equation $dy/dx = 1/(y - 3)$ has no critical points. Nevertheless, place 3 on the phase line and obtain a phase portrait of the equation. Compute d^2y/dx^2 to determine where solution curves are concave up and where they are concave down (see Problems 35 and 36 in Exercises 2.1). Use the phase portrait and concavity to sketch, by hand, some typical solution curves.

(b) Find explicit solutions $y_1(x)$, $y_2(x)$, $y_3(x)$, and $y_4(x)$ of the differential equation in part (a) that satisfy, in turn, the initial conditions $y_1(0) = 4$, $y_2(0) = 2$,

$y_3(1) = 2$, and $y_4(-1) = 4$. Graph each solution and compare with your sketches in part (a). Give the exact interval of definition for each solution.

41. (a) Find an explicit solution of the initial-value problem

$$\frac{dy}{dx} = \frac{2x + 1}{2y}, \quad y(-2) = -1.$$

(b) Use a graphing utility to plot the graph of the solution in part (a). Use the graph to estimate the interval I of definition of the solution.

(c) Determine the exact interval I of definition by analytical methods.

42. Repeat parts (a)–(c) of Problem 41 for the IVP consisting of the differential equation in Problem 7 and the initial condition $y(0) = 0$.

Discussion Problems

43. (a) Explain why the interval of definition of the explicit solution $y = \phi_2(x)$ of the initial-value problem in Example 2 is the *open* interval $(-5, 5)$.

(b) Can any solution of the differential equation cross the x-axis? Do you think that $x^2 + y^2 = 1$ is an implicit solution of the initial-value problem $dy/dx = -x/y, y(1) = 0$?

44. (a) If $a > 0$, discuss the differences, if any, between the solutions of the initial-value problems consisting of the differential equation $dy/dx = x/y$ and each of the initial conditions $y(a) = a$, $y(a) = -a$, $y(-a) = a$, and $y(-a) = -a$.

(b) Does the initial-value problem $dy/dx = x/y$, $y(0) = 0$ have a solution?

(c) Solve $dy/dx = x/y$, $y(1) = 2$ and give the exact interval I of definition of its solution.

45. In Problems 39 and 40 we saw that every autonomous first-order differential equation $dy/dx = f(y)$ is separable. Does this fact help in the solution of the initial-value problem $\dfrac{dy}{dx} = \sqrt{1 + y^2} \sin^2 y, \quad y(0) = \frac{1}{2}$? Discuss. Sketch, by hand, a plausible solution curve of the problem.

46. Without the use of technology, how would you solve

$$\left(\sqrt{x} + x\right)\frac{dy}{dx} = \sqrt{y} + y?$$

Carry out your ideas.

47. Find a function whose square plus the square of its derivative is 1.

48. (a) The differential equation in Problem 27 is equivalent to the normal form

$$\frac{dy}{dx} = \sqrt{\frac{1 - y^2}{1 - x^2}}$$

in the square region in the xy-plane defined by $|x| < 1, |y| < 1$. But the quantity under the radical is nonnegative also in the regions defined by $|x| > 1$, $|y| > 1$. Sketch all regions in the xy-plane for which this differential equation possesses real solutions.

(b) Solve the DE in part (a) in the regions defined by $|x| > 1, |y| > 1$. Then find an implicit and an explicit solution of the differential equation subject to $y(2) = 2$.

Mathematical Model

49. Suspension Bridge In (16) of Section 1.3 we saw that a mathematical model for the shape of a flexible cable strung between two vertical supports is

$$\frac{dy}{dx} = \frac{W}{T_1}, \qquad (10)$$

where W denotes the portion of the total vertical load between the points P_1 and P_2 shown in Figure 1.3.7. The DE (10) is separable under the following conditions that describe a suspension bridge.

Let us assume that the x- and y-axes are as shown in Figure 2.2.5—that is, the x-axis runs along the horizontal roadbed, and the y-axis passes through $(0, a)$, which is the lowest point on one cable over the span of the bridge, coinciding with the interval $[-L/2, L/2]$. In the case of a suspension bridge, the usual assumption is that the vertical load in (10) is only a uniform roadbed distributed along the horizontal axis. In other words, it is assumed that the weight of all cables is negligible in comparison to the weight of the roadbed and that the weight per unit length of the roadbed (say, pounds per horizontal foot) is a constant ρ. Use this information to set up and solve an appropriate initial-value problem from which the shape (a curve with equation $y = \phi(x)$) of each of the two cables in a suspension bridge is determined. Express your solution of the IVP in terms of the sag h and span L. See Figure 2.2.5.

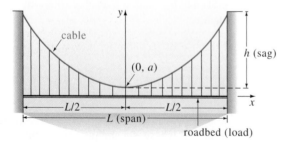

FIGURE 2.2.5 Shape of a cable in Problem 49

Computer Lab Assignments

50. (a) Use a CAS and the concept of level curves to plot representative graphs of members of the

family of solutions of the differential equation $\frac{dy}{dx} = -\frac{8x + 5}{3y^2 + 1}$. Experiment with different numbers of level curves as well as various rectangular regions defined by $a \le x \le b, c \le y \le d$.

(b) On separate coordinate axes plot the graphs of the particular solutions corresponding to the initial conditions: $y(0) = -1$; $y(0) = 2$; $y(-1) = 4$; $y(-1) = -3$.

51. (a) Find an implicit solution of the IVP

$$(2y + 2)\, dy - (4x^3 + 6x)\, dx = 0, \quad y(0) = -3.$$

(b) Use part (a) to find an explicit solution $y = \phi(x)$ of the IVP.

(c) Consider your answer to part (b) as a *function* only. Use a graphing utility or a CAS to graph this function, and then use the graph to estimate its domain.

(d) With the aid of a root-finding application of a CAS, determine the approximate largest interval I of definition of the *solution* $y = \phi(x)$ in part (b). Use a graphing utility or a CAS to graph the solution curve for the IVP on this interval.

52. (a) Use a CAS and the concept of level curves to plot representative graphs of members of the family of solutions of the differential equation $\frac{dy}{dx} = \frac{x(1 - x)}{y(-2 + y)}$. Experiment with different numbers of level curves as well as various rectangular regions in the xy-plane until your result resembles Figure 2.2.6.

(b) On separate coordinate axes, plot the graph of the implicit solution corresponding to the initial condition $y(0) = \frac{3}{2}$. Use a colored pencil to mark off that segment of the graph that corresponds to the solution curve of a solution ϕ that satisfies the initial condition. With the aid of a root-finding application of a CAS, determine the approximate largest interval I of definition of the solution ϕ. [*Hint*: First find the points on the curve in part (a) where the tangent is vertical.]

(c) Repeat part (b) for the initial condition $y(0) = -2$.

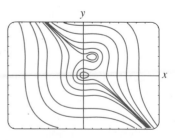

FIGURE 2.2.6 Level curves in Problem 52

2.3 LINEAR EQUATIONS

REVIEW MATERIAL

• Review the definition of linear DEs in (6) and (7) of Section 1.1

INTRODUCTION We continue our quest for solutions of first-order DEs by next examining linear equations. Linear differential equations are an especially "friendly" family of differential equations in that, given a linear equation, whether first order or a higher-order kin, there is always a good possibility that we can find some sort of solution of the equation that we can examine.

A DEFINITION The form of a linear first-order DE was given in (7) of Section 1.1. This form, the case when $n = 1$ in (6) of that section, is reproduced here for convenience.

DEFINITION 2.3.1 Linear Equation

A first-order differential equation of the form

$$a_1(x)\frac{dy}{dx} + a_0(x)y = g(x) \tag{1}$$

is said to be a **linear equation** in the dependent variable y.

When $g(x) = 0$, the linear equation (1) is said to be **homogeneous;** otherwise, it is **nonhomogeneous.**

STANDARD FORM By dividing both sides of (1) by the lead coefficient $a_1(x)$, we obtain a more useful form, the **standard form,** of a linear equation:

$$\frac{dy}{dx} + P(x)y = f(x). \tag{2}$$

We seek a solution of (2) on an interval I for which both coefficient functions P and f are continuous.

In the discussion that follows we illustrate a property and a procedure and end up with a formula representing the form that every solution of (2) must have. But more than the formula, the property and the procedure are important, because these two concepts carry over to linear equations of higher order.

THE PROPERTY The differential equation (2) has the property that its solution is the **sum** of the two solutions: $y = y_c + y_p$, where y_c is a solution of the associated homogeneous equation

$$\frac{dy}{dx} + P(x)y = 0 \tag{3}$$

and y_p is a particular solution of the nonhomogeneous equation (2). To see this, observe that

$$\frac{d}{dx}[y_c + y_p] + P(x)[y_c + y_p] = \underbrace{\left[\frac{dy_c}{dx} + P(x)y_c\right]}_{0} + \underbrace{\left[\frac{dy_p}{dx} + P(x)y_p\right]}_{f(x)} = f(x).$$

Now the homogeneous equation (3) is also separable. This fact enables us to find y_c by writing (3) as

$$\frac{dy}{y} + P(x)\, dx = 0$$

and integrating. Solving for y gives $y_c = ce^{-\int P(x)dx}$. For convenience let us write $y_c = cy_1(x)$, where $y_1 = e^{-\int P(x)dx}$. The fact that $dy_1/dx + P(x)y_1 = 0$ will be used next to determine y_p.

THE PROCEDURE We can now find a particular solution of equation (2) by a procedure known as **variation of parameters.** The basic idea here is to find a function u so that $y_p = u(x)y_1(x) = u(x)e^{-\int P(x)dx}$ is a solution of (2). In other words, our assumption for y_p is the same as $y_c = cy_1(x)$ except that c is replaced by the "variable parameter" u. Substituting $y_p = uy_1$ into (2) gives

Product Rule ↓ zero ↓

$$u\frac{dy_1}{dx} + y_1\frac{du}{dx} + P(x)uy_1 = f(x) \qquad \text{or} \qquad u\left[\frac{dy_1}{dx} + P(x)y_1\right] + y_1\frac{du}{dx} = f(x)$$

so

$$y_1\frac{du}{dx} = f(x).$$

Separating variables and integrating then gives

$$du = \frac{f(x)}{y_1(x)}\, dx \qquad \text{and} \qquad u = \int \frac{f(x)}{y_1(x)}\, dx.$$

Since $y_1(x) = e^{-\int P(x)dx}$, we see that $1/y_1(x) = e^{\int P(x)dx}$. Therefore

$$y_p = uy_1 = \left(\int \frac{f(x)}{y_1(x)}\, dx\right)e^{-\int P(x)dx} = e^{-\int P(x)dx}\int e^{\int P(x)dx}f(x)\, dx,$$

and

$$y = \underbrace{ce^{-\int P(x)dx}}_{y_c} + \underbrace{e^{-\int P(x)dx}\int e^{\int P(x)dx}f(x)\, dx}_{y_p}. \qquad (4)$$

Hence if (2) has a solution, it must be of form (4). Conversely, it is a straightforward exercise in differentiation to verify that (4) constitutes a one-parameter family of solutions of equation (2).

You should not memorize the formula given in (4). However, you should remember the special term

$$e^{\int P(x)dx} \qquad (5)$$

because it is used in an equivalent but easier way of solving (2). If equation (4) is multiplied by (5),

$$e^{\int P(x)dx}y = c + \int e^{\int P(x)dx}f(x)\, dx, \qquad (6)$$

and then (6) is differentiated,

$$\frac{d}{dx}\left[e^{\int P(x)dx}y\right] = e^{\int P(x)dx}f(x), \qquad (7)$$

we get

$$e^{\int P(x)dx}\frac{dy}{dx} + P(x)e^{\int P(x)dx}y = e^{\int P(x)dx}f(x). \qquad (8)$$

Dividing the last result by $e^{\int P(x)dx}$ gives (2).

METHOD OF SOLUTION   The recommended method of solving (2) actually consists of (6)–(8) worked in reverse order. In other words, if (2) is multiplied by (5), we get (8). The left-hand side of (8) is recognized as the derivative of the product of $e^{\int P(x)dx}$ and y. This gets us to (7). We then integrate both sides of (7) to get the solution (6). Because we can solve (2) by integration after multiplication by $e^{\int P(x)dx}$, we call this function an **integrating factor** for the differential equation. For convenience we summarize these results. We again emphasize that you should not memorize formula (4) but work through the following procedure each time.

SOLVING A LINEAR FIRST-ORDER EQUATION

   (*i*)   Put a linear equation of form (1) into the standard form (2).

   (*ii*)   From the standard form identify $P(x)$ and then find the integrating factor $e^{\int P(x)dx}$.

   (*iii*)   Multiply the standard form of the equation by the integrating factor. The left-hand side of the resulting equation is automatically the derivative of the integrating factor and y:

$$\frac{d}{dx}\left[e^{\int P(x)dx}y\right] = e^{\int P(x)dx}f(x).$$

   (*iv*)   Integrate both sides of this last equation.

EXAMPLE 1   Solving a Homogeneous Linear DE

Solve $\dfrac{dy}{dx} - 3y = 0$.

SOLUTION   This linear equation can be solved by separation of variables. Alternatively, since the equation is already in the standard form (2), we see that $P(x) = -3$, and so the integrating factor is $e^{\int(-3)dx} = e^{-3x}$. We multiply the equation by this factor and recognize that

$$e^{-3x}\frac{dy}{dx} - 3e^{-3x}y = 0 \qquad \text{is the same as} \qquad \frac{d}{dx}[e^{-3x}y] = 0.$$

Integrating both sides of the last equation gives $e^{-3x}y = c$. Solving for y gives us the explicit solution $y = ce^{3x}$, $-\infty < x < \infty$.   ∎

EXAMPLE 2   Solving a Nonhomogeneous Linear DE

Solve $\dfrac{dy}{dx} - 3y = 6$.

SOLUTION   The associated homogeneous equation for this DE was solved in Example 1. Again the equation is already in the standard form (2), and the integrating factor is still $e^{\int(-3)dx} = e^{-3x}$. This time multiplying the given equation by this factor gives

$$e^{-3x}\frac{dy}{dx} - 3e^{-3x}y = 6e^{-3x}, \qquad \text{which is the same as} \qquad \frac{d}{dx}[e^{-3x}y] = 6e^{-3x}.$$

Integrating both sides of the last equation gives $e^{-3x}y = -2e^{-3x} + c$ or $y = -2 + ce^{3x}$, $-\infty < x < \infty$.   ∎

The final solution in Example 2 is the sum of two solutions: $y = y_c + y_p$, where $y_c = ce^{3x}$ is the solution of the homogeneous equation in Example 1 and $y_p = -2$ is a particular solution of the nonhomogeneous equation $y' - 3y = 6$. You need not be concerned about whether a linear first-order equation is homogeneous or nonhomogeneous; when you follow the solution procedure outlined above, a solution of a nonhomogeneous equation necessarily turns out to be $y = y_c + y_p$. However, the distinction between solving a homogeneous DE and solving a nonhomogeneous DE becomes more important in Chapter 4, where we solve linear higher-order equations.

When a_1, a_0, and g in (1) are constants, the differential equation is autonomous. In Example 2 you can verify from the normal form $dy/dx = 3(y + 2)$ that -2 is a critical point and that it is unstable (a repeller). Thus a solution curve with an initial point either above or below the graph of the equilibrium solution $y = -2$ pushes away from this horizontal line as x increases. Figure 2.3.1, obtained with the aid of a graphing utility, shows the graph of $y = -2$ along with some additional solution curves.

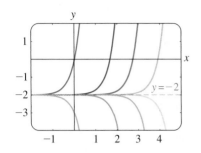

FIGURE 2.3.1   Some solutions of $y' - 3y = 6$

CONSTANT OF INTEGRATION   Notice that in the general discussion and in Examples 1 and 2 we disregarded a constant of integration in the evaluation of the indefinite integral in the exponent of $e^{\int P(x)dx}$. If you think about the laws of exponents and the fact that the integrating factor multiplies both sides of the differential equation, you should be able to explain why writing $\int P(x)\,dx + c$ is unnecessary. See Problem 44 in Exercises 2.3.

GENERAL SOLUTION   Suppose again that the functions P and f in (2) are continuous on a common interval I. In the steps leading to (4) we showed that *if* (2) has a solution on I, then it must be of the form given in (4). Conversely, it is a straightforward exercise in differentiation to verify that any function of the form given in (4) is a solution of the differential equation (2) on I. In other words, (4) is a one-parameter family of solutions of equation (2) and *every solution of* (2) *defined on I is a member of this family*. Therefore we call (4) the **general solution** of the differential equation on the interval I. (See the *Remarks* at the end of Section 1.1.) Now by writing (2) in the normal form $y' = F(x, y)$, we can identify $F(x, y) = -P(x)y + f(x)$ and $\partial F/\partial y = -P(x)$. From the continuity of P and f on the interval I we see that F and $\partial F/\partial y$ are also continuous on I. With Theorem 1.2.1 as our justification, we conclude that there exists one and only one solution of the initial-value problem

$$\frac{dy}{dx} + P(x)y = f(x), \quad y(x_0) = y_0 \tag{9}$$

defined on *some* interval I_0 containing x_0. But when x_0 is in I, finding a solution of (9) is just a matter of finding an appropriate value of c in (4)—that is, to each x_0 in I there corresponds a distinct c. In other words, the interval I_0 of existence and uniqueness in Theorem 1.2.1 for the initial-value problem (9) is the entire interval I.

EXAMPLE 3   **General Solution**

Solve $x\dfrac{dy}{dx} - 4y = x^6 e^x$.

SOLUTION   Dividing by x, we get the standard form

$$\frac{dy}{dx} - \frac{4}{x}y = x^5 e^x. \tag{10}$$

From this form we identify $P(x) = -4/x$ and $f(x) = x^5 e^x$ and further observe that P and f are continuous on $(0, \infty)$. Hence the integrating factor is

we can use $\ln x$ instead of $\ln |x|$ since $x > 0$
$$\downarrow$$
$$e^{-4\int dx/x} = e^{-4\ln x} = e^{\ln x^{-4}} = x^{-4}.$$

Here we have used the basic identity $b^{\log_b N} = N$, $N > 0$. Now we multiply (10) by x^{-4} and rewrite

$$x^{-4} \frac{dy}{dx} - 4x^{-5}y = xe^x \qquad \text{as} \qquad \frac{d}{dx}[x^{-4}y] = xe^x.$$

It follows from integration by parts that the general solution defined on the interval $(0, \infty)$ is $x^{-4}y = xe^x - e^x + c$ or $y = x^5 e^x - x^4 e^x + cx^4$. ∎

Except in the case in which the lead coefficient is 1, the recasting of equation (1) into the standard form (2) requires division by $a_1(x)$. Values of x for which $a_1(x) = 0$ are called **singular points** of the equation. Singular points are potentially troublesome. Specifically, in (2), if $P(x)$ (formed by dividing $a_0(x)$ by $a_1(x)$) is discontinuous at a point, the discontinuity may carry over to solutions of the differential equation.

EXAMPLE 4 General Solution

Find the general solution of $(x^2 - 9) \dfrac{dy}{dx} + xy = 0$.

SOLUTION We write the differential equation in standard form

$$\frac{dy}{dx} + \frac{x}{x^2 - 9}y = 0 \tag{11}$$

and identify $P(x) = x/(x^2 - 9)$. Although P is continuous on $(-\infty, -3)$, $(-3, 3)$, and $(3, \infty)$, we shall solve the equation on the first and third intervals. On these intervals the integrating factor is

$$e^{\int x\, dx/(x^2-9)} = e^{\frac{1}{2}\int 2x\, dx/(x^2-9)} = e^{\frac{1}{2}\ln|x^2-9|} = \sqrt{x^2 - 9}.$$

After multiplying the standard form (11) by this factor, we get

$$\frac{d}{dx}\left[\sqrt{x^2 - 9}\, y\right] = 0.$$

Integrating both sides of the last equation gives $\sqrt{x^2 - 9}\, y = c$. Thus for either $x > 3$ or $x < -3$ the general solution of the equation is $y = \dfrac{c}{\sqrt{x^2 - 9}}$. ∎

Notice in Example 4 that $x = 3$ and $x = -3$ are singular points of the equation and that every function in the general solution $y = c/\sqrt{x^2 - 9}$ is discontinuous at these points. On the other hand, $x = 0$ is a singular point of the differential equation in Example 3, but the general solution $y = x^5 e^x - x^4 e^x + cx^4$ is noteworthy in that every function in this one-parameter family is continuous at $x = 0$ and is defined on the interval $(-\infty, \infty)$ and not just on $(0, \infty)$, as stated in the solution. However, the family $y = x^5 e^x - x^4 e^x + cx^4$ defined on $(-\infty, \infty)$ cannot be considered the general solution of the DE, since the singular point $x = 0$ still causes a problem. See Problem 39 in Exercises 2.3.

EXAMPLE 5 **An Initial-Value Problem**

Solve $\dfrac{dy}{dx} + y = x$, $\quad y(0) = 4$.

SOLUTION The equation is in standard form, and $P(x) = 1$ and $f(x) = x$ are continuous on $(-\infty, \infty)$. The integrating factor is $e^{\int dx} = e^x$, so integrating

$$\frac{d}{dx}[e^x y] = xe^x$$

gives $e^x y = xe^x - e^x + c$. Solving this last equation for y yields the general solution $y = x - 1 + ce^{-x}$. But from the initial condition we know that $y = 4$ when $x = 0$. Substituting these values into the general solution implies that $c = 5$. Hence the solution of the problem is

$$y = x - 1 + 5e^{-x}, \quad -\infty < x < \infty. \tag{12} \quad \blacksquare$$

Figure 2.3.2, obtained with the aid of a graphing utility, shows the graph of (12) in dark blue, along with the graphs of other representative solutions in the one-parameter family $y = x - 1 + ce^{-x}$. In this general solution we identify $y_c = ce^{-x}$ and $y_p = x - 1$. It is interesting to observe that as x increases, the graphs of *all* members of the family are close to the graph of the particular solution $y_p = x - 1$, which is shown in solid green in Figure 2.3.2. This is because the contribution of $y_c = ce^{-x}$ to the values of a solution becomes negligible for increasing values of x. We say that $y_c = ce^{-x}$ is a **transient term,** since $y_c \to 0$ as $x \to \infty$. While this behavior is not a characteristic of all general solutions of linear equations (see Example 2), the notion of a transient is often important in applied problems.

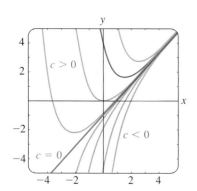

FIGURE 2.3.2 Some solutions of $y' + y = x$

DISCONTINUOUS COEFFICIENTS In applications the coefficients $P(x)$ and $f(x)$ in (2) may be piecewise continuous. In the next example $f(x)$ is piecewise continuous on $[0, \infty)$ with a single discontinuity, namely, a (finite) jump discontinuity at $x = 1$. We solve the problem in two parts corresponding to the two intervals over which f is defined. It is then possible to piece together the two solutions at $x = 1$ so that $y(x)$ is continuous on $[0, \infty)$.

EXAMPLE 6 **An Initial-Value Problem**

Solve $\dfrac{dy}{dx} + y = f(x)$, $\quad y(0) = 0$ $\quad$ where $\quad f(x) = \begin{cases} 1, & 0 \le x \le 1, \\ 0, & x > 1. \end{cases}$

SOLUTION The graph of the discontinuous function f is shown in Figure 2.3.3. We solve the DE for $y(x)$ first on the interval $[0, 1]$ and then on the interval $(1, \infty)$. For $0 \le x \le 1$ we have

$$\frac{dy}{dx} + y = 1 \qquad \text{or, equivalently,} \qquad \frac{d}{dx}[e^x y] = e^x.$$

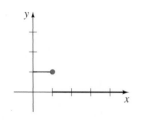

FIGURE 2.3.3 Discontinuous $f(x)$

Integrating this last equation and solving for y gives $y = 1 + c_1 e^{-x}$. Since $y(0) = 0$, we must have $c_1 = -1$, and therefore $y = 1 - e^{-x}$, $0 \le x \le 1$. Then for $x > 1$ the equation

$$\frac{dy}{dx} + y = 0$$

leads to $y = c_2 e^{-x}$. Hence we can write

$$y = \begin{cases} 1 - e^{-x}, & 0 \le x \le 1, \\ c_2 e^{-x}, & x > 1. \end{cases}$$

By appealing to the definition of continuity at a point, it is possible to determine c_2 so that the foregoing function is continuous at $x = 1$. The requirement that $\lim_{x \to 1^+} y(x) = y(1)$ implies that $c_2 e^{-1} = 1 - e^{-1}$ or $c_2 = e - 1$. As seen in Figure 2.3.4, the function

$$y = \begin{cases} 1 - e^{-x}, & 0 \le x \le 1, \\ (e - 1)e^{-x}, & x > 1 \end{cases} \tag{13}$$

is continuous on $(0, \infty)$. ∎

It is worthwhile to think about (13) and Figure 2.3.4 a little bit; you are urged to read and answer Problem 42 in Exercises 2.3.

FUNCTIONS DEFINED BY INTEGRALS At the end of Section 2.2 we discussed the fact that some simple continuous functions do not possess antiderivatives that are elementary functions and that integrals of these kinds of functions are called **nonelementary.** For example, you may have seen in calculus that $\int e^{-x^2} dx$ and $\int \sin x^2 \, dx$ are nonelementary integrals. In applied mathematics some important functions are *defined* in terms of nonelementary integrals. Two such **special functions** are the **error function** and **complementary error function:**

$$\operatorname{erf}(x) = \frac{2}{\sqrt{\pi}} \int_0^x e^{-t^2} dt \quad \text{and} \quad \operatorname{erfc}(x) = \frac{2}{\sqrt{\pi}} \int_x^\infty e^{-t^2} dt. \tag{14}$$

From the known result $\int_0^\infty e^{-t^2} dt = \sqrt{\pi}/2$[*] we can write $(2/\sqrt{\pi}) \int_0^\infty e^{-t^2} dt = 1$. Then from $\int_0^\infty = \int_0^x + \int_x^\infty$ it is seen from (14) that the complementary error function $\operatorname{erfc}(x)$ is related to $\operatorname{erf}(x)$ by $\operatorname{erf}(x) + \operatorname{erfc}(x) = 1$. Because of its importance in probability, statistics, and applied partial differential equations, the error function has been extensively tabulated. Note that $\operatorname{erf}(0) = 0$ is one obvious function value. Values of $\operatorname{erf}(x)$ can also be found by using a CAS.

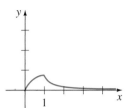

FIGURE 2.3.4 Graph of function in (13)

| **EXAMPLE 7** **The Error Function** |

Solve the initial-value problem $\dfrac{dy}{dx} - 2xy = 2, \quad y(0) = 1.$

SOLUTION Since the equation is already in standard form, we see that the integrating factor is $e^{-x^2} dx$, so from

$$\frac{d}{dx}[e^{-x^2}y] = 2e^{-x^2} \quad \text{we get} \quad y = 2e^{x^2} \int_0^x e^{-t^2} dt + ce^{x^2}. \tag{15}$$

Applying $y(0) = 1$ to the last expression then gives $c = 1$. Hence the solution of the problem is

$$y = 2e^{x^2} \int_0^x e^{-t^2} dt + e^{x^2} \text{ or } y = e^{x^2}[1 + \sqrt{\pi} \operatorname{erf}(x)].$$

The graph of this solution on the interval $(-\infty, \infty)$, shown in dark blue in Figure 2.3.5 among other members of the family defined in (15), was obtained with the aid of a computer algebra system. ∎

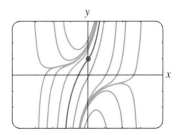

FIGURE 2.3.5 Some solutions of $y' - 2xy = 2$

---

[*]This result is usually proved in the third semester of calculus.

USE OF COMPUTERS The computer algebra systems *Mathematica* and *Maple* are capable of producing implicit or explicit solutions for some kinds of differential equations using their *dsolve* commands.[*]

REMARKS

(*i*) In general, a linear DE of any order is said to be homogeneous when $g(x) = 0$ in (6) of Section 1.1. For example, the linear second-order DE $y'' - 2y' + 6y = 0$ is homogeneous. As can be seen in this example and in the special case (3) of this section, the trivial solution $y = 0$ is always a solution of a homogeneous linear DE.

(*ii*) Occasionally, a first-order differential equation is not linear in one variable but is linear in the other variable. For example, the differential equation

$$\frac{dy}{dx} = \frac{1}{x + y^2}$$

is not linear in the variable y. But its reciprocal

$$\frac{dx}{dy} = x + y^2 \qquad \text{or} \qquad \frac{dx}{dy} - x = y^2$$

is recognized as linear in the variable x. You should verify that the integrating factor $e^{\int(-1)dy} = e^{-y}$ and integration by parts yield the explicit solution $x = -y^2 - 2y - 2 + ce^y$ for the second equation. This expression is, then, an implicit solution of the first equation.

(*iii*) Mathematicians have adopted as their own certain words from engineering, which they found appropriately descriptive. The word *transient,* used earlier, is one of these terms. In future discussions the words *input* and *output* will occasionally pop up. The function f in (2) is called the **input** or **driving function;** a solution $y(x)$ of the differential equation for a given input is called the **output** or **response.**

(*iv*) The term **special functions** mentioned in conjunction with the error function also applies to the **sine integral function** and the **Fresnel sine integral** introduced in Problems 49 and 50 in Exercises 2.3. "Special Functions" is actually a well-defined branch of mathematics. More special functions are studied in Section 6.3.

---

[*]Certain commands have the same spelling, but in *Mathematica* commands begin with a capital letter (**Dsolve**), whereas in *Maple* the same command begins with a lower case letter (**dsolve**). When discussing such common syntax, we compromise and write, for example, *dsolve*. See the *Student Resource and Solutions Manual* for the complete input commands used to solve a linear first-order DE.

EXERCISES 2.3

Answers to selected odd-numbered problems begin on page ANS-2.

In Problems 1–24 find the general solution of the given differential equation. Give the largest interval I over which the general solution is defined. Determine whether there are any transient terms in the general solution.

1. $\dfrac{dy}{dx} = 5y$

2. $\dfrac{dy}{dx} + 2y = 0$

3. $\dfrac{dy}{dx} + y = e^{3x}$

4. $3\dfrac{dy}{dx} + 12y = 4$

5. $y' + 3x^2y = x^2$

6. $y' + 2xy = x^3$

7. $x^2y' + xy = 1$

8. $y' = 2y + x^2 + 5$

9. $x\dfrac{dy}{dx} - y = x^2 \sin x$

10. $x\dfrac{dy}{dx} + 2y = 3$

11. $x\dfrac{dy}{dx} + 4y = x^3 - x$

12. $(1 + x)\dfrac{dy}{dx} - xy = x + x^2$

13. $x^2y' + x(x + 2)y = e^x$

14. $xy' + (1 + x)y = e^{-x} \sin 2x$

15. $y\,dx - 4(x + y^6)\,dy = 0$

16. $y\,dx = (ye^y - 2x)\,dy$

17. $\cos x \dfrac{dy}{dx} + (\sin x)y = 1$

18. $\cos^2 x \sin x \dfrac{dy}{dx} + (\cos^3 x)y = 1$

19. $(x + 1)\dfrac{dy}{dx} + (x + 2)y = 2xe^{-x}$

20. $(x + 2)^2 \dfrac{dy}{dx} = 5 - 8y - 4xy$

21. $\dfrac{dr}{d\theta} + r \sec \theta = \cos \theta$

22. $\dfrac{dP}{dt} + 2tP = P + 4t - 2$

23. $x\dfrac{dy}{dx} + (3x + 1)y = e^{-3x}$

24. $(x^2 - 1)\dfrac{dy}{dx} + 2y = (x + 1)^2$

In Problems 25–30 solve the given initial-value problem. Give the largest interval I over which the solution is defined.

25. $xy' + y = e^x, \quad y(1) = 2$

26. $y\dfrac{dx}{dy} - x = 2y^2, \quad y(1) = 5$

27. $L\dfrac{di}{dt} + Ri = E, \quad i(0) = i_0,$

$L, R, E,$ and i_0 constants

28. $\dfrac{dT}{dt} = k(T - T_m); \quad T(0) = T_0,$

$k, T_m,$ and T_0 constants

29. $(x + 1)\dfrac{dy}{dx} + y = \ln x, \quad y(1) = 10$

30. $y' + (\tan x)y = \cos^2 x, \quad y(0) = -1$

In Problems 31–34 proceed as in Example 6 to solve the given initial-value problem. Use a graphing utility to graph the continuous function $y(x)$.

31. $\dfrac{dy}{dx} + 2y = f(x), y(0) = 0,$ where

$$f(x) = \begin{cases} 1, & 0 \le x \le 3 \\ 0, & x > 3 \end{cases}$$

32. $\dfrac{dy}{dx} + y = f(x), y(0) = 1,$ where

$$f(x) = \begin{cases} 1, & 0 \le x \le 1 \\ -1, & x > 1 \end{cases}$$

33. $\dfrac{dy}{dx} + 2xy = f(x), y(0) = 2,$ where

$$f(x) = \begin{cases} x, & 0 \le x < 1 \\ 0, & x \ge 1 \end{cases}$$

34. $(1 + x^2)\dfrac{dy}{dx} + 2xy = f(x), y(0) = 0,$ where

$$f(x) = \begin{cases} x, & 0 \le x < 1 \\ -x, & x \ge 1 \end{cases}$$

35. Proceed in a manner analogous to Example 6 to solve the initial-value problem $y' + P(x)y = 4x, y(0) = 3,$ where

$$P(x) = \begin{cases} 2, & 0 \le x \le 1, \\ -2/x, & x > 1. \end{cases}$$

Use a graphing utility to graph the continuous function $y(x)$.

36. Consider the initial-value problem $y' + e^x y = f(x),$ $y(0) = 1.$ Express the solution of the IVP for $x > 0$ as a nonelementary integral when $f(x) = 1.$ What is the solution when $f(x) = 0$? When $f(x) = e^x$?

37. Express the solution of the initial-value problem $y' - 2xy = 1, y(1) = 1,$ in terms of $\mathrm{erf}(x).$

Discussion Problems

38. Reread the discussion following Example 2. Construct a linear first-order differential equation for which all nonconstant solutions approach the horizontal asymptote $y = 4$ as $x \to \infty.$

39. Reread Example 3 and then discuss, with reference to Theorem 1.2.1, the existence and uniqueness of a solution of the initial-value problem consisting of $xy' - 4y = x^6 e^x$ and the given initial condition.
   (a) $y(0) = 0$ **(b)** $y(0) = y_0, y_0 > 0$
   (c) $y(x_0) = y_0, x_0 > 0, y_0 > 0$

40. Reread Example 4 and then find the general solution of the differential equation on the interval $(-3, 3).$

41. Reread the discussion following Example 5. Construct a linear first-order differential equation for which all solutions are asymptotic to the line $y = 3x - 5$ as $x \to \infty.$

42. Reread Example 6 and then discuss why it is technically incorrect to say that the function in (13) is a "solution" of the IVP on the interval $[0, \infty).$

43. (a) Construct a linear first-order differential equation of the form $xy' + a_0(x)y = g(x)$ for which $y_c = c/x^3$ and $y_p = x^3.$ Give an interval on which $y = x^3 + c/x^3$ is the general solution of the DE.

    (b) Give an initial condition $y(x_0) = y_0$ for the DE found in part (a) so that the solution of the IVP is $y = x^3 - 1/x^3.$ Repeat if the solution is

$y = x^3 + 2/x^3$. Give an interval I of definition of each of these solutions. Graph the solution curves. Is there an initial-value problem whose solution is defined on $(-\infty, \infty)$?

(c) Is each IVP found in part (b) unique? That is, can there be more than one IVP for which, say, $y = x^3 - 1/x^3$, x in some interval I, is the solution?

44. In determining the integrating factor (5), we did not use a constant of integration in the evaluation of $\int P(x)\, dx$. Explain why using $\int P(x)\, dx + c$ has no effect on the solution of (2).

45. Suppose $P(x)$ is continuous on some interval I and a is a number in I. What can be said about the solution of the initial-value problem $y' + P(x)y = 0$, $y(a) = 0$?

Mathematical Models

46. Radioactive Decay Series The following system of differential equations is encountered in the study of the decay of a special type of radioactive series of elements:

$$\frac{dx}{dt} = -\lambda_1 x$$

$$\frac{dy}{dt} = \lambda_1 x - \lambda_2 y,$$

where λ_1 and λ_2 are constants. Discuss how to solve this system subject to $x(0) = x_0$, $y(0) = y_0$. Carry out your ideas.

47. Heart Pacemaker A heart pacemaker consists of a switch, a battery of constant voltage E_0, a capacitor with constant capacitance C, and the heart as a resistor with constant resistance R. When the switch is closed, the capacitor charges; when the switch is open, the capacitor discharges, sending an electrical stimulus to the heart. During the time the heart is being stimulated, the voltage E across the heart satisfies the linear differential equation

$$\frac{dE}{dt} = -\frac{1}{RC}E.$$

Solve the DE subject to $E(4) = E_0$.

Computer Lab Assignments

48. (a) Express the solution of the initial-value problem $y' - 2xy = -1$, $y(0) = \sqrt{\pi}/2$, in terms of erfc(x).

(b) Use tables or a CAS to find the value of $y(2)$. Use a CAS to graph the solution curve for the IVP on $(-\infty, \infty)$.

49. (a) The **sine integral function** is defined by $\text{Si}(x) = \int_0^x (\sin t/t)\, dt$, where the integrand is defined to be 1 at $t = 0$. Express the solution $y(x)$ of the initial-value problem $x^3 y' + 2x^2 y = 10\sin x$, $y(1) = 0$ in terms of Si(x).

(b) Use a CAS to graph the solution curve for the IVP for $x > 0$.

(c) Use a CAS to find the value of the absolute maximum of the solution $y(x)$ for $x > 0$.

50. (a) The **Fresnel sine integral** is defined by $S(x) = \int_0^x \sin(\pi t^2/2)\, dt$. Express the solution $y(x)$ of the initial-value problem $y' - (\sin x^2)y = 0$, $y(0) = 5$, in terms of $S(x)$.

(b) Use a CAS to graph the solution curve for the IVP on $(-\infty, \infty)$.

(c) It is known that $S(x) \to \frac{1}{2}$ as $x \to \infty$ and $S(x) \to -\frac{1}{2}$ as $x \to -\infty$. What does the solution $y(x)$ approach as $x \to \infty$? As $x \to -\infty$?

(d) Use a CAS to find the values of the absolute maximum and the absolute minimum of the solution $y(x)$.

2.4	**EXACT EQUATIONS**

REVIEW MATERIAL

- Multivariate calculus
- Partial differentiation and partial integration
- Differential of a function of two variables

INTRODUCTION Although the simple first-order equation

$$y\, dx + x\, dy = 0$$

is separable, we can solve the equation in an alternative manner by recognizing that the expression on the left-hand side of the equality is the differential of the function $f(x, y) = xy$; that is,

$$d(xy) = y\, dx + x\, dy.$$

In this section we examine first-order equations in differential form $M(x, y)\, dx + N(x, y)\, dy = 0$. By applying a simple test to M and N, we can determine whether $M(x, y)\, dx + N(x, y)\, dy$ is a differential of a function $f(x, y)$. If the answer is yes, we can construct f by partial integration.

DIFFERENTIAL OF A FUNCTION OF TWO VARIABLES If $z = f(x, y)$ is a function of two variables with continuous first partial derivatives in a region R of the xy-plane, then its differential is

$$dz = \frac{\partial f}{\partial x}\, dx + \frac{\partial f}{\partial y}\, dy. \tag{1}$$

In the special case when $f(x, y) = c$, where c is a constant, then (1) implies

$$\frac{\partial f}{\partial x}\, dx + \frac{\partial f}{\partial y}\, dy = 0. \tag{2}$$

In other words, given a one-parameter family of functions $f(x, y) = c$, we can generate a first-order differential equation by computing the differential of both sides of the equality. For example, if $x^2 - 5xy + y^3 = c$, then (2) gives the first-order DE

$$(2x - 5y)\, dx + (-5x + 3y^2)\, dy = 0. \tag{3}$$

A DEFINITION Of course, not every first-order DE written in differential form $M(x, y)\, dx + N(x, y)\, dy = 0$ corresponds to a differential of $f(x, y) = c$. So for our purposes it is more important to turn the foregoing example around; namely, if we are given a first-order DE such as (3), is there some way we can recognize that the differential expression $(2x - 5y)\, dx + (-5x + 3y^2)\, dy$ is the differential $d(x^2 - 5xy + y^3)$? If there is, then an implicit solution of (3) is $x^2 - 5xy + y^3 = c$. We answer this question after the next definition.

DEFINITION 2.4.1 Exact Equation

A differential expression $M(x, y)\, dx + N(x, y)\, dy$ is an **exact differential** in a region R of the xy-plane if it corresponds to the differential of some function $f(x, y)$ defined in R. A first-order differential equation of the form

$$M(x, y)\, dx + N(x, y)\, dy = 0$$

is said to be an **exact equation** if the expression on the left-hand side is an exact differential.

For example, $x^2y^3\, dx + x^3y^2\, dy = 0$ is an exact equation, because its left-hand side is an exact differential:

$$d\left(\tfrac{1}{3} x^3 y^3\right) = x^2 y^3\, dx + x^3 y^2\, dy.$$

Notice that if we make the identifications $M(x, y) = x^2y^3$ and $N(x, y) = x^3y^2$, then $\partial M/\partial y = 3x^2y^2 = \partial N/\partial x$. Theorem 2.4.1, given next, shows that the equality of the partial derivatives $\partial M/\partial y$ and $\partial N/\partial x$ is no coincidence.

THEOREM 2.4.1 Criterion for an Exact Differential

Let $M(x, y)$ and $N(x, y)$ be continuous and have continuous first partial derivatives in a rectangular region R defined by $a < x < b, c < y < d$. Then a necessary and sufficient condition that $M(x, y)\, dx + N(x, y)\, dy$ be an exact differential is

$$\frac{\partial M}{\partial y} = \frac{\partial N}{\partial x}. \tag{4}$$

PROOF OF THE NECESSITY For simplicity let us assume that $M(x, y)$ and $N(x, y)$ have continuous first partial derivatives for all (x, y). Now if the expression $M(x, y)\, dx + N(x, y)\, dy$ is exact, there exists some function f such that for all x in R,

$$M(x, y)\, dx + N(x, y)\, dy = \frac{\partial f}{\partial x}\, dx + \frac{\partial f}{\partial y}\, dy.$$

Therefore

$$M(x, y) = \frac{\partial f}{\partial x}, \qquad N(x, y) = \frac{\partial f}{\partial y},$$

and

$$\frac{\partial M}{\partial y} = \frac{\partial}{\partial y}\left(\frac{\partial f}{\partial x}\right) = \frac{\partial^2 f}{\partial y\, \partial x} = \frac{\partial}{\partial x}\left(\frac{\partial f}{\partial y}\right) = \frac{\partial N}{\partial x}.$$

The equality of the mixed partials is a consequence of the continuity of the first partial derivatives of $M(x, y)$ and $N(x, y)$. ∎

The sufficiency part of Theorem 2.4.1 consists of showing that there exists a function f for which $\partial f/\partial x = M(x, y)$ and $\partial f/\partial y = N(x, y)$ whenever (4) holds. The construction of the function f actually reflects a basic procedure for solving exact equations.

METHOD OF SOLUTION Given an equation in the differential form $M(x, y)\, dx + N(x, y)\, dy = 0$, determine whether the equality in (4) holds. If it does, then there exists a function f for which

$$\frac{\partial f}{\partial x} = M(x, y).$$

We can find f by integrating $M(x, y)$ with respect to x while holding y constant:

$$f(x, y) = \int M(x, y)\, dx + g(y), \tag{5}$$

where the arbitrary function $g(y)$ is the "constant" of integration. Now differentiate (5) with respect to y and assume that $\partial f/\partial y = N(x, y)$:

$$\frac{\partial f}{\partial y} = \frac{\partial}{\partial y}\int M(x, y)\, dx + g'(y) = N(x, y).$$

This gives

$$g'(y) = N(x, y) - \frac{\partial}{\partial y}\int M(x, y)\, dx. \tag{6}$$

Finally, integrate (6) with respect to y and substitute the result in (5). The implicit solution of the equation is $f(x, y) = c$.

Some observations are in order. First, it is important to realize that the expression $N(x, y) - (\partial/\partial y)\int M(x, y)\, dx$ in (6) is independent of x, because

$$\frac{\partial}{\partial x}\left[N(x, y) - \frac{\partial}{\partial y}\int M(x, y)\, dx\right] = \frac{\partial N}{\partial x} - \frac{\partial}{\partial y}\left(\frac{\partial}{\partial x}\int M(x, y)\, dx\right) = \frac{\partial N}{\partial x} - \frac{\partial M}{\partial y} = 0.$$

Second, we could just as well start the foregoing procedure with the assumption that $\partial f/\partial y = N(x, y)$. After integrating N with respect to y and then differentiating that result, we would find the analogues of (5) and (6) to be, respectively,

$$f(x, y) = \int N(x, y)\, dy + h(x) \qquad \text{and} \qquad h'(x) = M(x, y) - \frac{\partial}{\partial x}\int N(x, y)\, dy.$$

In either case *none of these formulas should be memorized.*

EXAMPLE 1   Solving an Exact DE

Solve $2xy\,dx + (x^2 - 1)\,dy = 0$.

SOLUTION   With $M(x, y) = 2xy$ and $N(x, y) = x^2 - 1$ we have

$$\frac{\partial M}{\partial y} = 2x = \frac{\partial N}{\partial x}.$$

Thus the equation is exact, and so by Theorem 2.4.1 there exists a function $f(x, y)$ such that

$$\frac{\partial f}{\partial x} = 2xy \qquad \text{and} \qquad \frac{\partial f}{\partial y} = x^2 - 1.$$

From the first of these equations we obtain, after integrating,

$$f(x, y) = x^2 y + g(y).$$

Taking the partial derivative of the last expression with respect to y and setting the result equal to $N(x, y)$ gives

$$\frac{\partial f}{\partial y} = x^2 + g'(y) = x^2 - 1. \qquad \leftarrow N(x, y)$$

It follows that $g'(y) = -1$ and $g(y) = -y$. Hence $f(x, y) = x^2 y - y$, so the solution of the equation in implicit form is $x^2 y - y = c$. The explicit form of the solution is easily seen to be $y = c/(1 - x^2)$ and is defined on any interval not containing either $x = 1$ or $x = -1$. ∎

NOTE   The solution of the DE in Example 1 is *not* $f(x, y) = x^2 y - y$. Rather, it is $f(x, y) = c$; if a constant is used in the integration of $g'(y)$, we can then write the solution as $f(x, y) = 0$. Note, too, that the equation could be solved by separation of variables.

EXAMPLE 2   Solving an Exact DE

Solve $(e^{2y} - y \cos xy)\,dx + (2xe^{2y} - x \cos xy + 2y)\,dy = 0$.

SOLUTION   The equation is exact because

$$\frac{\partial M}{\partial y} = 2e^{2y} + xy \sin xy - \cos xy = \frac{\partial N}{\partial x}.$$

Hence a function $f(x, y)$ exists for which

$$M(x, y) = \frac{\partial f}{\partial x} \qquad \text{and} \qquad N(x, y) = \frac{\partial f}{\partial y}.$$

Now for variety we shall start with the assumption that $\partial f/\partial y = N(x, y)$; that is,

$$\frac{\partial f}{\partial y} = 2xe^{2y} - x \cos xy + 2y$$

$$f(x, y) = 2x \int e^{2y}\,dy - x \int \cos xy\,dy + 2 \int y\,dy.$$

Remember, the reason x can come out in front of the symbol $\int$ is that in the integration with respect to y, x is treated as an ordinary constant. It follows that

$$f(x, y) = xe^{2y} - \sin xy + y^2 + h(x)$$

$$\frac{\partial f}{\partial x} = e^{2y} - y \cos xy + h'(x) = e^{2y} - y \cos xy, \quad \leftarrow M(x, y)$$

and so $h'(x) = 0$ or $h(x) = c$. Hence a family of solutions is

$$xe^{2y} - \sin xy + y^2 + c = 0. \qquad \blacksquare$$

EXAMPLE 3 An Initial-Value Problem

Solve $\dfrac{dy}{dx} = \dfrac{xy^2 - \cos x \sin x}{y(1 - x^2)}$, $\quad y(0) = 2$.

SOLUTION By writing the differential equation in the form

$$(\cos x \sin x - xy^2)\, dx + y(1 - x^2)\, dy = 0,$$

we recognize that the equation is exact because

$$\frac{\partial M}{\partial y} = -2xy = \frac{\partial N}{\partial x}.$$

Now

$$\frac{\partial f}{\partial y} = y(1 - x^2)$$

$$f(x, y) = \frac{y^2}{2}(1 - x^2) + h(x)$$

$$\frac{\partial f}{\partial x} = -xy^2 + h'(x) = \cos x \sin x - xy^2.$$

The last equation implies that $h'(x) = \cos x \sin x$. Integrating gives

$$h(x) = -\int (\cos x)(-\sin x\, dx) = -\frac{1}{2}\cos^2 x.$$

Thus $\quad \dfrac{y^2}{2}(1 - x^2) - \dfrac{1}{2}\cos^2 x = c_1 \quad$ or $\quad y^2(1 - x^2) - \cos^2 x = c, \qquad$ (7)

where $2c_1$ has been replaced by c. The initial condition $y = 2$ when $x = 0$ demands that $4(1) - \cos^2(0) = c$, and so $c = 3$. An implicit solution of the problem is then $y^2(1 - x^2) - \cos^2 x = 3$.

The solution curve of the IVP is the curve drawn in dark blue in Figure 2.4.1; it is part of an interesting family of curves. The graphs of the members of the one-parameter family of solutions given in (7) can be obtained in several ways, two of which are using software to graph level curves (as discussed in Section 2.2) and using a graphing utility to carefully graph the explicit functions obtained for various values of c by solving $y^2 = (c + \cos^2 x)/(1 - x^2)$ for y. $\qquad \blacksquare$

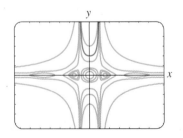

FIGURE 2.4.1 Some graphs of members of the family $y^2(1 - x^2) - \cos^2 x = c$

INTEGRATING FACTORS Recall from Section 2.3 that the left-hand side of the linear equation $y' + P(x)y = f(x)$ can be transformed into a derivative when we multiply the equation by an integrating factor. The same basic idea sometimes works for a nonexact differential equation $M(x, y)\, dx + N(x, y)\, dy = 0$. That is, it is sometimes possible to find an **integrating factor** $\mu(x, y)$ so that after multiplying, the left-hand side of

$$\mu(x, y)M(x, y)\,dx + \mu(x, y)N(x, y)\,dy = 0 \tag{8}$$

is an exact differential. In an attempt to find μ, we turn to the criterion (4) for exactness. Equation (8) is exact if and only if $(\mu M)_y = (\mu N)_x$, where the subscripts denote partial derivatives. By the Product Rule of differentiation the last equation is the same as $\mu M_y + \mu_y M = \mu N_x + \mu_x N$ or

$$\mu_x N - \mu_y M = (M_y - N_x)\mu. \tag{9}$$

Although M, N, M_y, and N_x are known functions of x and y, the difficulty here in determining the unknown $\mu(x, y)$ from (9) is that we must solve a partial differential equation. Since we are not prepared to do that, we make a simplifying assumption. Suppose μ is a function of one variable; for example, say that μ depends only on x. In this case, $\mu_x = d\mu/dx$ and $\mu_y = 0$, so (9) can be written as

$$\frac{d\mu}{dx} = \frac{M_y - N_x}{N}\,\mu. \tag{10}$$

We are still at an impasse if the quotient $(M_y - N_x)/N$ depends on both x and y. However, if after all obvious algebraic simplifications are made, the quotient $(M_y - N_x)/N$ turns out to depend solely on the variable x, then (10) is a first-order ordinary differential equation. We can finally determine μ because (10) is *separable* as well as *linear*. It follows from either Section 2.2 or Section 2.3 that $\mu(x) = e^{\int ((M_y - N_x)/N)\,dx}$. In like manner, it follows from (9) that if μ depends only on the variable y, then

$$\frac{d\mu}{dy} = \frac{N_x - M_y}{M}\,\mu. \tag{11}$$

In this case, if $(N_x - M_y)/M$ is a function of y only, then we can solve (11) for μ.

We summarize the results for the differential equation

$$M(x, y)\,dx + N(x, y)\,dy = 0. \tag{12}$$

- If $(M_y - N_x)/N$ is a function of x alone, then an integrating factor for (12) is

$$\mu(x) = e^{\int \frac{M_y - N_x}{N}\,dx}. \tag{13}$$

- If $(N_x - M_y)/M$ is a function of y alone, then an integrating factor for (12) is

$$\mu(y) = e^{\int \frac{N_x - M_y}{M}\,dy}. \tag{14}$$

EXAMPLE 4   A Nonexact DE Made Exact

The nonlinear first-order differential equation

$$xy\,dx + (2x^2 + 3y^2 - 20)\,dy = 0$$

is not exact. With the identifications $M = xy$, $N = 2x^2 + 3y^2 - 20$, we find the partial derivatives $M_y = x$ and $N_x = 4x$. The first quotient from (13) gets us nowhere, since

$$\frac{M_y - N_x}{N} = \frac{x - 4x}{2x^2 + 3y^2 - 20} = \frac{-3x}{2x^2 + 3y^2 - 20}$$

depends on x and y. However, (14) yields a quotient that depends only on y:

$$\frac{N_x - M_y}{M} = \frac{4x - x}{xy} = \frac{3x}{xy} = \frac{3}{y}.$$

The integrating factor is then $e^{\int 3dy/y} = e^{3\ln y} = e^{\ln y^3} = y^3$. After we multiply the given DE by $\mu(y) = y^3$, the resulting equation is

$$xy^4\,dx + (2x^2y^3 + 3y^5 - 20y^3)\,dy = 0.$$

You should verify that the last equation is now exact as well as show, using the method of this section, that a family of solutions is $\frac{1}{2}x^2y^4 + \frac{1}{2}y^6 - 5y^4 = c$. ∎

REMARKS

(*i*) When testing an equation for exactness, make sure it is of the precise form $M(x, y)\,dx + N(x, y)\,dy = 0$. Sometimes a differential equation is written $G(x, y)\,dx = H(x, y)\,dy$. In this case, first rewrite it as $G(x, y)\,dx - H(x, y)\,dy = 0$ and then identify $M(x, y) = G(x, y)$ and $N(x, y) = -H(x, y)$ before using (4).

(*ii*) In some texts on differential equations the study of exact equations precedes that of linear DEs. Then the method for finding integrating factors just discussed can be used to derive an integrating factor for $y' + P(x)y = f(x)$. By rewriting the last equation in the differential form $(P(x)y - f(x))\,dx + dy = 0$, we see that

$$\frac{M_y - N_x}{N} = P(x).$$

From (13) we arrive at the already familiar integrating factor $e^{\int P(x)dx}$, used in Section 2.3.

EXERCISES 2.4

Answers to selected odd-numbered problems begin on page ANS-2.

In Problems 1–20 determine whether the given differential equation is exact. If it is exact, solve it.

1. $(2x - 1)\,dx + (3y + 7)\,dy = 0$

2. $(2x + y)\,dx - (x + 6y)\,dy = 0$

3. $(5x + 4y)\,dx + (4x - 8y^3)\,dy = 0$

4. $(\sin y - y\sin x)\,dx + (\cos x + x\cos y - y)\,dy = 0$

5. $(2xy^2 - 3)\,dx + (2x^2y + 4)\,dy = 0$

6. $\left(2y - \dfrac{1}{x} + \cos 3x\right)\dfrac{dy}{dx} + \dfrac{y}{x^2} - 4x^3 + 3y\sin 3x = 0$

7. $(x^2 - y^2)\,dx + (x^2 - 2xy)\,dy = 0$

8. $\left(1 + \ln x + \dfrac{y}{x}\right)dx = (1 - \ln x)\,dy$

9. $(x - y^3 + y^2\sin x)\,dx = (3xy^2 + 2y\cos x)\,dy$

10. $(x^3 + y^3)\,dx + 3xy^2\,dy = 0$

11. $(y\ln y - e^{-xy})\,dx + \left(\dfrac{1}{y} + x\ln y\right)dy = 0$

12. $(3x^2y + e^y)\,dx + (x^3 + xe^y - 2y)\,dy = 0$

13. $x\dfrac{dy}{dx} = 2xe^x - y + 6x^2$

14. $\left(1 - \dfrac{3}{y} + x\right)\dfrac{dy}{dx} + y = \dfrac{3}{x} - 1$

15. $\left(x^2y^3 - \dfrac{1}{1 + 9x^2}\right)\dfrac{dx}{dy} + x^3y^2 = 0$

16. $(5y - 2x)y' - 2y = 0$

17. $(\tan x - \sin x\sin y)\,dx + \cos x\cos y\,dy = 0$

18. $(2y\sin x\cos x - y + 2y^2e^{xy^2})\,dx$
$$= (x - \sin^2 x - 4xye^{xy^2})\,dy$$

19. $(4t^3y - 15t^2 - y)\,dt + (t^4 + 3y^2 - t)\,dy = 0$

20. $\left(\dfrac{1}{t} + \dfrac{1}{t^2} - \dfrac{y}{t^2 + y^2}\right)dt + \left(ye^y + \dfrac{t}{t^2 + y^2}\right)dy = 0$

In Problems 21–26 solve the given initial-value problem.

21. $(x + y)^2 \, dx + (2xy + x^2 - 1) \, dy = 0, \quad y(1) = 1$

22. $(e^x + y) \, dx + (2 + x + ye^y) \, dy = 0, \quad y(0) = 1$

23. $(4y + 2t - 5) \, dt + (6y + 4t - 1) \, dy = 0, \quad y(-1) = 2$

24. $\left(\dfrac{3y^2 - t^2}{y^5} \right) \dfrac{dy}{dt} + \dfrac{t}{2y^4} = 0, \quad y(1) = 1$

25. $(y^2 \cos x - 3x^2 y - 2x) \, dx$
$+ (2y \sin x - x^3 + \ln y) \, dy = 0, \quad y(0) = e$

26. $\left(\dfrac{1}{1 + y^2} + \cos x - 2xy \right) \dfrac{dy}{dx} = y(y + \sin x), \quad y(0) = 1$

In Problems 27 and 28 find the value of k so that the given differential equation is exact.

27. $(y^3 + kxy^4 - 2x) \, dx + (3xy^2 + 20x^2 y^3) \, dy = 0$

28. $(6xy^3 + \cos y) \, dx + (2kx^2 y^2 - x \sin y) \, dy = 0$

In Problems 29 and 30 verify that the given differential equation is not exact. Multiply the given differential equation by the indicated integrating factor $\mu(x, y)$ and verify that the new equation is exact. Solve.

29. $(-xy \sin x + 2y \cos x) \, dx + 2x \cos x \, dy = 0;$
$\mu(x, y) = xy$

30. $(x^2 + 2xy - y^2) \, dx + (y^2 + 2xy - x^2) \, dy = 0;$
$\mu(x, y) = (x + y)^{-2}$

In Problems 31–36 solve the given differential equation by finding, as in Example 4, an appropriate integrating factor.

31. $(2y^2 + 3x) \, dx + 2xy \, dy = 0$

32. $y(x + y + 1) \, dx + (x + 2y) \, dy = 0$

33. $6xy \, dx + (4y + 9x^2) \, dy = 0$

34. $\cos x \, dx + \left(1 + \dfrac{2}{y} \right) \sin x \, dy = 0$

35. $(10 - 6y + e^{-3x}) \, dx - 2 \, dy = 0$

36. $(y^2 + xy^3) \, dx + (5y^2 - xy + y^3 \sin y) \, dy = 0$

In Problems 37 and 38 solve the given initial-value problem by finding, as in Example 4, an appropriate integrating factor.

37. $x \, dx + (x^2 y + 4y) \, dy = 0, \quad y(4) = 0$

38. $(x^2 + y^2 - 5) \, dx = (y + xy) \, dy, \quad y(0) = 1$

39. (a) Show that a one-parameter family of solutions of the equation

$$(4xy + 3x^2) \, dx + (2y + 2x^2) \, dy = 0$$

is $x^3 + 2x^2 y + y^2 = c$.

(b) Show that the initial conditions $y(0) = -2$ and $y(1) = 1$ determine the same implicit solution.

(c) Find explicit solutions $y_1(x)$ and $y_2(x)$ of the differential equation in part (a) such that $y_1(0) = -2$ and $y_2(1) = 1$. Use a graphing utility to graph $y_1(x)$ and $y_2(x)$.

Discussion Problems

40. Consider the concept of an integrating factor used in Problems 29–38. Are the two equations $M \, dx + N \, dy = 0$ and $\mu M \, dx + \mu N \, dy = 0$ necessarily equivalent in the sense that a solution of one is also a solution of the other? Discuss.

41. Reread Example 3 and then discuss why we can conclude that the interval of definition of the explicit solution of the IVP (the blue curve in Figure 2.4.1) is $(-1, 1)$.

42. Discuss how the functions $M(x, y)$ and $N(x, y)$ can be found so that each differential equation is exact. Carry out your ideas.

(a) $M(x, y) \, dx + \left(xe^{xy} + 2xy + \dfrac{1}{x} \right) dy = 0$

(b) $\left(x^{-1/2} y^{1/2} + \dfrac{x}{x^2 + y} \right) dx + N(x, y) \, dy = 0$

43. Differential equations are sometimes solved by having a clever idea. Here is a little exercise in cleverness: Although the differential equation $(x - \sqrt{x^2 + y^2}) \, dx + y \, dy = 0$ is not exact, show how the rearrangement $(x \, dx + y \, dy) / \sqrt{x^2 + y^2} = dx$ and the observation $\frac{1}{2} d(x^2 + y^2) = x \, dx + y \, dy$ can lead to a solution.

44. True or False: Every separable first-order equation $dy/dx = g(x)h(y)$ is exact.

Mathematical Model

45. Falling Chain A portion of a uniform chain of length 8 ft is loosely coiled around a peg at the edge of a high horizontal platform, and the remaining portion of the chain hangs at rest over the edge of the platform. See Figure 2.4.2. Suppose that the length of the overhanging chain is 3 ft, that the chain weighs 2 lb/ft, and that the positive direction is downward. Starting at $t = 0$ seconds, the weight of the overhanging portion causes the chain on the table to uncoil smoothly and to fall to the floor. If $x(t)$ denotes the length of the chain overhanging the table at time $t > 0$, then $v = dx/dt$ is its velocity. When all resistive forces are ignored, it can be shown that a mathematical model relating v to x is given by

$$xv\frac{dv}{dx} + v^2 = 32x.$$

(a) Rewrite this model in differential form. Proceed as in Problems 31–36 and solve the DE for v in terms of x by finding an appropriate integrating factor. Find an explicit solution $v(x)$.

(b) Determine the velocity with which the chain leaves the platform.

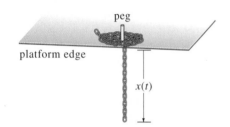

FIGURE 2.4.2 Uncoiling chain in Problem 45

Computer Lab Assignments

46. Streamlines

(a) The solution of the differential equation

$$\frac{2xy}{(x^2 + y^2)^2}\,dx + \left[1 + \frac{y^2 - x^2}{(x^2 + y^2)^2}\right]dy = 0$$

is a family of curves that can be interpreted as streamlines of a fluid flow around a circular object whose boundary is described by the equation $x^2 + y^2 = 1$. Solve this DE and note the solution $f(x, y) = c$ for $c = 0$.

(b) Use a CAS to plot the streamlines for $c = 0,\ \pm0.2,\ \pm0.4,\ \pm0.6,$ and ±0.8 in three different ways. First, use the *contourplot* of a CAS. Second, solve for x in terms of the variable y. Plot the resulting two functions of y for the given values of c, and then combine the graphs. Third, use the CAS to solve a cubic equation for y in terms of x.

2.5 SOLUTIONS BY SUBSTITUTIONS

REVIEW MATERIAL

- Techniques of integration
- Separation of variables
- Solution of linear DEs

INTRODUCTION We usually solve a differential equation by recognizing it as a certain kind of equation (say, separable, linear, or exact) and then carrying out a procedure, consisting of *equation-specific mathematical steps*, that yields a solution of the equation. But it is not uncommon to be stumped by a differential equation because it does not fall into one of the classes of equations that we know how to solve. The procedures that are discussed in this section may be helpful in this situation.

SUBSTITUTIONS Often the first step in solving a differential equation consists of transforming it into another differential equation by means of a **substitution.** For example, suppose we wish to transform the first-order differential equation $dy/dx = f(x, y)$ by the substitution $y = g(x, u)$, where u is regarded as a function of the variable x. If g possesses first-partial derivatives, then the Chain Rule

$$\frac{dy}{dx} = \frac{\partial g}{\partial x}\frac{dx}{dx} + \frac{\partial g}{\partial u}\frac{du}{dx} \qquad \text{gives} \qquad \frac{dy}{dx} = g_x(x, u) + g_u(x, u)\frac{du}{dx}.$$

If we replace dy/dx by the foregoing derivative and replace y in $f(x, y)$ by $g(x, u)$, then the DE $dy/dx = f(x, y)$ becomes $g_x(x, u) + g_u(x, u)\dfrac{du}{dx} = f(x, g(x, u))$, which, solved for du/dx, has the form $\dfrac{du}{dx} = F(x, u)$. If we can determine a solution $u = \phi(x)$ of this last equation, then a solution of the original differential equation is $y = g(x, \phi(x))$.

In the discussion that follows we examine three different kinds of first-order differential equations that are solvable by means of a substitution.

HOMOGENEOUS EQUATIONS If a function f possesses the property $f(tx, ty) = t^\alpha f(x, y)$ for some real number α, then f is said to be a **homogeneous function** of degree α. For example, $f(x, y) = x^3 + y^3$ is a homogeneous function of degree 3, since

$$f(tx, ty) = (tx)^3 + (ty)^3 = t^3(x^3 + y^3) = t^3 f(x, y),$$

whereas $f(x, y) = x^3 + y^3 + 1$ is not homogeneous. A first-order DE in differential form

$$M(x, y)\, dx + N(x, y)\, dy = 0 \tag{1}$$

is said to be **homogeneous**[*] if both coefficient functions M and N are homogeneous functions of the *same* degree. In other words, (1) is homogeneous if

$$M(tx, ty) = t^\alpha M(x, y) \qquad \text{and} \qquad N(tx, ty) = t^\alpha N(x, y).$$

In addition, if M and N are homogeneous functions of degree α, we can also write

$$M(x, y) = x^\alpha M(1, u) \qquad \text{and} \qquad N(x, y) = x^\alpha N(1, u), \quad \text{where } u = y/x, \tag{2}$$

and

$$M(x, y) = y^\alpha M(v, 1) \qquad \text{and} \qquad N(x, y) = y^\alpha N(v, 1), \quad \text{where } v = x/y. \tag{3}$$

See Problem 31 in Exercises 2.5. Properties (2) and (3) suggest the substitutions that can be used to solve a homogeneous differential equation. Specifically, *either* of the substitutions $y = ux$ or $x = vy$, where u and v are new dependent variables, will reduce a homogeneous equation to a *separable* first-order differential equation. To show this, observe that as a consequence of (2) a homogeneous equation $M(x, y)\, dx + N(x, y)\, dy = 0$ can be rewritten as

$$x^\alpha M(1, u)\, dx + x^\alpha N(1, u)\, dy = 0 \qquad \text{or} \qquad M(1, u)\, dx + N(1, u)\, dy = 0,$$

where $u = y/x$ or $y = ux$. By substituting the differential $dy = u\, dx + x\, du$ into the last equation and gathering terms, we obtain a separable DE in the variables u and x:

$$M(1, u)\, dx + N(1, u)[u\, dx + x\, du] = 0$$

$$[M(1, u) + uN(1, u)]\, dx + xN(1, u)\, du = 0$$

or

$$\frac{dx}{x} + \frac{N(1, u)\, du}{M(1, u) + uN(1, u)} = 0.$$

At this point we offer the same advice as in the preceding sections: Do not memorize anything here (especially the last formula); rather, *work through the procedure each time.* The proof that the substitutions $x = vy$ and $dx = v\, dy + y\, dv$ also lead to a separable equation follows in an analogous manner from (3).

| **EXAMPLE 1** | **Solving a Homogeneous DE** |

Solve $(x^2 + y^2)\, dx + (x^2 - xy)\, dy = 0$.

SOLUTION Inspection of $M(x, y) = x^2 + y^2$ and $N(x, y) = x^2 - xy$ shows that these coefficients are homogeneous functions of degree 2. If we let $y = ux$, then

---

[*]Here the word *homogeneous* does not mean the same as it did in Section 2.3. Recall that a linear first-order equation $a_1(x)y' + a_0(x)y = g(x)$ is homogeneous when $g(x) = 0$.

$dy = u\,dx + x\,du$, so after substituting, the given equation becomes

$$(x^2 + u^2x^2)\,dx + (x^2 - ux^2)[u\,dx + x\,du] = 0$$

$$x^2(1 + u)\,dx + x^3(1 - u)\,du = 0$$

$$\frac{1 - u}{1 + u}\,du + \frac{dx}{x} = 0$$

$$\left[-1 + \frac{2}{1 + u}\right]du + \frac{dx}{x} = 0. \quad \leftarrow \text{long division}$$

After integration the last line gives

$$-u + 2\ln|1 + u| + \ln|x| = \ln|c|$$

$$-\frac{y}{x} + 2\ln\left|1 + \frac{y}{x}\right| + \ln|x| = \ln|c|. \quad \leftarrow \text{resubstituting } u = y/x$$

Using the properties of logarithms, we can write the preceding solution as

$$\ln\left|\frac{(x + y)^2}{cx}\right| = \frac{y}{x} \quad \text{or} \quad (x + y)^2 = cxe^{y/x}. \qquad \blacksquare$$

Although either of the indicated substitutions can be used for every homogeneous differential equation, in practice we try $x = vy$ whenever the function $M(x, y)$ is simpler than $N(x, y)$. Also it could happen that after using one substitution, we may encounter integrals that are difficult or impossible to evaluate in closed form; switching substitutions may result in an easier problem.

BERNOULLI'S EQUATION   The differential equation

$$\frac{dy}{dx} + P(x)y = f(x)y^n, \tag{4}$$

where n is any real number, is called **Bernoulli's equation.** Note that for $n = 0$ and $n = 1$, equation (4) is linear. For $n \neq 0$ and $n \neq 1$ the substitution $u = y^{1-n}$ reduces any equation of form (4) to a linear equation.

EXAMPLE 2   Solving a Bernoulli DE

Solve $x\dfrac{dy}{dx} + y = x^2y^2$.

SOLUTION   We first rewrite the equation as

$$\frac{dy}{dx} + \frac{1}{x}y = xy^2$$

by dividing by x. With $n = 2$ we have $u = y^{-1}$ or $y = u^{-1}$. We then substitute

$$\frac{dy}{dx} = \frac{dy}{du}\frac{du}{dx} = -u^{-2}\frac{du}{dx} \qquad \leftarrow \text{Chain Rule}$$

into the given equation and simplify. The result is

$$\frac{du}{dx} - \frac{1}{x}u = -x.$$

The integrating factor for this linear equation on, say, $(0, \infty)$ is

$$e^{-\int dx/x} = e^{-\ln x} = e^{\ln x^{-1}} = x^{-1}.$$

Integrating
$$\frac{d}{dx}[x^{-1}u] = -1$$

gives $x^{-1}u = -x + c$ or $u = -x^2 + cx$. Since $u = y^{-1}$, we have $y = 1/u$, so a solution of the given equation is $y = 1/(-x^2 + cx)$. ∎

Note that we have not obtained the general solution of the original nonlinear differential equation in Example 2, since $y = 0$ is a singular solution of the equation.

REDUCTION TO SEPARATION OF VARIABLES   A differential equation of the form

$$\frac{dy}{dx} = f(Ax + By + C) \qquad . \tag{5}$$

can always be reduced to an equation with separable variables by means of the substitution $u = Ax + By + C,\ B \neq 0$. Example 3 illustrates the technique.

EXAMPLE 3   An Initial-Value Problem

Solve $\dfrac{dy}{dx} = (-2x + y)^2 - 7, \quad y(0) = 0.$

SOLUTION   If we let $u = -2x + y$, then $du/dx = -2 + dy/dx$, so the differential equation is transformed into

$$\frac{du}{dx} + 2 = u^2 - 7 \qquad \text{or} \qquad \frac{du}{dx} = u^2 - 9.$$

The last equation is separable. Using partial fractions

$$\frac{du}{(u-3)(u+3)} = dx \qquad \text{or} \qquad \frac{1}{6}\left[\frac{1}{u-3} - \frac{1}{u+3}\right]du = dx$$

and then integrating yields

$$\frac{1}{6}\ln\left|\frac{u-3}{u+3}\right| = x + c_1 \qquad \text{or} \qquad \frac{u-3}{u+3} = e^{6x+6c_1} = ce^{6x}. \qquad \leftarrow \text{replace } e^{6c_1} \text{ by } c$$

Solving the last equation for u and then resubstituting gives the solution

$$u = \frac{3(1 + ce^{6x})}{1 - ce^{6x}} \qquad \text{or} \qquad y = 2x + \frac{3(1 + ce^{6x})}{1 - ce^{6x}}. \tag{6}$$

Finally, applying the initial condition $y(0) = 0$ to the last equation in (6) gives $c = -1$. Figure 2.5.1, obtained with the aid of a graphing utility, shows the graph of the particular solution $y = 2x + \dfrac{3(1 - e^{6x})}{1 + e^{6x}}$ in dark blue, along with the graphs of some other members of the family of solutions (6). ∎

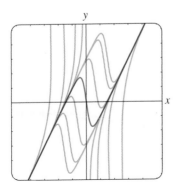

FIGURE 2.5.1   Some solutions of $y' = (-2x + y)^2 - 7$

EXERCISES 2.5

Each DE in Problems 1–14 is homogeneous.

In Problems 1–10 solve the given differential equation by using an appropriate substitution.

1. $(x - y)\,dx + x\,dy = 0$ **2.** $(x + y)\,dx + x\,dy = 0$

3. $x\,dx + (y - 2x)\,dy = 0$ **4.** $y\,dx = 2(x + y)\,dy$

5. $(y^2 + yx)\,dx - x^2\,dy = 0$

6. $(y^2 + yx)\,dx + x^2\,dy = 0$

7. $\dfrac{dy}{dx} = \dfrac{y - x}{y + x}$

8. $\dfrac{dy}{dx} = \dfrac{x + 3y}{3x + y}$

9. $-y\,dx + \left(x + \sqrt{xy}\right) dy = 0$

10. $x\dfrac{dy}{dx} = y + \sqrt{x^2 - y^2}, \quad x > 0$

In Problems 11–14 solve the given initial-value problem.

11. $xy^2 \dfrac{dy}{dx} = y^3 - x^3, \quad y(1) = 2$

12. $(x^2 + 2y^2)\dfrac{dx}{dy} = xy, \quad y(-1) = 1$

13. $(x + ye^{y/x})\,dx - xe^{y/x}\,dy = 0, \quad y(1) = 0$

14. $y\,dx + x(\ln x - \ln y - 1)\,dy = 0, \quad y(1) = e$

Each DE in Problems 15–22 is a Bernoulli equation.

In Problems 15–20 solve the given differential equation by using an appropriate substitution.

15. $x\dfrac{dy}{dx} + y = \dfrac{1}{y^2}$ **16.** $\dfrac{dy}{dx} - y = e^x y^2$

17. $\dfrac{dy}{dx} = y(xy^3 - 1)$ **18.** $x\dfrac{dy}{dx} - (1 + x)y = xy^2$

19. $t^2 \dfrac{dy}{dt} + y^2 = ty$ **20.** $3(1 + t^2)\dfrac{dy}{dt} = 2ty(y^3 - 1)$

In Problems 21 and 22 solve the given initial-value problem.

21. $x^2 \dfrac{dy}{dx} - 2xy = 3y^4, \quad y(1) = \frac{1}{2}$

22. $y^{1/2}\dfrac{dy}{dx} + y^{3/2} = 1, \quad y(0) = 4$

Each DE in Problems 23–30 is of the form given in (5).

In Problems 23–28 solve the given differential equation by using an appropriate substitution.

23. $\dfrac{dy}{dx} = (x + y + 1)^2$ **24.** $\dfrac{dy}{dx} = \dfrac{1 - x - y}{x + y}$

25. $\dfrac{dy}{dx} = \tan^2(x + y)$ **26.** $\dfrac{dy}{dx} = \sin(x + y)$

27. $\dfrac{dy}{dx} = 2 + \sqrt{y - 2x + 3}$ **28.** $\dfrac{dy}{dx} = 1 + e^{y-x+5}$

In Problems 29 and 30 solve the given initial-value problem.

29. $\dfrac{dy}{dx} = \cos(x + y), \quad y(0) = \pi/4$

30. $\dfrac{dy}{dx} = \dfrac{3x + 2y}{3x + 2y + 2}, \quad y(-1) = -1$

Discussion Problems

31. Explain why it is always possible to express any homogeneous differential equation $M(x, y)\,dx + N(x, y)\,dy = 0$ in the form

$$\frac{dy}{dx} = F\left(\frac{y}{x}\right).$$

You might start by proving that

$$M(x, y) = x^\alpha M(1, y/x) \quad \text{and} \quad N(x, y) = x^\alpha N(1, y/x).$$

32. Put the homogeneous differential equation

$$(5x^2 - 2y^2)\,dx - xy\,dy = 0$$

into the form given in Problem 31.

33. **(a)** Determine two singular solutions of the DE in Problem 10.

  (b) If the initial condition $y(5) = 0$ is as prescribed in Problem 10, then what is the largest interval I over which the solution is defined? Use a graphing utility to graph the solution curve for the IVP.

34. In Example 3 the solution $y(x)$ becomes unbounded as $x \to \pm\infty$. Nevertheless, $y(x)$ is asymptotic to a curve as $x \to -\infty$ and to a different curve as $x \to \infty$. What are the equations of these curves?

35. The differential equation $dy/dx = P(x) + Q(x)y + R(x)y^2$ is known as **Riccati's equation.**

  (a) A Riccati equation can be solved by a succession of two substitutions *provided* that we know a particular solution y_1 of the equation. Show that the substitution $y = y_1 + u$ reduces Riccati's equation to a Bernoulli equation (4) with $n = 2$. The Bernoulli equation can then be reduced to a linear equation by the substitution $w = u^{-1}$.

(b) Find a one-parameter family of solutions for the differential equation

$$\frac{dy}{dx} = -\frac{4}{x^2} - \frac{1}{x}y + y^2$$

where $y_1 = 2/x$ is a known solution of the equation.

36. Determine an appropriate substitution to solve

$$xy' = y \ln(xy).$$

Mathematical Models

37. Falling Chain In Problem 45 in Exercises 2.4 we saw that a mathematical model for the velocity v of a chain slipping off the edge of a high horizontal platform is

$$xv\frac{dv}{dx} + v^2 = 32x.$$

In that problem you were asked to solve the DE by converting it into an exact equation using an integrating factor. This time solve the DE using the fact that it is a Bernoulli equation.

38. Population Growth In the study of population dynamics one of the most famous models for a growing but bounded population is the **logistic equation**

$$\frac{dP}{dt} = P(a - bP),$$

where a and b are positive constants. Although we will come back to this equation and solve it by an alternative method in Section 3.2, solve the DE this first time using the fact that it is a Bernoulli equation.

2.6 A NUMERICAL METHOD

INTRODUCTION   A first-order differential equation $dy/dx = f(x, y)$ is a source of information. We started this chapter by observing that we could garner *qualitative* information from a first-order DE about its solutions even before we attempted to solve the equation. Then in Sections 2.2–2.5 we examined first-order DEs *analytically*—that is, we developed some procedures for obtaining explicit and implicit solutions. But a differential equation can a possess a solution yet we may not be able to obtain it analytically. So to round out the picture of the different types of analyses of differential equations, we conclude this chapter with a method by which we can "solve" the differential equation *numerically*—this means that the DE is used as the cornerstone of an algorithm for approximating the unknown solution.

In this section we are going to develop only the simplest of numerical methods—a method that utilizes the idea that a tangent line can be used to approximate the values of a function in a small neighborhood of the point of tangency. A more extensive treatment of numerical methods for ordinary differential equations is given in Chapter 9.

USING THE TANGENT LINE   Let us assume that the first-order initial-value problem

$$y' = f(x, y), \quad y(x_0) = y_0 \tag{1}$$

possesses a solution. One way of approximating this solution is to use tangent lines. For example, let $y(x)$ denote the unknown solution of the first-order initial-value problem $y' = 0.1\sqrt{y} + 0.4x^2$, $y(2) = 4$. The nonlinear differential equation in this IVP cannot be solved directly by any of the methods considered in Sections 2.2, 2.4, and 2.5; nevertheless, we can still find approximate numerical values of the unknown $y(x)$. Specifically, suppose we wish to know the value of $y(2.5)$. The IVP has a solution, and as the flow of the direction field of the DE in Figure 2.6.1(a) suggests, a solution curve must have a shape similar to the curve shown in blue.

The direction field in Figure 2.6.1(a) was generated with lineal elements passing through points in a grid with integer coordinates. As the solution curve passes through the initial point $(2, 4)$, the lineal element at this point is a tangent line with slope given by $f(2, 4) = 0.1\sqrt{4} + 0.4(2)^2 = 1.8$. As is apparent in Figure 2.6.1(a) and the "zoom in" in Figure 2.6.1(b), when x is close to 2, the points on the solution curve are close to the points on the tangent line (the lineal element). Using the point $(2, 4)$, the slope $f(2, 4) = 1.8$, and the point-slope form of a line, we find that an equation of the tangent line is $y = L(x)$, where $L(x) = 1.8x + 0.4$. This last equation, called a **linearization** of $y(x)$ at $x = 2$, can be used to approximate values of $y(x)$ within a small neighborhood of $x = 2$. If $y_1 = L(x_1)$ denotes the y-coordinate on the tangent line and $y(x_1)$ is the y-coordinate on the solution curve corresponding to an x-coordinate x_1 that is close to $x = 2$, then $y(x_1) \approx y_1$. If we choose, say, $x_1 = 2.1$, then $y_1 = L(2.1) = 1.8(2.1) + 0.4 = 4.18$, so $y(2.1) \approx 4.18$.

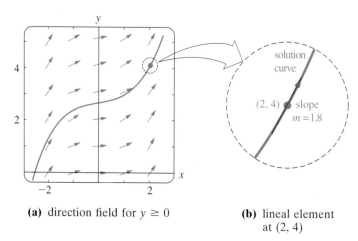

(a) direction field for $y \geq 0$

(b) lineal element at $(2, 4)$

FIGURE 2.6.1 Magnification of a neighborhood about the point $(2, 4)$

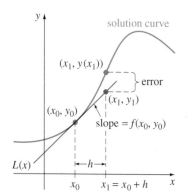

FIGURE 2.6.2 Approximating $y(x_1)$ using a tangent line

EULER'S METHOD To generalize the procedure just illustrated, we use the linearization of the unknown solution $y(x)$ of (1) at $x = x_0$:

$$L(x) = y_0 + f(x_0, y_0)(x - x_0). \tag{2}$$

The graph of this linearization is a straight line tangent to the graph of $y = y(x)$ at the point (x_0, y_0). We now let h be a positive increment of the x-axis, as shown in Figure 2.6.2. Then by replacing x by $x_1 = x_0 + h$ in (2), we get

$$L(x_1) = y_0 + f(x_0, y_0)(x_0 + h - x_0) \quad \text{or} \quad y_1 = y_0 + hf(x_1, y_1),$$

where $y_1 = L(x_1)$. The point (x_1, y_1) on the tangent line is an approximation to the point $(x_1, y(x_1))$ on the solution curve. Of course, the accuracy of the approximation $L(x_1) \approx y(x_1)$ or $y_1 \approx y(x_1)$ depends heavily on the size of the increment h. Usually, we must choose this **step size** to be "reasonably small." We now repeat the process using a second "tangent line" at (x_1, y_1).[*] By identifying the new starting point as (x_1, y_1) with (x_0, y_0) in the above discussion, we obtain an approximation $y_2 \approx y(x_2)$ corresponding to two steps of length h from x_0, that is, $x_2 = x_1 + h = x_0 + 2h$, and

$$y(x_2) = y(x_0 + 2h) = y(x_1 + h) \approx y_2 = y_1 + hf(x_1, y_1).$$

Continuing in this manner, we see that $y_1, y_2, y_3, \ldots,$ can be defined recursively by the general formula

$$y_{n+1} = y_n + hf(x_n, y_n), \tag{3}$$

where $x_n = x_0 + nh$, $n = 0, 1, 2, \ldots.$ This procedure of using successive "tangent lines" is called **Euler's method.**

---

[*]This is not an actual tangent line, since (x_1, y_1) lies on the first tangent and not on the solution curve.

EXAMPLE 1 Euler's Method

Consider the initial-value problem $y' = 0.1\sqrt{y} + 0.4x^2$, $y(2) = 4$. Use Euler's method to obtain an approximation of $y(2.5)$ using first $h = 0.1$ and then $h = 0.05$.

SOLUTION With the identification $f(x, y) = 0.1\sqrt{y} + 0.4x^2$, (3) becomes

$$y_{n+1} = y_n + h\left(0.1\sqrt{y_n} + 0.4x_n^2\right).$$

Then for $h = 0.1$, $x_0 = 2$, $y_0 = 4$, and $n = 0$ we find

$$y_1 = y_0 + h\left(0.1\sqrt{y_0} + 0.4x_0^2\right) = 4 + 0.1\left(0.1\sqrt{4} + 0.4(2)^2\right) = 4.18,$$

which, as we have already seen, is an estimate to the value of $y(2.1)$. However, if we use the smaller step size $h = 0.05$, it takes two steps to reach $x = 2.1$. From

$$y_1 = 4 + 0.05\left(0.1\sqrt{4} + 0.4(2)^2\right) = 4.09$$
$$y_2 = 4.09 + 0.05\left(0.1\sqrt{4.09} + 0.4(2.05)^2\right) = 4.18416187$$

we have $y_1 \approx y(2.05)$ and $y_2 \approx y(2.1)$. The remainder of the calculations were carried out by using software. The results are summarized in Tables 2.1 and 2.2, where each entry has been rounded to four decimal places. We see in Tables 2.1 and 2.2 that it takes five steps with $h = 0.1$ and 10 steps with $h = 0.05$, respectively, to get to $x = 2.5$. Intuitively, we would expect that $y_{10} = 5.0997$ corresponding to $h = 0.05$ is the better approximation of $y(2.5)$ than the value $y_5 = 5.0768$ corresponding to $h = 0.1$. ∎

In Example 2 we apply Euler's method to a differential equation for which we have already found a solution. We do this to compare the values of the approximations y_n at each step with the true or actual values of the solution $y(x_n)$ of the initial-value problem.

EXAMPLE 2 Comparison of Approximate and Actual Values

Consider the initial-value problem $y' = 0.2xy$, $y(1) = 1$. Use Euler's method to obtain an approximation of $y(1.5)$ using first $h = 0.1$ and then $h = 0.05$.

SOLUTION With the identification $f(x, y) = 0.2xy$, (3) becomes

$$y_{n+1} = y_n + h(0.2x_n y_n)$$

where $x_0 = 1$ and $y_0 = 1$. Again with the aid of computer software we obtain the values in Tables 2.3 and 2.4.

TABLE 2.1 $h = 0.1$

x_n	y_n
2.00	4.0000
2.10	4.1800
2.20	4.3768
2.30	4.5914
2.40	4.8244
2.50	5.0768

TABLE 2.2 $h = 0.05$

x_n	y_n
2.00	4.0000
2.05	4.0900
2.10	4.1842
2.15	4.2826
2.20	4.3854
2.25	4.4927
2.30	4.6045
2.35	4.7210
2.40	4.8423
2.45	4.9686
2.50	5.0997

TABLE 2.3 $h = 0.1$

x_n	y_n	Actual value	Abs. error	% Rel. error
1.00	1.0000	1.0000	0.0000	0.00
1.10	1.0200	1.0212	0.0012	0.12
1.20	1.0424	1.0450	0.0025	0.24
1.30	1.0675	1.0714	0.0040	0.37
1.40	1.0952	1.1008	0.0055	0.50
1.50	1.1259	1.1331	0.0073	0.64

TABLE 2.4 $h = 0.05$

x_n	y_n	Actual value	Abs. error	% Rel. error
1.00	1.0000	1.0000	0.0000	0.00
1.05	1.0100	1.0103	0.0003	0.03
1.10	1.0206	1.0212	0.0006	0.06
1.15	1.0318	1.0328	0.0009	0.09
1.20	1.0437	1.0450	0.0013	0.12
1.25	1.0562	1.0579	0.0016	0.16
1.30	1.0694	1.0714	0.0020	0.19
1.35	1.0833	1.0857	0.0024	0.22
1.40	1.0980	1.1008	0.0028	0.25
1.45	1.1133	1.1166	0.0032	0.29
1.50	1.1295	1.1331	0.0037	0.32

In Example 1 the true or actual values were calculated from the known solution $y = e^{0.1(x^2-1)}$. (Verify.) The **absolute error** is defined to be

$$|actual\ value - approximation|.$$

The **relative error** and **percentage relative error** are, in turn,

$$\frac{absolute\ error}{|actual\ value|} \quad \text{and} \quad \frac{absolute\ error}{|actual\ value|} \times 100.$$

It is apparent from Tables 2.3 and 2.4 that the accuracy of the approximations improves as the step size h decreases. Also, we see that even though the percentage relative error is growing with each step, it does not appear to be that bad. But you should not be deceived by one example. If we simply change the coefficient of the right side of the DE in Example 2 from 0.2 to 2, then at $x_n = 1.5$ the percentage relative errors increase dramatically. See Problem 4 in Exercises 2.6.

A CAVEAT Euler's method is just one of many different ways in which a solution of a differential equation can be approximated. Although attractive for its simplicity, *Euler's method is seldom used in serious calculations.* It was introduced here simply to give you a first taste of numerical methods. We will go into greater detail in discussing numerical methods that give significantly greater accuracy, notably the **fourth order Runge-Kutta method,** referred to as the **RK4 method,** in Chapter 9.

NUMERICAL SOLVERS Regardless of whether we can actually find an explicit or implicit solution, if a solution of a differential equation exists, it represents a smooth curve in the Cartesian plane. The basic idea behind *any* numerical method for first-order ordinary differential equations is to somehow approximate the y-values of a solution for preselected values of x. We start at a specified initial point (x_0, y_0) on a solution curve and proceed to calculate in a step-by-step fashion a sequence of points $(x_1, y_1), (x_2, y_2), \dots, (x_n, y_n)$ whose y-coordinates y_i approximate the y-coordinates $y(x_i)$ of points $(x_1, y(x_1)), (x_2, y(x_2)), \dots, (x_n, y(x_n))$ that lie on the graph of the usually unknown solution $y(x)$. By taking the x-coordinates close together (that is, for small values of h) and by joining the points (x_1, y_1), $(x_2, y_2), \dots, (x_n, y_n)$ with short line segments, we obtain a polygonal curve whose qualitative characteristics we hope are close to those of an actual solution curve. Drawing curves is something that is well suited to a computer. A computer program written to either implement a numerical method or render a visual representation of an approximate solution curve fitting the numerical data produced by this method is referred to as a **numerical solver.** Many different numerical solvers are commercially available, either embedded in a larger software package, such as a computer algebra system, or provided as a stand-alone package. Some software packages simply plot the generated numerical approximations, whereas others generate hard numerical data as well as the corresponding approximate or **numerical solution curves.** By way of illustration of the connect-the-dots nature of the graphs produced by a numerical solver, the two colored polygonal graphs in Figure 2.6.3 are the numerical solution curves for the initial-value problem $y' = 0.2xy$, $y(0) = 1$ on the interval $[0, 4]$ obtained from Euler's method and the RK4 method using the step size $h = 1$. The blue smooth curve is the graph of the exact solution $y = e^{0.1x^2}$ of the IVP. Notice in Figure 2.6.3 that, even with the ridiculously large step size of $h = 1$, the RK4 method produces the more believable "solution curve." The numerical solution curve obtained from the RK4 method is indistinguishable from the actual solution curve on the interval $[0, 4]$ when a more typical step size of $h = 0.1$ is used.

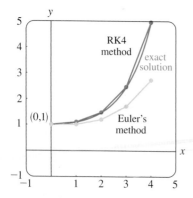

FIGURE 2.6.3 Comparison of the Runge-Kutta (RK4) and Euler methods

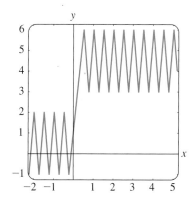

FIGURE 2.6.4 A not very helpful numerical solution curve

USING A NUMERICAL SOLVER Knowledge of the various numerical methods is not necessary in order to use a numerical solver. A solver usually requires that the differential equation be expressed in normal form $dy/dx = f(x, y)$. Numerical solvers that generate only curves usually require that you supply $f(x, y)$ and the initial data x_0 and y_0 and specify the desired numerical method. If the idea is to approximate the numerical value of $y(a)$, then a solver may additionally require that you state a value for h or, equivalently, give the number of steps that you want to take to get from $x = x_0$ to $x = a$. For example, if we wanted to approximate $y(4)$ for the IVP illustrated in Figure 2.6.3, then, starting at $x = 0$ it would take four steps to reach $x = 4$ with a step size of $h = 1$; 40 steps is equivalent to a step size of $h = 0.1$. Although we will not delve here into the many problems that one can encounter when attempting to approximate mathematical quantities, you should at least be aware of the fact that a numerical solver may break down near certain points or give an incomplete or misleading picture when applied to some first-order differential equations in the normal form. Figure 2.6.4 illustrates the graph obtained by applying Euler's method to a certain first-order initial-value problem $dy/dx = f(x, y)$, $y(0) = 1$. Equivalent results were obtained using three different commercial numerical solvers, yet the graph is hardly a plausible solution curve. (Why?) There are several avenues of recourse when a numerical solver has difficulties; three of the more obvious are decrease the step size, use another numerical method, and try a different numerical solver.

EXERCISES 2.6

Answers to selected odd-numbered problems begin on page ANS-2.

In Problems 1 and 2 use Euler's method to obtain a four-decimal approximation of the indicated value. Carry out the recursion of (3) by hand, first using $h = 0.1$ and then using $h = 0.05$.

1. $y' = 2x - 3y + 1$, $y(1) = 5$; $y(1.2)$

2. $y' = x + y^2$, $y(0) = 0$; $y(0.2)$

In Problems 3 and 4 use Euler's method to obtain a four-decimal approximation of the indicated value. First use $h = 0.1$ and then use $h = 0.05$. Find an explicit solution for each initial-value problem and then construct tables similar to Tables 2.3 and 2.4.

3. $y' = y$, $y(0) = 1$; $y(1.0)$

4. $y' = 2xy$, $y(1) = 1$; $y(1.5)$

In Problems 5–10 use a numerical solver and Euler's method to obtain a four-decimal approximation of the indicated value. First use $h = 0.1$ and then use $h = 0.05$.

5. $y' = e^{-y}$, $y(0) = 0$; $y(0.5)$

6. $y' = x^2 + y^2$, $y(0) = 1$; $y(0.5)$

7. $y' = (x - y)^2$, $y(0) = 0.5$; $y(0.5)$

8. $y' = xy + \sqrt{y}$, $y(0) = 1$; $y(0.5)$

9. $y' = xy^2 - \dfrac{y}{x}$, $y(1) = 1$; $y(1.5)$

10. $y' = y - y^2$, $y(0) = 0.5$; $y(0.5)$

In Problems 11 and 12 use a numerical solver to obtain a numerical solution curve for the given initial-value problem. First use Euler's method and then the RK4 method. Use $h = 0.25$ in each case. Superimpose both solution curves on the same coordinate axes. If possible, use a different color for each curve. Repeat, using $h = 0.1$ and $h = 0.05$.

11. $y' = 2(\cos x)y$, $y(0) = 1$

12. $y' = y(10 - 2y)$, $y(0) = 1$

Discussion Problems

13. Use a numerical solver and Euler's method to approximate $y(1.0)$, where $y(x)$ is the solution to $y' = 2xy^2$, $y(0) = 1$. First use $h = 0.1$ and then use $h = 0.05$. Repeat, using the RK4 method. Discuss what might cause the approximations to $y(1.0)$ to differ so greatly.

Computer Lab Assignments

14. (a) Use a numerical solver and the RK4 method to graph the solution of the initial-value problem $y' = -2xy + 1$, $y(0) = 0$.

(b) Solve the initial-value problem by one of the analytic procedures developed earlier in this chapter.

(c) Use the analytic solution $y(x)$ found in part (b) and a CAS to find the coordinates of all relative extrema.

CHAPTER 2 IN REVIEW

Answers to selected odd-numbered problems begin on page ANS-3.

Answer Problems 1–4 without referring back to the text. Fill in the blanks or answer true or false.

1. The linear DE, $y' - ky = A$, where k and A are constants, is autonomous. The critical point _____ of the equation is a(n) _____ (attractor or repeller) for $k > 0$ and a(n) _____ (attractor or repeller) for $k < 0$.

2. The initial-value problem $x\dfrac{dy}{dx} - 4y = 0$, $y(0) = k$, has an infinite number of solutions for $k = $ _____ and no solution for $k = $ _____.

3. The linear DE, $y' + k_1y = k_2$, where k_1 and k_2 are nonzero constants, always possesses a constant solution. _____

4. The linear DE, $a_1(x)y' + a_2(x)y = 0$ is also separable. _____

In Problems 5 and 6 construct an autonomous first-order differential equation $dy/dx = f(y)$ whose phase portrait is consistent with the given figure.

5.

FIGURE 2.R.1 Graph for Problem 5

6.

FIGURE 2.R.2 Graph for Problem 6

7. The number 0 is a critical point of the autonomous differential equation $dx/dt = x^n$, where n is a positive integer. For what values of n is 0 asymptotically stable? Semi-stable? Unstable? Repeat for the differential equation $dx/dt = -x^n$.

8. Consider the differential equation $dP/dt = f(P)$, where

$$f(P) = -0.5P^3 - 1.7P + 3.4.$$

The function $f(P)$ has one real zero, as shown in Figure 2.R.3. Without attempting to solve the differential equation, estimate the value of $\lim_{t \to \infty} P(t)$.

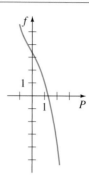

FIGURE 2.R.3 Graph for Problem 8

9. Figure 2.R.4 is a portion of a direction field of a differential equation $dy/dx = f(x, y)$. By hand, sketch two different solution curves—one that is tangent to the lineal element shown in black and one that is tangent to the lineal element shown in color.

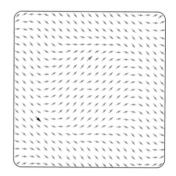

FIGURE 2.R.4 Portion of a direction field for Problem 9

10. Classify each differential equation as separable, exact, linear, homogeneous, or Bernoulli. Some equations may be more than one kind. Do not solve.

(a) $\dfrac{dy}{dx} = \dfrac{x - y}{x}$

(b) $\dfrac{dy}{dx} = \dfrac{1}{y - x}$

(c) $(x + 1)\dfrac{dy}{dx} = -y + 10$

(d) $\dfrac{dy}{dx} = \dfrac{1}{x(x - y)}$

(e) $\dfrac{dy}{dx} = \dfrac{y^2 + y}{x^2 + x}$

(f) $\dfrac{dy}{dx} = 5y + y^2$

(g) $y\,dx = (y - xy^2)\,dy$

(h) $x\dfrac{dy}{dx} = ye^{x/y} - x$

(i) $xy\,y' + y^2 = 2x$

(j) $2xy\,y' + y^2 = 2x^2$

(k) $y\,dx + x\,dy = 0$

(l) $\left(x^2 + \dfrac{2y}{x}\right)dx = (3 - \ln x^2)\,dy$

(m) $\dfrac{dy}{dx} = \dfrac{x}{y} + \dfrac{y}{x} + 1$

(n) $\dfrac{y}{x^2}\dfrac{dy}{dx} + e^{2x^3 + y^2} = 0$

In Problems 11–18 solve the given differential equation.

11. $(y^2 + 1) \, dx = y \sec^2 x \, dy$

12. $y(\ln x - \ln y) \, dx = (x \ln x - x \ln y - y) \, dy$

13. $(6x + 1)y^2 \dfrac{dy}{dx} + 3x^2 + 2y^3 = 0$

14. $\dfrac{dx}{dy} = -\dfrac{4y^2 + 6xy}{3y^2 + 2x}$

15. $t\dfrac{dQ}{dt} + Q = t^4 \ln t$

16. $(2x + y + 1)y' = 1$

17. $(x^2 + 4) \, dy = (2x - 8xy) \, dx$

18. $(2r^2 \cos \theta \sin \theta + r \cos \theta) \, d\theta$
$$+ \, (4r + \sin \theta - 2r \cos^2 \theta) \, dr = 0$$

In Problems 19 and 20 solve the given initial-value problem and give the largest interval I on which the solution is defined.

19. $\sin x \dfrac{dy}{dx} + (\cos x)y = 0, \quad y\left(\dfrac{7\pi}{6}\right) = -2$

20. $\dfrac{dy}{dt} + 2(t + 1)y^2 = 0, \quad y(0) = -\dfrac{1}{8}$

21. (a) Without solving, explain why the initial-value problem

$$\dfrac{dy}{dx} = \sqrt{y}, \quad y(x_0) = y_0$$

has no solution for $y_0 < 0$.

(b) Solve the initial-value problem in part (a) for $y_0 > 0$ and find the largest interval I on which the solution is defined.

22. (a) Find an implicit solution of the initial-value problem

$$\dfrac{dy}{dx} = \dfrac{y^2 - x^2}{xy}, \quad y(1) = -\sqrt{2}.$$

(b) Find an explicit solution of the problem in part (a) and give the largest interval I over which the solution is defined. A graphing utility may be helpful here.

23. Graphs of some members of a family of solutions for a first-order differential equation $dy/dx = f(x, y)$ are shown in Figure 2.R.5. The graphs of two implicit solutions, one that passes through the point $(1, -1)$ and one that passes through $(-1, 3)$, are shown in red. Reproduce the figure on a piece of paper. With colored pencils trace out the solution curves for the solutions $y = y_1(x)$ and $y = y_2(x)$ defined by the implicit solutions such that $y_1(1) = -1$ and $y_2(-1) = 3$, respectively. Estimate the intervals on which the solutions $y = y_1(x)$ and $y = y_2(x)$ are defined.

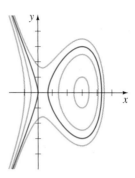

FIGURE 2.R.5 Graph for Problem 23

24. Use Euler's method with step size $h = 0.1$ to approximate $y(1.2)$, where $y(x)$ is a solution of the initial-value problem $y' = 1 + x\sqrt{y}$, $y(1) = 9$.

In Problems 25 and 26 each figure represents a portion of a direction field of an autonomous first-order differential equation $dy/dx = f(y)$. Reproduce the figure on a separate piece of paper and then complete the direction field over the grid. The points of the grid are (mh, nh), where $h = \frac{1}{2}$, m and n integers, $-7 \le m \le 7$, $-7 \le n \le 7$. In each direction field, sketch by hand an approximate solution curve that passes through each of the solid points shown in red. Discuss: Does it appear that the DE possesses critical points in the interval $-3.5 \le y \le 3.5$? If so, classify the critical points as asymptotically stable, unstable, or semi-stable.

25.

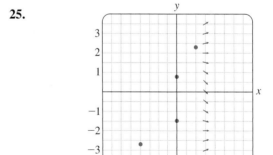

FIGURE 2.R.6 Portion of a direction field for Problem 25

26.

FIGURE 2.R.7 Portion of a direction field for Problem 26

3 MODELING WITH FIRST-ORDER DIFFERENTIAL EQUATIONS

3.1 Linear Models

3.2 Nonlinear Models

3.3 Modeling with Systems of First-Order DEs

CHAPTER 3 IN REVIEW

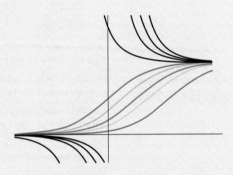

In Section 1.3 we saw how a first-order differential equation could be used as a mathematical model in the study of population growth, radioactive decay, continuous compound interest, cooling of bodies, mixtures, chemical reactions, fluid draining from a tank, velocity of a falling body, and current in a series circuit. Using the methods of Chapter 2, we are now able to solve some of the linear DEs (Section 3.1) and nonlinear DEs (Section 3.2) that commonly appear in applications. The chapter concludes with the natural next step: In Section 3.3 we examine how systems of first-order DEs can arise as mathematical models in coupled physical systems (for example, a population of predators such as foxes interacting with a population of prey such as rabbits).

3.1 LINEAR MODELS

REVIEW MATERIAL

- A differential equation as a mathematical model in Section 1.3
- Reread "Solving a Linear First-Order Equation" on page 55 in Section 2.3

INTRODUCTION In this section we solve some of the linear first-order models that were introduced in Section 1.3.

GROWTH AND DECAY The initial-value problem

$$\frac{dx}{dt} = kx, \quad x(t_0) = x_0, \tag{1}$$

where k is a constant of proportionality, serves as a model for diverse phenomena involving either growth or decay. We saw in Section 1.3 that in biological applications the rate of growth of certain populations (bacteria, small animals) over short periods of time is proportional to the population present at time t. Knowing the population at some arbitrary initial time t_0, we can then use the solution of (1) to predict the population in the future—that is, at times $t > t_0$. The constant of proportionality k in (1) can be determined from the solution of the initial-value problem, using a subsequent measurement of x at a time $t_1 > t_0$. In physics and chemistry (1) is seen in the form of a *first-order reaction*—that is, a reaction whose rate, or velocity, dx/dt is directly proportional to the amount x of a substance that is unconverted or remaining at time t. The decomposition, or decay, of U-238 (uranium) by radioactivity into Th-234 (thorium) is a first-order reaction.

EXAMPLE 1 Bacterial Growth

A culture initially has P_0 number of bacteria. At $t = 1$ h the number of bacteria is measured to be $\frac{3}{2}P_0$. If the rate of growth is proportional to the number of bacteria $P(t)$ present at time t, determine the time necessary for the number of bacteria to triple.

SOLUTION We first solve the differential equation in (1), with the symbol x replaced by P. With $t_0 = 0$ the initial condition is $P(0) = P_0$. We then use the empirical observation that $P(1) = \frac{3}{2}P_0$ to determine the constant of proportionality k.

Notice that the differential equation $dP/dt = kP$ is both separable and linear. When it is put in the standard form of a linear first-order DE,

$$\frac{dP}{dt} - kP = 0,$$

we can see by inspection that the integrating factor is e^{-kt}. Multiplying both sides of the equation by this term and integrating gives, in turn,

$$\frac{d}{dt}[e^{-kt}P] = 0 \quad \text{and} \quad e^{-kt}P = c.$$

Therefore $P(t) = ce^{kt}$. At $t = 0$ it follows that $P_0 = ce^0 = c$, so $P(t) = P_0 e^{kt}$. At $t = 1$ we have $\frac{3}{2}P_0 = P_0 e^k$ or $e^k = \frac{3}{2}$. From the last equation we get $k = \ln \frac{3}{2} = 0.4055$, so $P(t) = P_0 e^{0.4055t}$. To find the time at which the number of bacteria has tripled, we solve $3P_0 = P_0 e^{0.4055t}$ for t. It follows that $0.4055t = \ln 3$, or

$$t = \frac{\ln 3}{0.4055} \approx 2.71 \text{ h.}$$

See Figure 3.1.1.

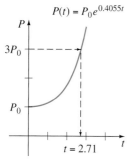

$P(t) = P_0 e^{0.4055t}$

FIGURE 3.1.1 Time in which population triples

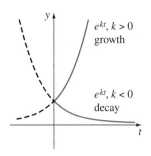

FIGURE 3.1.2 Growth ($k > 0$) and decay ($k < 0$)

Notice in Example 1 that the actual number P_0 of bacteria present at time $t = 0$ played no part in determining the time required for the number in the culture to triple. The time necessary for an initial population of, say, 100 or 1,000,000 bacteria to triple is still approximately 2.71 hours.

As shown in Figure 3.1.2, the exponential function e^{kt} increases as t increases for $k > 0$ and decreases as t increases for $k < 0$. Thus problems describing growth (whether of populations, bacteria, or even capital) are characterized by a positive value of k, whereas problems involving decay (as in radioactive disintegration) yield a negative k value. Accordingly, we say that k is either a **growth constant** ($k > 0$) or a **decay constant** ($k < 0$).

HALF-LIFE In physics the **half-life** is a measure of the stability of a radioactive substance. The half-life is simply the time it takes for one-half of the atoms in an initial amount A_0 to disintegrate, or transmute, into the atoms of another element. The longer the half-life of a substance, the more stable it is. For example, the half-life of highly radioactive radium, Ra-226, is about 1700 years. In 1700 years one-half of a given quantity of Ra-226 is transmuted into radon, Rn-222. The most commonly occurring uranium isotope, U-238, has a half-life of approximately 4,500,000,000 years. In about 4.5 billion years, one-half of a quantity of U-238 is transmuted into lead, Pb-206.

EXAMPLE 2   Half-Life of Plutonium

A breeder reactor converts relatively stable uranium 238 into the isotope plutonium 239. After 15 years it is determined that 0.043% of the initial amount A_0 of plutonium has disintegrated. Find the half-life of this isotope if the rate of disintegration is proportional to the amount remaining.

SOLUTION Let $A(t)$ denote the amount of plutonium remaining at time t. As in Example 1 the solution of the initial-value problem

$$\frac{dA}{dt} = kA, \quad A(0) = A_0$$

is $A(t) = A_0 e^{kt}$. If 0.043% of the atoms of A_0 have disintegrated, then 99.957% of the substance remains. To find the decay constant k, we use $0.99957A_0 = A(15)$—that is, $0.99957A_0 = A_0 e^{15k}$. Solving for k then gives $k = \frac{1}{15} \ln 0.99957 = -0.00002867$. Hence $A(t) = A_0 e^{-0.00002867t}$. Now the half-life is the corresponding value of time at which $A(t) = \frac{1}{2}A_0$. Solving for t gives $\frac{1}{2}A_0 = A_0 e^{-0.00002867t}$, or $\frac{1}{2} = e^{-0.00002867t}$. The last equation yields

$$t = \frac{\ln 2}{0.00002867} \approx 24,180 \text{ yr.} \quad \blacksquare$$

CARBON DATING About 1950 the chemist Willard Libby devised a method of using radioactive carbon as a means of determining the approximate ages of fossils. The theory of **carbon dating** is based on the fact that the isotope carbon 14 is produced in the atmosphere by the action of cosmic radiation on nitrogen. The ratio of the amount of C-14 to ordinary carbon in the atmosphere appears to be a constant, and as a consequence the proportionate amount of the isotope present in all living organisms is the same as that in the atmosphere. When an organism dies, the absorption of C-14, by either breathing or eating, ceases. Thus by comparing the proportionate amount of C-14 present, say, in a fossil with the constant ratio found in the atmosphere, it is possible to obtain a reasonable estimation of the fossil's age. The method is based on the knowledge that the half-life of radioactive C-14 is approximately 5600 years. For his work Libby won the Nobel Prize for chemistry in

1960. Libby's method has been used to date wooden furniture in Egyptian tombs, the woven flax wrappings of the Dead Sea scrolls, and the cloth of the enigmatic shroud of Turin.

EXAMPLE 3 Age of a Fossil

A fossilized bone is found to contain one-thousandth of the C-14 level found in living matter. Estimate the age of the fossil.

SOLUTION The starting point is again $A(t) = A_0 e^{kt}$. To determine the value of the decay constant k, we use the fact that $\frac{1}{2}A_0 = A(5600)$ or $\frac{1}{2}A_0 = A_0 e^{5600k}$. From $5600k = \ln \frac{1}{2} = -\ln 2$ we then get $k = -(\ln 2)/5600 = -0.00012378$. Therefore $A(t) = A_0 e^{-0.00012378t}$. With $A(t) = \frac{1}{1000}A_0$ we have $\frac{1}{1000}A_0 = A_0 e^{-0.00012378t}$, so $-0.00012378t = \ln \frac{1}{1000} = -\ln 1000$. Thus the age of the fossil is about

$$t = \frac{\ln 1000}{0.00012378} \approx 55{,}800 \text{ yr.} \qquad \blacksquare$$

The age found in Example 3 is really at the border of accuracy for this method. The usual carbon-14 technique is limited to about 9 half-lives of the isotope, or about 50,000 years. One reason for this limitation is that the chemical analysis needed to obtain an accurate measurement of the remaining C-14 becomes somewhat formidable around the point of $\frac{1}{1000} A_0$. Also, this analysis demands the destruction of a rather large sample of the specimen. If this measurement is accomplished indirectly, based on the actual radioactivity of the specimen, then it is very difficult to distinguish between the radiation from the fossil and the normal background radiation.[*] But recently, the use of a particle accelerator has enabled scientists to separate C-14 from stable C-12 directly. When the precise value of the ratio of C-14 to C-12 is computed, the accuracy of this method can be extended to 70,000–100,000 years. Other isotopic techniques such as using potassium 40 and argon 40 can give ages of several million years.[†] Nonisotopic methods based on the use of amino acids are also sometimes possible.

NEWTON'S LAW OF COOLING/WARMING In equation (3) of Section 1.3 we saw that the mathematical formulation of Newton's empirical law of cooling/warming of an object is given by the linear first-order differential equation

$$\frac{dT}{dt} = k(T - T_m), \qquad (2)$$

where k is a constant of proportionality, $T(t)$ is the temperature of the object for $t > 0$, and T_m is the ambient temperature—that is, the temperature of the medium around the object. In Example 4 we assume that T_m is constant.

EXAMPLE 4 Cooling of a Cake

When a cake is removed from an oven, its temperature is measured at 300° F. Three minutes later its temperature is 200° F. How long will it take for the cake to cool off to a room temperature of 70° F?

---

[*]The number of disintegrations per minute per gram of carbon is recorded by using a Geiger counter. The lower level of detectability is about 0.1 disintegrations per minute per gram.
[†]Potassium-argon dating is used in dating terrestrial materials such as minerals, rocks, and lava and extraterrestrial materials such as meteorites and lunar rocks. The age of a fossil can be estimated by determining the age of the rock stratum in which it was found.

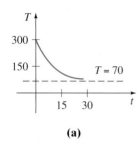

(a)

$T(t)$	t (min)
75°	20.1
74°	21.3
73°	22.8
72°	24.9
71°	28.6
70.5°	32.3

(b)

FIGURE 3.1.3 Temperature of cooling cake approaches room temperature

SOLUTION In (2) we make the identification $T_m = 70$. We must then solve the initial-value problem

$$\frac{dT}{dt} = k(T - 70), \quad T(0) = 300 \tag{3}$$

and determine the value of k so that $T(3) = 200$.

Equation (3) is both linear and separable. If we separate variables,

$$\frac{dT}{T - 70} = k\,dt,$$

yields $\ln|T - 70| = kt + c_1$, and so $T = 70 + c_2 e^{kt}$. When $t = 0$, $T = 300$, so $300 = 70 + c_2$ gives $c_2 = 230$; therefore $T = 70 + 230 e^{kt}$. Finally, the measurement $T(3) = 200$ leads to $e^{3k} = \frac{13}{23}$, or $k = \frac{1}{3} \ln \frac{13}{23} = -0.19018$. Thus

$$T(t) = 70 + 230 e^{-0.19018 t}. \tag{4}$$

We note that (4) furnishes no finite solution to $T(t) = 70$, since $\lim_{t \to \infty} T(t) = 70$. Yet we intuitively expect the cake to reach room temperature after a reasonably long period of time. How long is "long"? Of course, we should not be disturbed by the fact that the model (3) does not quite live up to our physical intuition. Parts (a) and (b) of Figure 3.1.3 clearly show that the cake will be approximately at room temperature in about one-half hour. ∎

The ambient temperature in (2) need not be a constant but could be a function $T_m(t)$ of time t. See Problem 18 in Exercises 3.1.

MIXTURES The mixing of two fluids sometimes gives rise to a linear first-order differential equation. When we discussed the mixing of two brine solutions in Section 1.3, we assumed that the rate $A'(t)$ at which the amount of salt in the mixing tank changes was a net rate:

$$\frac{dA}{dt} = (\text{input rate of salt}) - (\text{output rate of salt}) = R_{in} - R_{out}. \tag{5}$$

In Example 5 we solve equation (8) of Section 1.3.

EXAMPLE 5 Mixture of Two Salt Solutions

Recall that the large tank considered in Section 1.3 held 300 gallons of a brine solution. Salt was entering and leaving the tank; a brine solution was being pumped into the tank at the rate of 3 gal/min; it mixed with the solution there, and then the mixture was pumped out at the rate of 3 gal/min. The concentration of the salt in the inflow, or solution entering, was 2 lb/gal, so salt was entering the tank at the rate $R_{in} = (2 \text{ lb/gal}) \cdot (3 \text{ gal/min}) = 6 \text{ lb/min}$ and leaving the tank at the rate $R_{out} = (A/300 \text{ lb/gal}) \cdot (3 \text{ gal/min}) = A/100 \text{ lb/min}$. From this data and (5) we get equation (8) of Section 1.3. Let us pose the question: If 50 pounds of salt were dissolved initially in the 300 gallons, how much salt is in the tank after a long time?

SOLUTION To find the amount of salt $A(t)$ in the tank at time t, we solve the initial-value problem

$$\frac{dA}{dt} + \frac{1}{100} A = 6, \quad A(0) = 50.$$

Note here that the side condition is the initial amount of salt $A(0) = 50$ in the tank and *not* the initial amount of liquid in the tank. Now since the integrating factor of the

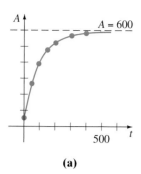

(a)

t (min)	A (lb)
50	266.41
100	397.67
150	477.27
200	525.57
300	572.62
400	589.93

(b)

FIGURE 3.1.4 Pounds of salt in tank as a function of time t

linear differential equation is $e^{t/100}$, we can write the equation as

$$\frac{d}{dt}\,[e^{t/100}A] = 6e^{t/100}.$$

Integrating the last equation and solving for A gives the general solution $A(t) = 600 + ce^{-t/100}$. When $t = 0$, $A = 50$, so we find that $c = -550$. Thus the amount of salt in the tank at time t is given by

$$A(t) = 600 - 550e^{-t/100}. \tag{6}$$

The solution (6) was used to construct the table in Figure 3.1.4(b). Also, it can be seen from (6) and Figure 3.1.4(a) that $A(t) \to 600$ as $t \to \infty$. Of course, this is what we would intuitively expect; over a long time the number of pounds of salt in the solution must be (300 gal)(2 lb/gal) = 600 lb. ∎

In Example 5 we assumed that the rate at which the solution was pumped in was the same as the rate at which the solution was pumped out. However, this need not be the case; the mixed brine solution could be pumped out at a rate r_{out} that is faster or slower than the rate r_{in} at which the other brine solution is pumped in. For example, if the well-stirred solution in Example 5 is pumped out at a slower rate of, say, $r_{out} = 2$ gal/min, then liquid will accumulate in the tank at the rate of $r_{in} - r_{out} = (3 - 2)$ gal/min = 1 gal/min. After t minutes, $(1 \text{ gal/min}) \cdot (t \text{ min}) = t$ gal will accumulate, so the tank will contain $300 + t$ gallons of brine. The concentration of the outflow is then $c(t) = A/(300 + t)$, and the output rate of salt is $R_{out} = c(t) \cdot r_{out}$, or

$$R_{out} = \left(\frac{A}{300 + t}\,\text{lb/gal}\right) \cdot (2 \text{ gal/min}) = \frac{2A}{300 + t}\,\text{lb/min}.$$

Hence equation (5) becomes

$$\frac{dA}{dt} = 6 - \frac{2A}{300 + t} \qquad \text{or} \qquad \frac{dA}{dt} + \frac{2}{300 + t}A = 6.$$

You should verify that the solution of the last equation, subject to $A(0) = 50$, is $A(t) = 600 + 2t - (4.95 \times 10^7)(300 + t)^{-2}$. See the discussion following (8) of Section 1.3, Problem 12 in Exercises 1.3, and Problems 25–28 in Exercises 3.1.

SERIES CIRCUITS For a series circuit containing only a resistor and an inductor, Kirchhoff's second law states that the sum of the voltage drop across the inductor $(L(di/dt))$ and the voltage drop across the resistor (iR) is the same as the impressed voltage $(E(t))$ on the circuit. See Figure 3.1.5.

Thus we obtain the linear differential equation for the current $i(t)$,

$$L\frac{di}{dt} + Ri = E(t), \tag{7}$$

where L and R are constants known as the inductance and the resistance, respectively. The current $i(t)$ is also called the **response** of the system.

The voltage drop across a capacitor with capacitance C is given by $q(t)/C$, where q is the charge on the capacitor. Hence, for the series circuit shown in Figure 3.1.6, Kirchhoff's second law gives

$$Ri + \frac{1}{C}q = E(t). \tag{8}$$

But current i and charge q are related by $i = dq/dt$, so (8) becomes the linear differential equation

$$R\frac{dq}{dt} + \frac{1}{C}q = E(t). \tag{9}$$

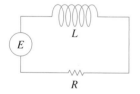

FIGURE 3.1.5 *LR* series circuit

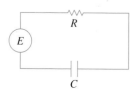

FIGURE 3.1.6 *RC* series circuit

EXAMPLE 6 Series Circuit

A 12-volt battery is connected to a series circuit in which the inductance is $\frac{1}{2}$ henry and the resistance is 10 ohms. Determine the current i if the initial current is zero.

SOLUTION From (7) we see that we must solve

$$\frac{1}{2}\frac{di}{dt} + 10i = 12,$$

subject to $i(0) = 0$. First, we multiply the differential equation by 2 and read off the integrating factor e^{20t}. We then obtain

$$\frac{d}{dt}[e^{20t}i] = 24e^{20t}.$$

Integrating each side of the last equation and solving for i gives $i(t) = \frac{6}{5} + ce^{-20t}$. Now $i(0) = 0$ implies that $0 = \frac{6}{5} + c$ or $c = -\frac{6}{5}$. Therefore the response is $i(t) = \frac{6}{5} - \frac{6}{5}e^{-20t}$. ∎

From (4) of Section 2.3 we can write a general solution of (7):

$$i(t) = \frac{e^{-(R/L)t}}{L}\int e^{(R/L)t}E(t)\,dt + ce^{-(R/L)t}. \tag{10}$$

In particular, when $E(t) = E_0$ is a constant, (10) becomes

$$i(t) = \frac{E_0}{R} + ce^{-(R/L)t}. \tag{11}$$

Note that as $t \to \infty$, the second term in equation (11) approaches zero. Such a term is usually called a **transient term;** any remaining terms are called the **steady-state** part of the solution. In this case E_0/R is also called the **steady-state current;** for large values of time it appears that the current in the circuit is simply governed by Ohm's law ($E = iR$).

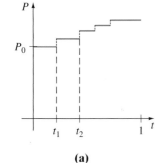

(a)

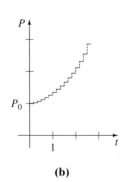

(b)

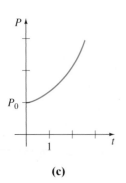

(c)

FIGURE 3.1.7 Population growth is a discrete process

REMARKS

The solution $P(t) = P_0 e^{0.4055t}$ of the initial-value problem in Example 1 described the population of a colony of bacteria at any time $t > 0$. Of course, $P(t)$ is a continuous function that takes on *all* real numbers in the interval $P_0 \le P < \infty$. But since we are talking about a population, common sense dictates that P can take on only positive integer values. Moreover, we would not expect the population to grow continuously—that is, every second, every microsecond, and so on—as predicted by our solution; there may be intervals of time $[t_1, t_2]$ over which there is no growth at all. Perhaps, then, the graph shown in Figure 3.1.7(a) is a more realistic description of P than is the graph of an exponential function. Using a continuous function to describe a discrete phenomenon is often more a matter of convenience than of accuracy. However, for some purposes we may be satisfied if our model describes the system fairly closely when viewed macroscopically in time, as in Figures 3.1.7(b) and 3.1.7(c), rather than microscopically, as in Figure 3.1.7(a).

EXERCISES 3.1

Answers to selected odd-numbered problems begin on page ANS-3.

Growth and Decay

1. The population of a community is known to increase at a rate proportional to the number of people present at time t. If an initial population P_0 has doubled in 5 years, how long will it take to triple? To quadruple?

2. Suppose it is known that the population of the community in Problem 1 is 10,000 after 3 years. What was the initial population P_0? What will be the population in 10 years? How fast is the population growing at $t = 10$?

3. The population of a town grows at a rate proportional to the population present at time t. The initial population of 500 increases by 15% in 10 years. What will be the population in 30 years? How fast is the population growing at $t = 30$?

4. The population of bacteria in a culture grows at a rate proportional to the number of bacteria present at time t. After 3 hours it is observed that 400 bacteria are present. After 10 hours 2000 bacteria are present. What was the initial number of bacteria?

5. The radioactive isotope of lead, Pb-209, decays at a rate proportional to the amount present at time t and has a half-life of 3.3 hours. If 1 gram of this isotope is present initially, how long will it take for 90% of the lead to decay?

6. Initially 100 milligrams of a radioactive substance was present. After 6 hours the mass had decreased by 3%. If the rate of decay is proportional to the amount of the substance present at time t, find the amount remaining after 24 hours.

7. Determine the half-life of the radioactive substance described in Problem 6.

8. (a) Consider the initial-value problem $dA/dt = kA$, $A(0) = A_0$ as the model for the decay of a radioactive substance. Show that, in general, the half-life T of the substance is $T = -(\ln 2)/k$.

   (b) Show that the solution of the initial-value problem in part (a) can be written $A(t) = A_0 2^{-t/T}$.

   (c) If a radioactive substance has the half-life T given in part (a), how long will it take an initial amount A_0 of the substance to decay to $\frac{1}{8}A_0$?

9. When a vertical beam of light passes through a transparent medium, the rate at which its intensity I decreases is proportional to $I(t)$, where t represents the thickness of the medium (in feet). In clear seawater, the intensity 3 feet below the surface is 25% of the initial intensity I_0 of the incident beam. What is the intensity of the beam 15 feet below the surface?

10. When interest is compounded continuously, the amount of money increases at a rate proportional to the amount S present at time t, that is, $dS/dt = rS$, where r is the annual rate of interest.

    (a) Find the amount of money accrued at the end of 5 years when $5000 is deposited in a savings account drawing $5\frac{3}{4}\%$ annual interest compounded continuously.

    (b) In how many years will the initial sum deposited have doubled?

    (c) Use a calculator to compare the amount obtained in part (a) with the amount $S = 5000(1 + \frac{1}{4}(0.0575))^{5(4)}$ that is accrued when interest is compounded quarterly.

Carbon Dating

11. Archaeologists used pieces of burned wood, or charcoal, found at the site to date prehistoric paintings and drawings on walls and ceilings of a cave in Lascaux, France. See Figure 3.1.8. Use the information on page 84 to determine the approximate age of a piece of burned wood, if it was found that 85.5% of the C-14 found in living trees of the same type had decayed.

© Prehistoric/The Bridgeman Art Library/Getty Images

FIGURE 3.1.8 Cave wall painting in Problem 11

12. The shroud of Turin, which shows the negative image of the body of a man who appears to have been crucified, is believed by many to be the burial shroud of Jesus of Nazareth. See Figure 3.1.9. In 1988 the Vatican granted permission to have the shroud carbon-dated. Three independent scientific laboratories analyzed the cloth and concluded that the shroud was approximately 660 years old,[*] an age consistent with its historical appearance.

© Bettmann/CORBIS

FIGURE 3.1.9 Shroud image in Problem 12

---

[*]Some scholars have disagreed with this finding. For more information on this fascinating mystery see the Shroud of Turin home page at http://www.shroud.com/.

Using this age, determine what percentage of the original amount of C-14 remained in the cloth as of 1988.

Newton's Law of Cooling/Warming

13. A thermometer is removed from a room where the temperature is 70° F and is taken outside, where the air temperature is 10° F. After one-half minute the thermometer reads 50° F. What is the reading of the thermometer at $t = 1$ min? How long will it take for the thermometer to reach 15° F?

14. A thermometer is taken from an inside room to the outside, where the air temperature is 5° F. After 1 minute the thermometer reads 55° F, and after 5 minutes it reads 30° F. What is the initial temperature of the inside room?

15. A small metal bar, whose initial temperature was 20° C, is dropped into a large container of boiling water. How long will it take the bar to reach 90° C if it is known that its temperature increases 2° in 1 second? How long will it take the bar to reach 98° C?

16. Two large containers A and B of the same size are filled with different fluids. The fluids in containers A and B are maintained at 0° C and 100° C, respectively. A small metal bar, whose initial temperature is 100° C, is lowered into container A. After 1 minute the temperature of the bar is 90° C. After 2 minutes the bar is removed and instantly transferred to the other container. After 1 minute in container B the temperature of the bar rises 10°. How long, measured from the start of the entire process, will it take the bar to reach 99.9° C?

17. A thermometer reading 70° F is placed in an oven preheated to a constant temperature. Through a glass window in the oven door, an observer records that the thermometer reads 110° F after $\frac{1}{2}$ minute and 145° F after 1 minute. How hot is the oven?

18. At $t = 0$ a sealed test tube containing a chemical is immersed in a liquid bath. The initial temperature of the chemical in the test tube is 80° F. The liquid bath has a controlled temperature (measured in degrees Fahrenheit) given by $T_m(t) = 100 - 40e^{-0.1t}$, $t \geq 0$, where t is measured in minutes.

   (a) Assume that $k = -0.1$ in (2). Before solving the IVP, describe in words what you expect the temperature $T(t)$ of the chemical to be like in the short term. In the long term.

   (b) Solve the initial-value problem. Use a graphing utility to plot the graph of $T(t)$ on time intervals of various lengths. Do the graphs agree with your predictions in part (a)?

19. A dead body was found within a closed room of a house where the temperature was a constant 70° F. At the time of discovery the core temperature of the body was determined to be 85° F. One hour later a second mea-

surement showed that the core temperature of the body was 80° F. Assume that the time of death corresponds to $t = 0$ and that the core temperature at that time was 98.6° F. Determine how many hours elapsed before the body was found. [*Hint:* Let $t_1 > 0$ denote the time that the body was discovered.]

20. The rate at which a body cools also depends on its exposed surface area S. If S is a constant, then a modification of (2) is

$$\frac{dT}{dt} = kS(T - T_m),$$

where $k < 0$ and T_m is a constant. Suppose that two cups A and B are filled with coffee at the same time. Initially, the temperature of the coffee is 150° F. The exposed surface area of the coffee in cup B is twice the surface area of the coffee in cup A. After 30 min the temperature of the coffee in cup A is 100° F. If $T_m = 70°$ F, then what is the temperature of the coffee in cup B after 30 min?

Mixtures

21. A tank contains 200 liters of fluid in which 30 grams of salt is dissolved. Brine containing 1 gram of salt per liter is then pumped into the tank at a rate of 4 L/min; the well-mixed solution is pumped out at the same rate. Find the number $A(t)$ of grams of salt in the tank at time t.

22. Solve Problem 21 assuming that pure water is pumped into the tank.

23. A large tank is filled to capacity with 500 gallons of pure water. Brine containing 2 pounds of salt per gallon is pumped into the tank at a rate of 5 gal/min. The well-mixed solution is pumped out at the same rate. Find the number $A(t)$ of pounds of salt in the tank at time t.

24. In Problem 23, what is the concentration $c(t)$ of the salt in the tank at time t? At $t = 5$ min? What is the concentration of the salt in the tank after a long time, that is, as $t \to \infty$? At what time is the concentration of the salt in the tank equal to one-half this limiting value?

25. Solve Problem 23 under the assumption that the solution is pumped out at a faster rate of 10 gal/min. When is the tank empty?

26. Determine the amount of salt in the tank at time t in Example 5 if the concentration of salt in the inflow is variable and given by $c_{in}(t) = 2 + \sin(t/4)$ lb/gal. Without actually graphing, conjecture what the solution curve of the IVP should look like. Then use a graphing utility to plot the graph of the solution on the interval [0, 300]. Repeat for the interval [0, 600] and compare your graph with that in Figure 3.1.4(a).

27. A large tank is partially filled with 100 gallons of fluid in which 10 pounds of salt is dissolved. Brine containing

$\frac{1}{2}$ pound of salt per gallon is pumped into the tank at a rate of 6 gal/min. The well-mixed solution is then pumped out at a slower rate of 4 gal/min. Find the number of pounds of salt in the tank after 30 minutes.

28. In Example 5 the size of the tank containing the salt mixture was not given. Suppose, as in the discussion following Example 5, that the rate at which brine is pumped into the tank is 3 gal/min but that the well-stirred solution is pumped out at a rate of 2 gal/min. It stands to reason that since brine is accumulating in the tank at the rate of 1 gal/min, any finite tank must eventually overflow. Now suppose that the tank has an open top and has a total capacity of 400 gallons.

(a) When will the tank overflow?

(b) What will be the number of pounds of salt in the tank at the instant it overflows?

(c) Assume that although the tank is overflowing, brine solution continues to be pumped in at a rate of 3 gal/min and the well-stirred solution continues to be pumped out at a rate of 2 gal/min. Devise a method for determining the number of pounds of salt in the tank at $t = 150$ minutes.

(d) Determine the number of pounds of salt in the tank as $t \rightarrow \infty$. Does your answer agree with your intuition?

(e) Use a graphing utility to plot the graph of $A(t)$ on the interval $[0, 500)$.

Series Circuits

29. A 30-volt electromotive force is applied to an LR series circuit in which the inductance is 0.1 henry and the resistance is 50 ohms. Find the current $i(t)$ if $i(0) = 0$. Determine the current as $t \rightarrow \infty$.

30. Solve equation (7) under the assumption that $E(t) = E_0 \sin \omega t$ and $i(0) = i_0$.

31. A 100-volt electromotive force is applied to an RC series circuit in which the resistance is 200 ohms and the capacitance is 10^{-4} farad. Find the charge $q(t)$ on the capacitor if $q(0) = 0$. Find the current $i(t)$.

32. A 200-volt electromotive force is applied to an RC series circuit in which the resistance is 1000 ohms and the capacitance is 5×10^{-6} farad. Find the charge $q(t)$ on the capacitor if $i(0) = 0.4$. Determine the charge and current at $t = 0.005$ s. Determine the charge as $t \rightarrow \infty$.

33. An electromotive force

$$E(t) = \begin{cases} 120, & 0 \leq t \leq 20 \\ 0, & t > 20 \end{cases}$$

is applied to an LR series circuit in which the inductance is 20 henries and the resistance is 2 ohms. Find the current $i(t)$ if $i(0) = 0$.

34. Suppose an RC series circuit has a variable resistor. If the resistance at time t is given by $R = k_1 + k_2 t$, where k_1 and k_2 are known positive constants, then (9) becomes

$$(k_1 + k_2 t) \frac{dq}{dt} + \frac{1}{C} q = E(t).$$

If $E(t) = E_0$ and $q(0) = q_0$, where E_0 and q_0 are constants, show that

$$q(t) = E_0 C + (q_0 - E_0 C) \left(\frac{k_1}{k_1 + k_2 t} \right)^{1/Ck_2}.$$

Additional Linear Models

35. Air Resistance In (14) of Section 1.3 we saw that a differential equation describing the velocity v of a falling mass subject to air resistance proportional to the instantaneous velocity is

$$m \frac{dv}{dt} = mg - kv,$$

where $k > 0$ is a constant of proportionality. The positive direction is downward.

(a) Solve the equation subject to the initial condition $v(0) = v_0$.

(b) Use the solution in part (a) to determine the limiting, or terminal, velocity of the mass. We saw how to determine the terminal velocity without solving the DE in Problem 40 in Exercises 2.1.

(c) If the distance s, measured from the point where the mass was released above ground, is related to velocity v by $ds/dt = v(t)$, find an explicit expression for $s(t)$ if $s(0) = 0$.

36. How High?—No Air Resistance Suppose a small cannonball weighing 16 pounds is shot vertically upward, as shown in Figure 3.1.10, with an initial velocity $v_0 = 300$ ft/s. The answer to the question "How high does the cannonball go?" depends on whether we take air resistance into account.

(a) Suppose air resistance is ignored. If the positive direction is upward, then a model for the state of the cannonball is given by $d^2s/dt^2 = -g$ (equation (12) of Section 1.3). Since $ds/dt = v(t)$ the last

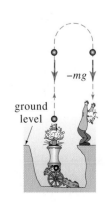

FIGURE 3.1.10 Find the maximum height of the cannonball in Problem 36

differential equation is the same as $dv/dt = -g$, where we take $g = 32$ ft/s^2. Find the velocity $v(t)$ of the cannonball at time t.

(b) Use the result obtained in part (a) to determine the height $s(t)$ of the cannonball measured from ground level. Find the maximum height attained by the cannonball.

37. How High?—Linear Air Resistance Repeat Problem 36, but this time assume that air resistance is proportional to instantaneous velocity. It stands to reason that the maximum height attained by the cannonball must be *less* than that in part (b) of Problem 36. Show this by supposing that the constant of proportionality is $k = 0.0025$. [*Hint*: Slightly modify the DE in Problem 35.]

38. Skydiving A skydiver weighs 125 pounds, and her parachute and equipment combined weigh another 35 pounds. After exiting from a plane at an altitude of 15,000 feet, she waits 15 seconds and opens her parachute. Assume that the constant of proportionality in the model in Problem 35 has the value $k = 0.5$ during free fall and $k = 10$ after the parachute is opened. Assume that her initial velocity on leaving the plane is zero. What is her velocity and how far has she traveled 20 seconds after leaving the plane? See Figure 3.1.11. How does her velocity at 20 seconds compare with her terminal velocity? How long does it take her to reach the ground? [*Hint*: Think in terms of two distinct IVPs.]

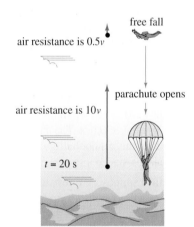

FIGURE 3.1.11
Find the time to reach the ground in Problem 38

39. Evaporating Raindrop As a raindrop falls, it evaporates while retaining its spherical shape. If we make the further assumptions that the rate at which the raindrop evaporates is proportional to its surface area and that air resistance is negligible, then a model for the velocity $v(t)$ of the raindrop is

$$\frac{dv}{dt} + \frac{3(k/\rho)}{(k/\rho)t + r_0} v = g.$$

Here ρ is the density of water, r_0 is the radius of the raindrop at $t = 0$, $k < 0$ is the constant of proportionality,

and the downward direction is taken to be the positive direction.

(a) Solve for $v(t)$ if the raindrop falls from rest.

(b) Reread Problem 34 of Exercises 1.3 and then show that the radius of the raindrop at time t is $r(t) = (k/\rho)t + r_0$.

(c) If $r_0 = 0.01$ ft and $r = 0.007$ ft 10 seconds after the raindrop falls from a cloud, determine the time at which the raindrop has evaporated completely.

40. Fluctuating Population The differential equation $dP/dt = (k \cos t)P$, where k is a positive constant, is a mathematical model for a population $P(t)$ that undergoes yearly seasonal fluctuations. Solve the equation subject to $P(0) = P_0$. Use a graphing utility to graph the solution for different choices of P_0.

41. Population Model In one model of the changing population $P(t)$ of a community, it is assumed that

$$\frac{dP}{dt} = \frac{dB}{dt} - \frac{dD}{dt},$$

where dB/dt and dD/dt are the birth and death rates, respectively.

(a) Solve for $P(t)$ if $dB/dt = k_1P$ and $dD/dt = k_2P$.

(b) Analyze the cases $k_1 > k_2$, $k_1 = k_2$, and $k_1 < k_2$.

42. Constant-Harvest Model A model that describes the population of a fishery in which harvesting takes place at a constant rate is given by

$$\frac{dP}{dt} = kP - h,$$

where k and h are positive constants.

(a) Solve the DE subject to $P(0) = P_0$.

(b) Describe the behavior of the population $P(t)$ for increasing time in the three cases $P_0 > h/k$, $P_0 = h/k$, and $0 < P_0 < h/k$.

(c) Use the results from part (b) to determine whether the fish population will ever go extinct in finite time, that is, whether there exists a time $T > 0$ such that $P(T) = 0$. If the population goes extinct, then find T.

43. Drug Dissemination A mathematical model for the rate at which a drug disseminates into the bloodstream is given by

$$\frac{dx}{dt} = r - kx,$$

where r and k are positive constants. The function $x(t)$ describes the concentration of the drug in the bloodstream at time t.

(a) Since the DE is autonomous, use the phase portrait concept of Section 2.1 to find the limiting value of $x(t)$ as $t \to \infty$.

(b) Solve the DE subject to $x(0) = 0$. Sketch the graph of $x(t)$ and verify your prediction in part (a). At what time is the concentration one-half this limiting value?

44. Memorization When forgetfulness is taken into account, the rate of memorization of a subject is given by

$$\frac{dA}{dt} = k_1(M - A) - k_2A,$$

where $k_1 > 0$, $k_2 > 0$, $A(t)$ is the amount memorized in time t, M is the total amount to be memorized, and $M - A$ is the amount remaining to be memorized.

(a) Since the DE is autonomous, use the phase portrait concept of Section 2.1 to find the limiting value of $A(t)$ as $t \to \infty$. Interpret the result.

(b) Solve the DE subject to $A(0) = 0$. Sketch the graph of $A(t)$ and verify your prediction in part (a).

45. Heart Pacemaker A heart pacemaker, shown in Figure 3.1.12, consists of a switch, a battery, a capacitor, and the heart as a resistor. When the switch S is at P, the capacitor charges; when S is at Q, the capacitor discharges, sending an electrical stimulus to the heart. In Problem 47 in Exercises 2.3 we saw that during this time the electrical stimulus is being applied to the heart, the voltage E across the heart satisfies the linear DE

$$\frac{dE}{dt} = -\frac{1}{RC}E.$$

(a) Let us assume that over the time interval of length t_1, $0 < t < t_1$, the switch S is at position P shown in Figure 3.1.12 and the capacitor is being charged. When the switch is moved to position Q at time t_1 the capacitor discharges, sending an impulse to the heart over the time interval of length t_2: $t_1 \le t < t_1 + t_2$. Thus over the initial charging/discharging interval $0 < t < t_1 + t_2$ the voltage to the heart is actually modeled by the piecewise-defined differential equation

$$\frac{dE}{dt} = \begin{cases} 0, & 0 \le t < t_1 \\ -\dfrac{1}{RC}E, & t_1 \le t < t_1 + t_2. \end{cases}$$

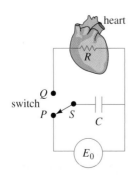

FIGURE 3.1.12 Model of a pacemaker in Problem 45

By moving S between P and Q, the charging and discharging over time intervals of lengths t_1 and t_2 is repeated indefinitely. Suppose $t_1 = 4$ s, $t_2 = 2$ s, $E_0 = 12$ V, and $E(0) = 0$, $E(4) = 12$, $E(6) = 0$, $E(10) = 12$, $E(12) = 0$, and so on. Solve for $E(t)$ for $0 \le t \le 24$.

(b) Suppose for the sake of illustration that $R = C = 1$. Use a graphing utility to graph the solution for the IVP in part (a) for $0 \le t \le 24$.

46. Sliding Box (a) A box of mass m slides down an inclined plane that makes an angle θ with the horizontal as shown in Figure 3.1.13. Find a differential equation for the velocity $v(t)$ of the box at time t in each of the following three cases:

    (i) No sliding friction and no air resistance

    (ii) With sliding friction and no air resistance

    (iii) With sliding friction and air resistance

In cases *(ii)* and *(iii)*, use the fact that the force of friction opposing the motion of the box is μN, where μ is the coefficient of sliding friction and N is the normal component of the weight of the box. In case *(iii)* assume that air resistance is proportional to the instantaneous velocity.

(b) In part (a), suppose that the box weighs 96 pounds, that the angle of inclination of the plane is $\theta = 30°$, that the coefficient of sliding friction is $\mu = \sqrt{3}/4$, and that the additional retarding force due to air resistance is numerically equal to $\frac{1}{4}v$. Solve the differential equation in each of the three cases, assuming that the box starts from rest from the highest point 50 ft above ground.

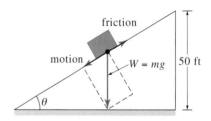

FIGURE 3.1.13 Box sliding down inclined plane in Problem 46

47. Sliding Box—Continued (a) In Problem 46 let $s(t)$ be the distance measured down the inclined plane from the highest point. Use $ds/dt = v(t)$ and the solution for each of the three cases in part (b) of Problem 46 to find the time that it takes the box to slide completely down the inclined plane. A root-finding application of a CAS may be useful here.

(b) In the case in which there is friction ($\mu \ne 0$) but no air resistance, explain why the box will not slide down the plane starting from *rest* from the highest point above ground when the inclination angle θ satisfies $\tan \theta \leq \mu$.

(c) The box *will* slide downward on the plane when $\tan \theta \leq \mu$ if it is given an initial velocity $v(0) = v_0 > 0$. Suppose that $\mu = \sqrt{3}/4$ and $\theta = 23°$. Verify that $\tan \theta \leq \mu$. How far will the box slide down the plane if $v_0 = 1$ ft/s?

(d) Using the values $\mu = \sqrt{3}/4$ and $\theta = 23°$, approximate the smallest initial velocity v_0 that can be given to the box so that, starting at the highest point 50 ft above ground, it will slide completely down the inclined plane. Then find the corresponding time it takes to slide down the plane.

48. What Goes Up . . . (a) It is well known that the model in which air resistance is ignored, part (a) of Problem 36, predicts that the time t_a it takes the cannonball to attain its maximum height is the same as the time t_d it takes the cannonball to fall from the maximum height to the ground. Moreover, the magnitude of the impact velocity v_i will be the same as the initial velocity v_0 of the cannonball. Verify both of these results.

(b) Then, using the model in Problem 37 that takes air resistance into account, compare the value of t_a with t_d and the value of the magnitude of v_i with v_0. A root-finding application of a CAS (or graphic calculator) may be useful here.

3.2 NONLINEAR MODELS

REVIEW MATERIAL

- Equations (5), (6), and (10) of Section 1.3 and Problems 7, 8, 13, 14, and 17 of Exercises 1.3
- Separation of variables in Section 2.2

INTRODUCTION We finish our study of single first-order differential equations with an examination of some nonlinear models.

POPULATION DYNAMICS If $P(t)$ denotes the size of a population at time t, the model for exponential growth begins with the assumption that $dP/dt = kP$ for some $k > 0$. In this model, the **relative**, or **specific, growth rate** defined by

$$\frac{dP/dt}{P} \tag{1}$$

is a constant k. True cases of exponential growth over long periods of time are hard to find because the limited resources of the environment will at some time exert restrictions on the growth of a population. Thus for other models, (1) can be expected to decrease as the population P increases in size.

The assumption that the rate at which a population grows (or decreases) is dependent only on the number P present and not on any time-dependent mechanisms such as seasonal phenomena (see Problem 31 in Exercises 1.3) can be stated as

$$\frac{dP/dt}{P} = f(P) \qquad \text{or} \qquad \frac{dP}{dt} = Pf(P). \tag{2}$$

The differential equation in (2), which is widely assumed in models of animal populations, is called the **density-dependent hypothesis.**

LOGISTIC EQUATION Suppose an environment is capable of sustaining no more than a fixed number K of individuals in its population. The quantity K is called the **carrying capacity** of the environment. Hence for the function f in (2) we have $f(K) = 0$, and we simply let $f(0) = r$. Figure 3.2.1 shows three functions f that satisfy these two conditions. The simplest assumption that we can make is that $f(P)$ is linear—that is, $f(P) = c_1P + c_2$. If we use the conditions $f(0) = r$ and

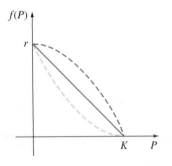

FIGURE 3.2.1 Simplest assumption for $f(P)$ is a straight line (blue color)

$f(K) = 0$, we find, in turn, $c_2 = r$ and $c_1 = -r/K$, and so f takes on the form $f(P) = r - (r/K)P$. Equation (2) becomes

$$\frac{dP}{dt} = P\left(r - \frac{r}{K}P\right).$$
(3)

With constants relabeled, the nonlinear equation (3) is the same as

$$\frac{dP}{dt} = P(a - bP).$$
(4)

Around 1840 the Belgian mathematician-biologist P. F. Verhulst was concerned with mathematical models for predicting the human populations of various countries. One of the equations he studied was (4), where $a > 0$ and $b > 0$. Equation (4) came to be known as the **logistic equation,** and its solution is called the **logistic function.** The graph of a logistic function is called a **logistic curve.**

The linear differential equation $dP/dt = kP$ does not provide a very accurate model for population when the population itself is very large. Overcrowded conditions, with the resulting detrimental effects on the environment such as pollution and excessive and competitive demands for food and fuel, can have an inhibiting effect on population growth. As we shall now see, the solution of (4) is bounded as $t \rightarrow \infty$. If we rewrite (4) as $dP/dt = aP - bP^2$, the nonlinear term $-bP^2$, $b > 0$, can be interpreted as an "inhibition" or "competition" term. Also, in most applications the positive constant a is much larger than the constant b.

Logistic curves have proved to be quite accurate in predicting the growth patterns, in a limited space, of certain types of bacteria, protozoa, water fleas (*Daphnia*), and fruit flies (*Drosophila*).

SOLUTION OF THE LOGISTIC EQUATION   One method of solving (4) is separation of variables. Decomposing the left side of $dP/P(a - bP) = dt$ into partial fractions and integrating gives

$$\left(\frac{1/a}{P} + \frac{b/a}{a - bP}\right)dP = dt$$

$$\frac{1}{a}\ln|P| - \frac{1}{a}\ln|a - bP| = t + c$$

$$\ln\left|\frac{P}{a - bP}\right| = at + ac$$

$$\frac{P}{a - bP} = c_1 e^{at}.$$

It follows from the last equation that

$$P(t) = \frac{ac_1 e^{at}}{1 + bc_1 e^{at}} = \frac{ac_1}{bc_1 + e^{-at}}.$$

If $P(0) = P_0$, $P_0 \neq a/b$, we find $c_1 = P_0/(a - bP_0)$, and so after substituting and simplifying, the solution becomes

$$P(t) = \frac{aP_0}{bP_0 + (a - bP_0)e^{-at}}.$$
(5)

GRAPHS OF $P(t)$ The basic shape of the graph of the logistic function $P(t)$ can be obtained without too much effort. Although the variable t usually represents time and we are seldom concerned with applications in which $t < 0$, it is nonetheless of some interest to include this interval in displaying the various graphs of P. From (5) we see that

$$P(t) \rightarrow \frac{aP_0}{bP_0} = \frac{a}{b} \quad \text{as} \quad t \rightarrow \infty \quad \text{and} \quad P(t) \rightarrow 0 \quad \text{as} \quad t \rightarrow -\infty.$$

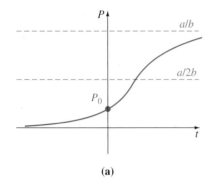

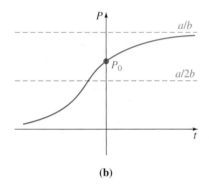

(b)

FIGURE 3.2.2 Logistic curves for different initial conditions

The dashed line $P = a/2b$ shown in Figure 3.2.2 corresponds to the ordinate of a point of inflection of the logistic curve. To show this, we differentiate (4) by the Product Rule:

$$\frac{d^2P}{dt^2} = P\left(-b\frac{dP}{dt}\right) + (a - bP)\frac{dP}{dt} = \frac{dP}{dt}(a - 2bP)$$

$$= P(a - bP)(a - 2bP)$$

$$= 2b^2P\left(P - \frac{a}{b}\right)\left(P - \frac{a}{2b}\right).$$

From calculus recall that the points where $d^2P/dt^2 = 0$ are possible points of inflection, but $P = 0$ and $P = a/b$ can obviously be ruled out. Hence $P = a/2b$ is the only possible ordinate value at which the concavity of the graph can change. For $0 < P < a/2b$ it follows that $P'' > 0$, and $a/2b < P < a/b$ implies that $P'' < 0$. Thus, as we read from left to right, the graph changes from concave up to concave down at the point corresponding to $P = a/2b$. When the initial value satisfies $0 < P_0 < a/2b$, the graph of $P(t)$ assumes the shape of an S, as we see in Figure 3.2.2(a). For $a/2b < P_0 < a/b$ the graph is still S-shaped, but the point of inflection occurs at a negative value of t, as shown in Figure 3.2.2(b).

We have already seen equation (4) in (5) of Section 1.3 in the form $dx/dt = kx(n + 1 - x)$, $k > 0$. This differential equation provides a reasonable model for describing the spread of an epidemic brought about initially by introducing an infected individual into a static population. The solution $x(t)$ represents the number of individuals infected with the disease at time t.

EXAMPLE 1   Logistic Growth

Suppose a student carrying a flu virus returns to an isolated college campus of 1000 students. If it is assumed that the rate at which the virus spreads is proportional not only to the number x of infected students but also to the number of students not infected, determine the number of infected students after 6 days if it is further observed that after 4 days $x(4) = 50$.

SOLUTION   Assuming that no one leaves the campus throughout the duration of the disease, we must solve the initial-value problem

$$\frac{dx}{dt} = kx(1000 - x), \quad x(0) = 1.$$

By making the identification $a = 1000k$ and $b = k$, we have immediately from (5) that

$$x(t) = \frac{1000k}{k + 999ke^{-1000kt}} = \frac{1000}{1 + 999e^{-1000kt}}.$$

Now, using the information $x(4) = 50$, we determine k from

$$50 = \frac{1000}{1 + 999e^{-4000k}}.$$

We find $-1000k = \frac{1}{4}\ln\frac{19}{999} = -0.9906$. Thus

$$x(t) = \frac{1000}{1 + 999e^{-0.9906t}}.$$

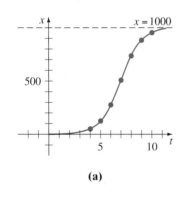

(a)

t (days)	x (number infected)
4	50 (observed)
5	124
6	276
7	507
8	735
9	882
10	953

(b)

FIGURE 3.2.3   Number of infected students $x(t)$ approaches 1000 as time t increases

Finally,
$$x(6) = \frac{1000}{1 + 999e^{-5.9436}} = 276 \text{ students.}$$

Additional calculated values of $x(t)$ are given in the table in Figure 3.2.3(b). ∎

MODIFICATIONS OF THE LOGISTIC EQUATION There are many variations of the logistic equation. For example, the differential equations

$$\frac{dP}{dt} = P(a - bP) - h \qquad \text{and} \qquad \frac{dP}{dt} = P(a - bP) + h \tag{6}$$

could serve, in turn, as models for the population in a fishery where fish are **harvested** or are **restocked** at rate h. When $h > 0$ is a constant, the DEs in (6) can be readily analyzed qualitatively or solved analytically by separation of variables. The equations in (6) could also serve as models of the human population decreased by emigration or increased by immigration, respectively. The rate h in (6) could be a function of time t or could be population dependent; for example, harvesting might be done periodically over time or might be done at a rate proportional to the population P at time t. In the latter instance, the model would look like $P' = P(a - bP) - cP$, $c > 0$. The human population of a community might change because of immigration in such a manner that the contribution due to immigration was large when the population P of the community was itself small but small when P was large; a reasonable model for the population of the community would then be $P' = P(a - bP) + ce^{-kP}$, $c > 0, k > 0$. See Problem 22 in Exercises 3.2. Another equation of the form given in (2),

$$\frac{dP}{dt} = P(a - b \ln P), \tag{7}$$

is a modification of the logistic equation known as the **Gompertz differential equation.** This DE is sometimes used as a model in the study of the growth or decline of populations, the growth of solid tumors, and certain kinds of actuarial predictions. See Problem 8 in Exercises 3.2.

CHEMICAL REACTIONS Suppose that a grams of chemical A are combined with b grams of chemical B. If there are M parts of A and N parts of B formed in the compound and $X(t)$ is the number of grams of chemical C formed, then the number of grams of chemical A and the number of grams of chemical B remaining at time t are, respectively,

$$a - \frac{M}{M + N}X \qquad \text{and} \qquad b - \frac{N}{M + N}X.$$

The law of mass action states that when no temperature change is involved, the rate at which the two substances react is proportional to the product of the amounts of A and B that are untransformed (remaining) at time t:

$$\frac{dX}{dt} \propto \left(a - \frac{M}{M + N}X\right)\left(b - \frac{N}{M + N}X\right). \tag{8}$$

If we factor out $M/(M + N)$ from the first factor and $N/(M + N)$ from the second and introduce a constant of proportionality $k > 0$, (8) has the form

$$\frac{dX}{dt} = k(\alpha - X)(\beta - X), \tag{9}$$

where $\alpha = a(M + N)/M$ and $\beta = b(M + N)/N$. Recall from (6) of Section 1.3 that a chemical reaction governed by the nonlinear differential equation (9) is said to be a **second-order reaction.**

EXAMPLE 2 Second-Order Chemical Reaction

A compound C is formed when two chemicals A and B are combined. The resulting reaction between the two chemicals is such that for each gram of A, 4 grams of B is used. It is observed that 30 grams of the compound C is formed in 10 minutes.

Determine the amount of C at time t if the rate of the reaction is proportional to the amounts of A and B remaining and if initially there are 50 grams of A and 32 grams of B. How much of the compound C is present at 15 minutes? Interpret the solution as $t \to \infty$.

SOLUTION Let $X(t)$ denote the number of grams of the compound C present at time t. Clearly, $X(0) = 0$ g and $X(10) = 30$ g.

If, for example, 2 grams of compound C is present, we must have used, say, a grams of A and b grams of B, so $a + b = 2$ and $b = 4a$. Thus we must use $a = \frac{2}{5} = 2\left(\frac{1}{5}\right)$ g of chemical A and $b = \frac{8}{5} = 2\left(\frac{4}{5}\right)$ g of B. In general, for X grams of C we must use

$$\frac{1}{5} X \text{ grams of } A \qquad \text{and} \qquad \frac{4}{5} X \text{ grams of } B.$$

The amounts of A and B remaining at time t are then

$$50 - \frac{1}{5} X \quad \text{and} \quad 32 - \frac{4}{5} X,$$

respectively.

Now we know that the rate at which compound C is formed satisfies

$$\frac{dX}{dt} \propto \left(50 - \frac{1}{5} X \right)\left(32 - \frac{4}{5} X \right).$$

To simplify the subsequent algebra, we factor $\frac{1}{5}$ from the first term and $\frac{4}{5}$ from the second and then introduce the constant of proportionality:

$$\frac{dX}{dt} = k(250 - X)(40 - X).$$

By separation of variables and partial fractions we can write

$$-\frac{\frac{1}{210}}{250 - X} dX + \frac{\frac{1}{210}}{40 - X} dX = k\, dt.$$

Integrating gives

$$\ln \frac{250 - X}{40 - X} = 210kt + c_1 \qquad \text{or} \qquad \frac{250 - X}{40 - X} = c_2 e^{210kt}. \qquad (10)$$

When $t = 0$, $X = 0$, so it follows at this point that $c_2 = \frac{25}{4}$. Using $X = 30$ g at $t = 10$, we find $210k = \frac{1}{10} \ln \frac{88}{25} = 0.1258$. With this information we solve the last equation in (10) for X:

$$X(t) = 1000 \frac{1 - e^{-0.1258t}}{25 - 4e^{-0.1258t}}. \qquad (11)$$

The behavior of X as a function of time is displayed in Figure 3.2.4. It is clear from the accompanying table and (11) that $X \to 40$ as $t \to \infty$. This means that 40 grams of compound C is formed, leaving

$$50 - \frac{1}{5}(40) = 42 \text{ g of } A \qquad \text{and} \qquad 32 - \frac{4}{5}(40) = 0 \text{ g of } B. \qquad \blacksquare$$

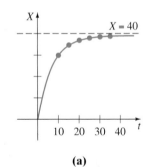

(a)

t (min)	X (g)
10	30 (measured)
15	34.78
20	37.25
25	38.54
30	39.22
35	39.59

(b)

FIGURE 3.2.4 $X(t)$ starts at 0 and approaches 40 as t increases

REMARKS

The indefinite integral $\int du/(a^2 - u^2)$ can be evaluated in terms of logarithms, the inverse hyperbolic tangent, or the inverse hyperbolic cotangent. For example, of the two results

$$\int \frac{du}{a^2 - u^2} = \frac{1}{a}\tanh^{-1}\frac{u}{a} + c, \quad |u| < a \tag{12}$$

$$\int \frac{du}{a^2 - u^2} = \frac{1}{2a}\ln\left|\frac{a+u}{a-u}\right| + c, \quad |u| \neq a, \tag{13}$$

(12) may be convenient in Problems 15 and 24 in Exercises 3.2, whereas (13) may be preferable in Problem 25.

EXERCISES 3.2

Answers to selected odd-numbered problems begin on page ANS-3.

Logistic Equation

1. The number $N(t)$ of supermarkets throughout the country that are using a computerized checkout system is described by the initial-value problem

$$\frac{dN}{dt} = N(1 - 0.0005N), \quad N(0) = 1.$$

(a) Use the phase portrait concept of Section 2.1 to predict how many supermarkets are expected to adopt the new procedure over a long period of time. By hand, sketch a solution curve of the given initial-value problem.

(b) Solve the initial-value problem and then use a graphing utility to verify the solution curve in part (a). How many companies are expected to adopt the new technology when $t = 10$?

2. The number $N(t)$ of people in a community who are exposed to a particular advertisement is governed by the logistic equation. Initially, $N(0) = 500$, and it is observed that $N(1) = 1000$. Solve for $N(t)$ if it is predicted that the limiting number of people in the community who will see the advertisement is 50,000.

3. A model for the population $P(t)$ in a suburb of a large city is given by the initial-value problem

$$\frac{dP}{dt} = P(10^{-1} - 10^{-7}P), \quad P(0) = 5000,$$

where t is measured in months. What is the limiting value of the population? At what time will the population be equal to one-half of this limiting value?

4. (a) Census data for the United States between 1790 and 1950 are given in Table 3.1. Construct a logistic population model using the data from 1790, 1850, and 1910.

(b) Construct a table comparing actual census population with the population predicted by the model in part (a). Compute the error and the percentage error for each entry pair.

TABLE 3.1

Year	Population (in millions)
1790	3.929
1800	5.308
1810	7.240
1820	9.638
1830	12.866
1840	17.069
1850	23.192
1860	31.433
1870	38.558
1880	50.156
1890	62.948
1900	75.996
1910	91.972
1920	105.711
1930	122.775
1940	131.669
1950	150.697

Modifications of the Logistic Model

5. (a) If a constant number h of fish are harvested from a fishery per unit time, then a model for the population $P(t)$ of the fishery at time t is given by

$$\frac{dP}{dt} = P(a - bP) - h, \quad P(0) = P_0,$$

where a, b, h, and P_0 are positive constants. Suppose $a = 5$, $b = 1$, and $h = 4$. Since the DE is autonomous, use the phase portrait concept of Section 2.1 to sketch representative solution curves corresponding to the cases $P_0 > 4$, $1 < P_0 < 4$, and $0 < P_0 < 1$. Determine the long-term behavior of the population in each case.

(b) Solve the IVP in part (a). Verify the results of your phase portrait in part (a) by using a graphing utility to plot the graph of $P(t)$ with an initial condition taken from each of the three intervals given.

(c) Use the information in parts (a) and (b) to determine whether the fishery population becomes extinct in finite time. If so, find that time.

6. Investigate the harvesting model in Problem 5 both qualitatively and analytically in the case $a = 5$, $b = 1$, $h = \frac{25}{4}$. Determine whether the population becomes extinct in finite time. If so, find that time.

7. Repeat Problem 6 in the case $a = 5$, $b = 1$, $h = 7$.

8. (a) Suppose $a = b = 1$ in the Gompertz differential equation (7). Since the DE is autonomous, use the phase portrait concept of Section 2.1 to sketch representative solution curves corresponding to the cases $P_0 > e$ and $0 < P_0 < e$.

(b) Suppose $a = 1$, $b = -1$ in (7). Use a new phase portrait to sketch representative solution curves corresponding to the cases $P_0 > e^{-1}$ and $0 < P_0 < e^{-1}$.

(c) Find an explicit solution of (7) subject to $P(0) = P_0$.

Chemical Reactions

9. Two chemicals A and B are combined to form a chemical C. The rate, or velocity, of the reaction is proportional to the product of the instantaneous amounts of A and B not converted to chemical C. Initially, there are 40 grams of A and 50 grams of B, and for each gram of B, 2 grams of A is used. It is observed that 10 grams of C is formed in 5 minutes. How much is formed in 20 minutes? What is the limiting amount of C after a long time? How much of chemicals A and B remains after a long time?

10. Solve Problem 9 if 100 grams of chemical A is present initially. At what time is chemical C half-formed?

Additional Nonlinear Models

11. **Leaking Cylindrical Tank** A tank in the form of a right-circular cylinder standing on end is leaking water through a circular hole in its bottom. As we saw in (10) of Section 1.3, when friction and contraction of water at the hole are ignored, the height h of water in the tank is described by

$$\frac{dh}{dt} = -\frac{A_h}{A_w}\sqrt{2gh},$$

where A_w and A_h are the cross-sectional areas of the water and the hole, respectively.

(a) Solve the DE if the initial height of the water is H. By hand, sketch the graph of $h(t)$ and give its interval

I of definition in terms of the symbols A_w, A_h, and H. Use $g = 32$ ft/s².

(b) Suppose the tank is 10 feet high and has radius 2 feet and the circular hole has radius $\frac{1}{2}$ inch. If the tank is initially full, how long will it take to empty?

12. **Leaking Cylindrical Tank—Continued** When friction and contraction of the water at the hole are taken into account, the model in Problem 11 becomes

$$\frac{dh}{dt} = -c\frac{A_h}{A_w}\sqrt{2gh},$$

where $0 < c < 1$. How long will it take the tank in Problem 11(b) to empty if $c = 0.6$? See Problem 13 in Exercises 1.3.

13. **Leaking Conical Tank** A tank in the form of a right-circular cone standing on end, vertex down, is leaking water through a circular hole in its bottom.

(a) Suppose the tank is 20 feet high and has radius 8 feet and the circular hole has radius 2 inches. In Problem 14 in Exercises 1.3 you were asked to show that the differential equation governing the height h of water leaking from a tank is

$$\frac{dh}{dt} = -\frac{5}{6h^{3/2}}.$$

In this model, friction and contraction of the water at the hole were taken into account with $c = 0.6$, and g was taken to be 32 ft/s². See Figure 1.3.12. If the tank is initially full, how long will it take the tank to empty?

(b) Suppose the tank has a vertex angle of 60° and the circular hole has radius 2 inches. Determine the differential equation governing the height h of water. Use $c = 0.6$ and $g = 32$ ft/s². If the height of the water is initially 9 feet, how long will it take the tank to empty?

14. **Inverted Conical Tank** Suppose that the conical tank in Problem 13(a) is inverted, as shown in Figure 3.2.5, and that water leaks out a circular hole of radius 2 inches in the center of its circular base. Is the time it takes to empty a full tank the same as for the tank with vertex down in Problem 13? Take the friction/contraction coefficient to be $c = 0.6$ and $g = 32$ ft/s².

FIGURE 3.2.5 Inverted conical tank in Problem 14

15. Air Resistance A differential equation for the velocity v of a falling mass m subjected to air resistance proportional to the square of the instantaneous velocity is

$$m\frac{dv}{dt} = mg - kv^2,$$

where $k > 0$ is a constant of proportionality. The positive direction is downward.

(a) Solve the equation subject to the initial condition $v(0) = v_0$.

(b) Use the solution in part (a) to determine the limiting, or terminal, velocity of the mass. We saw how to determine the terminal velocity without solving the DE in Problem 41 in Exercises 2.1.

(c) If the distance s, measured from the point where the mass was released above ground, is related to velocity v by $ds/dt = v(t)$, find an explicit expression for $s(t)$ if $s(0) = 0$.

16. How High?—Nonlinear Air Resistance Consider the 16-pound cannonball shot vertically upward in Problems 36 and 37 in Exercises 3.1 with an initial velocity $v_0 = 300$ ft/s. Determine the maximum height attained by the cannonball if air resistance is assumed to be proportional to the square of the instantaneous velocity. Assume that the positive direction is upward and take $k = 0.0003$. [*Hint*: Slightly modify the DE in Problem 15.]

17. That Sinking Feeling (a) Determine a differential equation for the velocity $v(t)$ of a mass m sinking in water that imparts a resistance proportional to the square of the instantaneous velocity and also exerts an upward buoyant force whose magnitude is given by Archimedes' principle. See Problem 18 in Exercises 1.3. Assume that the positive direction is downward.

(b) Solve the differential equation in part (a).

(c) Determine the limiting, or terminal, velocity of the sinking mass.

18. Solar Collector The differential equation

$$\frac{dy}{dx} = \frac{-x + \sqrt{x^2 + y^2}}{y}$$

describes the shape of a plane curve C that will reflect all incoming light beams to the same point and could be a model for the mirror of a reflecting telescope, a satellite antenna, or a solar collector. See Problem 27 in Exercises 1.3. There are several ways of solving this DE.

(a) Verify that the differential equation is homogeneous (see Section 2.5). Show that the substitution $y = ux$ yields

$$\frac{u\,du}{\sqrt{1 + u^2}\left(1 - \sqrt{1 + u^2}\right)} = \frac{dx}{x}.$$

Use a CAS (or another judicious substitution) to integrate the left-hand side of the equation. Show that the curve C must be a parabola with focus at the origin and is symmetric with respect to the x-axis.

(b) Show that the first differential equation can also be solved by means of the substitution $u = x^2 + y^2$.

19. Tsunami (a) A simple model for the shape of a tsunami, or tidal wave, is given by

$$\frac{dW}{dx} = W\sqrt{4 - 2W},$$

where $W(x) > 0$ is the height of the wave expressed as a function of its position relative to a point offshore. By inspection, find all constant solutions of the DE.

(b) Solve the differential equation in part (a). A CAS may be useful for integration.

(c) Use a graphing utility to obtain the graphs of all solutions that satisfy the initial condition $W(0) = 2$.

20. Evaporation An outdoor decorative pond in the shape of a hemispherical tank is to be filled with water pumped into the tank through an inlet in its bottom. Suppose that the radius of the tank is $R = 10$ ft, that water is pumped in at a rate of π ft³/min, and that the tank is initially empty. See Figure 3.2.6. As the tank fills, it loses water through evaporation. Assume that the rate of evaporation is proportional to the area A of the surface of the water and that the constant of proportionality is $k = 0.01$.

(a) The rate of change dV/dt of the volume of the water at time t is a net rate. Use this net rate to determine a differential equation for the height h of the water at time t. The volume of the water shown in the figure is $V = \pi Rh^2 - \frac{1}{3}\pi h^3$, where $R = 10$. Express the area of the surface of the water $A = \pi r^2$ in terms of h.

(b) Solve the differential equation in part (a). Graph the solution.

(c) If there were no evaporation, how long would it take the tank to fill?

(d) With evaporation, what is the depth of the water at the time found in part (c)? Will the tank ever be filled? Prove your assertion.

Output: water evaporates
at rate proportional
to area A of surface

Input: water pumped in
at rate π ft³/min

(a) hemispherical tank

(b) cross-section of tank

FIGURE 3.2.6 Decorative pond in Problem 20

Project Problems

21. Regression Line Read the documentation for your CAS on *scatter plots* (or *scatter diagrams*) and *least-squares linear fit*. The straight line that best fits a set of data points is called a **regression line** or a **least squares line.** Your task is to construct a logistic model for the population of the United States, defining $f(P)$ in (2) as an equation of a regression line based on the population data in the table in Problem 4. One way of doing this is to approximate the left-hand side $\dfrac{1}{P}\dfrac{dP}{dt}$ of the first equation in (2), using the forward difference quotient in place of dP/dt:

$$Q(t) = \frac{1}{P(t)}\frac{P(t+h) - P(t)}{h}.$$

(a) Make a table of the values t, $P(t)$, and $Q(t)$ using $t = 0, 10, 20, \ldots, 160$ and $h = 10$. For example, the first line of the table should contain $t = 0$, $P(0)$, and $Q(0)$. With $P(0) = 3.929$ and $P(10) = 5.308$,

$$Q(0) = \frac{1}{P(0)}\frac{P(10) - P(0)}{10} = 0.035.$$

Note that $Q(160)$ depends on the 1960 census population $P(170)$. Look up this value.

(b) Use a CAS to obtain a scatter plot of the data $(P(t), Q(t))$ computed in part (a). Also use a CAS to find an equation of the regression line and to superimpose its graph on the scatter plot.

(c) Construct a logistic model $dP/dt = Pf(P)$, where $f(P)$ is the equation of the regression line found in part (b).

(d) Solve the model in part (c) using the initial condition $P(0) = 3.929$.

(e) Use a CAS to obtain another scatter plot, this time of the ordered pairs $(t, P(t))$ from your table in part (a). Use your CAS to superimpose the graph of the solution in part (d) on the scatter plot.

(f) Look up the U.S. census data for 1970, 1980, and 1990. What population does the logistic model in part (c) predict for these years? What does the model predict for the U.S. population $P(t)$ as $t \to \infty$?

22. Immigration Model **(a)** In Examples 3 and 4 of Section 2.1 we saw that any solution $P(t)$ of (4) possesses the asymptotic behavior $P(t) \to a/b$ as $t \to \infty$ for $P_0 > a/b$ and for $0 < P_0 < a/b$; as a consequence the equilibrium solution $P = a/b$ is called an attractor. Use a root-finding application of a CAS (or a graphic calculator) to approximate the equilibrium solution of the immigration model

$$\frac{dP}{dt} = P(1 - P) + 0.3e^{-P}.$$

(b) Use a graphing utility to graph the function $F(P) = P(1 - P) + 0.3e^{-P}$. Explain how this graph

can be used to determine whether the number found in part (a) is an attractor.

(c) Use a numerical solver to compare the solution curves for the IVPs

$$\frac{dP}{dt} = P(1 - P), \quad P(0) = P_0$$

for $P_0 = 0.2$ and $P_0 = 1.2$ with the solution curves for the IVPs

$$\frac{dP}{dt} = P(1 - P) + 0.3e^{-P}, \quad P(0) = P_0$$

for $P_0 = 0.2$ and $P_0 = 1.2$. Superimpose all curves on the same coordinate axes but, if possible, use a different color for the curves of the second initial-value problem. Over a long period of time, what percentage increase does the immigration model predict in the population compared to the logistic model?

23. What Goes Up . . . In Problem 16 let t_a be the time it takes the cannonball to attain its maximum height and let t_d be the time it takes the cannonball to fall from the maximum height to the ground. Compare the value of t_a with the value of t_d and compare the magnitude of the impact velocity v_i with the initial velocity v_0. See Problem 48 in Exercises 3.1. A root-finding application of a CAS might be useful here. [*Hint*: Use the model in Problem 15 when the cannonball is falling.]

24. Skydiving A skydiver is equipped with a stopwatch and an altimeter. As shown in Figure 3.2.7, he opens his parachute 25 seconds after exiting a plane flying at an altitude of 20,000 feet and observes that his altitude is 14,800 feet. Assume that air resistance is proportional to the square of the instantaneous velocity, his initial velocity on leaving the plane is zero, and $g = 32 \text{ ft/s}^2$.

(a) Find the distance $s(t)$, measured from the plane, the skydiver has traveled during freefall in time t. [*Hint*: The constant of proportionality k in the model given in Problem 15 is not specified. Use the expression for terminal velocity v_t obtained in part (b) of Problem 15 to eliminate k from the IVP. Then eventually solve for v_t.]

(b) How far does the skydiver fall and what is his velocity at $t = 15$ s?

FIGURE 3.2.7 Skydiver in Problem 24

25. **Hitting Bottom**   A helicopter hovers 500 feet above a large open tank full of liquid (not water). A dense compact object weighing 160 pounds is dropped (released from rest) from the helicopter into the liquid. Assume that air resistance is proportional to instantaneous velocity v while the object is in the air and that viscous damping is proportional to v^2 after the object has entered the liquid. For air take $k = \frac{1}{4}$, and for the liquid take $k = 0.1$. Assume that the positive direction is downward. If the tank is 75 feet high, determine the time and the impact velocity when the object hits the bottom of the tank. [*Hint*: Think in terms of two distinct IVPs. If you use (13), be careful in removing the absolute value sign. You might compare the velocity when the object hits the liquid—the initial velocity for the second problem—with the terminal velocity v_t of the object falling through the liquid.]

26. **Old Man River . . .**   In Figure 3.2.8(a) suppose that the y-axis and the dashed vertical line $x = 1$ represent, respectively, the straight west and east beaches of a river that is 1 mile wide. The river flows northward with a velocity $\mathbf{v}_r$, where $|\mathbf{v}_r| = v_r$ mi/h is a constant. A man enters the current at the point (1, 0) on the east shore and swims in a direction and rate relative to the river given by the vector $\mathbf{v}_s$, where the speed $|\mathbf{v}_s| = v_s$ mi/h is a constant. The man wants to reach the west beach exactly at (0, 0) and so swims in such a manner that keeps his velocity vector $\mathbf{v}_s$ always directed toward the point (0, 0). Use Figure 3.2.8(b) as an aid in showing that a mathematical model for the path of the swimmer in the river is

$$\frac{dy}{dx} = \frac{v_s y - v_r \sqrt{x^2 + y^2}}{v_s x}.$$

[*Hint*: The velocity $\mathbf{v}$ of the swimmer along the path or curve shown in Figure 3.2.8 is the resultant $\mathbf{v} = \mathbf{v}_s + \mathbf{v}_r$. Resolve $\mathbf{v}_s$ and $\mathbf{v}_r$ into components in the x- and y-directions. If $x = x(t)$, $y = y(t)$ are parametric equations of the swimmer's path, then $\mathbf{v} = (dx/dt, dy/dt)$.]

27. **(a)** Solve the DE in Problem 26 subject to $y(1) = 0$. For convenience let $k = v_r/v_s$.

   (b) Determine the values of v_s for which the swimmer will reach the point (0, 0) by examining $\lim\limits_{x \to 0^+} y(x)$ in the cases $k = 1$, $k > 1$, and $0 < k < 1$.

28. **Old Man River Keeps Moving . . .**   Suppose the man in Problem 26 again enters the current at (1, 0) but this time decides to swim so that his velocity vector $\mathbf{v}_s$ is always directed toward the west beach. Assume that the speed $|\mathbf{v}_s| = v_s$ mi/h is a constant. Show that a mathematical model for the path of the swimmer in the river is now

$$\frac{dy}{dx} = -\frac{v_r}{v_s}.$$

29. The current speed v_r of a straight river such as that in Problem 26 is usually not a constant. Rather, an approximation to the current speed (measured in miles per hour) could be a function such as $v_r(x) = 30x(1 - x)$, $0 \leq x \leq 1$, whose values are small at the shores (in this case, $v_r(0) = 0$ and $v_r(1) = 0$) and largest in the middle of the river. Solve the DE in Problem 28 subject to $y(1) = 0$, where $v_s = 2$ mi/h and $v_r(x)$ is as given. When the swimmer makes it across the river, how far will he have to walk along the beach to reach the point (0, 0)?

30. **Raindrops Keep Falling . . .**   When a bottle of liquid refreshment was opened recently, the following factoid was found inside the bottle cap:

   The average velocity of a falling raindrop is 7 miles/hour.

   A quick search of the Internet found that meteorologist Jeff Haby offers the additional information that an "average" spherical raindrop has a radius of 0.04 in. and an approximate volume of 0.000000155 ft^3. Use this data and, if need be, dig up other data and make other reasonable assumptions to determine whether *"average velocity of . . . 7 mph"* is consistent with the models in Problems 35 and 36 in Exercises 3.1 and Problem 15 in this exercise set. Also see Problem 34 in Exercises 1.3.

31. **Time Drips By**   The **clepsydra,** or water clock, was a device that the ancient Egyptians, Greeks, Romans, and Chinese used to measure the passage of time by observing the change in the height of water that was permitted to flow out of a small hole in the bottom of a container or tank.

   (a) Suppose a tank is made of glass and has the shape of a right-circular cylinder of radius 1 ft. Assume that $h(0) = 2$ ft corresponds to water filled to the top of the tank, a hole in the bottom is circular with radius $\frac{1}{32}$ in., $g = 32$ ft/s^2, and $c = 0.6$. Use the differential equation in Problem 12 to find the height $h(t)$ of the water.

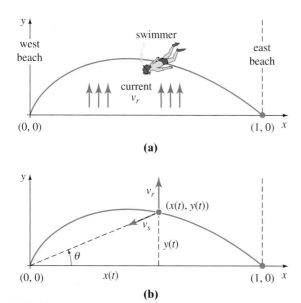

FIGURE 3.2.8   Path of swimmer in Problem 26

(For figure (a): labels include *west beach*, *swimmer*, *east beach*, *current* v_r, points (0, 0) and (1, 0), y and x axes.)

(For figure (b): labels include v_r, v_s, $(x(t), y(t))$, $y(t)$, θ, $x(t)$, points (0, 0) and (1, 0), y and x axes.)

(b) For the tank in part (a), how far up from its bottom should a mark be made on its side, as shown in Figure 3.2.9, that corresponds to the passage of one hour? Next determine where to place the marks corresponding to the passage of 2 hr, 3 hr, ..., 12 hr. Explain why these marks are not evenly spaced.

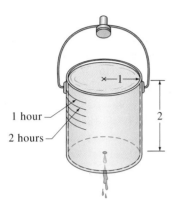

FIGURE 3.2.9 Clepsydra in Problem 31

32. (a) Suppose that a glass tank has the shape of a cone with circular cross section as shown in Figure 3.2.10. As in part (a) of Problem 31, assume that $h(0) = 2$ ft corresponds to water filled to the top of the tank, a hole in the bottom is circular with radius $\frac{1}{32}$ in., $g = 32$ ft/s^2, and $c = 0.6$. Use the differential equation in Problem 12 to find the height $h(t)$ of the water.

(b) Can this water clock measure 12 time intervals of length equal to 1 hour? Explain using sound mathematics.

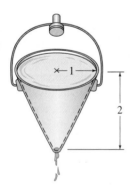

FIGURE 3.2.10 Clepsydra in Problem 32

33. Suppose that $r = f(h)$ defines the shape of a water clock for which the time marks are equally spaced. Use the differential equation in Problem 12 to find $f(h)$ and sketch a typical graph of h as a function of r. Assume that the cross-sectional area A_h of the hole is constant. [*Hint*: In this situation $dh/dt = -a$, where $a > 0$ is a constant.]

Contributed Problem | Michael Prophet, Ph.D Doug Shaw, Ph.D Associate Professors Mathematics Department University of Northern Iowa

34. A Logistic Model of Sunflower Growth This problem involves planting a sunflower seed and plotting the height of the sunflower versus time. It should take 3–4 months to gather the data, so start early! You can substitute a different plant if you like, but you may then have to adjust the time scale and the height scale appropriately.

(a) You are going to be creating a plot of the sunflower height (in cm) versus the time (in days). Before beginning, guess what this curve is going to look like, and fill in your guess on the grid.

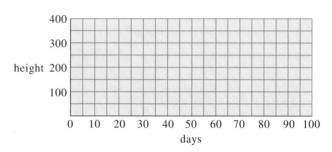

(b) Now plant your sunflower. Take a height measurement the first day that your flower sprouts, and call that day 0. Then take a measurement at least once a week until it is time to start writing up your data.

(c) Do your data points more closely resemble exponential growth or logistic growth? Why?

(d) If your data more closely resemble exponential growth, the equation for height versus time will be $dH/dt = kH$. If your data more closely resemble logistic growth, the equation for height versus time will be $dH/dt = kH(C - H)$. What is the physical meaning of C? Use your data to estimate C.

(e) We now experimentally determine k. At each of your t values, estimate dH/dt by using difference quotients. Then use the fact that $k = \dfrac{dH/dt}{H(C - H)}$ to get a best estimate of k.

(f) Solve your differential equation. Now graph your solution along with the data points. Did you come up with a good model? Do you think that k will change if you plant a different sunflower next year?

Contributed Problem | Ben Fitzpatrick, Ph.D Clarence Wallen Chair of Mathematics Mathematics Department Loyola Marymount University

35. Torricelli's Law If we punch a hole in a bucket full of water, the fluid drains at a rate governed by Torricelli's law, which states that the rate of change of volume is proportional to the square root of the height of the fluid.

The rate equation given in Figure 3.2.11 arises from Bernoulli's principle in fluid dynamics, which states that the quantity $P + \frac{1}{2}\rho v^2 + \rho g h$ is constant. Here P is pressure, ρ is fluid density, v is velocity, and g is the acceleration due to gravity. Comparing the top of the fluid, at the height h, to the fluid at the hole, we have

$$P_{top} + \frac{1}{2}\rho v_{top}^2 + \rho g h = P_{hole} + \frac{1}{2}\rho v_{hole}^2 + \rho g \cdot 0.$$

If the pressure at the top and the pressure at the bottom are both atmospheric pressure and if the drainage hole radius is much less than the radius of the bucket, then $P_{top} = P_{hole}$ and $v_{top} = 0$, so $\rho g h = \frac{1}{2}\rho v_{hole}^2$ leads to Torricelli's law: $v = \sqrt{2gh}$. Since $\dfrac{dV}{dt} = -A_{hole}v$, we have the differential equation

$$\frac{dV}{dt} = -A_{hole}\sqrt{2gh}.$$

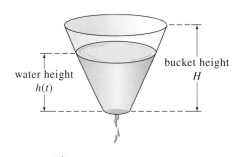

rate equation: $\dfrac{dV}{dt} = -A_{hole}\sqrt{2gh}$

FIGURE 3.2.11 Bucket Drainage

In this problem, we seek a comparison of Torricelli's differential equation with actual data.

(a) If the water is at a height h, we can find the volume of water in the bucket by the formula

$$V(h) = \frac{\pi}{3m}\left[(mh + R_B)^3 - R_B^3\right]$$

in which $m = (R_T - R_B)/H$. Here R_T and R_B denote the top and bottom radii of the bucket, respectively, and H denotes the height of the bucket. Taking this formula as given, differentiate to find a relationship between the rates dV/dt and dh/dt.

(b) Use the relationship derived in part (a) to find a differential equation for $h(t)$ (that is, you should have an independent variable t, a dependent variable h, and constants in the equation).

(c) Solve this differential equation using separation of variables. It is relatively straightforward to determine time as a function of height, but solving for height as a function of time may be difficult.

(d) Obtain a flowerpot, fill it with water, and watch it drain. At a fixed set of heights, record the time at which the water reaches the height. Compare the results to the differential equation's solution.

(e) It has been observed that a more accurate differential equation is

$$\frac{dV}{dt} = -(0.84)A_{hole}\sqrt{gh}.$$

Solve this differential equation and compare to the results of part (d).

3.3 MODELING WITH SYSTEMS OF FIRST-ORDER DEs

REVIEW MATERIAL

● Section 1.3

INTRODUCTION This section is similar to Section 1.3 in that we are just going to discuss certain mathematical models, but instead of a single differential equation the models will be systems of first-order differential equations. Although some of the models will be based on topics that we explored in the preceding two sections, we are not going to develop any general methods for solving these systems. There are reasons for this: First, we do not possess the necessary mathematical tools for solving systems at this point. Second, some of the systems that we discuss—notably the systems of *nonlinear* first-order DEs—simply cannot be solved analytically. We shall examine solution methods for systems of *linear* DEs in Chapters 4, 7, and 8.

LINEAR/NONLINEAR SYSTEMS We have seen that a single differential equation can serve as a mathematical model for a single population in an environment. But if there are, say, two interacting and perhaps competing species living in the same environment (for example, rabbits and foxes), then a model for their populations $x(t)$

and $y(t)$ might be a system of two first-order differential equations such as

$$\frac{dx}{dt} = g_1(t, x, y)$$

$$\frac{dy}{dt} = g_2(t, x, y). \tag{1}$$

When g_1 and g_2 are linear in the variables x and y—that is, g_1 and g_2 have the forms

$$g_1(t, x, y) = c_1 x + c_2 y + f_1(t) \qquad \text{and} \qquad g_2(t, x, y) = c_3 x + c_4 y + f_2(t),$$

where the coefficients c_i could depend on t—then (1) is said to be a **linear system.** A system of differential equations that is not linear is said to be **nonlinear.**

RADIOACTIVE SERIES In the discussion of radioactive decay in Sections 1.3 and 3.1 we assumed that the rate of decay was proportional to the number $A(t)$ of nuclei of the substance present at time t. When a substance decays by radioactivity, it usually doesn't just transmute in one step into a stable substance; rather, the first substance decays into another radioactive substance, which in turn decays into a third substance, and so on. This process, called a **radioactive decay series,** continues until a stable element is reached. For example, the uranium decay series is U-238 $\rightarrow$ Th-234 $\rightarrow \cdots \rightarrow$ Pb-206, where Pb-206 is a stable isotope of lead. The half-lives of the various elements in a radioactive series can range from billions of years (4.5×10^9 years for U-238) to a fraction of a second. Suppose a radioactive series is described schematically by $X \xrightarrow{-\lambda_1} Y \xrightarrow{-\lambda_2} Z$, where $k_1 = -\lambda_1 < 0$ and $k_2 = -\lambda_2 < 0$ are the decay constants for substances X and Y, respectively, and Z is a stable element. Suppose, too, that $x(t)$, $y(t)$, and $z(t)$ denote amounts of substances X, Y, and Z, respectively, remaining at time t. The decay of element X is described by

$$\frac{dx}{dt} = -\lambda_1 x,$$

whereas the rate at which the second element Y decays is the net rate

$$\frac{dy}{dt} = \lambda_1 x - \lambda_2 y,$$

since Y is *gaining* atoms from the decay of X and at the same time *losing* atoms because of its own decay. Since Z is a stable element, it is simply gaining atoms from the decay of element Y:

$$\frac{dz}{dt} = \lambda_2 y.$$

In other words, a model of the radioactive decay series for three elements is the linear system of three first-order differential equations

$$\frac{dx}{dt} = -\lambda_1 x$$

$$\frac{dy}{dt} = \lambda_1 x - \lambda_2 y \tag{2}$$

$$\frac{dz}{dt} = \lambda_2 y.$$

MIXTURES Consider the two tanks shown in Figure 3.3.1. Let us suppose for the sake of discussion that tank A contains 50 gallons of water in which 25 pounds of salt is dissolved. Suppose tank B contains 50 gallons of pure water. Liquid is pumped into and out of the tanks as indicated in the figure; the mixture exchanged between the two tanks and the liquid pumped out of tank B are assumed to be well stirred.

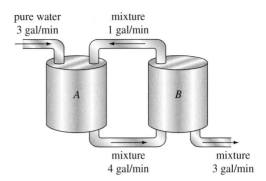

pure water
3 gal/min

mixture
1 gal/min

mixture
4 gal/min

mixture
3 gal/min

FIGURE 3.3.1   Connected mixing tanks

We wish to construct a mathematical model that describes the number of pounds $x_1(t)$ and $x_2(t)$ of salt in tanks A and B, respectively, at time t.

By an analysis similar to that on page 23 in Section 1.3 and Example 5 of Section 3.1 we see that the net rate of change of $x_1(t)$ for tank A is

$$\frac{dx_1}{dt} = \overbrace{(3 \text{ gal/min}) \cdot (0 \text{ lb/gal}) + (1 \text{ gal/min}) \cdot \left(\frac{x_2}{50} \text{ lb/gal}\right)}^{\substack{\text{input rate} \\ \text{of salt}}} - \overbrace{(4 \text{ gal/min}) \cdot \left(\frac{x_1}{50} \text{ lb/gal}\right)}^{\substack{\text{output rate} \\ \text{of salt}}}$$

$$= -\frac{2}{25} x_1 + \frac{1}{50} x_2.$$

Similarly, for tank B the net rate of change of $x_2(t)$ is

$$\frac{dx_2}{dt} = 4 \cdot \frac{x_1}{50} - 3 \cdot \frac{x_2}{50} - 1 \cdot \frac{x_2}{50}$$

$$= \frac{2}{25} x_1 - \frac{2}{25} x_2.$$

Thus we obtain the linear system

$$\begin{aligned} \frac{dx_1}{dt} &= -\frac{2}{25} x_1 + \frac{1}{50} x_2 \\ \frac{dx_2}{dt} &= \frac{2}{25} x_1 - \frac{2}{25} x_2. \end{aligned} \tag{3}$$

Observe that the foregoing system is accompanied by the initial conditions $x_1(0) = 25$, $x_2(0) = 0$.

A PREDATOR-PREY MODEL   Suppose that two different species of animals interact within the same environment or ecosystem, and suppose further that the first species eats only vegetation and the second eats only the first species. In other words, one species is a predator and the other is a prey. For example, wolves hunt grass-eating caribou, sharks devour little fish, and the snowy owl pursues an arctic rodent called the lemming. For the sake of discussion, let us imagine that the predators are foxes and the prey are rabbits.

Let $x(t)$ and $y(t)$ denote the fox and rabbit populations, respectively, at time t. If there were no rabbits, then one might expect that the foxes, lacking an adequate food supply, would decline in number according to

$$\frac{dx}{dt} = -ax, \qquad a > 0. \tag{4}$$

When rabbits are present in the environment, however, it seems reasonable that the number of encounters or interactions between these two species per unit time is jointly proportional to their populations x and y—that is, proportional to the product xy. Thus when rabbits are present, there is a supply of food, so foxes are added to the system at a rate bxy, $b > 0$. Adding this last rate to (4) gives a model for the fox population:

$$\frac{dx}{dt} = -ax + bxy. \tag{5}$$

On the other hand, if there were no foxes, then the rabbits would, with an added assumption of unlimited food supply, grow at a rate that is proportional to the number of rabbits present at time t:

$$\frac{dy}{dt} = dy, \qquad d > 0. \tag{6}$$

But when foxes are present, a model for the rabbit population is (6) decreased by cxy, $c > 0$—that is, decreased by the rate at which the rabbits are eaten during their encounters with the foxes:

$$\frac{dy}{dt} = dy - cxy. \tag{7}$$

Equations (5) and (7) constitute a system of nonlinear differential equations

$$\frac{dx}{dt} = -ax + bxy = x(-a + by)$$
$$\frac{dy}{dt} = dy - cxy = y(d - cx), \tag{8}$$

where a, b, c, and d are positive constants. This famous system of equations is known as the **Lotka-Volterra predator-prey model.**

Except for two constant solutions, $x(t) = 0$, $y(t) = 0$ and $x(t) = d/c$, $y(t) = a/b$, the nonlinear system (8) cannot be solved in terms of elementary functions. However, we can analyze such systems quantitatively and qualitatively. See Chapter 9, "Numerical Solutions of Ordinary Differential Equations," and Chapter 10, "Plane Autonomous Systems."*

EXAMPLE 1   Predator-Prey Model

Suppose

$$\frac{dx}{dt} = -0.16x + 0.08xy$$

$$\frac{dy}{dt} = 4.5y - 0.9xy$$

represents a predator-prey model. Because we are dealing with populations, we have $x(t) \geq 0$, $y(t) \geq 0$. Figure 3.3.2, obtained with the aid of a numerical solver, shows typical population curves of the predators and prey for this model superimposed on the same coordinate axes. The initial conditions used were $x(0) = 4$, $y(0) = 4$. The curve in red represents the population $x(t)$ of the predators (foxes), and the blue curve is the population $y(t)$ of the prey (rabbits). Observe that the model seems to predict that both populations $x(t)$ and $y(t)$ are periodic in time. This makes intuitive sense because as the number of prey decreases, the predator population eventually decreases because of a diminished food supply; but attendant to a decrease in the number of predators is an increase in the number of prey; this in turn gives rise to an increased number of predators, which ultimately brings about another decrease in the number of prey. ∎

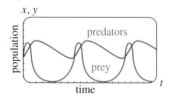

FIGURE 3.3.2 Populations of predators (red) and prey (blue) appear to be periodic

---

*Chapters 10–15 are in the expanded version of this text, *Differential Equations with Boundary-Value Problems.*

COMPETITION MODELS Now suppose two different species of animals occupy the same ecosystem, not as predator and prey but rather as competitors for the same resources (such as food and living space) in the system. In the absence of the other, let us assume that the rate at which each population grows is given by

$$\frac{dx}{dt} = ax \quad \text{and} \quad \frac{dy}{dt} = cy, \tag{9}$$

respectively.

Since the two species compete, another assumption might be that each of these rates is diminished simply by the influence, or existence, of the other population. Thus a model for the two populations is given by the linear system

$$\frac{dx}{dt} = ax - by$$
$$\frac{dy}{dt} = cy - dx, \tag{10}$$

where a, b, c, and d are positive constants.

On the other hand, we might assume, as we did in (5), that each growth rate in (9) should be reduced by a rate proportional to the number of interactions between the two species:

$$\frac{dx}{dt} = ax - bxy$$
$$\frac{dy}{dt} = cy - dxy. \tag{11}$$

Inspection shows that this nonlinear system is similar to the Lotka-Volterra predator-prey model. Finally, it might be more realistic to replace the rates in (9), which indicate that the population of each species in isolation grows exponentially, with rates indicating that each population grows logistically (that is, over a long time the population is bounded):

$$\frac{dx}{dt} = a_1 x - b_1 x^2 \quad \text{and} \quad \frac{dy}{dt} = a_2 y - b_2 y^2. \tag{12}$$

When these new rates are decreased by rates proportional to the number of interactions, we obtain another nonlinear model:

$$\frac{dx}{dt} = a_1 x - b_1 x^2 - c_1 xy = x(a_1 - b_1 x - c_1 y)$$
$$\frac{dy}{dt} = a_2 y - b_2 y^2 - c_2 xy = y(a_2 - b_2 y - c_2 x), \tag{13}$$

where all coefficients are positive. The linear system (10) and the nonlinear systems (11) and (13) are, of course, called **competition models.**

NETWORKS An electrical network having more than one loop also gives rise to simultaneous differential equations. As shown in Figure 3.3.3, the current $i_1(t)$ splits in the directions shown at point B_1, called a *branch point* of the network. By **Kirchhoff's first law** we can write

$$i_1(t) = i_2(t) + i_3(t). \tag{14}$$

We can also apply **Kirchhoff's second law** to each loop. For loop $A_1 B_1 B_2 A_2 A_1$, summing the voltage drops across each part of the loop gives

$$E(t) = i_1 R_1 + L_1 \frac{di_2}{dt} + i_2 R_2. \tag{15}$$

Similarly, for loop $A_1 B_1 C_1 C_2 B_2 A_2 A_1$ we find

$$E(t) = i_1 R_1 + L_2 \frac{di_3}{dt}. \tag{16}$$

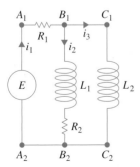

FIGURE 3.3.3 Network whose model is given in (17)

Using (14) to eliminate i_1 in (15) and (16) yields two linear first-order equations for the currents $i_2(t)$ and $i_3(t)$:

$$L_1\frac{di_2}{dt} + (R_1 + R_2)i_2 + R_1i_3 = E(t)$$

$$L_2\frac{di_3}{dt} + \qquad R_1i_2 + R_1i_3 = E(t). \tag{17}$$

We leave it as an exercise (see Problem 14) to show that the system of differential equations describing the currents $i_1(t)$ and $i_2(t)$ in the network containing a resistor, an inductor, and a capacitor shown in Figure 3.3.4 is

$$L\frac{di_1}{dt} + Ri_2 = E(t)$$

$$RC\frac{di_2}{dt} + i_2 - i_1 = 0. \tag{18}$$

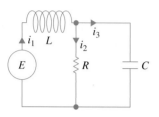

FIGURE 3.3.4 Network whose model is given in (18)

EXERCISES 3.3

Answers to selected odd-numbered problems begin on page ANS-4.

Radioactive Series

1. We have not discussed methods by which systems of first-order differential equations can be solved. Nevertheless, systems such as (2) can be solved with no knowledge other than how to solve a single linear first-order equation. Find a solution of (2) subject to the initial conditions $x(0) = x_0$, $y(0) = 0$, $z(0) = 0$.

2. In Problem 1 suppose that time is measured in days, that the decay constants are $k_1 = -0.138629$ and $k_2 = -0.004951$, and that $x_0 = 20$. Use a graphing utility to obtain the graphs of the solutions $x(t)$, $y(t)$, and $z(t)$ on the same set of coordinate axes. Use the graphs to approximate the half-lives of substances X and Y.

3. Use the graphs in Problem 2 to approximate the times when the amounts $x(t)$ and $y(t)$ are the same, the times when the amounts $x(t)$ and $z(t)$ are the same, and the times when the amounts $y(t)$ and $z(t)$ are the same. Why does the time that is determined when the amounts $y(t)$ and $z(t)$ are the same make intuitive sense?

4. Construct a mathematical model for a radioactive series of four elements W, X, Y, and Z, where Z is a stable element.

Mixtures

5. Consider two tanks A and B, with liquid being pumped in and out at the same rates, as described by the system of equations (3). What is the system of differential equations if, instead of pure water, a brine solution containing 2 pounds of salt per gallon is pumped into tank A?

6. Use the information given in Figure 3.3.5 to construct a mathematical model for the number of pounds of salt $x_1(t)$, $x_2(t)$, and $x_3(t)$ at time t in tanks A, B, and C, respectively.

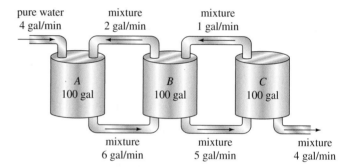

FIGURE 3.3.5 Mixing tanks in Problem 6

7. Two very large tanks A and B are each partially filled with 100 gallons of brine. Initially, 100 pounds of salt is dissolved in the solution in tank A and 50 pounds of salt is dissolved in the solution in tank B. The system is closed in that the well-stirred liquid is pumped only between the tanks, as shown in Figure 3.3.6.

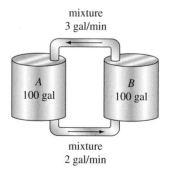

FIGURE 3.3.6 Mixing tanks in Problem 7

(a) Use the information given in the figure to construct a mathematical model for the number of pounds of salt $x_1(t)$ and $x_2(t)$ at time t in tanks A and B, respectively.

(b) Find a relationship between the variables $x_1(t)$ and $x_2(t)$ that holds at time t. Explain why this relationship makes intuitive sense. Use this relationship to help find the amount of salt in tank B at $t = 30$ min.

8. Three large tanks contain brine, as shown in Figure 3.3.7. Use the information in the figure to construct a mathematical model for the number of pounds of salt $x_1(t)$, $x_2(t)$, and $x_3(t)$ at time t in tanks A, B, and C, respectively. Without solving the system, predict limiting values of $x_1(t)$, $x_2(t)$, and $x_3(t)$ as $t \to \infty$.

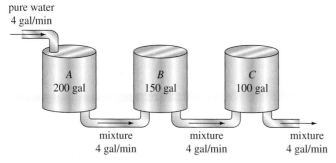

FIGURE 3.3.7 Mixing tanks in Problem 8

Predator-Prey Models

9. Consider the Lotka-Volterra predator-prey model defined by

$$\frac{dx}{dt} = -0.1x + 0.02xy$$

$$\frac{dy}{dt} = 0.2y - 0.025xy,$$

where the populations $x(t)$ (predators) and $y(t)$ (prey) are measured in thousands. Suppose $x(0) = 6$ and $y(0) = 6$. Use a numerical solver to graph $x(t)$ and $y(t)$. Use the graphs to approximate the time $t > 0$ when the two populations are first equal. Use the graphs to approximate the period of each population.

Competition Models

10. Consider the competition model defined by

$$\frac{dx}{dt} = x(2 - 0.4x - 0.3y)$$

$$\frac{dy}{dt} = y(1 - 0.1y - 0.3x),$$

where the populations $x(t)$ and $y(t)$ are measured in thousands and t in years. Use a numerical solver to analyze the populations over a long period of time for each of the following cases:
(a) $x(0) = 1.5, \quad y(0) = 3.5$
(b) $x(0) = 1, \quad y(0) = 1$
(c) $x(0) = 2, \quad y(0) = 7$
(d) $x(0) = 4.5, \quad y(0) = 0.5$

11. Consider the competition model defined by

$$\frac{dx}{dt} = x(1 - 0.1x - 0.05y)$$

$$\frac{dy}{dt} = y(1.7 - 0.1y - 0.15x),$$

where the populations $x(t)$ and $y(t)$ are measured in thousands and t in years. Use a numerical solver to analyze the populations over a long period of time for each of the following cases:
(a) $x(0) = 1, \quad y(0) = 1$
(b) $x(0) = 4, \quad y(0) = 10$
(c) $x(0) = 9, \quad y(0) = 4$
(d) $x(0) = 5.5, \quad y(0) = 3.5$

Networks

12. Show that a system of differential equations that describes the currents $i_2(t)$ and $i_3(t)$ in the electrical network shown in Figure 3.3.8 is

$$L\frac{di_2}{dt} + L\frac{di_3}{dt} + R_1 i_2 = E(t)$$

$$-R_1\frac{di_2}{dt} + R_2\frac{di_3}{dt} + \frac{1}{C}i_3 = 0.$$

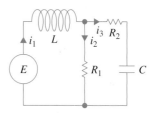

FIGURE 3.3.8 Network in Problem 12

13. Determine a system of first-order differential equations that describes the currents $i_2(t)$ and $i_3(t)$ in the electrical network shown in Figure 3.3.9.

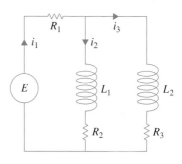

FIGURE 3.3.9 Network in Problem 13

14. Show that the linear system given in (18) describes the currents $i_1(t)$ and $i_2(t)$ in the network shown in Figure 3.3.4. [*Hint*: $dq/dt = i_3$.]

Additional Nonlinear Models

15. SIR Model A communicable disease is spread throughout a small community, with a fixed population of n people, by contact between infected individuals and people who are susceptible to the disease. Suppose that everyone is initially susceptible to the disease and that no one leaves the community while the epidemic is spreading. At time t, let $s(t)$, $i(t)$, and $r(t)$ denote, in turn, the number of people in the community (measured in hundreds) who are *susceptible* to the disease but not yet infected with it, the number of people who are *infected* with the disease, and the number of people who have *recovered* from the disease. Explain why the system of differential equations

$$\frac{ds}{dt} = -k_1 s i$$

$$\frac{di}{dt} = -k_2 i + k_1 s i$$

$$\frac{dr}{dt} = k_2 i,$$

where k_1 (called the *infection rate*) and k_2 (called the *removal rate*) are positive constants, is a reasonable mathematical model, commonly called a **SIR model**, for the spread of the epidemic throughout the community. Give plausible initial conditions associated with this system of equations.

16. (a) In Problem 15, explain why it is sufficient to analyze only

$$\frac{ds}{dt} = -k_1 s i$$

$$\frac{di}{dt} = -k_2 i + k_1 s i.$$

(b) Suppose $k_1 = 0.2$, $k_2 = 0.7$, and $n = 10$. Choose various values of $i(0) = i_0$, $0 < i_0 < 10$. Use a numerical solver to determine what the model predicts about the epidemic in the two cases $s_0 > k_2/k_1$ and $s_0 \leq k_2/k_1$. In the case of an epidemic, estimate the number of people who are eventually infected.

Project Problems

17. Concentration of a Nutrient Suppose compartments A and B shown in Figure 3.3.10 are filled with fluids and are separated by a permeable membrane. The figure is a compartmental representation of the exterior and interior of a cell. Suppose, too, that a nutrient necessary for cell growth passes through the membrane. A model for the concentrations $x(t)$ and $y(t)$ of the nutrient in compartments A and B, respectively, at time t is given by the linear system of differential equations

$$\frac{dx}{dt} = \frac{\kappa}{V_A}(y - x)$$

$$\frac{dy}{dt} = \frac{\kappa}{V_B}(x - y),$$

where V_A and V_B are the volumes of the compartments, and $\kappa > 0$ is a permeability factor. Let $x(0) = x_0$ and $y(0) = y_0$ denote the initial concentrations of the nutrient. Solely on the basis of the equations in the system and the assumption $x_0 > y_0 > 0$, sketch, on the same set of coordinate axes, possible solution curves of the system. Explain your reasoning. Discuss the behavior of the solutions over a long period of time.

18. The system in Problem 17, like the system in (2), can be solved with no advanced knowledge. Solve for $x(t)$ and $y(t)$ and compare their graphs with your sketches in Problem 17. Determine the limiting values of $x(t)$ and $y(t)$ as $t \rightarrow \infty$. Explain why the answer to the last question makes intuitive sense.

19. Solely on the basis of the physical description of the mixture problem on page 107 and in Figure 3.3.1, discuss the nature of the functions $x_1(t)$ and $x_2(t)$. What is the behavior of each function over a long period of time? Sketch possible graphs of $x_1(t)$ and $x_2(t)$. Check your conjectures by using a numerical solver to obtain numerical solution curves of (3) subject to the initial conditions $x_1(0) = 25$, $x_2(0) = 0$.

20. Newton's Law of Cooling/Warming As shown in Figure 3.3.11, a small metal bar is placed inside container A, and container A then is placed within a much larger container B. As the metal bar cools, the ambient temperature $T_A(t)$ of the medium within container A changes according to Newton's law of cooling. As container A cools, the temperature of the medium inside container B does not change significantly and can be considered to be a constant T_B. Construct a mathematical

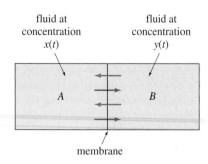

fluid at concentration $x(t)$ fluid at concentration $y(t)$

A B

membrane

FIGURE 3.3.10 Nutrient flow through a membrane in Problem 17

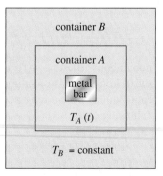

container B

container A

metal bar

$T_A(t)$

T_B = constant

FIGURE 3.3.11 Container within a container in Problem 20

model for the temperatures $T(t)$ and $T_A(t)$, where $T(t)$ is the temperature of the metal bar inside container A. As in Problems 1 and 18, this model can be solved by using prior knowledge. Find a solution of the system subject to the initial conditions $T(0) = T_0$, $T_A(0) = T_1$.

Contributed Problem

Michael Prophet, Ph.D
Doug Shaw, Ph.D
Associate Professors
Mathematics Department
University of Northern Iowa

21. A Mixing Problem A pair of tanks are connected as shown in Figure 3.3.12. At $t = 0$, tank A contains 500 liters of liquid, 200 of which are ethanol, and tank B contains 100 liters of liquid, 7 of which are ethanol. Beginning at $t = 0$, 3 liters of 20% ethanol solution are added per minute. An additional 2 L/min are pumped from tank B back into tank A. The result is continuously mixed, and 5 L/min are pumped into tank B. The contents of tank B are also continuously mixed. In addition to the 2 liters that are returned to tank A, 3 L/min are discharged from the system. Let $P(t)$ and $Q(t)$ denote the number of liters of ethanol in tanks A and B at time t. We wish to find $P(t)$. Using the principle that

rate of change = input rate of ethanol − output rate of ethanol,

we obtain the system of first-order differential equations

$$\frac{dP}{dt} = 3(0.2) + 2\left(\frac{Q}{100}\right) - 5\left(\frac{P}{500}\right) = 0.6 + \frac{Q}{50} - \frac{P}{100} \quad (19)$$

$$\frac{dQ}{dt} = 5\left(\frac{P}{500}\right) - 5\left(\frac{Q}{100}\right) = \frac{P}{100} - \frac{Q}{20}. \quad (20)$$

(a) Qualitatively discuss the behavior of the system. What is happening in the short term? What happens in the long term?

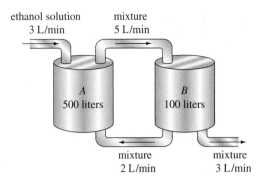

ethanol solution
3 L/min

mixture
5 L/min

A
500 liters

B
100 liters

mixture
2 L/min

mixture
3 L/min

FIGURE 3.3.12 Mixing tanks in Problem 21

(b) We now attempt to solve this system. When (19) is differentiated with respect to t, we obtain

$$\frac{d^2P}{dt^2} = \frac{1}{50}\frac{dQ}{dt} - \frac{1}{100}\frac{dP}{dt}.$$

Substitute (20) into this equation and simplify.

(c) Show that when we solve (19) for Q and substitute it into our answer in part (b), we obtain

$$100\frac{d^2P}{dt^2} + 6\frac{dP}{dt} + \frac{3}{100}P = 3.$$

(d) We are given that $P(0) = 200$. Show that $P'(0) = -\frac{63}{50}$. Then solve the differential equation in part (c) subject to these initial conditions.

(e) Substitute the solution of part (d) back into (19) and solve for $Q(t)$.

(f) What happens to $P(t)$ and $Q(t)$ as $t \to \infty$?

CHAPTER 3 IN REVIEW

Answers to selected odd-numbered problems begin on page ANS-4.

Answer Problems 1 and 2 without referring back to the text. Fill in the blank or answer true or false.

1. If $P(t) = P_0 e^{0.15t}$ gives the population in an environment at time t, then a differential equation satisfied by $P(t)$ is _____.

2. If the rate of decay of a radioactive substance is proportional to the amount $A(t)$ remaining at time t, then the half-life of the substance is necessarily $T = -(\ln 2)/k$. The rate of decay of the substance at time $t = T$ is one-half the rate of decay at $t = 0$. _____

3. In March 1976 the world population reached 4 billion. At that time, a popular news magazine predicted that with an average yearly growth rate of 1.8%, the world population would be 8 billion in 45 years. How does this value compare with the value predicted by the model

that assumes that the rate of increase in population is proportional to the population present at time t?

4. Air containing 0.06% carbon dioxide is pumped into a room whose volume is 8000 ft³. The air is pumped in at a rate of 2000 ft³/min, and the circulated air is then pumped out at the same rate. If there is an initial concentration of 0.2% carbon dioxide in the room, determine the subsequent amount in the room at time t. What is the concentration of carbon dioxide at 10 minutes? What is the steady-state, or equilibrium, concentration of carbon dioxide?

5. Solve the differential equation

$$\frac{dy}{dx} = -\frac{y}{\sqrt{s^2 - y^2}}$$

of the tractrix. See Problem 26 in Exercises 1.3. Assume that the initial point on the y-axis in $(0, 10)$ and that the length of the rope is $x = 10$ ft.

6. Suppose a cell is suspended in a solution containing a solute of constant concentration C_s. Suppose further that the cell has constant volume V and that the area of its permeable membrane is the constant A. By **Fick's law** the rate of change of its mass m is directly proportional to the area A and the difference $C_s - C(t)$, where $C(t)$ is the concentration of the solute inside the cell at time t. Find $C(t)$ if $m = V \cdot C(t)$ and $C(0) = C_0$. See Figure 3.R.1.

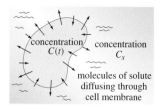

FIGURE 3.R.1 Cell in Problem 6

7. Suppose that as a body cools, the temperature of the surrounding medium increases because it completely absorbs the heat being lost by the body. Let $T(t)$ and $T_m(t)$ be the temperatures of the body and the medium at time t, respectively. If the initial temperature of the body is T_1 and the initial temperature of the medium is T_2, then it can be shown in this case that Newton's law of cooling is $dT/dt = k(T - T_m)$, $k < 0$, where $T_m = T_2 + B(T_1 - T)$, $B > 0$ is a constant.

   (a) The foregoing DE is autonomous. Use the phase portrait concept of Section 2.1 to determine the limiting value of the temperature $T(t)$ as $t \to \infty$. What is the limiting value of $T_m(t)$ as $t \to \infty$?

   (b) Verify your answers in part (a) by actually solving the differential equation.

   (c) Discuss a physical interpretation of your answers in part (a).

8. According to **Stefan's law of radiation** the absolute temperature T of a body cooling in a medium at constant absolute temperature T_m is given by

$$\frac{dT}{dt} = k(T^4 - T_m^4),$$

where k is a constant. Stefan's law can be used over a greater temperature range than Newton's law of cooling.

   (a) Solve the differential equation.

   (b) Show that when $T - T_m$ is small in comparison to T_m then Newton's law of cooling approximates Stefan's law. [*Hint*: Think binomial series of the right-hand side of the DE.]

9. An *LR* series circuit has a variable inductor with the inductance defined by

$$L(t) = \begin{cases} 1 - \dfrac{1}{10}t, & 0 \le t < 10 \\ 0, & t \ge 10. \end{cases}$$

Find the current $i(t)$ if the resistance is 0.2 ohm, the impressed voltage is $E(t) = 4$, and $i(0) = 0$. Graph $i(t)$.

10. A classical problem in the calculus of variations is to find the shape of a curve $\mathscr{C}$ such that a bead, under the influence of gravity, will slide from point $A(0, 0)$ to point $B(x_1, y_1)$ in the least time. See Figure 3.R.2. It can be shown that a nonlinear differential for the shape $y(x)$ of the path is $y[1 + (y')^2] = k$, where k is a constant. First solve for dx in terms of y and dy, and then use the substitution $y = k \sin^2\theta$ to obtain a parametric form of the solution. The curve $\mathscr{C}$ turns out to be a cycloid.

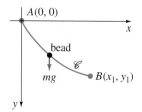

FIGURE 3.R.2 Sliding bead in Problem 10

11. A model for the populations of two interacting species of animals is

$$\frac{dx}{dt} = k_1 x(\alpha - x)$$

$$\frac{dy}{dt} = k_2 xy.$$

Solve for x and y in terms of t.

12. Initially, two large tanks A and B each hold 100 gallons of brine. The well-stirred liquid is pumped between the tanks as shown in Figure 3.R.3. Use the information given in the figure to construct a mathematical model for the number of pounds of salt $x_1(t)$ and $x_2(t)$ at time t in tanks A and B, respectively.

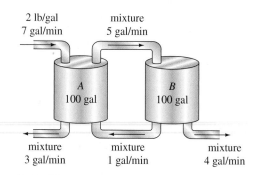

FIGURE 3.R.3 Mixing tanks in Problem 12

When all the curves in a family $G(x, y, c_1) = 0$ intersect orthogonally all the curves in another family $H(x, y, c_2) = 0$, the families are said to be **orthogonal trajectories** of each other. See Figure 3.R.4. If $dy/dx = f(x, y)$ is the differential equation of one family, then the differential equation for the orthogonal trajectories of this family is $dy/dx = -1/f(x, y)$. In Problems 13 and 14 find the differential equation of the given family. Find the orthogonal trajectories of this family. Use a graphing utility to graph both families on the same set of coordinate axes.

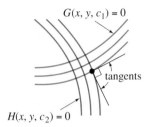

FIGURE 3.R.4 Orthogonal trajectories

13. $y = -x - 1 + c_1 e^x$ **14.** $y = \dfrac{1}{x + c_1}$

Contributed Problem

David Zeigler
Assistant Professor
Department of Mathematics and Statistics
CSU Sacramento

15. Aquifers and Darcy's Law According to the Sacramento, California, Department of Utilities, approximately 15% of the water source for Sacramento comes from **aquifers.** Unlike water sources such as rivers or lakes that lie above ground, an aquifer is an underground layer of a porous material that contains water. The water may reside in the void spaces between rocks or in the cracks of the rocks. Because of the material lying above, the water is subjected to pressure that drives the fluid motion.

Darcy's law is a generalized relationship to describe the flow of a fluid through a porous medium. It shows the flow rate of a fluid through a container as a function of the cross sectional area, elevation and fluid pressure. The configuration that we will consider in this problem is what is called a *one-dimensional flow problem.* Consider the flow column as shown in Figure 3.R.5. As indicated by the arrows, the fluid flow is from left to right through a container with a circular cross section. The container is filled with a porous material (for example, pebbles, sand, or cotton) that allows for the fluid to flow. At the entrance and the exit of the container are piezometers that measure the hydraulic head, that is, the water pressure per unit weight, by reporting the height of the water column. The difference in the water heights in the pizeometers is denoted Δh. For this configuration Darcy experimentally calculated that

$$Q = AK \frac{\Delta h}{L}$$

where length is measured in meters (m) and time in seconds (s):

Q = volumetric flow rate (m³/s)
A = cross-sectional flow area, perpendicular to the flow direction (m²)
K = hydraulic conductivity (m/s)
L = flow path length (m)
Δh = hydraulic head difference (m).

Since the hydraulic head at a specific point is the sum of the pressure head and the elevation, the flow rate can be rewritten as

$$Q = AK \frac{\Delta \left[\dfrac{p}{\rho g} + y \right]}{L},$$

where

p = water pressure (N/m²)
ρ = water density (kg/m³)
g = gravitational acceleration (m/s²)
y = elevation (m).

A more general form of the equation results when the limit of Δh with respect to the flow direction (x as shown in Figure 3.R.5) is evaluated as the flow path length $L \to 0$. Performing this calculation yields

$$Q = -AK \frac{d}{dx} \left[\frac{p}{\rho g} + y \right],$$

where the sign change reflects the fact that the hydraulic head always decreases in the direction of flow. The volumetric flow per unit area is called the **Darcy flux q** and is defined by the differential equation

$$q = \frac{Q}{A} = -K \frac{d}{dx} \left[\frac{p}{\rho g} + y \right], \qquad (1)$$

where q is measured in m/s.

(a) Assume that the fluid density ρ and the Darcy flux q are functions of x. Solve (1) for the pressure p. You may assume that K and g are constants.

(b) Suppose the Darcy flux is negatively valued, that is, $q < 0$. What does this say about the ratio p/ρ? Specifically, is the ratio between the pressure and the density increasing or decreasing with respect to x? Assume that the elevation y of the cylinder is fixed. What can be said about the ratio p/ρ if the Darcy flux is zero?

(c) Assume that the fluid density ρ is constant. Solve (1) for the pressure $p(x)$ when the Darcy flux is proportional to the pressure, that is, $q = \alpha p$, where α is a constant of proportionality. Sketch the family of solutions for the pressure.

(d) Now if we assume that the pressure p is constant but the density ρ is a function of x, then Darcy flux is a function of x. Solve (1) for the density $\rho(x)$.

Solve (1) for the density $\rho(x)$ when the Darcy flux is proportional to the density, $q = \beta\rho$, where β is a constant of proportionality.

(e) Assume that the Darcy flux is $q(x) = \sin e^{-x}$ and the density function is

$$\rho(x) = \frac{1}{1 + \ln(2 + x)}.$$

Use a CAS to plot the pressure $p(x)$ over the interval $0 \le x \le 2\pi$. Suppose that $K/g = -1$ and that the pressure at the left end point $(x = 0)$ is normalized to 1. Assume that the elevation y is constant. Explain the physical implications of your result.

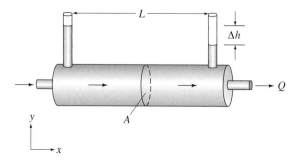

FIGURE 3.R.5 Flow in Problem 15

Contributed Problem

Michael Prophet, Ph.D
Doug Shaw, Ph.D
Associate Professors
Mathematics Department
University of Northern Iowa

16. Population Growth Models We can use direction fields to obtain a great deal of information about population growth models. In this problem you can create direction fields by hand or use a computer algebra system to create detailed ones. At time $t = 0$ a thin sheet of water begins pouring over the concrete spillway of a dam. At the same time, 1000 algae are attached to the spillway. We will be modeling $P(t)$, the number of algae (in thousands) present after t hours.

Exponential Growth Model: We assume that the rate of population change is proportional to the population present: $dP/dt = kP$. In this particular case take $k = \frac{1}{12}$.

(a) Create a direction field for this differential equation and sketch the solution curve.

(b) Solve this differential equation and graph the solution. Compare your graph to the sketch from part (a).

(c) Describe the equilibrium solutions of this autonomous differential equation.

(d) According to this model, what happens as $t \to \infty$?

(e) In our model, $P(0) = 1$. Describe how a change in $P(0)$ would affect the solution.

(f) Consider the solution corresponding to $P(0) = 0$. How would a small change in $P(0)$ affect that solution?

Logistic Growth Model: As you saw in part (d), the exponential growth model above becomes unrealistic for very large t. What limits the algae population? Assume that the water flow provides a steady source of nutrients and carries away all waste materials. In that case the major limiting factor is the area of the spillway. We might model this as follows: Each algae-algae interaction stresses the organisms involved. This causes additional mortality. The number of such possible interactions is proportional to the *square* of the number of organisms present. Thus a reasonable model would be

$$\frac{dP}{dt} = kP - mP^2,$$

where k and m are positive constants. In this particular case take $k = \frac{1}{12}$ and $m = \frac{1}{500}$.

(g) Create a direction field for this differential equation and sketch the solution curve.

(h) Solve this differential equation and graph the solution. Compare your graph to the sketch from part (g).

(i) Describe the equilibrium solutions of this autonomous differential equation.

(j) According to this model, what happens as $t \to \infty$?

(k) In our model, $P(0) = 1$. Describe how a change in $P(0)$ would affect the solution.

(l) Consider the solution corresponding to $P(0) = 0$. How would a small change in $P(0)$ affect that solution?

(m) Consider the solution corresponding to $P(0) = k/m$. How would a small change in $P(0)$ affect that solution?

A Nonautonomous Model: Suppose that the flow of water across the spillway is decreasing in time, so the prime algae habitat also shrinks in time. This would increase the effect of crowding. A reasonable model now would be

$$\frac{dP}{dt} = kP - m(1 + nt)P^2,$$

where n would be determined by the rate at which the spillway is drying. In our example, take k and m as above and $n = \frac{1}{10}$.

(n) Create a direction field for this differential equation and sketch the solution curve.

(o) Describe the constant solutions of this nonautonomous differential equation.

(p) According to this model, what happens as $t \to \infty$? What happens if you change the value of $P(0)$?

4 HIGHER-ORDER DIFFERENTIAL EQUATIONS

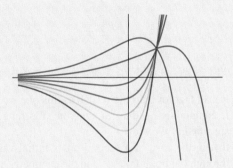

We turn now to the solution of ordinary differential equations of order two or higher. In the first seven sections of this chapter we examine the underlying theory and solution methods for certain kinds of *linear* equations. The elimination method for solving systems of linear equations is introduced in Section 4.8 because this method simply uncouples a system into individual linear equations in each dependent variable. The chapter concludes with a brief examinations of *nonlinear* higher-order equations.

| 4.1 | PRELIMINARY THEORY—LINEAR EQUATIONS |

REVIEW MATERIAL

- Reread the *Remarks* at the end of Section 1.1
- Section 2.3 (especially pages 54–58)

INTRODUCTION In Chapter 2 we saw that we could solve a few first-order differential equations by recognizing them as separable, linear, exact, homogeneous, or perhaps Bernoulli equations. Even though the solutions of these equations were in the form of a one-parameter family, this family, with one exception, did not represent the general solution of the differential equation. Only in the case of *linear* first-order differential equations were we able to obtain general solutions, by paying attention to certain continuity conditions imposed on the coefficients. Recall that a **general solution** is a family of solutions defined on some interval *I* that contains *all* solutions of the DE that are defined on *I*. Because our primary goal in this chapter is to find general solutions of linear higher-order DEs, we first need to examine some of the theory of linear equations.

4.1.1 INITIAL-VALUE AND BOUNDARY-VALUE PROBLEMS

INITIAL-VALUE PROBLEM In Section 1.2 we defined an initial-value problem for a general *n*th-order differential equation. For a linear differential equation an **nth-order initial-value problem** is

$$\textit{Solve:} \qquad a_n(x)\frac{d^n y}{dx^n} + a_{n-1}(x)\frac{d^{n-1}y}{dx^{n-1}} + \cdots + a_1(x)\frac{dy}{dx} + a_0(x)y = g(x) \qquad (1)$$

$$\textit{Subject to:} \qquad y(x_0) = y_0, \quad y'(x_0) = y_1, \ldots, \quad y^{(n-1)}(x_0) = y_{n-1}.$$

Recall that for a problem such as this one we seek a function defined on some interval *I*, containing x_0, that satisfies the differential equation and the *n* initial conditions specified at x_0: $y(x_0) = y_0, y'(x_0) = y_1, \ldots, y^{(n-1)}(x_0) = y_{n-1}$. We have already seen that in the case of a second-order initial-value problem a solution curve must pass through the point (x_0, y_0) and have slope y_1 at this point.

EXISTENCE AND UNIQUENESS In Section 1.2 we stated a theorem that gave conditions under which the existence and uniqueness of a solution of a first-order initial-value problem were guaranteed. The theorem that follows gives sufficient conditions for the existence of a unique solution of the problem in (1).

THEOREM 4.1.1 **Existence of a Unique Solution**

Let $a_n(x), a_{n-1}(x), \ldots, a_1(x), a_0(x)$ and $g(x)$ be continuous on an interval *I* and let $a_n(x) \neq 0$ for every *x* in this interval. If $x = x_0$ is any point in this interval, then a solution $y(x)$ of the initial-value problem (1) exists on the interval and is unique.

EXAMPLE 1 **Unique Solution of an IVP**

The initial-value problem

$$3y''' + 5y'' - y' + 7y = 0, \quad y(1) = 0, \quad y'(1) = 0, \quad y''(1) = 0$$

possesses the trivial solution $y = 0$. Because the third-order equation is linear with constant coefficients, it follows that all the conditions of Theorem 4.1.1 are fulfilled. Hence $y = 0$ is the *only* solution on any interval containing $x = 1$. ∎

EXAMPLE 2   Unique Solution of an IVP

You should verify that the function $y = 3e^{2x} + e^{-2x} - 3x$ is a solution of the initial-value problem

$$y'' - 4y = 12x, \quad y(0) = 4, \quad y'(0) = 1.$$

Now the differential equation is linear, the coefficients as well as $g(x) = 12x$ are continuous, and $a_2(x) = 1 \neq 0$ on any interval I containing $x = 0$. We conclude from Theorem 4.1.1 that the given function is the unique solution on I. ∎

The requirements in Theorem 4.1.1 that $a_i(x)$, $i = 0, 1, 2, \ldots, n$ be continuous and $a_n(x) \neq 0$ for every x in I are both important. Specifically, if $a_n(x) = 0$ for some x in the interval, then the solution of a linear initial-value problem may not be unique or even exist. For example, you should verify that the function $y = cx^2 + x + 3$ is a solution of the initial-value problem

$$x^2 y'' - 2xy' + 2y = 6, \quad y(0) = 3, \quad y'(0) = 1$$

on the interval $(-\infty, \infty)$ for any choice of the parameter c. In other words, there is no unique solution of the problem. Although most of the conditions of Theorem 4.1.1 are satisfied, the obvious difficulties are that $a_2(x) = x^2$ is zero at $x = 0$ and that the initial conditions are also imposed at $x = 0$.

BOUNDARY-VALUE PROBLEM   Another type of problem consists of solving a linear differential equation of order two or greater in which the dependent variable y or its derivatives are specified at *different points*. A problem such as

Solve: $\quad a_2(x)\dfrac{d^2 y}{dx^2} + a_1(x)\dfrac{dy}{dx} + a_0(x)y = g(x)$

Subject to: $\quad y(a) = y_0, \quad y(b) = y_1$

is called a **boundary-value problem (BVP).** The prescribed values $y(a) = y_0$ and $y(b) = y_1$ are called **boundary conditions.** A solution of the foregoing problem is a function satisfying the differential equation on some interval I, containing a and b, whose graph passes through the two points (a, y_0) and (b, y_1). See Figure 4.1.1.

For a second-order differential equation other pairs of boundary conditions could be

$$y'(a) = y_0, \qquad y(b) = y_1$$
$$y(a) = y_0, \qquad y'(b) = y_1$$
$$y'(a) = y_0, \qquad y'(b) = y_1,$$

where y_0 and y_1 denote arbitrary constants. These three pairs of conditions are just special cases of the general boundary conditions

$$\alpha_1 y(a) + \beta_1 y'(a) = \gamma_1$$
$$\alpha_2 y(b) + \beta_2 y'(b) = \gamma_2.$$

The next example shows that even when the conditions of Theorem 4.1.1 are fulfilled, a boundary-value problem may have several solutions (as suggested in Figure 4.1.1), a unique solution, or no solution at all.

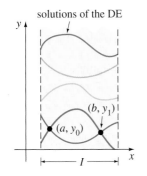

solutions of the DE

(b, y_1)

(a, y_0)

I

FIGURE 4.1.1   Solution curves of a BVP that pass through two points

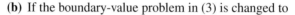

EXAMPLE 3   A BVP Can Have Many, One, or No Solutions

In Example 4 of Section 1.1 we saw that the two-parameter family of solutions of the differential equation $x'' + 16x = 0$ is

$$x = c_1 \cos 4t + c_2 \sin 4t. \tag{2}$$

(a) Suppose we now wish to determine the solution of the equation that further satisfies the boundary conditions $x(0) = 0$, $x(\pi/2) = 0$. Observe that the first condition $0 = c_1 \cos 0 + c_2 \sin 0$ implies that $c_1 = 0$, so $x = c_2 \sin 4t$. But when $t = \pi/2$, $0 = c_2 \sin 2\pi$ is satisfied for any choice of c_2, since $\sin 2\pi = 0$. Hence the boundary-value problem

$$x'' + 16x = 0, \quad x(0) = 0, \quad x\left(\frac{\pi}{2}\right) = 0 \tag{3}$$

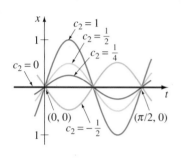

FIGURE 4.1.2 Some solution curves of (3)

has infinitely many solutions. Figure 4.1.2 shows the graphs of some of the members of the one-parameter family $x = c_2 \sin 4t$ that pass through the two points $(0, 0)$ and $(\pi/2, 0)$.

(b) If the boundary-value problem in (3) is changed to

$$x'' + 16x = 0, \quad x(0) = 0, \quad x\left(\frac{\pi}{8}\right) = 0, \tag{4}$$

then $x(0) = 0$ still requires $c_1 = 0$ in the solution (2). But applying $x(\pi/8) = 0$ to $x = c_2 \sin 4t$ demands that $0 = c_2 \sin(\pi/2) = c_2 \cdot 1$. Hence $x = 0$ is a solution of this new boundary-value problem. Indeed, it can be proved that $x = 0$ is the *only* solution of (4).

(c) Finally, if we change the problem to

$$x'' + 16x = 0, \quad x(0) = 0, \quad x\left(\frac{\pi}{2}\right) = 1, \tag{5}$$

we find again from $x(0) = 0$ that $c_1 = 0$, but applying $x(\pi/2) = 1$ to $x = c_2 \sin 4t$ leads to the contradiction $1 = c_2 \sin 2\pi = c_2 \cdot 0 = 0$. Hence the boundary-value problem (5) has no solution. ∎

4.1.2 HOMOGENEOUS EQUATIONS

A linear nth-order differential equation of the form

$$a_n(x)\frac{d^n y}{dx^n} + a_{n-1}(x)\frac{d^{n-1}y}{dx^{n-1}} + \cdots + a_1(x)\frac{dy}{dx} + a_0(x)y = 0 \tag{6}$$

is said to be **homogeneous,** whereas an equation

$$a_n(x)\frac{d^n y}{dx^n} + a_{n-1}(x)\frac{d^{n-1}y}{dx^{n-1}} + \cdots + a_1(x)\frac{dy}{dx} + a_0(x)y = g(x), \tag{7}$$

with $g(x)$ not identically zero, is said to be **nonhomogeneous.** For example, $2y'' + 3y' - 5y = 0$ is a homogeneous linear second-order differential equation, whereas $x^3 y''' + 6y' + 10y = e^x$ is a nonhomogeneous linear third-order differential equation. The word *homogeneous* in this context does not refer to coefficients that are homogeneous functions, as in Section 2.5.

We shall see that to solve a nonhomogeneous linear equation (7), we must first be able to solve the **associated homogeneous equation** (6).

To avoid needless repetition throughout the remainder of this text, we shall, as a matter of course, make the following important assumptions when stating definitions and theorems about linear equations (1). On some common interval I,

■ Please remember these two assumptions.

- the coefficient functions $a_i(x)$, $i = 0, 1, 2, \ldots, n$ and $g(x)$ are continuous;
- $a_n(x) \neq 0$ for every x in the interval.

DIFFERENTIAL OPERATORS In calculus differentiation is often denoted by the capital letter D—that is, $dy/dx = Dy$. The symbol D is called a **differential operator** because it transforms a differentiable function into another function. For example, $D(\cos 4x) = -4 \sin 4x$ and $D(5x^3 - 6x^2) = 15x^2 - 12x$. Higher-order derivatives can be expressed in terms of D in a natural manner:

$$\frac{d}{dx}\left(\frac{dy}{dx}\right) = \frac{d^2y}{dx^2} = D(Dy) = D^2y \quad \text{and, in general,} \quad \frac{d^ny}{dx^n} = D^ny,$$

where y represents a sufficiently differentiable function. Polynomial expressions involving D, such as $D + 3$, $D^2 + 3D - 4$, and $5x^3D^3 - 6x^2D^2 + 4xD + 9$, are also differential operators. In general, we define an **nth-order differential operator** or **polynomial operator** to be

$$L = a_n(x)D^n + a_{n-1}(x)D^{n-1} + \cdots + a_1(x)D + a_0(x). \quad (8)$$

As a consequence of two basic properties of differentiation, $D(cf(x)) = cDf(x)$, c is a constant, and $D\{f(x) + g(x)\} = Df(x) + Dg(x)$, the differential operator L possesses a linearity property; that is, L operating on a linear combination of two differentiable functions is the same as the linear combination of L operating on the individual functions. In symbols this means that

$$L\{\alpha f(x) + \beta g(x)\} = \alpha L(f(x)) + \beta L(g(x)), \quad (9)$$

where α and β are constants. Because of (9) we say that the nth-order differential operator L is a **linear operator.**

DIFFERENTIAL EQUATIONS Any linear differential equation can be expressed in terms of the D notation. For example, the differential equation $y'' + 5y' + 6y = 5x - 3$ can be written as $D^2y + 5Dy + 6y = 5x - 3$ or $(D^2 + 5D + 6)y = 5x - 3$. Using (8), we can write the linear nth-order differential equations (6) and (7) compactly as

$$L(y) = 0 \quad \text{and} \quad L(y) = g(x),$$

respectively.

SUPERPOSITION PRINCIPLE In the next theorem we see that the sum, or **superposition,** of two or more solutions of a homogeneous linear differential equation is also a solution.

THEOREM 4.1.2 **Superposition Principle—Homogeneous Equations**

Let $y_1, y_2, \ldots, y_k$ be solutions of the homogeneous nth-order differential equation (6) on an interval I. Then the linear combination

$$y = c_1y_1(x) + c_2y_2(x) + \cdots + c_ky_k(x),$$

where the c_i, $i = 1, 2, \ldots, k$ are arbitrary constants, is also a solution on the interval.

PROOF We prove the case $k = 2$. Let L be the differential operator defined in (8), and let $y_1(x)$ and $y_2(x)$ be solutions of the homogeneous equation $L(y) = 0$. If we define $y = c_1y_1(x) + c_2y_2(x)$, then by linearity of L we have

$$L(y) = L\{c_1y_1(x) + c_2y_2(x)\} = c_1 L(y_1) + c_2 L(y_2) = c_1 \cdot 0 + c_2 \cdot 0 = 0. \quad ■$$

COROLLARIES TO THEOREM 4.1.2

(A) A constant multiple $y = c_1y_1(x)$ of a solution $y_1(x)$ of a homogeneous linear differential equation is also a solution.

(B) A homogeneous linear differential equation always possesses the trivial solution $y = 0$.

EXAMPLE 4 Superposition—Homogeneous DE

The functions $y_1 = x^2$ and $y_2 = x^2 \ln x$ are both solutions of the homogeneous linear equation $x^3y''' - 2xy' + 4y = 0$ on the interval $(0, \infty)$. By the superposition principle the linear combination

$$y = c_1x^2 + c_2x^2 \ln x$$

is also a solution of the equation on the interval. ∎

The function $y = e^{7x}$ is a solution of $y'' - 9y' + 14y = 0$. Because the differential equation is linear and homogeneous, the constant multiple $y = ce^{7x}$ is also a solution. For various values of c we see that $y = 9e^{7x}$, $y = 0$, $y = -\sqrt{5}e^{7x}, \ldots$ are all solutions of the equation.

LINEAR DEPENDENCE AND LINEAR INDEPENDENCE The next two concepts are basic to the study of linear differential equations.

DEFINITION 4.1.1 Linear Dependence/Independence

A set of functions $f_1(x), f_2(x), \ldots, f_n(x)$ is said to be **linearly dependent** on an interval I if there exist constants $c_1, c_2, \ldots, c_n$, not all zero, such that

$$c_1f_1(x) + c_2f_2(x) + \cdots + c_nf_n(x) = 0$$

for every x in the interval. If the set of functions is not linearly dependent on the interval, it is said to be **linearly independent.**

In other words, a set of functions is linearly independent on an interval I if the only constants for which

$$c_1f_1(x) + c_2f_2(x) + \cdots + c_nf_n(x) = 0$$

for every x in the interval are $c_1 = c_2 = \cdots = c_n = 0$.

It is easy to understand these definitions for a set consisting of two functions $f_1(x)$ and $f_2(x)$. If the set of functions is linearly dependent on an interval, then there exist constants c_1 and c_2 that are not both zero such that for every x in the interval, $c_1f_1(x) + c_2f_2(x) = 0$. Therefore if we assume that $c_1 \neq 0$, it follows that $f_1(x) = (-c_2/c_1)f_2(x)$; that is, *if a set of two functions is linearly dependent, then one function is simply a constant multiple of the other.* Conversely, if $f_1(x) = c_2f_2(x)$ for some constant c_2, then $(-1) \cdot f_1(x) + c_2f_2(x) = 0$ for every x in the interval. Hence the set of functions is linearly dependent because at least one of the constants (namely, $c_1 = -1$) is not zero. We conclude that *a set of two functions $f_1(x)$ and $f_2(x)$ is linearly independent when neither function is a constant multiple of the other* on the interval. For example, the set of functions $f_1(x) = \sin 2x$, $f_2(x) = \sin x \cos x$ is linearly dependent on $(-\infty, \infty)$ because $f_1(x)$ is a constant multiple of $f_2(x)$. Recall from the double-angle formula for the sine that $\sin 2x = 2 \sin x \cos x$. On the other hand, the set of functions $f_1(x) = x$, $f_2(x) = |x|$ is linearly independent on $(-\infty, \infty)$. Inspection of Figure 4.1.3 should convince you that neither function is a constant multiple of the other on the interval.

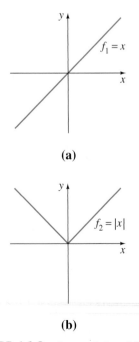

(a)

(b)

FIGURE 4.1.3 Set consisting of f_1 and f_2 is linearly independent on $(-\infty, \infty)$

It follows from the preceding discussion that the quotient $f_2(x)/f_1(x)$ is not a constant on an interval on which the set $f_1(x), f_2(x)$ is linearly independent. This little fact will be used in the next section.

EXAMPLE 5   Linearly Dependent Set of Functions

The set of functions $f_1(x) = \cos^2 x$, $f_2(x) = \sin^2 x$, $f_3(x) = \sec^2 x$, $f_4(x) = \tan^2 x$ is linearly dependent on the interval $(-\pi/2, \pi/2)$ because

$$c_1 \cos^2 x + c_2 \sin^2 x + c_3 \sec^2 x + c_4 \tan^2 x = 0$$

when $c_1 = c_2 = 1$, $c_3 = -1$, $c_4 = 1$. We used here $\cos^2 x + \sin^2 x = 1$ and $1 + \tan^2 x = \sec^2 x$. ∎

A set of functions $f_1(x), f_2(x), \ldots, f_n(x)$ is linearly dependent on an interval if at least one function can be expressed as a linear combination of the remaining functions.

EXAMPLE 6   Linearly Dependent Set of Functions

The set of functions $f_1(x) = \sqrt{x} + 5, f_2(x) = \sqrt{x} + 5x, f_3(x) = x - 1, f_4(x) = x^2$ is linearly dependent on the interval $(0, \infty)$ because f_2 can be written as a linear combination of f_1, f_3, and f_4. Observe that

$$f_2(x) = 1 \cdot f_1(x) + 5 \cdot f_3(x) + 0 \cdot f_4(x)$$

for every x in the interval $(0, \infty)$. ∎

SOLUTIONS OF DIFFERENTIAL EQUATIONS   We are primarily interested in linearly independent functions or, more to the point, linearly independent solutions of a linear differential equation. Although we could always appeal directly to Definition 4.1.1, it turns out that the question of whether the set of n solutions $y_1, y_2, \ldots, y_n$ of a homogeneous linear nth-order differential equation (6) is linearly independent can be settled somewhat mechanically by using a determinant.

DEFINITION 4.1.2   Wronskian

Suppose each of the functions $f_1(x), f_2(x), \ldots, f_n(x)$ possesses at least $n - 1$ derivatives. The determinant

$$W(f_1, f_2, \ldots, f_n) = \begin{vmatrix} f_1 & f_2 & \cdots & f_n \\ f_1' & f_2' & \cdots & f_n' \\ \vdots & \vdots & & \vdots \\ f_1^{(n-1)} & f_2^{(n-1)} & \cdots & f_n^{(n-1)} \end{vmatrix},$$

where the primes denote derivatives, is called the **Wronskian** of the functions.

THEOREM 4.1.3   Criterion for Linearly Independent Solutions

Let $y_1, y_2, \ldots, y_n$ be n solutions of the homogeneous linear nth-order differential equation (6) on an interval I. Then the set of solutions is **linearly independent** on I if and only if $W(y_1, y_2, \ldots, y_n) \neq 0$ for every x in the interval.

It follows from Theorem 4.1.3 that when $y_1, y_2, \ldots, y_n$ are n solutions of (6) on an interval I, the Wronskian $W(y_1, y_2, \ldots, y_n)$ is either identically zero or never zero on the interval.

A set of n linearly independent solutions of a homogeneous linear nth-order differential equation is given a special name.

DEFINITION 4.1.3 **Fundamental Set of Solutions**

Any set $y_1, y_2, \ldots, y_n$ of n linearly independent solutions of the homogeneous linear nth-order differential equation (6) on an interval I is said to be a **fundamental set of solutions** on the interval.

The basic question of whether a fundamental set of solutions exists for a linear equation is answered in the next theorem.

THEOREM 4.1.4 **Existence of a Fundamental Set**

There exists a fundamental set of solutions for the homogeneous linear nth-order differential equation (6) on an interval I.

Analogous to the fact that any vector in three dimensions can be expressed as a linear combination of the *linearly independent* vectors **i, j, k,** any solution of an nth-order homogeneous linear differential equation on an interval I can be expressed as a linear combination of n linearly independent solutions on I. In other words, n linearly independent solutions $y_1, y_2, \ldots, y_n$ are the basic building blocks for the general solution of the equation.

THEOREM 4.1.5 **General Solution—Homogeneous Equations**

Let $y_1, y_2, \ldots, y_n$ be a fundamental set of solutions of the homogeneous linear nth-order differential equation (6) on an interval I. Then the **general solution** of the equation on the interval is

$$y = c_1 y_1(x) + c_2 y_2(x) + \cdots + c_n y_n(x),$$

where c_i, $i = 1, 2, \ldots, n$ are arbitrary constants.

Theorem 4.1.5 states that if $Y(x)$ is any solution of (6) on the interval, then constants $C_1, C_2, \ldots, C_n$ can always be found so that

$$Y(x) = C_1 y_1(x) + C_2 y_2(x) + \cdots + C_n y_n(x).$$

We will prove the case when $n = 2$.

PROOF Let Y be a solution and let y_1 and y_2 be linearly independent solutions of $a_2 y'' + a_1 y' + a_0 y = 0$ on an interval I. Suppose that $x = t$ is a point in I for which $W(y_1(t), y_2(t)) \neq 0$. Suppose also that $Y(t) = k_1$ and $Y'(t) = k_2$. If we now examine the equations

$$C_1 y_1(t) + C_2 y_2(t) = k_1$$

$$C_1 y_1'(t) + C_2 y_2'(t) = k_2,$$

it follows that we can determine C_1 and C_2 uniquely, provided that the determinant of the coefficients satisfies

$$\begin{vmatrix} y_1(t) & y_2(t) \\ y_1'(t) & y_2'(t) \end{vmatrix} \neq 0.$$

But this determinant is simply the Wronskian evaluated at $x = t$, and by assumption, $W \neq 0$. If we define $G(x) = C_1 y_1(x) + C_2 y_2(x)$, we observe that $G(x)$ satisfies the differential equation since it is a superposition of two known solutions; $G(x)$ satisfies the initial conditions

$$G(t) = C_1 y_1(t) + C_2 y_2(t) = k_1 \qquad \text{and} \qquad G'(t) = C_1 y_1'(t) + C_2 y_2'(t) = k_2;$$

and $Y(x)$ satisfies the *same* linear equation and the *same* initial conditions. Because the solution of this linear initial-value problem is unique (Theorem 4.1.1), we have $Y(x) = G(x)$ or $Y(x) = C_1 y_1(x) + C_2 y_2(x)$. ∎

EXAMPLE 7 General Solution of a Homogeneous DE

The functions $y_1 = e^{3x}$ and $y_2 = e^{-3x}$ are both solutions of the homogeneous linear equation $y'' - 9y = 0$ on the interval $(-\infty, \infty)$. By inspection the solutions are linearly independent on the x-axis. This fact can be corroborated by observing that the Wronskian

$$W(e^{3x}, e^{-3x}) = \begin{vmatrix} e^{3x} & e^{-3x} \\ 3e^{3x} & -3e^{-3x} \end{vmatrix} = -6 \neq 0$$

for every x. We conclude that y_1 and y_2 form a fundamental set of solutions, and consequently, $y = c_1 e^{3x} + c_2 e^{-3x}$ is the general solution of the equation on the interval. ∎

EXAMPLE 8 A Solution Obtained from a General Solution

The function $y = 4\sinh 3x - 5e^{3x}$ is a solution of the differential equation in Example 7. (Verify this.) In view of Theorem 4.1.5 we must be able to obtain this solution from the general solution $y = c_1 e^{3x} + c_2 e^{-3x}$. Observe that if we choose $c_1 = 2$ and $c_2 = -7$, then $y = 2e^{3x} - 7e^{-3x}$ can be rewritten as

$$y = 2e^{3x} - 2e^{-3x} - 5e^{-3x} = 4\left(\frac{e^{3x} - e^{-3x}}{2}\right) - 5e^{-3x}.$$

The last expression is recognized as $y = 4 \sinh 3x - 5e^{-3x}$. ∎

EXAMPLE 9 General Solution of a Homogeneous DE

The functions $y_1 = e^x$, $y_2 = e^{2x}$, and $y_3 = e^{3x}$ satisfy the third-order equation $y''' - 6y'' + 11y' - 6y = 0$. Since

$$W(e^x, e^{2x}, e^{3x}) = \begin{vmatrix} e^x & e^{2x} & e^{3x} \\ e^x & 2e^{2x} & 3e^{3x} \\ e^x & 4e^{2x} & 9e^{3x} \end{vmatrix} = 2e^{6x} \neq 0$$

for every real value of x, the functions y_1, y_2, and y_3 form a fundamental set of solutions on $(-\infty, \infty)$. We conclude that $y = c_1 e^x + c_2 e^{2x} + c_3 e^{3x}$ is the general solution of the differential equation on the interval. ∎

4.1.3 NONHOMOGENEOUS EQUATIONS

Any function y_p, free of arbitrary parameters, that satisfies (7) is said to be a **particular solution** or **particular integral** of the equation. For example, it is a straightforward task to show that the constant function $y_p = 3$ is a particular solution of the nonhomogeneous equation $y'' + 9y = 27$.

Now if $y_1, y_2, \ldots, y_k$ are solutions of (6) on an interval I and y_p is any particular solution of (7) on I, then the linear combination

$$y = c_1 y_1(x) + c_2 y_2(x) + \cdots + c_k y_k(x) + y_p \qquad (10)$$

is also a solution of the nonhomogeneous equation (7). If you think about it, this makes sense, because the linear combination $c_1 y_1(x) + c_2 y_2(x) + \cdots + c_k y_k(x)$ is transformed into 0 by the operator $L = a_n D^n + a_{n-1} D^{n-1} + \cdots + a_1 D + a_0$, whereas y_p is transformed into $g(x)$. If we use $k = n$ linearly independent solutions of the nth-order equation (6), then the expression in (10) becomes the general solution of (7).

THEOREM 4.1.6   General Solution—Nonhomogeneous Equations

Let y_p be any particular solution of the nonhomogeneous linear nth-order differential equation (7) on an interval I, and let $y_1, y_2, \ldots, y_n$ be a fundamental set of solutions of the associated homogeneous differential equation (6) on I. Then the **general solution** of the equation on the interval is

$$y = c_1 y_1(x) + c_2 y_2(x) + \cdots + c_n y_n(x) + y_p,$$

where the c_i, $i = 1, 2, \ldots, n$ are arbitrary constants.

PROOF   Let L be the differential operator defined in (8) and let $Y(x)$ and $y_p(x)$ be particular solutions of the nonhomogeneous equation $L(y) = g(x)$. If we define $u(x) = Y(x) - y_p(x)$, then by linearity of L we have

$$L(u) = L\{Y(x) - y_p(x)\} = L(Y(x)) - L(y_p(x)) = g(x) - g(x) = 0.$$

This shows that $u(x)$ is a solution of the homogeneous equation $L(y) = 0$. Hence by Theorem 4.1.5, $u(x) = c_1 y_1(x) + c_2 y_2(x) + \cdots + c_n y_n(x)$, and so

$$Y(x) - y_p(x) = c_1 y_1(x) + c_2 y_2(x) + \cdots + c_n y_n(x)$$

or $\qquad\qquad Y(x) = c_1 y_1(x) + c_2 y_2(x) + \cdots + c_n y_n(x) + y_p(x).$ ∎

COMPLEMENTARY FUNCTION   We see in Theorem 4.1.6 that the general solution of a nonhomogeneous linear equation consists of the sum of two functions:

$$y = c_1 y_1(x) + c_2 y_2(x) + \cdots + c_n y_n(x) + y_p(x) = y_c(x) + y_p(x).$$

The linear combination $y_c(x) = c_1 y_1(x) + c_2 y_2(x) + \cdots + c_n y_n(x)$, which is the general solution of (6), is called the **complementary function** for equation (7). In other words, to solve a nonhomogeneous linear differential equation, we first solve the associated homogeneous equation and then find any particular solution of the nonhomogeneous equation. The general solution of the nonhomogeneous equation is then

$$y = complementary\ function + any\ particular\ solution$$
$$= y_c + y_p.$$

EXAMPLE 10   General Solution of a Nonhomogeneous DE

By substitution the function $y_p = -\frac{11}{12} - \frac{1}{2}x$ is readily shown to be a particular solution of the nonhomogeneous equation

$$y''' - 6y'' + 11y' - 6y = 3x. \qquad (11)$$

To write the general solution of (11), we must also be able to solve the associated homogeneous equation

$$y''' - 6y'' + 11y' - 6y = 0.$$

But in Example 9 we saw that the general solution of this latter equation on the interval $(-\infty, \infty)$ was $y_c = c_1 e^x + c_2 e^{2x} + c_3 e^{3x}$. Hence the general solution of (11) on the interval is

$$y = y_c + y_p = c_1 e^x + c_2 e^{2x} + c_3 e^{3x} - \frac{11}{12} - \frac{1}{2}x. \qquad \blacksquare$$

ANOTHER SUPERPOSITION PRINCIPLE The last theorem of this discussion will be useful in Section 4.4 when we consider a method for finding particular solutions of nonhomogeneous equations.

THEOREM 4.1.7 Superposition Principle—Nonhomogeneous Equations

Let $y_{p_1}, y_{p_2}, \ldots, y_{p_k}$ be k particular solutions of the nonhomogeneous linear nth-order differential equation (7) on an interval I corresponding, in turn, to k distinct functions $g_1, g_2, \ldots, g_k$. That is, suppose y_{p_i} denotes a particular solution of the corresponding differential equation

$$a_n(x)y^{(n)} + a_{n-1}(x)y^{(n-1)} + \cdots + a_1(x)y' + a_0(x)y = g_i(x), \quad (12)$$

where $i = 1, 2, \ldots, k$. Then

$$y_p = y_{p_1}(x) + y_{p_2}(x) + \cdots + y_{p_k}(x) \qquad (13)$$

is a particular solution of

$$a_n(x)y^{(n)} + a_{n-1}(x)y^{(n-1)} + \cdots + a_1(x)y' + a_0(x)y$$
$$= g_1(x) + g_2(x) + \cdots + g_k(x). \qquad (14)$$

PROOF We prove the case $k = 2$. Let L be the differential operator defined in (8) and let $y_{p_1}(x)$ and $y_{p_2}(x)$ be particular solutions of the nonhomogeneous equations $L(y) = g_1(x)$ and $L(y) = g_2(x)$, respectively. If we define $y_p = y_{p_1}(x) + y_{p_2}(x)$, we want to show that y_p is a particular solution of $L(y) = g_1(x) + g_2(x)$. The result follows again by the linearity of the operator L:

$$L(y_p) = L\{y_{p_1}(x) + y_{p_2}(x)\} = L(y_{p_1}(x)) + L(y_{p_2}(x)) = g_1(x) + g_2(x). \quad \blacksquare$$

EXAMPLE 11 Superposition—Nonhomogeneous DE

You should verify that

$y_{p_1} = -4x^2$ is a particular solution of $y'' - 3y' + 4y = -16x^2 + 24x - 8,$

$y_{p_2} = e^{2x}$ is a particular solution of $y'' - 3y' + 4y = 2e^{2x},$

$y_{p_3} = xe^x$ is a particular solution of $y'' - 3y' + 4y = 2xe^x - e^x.$

It follows from (13) of Theorem 4.1.7 that the superposition of y_{p_1}, y_{p_2}, and y_{p_3},

$$y = y_{p_1} + y_{p_2} + y_{p_3} = -4x^2 + e^{2x} + xe^x,$$

is a solution of

$$y'' - 3y' + 4y = \underbrace{-16x^2 + 24x - 8}_{g_1(x)} + \underbrace{2e^{2x}}_{g_2(x)} + \underbrace{2xe^x - e^x}_{g_3(x)}. \qquad \blacksquare$$

NOTE If the y_{p_i} are particular solutions of (12) for $i = 1, 2, \ldots, k$, then the linear combination

$$y_p = c_1 y_{p_1} + c_2 y_{p_2} + \cdots + c_k y_{p_k},$$

where the c_i are constants, is also a particular solution of (14) when the right-hand member of the equation is the linear combination

$$c_1 g_1(x) + c_2 g_2(x) + \cdots + c_k g_k(x).$$

Before we actually start solving homogeneous and nonhomogeneous linear differential equations, we need one additional bit of theory, which is presented in the next section.

REMARKS

This remark is a continuation of the brief discussion of dynamical systems given at the end of Section 1.3.

A dynamical system whose rule or mathematical model is a linear nth-order differential equation

$$a_n(t)y^{(n)} + a_{n-1}(t)y^{(n-1)} + \cdots + a_1(t)y' + a_0(t)y = g(t)$$

is said to be an nth-order **linear system.** The n time-dependent functions $y(t)$, $y'(t), \ldots, y^{(n-1)}(t)$ are the **state variables** of the system. Recall that their values at some time t give the **state of the system.** The function g is variously called the **input function, forcing function,** or **excitation function.** A solution $y(t)$ of the differential equation is said to be the **output** or **response of the system.** Under the conditions stated in Theorem 4.1.1, the output or response $y(t)$ is uniquely determined by the input and the state of the system prescribed at a time t_0—that is, by the initial conditions $y(t_0), y'(t_0), \ldots, y^{(n-1)}(t_0)$.

For a dynamical system to be a linear system, it is necessary that the superposition principle (Theorem 4.1.7) holds in the system; that is, the response of the system to a superposition of inputs is a superposition of outputs. We have already examined some simple linear systems in Section 3.1 (linear first-order equations); in Section 5.1 we examine linear systems in which the mathematical models are second-order differential equations.

EXERCISES 4.1

Answers to selected odd-numbered problems begin on page ANS-4.

4.1.1 INITIAL-VALUE AND BOUNDARY-VALUE PROBLEMS

In Problems 1–4 the given family of functions is the general solution of the differential equation on the indicated interval. Find a member of the family that is a solution of the initial-value problem.

1. $y = c_1 e^x + c_2 e^{-x}, (-\infty, \infty);$
$y'' - y = 0, \quad y(0) = 0, \quad y'(0) = 1$

2. $y = c_1 e^{4x} + c_2 e^{-x}, (-\infty, \infty);$
$y'' - 3y' - 4y = 0, \quad y(0) = 1, \quad y'(0) = 2$

3. $y = c_1 x + c_2 x \ln x, (0, \infty);$
$x^2 y'' - xy' + y = 0, \quad y(1) = 3, \quad y'(1) = -1$

4. $y = c_1 + c_2 \cos x + c_3 \sin x, (-\infty, \infty);$
$y''' + y' = 0, \quad y(\pi) = 0, \quad y'(\pi) = 2, \quad y''(\pi) = -1$

5. Given that $y = c_1 + c_2 x^2$ is a two-parameter family of solutions of $xy'' - y' = 0$ on the interval $(-\infty, \infty)$, show that constants c_1 and c_2 cannot be found so that a member of the family satisfies the initial conditions $y(0) = 0, y'(0) = 1$. Explain why this does not violate Theorem 4.1.1.

6. Find two members of the family of solutions in Problem 5 that satisfy the initial conditions $y(0) = 0$, $y'(0) = 0$.

7. Given that $x(t) = c_1 \cos \omega t + c_2 \sin \omega t$ is the general solution of $x'' + \omega^2 x = 0$ on the interval $(-\infty, \infty)$, show that a solution satisfying the initial conditions $x(0) = x_0, x'(0) = x_1$ is given by

$$x(t) = x_0 \cos \omega t + \frac{x_1}{\omega} \sin \omega t.$$

8. Use the general solution of $x'' + \omega^2 x = 0$ given in Problem 7 to show that a solution satisfying the initial conditions $x(t_0) = x_0, x'(t_0) = x_1$ is the solution given in Problem 7 shifted by an amount t_0:

$$x(t) = x_0 \cos \omega(t - t_0) + \frac{x_1}{\omega} \sin \omega(t - t_0).$$

In Problems 9 and 10 find an interval centered about $x = 0$ for which the given initial-value problem has a unique solution.

9. $(x - 2)y'' + 3y = x, \quad y(0) = 0, \quad y'(0) = 1$

10. $y'' + (\tan x)y = e^x, \quad y(0) = 1, \quad y'(0) = 0$

11. (a) Use the family in Problem 1 to find a solution of $y'' - y = 0$ that satisfies the boundary conditions $y(0) = 0, y(1) = 1$.

   (b) The DE in part (a) has the alternative general solution $y = c_3 \cosh x + c_4 \sinh x$ on $(-\infty, \infty)$. Use this family to find a solution that satisfies the boundary conditions in part (a).

   (c) Show that the solutions in parts (a) and (b) are equivalent

12. Use the family in Problem 5 to find a solution of $xy'' - y' = 0$ that satisfies the boundary conditions $y(0) = 1, y'(1) = 6$.

In Problems 13 and 14 the given two-parameter family is a solution of the indicated differential equation on the interval $(-\infty, \infty)$. Determine whether a member of the family can be found that satisfies the boundary conditions.

13. $y = c_1 e^x \cos x + c_2 e^x \sin x; \quad y'' - 2y' + 2y = 0$

   (a) $y(0) = 1, \quad y'(\pi) = 0$ **(b)** $y(0) = 1, \quad y(\pi) = -1$

   (c) $y(0) = 1, \quad y\left(\dfrac{\pi}{2}\right) = 1$ **(d)** $y(0) = 0, \quad y(\pi) = 0.$

14. $y = c_1 x^2 + c_2 x^4 + 3; \quad x^2 y'' - 5xy' + 8y = 24$

   (a) $y(-1) = 0, \quad y(1) = 4$ **(b)** $y(0) = 1, \quad y(1) = 2$

   (c) $y(0) = 3, \quad y(1) = 0$ **(d)** $y(1) = 3, \quad y(2) = 15$

4.1.2 HOMOGENEOUS EQUATIONS

In Problems 15–22 determine whether the given set of functions is linearly independent on the interval $(-\infty, \infty)$.

15. $f_1(x) = x, \quad f_2(x) = x^2, \quad f_3(x) = 4x - 3x^2$

16. $f_1(x) = 0, \quad f_2(x) = x, \quad f_3(x) = e^x$

17. $f_1(x) = 5, \quad f_2(x) = \cos^2 x, \quad f_3(x) = \sin^2 x$

18. $f_1(x) = \cos 2x, \quad f_2(x) = 1, \quad f_3(x) = \cos^2 x$

19. $f_1(x) = x, \quad f_2(x) = x - 1, \quad f_3(x) = x + 3$

20. $f_1(x) = 2 + x, \quad f_2(x) = 2 + |x|$

21. $f_1(x) = 1 + x, \quad f_2(x) = x, \quad f_3(x) = x^2$

22. $f_1(x) = e^x, \quad f_2(x) = e^{-x}, \quad f_3(x) = \sinh x$

In Problems 23–30 verify that the given functions form a fundamental set of solutions of the differential equation on the indicated interval. Form the general solution.

23. $y'' - y' - 12y = 0; \quad e^{-3x}, e^{4x}, (-\infty, \infty)$

24. $y'' - 4y = 0; \quad \cosh 2x, \sinh 2x, (-\infty, \infty)$

25. $y'' - 2y' + 5y = 0; \quad e^x \cos 2x, e^x \sin 2x, (-\infty, \infty)$

26. $4y'' - 4y' + y = 0; \quad e^{x/2}, xe^{x/2}, (-\infty, \infty)$

27. $x^2 y'' - 6xy' + 12y = 0; \quad x^3, x^4, (0, \infty)$

28. $x^2 y'' + xy' + y = 0; \quad \cos(\ln x), \sin(\ln x), (0, \infty)$

29. $x^3 y''' + 6x^2 y'' + 4xy' - 4y = 0; \quad x, x^{-2}, x^{-2} \ln x, (0, \infty)$

30. $y^{(4)} + y'' = 0; \quad 1, x, \cos x, \sin x, (-\infty, \infty)$

4.1.3 NONHOMOGENEOUS EQUATIONS

In Problems 31–34 verify that the given two-parameter family of functions is the general solution of the nonhomogeneous differential equation on the indicated interval.

31. $y'' - 7y' + 10y = 24e^x;$
   $y = c_1 e^{2x} + c_2 e^{5x} + 6e^x, (-\infty, \infty)$

32. $y'' + y = \sec x;$
   $y = c_1 \cos x + c_2 \sin x + x \sin x + (\cos x) \ln(\cos x),$
   $(-\pi/2, \pi/2)$

33. $y'' - 4y' + 4y = 2e^{2x} + 4x - 12;$
   $y = c_1 e^{2x} + c_2 xe^{2x} + x^2 e^{2x} + x - 2, (-\infty, \infty)$

34. $2x^2 y'' + 5xy' + y = x^2 - x;$
   $y = c_1 x^{-1/2} + c_2 x^{-1} + \frac{1}{15} x^2 - \frac{1}{6} x, (0, \infty)$

35. (a) Verify that $y_{p_1} = 3e^{2x}$ and $y_{p_2} = x^2 + 3x$ are, respectively, particular solutions of

$$y'' - 6y' + 5y = -9e^{2x}$$

and $y'' - 6y' + 5y = 5x^2 + 3x - 16.$

   (b) Use part (a) to find particular solutions of

$$y'' - 6y' + 5y = 5x^2 + 3x - 16 - 9e^{2x}$$

and $y'' - 6y' + 5y = -10x^2 - 6x + 32 + e^{2x}.$

36. (a) By inspection find a particular solution of

$$y'' + 2y = 10.$$

   (b) By inspection find a particular solution of

$$y'' + 2y = -4x.$$

   (c) Find a particular solution of $y'' + 2y = -4x + 10.$

   (d) Find a particular solution of $y'' + 2y = 8x + 5.$

Discussion Problems

37. Let $n = 1, 2, 3, \ldots$. Discuss how the observations $D^n x^{n-1} = 0$ and $D^n x^n = n!$ can be used to find the general solutions of the given differential equations.

    (a) $y'' = 0$ **(b)** $y''' = 0$ **(c)** $y^{(4)} = 0$

    (d) $y'' = 2$ **(e)** $y''' = 6$ **(f)** $y^{(4)} = 24$

38. Suppose that $y_1 = e^x$ and $y_2 = e^{-x}$ are two solutions of a homogeneous linear differential equation. Explain why $y_3 = \cosh x$ and $y_4 = \sinh x$ are also solutions of the equation.

39. (a) Verify that $y_1 = x^3$ and $y_2 = |x|^3$ are linearly independent solutions of the differential equation $x^2 y'' - 4xy' + 6y = 0$ on the interval $(-\infty, \infty)$.

    (b) Show that $W(y_1, y_2) = 0$ for every real number x. Does this result violate Theorem 4.1.3? Explain.

    (c) Verify that $Y_1 = x^3$ and $Y_2 = x^2$ are also linearly independent solutions of the differential equation in part (a) on the interval $(-\infty, \infty)$.

    (d) Find a solution of the differential equation satisfying $y(0) = 0$, $y'(0) = 0$.

(e) By the superposition principle, Theorem 4.1.2, both linear combinations $y = c_1 y_1 + c_2 y_2$ and $Y = c_1 Y_1 + c_2 Y_2$ are solutions of the differential equation. Discuss whether one, both, or neither of the linear combinations is a general solution of the differential equation on the interval $(-\infty, \infty)$.

40. Is the set of functions $f_1(x) = e^{x+2}$, $f_2(x) = e^{x-3}$ linearly dependent or linearly independent on $(-\infty, \infty)$? Discuss.

41. Suppose $y_1, y_2, \ldots, y_k$ are k linearly independent solutions on $(-\infty, \infty)$ of a homogeneous linear nth-order differential equation with constant coefficients. By Theorem 4.1.2 it follows that $y_{k+1} = 0$ is also a solution of the differential equation. Is the set of solutions $y_1, y_2, \ldots, y_k, y_{k+1}$ linearly dependent or linearly independent on $(-\infty, \infty)$? Discuss.

42. Suppose that $y_1, y_2, \ldots, y_k$ are k nontrivial solutions of a homogeneous linear nth-order differential equation with constant coefficients and that $k = n + 1$. Is the set of solutions $y_1, y_2, \ldots, y_k$ linearly dependent or linearly independent on $(-\infty, \infty)$? Discuss.

4.2   REDUCTION OF ORDER

REVIEW MATERIAL

- Section 2.5 (using a substitution)
- Section 4.1

INTRODUCTION   In the preceding section we saw that the general solution of a homogeneous linear second-order differential equation

$$a_2(x)y'' + a_1(x)y' + a_0(x)y = 0 \tag{1}$$

is a linear combination $y = c_1 y_1 + c_2 y_2$, where y_1 and y_2 are solutions that constitute a linearly independent set on some interval I. Beginning in the next section, we examine a method for determining these solutions when the coefficients of the differential equation in (1) are constants. This method, which is a straightforward exercise in algebra, breaks down in a few cases and yields only a single solution y_1 of the DE. It turns out that we can construct a second solution y_2 of a homogeneous equation (1) (even when the coefficients in (1) are variable) provided that we know a nontrivial solution y_1 of the DE. The basic idea described in this section is that *equation (1) can be reduced to a linear first-order DE by means of a substitution* involving the known solution y_1. A second solution y_2 of (1) is apparent after this first-order differential equation is solved.

REDUCTION OF ORDER   Suppose that y_1 denotes a nontrivial solution of (1) and that y_1 is defined on an interval I. We seek a second solution y_2 so that the set consisting of y_1 and y_2 is linearly independent on I. Recall from Section 4.1 that if y_1 and y_2 are linearly independent, then their quotient y_2/y_1 is nonconstant on I—that is, $y_2(x)/y_1(x) = u(x)$ or $y_2(x) = u(x)y_1(x)$. The function $u(x)$ can be found by substituting $y_2(x) = u(x)y_1(x)$ into the given differential equation. This method is called **reduction of order** because we must solve a linear first-order differential equation to find u.

EXAMPLE 1   A Second Solution by Reduction of Order

Given that $y_1 = e^x$ is a solution of $y'' - y = 0$ on the interval $(-\infty, \infty)$, use reduction of order to find a second solution y_2.

SOLUTION If $y = u(x)y_1(x) = u(x)e^x$, then the Product Rule gives

$$y' = ue^x + e^x u', \quad y'' = ue^x + 2e^x u' + e^x u'',$$

and so
$$y'' - y = e^x(u'' + 2u') = 0.$$

Since $e^x \neq 0$, the last equation requires $u'' + 2u' = 0$. If we make the substitution $w = u'$, this linear second-order equation in u becomes $w' + 2w = 0$, which is a linear first-order equation in w. Using the integrating factor e^{2x}, we can write $\dfrac{d}{dx}[e^{2x}w] = 0$. After integrating, we get $w = c_1 e^{-2x}$ or $u' = c_1 e^{-2x}$. Integrating again then yields $u = -\frac{1}{2}c_1 e^{-2x} + c_2$. Thus

$$y = u(x)e^x = -\frac{c_1}{2}e^{-x} + c_2 e^x. \tag{2}$$

By picking $c_2 = 0$ and $c_1 = -2$, we obtain the desired second solution, $y_2 = e^{-x}$. Because $W(e^x, e^{-x}) \neq 0$ for every x, the solutions are linearly independent on $(-\infty, \infty)$. ∎

Since we have shown that $y_1 = e^x$ and $y_2 = e^{-x}$ are linearly independent solutions of a linear second-order equation, the expression in (2) is actually the general solution of $y'' - y = 0$ on $(-\infty, \infty)$.

GENERAL CASE Suppose we divide by $a_2(x)$ to put equation (1) in the **standard form**

$$y'' + P(x)y' + Q(x)y = 0, \tag{3}$$

where $P(x)$ and $Q(x)$ are continuous on some interval I. Let us suppose further that $y_1(x)$ is a known solution of (3) on I and that $y_1(x) \neq 0$ for every x in the interval. If we define $y = u(x)y_1(x)$, it follows that

$$y' = uy_1' + y_1 u', \quad y'' = uy_1'' + 2y_1' u' + y_1 u''$$

$$y'' + Py' + Qy = u[\underbrace{y_1'' + Py_1' + Qy_1}_{\text{zero}}] + y_1 u'' + (2y_1' + Py_1)u' = 0.$$

This implies that we must have

$$y_1 u'' + (2y_1' + Py_1)u' = 0 \quad \text{or} \quad y_1 w' + (2y_1' + Py_1)w = 0, \tag{4}$$

where we have let $w = u'$. Observe that the last equation in (4) is both linear and separable. Separating variables and integrating, we obtain

$$\frac{dw}{w} + 2\frac{y_1'}{y_1}\,dx + P\,dx = 0$$

$$\ln|wy_1^2| = -\int P\,dx + c \quad \text{or} \quad wy_1^2 = c_1 e^{-\int P\,dx}.$$

We solve the last equation for w, use $w = u'$, and integrate again:

$$u = c_1 \int \frac{e^{-\int P\,dx}}{y_1^2}\,dx + c_2.$$

By choosing $c_1 = 1$ and $c_2 = 0$, we find from $y = u(x)y_1(x)$ that a second solution of equation (3) is

$$y_2 = y_1(x) \int \frac{e^{-\int P(x)\,dx}}{y_1^2(x)}\,dx. \qquad (5)$$

It makes a good review of differentiation to verify that the function $y_2(x)$ defined in (5) satisfies equation (3) and that y_1 and y_2 are linearly independent on any interval on which $y_1(x)$ is not zero.

EXAMPLE 2   A Second Solution by Formula (5)

The function $y_1 = x^2$ is a solution of $x^2 y'' - 3xy' + 4y = 0$. Find the general solution of the differential equation on the interval $(0, \infty)$.

SOLUTION   From the standard form of the equation,

$$y'' - \frac{3}{x}y' + \frac{4}{x^2}y = 0,$$

we find from (5)

$$y_2 = x^2 \int \frac{e^{3\int dx/x}}{x^4}\,dx \quad \leftarrow e^{3\int dx/x} = e^{\ln x^3} = x^3$$

$$= x^2 \int \frac{dx}{x} = x^2 \ln x.$$

The general solution on the interval $(0, \infty)$ is given by $y = c_1 y_1 + c_2 y_2$; that is, $y = c_1 x^2 + c_2 x^2 \ln x$. ∎

REMARKS

(*i*) The derivation and use of formula (5) have been illustrated here because this formula appears again in the next section and in Sections 4.7 and 6.2. We use (5) simply to save time in obtaining a desired result. Your instructor will tell you whether you should memorize (5) or whether you should know the first principles of reduction of order.

(*ii*) Reduction of order can be used to find the general solution of a nonhomogeneous equation $a_2(x)y'' + a_1(x)y' + a_0(x)y = g(x)$ whenever a solution y_1 of the associated homogeneous equation is known. See Problems 17–20 in Exercises 4.2.

EXERCISES 4.2   *Answers to selected odd-numbered problems begin on page ANS-4.*

In Problems 1–16 the indicated function $y_1(x)$ is a solution of the given differential equation. Use reduction of order or formula (5), as instructed, to find a second solution $y_2(x)$.

1. $y'' - 4y' + 4y = 0;$ $y_1 = e^{2x}$

2. $y'' + 2y' + y = 0;$ $y_1 = xe^{-x}$

3. $y'' + 16y = 0;$ $y_1 = \cos 4x$

4. $y'' + 9y = 0;$ $y_1 = \sin 3x$

5. $y'' - y = 0;$ $y_1 = \cosh x$

6. $y'' - 25y = 0;$ $y_1 = e^{5x}$

7. $9y'' - 12y' + 4y = 0;$ $y_1 = e^{2x/3}$

8. $6y'' + y' - y = 0;$ $y_1 = e^{x/3}$

9. $x^2 y'' - 7xy' + 16y = 0;$ $y_1 = x^4$

10. $x^2 y'' + 2xy' - 6y = 0;$ $y_1 = x^2$

11. $xy'' + y' = 0;$ $y_1 = \ln x$

12. $4x^2 y'' + y = 0;$ $y_1 = x^{1/2} \ln x$

13. $x^2 y'' - xy' + 2y = 0;$ $y_1 = x \sin(\ln x)$

14. $x^2 y'' - 3xy' + 5y = 0;$ $y_1 = x^2 \cos(\ln x)$

15. $(1 - 2x - x^2)y'' + 2(1 + x)y' - 2y = 0$; $y_1 = x + 1$

16. $(1 - x^2)y'' + 2xy' = 0$; $y_1 = 1$

In Problems 17–20 the indicated function $y_1(x)$ is a solution of the associated homogeneous equation. Use the method of reduction of order to find a second solution $y_2(x)$ of the homogeneous equation and a particular solution of the given nonhomogeneous equation.

17. $y'' - 4y = 2$; $y_1 = e^{-2x}$

18. $y'' + y' = 1$; $y_1 = 1$

19. $y'' - 3y' + 2y = 5e^{3x}$; $y_1 = e^x$

20. $y'' - 4y' + 3y = x$; $y_1 = e^x$

Discussion Problems

21. (a) Give a convincing demonstration that the second-order equation $ay'' + by' + cy = 0$, a, b, and c constants, always possesses at least one solution of the form $y_1 = e^{m_1 x}$, m_1 a constant.

(b) Explain why the differential equation in part (a) must then have a second solution either of the form $y_2 = e^{m_2 x}$ or of the form $y_2 = xe^{m_1 x}$, m_1 and m_2 constants.

(c) Reexamine Problems 1–8. Can you explain why the statements in parts (a) and (b) above are not contradicted by the answers to Problems 3–5?

22. Verify that $y_1(x) = x$ is a solution of $xy'' - xy' + y = 0$. Use reduction of order to find a second solution $y_2(x)$ in the form of an infinite series. Conjecture an interval of definition for $y_2(x)$.

Computer Lab Assignments

23. (a) Verify that $y_1(x) = e^x$ is a solution of
$$xy'' - (x + 10)y' + 10y = 0.$$

(b) Use (5) to find a second solution $y_2(x)$. Use a CAS to carry out the required integration.

(c) Explain, using Corollary (A) of Theorem 4.1.2, why the second solution can be written compactly as
$$y_2(x) = \sum_{n=0}^{10} \frac{1}{n!} x^n.$$

| **4.3** | HOMOGENEOUS LINEAR EQUATIONS WITH CONSTANT COEFFICIENTS |

REVIEW MATERIAL

- Review Problem 27 in Exercises 1.1 and Theorem 4.1.5
- Review the algebra of solving polynomial equations (see the *Student Resource and Solutions Manual*)

INTRODUCTION   As a means of motivating the discussion in this section, let us return to first-order differential equations—more specifically, to *homogeneous* linear equations $ay' + by = 0$, where the coefficients $a \neq 0$ and b are constants. This type of equation can be solved either by separation of variables or with the aid of an integrating factor, but there is another solution method, one that uses only algebra. Before illustrating this alternative method, we make one observation: Solving $ay' + by = 0$ for y' yields $y' = ky$, where k is a constant. This observation reveals the nature of the unknown solution y; the only nontrivial elementary function whose derivative is a constant multiple of itself is an exponential function e^{mx}. Now the new solution method: If we substitute $y = e^{mx}$ and $y' = me^{mx}$ into $ay' + by = 0$, we get
$$ame^{mx} + be^{mx} = 0 \quad \text{or} \quad e^{mx}(am + b) = 0.$$

Since e^{mx} is never zero for real values of x, the last equation is satisfied only when m is a solution or root of the first-degree polynomial equation $am + b = 0$. For this single value of m, $y = e^{mx}$ is a solution of the DE. To illustrate, consider the constant-coefficient equation $2y' + 5y = 0$. It is not necessary to go through the differentiation and substitution of $y = e^{mx}$ into the DE; we merely have to form the equation $2m + 5 = 0$ and solve it for m. From $m = -\frac{5}{2}$ we conclude that $y = e^{-5x/2}$ is a solution of $2y' + 5y = 0$, and its general solution on the interval $(-\infty, \infty)$ is $y = c_1 e^{-5x/2}$.

In this section we will see that the foregoing procedure can produce exponential solutions for homogeneous linear higher-order DEs,
$$a_n y^{(n)} + a_{n-1} y^{(n-1)} + \cdots + a_2 y'' + a_1 y' + a_0 y = 0, \tag{1}$$
where the coefficients a_i, $i = 0, 1, \ldots, n$ are real constants and $a_n \neq 0$.

AUXILIARY EQUATION   We begin by considering the special case of the second-order equation

$$ay'' + by' + cy = 0, \tag{2}$$

where a, b, and c are constants. If we try to find a solution of the form $y = e^{mx}$, then after substitution of $y' = me^{mx}$ and $y'' = m^2 e^{mx}$, equation (2) becomes

$$am^2 e^{mx} + bm e^{mx} + ce^{mx} = 0 \quad \text{or} \quad e^{mx}(am^2 + bm + c) = 0.$$

As in the introduction we argue that because $e^{mx} \neq 0$ for all x, it is apparent that the only way $y = e^{mx}$ can satisfy the differential equation (2) is when m is chosen as a root of the quadratic equation

$$am^2 + bm + c = 0. \tag{3}$$

This last equation is called the **auxiliary equation** of the differential equation (2). Since the two roots of (3) are $m_1 = (-b + \sqrt{b^2 - 4ac})/2a$ and $m_2 = (-b - \sqrt{b^2 - 4ac})/2a$, there will be three forms of the general solution of (2) corresponding to the three cases:

- m_1 and m_2 real and distinct ($b^2 - 4ac > 0$),
- m_1 and m_2 real and equal ($b^2 - 4ac = 0$), and
- m_1 and m_2 conjugate complex numbers ($b^2 - 4ac < 0$).

We discuss each of these cases in turn.

CASE I: DISTINCT REAL ROOTS   Under the assumption that the auxiliary equation (3) has two unequal real roots m_1 and m_2, we find two solutions, $y_1 = e^{m_1 x}$ and $y_2 = e^{m_2 x}$. We see that these functions are linearly independent on $(-\infty, \infty)$ and hence form a fundamental set. It follows that the general solution of (2) on this interval is

$$y = c_1 e^{m_1 x} + c_2 e^{m_2 x}. \tag{4}$$

CASE II: REPEATED REAL ROOTS   When $m_1 = m_2$, we necessarily obtain only one exponential solution, $y_1 = e^{m_1 x}$. From the quadratic formula we find that $m_1 = -b/2a$ since the only way to have $m_1 = m_2$ is to have $b^2 - 4ac = 0$. It follows from (5) in Section 4.2 that a second solution of the equation is

$$y_2 = e^{m_1 x} \int \frac{e^{2m_1 x}}{e^{2m_1 x}} \, dx = e^{m_1 x} \int dx = x e^{m_1 x}. \tag{5}$$

In (5) we have used the fact that $-b/a = 2m_1$. The general solution is then

$$y = c_1 e^{m_1 x} + c_2 x e^{m_1 x}. \tag{6}$$

CASE III: CONJUGATE COMPLEX ROOTS   If m_1 and m_2 are complex, then we can write $m_1 = \alpha + i\beta$ and $m_2 = \alpha - i\beta$, where α and $\beta > 0$ are real and $i^2 = -1$. Formally, there is no difference between this case and Case I, and hence

$$y = C_1 e^{(\alpha + i\beta)x} + C_2 e^{(\alpha - i\beta)x}.$$

However, in practice we prefer to work with real functions instead of complex exponentials. To this end we use **Euler's formula:**

$$e^{i\theta} = \cos\theta + i \sin\theta,$$

where θ is any real number.[*] It follows from this formula that

$$e^{i\beta x} = \cos\beta x + i \sin\beta x \quad \text{and} \quad e^{-i\beta x} = \cos\beta x - i \sin\beta x, \tag{7}$$

---

[*]A formal derivation of Euler's formula can be obtained from the Maclaurin series $e^x = \sum\limits_{n=0}^{\infty} \dfrac{x^n}{n!}$ by substituting $x = i\theta$, using $i^2 = -1$, $i^3 = -i$, ..., and then separating the series into real and imaginary parts. The plausibility thus established, we can adopt $\cos\theta + i \sin\theta$ as the *definition* of $e^{i\theta}$.

where we have used $\cos(-\beta x) = \cos \beta x$ and $\sin(-\beta x) = -\sin \beta x$. Note that by first adding and then subtracting the two equations in (7), we obtain, respectively,

$$e^{i\beta x} + e^{-i\beta x} = 2 \cos \beta x \qquad \text{and} \qquad e^{i\beta x} - e^{-i\beta x} = 2i \sin \beta x.$$

Since $y = C_1 e^{(\alpha+i\beta)x} + C_2 e^{(\alpha-i\beta)x}$ is a solution of (2) for any choice of the constants C_1 and C_2, the choices $C_1 = C_2 = 1$ and $C_1 = 1, C_2 = -1$ give, in turn, two solutions:

$$y_1 = e^{(\alpha+i\beta)x} + e^{(\alpha-i\beta)x} \qquad \text{and} \qquad y_2 = e^{(\alpha+i\beta)x} - e^{(\alpha-i\beta)x}.$$

But

$$y_1 = e^{\alpha x}(e^{i\beta x} + e^{-i\beta x}) = 2e^{\alpha x} \cos \beta x$$

and

$$y_2 = e^{\alpha x}(e^{i\beta x} - e^{-i\beta x}) = 2ie^{\alpha x} \sin \beta x.$$

Hence from Corollary (A) of Theorem 4.1.2 the last two results show that $e^{\alpha x} \cos \beta x$ and $e^{\alpha x} \sin \beta x$ are *real* solutions of (2). Moreover, these solutions form a fundamental set on $(-\infty, \infty)$. Consequently, the general solution is

$$y = c_1 e^{\alpha x} \cos \beta x + c_2 e^{\alpha x} \sin \beta x = e^{\alpha x}(c_1 \cos \beta x + c_2 \sin \beta x). \tag{8}$$

EXAMPLE 1 Second-Order DEs

Solve the following differential equations.

(a) $2y'' - 5y' - 3y = 0$ **(b)** $y'' - 10y' + 25y = 0$ **(c)** $y'' + 4y' + 7y = 0$

SOLUTION We give the auxiliary equations, the roots, and the corresponding general solutions.

(a) $2m^2 - 5m - 3 = (2m + 1)(m - 3) = 0, \quad m_1 = -\frac{1}{2}, m_2 = 3$

From (4), $y = c_1 e^{-x/2} + c_2 e^{3x}$.

(b) $m^2 - 10m + 25 = (m - 5)^2 = 0, \quad m_1 = m_2 = 5$

From (6), $y = c_1 e^{5x} + c_2 x e^{5x}$.

(c) $m^2 + 4m + 7 = 0, \quad m_1 = -2 + \sqrt{3}i, \quad m_2 = -2 - \sqrt{3}i$

From (8) with $\alpha = -2, \beta = \sqrt{3}, y = e^{-2x}(c_1 \cos \sqrt{3}x + c_2 \sin \sqrt{3}x)$. ∎

EXAMPLE 2 An Initial-Value Problem

Solve $4y'' + 4y' + 17y = 0, y(0) = -1, y'(0) = 2$.

SOLUTION By the quadratic formula we find that the roots of the auxiliary equation $4m^2 + 4m + 17 = 0$ are $m_1 = -\frac{1}{2} + 2i$ and $m_2 = -\frac{1}{2} - 2i$. Thus from (8) we have $y = e^{-x/2}(c_1 \cos 2x + c_2 \sin 2x)$. Applying the condition $y(0) = -1$, we see from $e^0(c_1 \cos 0 + c_2 \sin 0) = -1$ that $c_1 = -1$. Differentiating $y = e^{-x/2}(-\cos 2x + c_2 \sin 2x)$ and then using $y'(0) = 2$ gives $2c_2 + \frac{1}{2} = 2$ or $c_2 = \frac{3}{4}$. Hence the solution of the IVP is $y = e^{-x/2}(-\cos 2x + \frac{3}{4} \sin 2x)$. In Figure 4.3.1 we see that the solution is oscillatory, but $y \to 0$ as $x \to \infty$. ∎

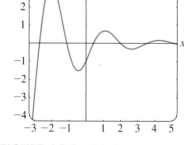

FIGURE 4.3.1 Solution curve of IVP in Example 2

TWO EQUATIONS WORTH KNOWING The two differential equations

$$y'' + k^2 y = 0 \qquad \text{and} \qquad y'' - k^2 y = 0,$$

where k is real, are important in applied mathematics. For $y'' + k^2 y = 0$ the auxiliary equation $m^2 + k^2 = 0$ has imaginary roots $m_1 = ki$ and $m_2 = -ki$. With $\alpha = 0$ and $\beta = k$ in (8) the general solution of the DE is seen to be

$$y = c_1 \cos kx + c_2 \sin kx. \tag{9}$$

On the other hand, the auxiliary equation $m^2 - k^2 = 0$ for $y'' - k^2 y = 0$ has distinct real roots $m_1 = k$ and $m_2 = -k$, and so by (4) the general solution of the DE is

$$y = c_1 e^{kx} + c_2 e^{-kx}. \tag{10}$$

Notice that if we choose $c_1 = c_2 = \frac{1}{2}$ and $c_1 = \frac{1}{2}, c_2 = -\frac{1}{2}$ in (10), we get the particular solutions $y = \frac{1}{2}(e^{kx} + e^{-kx}) = \cosh kx$ and $y = \frac{1}{2}(e^{kx} - e^{-kx}) = \sinh kx$. Since $\cosh kx$ and $\sinh kx$ are linearly independent on any interval of the x-axis, an alternative form for the general solution of $y'' - k^2 y = 0$ is

$$y = c_1 \cosh kx + c_2 \sinh kx. \tag{11}$$

See Problems 41 and 42 in Exercises 4.3.

HIGHER-ORDER EQUATIONS In general, to solve an nth-order differential equation (1), where the a_i, $i = 0, 1, \ldots, n$ are real constants, we must solve an nth-degree polynomial equation

$$a_n m^n + a_{n-1} m^{n-1} + \cdots + a_2 m^2 + a_1 m + a_0 = 0. \tag{12}$$

If all the roots of (12) are real and distinct, then the general solution of (1) is

$$y = c_1 e^{m_1 x} + c_2 e^{m_2 x} + \cdots + c_n e^{m_n x}.$$

It is somewhat harder to summarize the analogues of Cases II and III because the roots of an auxiliary equation of degree greater than two can occur in many combinations. For example, a fifth-degree equation could have five distinct real roots, or three distinct real and two complex roots, or one real and four complex roots, or five real but equal roots, or five real roots but two of them equal, and so on. When m_1 is a root of multiplicity k of an nth-degree auxiliary equation (that is, k roots are equal to m_1), it can be shown that the linearly independent solutions are

$$e^{m_1 x}, \quad x e^{m_1 x}, \quad x^2 e^{m_1 x}, \ldots, \quad x^{k-1} e^{m_1 x}$$

and the general solution must contain the linear combination

$$c_1 e^{m_1 x} + c_2 x e^{m_1 x} + c_3 x^2 e^{m_1 x} + \cdots + c_k x^{k-1} e^{m_1 x}.$$

Finally, it should be remembered that when the coefficients are real, complex roots of an auxiliary equation always appear in conjugate pairs. Thus, for example, a cubic polynomial equation can have at most two complex roots.

EXAMPLE 3 **Third-Order DE**

Solve $y''' + 3y'' - 4y = 0$.

SOLUTION It should be apparent from inspection of $m^3 + 3m^2 - 4 = 0$ that one root is $m_1 = 1$, so $m - 1$ is a factor of $m^3 + 3m^2 - 4$. By division we find

$$m^3 + 3m^2 - 4 = (m - 1)(m^2 + 4m + 4) = (m - 1)(m + 2)^2,$$

so the other roots are $m_2 = m_3 = -2$. Thus the general solution of the DE is $y = c_1 e^x + c_2 e^{-2x} + c_3 x e^{-2x}$. ∎

EXAMPLE 4   Fourth-Order DE

Solve $\dfrac{d^4 y}{dx^4} + 2\dfrac{d^2 y}{dx^2} + y = 0$.

SOLUTION The auxiliary equation $m^4 + 2m^2 + 1 = (m^2 + 1)^2 = 0$ has roots $m_1 = m_3 = i$ and $m_2 = m_4 = -i$. Thus from Case II the solution is

$$y = C_1 e^{ix} + C_2 e^{-ix} + C_3 x e^{ix} + C_4 x e^{-ix}.$$

By Euler's formula the grouping $C_1 e^{ix} + C_2 e^{-ix}$ can be rewritten as

$$c_1 \cos x + c_2 \sin x$$

after a relabeling of constants. Similarly, $x(C_3 e^{ix} + C_4 e^{-ix})$ can be expressed as $x(c_3 \cos x + c_4 \sin x)$. Hence the general solution is

$$y = c_1 \cos x + c_2 \sin x + c_3 x \cos x + c_4 x \sin x. \qquad \blacksquare$$

Example 4 illustrates a special case when the auxiliary equation has repeated complex roots. In general, if $m_1 = \alpha + i\beta$, $\beta > 0$ is a complex root of multiplicity k of an auxiliary with real coefficients, then its conjugate $m_2 = \alpha - i\beta$ is also a root of multiplicity k. From the $2k$ complex-valued solutions

$$e^{(\alpha+i\beta)x}, \quad x e^{(\alpha+i\beta)x}, \quad x^2 e^{(\alpha+i\beta)x}, \quad \ldots, \quad x^{k-1} e^{(\alpha+i\beta)x},$$

$$e^{(\alpha-i\beta)x}, \quad x e^{(\alpha-i\beta)x}, \quad x^2 e^{(\alpha-i\beta)x}, \quad \ldots, \quad x^{k-1} e^{(\alpha-i\beta)x},$$

we conclude, with the aid of Euler's formula, that the general solution of the corresponding differential equation must then contain a linear combination of the $2k$ real linearly independent solutions

$$e^{\alpha x} \cos \beta x, \quad x e^{\alpha x} \cos \beta x, \quad x^2 e^{\alpha x} \cos \beta x, \quad \ldots, \quad x^{k-1} e^{\alpha x} \cos \beta x,$$

$$e^{\alpha x} \sin \beta x, \quad x e^{\alpha x} \sin \beta x, \quad x^2 e^{\alpha x} \sin \beta x, \quad \ldots, \quad x^{k-1} e^{\alpha x} \sin \beta x.$$

In Example 4 we identify $k = 2$, $\alpha = 0$, and $\beta = 1$.

Of course the most difficult aspect of solving constant-coefficient differential equations is finding roots of auxiliary equations of degree greater than two. For example, to solve $3y''' + 5y'' + 10y' - 4y = 0$, we must solve $3m^3 + 5m^2 + 10m - 4 = 0$. Something we can try is to test the auxiliary equation for rational roots. Recall that if $m_1 = p/q$ is a rational root (expressed in lowest terms) of an auxiliary equation $a_n m^n + \cdots + a_1 m + a_0 = 0$ with integer coefficients, then p is a factor of a_0 and q is a factor of a_n. For our specific cubic auxiliary equation, all the factors of $a_0 = -4$ and $a_n = 3$ are p: $\pm 1, \pm 2, \pm 4$ and q: $\pm 1, \pm 3$, so the possible rational roots are p/q: $\pm 1, \pm 2, \pm 4, \pm\frac{1}{3}, \pm\frac{2}{3}, \pm\frac{4}{3}$. Each of these numbers can then be tested—say, by synthetic division. In this way we discover both the root $m_1 = \frac{1}{3}$ and the factorization

$$3m^3 + 5m^2 + 10m - 4 = \left(m - \tfrac{1}{3}\right)(3m^2 + 6m + 12).$$

The quadratic formula then yields the remaining roots $m_2 = -1 + \sqrt{3}i$ and $m_3 = -1 - \sqrt{3}i$. Therefore the general solution of $3y''' + 5y'' + 10y' - 4y = 0$ is $y = c_1 e^{x/3} + e^{-x}(c_2 \cos \sqrt{3}x + c_3 \sin \sqrt{3}x)$.

USE OF COMPUTERS Finding roots or approximation of roots of auxiliary equations is a routine problem with an appropriate calculator or computer software. Polynomial equations (in one variable) of degree less than five can be solved by means of algebraic formulas using the *solve* commands in *Mathematica* and *Maple*. For auxiliary equations of degree five or greater it might be necessary to resort to numerical commands such as **NSolve** and **FindRoot** in *Mathematica*. Because of their capability of solving polynomial equations, it is not surprising that these computer algebra

■ There is more on this in the *SRSM*.

systems are also able, by means of their *dsolve* commands, to provide explicit solutions of homogeneous linear constant-coefficient differential equations.

In the classic text *Differential Equations* by Ralph Palmer Agnew[*] (used by the author as a student) the following statement is made:

> *It is not reasonable to expect students in this course to have computing skill and equipment necessary for efficient solving of equations such as*

$$4.317\frac{d^4y}{dx^4} + 2.179\frac{d^3y}{dx^3} + 1.416\frac{d^2y}{dx^2} + 1.295\frac{dy}{dx} + 3.169y = 0. \tag{13}$$

Although it is debatable whether computing skills have improved in the intervening years, it is a certainty that technology has. If one has access to a computer algebra system, equation (13) could now be considered reasonable. After simplification and some relabeling of output, *Mathematica* yields the (approximate) general solution

$$y = c_1 e^{-0.728852x}\cos(0.618605x) + c_2 e^{-0.728852x}\sin(0.618605x)$$
$$+ c_3 e^{0.476478x}\cos(0.759081x) + c_4 e^{0.476478x}\sin(0.759081x).$$

Finally, if we are faced with an initial-value problem consisting of, say, a fourth-order equation, then to fit the general solution of the DE to the four initial conditions, we must solve four linear equations in four unknowns (the c_1, c_2, c_3, c_4 in the general solution). Using a CAS to solve the system can save lots of time. See Problems 59 and 60 in Exercises 4.3 and Problem 35 in Chapter 4 in Review.

---

[*]McGraw-Hill, New York, 1960.

EXERCISES 4.3

Answers to selected odd-numbered problems begin on page ANS-4.

In Problems 1–14 find the general solution of the given second-order differential equation.

1. $4y'' + y' = 0$

2. $y'' - 36y = 0$

3. $y'' - y' - 6y = 0$

4. $y'' - 3y' + 2y = 0$

5. $y'' + 8y' + 16y = 0$

6. $y'' - 10y' + 25y = 0$

7. $12y'' - 5y' - 2y = 0$

8. $y'' + 4y' - y = 0$

9. $y'' + 9y = 0$

10. $3y'' + y = 0$

11. $y'' - 4y' + 5y = 0$

12. $2y'' + 2y' + y = 0$

13. $3y'' + 2y' + y = 0$

14. $2y'' - 3y' + 4y = 0$

In Problems 15–28 find the general solution of the given higher-order differential equation.

15. $y''' - 4y'' - 5y' = 0$

16. $y''' - y = 0$

17. $y''' - 5y'' + 3y' + 9y = 0$

18. $y''' + 3y'' - 4y' - 12y = 0$

19. $\dfrac{d^3u}{dt^3} + \dfrac{d^2u}{dt^2} - 2u = 0$

20. $\dfrac{d^3x}{dt^3} - \dfrac{d^2x}{dt^2} - 4x = 0$

21. $y''' + 3y'' + 3y' + y = 0$

22. $y''' - 6y'' + 12y' - 8y = 0$

23. $y^{(4)} + y''' + y'' = 0$

24. $y^{(4)} - 2y'' + y = 0$

25. $16\dfrac{d^4y}{dx^4} + 24\dfrac{d^2y}{dx^2} + 9y = 0$

26. $\dfrac{d^4y}{dx^4} - 7\dfrac{d^2y}{dx^2} - 18y = 0$

27. $\dfrac{d^5u}{dr^5} + 5\dfrac{d^4u}{dr^4} - 2\dfrac{d^3u}{dr^3} - 10\dfrac{d^2u}{dr^2} + \dfrac{du}{dr} + 5u = 0$

28. $2\dfrac{d^5x}{ds^5} - 7\dfrac{d^4x}{ds^4} + 12\dfrac{d^3x}{ds^3} + 8\dfrac{d^2x}{ds^2} = 0$

In Problems 29–36 solve the given initial-value problem.

29. $y'' + 16y = 0$, $y(0) = 2$, $y'(0) = -2$

30. $\dfrac{d^2y}{d\theta^2} + y = 0$, $y\left(\dfrac{\pi}{3}\right) = 0$, $y'\left(\dfrac{\pi}{3}\right) = 2$

31. $\dfrac{d^2y}{dt^2} - 4\dfrac{dy}{dt} - 5y = 0, \quad y(1) = 0, y'(1) = 2$

32. $4y'' - 4y' - 3y = 0, \quad y(0) = 1, y'(0) = 5$

33. $y'' + y' + 2y = 0, \quad y(0) = y'(0) = 0$

34. $y'' - 2y' + y = 0, \quad y(0) = 5, y'(0) = 10$

35. $y''' + 12y'' + 36y' = 0, \quad y(0) = 0, y'(0) = 1, y''(0) = -7$

36. $y''' + 2y'' - 5y' - 6y = 0, \quad y(0) = y'(0) = 0, y''(0) = 1$

In Problems 37–40 solve the given boundary-value problem.

37. $y'' - 10y' + 25y = 0, \quad y(0) = 1, y(1) = 0$

38. $y'' + 4y = 0, \quad y(0) = 0, y(\pi) = 0$

39. $y'' + y = 0, \quad y'(0) = 0, y'\left(\dfrac{\pi}{2}\right) = 0$

40. $y'' - 2y' + 2y = 0, \quad y(0) = 1, y(\pi) = 1$

In Problems 41 and 42 solve the given problem first using the form of the general solution given in (10). Solve again, this time using the form given in (11).

41. $y'' - 3y = 0, \quad y(0) = 1, y'(0) = 5$

42. $y'' - y = 0, \quad y(0) = 1, y'(1) = 0$

In Problems 43–48 each figure represents the graph of a particular solution of one of the following differential equations:

    (a) $y'' - 3y' - 4y = 0$ **(b)** $y'' + 4y = 0$
    (c) $y'' + 2y' + y = 0$ **(d)** $y'' + y = 0$
    (e) $y'' + 2y' + 2y = 0$ **(f)** $y'' - 3y' + 2y = 0$

Match a solution curve with one of the differential equations. Explain your reasoning.

43.

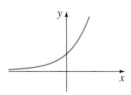

FIGURE 4.3.2   Graph for Problem 43

44.

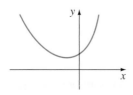

FIGURE 4.3.3   Graph for Problem 44

45.

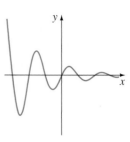

FIGURE 4.3.4   Graph for Problem 45

46.

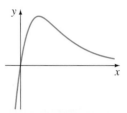

FIGURE 4.3.5   Graph for Problem 46

47.

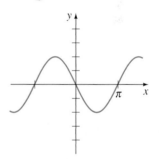

FIGURE 4.3.6   Graph for Problem 47

48.

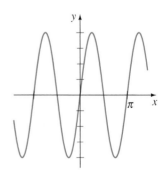

FIGURE 4.3.7   Graph for Problem 48

Discussion Problems

49. The roots of a cubic auxiliary equation are $m_1 = 4$ and $m_2 = m_3 = -5$. What is the corresponding homogeneous linear differential equation? Discuss: Is your answer unique?

50. Two roots of a cubic auxiliary equation with real coefficients are $m_1 = -\frac{1}{2}$ and $m_2 = 3 + i$. What is the corresponding homogeneous linear differential equation?

51. Find the general solution of $y''' + 6y'' + y' - 34y = 0$ if it is known that $y_1 = e^{-4x} \cos x$ is one solution.

52. To solve $y^{(4)} + y = 0$, we must find the roots of $m^4 + 1 = 0$. This is a trivial problem using a CAS but can also be done by hand working with complex numbers. Observe that $m^4 + 1 = (m^2 + 1)^2 - 2m^2$. How does this help? Solve the differential equation.

53. Verify that $y = \sinh x - 2 \cos (x + \pi/6)$ is a particular solution of $y^{(4)} - y = 0$. Reconcile this particular solution with the general solution of the DE.

54. Consider the boundary-value problem $y'' + \lambda y = 0$, $y(0) = 0$, $y(\pi/2) = 0$. Discuss: Is it possible to determine values of λ so that the problem possesses (**a**) trivial solutions? (**b**) nontrivial solutions?

Computer Lab Assignments

In Problems 55–58 use a computer either as an aid in solving the auxiliary equation or as a means of directly obtaining the general solution of the given differential equation. If you use a CAS to obtain the general solution, simplify the output and, if necessary, write the solution in terms of real functions.

55. $y''' - 6y'' + 2y' + y = 0$

56. $6.11y''' + 8.59y'' + 7.93y' + 0.778y = 0$

57. $3.15y^{(4)} - 5.34y'' + 6.33y' - 2.03y = 0$

58. $y^{(4)} + 2y'' - y' + 2y = 0$

In Problems 59 and 60 use a CAS as an aid in solving the auxiliary equation. Form the general solution of the differential equation. Then use a CAS as an aid in solving the system of equations for the coefficients c_i, $i = 1, 2, 3, 4$ that results when the initial conditions are applied to the general solution.

59. $2y^{(4)} + 3y''' - 16y'' + 15y' - 4y = 0$,
$y(0) = -2, y'(0) = 6, y''(0) = 3, y'''(0) = \frac{1}{2}$

60. $y^{(4)} - 3y''' + 3y'' - y' = 0$,
$y(0) = y'(0) = 0, y''(0) = y'''(0) = 1$

4.4 UNDETERMINED COEFFICIENTS—SUPERPOSITION APPROACH*

REVIEW MATERIAL
- Review Theorems 4.1.6 and 4.1.7 (Section 4.1)

INTRODUCTION To solve a nonhomogeneous linear differential equation

$$a_n y^{(n)} + a_{n-1} y^{(n-1)} + \cdots + a_1 y' + a_0 y = g(x), \tag{1}$$

we must do two things:
- find the complementary function y_c and
- find *any* particular solution y_p of the nonhomogeneous equation (1).

Then, as was discussed in Section 4.1, the general solution of (1) is $y = y_c + y_p$. The complementary function y_c is the general solution of the associated homogeneous DE of (1), that is,

$$a_n y^{(n)} + a_{n-1} y^{(n-1)} + \cdots + a_1 y' + a_0 y = 0.$$

In Section 4.3 we saw how to solve these kinds of equations when the coefficients were constants. Our goal in the present section is to develop a method for obtaining particular solutions.

---

*Note to the Instructor: In this section the method of undetermined coefficients is developed from the viewpoint of the superposition principle for nonhomogeneous equations (Theorem 4.7.1). In Section 4.5 an entirely different approach will be presented, one utilizing the concept of differential annihilator operators. Take your pick.

METHOD OF UNDETERMINED COEFFICIENTS The first of two ways we shall consider for obtaining a particular solution y_p for a nonhomogeneous linear DE is called the **method of undetermined coefficients.** The underlying idea behind this method is a conjecture about the form of y_p, an educated guess really, that is motivated by the kinds of functions that make up the input function $g(x)$. The general method is limited to linear DEs such as (1) where

- the coefficients a_i, $i = 0, 1, \ldots, n$ are constants and
- $g(x)$ is a constant k, a polynomial function, an exponential function $e^{\alpha x}$, a sine or cosine function $\sin \beta x$ or $\cos \beta x$, or finite sums and products of these functions.

NOTE Strictly speaking, $g(x) = k$ (constant) is a polynomial function. Since a constant function is probably not the first thing that comes to mind when you think of polynomial functions, for emphasis we shall continue to use the redundancy "constant functions, polynomials, ..."

The following functions are some examples of the types of inputs $g(x)$ that are appropriate for this discussion:

$$g(x) = 10, \quad g(x) = x^2 - 5x, \quad g(x) = 15x - 6 + 8e^{-x},$$

$$g(x) = \sin 3x - 5x \cos 2x, \quad g(x) = xe^x \sin x + (3x^2 - 1)e^{-4x}.$$

That is, $g(x)$ is a linear combination of functions of the type

$$P(x) = a_n x^n + a_{n-1} x^{n-1} + \cdots + a_1 x + a_0, \quad P(x) e^{\alpha x}, \quad P(x) e^{\alpha x} \sin \beta x, \quad \text{and} \quad P(x) e^{\alpha x} \cos \beta x,$$

where n is a nonnegative integer and α and β are real numbers. The method of undetermined coefficients is not applicable to equations of form (1) when

$$g(x) = \ln x, \quad g(x) = \frac{1}{x}, \quad g(x) = \tan x, \quad g(x) = \sin^{-1} x,$$

and so on. Differential equations in which the input $g(x)$ is a function of this last kind will be considered in Section 4.6.

The set of functions that consists of constants, polynomials, exponentials $e^{\alpha x}$, sines, and cosines has the remarkable property that derivatives of their sums and products are again sums and products of constants, polynomials, exponentials $e^{\alpha x}$, sines, and cosines. Because the linear combination of derivatives $a_n y_p^{(n)} + a_{n-1} y_p^{(n-1)} + \cdots + a_1 y_p' + a_0 y_p$ must be identical to $g(x)$, it seems reasonable to assume that y_p *has the same form as* $g(x)$.

The next two examples illustrate the basic method.

EXAMPLE 1 General Solution Using Undetermined Coefficients

Solve $y'' + 4y' - 2y = 2x^2 - 3x + 6$. $\hspace{2cm}$ (2)

SOLUTION **Step 1.** We first solve the associated homogeneous equation $y'' + 4y' - 2y = 0$. From the quadratic formula we find that the roots of the auxiliary equation $m^2 + 4m - 2 = 0$ are $m_1 = -2 - \sqrt{6}$ and $m_2 = -2 + \sqrt{6}$. Hence the complementary function is

$$y_c = c_1 e^{-(2+\sqrt{6})x} + c_2 e^{(-2+\sqrt{6})x}.$$

Step 2. Now, because the function $g(x)$ is a quadratic polynomial, let us assume a particular solution that is also in the form of a quadratic polynomial:

$$y_p = Ax^2 + Bx + C.$$

We seek to determine *specific* coefficients A, B, and C for which y_p is a solution of (2). Substituting y_p and the derivatives

$$y_p' = 2Ax + B \qquad \text{and} \qquad y_p'' = 2A$$

into the given differential equation (2), we get

$$y_p'' + 4y_p' - 2y_p = 2A + 8Ax + 4B - 2Ax^2 - 2Bx - 2C = 2x^2 - 3x + 6.$$

Because the last equation is supposed to be an identity, the coefficients of like powers of x must be equal:

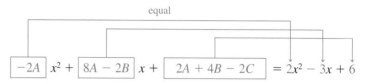

$$\boxed{-2A}\, x^2 + \boxed{8A - 2B}\, x + \boxed{2A + 4B - 2C} = 2x^2 - 3x + 6.$$

That is, $\quad -2A = 2, \quad\quad 8A - 2B = -3, \quad\quad 2A + 4B - 2C = 6.$

Solving this system of equations leads to the values $A = -1$, $B = -\frac{5}{2}$, and $C = -9$. Thus a particular solution is

$$y_p = -x^2 - \frac{5}{2}x - 9.$$

Step 3. The general solution of the given equation is

$$y = y_c + y_p = c_1 e^{-(2+\sqrt{6})x} + c_1 e^{(-2+\sqrt{6})x} - x^2 - \frac{5}{2}x - 9.$$ ∎

EXAMPLE 2 Particular Solution Using Undetermined Coefficients

Find a particular solution of $y'' - y' + y = 2 \sin 3x$.

SOLUTION A natural first guess for a particular solution would be $A \sin 3x$. But because successive differentiations of $\sin 3x$ produce $\sin 3x$ *and* $\cos 3x$, we are prompted instead to assume a particular solution that includes both of these terms:

$$y_p = A \cos 3x + B \sin 3x.$$

Differentiating y_p and substituting the results into the differential equation gives, after regrouping,

$$y_p'' - y_p' + y_p = (-8A - 3B) \cos 3x + (3A - 8B) \sin 3x = 2 \sin 3x$$

or

$$\boxed{-8A - 3B}\, \cos 3x + \boxed{3A - 8B}\, \sin 3x = 0 \cos 3x + 2 \sin 3x.$$

From the resulting system of equations,

$$-8A - 3B = 0, \qquad 3A - 8B = 2,$$

we get $A = \frac{6}{73}$ and $B = -\frac{16}{73}$. A particular solution of the equation is

$$y_p = \frac{6}{73} \cos 3x - \frac{16}{73} \sin 3x.$$ ∎

As we mentioned, the form that we assume for the particular solution y_p is an educated guess; it is not a blind guess. This educated guess must take into consideration not only the types of functions that make up $g(x)$ but also, as we shall see in Example 4, the functions that make up the complementary function y_c.

EXAMPLE 3 Forming y_p by Superposition

Solve $y'' - 2y' - 3y = 4x - 5 + 6xe^{2x}$. $\qquad\qquad$ (3)

SOLUTION Step 1. First, the solution of the associated homogeneous equation $y'' - 2y' - 3y = 0$ is found to be $y_c = c_1e^{-x} + c_2e^{3x}$.

Step 2. Next, the presence of $4x - 5$ in $g(x)$ suggests that the particular solution includes a linear polynomial. Furthermore, because the derivative of the product xe^{2x} produces $2xe^{2x}$ and e^{2x}, we also assume that the particular solution includes both xe^{2x} and e^{2x}. In other words, g is the sum of two basic kinds of functions:

$$g(x) = g_1(x) + g_2(x) = polynomial + exponentials.$$

Correspondingly, the superposition principle for nonhomogeneous equations (Theorem 4.1.7) suggests that we seek a particular solution

$$y_p = y_{p_1} + y_{p_2},$$

where $y_{p_1} = Ax + B$ and $y_{p_2} = Cxe^{2x} + Ee^{2x}$. Substituting

$$y_p = Ax + B + Cxe^{2x} + Ee^{2x}$$

into the given equation (3) and grouping like terms gives

$$y_p'' - 2y_p' - 3y_p = -3Ax - 2A - 3B - 3Cxe^{2x} + (2C - 3E)e^{2x} = 4x - 5 + 6xe^{2x}. \quad (4)$$

From this identity we obtain the four equations

$$-3A = 4, \qquad -2A - 3B = -5, \qquad -3C = 6, \qquad 2C - 3E = 0.$$

The last equation in this system results from the interpretation that the coefficient of e^{2x} in the right member of (4) is zero. Solving, we find $A = -\frac{4}{3}$, $B = \frac{23}{9}$, $C = -2$, and $E = -\frac{4}{3}$. Consequently,

$$y_p = -\frac{4}{3}x + \frac{23}{9} - 2xe^{2x} - \frac{4}{3}e^{2x}.$$

Step 3. The general solution of the equation is

$$y = c_1e^{-x} + c_2e^{3x} - \frac{4}{3}x + \frac{23}{9} - \left(2x + \frac{4}{3}\right)e^{2x}. \qquad \blacksquare$$

In light of the superposition principle (Theorem 4.1.7) we can also approach Example 3 from the viewpoint of solving two simpler problems. You should verify that substituting

$$y_{p_1} = Ax + B \qquad \text{into} \qquad y'' - 2y' - 3y = 4x - 5$$

and $\qquad y_{p_2} = Cxe^{2x} + Ee^{2x} \qquad \text{into} \qquad y'' - 2y' - 3y = 6xe^{2x}$

yields, in turn, $y_{p_1} = -\frac{4}{3}x + \frac{23}{9}$ and $y_{p_2} = -(2x + \frac{4}{3})e^{2x}$. A particular solution of (3) is then $y_p = y_{p_1} + y_{p_2}$.

The next example illustrates that sometimes the "obvious" assumption for the form of y_p is not a correct assumption.

EXAMPLE 4 A Glitch in the Method

Find a particular solution of $y'' - 5y' + 4y = 8e^x$.

SOLUTION Differentiation of e^x produces no new functions. Therefore proceeding as we did in the earlier examples, we can reasonably assume a particular solution of the form $y_p = Ae^x$. But substitution of this expression into the differential equation yields the contradictory statement $0 = 8e^x$, so we have clearly made the wrong guess for y_p.

The difficulty here is apparent on examining the complementary function $y_c = c_1 e^x + c_2 e^{4x}$. Observe that our assumption Ae^x is already present in y_c. This means that e^x is a solution of the associated homogeneous differential equation, and a constant multiple Ae^x when substituted into the differential equation necessarily produces zero.

What then should be the form of y_p? Inspired by Case II of Section 4.3, let's see whether we can find a particular solution of the form

$$y_p = Axe^x.$$

Substituting $y_p' = Axe^x + Ae^x$ and $y_p'' = Axe^x + 2Ae^x$ into the differential equation and simplifying gives

$$y_p'' - 5y_p' + 4y_p = -3Ae^x = 8e^x.$$

From the last equality we see that the value of A is now determined as $A = -\frac{8}{3}$. Therefore a particular solution of the given equation is $y_p = -\frac{8}{3}xe^x$. ∎

The difference in the procedures used in Examples 1–3 and in Example 4 suggests that we consider two cases. The first case reflects the situation in Examples 1–3.

CASE I No function in the assumed particular solution is a solution of the associated homogeneous differential equation.

In Table 4.1 we illustrate some specific examples of $g(x)$ in (1) along with the corresponding form of the particular solution. We are, of course, taking for granted that no function in the assumed particular solution y_p is duplicated by a function in the complementary function y_c.

TABLE 4.1 Trial Particular Solutions

$g(x)$	Form of y_p
1. 1 (any constant)	A
2. $5x + 7$	$Ax + B$
3. $3x^2 - 2$	$Ax^2 + Bx + C$
4. $x^3 - x + 1$	$Ax^3 + Bx^2 + Cx + E$
5. $\sin 4x$	$A \cos 4x + B \sin 4x$
6. $\cos 4x$	$A \cos 4x + B \sin 4x$
7. e^{5x}	Ae^{5x}
8. $(9x - 2)e^{5x}$	$(Ax + B)e^{5x}$
9. $x^2 e^{5x}$	$(Ax^2 + Bx + C)e^{5x}$
10. $e^{3x} \sin 4x$	$Ae^{3x} \cos 4x + Be^{3x} \sin 4x$
11. $5x^2 \sin 4x$	$(Ax^2 + Bx + C) \cos 4x + (Ex^2 + Fx + G) \sin 4x$
12. $xe^{3x} \cos 4x$	$(Ax + B)e^{3x} \cos 4x + (Cx + E)e^{3x} \sin 4x$

EXAMPLE 5   Forms of Particular Solutions—Case I

Determine the form of a particular solution of

(a) $y'' - 8y' + 25y = 5x^3 e^{-x} - 7e^{-x}$ **(b)** $y'' + 4y = x \cos x$

SOLUTION **(a)** We can write $g(x) = (5x^3 - 7)e^{-x}$. Using entry 9 in Table 4.1 as a model, we assume a particular solution of the form

$$y_p = (Ax^3 + Bx^2 + Cx + E)e^{-x}.$$

Note that there is no duplication between the terms in y_p and the terms in the complementary function $y_c = e^{4x}(c_1 \cos 3x + c_2 \sin 3x)$.

(b) The function $g(x) = x \cos x$ is similar to entry 11 in Table 4.1 except, of course, that we use a linear rather than a quadratic polynomial and $\cos x$ and $\sin x$ instead of $\cos 4x$ and $\sin 4x$ in the form of y_p:

$$y_p = (Ax + B)\cos x + (Cx + E)\sin x.$$

Again observe that there is no duplication of terms between y_p and $y_c = c_1 \cos 2x + c_2 \sin 2x$. ∎

If $g(x)$ consists of a sum of, say, m terms of the kind listed in the table, then (as in Example 3) the assumption for a particular solution y_p consists of the sum of the trial forms $y_{p_1}, y_{p_2}, \ldots, y_{p_m}$ corresponding to these terms:

$$y_p = y_{p_1} + y_{p_2} + \cdots + y_{p_m}.$$

The foregoing sentence can be put another way.

> **Form Rule for Case I** *The form of y_p is a linear combination of all linearly independent functions that are generated by repeated differentiations of $g(x)$.*

EXAMPLE 6   **Forming y_p by Superposition—Case I**

Determine the form of a particular solution of

$$y'' - 9y' + 14y = 3x^2 - 5\sin 2x + 7xe^{6x}.$$

SOLUTION

Corresponding to $3x^2$ we assume $y_{p_1} = Ax^2 + Bx + C.$

Corresponding to $-5\sin 2x$ we assume $y_{p_2} = E\cos 2x + F\sin 2x.$

Corresponding to $7xe^{6x}$ we assume $y_{p_3} = (Gx + H)e^{6x}.$

The assumption for the particular solution is then

$$y_p = y_{p_1} + y_{p_2} + y_{p_3} = Ax^2 + Bx + C + E\cos 2x + F\sin 2x + (Gx + H)e^{6x}.$$

No term in this assumption duplicates a term in $y_c = c_1 e^{2x} + c_2 e^{7x}$. ∎

CASE II   A function in the assumed particular solution is also a solution of the associated homogeneous differential equation.

The next example is similar to Example 4.

EXAMPLE 7   **Particular Solution—Case II**

Find a particular solution of $y'' - 2y' + y = e^x$.

SOLUTION   The complementary function is $y_c = c_1 e^x + c_2 x e^x$. As in Example 4, the assumption $y_p = Ae^x$ will fail, since it is apparent from y_c that e^x is a solution of the associated homogeneous equation $y'' - 2y' + y = 0$. Moreover, we will not be able to find a particular solution of the form $y_p = Axe^x$, since the term xe^x is also duplicated in y_c. We next try

$$y_p = Ax^2 e^x.$$

Substituting into the given differential equation yields $2Ae^x = e^x$, so $A = \frac{1}{2}$. Thus a particular solution is $y_p = \frac{1}{2}x^2 e^x$. ∎

Suppose again that $g(x)$ consists of m terms of the kind given in Table 4.1, and suppose further that the usual assumption for a particular solution is

$$y_p = y_{p_1} + y_{p_2} + \cdots + y_{p_m},$$

where the y_{p_i}, $i = 1, 2, \ldots, m$ are the trial particular solution forms corresponding to these terms. Under the circumstances described in Case II, we can make up the following general rule.

Multiplication Rule for Case II   *If any y_{p_i} contains terms that duplicate terms in y_c, then that y_{p_i} must be multiplied by x^n, where n is the smallest positive integer that eliminates that duplication.*

EXAMPLE 8   An Initial-Value Problem

Solve $y'' + y = 4x + 10 \sin x$, $y(\pi) = 0$, $y'(\pi) = 2$.

SOLUTION   The solution of the associated homogeneous equation $y'' + y = 0$ is $y_c = c_1 \cos x + c_2 \sin x$. Because $g(x) = 4x + 10 \sin x$ is the sum of a linear polynomial and a sine function, our normal assumption for y_p, from entries 2 and 5 of Table 4.1, would be the sum of $y_{p_1} = Ax + B$ and $y_{p_2} = C \cos x + E \sin x$:

$$y_p = Ax + B + C \cos x + E \sin x. \tag{5}$$

But there is an obvious duplication of the terms $\cos x$ and $\sin x$ in this assumed form and two terms in the complementary function. This duplication can be eliminated by simply multiplying y_{p_2} by x. Instead of (5) we now use

$$y_p = Ax + B + Cx \cos x + Ex \sin x. \tag{6}$$

Differentiating this expression and substituting the results into the differential equation gives

$$y_p'' + y_p = Ax + B - 2C \sin x + 2E \cos x = 4x + 10 \sin x,$$

and so $A = 4$, $B = 0$, $-2C = 10$, and $2E = 0$. The solutions of the system are immediate: $A = 4$, $B = 0$, $C = -5$, and $E = 0$. Therefore from (6) we obtain $y_p = 4x - 5x \cos x$. The general solution of the given equation is

$$y = y_c + y_p = c_1 \cos x + c_2 \sin x + 4x - 5x \cos x.$$

We now apply the prescribed initial conditions to the general solution of the equation. First, $y(\pi) = c_1 \cos \pi + c_2 \sin \pi + 4\pi - 5\pi \cos \pi = 0$ yields $c_1 = 9\pi$, since $\cos \pi = -1$ and $\sin \pi = 0$. Next, from the derivative

$$y' = -9\pi \sin x + c_2 \cos x + 4 + 5x \sin x - 5 \cos x$$

and $y'(\pi) = -9\pi \sin \pi + c_2 \cos \pi + 4 + 5\pi \sin \pi - 5 \cos \pi = 2$

we find $c_2 = 7$. The solution of the initial-value is then

$$y = 9\pi \cos x + 7 \sin x + 4x - 5x \cos x. \qquad \blacksquare$$

EXAMPLE 9   Using the Multiplication Rule

Solve $y'' - 6y' + 9y = 6x^2 + 2 - 12e^{3x}$.

SOLUTION   The complementary function is $y_c = c_1 e^{3x} + c_2 x e^{3x}$. And so, based on entries 3 and 7 of Table 4.1, the usual assumption for a particular solution would be

$$y_p = \underbrace{Ax^2 + Bx + C}_{y_{p_1}} + \underbrace{Ee^{3x}}_{y_{p_2}}.$$

Inspection of these functions shows that the one term in y_{p_2} is duplicated in y_c. If we multiply y_{p_2} by x, we note that the term xe^{3x} is still part of y_c. But multiplying y_{p_2} by x^2 eliminates all duplications. Thus the operative form of a particular solution is

$$y_p = Ax^2 + Bx + C + Ex^2e^{3x}.$$

Differentiating this last form, substituting into the differential equation, and collecting like terms gives

$$y_p'' - 6y_p' + 9y_p = 9Ax^2 + (-12A + 9B)x + 2A - 6B + 9C + 2Ee^{3x} = 6x^2 + 2 - 12e^{3x}.$$

It follows from this identity that $A = \frac{2}{3}$, $B = \frac{8}{9}$, $C = \frac{2}{3}$, and $E = -6$. Hence the general solution $y = y_c + y_p$ is $y = c_1e^{3x} + c_2xe^{3x} + \frac{2}{3}x^2 + \frac{8}{9}x + \frac{2}{3} - 6x^2e^{3x}$. ∎

EXAMPLE 10   Third-Order DE—Case I

Solve $y''' + y'' = e^x \cos x$.

SOLUTION From the characteristic equation $m^3 + m^2 = 0$ we find $m_1 = m_2 = 0$ and $m_3 = -1$. Hence the complementary function of the equation is $y_c = c_1 + c_2x + c_3e^{-x}$. With $g(x) = e^x \cos x$, we see from entry 10 of Table 4.1 that we should assume that

$$y_p = Ae^x \cos x + Be^x \sin x.$$

Because there are no functions in y_p that duplicate functions in the complementary solution, we proceed in the usual manner. From

$$y_p''' + y_p'' = (-2A + 4B)e^x \cos x + (-4A - 2B)e^x \sin x = e^x \cos x$$

we get $-2A + 4B = 1$ and $-4A - 2B = 0$. This system gives $A = -\frac{1}{10}$ and $B = \frac{1}{5}$, so a particular solution is $y_p = -\frac{1}{10}e^x \cos x + \frac{1}{5}e^x \sin x$. The general solution of the equation is

$$y = y_c + y_p = c_1 + c_2x + c_3e^{-x} - \frac{1}{10}e^x \cos x + \frac{1}{5}e^x \sin x.$$ ∎

EXAMPLE 11   Fourth-Order DE—Case II

Determine the form of a particular solution of $y^{(4)} + y''' = 1 - x^2e^{-x}$.

SOLUTION Comparing $y_c = c_1 + c_2x + c_3x^2 + c_4e^{-x}$ with our normal assumption for a particular solution

$$y_p = \underbrace{A}_{y_{p_1}} + \underbrace{Bx^2e^{-x} + Cxe^{-x} + Ee^{-x}}_{y_{p_2}},$$

we see that the duplications between y_c and y_p are eliminated when y_{p_1} is multiplied by x^3 and y_{p_2} is multiplied by x. Thus the correct assumption for a particular solution is $y_p = Ax^3 + Bx^3e^{-x} + Cx^2e^{-x} + Exe^{-x}$. ∎

REMARKS

(*i*) In Problems 27–36 in Exercises 4.4 you are asked to solve initial-value problems, and in Problems 37–40 you are asked to solve boundary-value problems. As illustrated in Example 8, be sure to apply the initial conditions or the boundary conditions to the general solution $y = y_c + y_p$. Students often make the mistake of applying these conditions only to the complementary function y_c because it is that part of the solution that contains the constants $c_1, c_2, \ldots, c_n$.

(*ii*) From the "Form Rule for Case I" on page 145 of this section you see why the method of undetermined coefficients is not well suited to nonhomogeneous linear DEs when the input function $g(x)$ is something other than one of the four basic types highlighted in color on page 141. For example, if $P(x)$ is a polynomial, then continued differentiation of $P(x)e^{\alpha x} \sin \beta x$ will generate an independent set containing only a *finite* number of functions—all of the same type, namely, a polynomial times $e^{\alpha x} \sin \beta x$ or a polynomial times $e^{\alpha x} \cos \beta x$. On the other hand, repeated differentiation of input functions such as $g(x) = \ln x$ or $g(x) = \tan^{-1} x$ generates an independent set containing an *infinite* number of functions:

$$\text{derivatives of } \ln x: \quad \frac{1}{x}, \frac{-1}{x^2}, \frac{2}{x^3}, \ldots,$$

$$\text{derivatives of } \tan^{-1} x: \quad \frac{1}{1 + x^2}, \frac{-2x}{(1 + x^2)^2}, \frac{-2 + 6x^2}{(1 + x^2)^3}, \ldots.$$

EXERCISES 4.4

Answers to selected odd-numbered problems begin on page ANS-5.

In Problems 1–26 solve the given differential equation by undetermined coefficients.

1. $y'' + 3y' + 2y = 6$

2. $4y'' + 9y = 15$

3. $y'' - 10y' + 25y = 30x + 3$

4. $y'' + y' - 6y = 2x$

5. $\frac{1}{4}y'' + y' + y = x^2 - 2x$

6. $y'' - 8y' + 20y = 100x^2 - 26xe^x$

7. $y'' + 3y = -48x^2 e^{3x}$

8. $4y'' - 4y' - 3y = \cos 2x$

9. $y'' - y' = -3$

10. $y'' + 2y' = 2x + 5 - e^{-2x}$

11. $y'' - y' + \frac{1}{4}y = 3 + e^{x/2}$

12. $y'' - 16y = 2e^{4x}$

13. $y'' + 4y = 3 \sin 2x$

14. $y'' - 4y = (x^2 - 3) \sin 2x$

15. $y'' + y = 2x \sin x$

16. $y'' - 5y' = 2x^3 - 4x^2 - x + 6$

17. $y'' - 2y' + 5y = e^x \cos 2x$

18. $y'' - 2y' + 2y = e^{2x}(\cos x - 3 \sin x)$

19. $y'' + 2y' + y = \sin x + 3 \cos 2x$

20. $y'' + 2y' - 24y = 16 - (x + 2)e^{4x}$

21. $y''' - 6y'' = 3 - \cos x$

22. $y''' - 2y'' - 4y' + 8y = 6xe^{2x}$

23. $y''' - 3y'' + 3y' - y = x - 4e^x$

24. $y''' - y'' - 4y' + 4y = 5 - e^x + e^{2x}$

25. $y^{(4)} + 2y'' + y = (x - 1)^2$

26. $y^{(4)} - y'' = 4x + 2xe^{-x}$

In Problems 27–36 solve the given initial-value problem.

27. $y'' + 4y = -2, \quad y\left(\frac{\pi}{8}\right) = \frac{1}{2}, y'\left(\frac{\pi}{8}\right) = 2$

28. $2y'' + 3y' - 2y = 14x^2 - 4x - 11, \quad y(0) = 0, y'(0) = 0$

29. $5y'' + y' = -6x, \quad y(0) = 0, y'(0) = -10$

30. $y'' + 4y' + 4y = (3 + x)e^{-2x}, \quad y(0) = 2, y'(0) = 5$

31. $y'' + 4y' + 5y = 35e^{-4x}, \quad y(0) = -3, y'(0) = 1$

32. $y'' - y = \cosh x, \quad y(0) = 2, y'(0) = 12$

33. $\dfrac{d^2x}{dt^2} + \omega^2 x = F_0 \sin \omega t, \quad x(0) = 0, x'(0) = 0$

34. $\dfrac{d^2x}{dt^2} + \omega^2 x = F_0 \cos \gamma t, \quad x(0) = 0, x'(0) = 0$

35. $y''' - 2y'' + y' = 2 - 24e^x + 40e^{5x}, \quad y(0) = \frac{1}{2}, \\ y'(0) = \frac{5}{2}, y''(0) = -\frac{9}{2}$

36. $y''' + 8y = 2x - 5 + 8e^{-2x}, \quad y(0) = -5, y'(0) = 3, \\ y''(0) = -4$

In Problems 37–40 solve the given boundary-value problem.

37. $y'' + y = x^2 + 1, \quad y(0) = 5, y(1) = 0$

38. $y'' - 2y' + 2y = 2x - 2, \quad y(0) = 0, y(\pi) = \pi$

39. $y'' + 3y = 6x, \quad y(0) = 0, y(1) + y'(1) = 0$

40. $y'' + 3y = 6x, \quad y(0) + y'(0) = 0, y(1) = 0$

In Problems 41 and 42 solve the given initial-value problem in which the input function $g(x)$ is discontinuous. [*Hint*: Solve each problem on two intervals, and then find a solution so that y and y' are continuous at $x = \pi/2$ (Problem 41) and at $x = \pi$ (Problem 42).]

41. $y'' + 4y = g(x), \quad y(0) = 1, y'(0) = 2, \quad$ where

$$g(x) = \begin{cases} \sin x, & 0 \le x \le \pi/2 \\ 0, & x > \pi/2 \end{cases}$$

42. $y'' - 2y' + 10y = g(x), \quad y(0) = 0, y'(0) = 0, \quad$ where

$$g(x) = \begin{cases} 20, & 0 \le x \le \pi \\ 0, & x > \pi \end{cases}$$

Discussion Problems

43. Consider the differential equation $ay'' + by' + cy = e^{kx}$, where a, b, c, and k are constants. The auxiliary equation of the associated homogeneous equation is $am^2 + bm + c = 0$.

   (a) If k is not a root of the auxiliary equation, show that we can find a particular solution of the form $y_p = Ae^{kx}$, where $A = 1/(ak^2 + bk + c)$.

   (b) If k is a root of the auxiliary equation of multiplicity one, show that we can find a particular solution of the form $y_p = Axe^{kx}$, where $A = 1/(2ak + b)$. Explain how we know that $k \ne -b/(2a)$.

   (c) If k is a root of the auxiliary equation of multiplicity two, show that we can find a particular solution of the form $y = Ax^2 e^{kx}$, where $A = 1/(2a)$.

44. Discuss how the method of this section can be used to find a particular solution of $y'' + y = \sin x \cos 2x$. Carry out your idea.

45. Without solving, match a solution curve of $y'' + y = f(x)$ shown in the figure with one of the following functions:

   (*i*) $f(x) = 1$,   (*ii*) $f(x) = e^{-x}$,

   (*iii*) $f(x) = e^x$,   (*iv*) $f(x) = \sin 2x$,

   (*v*) $f(x) = e^x \sin x$,   (*vi*) $f(x) = \sin x$.

Briefly discuss your reasoning.

(a)

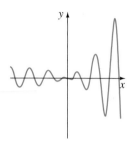

FIGURE 4.4.1   Solution curve

(b)

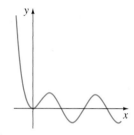

FIGURE 4.4.2   Solution curve

(c)

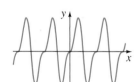

FIGURE 4.4.3   Solution curve

(d)

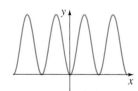

FIGURE 4.4.4   Solution curve

Computer Lab Assignments

In Problems 46 and 47 find a particular solution of the given differential equation. Use a CAS as an aid in carrying out differentiations, simplifications, and algebra.

46. $y'' - 4y' + 8y = (2x^2 - 3x)e^{2x} \cos 2x \\ \qquad\qquad\qquad + (10x^2 - x - 1)e^{2x} \sin 2x$

47. $y^{(4)} + 2y'' + y = 2 \cos x - 3x \sin x$

4.5	UNDETERMINED COEFFICIENTS—ANNIHILATOR APPROACH

REVIEW MATERIAL

• Review Theorems 4.1.6 and 4.1.7 (Section 4.1)

INTRODUCTION   We saw in Section 4.1 that an nth-order differential equation can be written

$$a_n D^n y + a_{n-1} D^{n-1} y + \cdots + a_1 Dy + a_0 y = g(x), \tag{1}$$

where $D^k y = d^k y / dx^k$, $k = 0, 1, \ldots, n$. When it suits our purpose, (1) is also written as $L(y) = g(x)$, where L denotes the linear nth-order differential, or polynomial, operator

$$a_n D^n + a_{n-1} D^{n-1} + \cdots + a_1 D + a_0. \tag{2}$$

Not only is the operator notation a helpful shorthand, but also on a very practical level the application of differential operators enables us to justify the somewhat mind-numbing rules for determining the form of particular solution y_p that were presented in the preceding section. In this section there are no special rules; the form of y_p follows almost automatically once we have found an appropriate linear differential operator that *annihilates* $g(x)$ in (1). Before investigating how this is done, we need to examine two concepts.

FACTORING OPERATORS   When the coefficients a_i, $i = 0, 1, \ldots, n$ are real constants, a linear differential operator (1) can be factored whenever the characteristic polynomial $a_n m^n + a_{n-1} m^{n-1} + \cdots + a_1 m + a_0$ factors. In other words, if r_1 is a root of the auxiliary equation

$$a_n m^n + a_{n-1} m^{n-1} + \cdots + a_1 m + a_0 = 0,$$

then $L = (D - r_1) P(D)$, where the polynomial expression $P(D)$ is a linear differential operator of order $n - 1$. For example, if we treat D as an algebraic quantity, then the operator $D^2 + 5D + 6$ can be factored as $(D + 2)(D + 3)$ or as $(D + 3)(D + 2)$. Thus if a function $y = f(x)$ possesses a second derivative, then

$$(D^2 + 5D + 6)y = (D + 2)(D + 3)y = (D + 3)(D + 2)y.$$

This illustrates a general property:

Factors of a linear differential operator with constant coefficients commute.

A differential equation such as $y'' + 4y' + 4y = 0$ can be written as

$$(D^2 + 4D + 4)y = 0 \quad \text{or} \quad (D + 2)(D + 2)y = 0 \quad \text{or} \quad (D + 2)^2 y = 0.$$

ANNIHILATOR OPERATOR   If L is a linear differential operator with constant coefficients and f is a sufficiently differentiable function such that

$$L(f(x)) = 0,$$

then L is said to be an **annihilator** of the function. For example, a constant function $y = k$ is annihilated by D, since $Dk = 0$. The function $y = x$ is annihilated by the differential operator D^2 since the first and second derivatives of x are 1 and 0, respectively. Similarly, $D^3 x^2 = 0$, and so on.

The differential operator D^n annihilates each of the functions

$$1, \quad x, \quad x^2, \quad \ldots, \quad x^{n-1}. \tag{3}$$

As an immediate consequence of (3) and the fact that differentiation can be done term by term, a polynomial

$$c_0 + c_1x + c_2x^2 + \cdots + c_{n-1}x^{n-1} \tag{4}$$

can be annihilated by finding an operator that annihilates the highest power of x.

The functions that are annihilated by a linear nth-order differential operator L are simply those functions that can be obtained from the general solution of the homogeneous differential equation $L(y) = 0$.

The differential operator $(D - \alpha)^n$ annihilates each of the functions

$$e^{\alpha x}, \quad xe^{\alpha x}, \quad x^2e^{\alpha x}, \quad \ldots, \quad x^{n-1}e^{\alpha x}. \tag{5}$$

To see this, note that the auxiliary equation of the homogeneous equation $(D - \alpha)^n y = 0$ is $(m - \alpha)^n = 0$. Since α is a root of multiplicity n, the general solution is

$$y = c_1e^{\alpha x} + c_2xe^{\alpha x} + \cdots + c_nx^{n-1}e^{\alpha x}. \tag{6}$$

EXAMPLE 1   Annihilator Operators

Find a differential operator that annihilates the given function.

(a) $1 - 5x^2 + 8x^3$ **(b)** e^{-3x} **(c)** $4e^{2x} - 10xe^{2x}$

SOLUTION   (a) From (3) we know that $D^4x^3 = 0$, so it follows from (4) that

$$D^4(1 - 5x^2 + 8x^3) = 0.$$

(b) From (5), with $\alpha = -3$ and $n = 1$, we see that

$$(D + 3)e^{-3x} = 0.$$

(c) From (5) and (6), with $\alpha = 2$ and $n = 2$, we have

$$(D - 2)^2(4e^{2x} - 10xe^{2x}) = 0. \qquad \blacksquare$$

When α and β, $\beta > 0$ are real numbers, the quadratic formula reveals that $[m^2 - 2\alpha m + (\alpha^2 + \beta^2)]^n = 0$ has complex roots $\alpha + i\beta$, $\alpha - i\beta$, both of multiplicity n. From the discussion at the end of Section 4.3 we have the next result.

The differential operator $[D^2 - 2\alpha D + (\alpha^2 + \beta^2)]^n$ annihilates each of the functions

$$e^{\alpha x}\cos\beta x, \quad xe^{\alpha x}\cos\beta x, \quad x^2e^{\alpha x}\cos\beta x, \quad \ldots, \quad x^{n-1}e^{\alpha x}\cos\beta x,$$
$$e^{\alpha x}\sin\beta x, \quad xe^{\alpha x}\sin\beta x, \quad x^2e^{\alpha x}\sin\beta x, \quad \ldots, \quad x^{n-1}e^{\alpha x}\sin\beta x. \tag{7}$$

EXAMPLE 2   Annihilator Operator

Find a differential operator that annihilates $5e^{-x}\cos 2x - 9e^{-x}\sin 2x$.

SOLUTION   Inspection of the functions $e^{-x}\cos 2x$ and $e^{-x}\sin 2x$ shows that $\alpha = -1$ and $\beta = 2$. Hence from (7) we conclude that $D^2 + 2D + 5$ will annihilate each function. Since $D^2 + 2D + 5$ is a linear operator, it will annihilate *any* linear combination of these functions such as $5e^{-x}\cos 2x - 9e^{-x}\sin 2x$. $\blacksquare$

When $\alpha = 0$ and $n = 1$, a special case of (7) is

$$(D^2 + \beta^2) \begin{cases} \cos \beta x \\ \sin \beta x \end{cases} = 0. \tag{8}$$

For example, $D^2 + 16$ will annihilate any linear combination of $\sin 4x$ and $\cos 4x$.

We are often interested in annihilating the sum of two or more functions. As we have just seen in Examples 1 and 2, if L is a linear differential operator such that $L(y_1) = 0$ and $L(y_2) = 0$, then L will annihilate the linear combination $c_1 y_1(x) + c_2 y_2(x)$. This is a direct consequence of Theorem 4.1.2. Let us now suppose that L_1 and L_2 are linear differential operators with constant coefficients such that L_1 annihilates $y_1(x)$ and L_2 annihilates $y_2(x)$, but $L_1(y_2) \neq 0$ and $L_2(y_1) \neq 0$. Then the *product* of differential operators $L_1 L_2$ annihilates the sum $c_1 y_1(x) + c_2 y_2(x)$. We can easily demonstrate this, using linearity and the fact that $L_1 L_2 = L_2 L_1$:

$$\begin{aligned} L_1 L_2(y_1 + y_2) &= L_1 L_2(y_1) + L_1 L_2(y_2) \\ &= L_2 L_1(y_1) + L_1 L_2(y_2) \\ &= L_2[\underbrace{L_1(y_1)}_{\text{zero}}] + L_1[\underbrace{L_2(y_2)}_{\text{zero}}] = 0. \end{aligned}$$

For example, we know from (3) that D^2 annihilates $7 - x$ and from (8) that $D^2 + 16$ annihilates $\sin 4x$. Therefore the product of operators $D^2(D^2 + 16)$ will annihilate the linear combination $7 - x + 6 \sin 4x$.

NOTE The differential operator that annihilates a function is not unique. We saw in part (b) of Example 1 that $D + 3$ will annihilate e^{-3x}, but so will differential operators of higher order as long as $D + 3$ is one of the factors of the operator. For example, $(D + 3)(D + 1)$, $(D + 3)^2$, and $D^3(D + 3)$ all annihilate e^{-3x}. (Verify this.) As a matter of course, when we seek a differential annihilator for a function $y = f(x)$, we want the operator of *lowest possible order* that does the job.

UNDETERMINED COEFFICIENTS This brings us to the point of the preceding discussion. Suppose that $L(y) = g(x)$ is a linear differential equation with constant coefficients and that the input $g(x)$ consists of finite sums and products of the functions listed in (3), (5), and (7)—that is, $g(x)$ is a linear combination of functions of the form

$$k \text{ (constant)}, \quad x^m, \quad x^m e^{\alpha x}, \quad x^m e^{\alpha x} \cos \beta x, \quad \text{and} \quad x^m e^{\alpha x} \sin \beta x,$$

where m is a nonnegative integer and α and β are real numbers. We now know that such a function $g(x)$ can be annihilated by a differential operator L_1 of lowest order, consisting of a product of the operators D^n, $(D - \alpha)^n$, and $(D^2 - 2\alpha D + \alpha^2 + \beta^2)^n$. Applying L_1 to both sides of the equation $L(y) = g(x)$ yields $L_1 L(y) = L_1(g(x)) = 0$. By solving the *homogeneous higher-order* equation $L_1 L(y) = 0$, we can discover the *form* of a particular solution y_p for the original *nonhomogeneous* equation $L(y) = g(x)$. We then substitute this assumed form into $L(y) = g(x)$ to find an explicit particular solution. This procedure for determining y_p, called the **method of undetermined coefficients**, is illustrated in the next several examples.

Before proceeding, recall that the general solution of a nonhomogeneous linear differential equation $L(y) = g(x)$ is $y = y_c + y_p$, where y_c is the complementary function—that is, the general solution of the associated homogeneous equation $L(y) = 0$. The general solution of each equation $L(y) = g(x)$ is defined on the interval $(-\infty, \infty)$.

EXAMPLE 3 General Solution Using Undetermined Coefficients

Solve $y'' + 3y' + 2y = 4x^2$. (9)

SOLUTION Step 1. First, we solve the homogeneous equation $y'' + 3y' + 2y = 0$. Then, from the auxiliary equation $m^2 + 3m + 2 = (m + 1)(m + 2) = 0$ we find $m_1 = -1$ and $m_2 = -2$, and so the complementary function is

$$y_c = c_1 e^{-x} + c_2 e^{-2x}.$$

Step 2. Now, since $4x^2$ is annihilated by the differential operator D^3, we see that $D^3(D^2 + 3D + 2)y = 4D^3 x^2$ is the same as

$$D^3(D^2 + 3D + 2)y = 0. \tag{10}$$

The auxiliary equation of the fifth-order equation in (10),

$$m^3(m^2 + 3m + 2) = 0 \quad \text{or} \quad m^3(m + 1)(m + 2) = 0,$$

has roots $m_1 = m_2 = m_3 = 0$, $m_4 = -1$, and $m_5 = -2$. Thus its general solution must be

$$y = c_1 + c_2 x + c_3 x^2 + \boxed{c_4 e^{-x} + c_5 e^{-2x}}. \tag{11}$$

The terms in the shaded box in (11) constitute the complementary function of the original equation (9). We can then argue that a particular solution y_p of (9) should also satisfy equation (10). This means that the terms remaining in (11) must be the basic form of y_p:

$$y_p = A + Bx + Cx^2, \tag{12}$$

where, for convenience, we have replaced c_1, c_2, and c_3 by A, B, and C, respectively. For (12) to be a particular solution of (9), it is necessary to find *specific* coefficients A, B, and C. Differentiating (12), we have

$$y_p' = B + 2Cx, \qquad y_p'' = 2C,$$

and substitution into (9) then gives

$$y_p'' + 3y_p' + 2y_p = 2C + 3B + 6Cx + 2A + 2Bx + 2Cx^2 = 4x^2.$$

Because the last equation is supposed to be an identity, the coefficients of like powers of x must be equal:

$$\boxed{2C}\,x^2 + \boxed{2B + 6C}\,x + \boxed{2A + 3B + 2C} = 4x^2 + 0x + 0.$$

That is $2C = 4$, $2B + 6C = 0$, $2A + 3B + 2C = 0$. (13)

Solving the equations in (13) gives $A = 7$, $B = -6$, and $C = 2$. Thus $y_p = 7 - 6x + 2x^2$.

Step 3. The general solution of the equation in (9) is $y = y_c + y_p$ or

$$y = c_1 e^{-x} + c_2 e^{-2x} + 7 - 6x + 2x^2. \qquad \blacksquare$$

EXAMPLE 4 **General Solution Using Undetermined Coefficients**

Solve $y'' - 3y' = 8e^{3x} + 4 \sin x$. $\qquad(14)$

SOLUTION **Step 1.** The auxiliary equation for the associated homogeneous equation $y'' - 3y' = 0$ is $m^2 - 3m = m(m - 3) = 0$, so $y_c = c_1 + c_2 e^{3x}$.

Step 2. Now, since $(D - 3)e^{3x} = 0$ and $(D^2 + 1) \sin x = 0$, we apply the differential operator $(D - 3)(D^2 + 1)$ to both sides of (14):

$$(D - 3)(D^2 + 1)(D^2 - 3D)y = 0. \qquad(15)$$

The auxiliary equation of (15) is

$$(m - 3)(m^2 + 1)(m^2 - 3m) = 0 \quad \text{or} \quad m(m - 3)^2(m^2 + 1) = 0.$$

Thus $\qquad y = \boxed{c_1 + c_2 e^{3x}} + c_3 x e^{3x} + c_4 \cos x + c_5 \sin x.$

After excluding the linear combination of terms in the box that corresponds to y_c, we arrive at the form of y_p:

$$y_p = Axe^{3x} + B \cos x + C \sin x.$$

Substituting y_p in (14) and simplifying yield

$$y_p'' - 3y_p' = 3Ae^{3x} + (-B - 3C) \cos x + (3B - C) \sin x = 8e^{3x} + 4 \sin x.$$

Equating coefficients gives $3A = 8$, $-B - 3C = 0$, and $3B - C = 4$. We find $A = \frac{8}{3}$, $B = \frac{6}{5}$, and $C = -\frac{2}{5}$, and consequently,

$$y_p = \frac{8}{3} xe^{3x} + \frac{6}{5} \cos x - \frac{2}{5} \sin x.$$

Step 3. The general solution of (14) is then

$$y = c_1 + c_2 e^{3x} + \frac{8}{3} xe^{3x} + \frac{6}{5} \cos x - \frac{2}{5} \sin x. \qquad\blacksquare$$

EXAMPLE 5 **General Solution Using Undetermined Coefficients**

Solve $y'' + y = x \cos x - \cos x$. $\qquad(16)$

SOLUTION The complementary function is $y_c = c_1 \cos x + c_2 \sin x$. Now by comparing $\cos x$ and $x \cos x$ with the functions in the first row of (7), we see that $\alpha = 0$ and $n = 1$, and so $(D^2 + 1)^2$ is an annihilator for the right-hand member of the equation in (16). Applying this operator to the differential equation gives

$$(D^2 + 1)^2 (D^2 + 1)y = 0 \quad \text{or} \quad (D^2 + 1)^3 y = 0.$$

Since i and $-i$ are both complex roots of multiplicity 3 of the auxiliary equation of the last differential equation, we conclude that

$$y = \boxed{c_1 \cos x + c_2 \sin x} + c_3 x \cos x + c_4 x \sin x + c_5 x^2 \cos x + c_6 x^2 \sin x.$$

We substitute

$$y_p = Ax \cos x + Bx \sin x + Cx^2 \cos x + Ex^2 \sin x$$

into (16) and simplify:

$$y_p'' + y_p = 4 Ex \cos x - 4 Cx \sin x + (2B + 2C) \cos x + (-2A + 2E) \sin x$$
$$= x \cos x - \cos x.$$

Equating coefficients gives the equations $4E = 1$, $-4C = 0$, $2B + 2C = -1$, and $-2A + 2E = 0$, from which we find $A = \frac{1}{4}$, $B = -\frac{1}{2}$, $C = 0$, and $E = \frac{1}{4}$. Hence the general solution of (16) is

$$y = c_1 \cos x + c_2 \sin x + \frac{1}{4}x \cos x - \frac{1}{2}x \sin x + \frac{1}{4}x^2 \sin x.$$ ∎

EXAMPLE 6   Form of a Particular Solution

Determine the form of a particular solution for

$$y'' - 2y' + y = 10e^{-2x}\cos x. \tag{17}$$

SOLUTION The complementary function for the given equation is $y_c = c_1 e^x + c_2 x e^x$.

Now from (7), with $\alpha = -2$, $\beta = 1$, and $n = 1$, we know that

$$(D^2 + 4D + 5)e^{-2x}\cos x = 0.$$

Applying the operator $D^2 + 4D + 5$ to (17) gives

$$(D^2 + 4D + 5)(D^2 - 2D + 1)y = 0. \tag{18}$$

Since the roots of the auxiliary equation of (18) are $-2 - i$, $-2 + i$, 1, and 1, we see from

$$y = c_1 e^x + c_2 x e^x + c_3 e^{-2x}\cos x + c_4 e^{-2x}\sin x$$

that a particular solution of (17) can be found with the form

$$y_p = Ae^{-2x}\cos x + Be^{-2x}\sin x.$$ ∎

EXAMPLE 7   Form of a Particular Solution

Determine the form of a particular solution for

$$y''' - 4y'' + 4y' = 5x^2 - 6x + 4x^2 e^{2x} + 3e^{5x}. \tag{19}$$

SOLUTION Observe that

$$D^3(5x^2 - 6x) = 0, \qquad (D - 2)^3 x^2 e^{2x} = 0, \qquad \text{and} \qquad (D - 5)e^{5x} = 0.$$

Therefore $D^3(D - 2)^3(D - 5)$ applied to (19) gives

$$D^3(D - 2)^3(D - 5)(D^3 - 4D^2 + 4D)y = 0$$

or

$$D^4(D - 2)^5(D - 5)y = 0.$$

The roots of the auxiliary equation for the last differential equation are easily seen to be $0, 0, 0, 0, 2, 2, 2, 2, 2$, and 5. Hence

$$y = c_1 + c_2 x + c_3 x^2 + c_4 x^3 + c_5 e^{2x} + c_6 x e^{2x} + c_7 x^2 e^{2x} + c_8 x^3 e^{2x} + c_9 x^4 e^{2x} + c_{10}e^{5x}. \tag{20}$$

Because the linear combination $c_1 + c_5 e^{2x} + c_6 x e^{2x}$ corresponds to the complementary function of (19), the remaining terms in (20) give the form of a particular solution of the differential equation:

$$y_p = Ax + Bx^2 + Cx^3 + Ex^2 e^{2x} + Fx^3 e^{2x} + Gx^4 e^{2x} + He^{5x}.$$ ∎

SUMMARY OF THE METHOD For your convenience the method of undetermined coefficients is summarized as follows.

UNDETERMINED COEFFICIENTS—ANNIHILATOR APPROACH

The differential equation $L(y) = g(x)$ has constant coefficients, and the function $g(x)$ consists of finite sums and products of constants, polynomials, exponential functions $e^{\alpha x}$, sines, and cosines.

(*i*) Find the complementary solution y_c for the homogeneous equation $L(y) = 0$.

(*ii*) Operate on both sides of the nonhomogeneous equation $L(y) = g(x)$ with a differential operator L_1 that annihilates the function $g(x)$.

(*iii*) Find the general solution of the higher-order homogeneous differential equation $L_1 L(y) = 0$.

(*iv*) Delete from the solution in step (*iii*) all those terms that are duplicated in the complementary solution y_c found in step (*i*). Form a linear combination y_p of the terms that remain. This is the form of a particular solution of $L(y) = g(x)$.

(*v*) Substitute y_p found in step (*iv*) into $L(y) = g(x)$. Match coefficients of the various functions on each side of the equality, and solve the resulting system of equations for the unknown coefficients in y_p.

(*vi*) With the particular solution found in step (*v*), form the general solution $y = y_c + y_p$ of the given differential equation.

REMARKS

The method of undetermined coefficients is not applicable to linear differential equations with variable coefficients nor is it applicable to linear equations with constant coefficients when $g(x)$ is a function such as

$$g(x) = \ln x, \qquad g(x) = \frac{1}{x}, \qquad g(x) = \tan x, \qquad g(x) = \sin^{-1} x,$$

and so on. Differential equations in which the input $g(x)$ is a function of this last kind will be considered in the next section.

EXERCISES 4.5

Answers to selected odd-numbered problems begin on page ANS-5.

In Problems 1–10 write the given differential equation in the form $L(y) = g(x)$, where L is a linear differential operator with constant coefficients. If possible, factor L.

1. $9y'' - 4y = \sin x$

2. $y'' - 5y = x^2 - 2x$

3. $y'' - 4y' - 12y = x - 6$

4. $2y'' - 3y' - 2y = 1$

5. $y''' + 10y'' + 25y' = e^x$

6. $y''' + 4y' = e^x \cos 2x$

7. $y''' + 2y'' - 13y' + 10y = xe^{-x}$

8. $y''' + 4y'' + 3y' = x^2 \cos x - 3x$

9. $y^{(4)} + 8y' = 4$

10. $y^{(4)} - 8y'' + 16y = (x^3 - 2x)e^{4x}$

In Problems 11–14 verify that the given differential operator annihilates the indicated functions.

11. D^4; $y = 10x^3 - 2x$

12. $2D - 1$; $y = 4e^{x/2}$

13. $(D - 2)(D + 5)$; $y = e^{2x} + 3e^{-5x}$

14. $D^2 + 64$; $y = 2 \cos 8x - 5 \sin 8x$

In Problems 15–26 find a linear differential operator that annihilates the given function.

15. $1 + 6x - 2x^3$

16. $x^3(1 - 5x)$

17. $1 + 7e^{2x}$

18. $x + 3xe^{6x}$

19. $\cos 2x$

20. $1 + \sin x$

21. $13x + 9x^2 - \sin 4x$

22. $8x - \sin x + 10 \cos 5x$

23. $e^{-x} + 2xe^x - x^2 e^x$

24. $(2 - e^x)^2$

25. $3 + e^x \cos 2x$

26. $e^{-x} \sin x - e^{2x} \cos x$

In Problems 27–34 find linearly independent functions that are annihilated by the given differential operator.

27. D^5

28. $D^2 + 4D$

29. $(D - 6)(2D + 3)$

30. $D^2 - 9D - 36$

31. $D^2 + 5$

32. $D^2 - 6D + 10$

33. $D^3 - 10D^2 + 25D$

34. $D^2(D - 5)(D - 7)$

In Problems 35–64 solve the given differential equation by undetermined coefficients.

35. $y'' - 9y = 54$

36. $2y'' - 7y' + 5y = -29$

37. $y'' + y' = 3$

38. $y''' + 2y'' + y' = 10$

39. $y'' + 4y' + 4y = 2x + 6$

40. $y'' + 3y' = 4x - 5$

41. $y''' + y'' = 8x^2$

42. $y'' - 2y' + y = x^3 + 4x$

43. $y'' - y' - 12y = e^{4x}$

44. $y'' + 2y' + 2y = 5e^{6x}$

45. $y'' - 2y' - 3y = 4e^x - 9$

46. $y'' + 6y' + 8y = 3e^{-2x} + 2x$

47. $y'' + 25y = 6 \sin x$

48. $y'' + 4y = 4 \cos x + 3 \sin x - 8$

49. $y'' + 6y' + 9y = -xe^{4x}$

50. $y'' + 3y' - 10y = x(e^x + 1)$

51. $y'' - y = x^2 e^x + 5$

52. $y'' + 2y' + y = x^2 e^{-x}$

53. $y'' - 2y' + 5y = e^x \sin x$

54. $y'' + y' + \dfrac{1}{4}y = e^x(\sin 3x - \cos 3x)$

55. $y'' + 25y = 20 \sin 5x$

56. $y'' + y = 4 \cos x - \sin x$

57. $y'' + y' + y = x \sin x$

58. $y'' + 4y = \cos^2 x$

59. $y''' + 8y'' = -6x^2 + 9x + 2$

60. $y''' - y'' + y' - y = xe^x - e^{-x} + 7$

61. $y''' - 3y'' + 3y' - y = e^x - x + 16$

62. $2y''' - 3y'' - 3y' + 2y = (e^x + e^{-x})^2$

63. $y^{(4)} - 2y''' + y'' = e^x + 1$

64. $y^{(4)} - 4y'' = 5x^2 - e^{2x}$

In Problems 65–72 solve the given initial-value problem.

65. $y'' - 64y = 16$, $\quad y(0) = 1, y'(0) = 0$

66. $y'' + y' = x$, $\quad y(0) = 1, y'(0) = 0$

67. $y'' - 5y' = x - 2$, $\quad y(0) = 0, y'(0) = 2$

68. $y'' + 5y' - 6y = 10e^{2x}$, $\quad y(0) = 1, y'(0) = 1$

69. $y'' + y = 8 \cos 2x - 4 \sin x$, $\quad y\left(\dfrac{\pi}{2}\right) = -1, y'\left(\dfrac{\pi}{2}\right) = 0$

70. $y''' - 2y'' + y' = xe^x + 5$, $\quad y(0) = 2, y'(0) = 2$, $y''(0) = -1$

71. $y'' - 4y' + 8y = x^3$, $\quad y(0) = 2, y'(0) = 4$

72. $y^{(4)} - y''' = x + e^x$, $\quad y(0) = 0, y'(0) = 0, y''(0) = 0$, $y'''(0) = 0$

Discussion Problems

73. Suppose L is a linear differential operator that factors but has variable coefficients. Do the factors of L commute? Defend your answer.

4.6 VARIATION OF PARAMETERS

REVIEW MATERIAL

- Variation of parameters was first introduced in Section 2.3 and used again in Section 4.2. A review of those sections is recommended.

INTRODUCTION The procedure that we used to find a particular solution y_p of a linear first-order differential equation on an interval is applicable to linear higher-order DEs as well. To adapt the method of **variation of parameters** to a linear second-order differential equation

$$a_2(x)y'' + a_1(x)y' + a_0(x)y = g(x), \tag{1}$$

we begin by putting the equation into the standard form

$$y'' + P(x)y' + Q(x)y = f(x) \tag{2}$$

by dividing through by the lead coefficient $a_2(x)$. Equation (2) is the second-order analogue of the standard form of a linear first-order equation: $dy/dx + P(x)y = f(x)$. In (2) we suppose that $P(x)$, $Q(x)$, and $f(x)$ are continuous on some common interval I. As we have already seen in Section 4.3, there is no difficulty in obtaining the complementary function y_c, the general solution of the associated homogeneous equation of (2), when the coefficients are constant.

ASSUMPTIONS Corresponding to the assumption $y_p = u_1(x)y_1(x)$ that we used in Section 2.3 to find a particular solution y_p of $dy/dx + P(x)y = f(x)$, for the linear second-order equation (2) we seek a solution of the form

$$y_p = u_1(x)y_1(x) + u_2(x)y_2(x), \tag{3}$$

where y_1 and y_2 form a fundamental set of solutions on I of the associated homogeneous form of (1). Using the Product Rule to differentiate y_p twice, we get

$$y'_p = u_1y'_1 + y_1u'_1 + u_2y'_2 + y_2u'_2$$

$$y''_p = u_1y''_1 + y'_1u'_1 + y_1u''_1 + u'_1y'_1 + u_2y''_2 + y'_2u'_2 + y_2u''_2 + u'_2y'_2.$$

Substituting (3) and the foregoing derivatives into (2) and grouping terms yields

$$y''_p + P(x)y'_p + Q(x)y_p = u_1[\overset{\text{zero}}{y''_1 + Py'_1 + Qy_1}] + u_2[\overset{\text{zero}}{y''_2 + Py'_2 + Qy_2}] + y_1u''_1 + u'_1y'_1$$

$$+ y_2u''_2 + u'_2y'_2 + P[y_1u'_1 + y_2u'_2] + y'_1u'_1 + y'_2u'_2$$

$$= \frac{d}{dx}[y_1u'_1] + \frac{d}{dx}[y_2u'_2] + P[y_1u'_1 + y_2u'_2] + y'_1u'_1 + y'_2u'_2$$

$$= \frac{d}{dx}[y_1u'_1 + y_2u'_2] + P[y_1u'_1 + y_2u'_2] + y'_1u'_1 + y'_2u'_2 = f(x). \tag{4}$$

Because we seek to determine two unknown functions u_1 and u_2, reason dictates that we need two equations. We can obtain these equations by making the further assumption that the functions u_1 and u_2 satisfy $y_1u'_1 + y_2u'_2 = 0$. This assumption does not come out of the blue but is prompted by the first two terms in (4), since if we demand that $y_1u'_1 + y_2u'_2 = 0$, then (4) reduces to $y'_1u'_1 + y'_2u'_2 = f(x)$. We now have our desired two equations, albeit two equations for determining the derivatives u'_1 and u'_2. By Cramer's Rule, the solution of the system

$$y_1u'_1 + y_2u'_2 = 0$$

$$y'_1u'_1 + y'_2u'_2 = f(x)$$

can be expressed in terms of determinants:

$$u'_1 = \frac{W_1}{W} = -\frac{y_2 f(x)}{W} \quad \text{and} \quad u'_2 = \frac{W_2}{W} = \frac{y_1 f(x)}{W}, \tag{5}$$

where

$$W = \begin{vmatrix} y_1 & y_2 \\ y'_1 & y'_2 \end{vmatrix}, \quad W_1 = \begin{vmatrix} 0 & y_2 \\ f(x) & y'_2 \end{vmatrix}, \quad W_2 = \begin{vmatrix} y_1 & 0 \\ y'_1 & f(x) \end{vmatrix}. \tag{6}$$

The functions u_1 and u_2 are found by integrating the results in (5). The determinant W is recognized as the Wronskian of y_1 and y_2. By linear independence of y_1 and y_2 on I, we know that $W(y_1(x), y_2(x)) \neq 0$ for every x in the interval.

SUMMARY OF THE METHOD Usually, it is not a good idea to memorize formulas in lieu of understanding a procedure. However, the foregoing procedure is too long and complicated to use each time we wish to solve a differential equation. In this case it is more efficient to simply use the formulas in (5). Thus to solve $a_2y'' + a_1y' + a_0y = g(x)$, first find the complementary function $y_c = c_1y_1 + c_2y_2$ and then compute the Wronskian $W(y_1(x), y_2(x))$. By dividing by a_2, we put the equation into the standard form $y'' + Py' + Qy = f(x)$ to determine $f(x)$. We find u_1 and u_2 by integrating $u'_1 = W_1/W$ and $u'_2 = W_2/W$, where W_1 and W_2 are defined as in (6). A particular solution is $y_p = u_1y_1 + u_2y_2$. The general solution of the equation is then $y = y_c + y_p$.

EXAMPLE 1   General Solution Using Variation of Parameters

Solve $y'' - 4y' + 4y = (x + 1)e^{2x}$.

SOLUTION   From the auxiliary equation $m^2 - 4m + 4 = (m - 2)^2 = 0$ we have $y_c = c_1 e^{2x} + c_2 x e^{2x}$. With the identifications $y_1 = e^{2x}$ and $y_2 = xe^{2x}$, we next compute the Wronskian:

$$W(e^{2x}, xe^{2x}) = \begin{vmatrix} e^{2x} & xe^{2x} \\ 2e^{2x} & 2xe^{2x} + e^{2x} \end{vmatrix} = e^{4x}.$$

Since the given differential equation is already in form (2) (that is, the coefficient of y'' is 1), we identify $f(x) = (x + 1)e^{2x}$. From (6) we obtain

$$W_1 = \begin{vmatrix} 0 & xe^{2x} \\ (x + 1)e^{2x} & 2xe^{2x} + e^{2x} \end{vmatrix} = -(x + 1)xe^{4x}, \qquad W_2 = \begin{vmatrix} e^{2x} & 0 \\ 2e^{2x} & (x + 1)e^{2x} \end{vmatrix} = (x + 1)e^{4x},$$

and so from (5)

$$u_1' = -\frac{(x + 1)xe^{4x}}{e^{4x}} = -x^2 - x, \qquad u_2' = \frac{(x + 1)e^{4x}}{e^{4x}} = x + 1.$$

It follows that $u_1 = -\frac{1}{3}x^3 - \frac{1}{2}x^2$ and $u_2 = \frac{1}{2}x^2 + x$. Hence

$$y_p = \left(-\frac{1}{3}x^3 - \frac{1}{2}x^2 \right)e^{2x} + \left(\frac{1}{2}x^2 + x \right)xe^{2x} = \frac{1}{6}x^3 e^{2x} + \frac{1}{2}x^2 e^{2x}$$

and

$$y = y_c + y_p = c_1 e^{2x} + c_2 x e^{2x} + \frac{1}{6}x^3 e^{2x} + \frac{1}{2}x^2 e^{2x}. \qquad \blacksquare$$

EXAMPLE 2   General Solution Using Variation of Parameters

Solve $4y'' + 36y = \csc 3x$.

SOLUTION   We first put the equation in the standard form (2) by dividing by 4:

$$y'' + 9y = \frac{1}{4}\csc 3x.$$

Because the roots of the auxiliary equation $m^2 + 9 = 0$ are $m_1 = 3i$ and $m_2 = -3i$, the complementary function is $y_c = c_1 \cos 3x + c_2 \sin 3x$. Using $y_1 = \cos 3x$, $y_2 = \sin 3x$, and $f(x) = \frac{1}{4}\csc 3x$, we obtain

$$W(\cos 3x, \sin 3x) = \begin{vmatrix} \cos 3x & \sin 3x \\ -3\sin 3x & 3\cos 3x \end{vmatrix} = 3,$$

$$W_1 = \begin{vmatrix} 0 & \sin 3x \\ \frac{1}{4}\csc 3x & 3\cos 3x \end{vmatrix} = -\frac{1}{4}, \qquad W_2 = \begin{vmatrix} \cos 3x & 0 \\ -3\sin 3x & \frac{1}{4}\csc 3x \end{vmatrix} = \frac{1}{4}\frac{\cos 3x}{\sin 3x}.$$

Integrating $u_1' = \dfrac{W_1}{W} = -\dfrac{1}{12}$ and $u_2' = \dfrac{W_2}{W} = \dfrac{1}{12}\dfrac{\cos 3x}{\sin 3x}$

gives $u_1 = -\frac{1}{12}x$ and $u_2 = \frac{1}{36}\ln|\sin 3x|$. Thus a particular solution is

$$y_p = -\frac{1}{12}x\cos 3x + \frac{1}{36}(\sin 3x)\ln|\sin 3x|.$$

The general solution of the equation is

$$y = y_c + y_p = c_1 \cos 3x + c_2 \sin 3x - \frac{1}{12}x\cos 3x + \frac{1}{36}(\sin 3x)\ln|\sin 3x|. \qquad (7) \quad \blacksquare$$

Equation (7) represents the general solution of the differential equation on, say, the interval $(0, \pi/6)$.

CONSTANTS OF INTEGRATION When computing the indefinite integrals of u_1' and u_2', we need not introduce any constants. This is because

$$y = y_c + y_p = c_1 y_1 + c_2 y_2 + (u_1 + a_1)y_1 + (u_2 + b_1)y_2$$
$$= (c_1 + a_1)y_1 + (c_2 + b_1)y_2 + u_1 y_1 + u_2 y_2$$
$$= C_1 y_1 + C_2 y_2 + u_1 y_1 + u_2 y_2.$$

EXAMPLE 3 **General Solution Using Variation of Parameters**

Solve $y'' - y = \dfrac{1}{x}$.

SOLUTION The auxiliary equation $m^2 - 1 = 0$ yields $m_1 = -1$ and $m_2 = 1$. Therefore $y_c = c_1 e^x + c_2 e^{-x}$. Now $W(e^x, e^{-x}) = -2$, and

$$u_1' = -\frac{e^{-x}(1/x)}{-2}, \qquad u_1 = \frac{1}{2}\int_{x_0}^x \frac{e^{-t}}{t}\, dt,$$

$$u_2' = \frac{e^x(1/x)}{-2}, \qquad u_2 = -\frac{1}{2}\int_{x_0}^x \frac{e^t}{t}\, dt.$$

Since the foregoing integrals are nonelementary, we are forced to write

$$y_p = \frac{1}{2}e^x \int_{x_0}^x \frac{e^{-t}}{t}\, dt - \frac{1}{2}e^{-x}\int_{x_0}^x \frac{e^t}{t}\, dt,$$

and so $\quad y = y_c + y_p = c_1 e^x + c_2 e^{-x} + \dfrac{1}{2}e^x \int_{x_0}^x \dfrac{e^{-t}}{t}\, dt - \dfrac{1}{2}e^{-x}\int_{x_0}^x \dfrac{e^t}{t}\, dt.$ (8) ∎

In Example 3 we can integrate on any interval $[x_0, x]$ that does not contain the origin.

HIGHER-ORDER EQUATIONS The method that we have just examined for nonhomogeneous second-order differential equations can be generalized to linear nth-order equations that have been put into the standard form

$$y^{(n)} + P_{n-1}(x)y^{(n-1)} + \cdots + P_1(x)y' + P_0(x)y = f(x). \tag{9}$$

If $y_c = c_1 y_1 + c_2 y_2 + \cdots + c_n y_n$ is the complementary function for (9), then a particular solution is

$$y_p = u_1(x)y_1(x) + u_2(x)y_2(x) + \cdots + u_n(x)y_n(x),$$

where the u_k', $k = 1, 2, \ldots, n$ are determined by the n equations

$$y_1 u_1' + y_2 u_2' + \cdots + y_n u_n' = 0$$
$$y_1' u_1' + y_2' u_2' + \cdots + y_n' u_n' = 0$$
$$\vdots \qquad\qquad\qquad \vdots \tag{10}$$
$$y_1^{(n-1)} u_1' + y_2^{(n-1)} u_2' + \cdots + y_n^{(n-1)} u_n' = f(x).$$

The first $n - 1$ equations in this system, like $y_1 u_1' + y_2 u_2' = 0$ in (4), are assumptions that are made to simplify the resulting equation after $y_p = u_1(x)y_1(x) + \cdots + u_n(x)y_n(x)$ is substituted in (9). In this case Cramer's rule gives

$$u_k' = \frac{W_k}{W}, \quad k = 1, 2, \ldots, n,$$

where W is the Wronskian of $y_1, y_2, \ldots, y_n$ and W_k is the determinant obtained by replacing the kth column of the Wronskian by the column consisting of the right-hand side of (10)—that is, the column consisting of $(0, 0, \ldots, f(x))$. When $n = 2$, we get (5). When $n = 3$, the particular solution is $y_p = u_1 y_1 + u_2 y_2 + u_3 y_3$, where y_1, y_2, and y_3 constitute a linearly independent set of solutions of the associated homogeneous DE and u_1, u_2, u_3 are determined from

$$u_1' = \frac{W_1}{W}, \quad u_2' = \frac{W_2}{W}, \quad u_3' = \frac{W_3}{W}, \tag{11}$$

$$W_1 = \begin{vmatrix} 0 & y_2 & y_3 \\ 0 & y_2' & y_3' \\ f(x) & y_2'' & y_3'' \end{vmatrix}, \quad W_2 = \begin{vmatrix} y_1 & 0 & y_3 \\ y_1' & 0 & y_3' \\ y_1'' & f(x) & y_3'' \end{vmatrix}, \quad W_3 = \begin{vmatrix} y_1 & y_2 & 0 \\ y_1' & y_2' & 0 \\ y_1'' & y_2'' & f(x) \end{vmatrix}, \quad \text{and} \quad W = \begin{vmatrix} y_1 & y_2 & y_3 \\ y_1' & y_2' & y_3' \\ y_1'' & y_2'' & y_3'' \end{vmatrix}.$$

See Problems 25 and 26 in Exercises 4.6.

REMARKS

(*i*) Variation of parameters has a distinct advantage over the method of undetermined coefficients in that it will *always* yield a particular solution y_p provided that the associated homogeneous equation can be solved. The present method is not limited to a function $f(x)$ that is a combination of the four types listed on page 141. As we shall see in the next section, variation of parameters, unlike undetermined coefficients, is applicable to linear DEs with variable coefficients.

(*ii*) In the problems that follow, do not hesitate to simplify the form of y_p. Depending on how the antiderivatives of u_1' and u_2' are found, you might not obtain the same y_p as given in the answer section. For example, in Problem 3 in Exercises 4.6 both $y_p = \frac{1}{2} \sin x - \frac{1}{2} x \cos x$ and $y_p = \frac{1}{4} \sin x - \frac{1}{2} x \cos x$ are valid answers. In either case the general solution $y = y_c + y_p$ simplifies to $y = c_1 \cos x + c_2 \sin x - \frac{1}{2} x \cos x$. Why?

EXERCISES 4.6

Answers to selected odd-numbered problems begin on page ANS-5.

In Problems 1–18 solve each differential equation by variation of parameters.

1. $y'' + y = \sec x$

2. $y'' + y = \tan x$

3. $y'' + y = \sin x$

4. $y'' + y = \sec \theta \tan \theta$

5. $y'' + y = \cos^2 x$

6. $y'' + y = \sec^2 x$

7. $y'' - y = \cosh x$

8. $y'' - y = \sinh 2x$

9. $y'' - 4y = \dfrac{e^{2x}}{x}$

10. $y'' - 9y = \dfrac{9x}{e^{3x}}$

11. $y'' + 3y' + 2y = \dfrac{1}{1 + e^x}$

12. $y'' - 2y' + y = \dfrac{e^x}{1 + x^2}$

13. $y'' + 3y' + 2y = \sin e^x$

14. $y'' - 2y' + y = e^t \arctan t$

15. $y'' + 2y' + y = e^{-t} \ln t$ **16.** $2y'' + 2y' + y = 4\sqrt{x}$

17. $3y'' - 6y' + 6y = e^x \sec x$

18. $4y'' - 4y' + y = e^{x/2}\sqrt{1 - x^2}$

In Problems 19–22 solve each differential equation by variation of parameters, subject to the initial conditions $y(0) = 1$, $y'(0) = 0$.

19. $4y'' - y = xe^{x/2}$

20. $2y'' + y' - y = x + 1$

21. $y'' + 2y' - 8y = 2e^{-2x} - e^{-x}$

22. $y'' - 4y' + 4y = (12x^2 - 6x)e^{2x}$

In Problems 23 and 24 the indicated functions are known linearly independent solutions of the associated homogeneous differential equation on $(0, \infty)$. Find the general solution of the given nonhomogeneous equation.

23. $x^2y'' + xy' + \left(x^2 - \frac{1}{4}\right)y = x^{3/2}$;

$y_1 = x^{-1/2} \cos x$, $y_2 = x^{-1/2} \sin x$

24. $x^2y'' + xy' + y = \sec(\ln x)$;

$y_1 = \cos(\ln x)$, $y_2 = \sin(\ln x)$

In Problems 25 and 26 solve the given third-order differential equation by variation of parameters.

25. $y''' + y' = \tan x$ **26.** $y''' + 4y' = \sec 2x$

Discussion Problems

In Problems 27 and 28 discuss how the methods of undetermined coefficients and variation of parameters can be combined to solve the given differential equation. Carry out your ideas.

27. $3y'' - 6y' + 30y = 15 \sin x + e^x \tan 3x$

28. $y'' - 2y' + y = 4x^2 - 3 + x^{-1}e^x$

29. What are the intervals of definition of the general solutions in Problems 1, 7, 9, and 18? Discuss why the interval of definition of the general solution in Problem 24 is *not* $(0, \infty)$.

30. Find the general solution of $x^4y'' + x^3y' - 4x^2y = 1$ given that $y_1 = x^2$ is a solution of the associated homogeneous equation.

31. Suppose $y_p(x) = u_1(x)y_1(x) + u_2(x)y_2(x)$, where u_1 and u_2 are defined by (5) is a particular solution of (2) on an interval I for which P, Q, and f are continuous. Show that y_p can be written as

$$y_p(x) = \int_{x_0}^{x} G(x, t)f(t) \, dt, \qquad (12)$$

where x and x_0 are in I,

$$G(x, t) = \frac{y_1(t)y_2(x) - y_1(x)y_2(t)}{W(t)}, \qquad (13)$$

and $W(t) = W(y_1(t), y_2(t))$ is the Wronskian. The function $G(x, t)$ in (13) is called the **Green's function** for the differential equation (2).

32. Use (13) to construct the Green's function for the differential equation in Example 3. Express the general solution given in (8) in terms of the particular solution (12).

33. Verify that (12) is a solution of the initial-value problem

$$\frac{d^2y}{dx^2} + P\frac{dy}{dx} + Qy = f(x), \quad y(x_0) = 0, \quad y'(x_0) = 0.$$

on the interval I. [*Hint*: Look up Leibniz's Rule for differentiation under an integral sign.]

34. Use the results of Problems 31 and 33 and the Green's function found in Problem 32 to find a solution of the initial-value problem

$$y'' - y = e^{2x}, \quad y(0) = 0, \quad y'(0) = 0$$

using (12). Evaluate the integral.

4.7	**CAUCHY-EULER EQUATION**

REVIEW MATERIAL
• Review the concept of the auxiliary equation in Section 4.3.

INTRODUCTION   The same relative ease with which we were able to find explicit solutions of higher-order linear differential equations with constant coefficients in the preceding sections does not, in general, carry over to linear equations with variable coefficients. We shall see in Chapter 6 that when a linear DE has variable coefficients, the best that we can *usually* expect is to find a solution in the form of an infinite series. However, the type of differential equation that we consider in this section is an exception to this rule; it is a linear equation with variable coefficients whose general solution can always be expressed in terms of powers of x, sines, cosines, and logarithmic functions. Moreover, its method of solution is quite similar to that for constant-coefficient equations in that an auxiliary equation must be solved.

CAUCHY-EULER EQUATION A linear differential equation of the form

$$a_n x^n \frac{d^n y}{dx^n} + a_{n-1} x^{n-1} \frac{d^{n-1} y}{dx^{n-1}} + \cdots + a_1 x \frac{dy}{dx} + a_0 y = g(x),$$

where the coefficients $a_n, a_{n-1}, \ldots, a_0$ are constants, is known as a **Cauchy-Euler equation.** The observable characteristic of this type of equation is that the degree $k = n, n - 1, \ldots, 1, 0$ of the monomial coefficients x^k matches the order k of differentiation $d^k y / dx^k$:

$$\overset{\text{same}}{a_n x^n} \frac{d^n y}{dx^n} + \overset{\text{same}}{a_{n-1} x^{n-1}} \frac{d^{n-1} y}{dx^{n-1}} + \cdots .$$

As in Section 4.3, we start the discussion with a detailed examination of the forms of the general solutions of the homogeneous second-order equation

$$ax^2 \frac{d^2 y}{dx^2} + bx \frac{dy}{dx} + cy = 0.$$

The solution of higher-order equations follows analogously. Also, we can solve the nonhomogeneous equation $ax^2 y'' + bxy' + cy = g(x)$ by variation of parameters, once we have determined the complementary function y_c.

NOTE The coefficient ax^2 of y'' is zero at $x = 0$. Hence to guarantee that the fundamental results of Theorem 4.1.1 are applicable to the Cauchy-Euler equation, we confine our attention to finding the general solutions defined on the interval $(0, \infty)$. Solutions on the interval $(-\infty, 0)$ can be obtained by substituting $t = -x$ into the differential equation. See Problems 37 and 38 in Exercises 4.7.

METHOD OF SOLUTION We try a solution of the form $y = x^m$, where m is to be determined. Analogous to what happened when we substituted e^{mx} into a linear equation with constant coefficients, when we substitute x^m, each term of a Cauchy-Euler equation becomes a polynomial in m times x^m, since

$$a_k x^k \frac{d^k y}{dx^k} = a_k x^k m(m-1)(m-2) \cdots (m-k+1) x^{m-k} = a_k m(m-1)(m-2) \cdots (m-k+1) x^m.$$

For example, when we substitute $y = x^m$, the second-order equation becomes

$$ax^2 \frac{d^2 y}{dx^2} + bx \frac{dy}{dx} + cy = am(m-1)x^m + bmx^m + cx^m = (am(m-1) + bm + c)x^m.$$

Thus $y = x^m$ is a solution of the differential equation whenever m is a solution of the **auxiliary equation**

$$am(m-1) + bm + c = 0 \quad \text{or} \quad am^2 + (b-a)m + c = 0. \tag{1}$$

There are three different cases to be considered, depending on whether the roots of this quadratic equation are real and distinct, real and equal, or complex. In the last case the roots appear as a conjugate pair.

CASE I: DISTINCT REAL ROOTS Let m_1 and m_2 denote the real roots of (1) such that $m_1 \neq m_2$. Then $y_1 = x^{m_1}$ and $y_2 = x^{m_2}$ form a fundamental set of solutions. Hence the general solution is

$$y = c_1 x^{m_1} + c_2 x^{m_2}. \tag{2}$$

EXAMPLE 1   Distinct Roots

Solve $x^2 \dfrac{d^2y}{dx^2} - 2x \dfrac{dy}{dx} - 4y = 0$.

SOLUTION   Rather than just memorizing equation (1), it is preferable to assume $y = x^m$ as the solution a few times to understand the origin and the difference between this new form of the auxiliary equation and that obtained in Section 4.3. Differentiate twice,

$$\frac{dy}{dx} = mx^{m-1}, \qquad \frac{d^2y}{dx^2} = m(m-1)x^{m-2},$$

and substitute back into the differential equation:

$$x^2 \frac{d^2y}{dx^2} - 2x \frac{dy}{dx} - 4y = x^2 \cdot m(m-1)x^{m-2} - 2x \cdot mx^{m-1} - 4x^m$$

$$= x^m(m(m-1) - 2m - 4) = x^m(m^2 - 3m - 4) = 0$$

if $m^2 - 3m - 4 = 0$. Now $(m + 1)(m - 4) = 0$ implies $m_1 = -1$, $m_2 = 4$, so $y = c_1 x^{-1} + c_2 x^4$.   ∎

CASE II: REPEATED REAL ROOTS   If the roots of (1) are repeated (that is, $m_1 = m_2$), then we obtain only one solution—namely, $y = x^{m_1}$. When the roots of the quadratic equation $am^2 + (b - a)m + c = 0$ are equal, the discriminant of the coefficients is necessarily zero. It follows from the quadratic formula that the root must be $m_1 = -(b - a)/2a$.

Now we can construct a second solution y_2, using (5) of Section 4.2. We first write the Cauchy-Euler equation in the standard form

$$\frac{d^2y}{dx^2} + \frac{b}{ax} \frac{dy}{dx} + \frac{c}{ax^2} y = 0$$

and make the identifications $P(x) = b/ax$ and $\int (b/ax)\, dx = (b/a) \ln x$. Thus

$$y_2 = x^{m_1} \int \frac{e^{-(b/a)\ln x}}{x^{2m_1}}\, dx$$

$$= x^{m_1} \int x^{-b/a} \cdot x^{-2m_1}\, dx \qquad \leftarrow e^{-(b/a)\ln x} = e^{\ln x^{-b/a}} = x^{-b/a}$$

$$= x^{m_1} \int x^{-b/a} \cdot x^{(b-a)/a}\, dx \qquad \leftarrow -2m_1 = (b - a)/a$$

$$= x^{m_1} \int \frac{dx}{x} = x^{m_1} \ln x.$$

The general solution is then

$$y = c_1 x^{m_1} + c_2 x^{m_1} \ln x. \tag{3}$$

EXAMPLE 2   Repeated Roots

Solve $4x^2 \dfrac{d^2y}{dx^2} + 8x \dfrac{dy}{dx} + y = 0$.

SOLUTION   The substitution $y = x^m$ yields

$$4x^2 \frac{d^2y}{dx^2} + 8x \frac{dy}{dx} + y = x^m(4m(m-1) + 8m + 1) = x^m(4m^2 + 4m + 1) = 0$$

when $4m^2 + 4m + 1 = 0$ or $(2m + 1)^2 = 0$. Since $m_1 = -\frac{1}{2}$, the general solution is $y = c_1 x^{-1/2} + c_2 x^{-1/2} \ln x$. ∎

For higher-order equations, if m_1 is a root of multiplicity k, then it can be shown that

$$x^{m_1}, \quad x^{m_1} \ln x, \quad x^{m_1}(\ln x)^2, \ldots, \quad x^{m_1}(\ln x)^{k-1}$$

are k linearly independent solutions. Correspondingly, the general solution of the differential equation must then contain a linear combination of these k solutions.

CASE III: CONJUGATE COMPLEX ROOTS If the roots of (1) are the conjugate pair $m_1 = \alpha + i\beta$, $m_2 = \alpha - i\beta$, where α and $\beta > 0$ are real, then a solution is

$$y = C_1 x^{\alpha + i\beta} + C_2 x^{\alpha - i\beta}.$$

But when the roots of the auxiliary equation are complex, as in the case of equations with constant coefficients, we wish to write the solution in terms of real functions only. We note the identity

$$x^{i\beta} = (e^{\ln x})^{i\beta} = e^{i\beta \ln x},$$

which, by Euler's formula, is the same as

$$x^{i\beta} = \cos(\beta \ln x) + i \sin(\beta \ln x).$$

Similarly,
$$x^{-i\beta} = \cos(\beta \ln x) - i \sin(\beta \ln x).$$

Adding and subtracting the last two results yields

$$x^{i\beta} + x^{-i\beta} = 2\cos(\beta \ln x) \qquad \text{and} \qquad x^{i\beta} - x^{-i\beta} = 2i \sin(\beta \ln x),$$

respectively. From the fact that $y = C_1 x^{\alpha + i\beta} + C_2 x^{\alpha - i\beta}$ is a solution for any values of the constants, we see, in turn, for $C_1 = C_2 = 1$ and $C_1 = 1$, $C_2 = -1$ that

$$y_1 = x^\alpha(x^{i\beta} + x^{-i\beta}) \qquad \text{and} \qquad y_2 = x^\alpha(x^{i\beta} - x^{-i\beta})$$

or
$$y_1 = 2x^\alpha \cos(\beta \ln x) \qquad \text{and} \qquad y_2 = 2ix^\alpha \sin(\beta \ln x)$$

are also solutions. Since $W(x^\alpha \cos(\beta \ln x), x^\alpha \sin(\beta \ln x)) = \beta x^{2\alpha - 1} \neq 0$, $\beta > 0$ on the interval $(0, \infty)$, we conclude that

$$y_1 = x^\alpha \cos(\beta \ln x) \qquad \text{and} \qquad y_2 = x^\alpha \sin(\beta \ln x)$$

constitute a fundamental set of real solutions of the differential equation. Hence the general solution is

$$y = x^\alpha[c_1 \cos(\beta \ln x) + c_2 \sin(\beta \ln x)]. \tag{4}$$

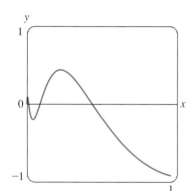

(a) solution for $0 < x \le 1$

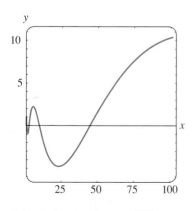

(b) solution for $0 < x \le 100$

FIGURE 4.7.1 Solution curve of IVP in Example 3

EXAMPLE 3 An Initial-Value Problem

Solve $4x^2 y'' + 17y = 0$, $y(1) = -1$, $y'(1) = -\frac{1}{2}$.

SOLUTION The y' term is missing in the given Cauchy-Euler equation; nevertheless, the substitution $y = x^m$ yields

$$4x^2 y'' + 17y = x^m(4m(m - 1) + 17) = x^m(4m^2 - 4m + 17) = 0$$

when $4m^2 - 4m + 17 = 0$. From the quadratic formula we find that the roots are $m_1 = \frac{1}{2} + 2i$ and $m_2 = \frac{1}{2} - 2i$. With the identifications $\alpha = \frac{1}{2}$ and $\beta = 2$ we see from (4) that the general solution of the differential equation is

$$y = x^{1/2}[c_1 \cos(2 \ln x) + c_2 \sin(2 \ln x)].$$

By applying the initial conditions $y(1) = -1$, $y'(1) = -\frac{1}{2}$ to the foregoing solution and using $\ln 1 = 0$, we then find, in turn, that $c_1 = -1$ and $c_2 = 0$. Hence the solution of the initial-value problem is $y = -x^{1/2} \cos(2 \ln x)$. The graph of this function, obtained with the aid of computer software, is given in Figure 4.7.1. The particular solution is seen to be oscillatory and unbounded as $x \rightarrow \infty$. ∎

The next example illustrates the solution of a third-order Cauchy-Euler equation.

EXAMPLE 4   Third-Order Equation

Solve $x^3 \dfrac{d^3 y}{dx^3} + 5x^2 \dfrac{d^2 y}{dx^2} + 7x \dfrac{dy}{dx} + 8y = 0$.

SOLUTION   The first three derivatives of $y = x^m$ are

$$\frac{dy}{dx} = m x^{m-1}, \qquad \frac{d^2 y}{dx^2} = m(m-1)x^{m-2}, \qquad \frac{d^3 y}{dx^3} = m(m-1)(m-2)x^{m-3},$$

so the given differential equation becomes

$$x^3 \frac{d^3 y}{dx^3} + 5x^2 \frac{d^2 y}{dx^2} + 7x \frac{dy}{dx} + 8y = x^3 m(m-1)(m-2)x^{m-3} + 5x^2 m(m-1)x^{m-2} + 7x m x^{m-1} + 8x^m$$

$$= x^m (m(m-1)(m-2) + 5m(m-1) + 7m + 8)$$

$$= x^m (m^3 + 2m^2 + 4m + 8) = x^m (m+2)(m^2 + 4) = 0.$$

In this case we see that $y = x^m$ will be a solution of the differential equation for $m_1 = -2$, $m_2 = 2i$, and $m_3 = -2i$. Hence the general solution is $y = c_1 x^{-2} + c_2 \cos(2 \ln x) + c_3 \sin(2 \ln x)$. ∎

The method of undetermined coefficients described in Sections 4.5 and 4.6 does not carry over, *in general,* to linear differential equations with variable coefficients. Consequently, in our next example the method of variation of parameters is employed.

EXAMPLE 5   Variation of Parameters

Solve $x^2 y'' - 3xy' + 3y = 2x^4 e^x$.

SOLUTION   Since the equation is nonhomogeneous, we first solve the associated homogeneous equation. From the auxiliary equation $(m-1)(m-3) = 0$ we find $y_c = c_1 x + c_2 x^3$. Now before using variation of parameters to find a particular solution $y_p = u_1 y_1 + u_2 y_2$, recall that the formulas $u_1' = W_1/W$ and $u_2' = W_2/W$, where W_1, W_2, and W are the determinants defined on page 158, were derived under the assumption that the differential equation has been put into the standard form $y'' + P(x)y' + Q(x)y = f(x)$. Therefore we divide the given equation by x^2, and from

$$y'' - \frac{3}{x}y' + \frac{3}{x^2}y = 2x^2 e^x$$

we make the identification $f(x) = 2x^2 e^x$. Now with $y_1 = x$, $y_2 = x^3$, and

$$W = \begin{vmatrix} x & x^3 \\ 1 & 3x^2 \end{vmatrix} = 2x^3, \quad W_1 = \begin{vmatrix} 0 & x^3 \\ 2x^2 e^x & 3x^2 \end{vmatrix} = -2x^5 e^x, \quad W_2 = \begin{vmatrix} x & 0 \\ 1 & 2x^2 e^x \end{vmatrix} = 2x^3 e^x,$$

we find $\qquad u_1' = -\dfrac{2x^5 e^x}{2x^3} = -x^2 e^x \quad$ and $\quad u_2' = \dfrac{2x^3 e^x}{2x^3} = e^x$.

The integral of the last function is immediate, but in the case of u_1' we integrate by parts twice. The results are $u_1 = -x^2e^x + 2xe^x - 2e^x$ and $u_2 = e^x$. Hence $y_p = u_1y_1 + u_2y_2$ is

$$y_p = (-x^2e^x + 2xe^x - 2e^x)x + e^xx^3 = 2x^2e^x - 2xe^x.$$

Finally, $\qquad\qquad y = y_c + y_p = c_1x + c_2x^3 + 2x^2e^x - 2xe^x.$ ∎

REDUCTION TO CONSTANT COEFFICIENTS

The similarities between the forms of solutions of Cauchy-Euler equations and solutions of linear equations with constant coefficients are not just a coincidence. For example, when the roots of the auxiliary equations for $ay'' + by' + cy = 0$ and $ax^2y'' + bxy' + cy = 0$ are distinct and real, the respective general solutions are

$$y = c_1e^{m_1x} + c_2e^{m_2x} \qquad \text{and} \qquad y = c_1x^{m_1} + c_2x^{m_2}, \quad x > 0. \qquad (5)$$

In view of the identity $e^{\ln x} = x$, $x > 0$, the second solution given in (5) can be expressed in the same form as the first solution:

$$y = c_1e^{m_1 \ln x} + c_2e^{m_2 \ln x} = c_1e^{m_1t} + c_2e^{m_2t},$$

where $t = \ln x$. This last result illustrates the fact that any Cauchy-Euler equation can *always* be rewritten as a linear differential equation with constant coefficients by means of the substitution $x = e^t$. The idea is to solve the new differential equation in terms of the variable t, using the methods of the previous sections, and, once the general solution is obtained, resubstitute $t = \ln x$. This method, illustrated in the last example, requires the use of the Chain Rule of differentiation.

EXAMPLE 6   Changing to Constant Coefficients

Solve $x^2y'' - xy' + y = \ln x$.

SOLUTION   With the substitution $x = e^t$ or $t = \ln x$, it follows that

$$\frac{dy}{dx} = \frac{dy}{dt}\frac{dt}{dx} = \frac{1}{x}\frac{dy}{dt} \qquad \leftarrow \text{Chain Rule}$$

$$\frac{d^2y}{dx^2} = \frac{1}{x}\frac{d}{dx}\left(\frac{dy}{dt}\right) + \frac{dy}{dt}\left(-\frac{1}{x^2}\right) \qquad \leftarrow \text{Product Rule and Chain Rule}$$

$$= \frac{1}{x}\left(\frac{d^2y}{dt^2}\frac{1}{x}\right) + \frac{dy}{dt}\left(-\frac{1}{x^2}\right) = \frac{1}{x^2}\left(\frac{d^2y}{dt^2} - \frac{dy}{dt}\right).$$

Substituting in the given differential equation and simplifying yields

$$\frac{d^2y}{dt^2} - 2\frac{dy}{dt} + y = t.$$

Since this last equation has constant coefficients, its auxiliary equation is $m^2 - 2m + 1 = 0$, or $(m - 1)^2 = 0$. Thus we obtain $y_c = c_1e^t + c_2te^t$.

By undetermined coefficients we try a particular solution of the form $y_p = A + Bt$. This assumption leads to $-2B + A + Bt = t$, so $A = 2$ and $B = 1$. Using $y = y_c + y_p$, we get

$$y = c_1e^t + c_2te^t + 2 + t,$$

so the general solution of the original differential equation on the interval $(0, \infty)$ is $y = c_1x + c_2x \ln x + 2 + \ln x$. ∎

EXERCISES 4.7

Answers to selected odd-numbered problems begin on page ANS-5.

In Problems 1–18 solve the given differential equation.

1. $x^2 y'' - 2y = 0$

2. $4x^2 y'' + y = 0$

3. $xy'' + y' = 0$

4. $xy'' - 3y' = 0$

5. $x^2 y'' + xy' + 4y = 0$

6. $x^2 y'' + 5xy' + 3y = 0$

7. $x^2 y'' - 3xy' - 2y = 0$

8. $x^2 y'' + 3xy' - 4y = 0$

9. $25x^2 y'' + 25xy' + y = 0$

10. $4x^2 y'' + 4xy' - y = 0$

11. $x^2 y'' + 5xy' + 4y = 0$

12. $x^2 y'' + 8xy' + 6y = 0$

13. $3x^2 y'' + 6xy' + y = 0$

14. $x^2 y'' - 7xy' + 41y = 0$

15. $x^3 y''' - 6y = 0$

16. $x^3 y''' + xy' - y = 0$

17. $xy^{(4)} + 6y''' = 0$

18. $x^4 y^{(4)} + 6x^3 y''' + 9x^2 y'' + 3xy' + y = 0$

In Problems 19–24 solve the given differential equation by variation of parameters.

19. $xy'' - 4y' = x^4$

20. $2x^2 y'' + 5xy' + y = x^2 - x$

21. $x^2 y'' - xy' + y = 2x$

22. $x^2 y'' - 2xy' + 2y = x^4 e^x$

23. $x^2 y'' + xy' - y = \ln x$

24. $x^2 y'' + xy' - y = \dfrac{1}{x + 1}$

In Problems 25–30 solve the given initial-value problem. Use a graphing utility to graph the solution curve.

25. $x^2 y'' + 3xy' = 0, \quad y(1) = 0, y'(1) = 4$

26. $x^2 y'' - 5xy' + 8y = 0, \quad y(2) = 32, y'(2) = 0$

27. $x^2 y'' + xy' + y = 0, \quad y(1) = 1, y'(1) = 2$

28. $x^2 y'' - 3xy' + 4y = 0, \quad y(1) = 5, y'(1) = 3$

29. $xy'' + y' = x, \quad y(1) = 1, y'(1) = -\tfrac{1}{2}$

30. $x^2 y'' - 5xy' + 8y = 8x^6, \quad y(\tfrac{1}{2}) = 0, y'(\tfrac{1}{2}) = 0$

In Problems 31–36 use the substitution $x = e^t$ to transform the given Cauchy-Euler equation to a differential equation with constant coefficients. Solve the original equation by solving the new equation using the procedures in Sections 4.3–4.5.

31. $x^2 y'' + 9xy' - 20y = 0$

32. $x^2 y'' - 9xy' + 25y = 0$

33. $x^2 y'' + 10xy' + 8y = x^2$

34. $x^2 y'' - 4xy' + 6y = \ln x^2$

35. $x^2 y'' - 3xy' + 13y = 4 + 3x$

36. $x^3 y''' - 3x^2 y'' + 6xy' - 6y = 3 + \ln x^3$

In Problems 37 and 38 solve the given initial-value problem on the interval $(-\infty, 0)$.

37. $4x^2 y'' + y = 0, \quad y(-1) = 2, y'(-1) = 4$

38. $x^2 y'' - 4xy' + 6y = 0, \quad y(-2) = 8, y'(-2) = 0$

Discussion Problems

39. How would you use the method of this section to solve

$$(x + 2)^2 y'' + (x + 2)y' + y = 0?$$

Carry out your ideas. State an interval over which the solution is defined.

40. Can a Cauchy-Euler differential equation of lowest order with real coefficients be found if it is known that 2 and $1 - i$ are roots of its auxiliary equation? Carry out your ideas.

41. The initial-conditions $y(0) = y_0$, $y'(0) = y_1$ apply to each of the following differential equations:

$$x^2 y'' = 0,$$
$$x^2 y'' - 2xy' + 2y = 0,$$
$$x^2 y'' - 4xy' + 6y = 0.$$

For what values of y_0 and y_1 does each initial-value problem have a solution?

42. What are the x-intercepts of the solution curve shown in Figure 4.7.1? How many x-intercepts are there for $0 < x < \tfrac{1}{2}$?

Computer Lab Assignments

In Problems 43–46 solve the given differential equation by using a CAS to find the (approximate) roots of the auxiliary equation.

43. $2x^3 y''' - 10.98x^2 y'' + 8.5xy' + 1.3y = 0$

44. $x^3 y''' + 4x^2 y'' + 5xy' - 9y = 0$

45. $x^4 y^{(4)} + 6x^3 y''' + 3x^2 y'' - 3xy' + 4y = 0$

46. $x^4 y^{(4)} - 6x^3 y''' + 33x^2 y'' - 105xy' + 169y = 0$

47. Solve $x^3 y''' - x^2 y'' - 2xy' + 6y = x^2$ by variation of parameters. Use a CAS as an aid in computing roots of the auxiliary equation and the determinants given in (10) of Section 4.6.

4.8 SOLVING SYSTEMS OF LINEAR DEs BY ELIMINATION

REVIEW MATERIAL

- Because the method of systematic elimination uncouples a system into distinct linear ODEs in each dependent variable, this section gives you an opportunity to practice what you learned in Sections 4.3, 4.4 (or 4.5), and 4.6.

INTRODUCTION Simultaneous ordinary differential equations involve two or more equations that contain derivatives of two or more dependent variables—the unknown functions—with respect to a single independent variable. The method of **systematic elimination** for solving systems of differential equations with constant coefficients is based on the algebraic principle of elimination of variables. We shall see that the analogue of *multiplying* an algebraic equation by a constant is *operating* on an ODE with some combination of derivatives.

SYSTEMATIC ELIMINATION The elimination of an unknown in a system of linear differential equations is expedited by rewriting each equation in the system in differential operator notation. Recall from Section 4.1 that a single linear equation

$$a_n y^{(n)} + a_{n-1} y^{(n-1)} + \cdots + a_1 y' + a_0 y = g(t),$$

where the a_i, $i = 0, 1, \ldots, n$ are constants, can be written as

$$(a_n D^n + a_{n-1} D^{(n-1)} + \cdots + a_1 D + a_0)y = g(t).$$

If the nth-order differential operator $a_n D^n + a_{n-1} D^{(n-1)} + \cdots + a_1 D + a_0$ factors into differential operators of lower order, then the factors commute. Now, for example, to rewrite the system

$$x'' + 2x' + y'' = x + 3y + \sin t$$
$$x' + y' = -4x + 2y + e^{-t}$$

in terms of the operator D, we first bring all terms involving the dependent variables to one side and group the same variables:

$$x'' + 2x' - x + y'' - 3y = \sin t \qquad \text{is the same as} \qquad (D^2 + 2D - 1)x + (D^2 - 3)y = \sin t$$
$$x' - 4x + y' - 2y = e^{-t} \qquad\qquad\qquad\qquad (D - 4)x + (D - 2)y = e^{-t}.$$

SOLUTION OF A SYSTEM A **solution** of a system of differential equations is a set of sufficiently differentiable functions $x = \phi_1(t)$, $y = \phi_2(t)$, $z = \phi_3(t)$, and so on that satisfies each equation in the system on some common interval I.

METHOD OF SOLUTION Consider the simple system of linear first-order equations

$$\frac{dx}{dt} = 3y$$
$$\frac{dy}{dt} = 2x \qquad \text{or, equivalently,} \qquad \begin{array}{l} Dx - 3y = 0 \\ 2x - Dy = 0. \end{array} \qquad (1)$$

Operating on the first equation in (1) by D while multiplying the second by -3 and then adding eliminates y from the system and gives $D^2 x - 6x = 0$. Since the roots of the auxiliary equation of the last DE are $m_1 = \sqrt{6}$ and $m_2 = -\sqrt{6}$, we obtain

$$x(t) = c_1 e^{-\sqrt{6}t} + c_2 e^{\sqrt{6}t}. \qquad (2)$$

Multiplying the first equation in (1) by 2 while operating on the second by D and then subtracting gives the differential equation for y, $D^2y - 6y = 0$. It follows immediately that

$$y(t) = c_3 e^{-\sqrt{6}t} + c_4 e^{\sqrt{6}t}. \tag{3}$$

Now (2) and (3) do not satisfy the system (1) for every choice of c_1, c_2, c_3, and c_4 because the system itself puts a constraint on the number of parameters in a solution that can be chosen arbitrarily. To see this, observe that substituting $x(t)$ and $y(t)$ into the first equation of the original system (1) gives, after simplification,

$$(-\sqrt{6}c_1 - 3c_3)e^{-\sqrt{6}t} + (\sqrt{6}c_2 - 3c_4)e^{\sqrt{6}t} = 0.$$

Since the latter expression is to be zero for all values of t, we must have $-\sqrt{6}c_1 - 3c_3 = 0$ and $\sqrt{6}c_2 - 3c_4 = 0$. These two equations enable us to write c_3 as a multiple of c_1 and c_4 as a multiple of c_2:

$$c_3 = -\frac{\sqrt{6}}{3}c_1 \quad \text{and} \quad c_4 = \frac{\sqrt{6}}{3}c_2. \tag{4}$$

Hence we conclude that a solution of the system must be

$$x(t) = c_1 e^{-\sqrt{6}t} + c_2 e^{\sqrt{6}t}, \quad y(t) = -\frac{\sqrt{6}}{3}c_1 e^{-\sqrt{6}t} + \frac{\sqrt{6}}{3}c_2 e^{\sqrt{6}t}.$$

You are urged to substitute (2) and (3) into the second equation of (1) and verify that the same relationship (4) holds between the constants.

EXAMPLE 1　Solution by Elimination

Solve
$$Dx + (D + 2)y = 0$$
$$(D - 3)x - \quad\quad 2y = 0. \tag{5}$$

SOLUTION　Operating on the first equation by $D - 3$ and on the second by D and then subtracting eliminates x from the system. It follows that the differential equation for y is

$$[(D - 3)(D + 2) + 2D]y = 0 \quad\text{or}\quad (D^2 + D - 6)y = 0.$$

Since the characteristic equation of this last differential equation is $m^2 + m - 6 = (m - 2)(m + 3) = 0$, we obtain the solution

$$y(t) = c_1 e^{2t} + c_2 e^{-3t}. \tag{6}$$

Eliminating y in a similar manner yields $(D^2 + D - 6)x = 0$, from which we find

$$x(t) = c_3 e^{2t} + c_4 e^{-3t}. \tag{7}$$

As we noted in the foregoing discussion, a solution of (5) does not contain four independent constants. Substituting (6) and (7) into the first equation of (5) gives

$$(4c_1 + 2c_3)e^{2t} + (-c_2 - 3c_4)e^{-3t} = 0.$$

From $4c_1 + 2c_3 = 0$ and $-c_2 - 3c_4 = 0$ we get $c_3 = -2c_1$ and $c_4 = -\frac{1}{3}c_2$. Accordingly, a solution of the system is

$$x(t) = -2c_1 e^{2t} - \frac{1}{3}c_2 e^{-3t}, \quad y(t) = c_1 e^{2t} + c_2 e^{-3t}. \quad\blacksquare$$

Because we could just as easily solve for c_3 and c_4 in terms of c_1 and c_2, the solution in Example 1 can be written in the alternative form

$$x(t) = c_3 e^{2t} + c_4 e^{-3t}, \quad y(t) = -\frac{1}{2}c_3 e^{2t} - 3c_4 e^{-3t}.$$

■ This might save
you some time.

It sometimes pays to keep one's eyes open when solving systems. Had we solved for x first in Example 1, then y could be found, along with the relationship between the constants, using the last equation in the system (5). You should verify that substituting $x(t)$ into $y = \frac{1}{2}(Dx - 3x)$ yields $y = -\frac{1}{2}c_3 e^{2t} - 3c_4 e^{-3t}$. Also note in the initial discussion that the relationship given in (4) and the solution $y(t)$ of (1) could also have been obtained by using $x(t)$ in (2) and the first equation of (1) in the form

$$y = \frac{1}{3} Dx = -\frac{1}{3}\sqrt{6}c_1 e^{-\sqrt{6}t} + \frac{1}{3}\sqrt{6}c_2 e^{\sqrt{6}t}.$$

EXAMPLE 2 Solution by Elimination

Solve
$$\begin{aligned}
x' - 4x + y'' &= t^2 \\
x' + x + y' &= 0.
\end{aligned} \tag{8}$$

SOLUTION First we write the system in differential operator notation:

$$\begin{aligned}
(D - 4)x + D^2 y &= t^2 \\
(D + 1)x + Dy &= 0.
\end{aligned} \tag{9}$$

Then, by eliminating x, we obtain

$$[(D + 1)D^2 - (D - 4)D]y = (D + 1)t^2 - (D - 4)0$$

or
$$(D^3 + 4D)y = t^2 + 2t.$$

Since the roots of the auxiliary equation $m(m^2 + 4) = 0$ are $m_1 = 0$, $m_2 = 2i$, and $m_3 = -2i$, the complementary function is $y_c = c_1 + c_2 \cos 2t + c_3 \sin 2t$. To determine the particular solution y_p, we use undetermined coefficients by assuming that $y_p = At^3 + Bt^2 + Ct$. Therefore $y_p' = 3At^2 + 2Bt + C$, $y_p'' = 6At + 2B$, $y_p''' = 6A$,

$$y_p''' + 4y_p' = 12At^2 + 8Bt + 6A + 4C = t^2 + 2t.$$

The last equality implies that $12A = 1$, $8B = 2$, and $6A + 4C = 0$; hence $A = \frac{1}{12}$, $B = \frac{1}{4}$, and $C = -\frac{1}{8}$. Thus

$$y = y_c + y_p = c_1 + c_2 \cos 2t + c_3 \sin 2t + \frac{1}{12}t^3 + \frac{1}{4}t^2 - \frac{1}{8}t. \tag{10}$$

Eliminating y from the system (9) leads to

$$[(D - 4) - D(D + 1)]x = t^2 \qquad \text{or} \qquad (D^2 + 4)x = -t^2.$$

It should be obvious that $x_c = c_4 \cos 2t + c_5 \sin 2t$ and that undetermined coefficients can be applied to obtain a particular solution of the form $x_p = At^2 + Bt + C$. In this case the usual differentiations and algebra yield $x_p = -\frac{1}{4}t^2 + \frac{1}{8}$, and so

$$x = x_c + x_p = c_4 \cos 2t + c_5 \sin 2t - \frac{1}{4}t^2 + \frac{1}{8}. \tag{11}$$

Now c_4 and c_5 can be expressed in terms of c_2 and c_3 by substituting (10) and (11) into either equation of (8). By using the second equation, we find, after combining terms,

$$(c_5 - 2c_4 - 2c_2) \sin 2t + (2c_5 + c_4 + 2c_3) \cos 2t = 0,$$

so $c_5 - 2c_4 - 2c_2 = 0$ and $2c_5 + c_4 + 2c_3 = 0$. Solving for c_4 and c_5 in terms of c_2 and c_3 gives $c_4 = -\frac{1}{5}(4c_2 + 2c_3)$ and $c_5 = \frac{1}{5}(2c_2 - 4c_3)$. Finally, a solution of (8) is found to be

$$x(t) = -\frac{1}{5}(4c_2 + 2c_3) \cos 2t + \frac{1}{5}(2c_2 - 4c_3) \sin 2t - \frac{1}{4}t^2 + \frac{1}{8},$$

$$y(t) = c_1 + c_2 \cos 2t + c_3 \sin 2t + \frac{1}{12}t^3 + \frac{1}{4}t^2 - \frac{1}{8}t. \qquad ■$$

EXAMPLE 3 A Mixture Problem Revisited

In (3) of Section 3.3 we saw that the system of linear first-order differential equations

$$\frac{dx_1}{dt} = -\frac{2}{25}x_1 + \frac{1}{50}x_2$$

$$\frac{dx_2}{dt} = \frac{2}{25}x_1 - \frac{2}{25}x_2$$

is a model for the number of pounds of salt $x_1(t)$ and $x_2(t)$ in brine mixtures in tanks A and B, respectively, shown in Figure 3.3.1. At that time we were not able to solve the system. But now, in terms of differential operators, the foregoing system can be written as

$$\left(D + \frac{2}{25}\right)x_1 - \frac{1}{50}x_2 = 0$$

$$-\frac{2}{25}x_1 + \left(D + \frac{2}{25}\right)x_2 = 0.$$

Operating on the first equation by $D + \frac{2}{25}$, multiplying the second equation by $\frac{1}{50}$, adding, and then simplifying gives $(625D^2 + 100D + 3)x_1 = 0$. From the auxiliary equation

$$625m^2 + 100m + 3 = (25m + 1)(25m + 3) = 0$$

we see immediately that $x_1(t) = c_1 e^{-t/25} + c_2 e^{-3t/25}$. We can now obtain $x_2(t)$ by using the first DE of the system in the form $x_2 = 50(D + \frac{2}{25})x_1$. In this manner we find the solution of the system to be

$$x_1(t) = c_1 e^{-t/25} + c_2 e^{-3t/25}, \qquad x_2(t) = 2c_1 e^{-t/25} - 2c_2 e^{-3t/25}.$$

In the original discussion on page 107 we assumed that the initial conditions were $x_1(0) = 25$ and $x_2(0) = 0$. Applying these conditions to the solution yields $c_1 + c_2 = 25$ and $2c_1 - 2c_2 = 0$. Solving these equations simultaneously gives $c_1 = c_2 = \frac{25}{2}$. Finally, a solution of the initial-value problem is

$$x_1(t) = \frac{25}{2}e^{-t/25} + \frac{25}{2}e^{-3t/25}, \qquad x_2(t) = 25e^{-t/25} - 25e^{-3t/25}.$$

The graphs of both of these equations are given in Figure 4.8.1. Consistent with the fact that pure water is being pumped into tank A we see in the figure that $x_1(t) \to 0$ and $x_2(t) \to 0$ as $t \to \infty$. ∎

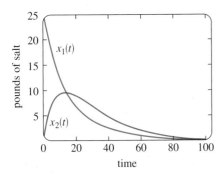

FIGURE 4.8.1 Pounds of salt in tanks A and B

EXERCISES 4.8

Answers to selected odd-numbered problems begin on page ANS-6.

In Problems 1–20 solve the given system of differential equations by systematic elimination.

1. $\dfrac{dx}{dt} = 2x - y$

$\dfrac{dy}{dt} = x$

2. $\dfrac{dx}{dt} = 4x + 7y$

$\dfrac{dy}{dt} = x - 2y$

3. $\dfrac{dx}{dt} = -y + t$

$\dfrac{dy}{dt} = x - t$

4. $\dfrac{dx}{dt} - 4y = 1$

$\dfrac{dy}{dt} + x = 2$

5. $(D^2 + 5)x - 2y = 0$
$-2x + (D^2 + 2)y = 0$

6. $(D + 1)x + (D - 1)y = 2$
$3x + (D + 2)y = -1$

7. $\dfrac{d^2x}{dt^2} = 4y + e^t$

$\dfrac{d^2y}{dt^2} = 4x - e^t$

8. $\dfrac{d^2x}{dt^2} + \dfrac{dy}{dt} = -5x$

$\dfrac{dx}{dt} + \dfrac{dy}{dt} = -x + 4y$

9. $Dx + D^2y = e^{3t}$
$(D + 1)x + (D - 1)y = 4e^{3t}$

10. $D^2x - \qquad Dy = t$
       $(D + 3)x + (D + 3)y = 2$

11. $(D^2 - 1)x - \quad y = 0$
       $(D - 1)x + Dy = 0$

12. $(2D^2 - D - 1)x - (2D + 1)y = 1$
          $(D - 1)x + \qquad Dy = -1$

13. $2\dfrac{dx}{dt} - 5x + \dfrac{dy}{dt} = e^t$

   $\dfrac{dx}{dt} - \quad x + \dfrac{dy}{dt} = 5e^t$

14. $\dfrac{dx}{dt} + \dfrac{dy}{dt} \qquad = e^t$

   $-\dfrac{d^2x}{dt^2} + \dfrac{dx}{dt} + x + y = 0$

15. $(D - 1)x + (D^2 + 1)y = 1$
       $(D^2 - 1)x + \ (D + 1)y = 2$

16. $D^2x - 2(D^2 + D)y = \sin t$
       $x + \qquad Dy = 0$

17. $Dx = y$ **18.** $Dx + \qquad z = e^t$
   $Dy = z$ $(D - 1)x + Dy + Dz = 0$
   $Dz = x$ $x + 2y + Dz = e^t$

19. $\dfrac{dx}{dt} = 6y$ **20.** $\dfrac{dx}{dt} = -x + z$

   $\dfrac{dy}{dt} = x + z$ $\dfrac{dy}{dt} = -y + z$

   $\dfrac{dz}{dt} = x + y$ $\dfrac{dz}{dt} = -x + y$

In Problems 21 and 22 solve the given initial-value problem.

21. $\dfrac{dx}{dt} = -5x - y$ **22.** $\dfrac{dx}{dt} = y - 1$

   $\dfrac{dy}{dt} = 4x - y$ $\dfrac{dy}{dt} = -3x + 2y$

   $x(1) = 0,\ y(1) = 1$ $x(0) = 0,\ y(0) = 0$

Mathematical Models

23. Projectile Motion   A projectile shot from a gun has weight $w = mg$ and velocity $\mathbf{v}$ tangent to its path of motion. Ignoring air resistance and all other forces acting on the projectile except its weight, determine a system of differential equations that describes its path of motion. See Figure 4.8.2. Solve the system. [*Hint*: Use Newton's second law of motion in the x and y directions.]

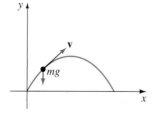

FIGURE 4.8.2   Path of projectile in Problem 23

24. Projectile Motion with Air Resistance   Determine a system of differential equations that describes the path of motion in Problem 23 if air resistance is a retarding force $\mathbf{k}$ (of magnitude k) acting tangent to the path of the projectile but opposite to its motion. See Figure 4.8.3. Solve the system. [*Hint*: $\mathbf{k}$ is a multiple of velocity, say, $c\mathbf{v}$.]

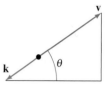

FIGURE 4.8.3   Forces in Problem 24

Discussion Problems

25. Examine and discuss the following system:

$$Dx \qquad - 2Dy = t^2$$
$$(D + 1)x - 2(D + 1)y = 1.$$

Computer Lab Assignments

26. Reexamine Figure 4.8.1 in Example 3. Then use a root-finding application to determine when tank B contains more salt than tank A.

27. (a) Reread Problem 8 of Exercises 3.3. In that problem you were asked to show that the system of differential equations

$$\frac{dx_1}{dt} = -\frac{1}{50}x_1$$
$$\frac{dx_2}{dt} = \frac{1}{50}x_1 - \frac{2}{75}x_2$$
$$\frac{dx_3}{dt} = \frac{2}{75}x_2 - \frac{1}{25}x_3$$

is a model for the amounts of salt in the connected mixing tanks A, B, and C shown in Figure 3.3.7. Solve the system subject to $x_1(0) = 15$, $x_2(t) = 10$, $x_3(t) = 5$.

(b) Use a CAS to graph $x_1(t)$, $x_2(t)$, and $x_3(t)$ in the same coordinate plane (as in Figure 4.8.1) on the interval [0, 200].

(c) Because only pure water is pumped into Tank A, it stands to reason that the salt will eventually be flushed out of all three tanks. Use a root-finding application of a CAS to determine the time when the amount of salt in each tank is less than or equal to 0.5 pound. When will the amounts of salt $x_1(t)$, $x_2(t)$, and $x_3(t)$ be simultaneously less than or equal to 0.5 pound?

4.9	NONLINEAR DIFFERENTIAL EQUATIONS

REVIEW MATERIAL

- Sections 2.2 and 2.5
- Section 4.2
- A review of Taylor series from calculus is also recommended.

INTRODUCTION   The difficulties that surround higher-order *nonlinear* differential equations and the few methods that yield analytic solutions are examined next. Two of the solution methods considered in this section employ a change of variable to reduce a second-order DE to a first-order DE. In that sense these methods are analogous to the material in Section 4.2.

SOME DIFFERENCES   There are several significant differences between linear and nonlinear differential equations. We saw in Section 4.1 that homogeneous linear equations of order two or higher have the property that a linear combination of solutions is also a solution (Theorem 4.1.2). Nonlinear equations do not possess this property of superposability. See Problems 1 and 18 in Exercises 4.9. We can find general solutions of linear first-order DEs and higher-order equations with constant coefficients. Even when we can solve a nonlinear first-order differential equation in the form of a one-parameter family, this family does not, as a rule, represent a general solution. Stated another way, nonlinear first-order DEs can possess singular solutions, whereas linear equations cannot. But the major difference between linear and nonlinear equations of order two or higher lies in the realm of solvability. Given a linear equation, there is a chance that we can find some form of a solution that we can look at—an explicit solution or perhaps a solution in the form of an infinite series (see Chapter 6). On the other hand, nonlinear higher-order differential equations virtually defy solution by analytical methods. Although this might sound disheartening, there are still things that can be done. As was pointed out at the end of Section 1.3, we can always analyze a nonlinear DE qualitatively and numerically.

Let us make it clear at the outset that nonlinear higher-order differential equations are important—dare we say even more important than linear equations?—because as we fine-tune the mathematical model of, say, a physical system, we also increase the likelihood that this higher-resolution model will be nonlinear.

We begin by illustrating an analytical method that *occasionally* enables us to find explicit/implicit solutions of special kinds of nonlinear second-order differential equations.

REDUCTION OF ORDER   Nonlinear second-order differential equations $F(x, y', y'') = 0$, where the dependent variable y is missing, and $F(y, y', y'') = 0$, where the independent variable x is missing, can sometimes be solved by using first-order methods. Each equation can be reduced to a first-order equation by means of the substitution $u = y'$.

The next example illustrates the substitution technique for an equation of the form $F(x, y', y'') = 0$. If $u = y'$, then the differential equation becomes $F(x, u, u') = 0$. If we can solve this last equation for u, we can find y by integration. Note that since we are solving a second-order equation, its solution will contain two arbitrary constants.

EXAMPLE 1   **Dependent Variable y Is Missing**

Solve $y'' = 2x(y')^2$.

SOLUTION If we let $u = y'$, then $du/dx = y''$. After substituting, the second-order equation reduces to a first-order equation with separable variables; the independent variable is x and the dependent variable is u:

$$\frac{du}{dx} = 2xu^2 \quad \text{or} \quad \frac{du}{u^2} = 2x\,dx$$

$$\int u^{-2}\,du = \int 2x\,dx$$

$$-u^{-1} = x^2 + c_1^2.$$

The constant of integration is written as c_1^2 for convenience. The reason should be obvious in the next few steps. Because $u^{-1} = 1/y'$, it follows that

$$\frac{dy}{dx} = -\frac{1}{x^2 + c_1^2},$$

and so $\qquad y = -\displaystyle\int \frac{dx}{x^2 + c_1^2} \quad$ or $\quad y = -\dfrac{1}{c_1}\tan^{-1}\dfrac{x}{c_1} + c_2.$ ∎

Next we show how to solve an equation that has the form $F(y, y', y'') = 0$. Once more we let $u = y'$, but because the independent variable x is missing, we use this substitution to transform the differential equation into one in which the independent variable is y and the dependent variable is u. To this end we use the Chain Rule to compute the second derivative of y:

$$y'' = \frac{du}{dx} = \frac{du}{dy}\frac{dy}{dx} = u\frac{du}{dy}.$$

In this case the first-order equation that we must now solve is

$$F\left(y, u, u\frac{du}{dy}\right) = 0.$$

■ **EXAMPLE 2** **Independent Variable x Is Missing**

Solve $yy'' = (y')^2$.

SOLUTION With the aid of $u = y'$, the Chain Rule shown above, and separation of variables, the given differential equation becomes

$$y\left(u\frac{du}{dy}\right) = u^2 \quad \text{or} \quad \frac{du}{u} = \frac{dy}{y}.$$

Integrating the last equation then yields $\ln|u| = \ln|y| + c_1$, which, in turn, gives $u = c_2 y$, where the constant $\pm e^{c_1}$ has been relabeled as c_2. We now resubstitute $u = dy/dx$, separate variables once again, integrate, and relabel constants a second time:

$$\int \frac{dy}{y} = c_2 \int dx \quad \text{or} \quad \ln|y| = c_2 x + c_3 \quad \text{or} \quad y = c_4 e^{c_2 x}. \quad ∎$$

USE OF TAYLOR SERIES In some instances a solution of a nonlinear initial-value problem, in which the initial conditions are specified at x_0, can be approximated by a Taylor series centered at x_0.

> ### EXAMPLE 3   Taylor Series Solution of an IVP

Let us assume that a solution of the initial-value problem

$$y'' = x + y - y^2, \quad y(0) = -1, \quad y'(0) = 1 \tag{1}$$

exists. If we further assume that the solution $y(x)$ of the problem is analytic at 0, then $y(x)$ possesses a Taylor series expansion centered at 0:

$$y(x) = y(0) + \frac{y'(0)}{1!}x + \frac{y''(0)}{2!}x^2 + \frac{y'''(0)}{3!}x^3 + \frac{y^{(4)}(0)}{4!}x^4 + \frac{y^{(5)}(0)}{5!}x^5 + \cdots. \tag{2}$$

Note that the values of the first and second terms in the series (2) are known since those values are the specified initial conditions $y(0) = -1$, $y'(0) = 1$. Moreover, the differential equation itself defines the value of the second derivative at 0: $y''(0) = 0 + y(0) - y(0)^2 = 0 + (-1) - (-1)^2 = -2$. We can then find expressions for the higher derivatives y''', $y^{(4)}, \ldots$ by calculating the successive derivatives of the differential equation:

$$y'''(x) = \frac{d}{dx}(x + y - y^2) = 1 + y' - 2yy' \tag{3}$$

$$y^{(4)}(x) = \frac{d}{dx}(1 + y' - 2yy') = y'' - 2yy'' - 2(y')^2 \tag{4}$$

$$y^{(5)}(x) = \frac{d}{dx}(y'' - 2yy'' - 2(y')^2) = y''' - 2yy''' - 6y'y'', \tag{5}$$

and so on. Now using $y(0) = -1$ and $y'(0) = 1$, we find from (3) that $y'''(0) = 4$. From the values $y(0) = -1$, $y'(0) = 1$, and $y''(0) = -2$ we find $y^{(4)}(0) = -8$ from (4). With the additional information that $y'''(0) = 4$, we then see from (5) that $y^{(5)}(0) = 24$. Hence from (2) the first six terms of a series solution of the initial-value problem (1) are

$$y(x) = -1 + x - x^2 + \frac{2}{3}x^3 - \frac{1}{3}x^4 + \frac{1}{5}x^5 + \cdots. \qquad \blacksquare$$

USE OF A NUMERICAL SOLVER Numerical methods, such as Euler's method or the Runge-Kutta method, are developed solely for first-order differential equations and then are extended to systems of first-order equations. To analyze an nth-order initial-value problem numerically, we express the nth-order ODE as a system of n first-order equations. In brief, here is how it is done for a second-order initial-value problem: First, solve for y''—that is, put the DE into normal form $y'' = f(x, y, y')$—and then let $y' = u$. For example, if we substitute $y' = u$ in

$$\frac{d^2y}{dx^2} = f(x, y, y'), \quad y(x_0) = y_0, \quad y'(x_0) = u_0, \tag{6}$$

then $y'' = u'$ and $y'(x_0) = u(x_0)$, so the initial-value problem (6) becomes

Solve: $\qquad \begin{cases} y' = u \\ u' = f(x, y, u) \end{cases}$

Subject to: $\qquad y(x_0) = y_0, u(x_0) = u_0.$

However, it should be noted that a commercial numerical solver *might not* require[*] that you supply the system.

---

[*]Some numerical solvers require only that a second-order differential equation be expressed in normal form $y'' = f(x, y, y')$. The translation of the single equation into a system of two equations is then built into the computer program, since the first equation of the system is always $y' = u$ and the second equation is $u' = f(x, y, u)$.

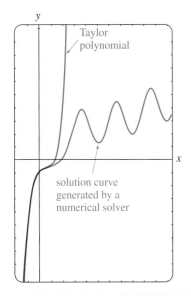

FIGURE 4.9.1 Comparison of two approximate solutions

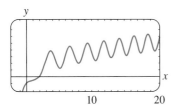

FIGURE 4.9.2 Numerical solution curve for the IVP in (1)

EXAMPLE 4 Graphical Analysis of Example 3

Following the foregoing procedure, we find that the second-order initial-value problem in Example 3 is equivalent to

$$\frac{dy}{dx} = u$$

$$\frac{du}{dx} = x + y - y^2$$

with initial conditions $y(0) = -1$, $u(0) = 1$. With the aid of a numerical solver we get the solution curve shown in blue in Figure 4.9.1. For comparison the graph of the fifth-degree Taylor polynomial $T_5(x) = -1 + x - x^2 + \frac{2}{3}x^3 - \frac{1}{3}x^4 + \frac{1}{5}x^5$ is shown in red. Although we do not know the interval of convergence of the Taylor series obtained in Example 3, the closeness of the two curves in a neighborhood of the origin suggests that the power series may converge on the interval $(-1, 1)$. ∎

QUALITATIVE QUESTIONS The blue graph in Figure 4.9.1 raises some questions of a qualitative nature: Is the solution of the original initial-value problem oscillatory as $x \to \infty$? The graph generated by a numerical solver on the larger interval shown in Figure 4.9.2 would seem to *suggest* that the answer is yes. But this single example—or even an assortment of examples—does not answer the basic question as to whether *all* solutions of the differential equation $y'' = x + y - y^2$ are oscillatory in nature. Also, what is happening to the solution curve in Figure 4.9.2 when x is near -1? What is the behavior of solutions of the differential equation as $x \to -\infty$? Are solutions bounded as $x \to \infty$? Questions such as these are not easily answered, in general, for nonlinear second-order differential equations. But certain kinds of second-order equations lend themselves to a systematic qualitative analysis, and these, like their first-order relatives encountered in Section 2.1, are the kind that have no explicit dependence on the independent variable. Second-order ODEs of the form

$$F(y, y', y'') = 0 \qquad \text{or} \qquad \frac{d^2y}{dx^2} = f(y, y'),$$

equations free of the independent variable x, are called **autonomous.** The differential equation in Example 2 is autonomous, and because of the presence of the x term on its right-hand side, the equation in Example 3 is nonautonomous. For an in-depth treatment of the topic of stability of autonomous second-order differential equations and autonomous systems of differential equations, refer to Chapter 10 in *Differential Equations with Boundary-Value Problems.*

EXERCISES 4.9

Answers to selected odd-numbered problems begin on page ANS-6.

In Problems 1 and 2 verify that y_1 and y_2 are solutions of the given differential equation but that $y = c_1 y_1 + c_2 y_2$ is, in general, not a solution.

1. $(y'')^2 = y^2$; $y_1 = e^x$, $y_2 = \cos x$

2. $yy'' = \frac{1}{2}(y')^2$; $y_1 = 1$, $y_2 = x^2$

In Problems 3–8 solve the given differential equation by using the substitution $u = y'$.

3. $y'' + (y')^2 + 1 = 0$ **4.** $y'' = 1 + (y')^2$

5. $x^2 y'' + (y')^2 = 0$ **6.** $(y + 1)y'' = (y')^2$

7. $y'' + 2y(y')^3 = 0$ **8.** $y^2 y'' = y'$

9. Consider the initial-value problem

$$y'' + yy' = 0, \quad y(0) = 1, y'(0) = -1.$$

(a) Use the DE and a numerical solver to graph the solution curve.

(b) Find an explicit solution of the IVP. Use a graphing utility to graph this solution.

(c) Find an interval of definition for the solution in part (b).

10. Find two solutions of the initial-value problem

$$(y'')^2 + (y')^2 = 1, \quad y\left(\frac{\pi}{2}\right) = \frac{1}{2}, \quad y'\left(\frac{\pi}{2}\right) = \frac{\sqrt{3}}{2}.$$

Use a numerical solver to graph the solution curves.

In Problems 11 and 12 show that the substitution $u = y'$ leads to a Bernoulli equation. Solve this equation (see Section 2.5).

11. $xy'' = y' + (y')^3$ **12.** $xy'' = y' + x(y')^2$

In Problems 13–16 proceed as in Example 3 and obtain the first six nonzero terms of a Taylor series solution, centered at 0, of the given initial-value problem. Use a numerical solver and a graphing utility to compare the solution curve with the graph of the Taylor polynomial.

13. $y'' = x + y^2$, $y(0) = 1, y'(0) = 1$

14. $y'' + y^2 = 1$, $y(0) = 2, y'(0) = 3$

15. $y'' = x^2 + y^2 - 2y'$, $y(0) = 1, y'(0) = 1$

16. $y'' = e^y$, $y(0) = 0, y'(0) = -1$

17. In calculus the curvature of a curve that is defined by a function $y = f(x)$ is defined as

$$\kappa = \frac{y''}{[1 + (y')^2]^{3/2}}.$$

Find $y = f(x)$ for which $\kappa = 1$. [*Hint:* For simplicity, ignore constants of integration.]

Discussion Problems

18. In Problem 1 we saw that $\cos x$ and e^x were solutions of the nonlinear equation $(y'')^2 - y^2 = 0$. Verify that $\sin x$ and e^{-x} are also solutions. Without attempting to solve the differential equation, discuss how these explicit solutions can be found by using knowledge about linear equations. Without attempting to verify, discuss why the linear combinations $y = c_1 e^x + c_2 e^{-x} + c_3 \cos x + c_4 \sin x$ and $y = c_2 e^{-x} + c_4 \sin x$ are not, in general, solutions, but

the two special linear combinations $y = c_1 e^x + c_2 e^{-x}$ and $y = c_3 \cos x + c_4 \sin x$ *must* satisfy the differential equation.

19. Discuss how the method of reduction of order considered in this section can be applied to the third-order differential equation $y''' = \sqrt{1 + (y'')^2}$. Carry out your ideas and solve the equation.

20. Discuss how to find an alternative two-parameter family of solutions for the nonlinear differential equation $y'' = 2x(y')^2$ in Example 1. [*Hint:* Suppose that $-c_1^2$ is used as the constant of integration instead of $+c_1^2$.]

Mathematical Models

21. Motion in a Force Field A mathematical model for the position $x(t)$ of a body moving rectilinearly on the x-axis in an inverse-square force field is given by

$$\frac{d^2x}{dt^2} = -\frac{k^2}{x^2}.$$

Suppose that at $t = 0$ the body starts from rest from the position $x = x_0$, $x_0 > 0$. Show that the velocity of the body at time t is given by $v^2 = 2k^2(1/x - 1/x_0)$. Use the last expression and a CAS to carry out the integration to express time t in terms of x.

22. A mathematical model for the position $x(t)$ of a moving object is

$$\frac{d^2x}{dt^2} + \sin x = 0.$$

Use a numerical solver to graphically investigate the solutions of the equation subject to $x(0) = 0$, $x'(0) = x_1$, $x_1 \geq 0$. Discuss the motion of the object for $t \geq 0$ and for various choices of x_1. Investigate the equation

$$\frac{d^2x}{dt^2} + \frac{dx}{dt} + \sin x = 0$$

in the same manner. Give a possible physical interpretation of the dx/dt term.

CHAPTER 4 IN REVIEW

Answers to selected odd-numbered problems begin on page ANS-6.

Answer Problems 1–4 without referring back to the text. Fill in the blank or answer true or false.

1. The only solution of the initial-value problem $y'' + x^2 y = 0$, $y(0) = 0$, $y'(0) = 0$ is _____.

2. For the method of undetermined coefficients, the assumed form of the particular solution y_p for $y'' - y = 1 + e^x$ is _____.

3. A constant multiple of a solution of a linear differential equation is also a solution. _____

4. If the set consisting of two functions f_1 and f_2 is linearly independent on an interval I, then the Wronskian $W(f_1, f_2) \neq 0$ for all x in I. _____

5. Give an interval over which the set of two functions $f_1(x) = x^2$ and $f_2(x) = x|x|$ is linearly independent.

Then give an interval over which the set consisting of f_1 and f_2 is linearly dependent.

6. Without the aid of the Wronskian, determine whether the given set of functions is linearly independent or linearly dependent on the indicated interval.

(a) $f_1(x) = \ln x, f_2(x) = \ln x^2, (0, \infty)$

(b) $f_1(x) = x^n, f_2(x) = x^{n+1}, n = 1, 2, \ldots, (-\infty, \infty)$

(c) $f_1(x) = x, f_2(x) = x + 1, (-\infty, \infty)$

(d) $f_1(x) = \cos\left(x + \dfrac{\pi}{2}\right), f_2(x) = \sin x, (-\infty, \infty)$

(e) $f_1(x) = 0, f_2(x) = x, (-5, 5)$

(f) $f_1(x) = 2, f_2(x) = 2x, (-\infty, \infty)$

(g) $f_1(x) = x^2, f_2(x) = 1 - x^2, f_3(x) = 2 + x^2, (-\infty, \infty)$

(h) $f_1(x) = xe^{x+1}, f_2(x) = (4x - 5)e^x,$
$\quad f_3(x) = xe^x, (-\infty, \infty)$

7. Suppose $m_1 = 3$, $m_2 = -5$, and $m_3 = 1$ are roots of multiplicity one, two, and three, respectively, of an auxiliary equation. Write down the general solution of the corresponding homogeneous linear DE if it is

(a) an equation with constant coefficients,

(b) a Cauchy-Euler equation.

8. Consider the differential equation $ay'' + by' + cy = g(x)$, where a, b, and c are constants. Choose the input functions $g(x)$ for which the method of undetermined coefficients is applicable and the input functions for which the method of variation of parameters is applicable.

(a) $g(x) = e^x \ln x$ (b) $g(x) = x^3 \cos x$

(c) $g(x) = \dfrac{\sin x}{e^x}$ (d) $g(x) = 2x^{-2}e^x$

(e) $g(x) = \sin^2 x$ (f) $g(x) = \dfrac{e^x}{\sin x}$

In Problems 9–24 use the procedures developed in this chapter to find the general solution of each differential equation.

9. $y'' - 2y' - 2y = 0$

10. $2y'' + 2y' + 3y = 0$

11. $y''' + 10y'' + 25y' = 0$

12. $2y''' + 9y'' + 12y' + 5y = 0$

13. $3y''' + 10y'' + 15y' + 4y = 0$

14. $2y^{(4)} + 3y''' + 2y'' + 6y' - 4y = 0$

15. $y'' - 3y' + 5y = 4x^3 - 2x$

16. $y'' - 2y' + y = x^2 e^x$

17. $y''' - 5y'' + 6y' = 8 + 2\sin x$

18. $y''' - y'' = 6$

19. $y'' - 2y' + 2y = e^x \tan x$

20. $y'' - y = \dfrac{2e^x}{e^x + e^{-x}}$

21. $6x^2 y'' + 5xy' - y = 0$

22. $2x^3 y''' + 19x^2 y'' + 39xy' + 9y = 0$

23. $x^2 y'' - 4xy' + 6y = 2x^4 + x^2$

24. $x^2 y'' - xy' + y = x^3$

25. Write down the form of the general solution $y = y_c + y_p$ of the given differential equation in the two cases $\omega \neq \alpha$ and $\omega = \alpha$. Do not determine the coefficients in y_p.

(a) $y'' + \omega^2 y = \sin \alpha x$ (b) $y'' - \omega^2 y = e^{\alpha x}$

26. (a) Given that $y = \sin x$ is a solution of

$$y^{(4)} + 2y''' + 11y'' + 2y' + 10y = 0,$$

find the general solution of the DE *without the aid of a calculator or a computer.*

(b) Find a linear second-order differential equation with constant coefficients for which $y_1 = 1$ and $y_2 = e^{-x}$ are solutions of the associated homogeneous equation and $y_p = \frac{1}{2}x^2 - x$ is a particular solution of the nonhomogeneous equation.

27. (a) Write the general solution of the fourth-order DE $y^{(4)} - 2y'' + y = 0$ entirely in terms of hyperbolic functions.

(b) Write down the form of a particular solution of $y^{(4)} - 2y'' + y = \sinh x$.

28. Consider the differential equation

$$x^2 y'' - (x^2 + 2x)y' + (x + 2)y = x^3.$$

Verify that $y_1 = x$ is one solution of the associated homogeneous equation. Then show that the method of reduction of order discussed in Section 4.2 leads to a second solution y_2 of the homogeneous equation as well as a particular solution y_p of the nonhomogeneous equation. Form the general solution of the DE on the interval $(0, \infty)$.

In Problems 29–34 solve the given differential equation subject to the indicated conditions.

29. $y'' - 2y' + 2y = 0$, $y\left(\dfrac{\pi}{2}\right) = 0, y(\pi) = -1$

30. $y'' + 2y' + y = 0$, $y(-1) = 0, y'(0) = 0$

31. $y'' - y = x + \sin x$, $y(0) = 2, y'(0) = 3$

32. $y'' + y = \sec^3 x$, $y(0) = 1, y'(0) = \dfrac{1}{2}$

33. $y'y'' = 4x$, $y(1) = 5, y'(1) = 2$

34. $2y'' = 3y^2$, $y(0) = 1, y'(0) = 1$

35. (a) Use a CAS as an aid in finding the roots of the auxiliary equation for

$$12y^{(4)} + 64y''' + 59y'' - 23y' - 12y = 0.$$

   Give the general solution of the equation.

   (b) Solve the DE in part (a) subject to the initial conditions $y(0) = -1$, $y'(0) = 2$, $y''(0) = 5$, $y'''(0) = 0$. Use a CAS as an aid in solving the resulting systems of four equations in four unknowns.

36. Find a member of the family of solutions of $xy'' + y' + \sqrt{x} = 0$ whose graph is tangent to the x-axis at $x = 1$. Use a graphing utility to graph the solution curve.

In Problems 37–40 use systematic elimination to solve the given system.

37. $\dfrac{dx}{dt} + \dfrac{dy}{dt} = 2x + 2y + 1$

$\dfrac{dx}{dt} + 2\dfrac{dy}{dt} = \qquad y + 3$

38. $\dfrac{dx}{dt} = 2x + \ y + \ t - 2$

$\dfrac{dy}{dt} = 3x + 4y - 4t$

39. $(D - 2)x \qquad\qquad - y = -e^t$

$\qquad -3x + (D - 4)\,y = -7e^t$

40. $(D + 2)x + (D + 1)y = \sin 2t$

$\qquad 5x + (D + 3)y = \cos 2t$

5 MODELING WITH HIGHER-ORDER DIFFERENTIAL EQUATIONS

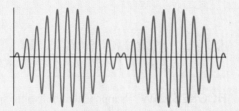

We have seen that a single differential equation can serve as a mathematical model for diverse physical systems. For this reason we examine just one application, the motion of a mass attached to a spring, in great detail in Section 5.1. Except for terminology and physical interpretations of the four terms in the linear equation $ay'' + by' + cy = g(t)$, the mathematics of, say, an electrical series circuit is identical to that of vibrating spring/mass system. Forms of this linear second-order DE appear in the analysis of problems in many diverse areas of science and engineering. In Section 5.1 we deal exclusively with initial-value problems, whereas in Section 5.2 we examine applications described by boundary-value problems. In Section 5.2 we also see how some boundary-value problems lead to the important concepts of *eigenvalues* and *eigenfunctions*. Section 5.3 begins with a discussion on the differences between linear and nonlinear springs; we then show how the simple pendulum and a suspended wire lead to nonlinear models.

5.1 | LINEAR MODELS: INITIAL-VALUE PROBLEMS

REVIEW MATERIAL

- Sections 4.1, 4.3, and 4.4
- Problems 29–36 in Exercises 4.3
- Problems 27–36 in Exercises 4.4

INTRODUCTION   In this section we are going to consider several linear dynamical systems in which each mathematical model is a second-order differential equation with constant coefficients along with initial conditions specified at a time that we shall take to be $t = 0$:

$$a\frac{d^2y}{dt^2} + b\frac{dy}{dt} + cy = g(t), \quad y(0) = y_0, \quad y'(0) = y_1.$$

Recall that the function g is the **input, driving function,** or **forcing function** of the system. A solution $y(t)$ of the differential equation on an interval I containing $t = 0$ that satisfies the initial conditions is called the **output** or **response** of the system.

5.1.1   SPRING/MASS SYSTEMS: FREE UNDAMPED MOTION

HOOKE'S LAW   Suppose that a flexible spring is suspended vertically from a rigid support and then a mass m is attached to its free end. The amount of stretch, or elongation, of the spring will of course depend on the mass; masses with different weights stretch the spring by differing amounts. By Hooke's law the spring itself exerts a restoring force F opposite to the direction of elongation and proportional to the amount of elongation s. Simply stated, $F = ks$, where k is a constant of proportionality called the **spring constant.** The spring is essentially characterized by the number k. For example, if a mass weighing 10 pounds stretches a spring $\frac{1}{2}$ foot, then $10 = k\left(\frac{1}{2}\right)$ implies $k = 20$ lb/ft. Necessarily then, a mass weighing, say, 8 pounds stretches the same spring only $\frac{2}{5}$ foot.

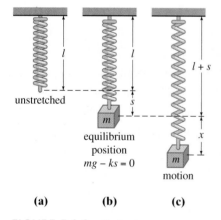

unstretched

equilibrium
position
$mg - ks = 0$

motion

(a)   (b)   (c)

FIGURE 5.1.1   Spring/mass system

NEWTON'S SECOND LAW   After a mass m is attached to a spring, it stretches the spring by an amount s and attains a position of equilibrium at which its weight W is balanced by the restoring force ks. Recall that weight is defined by $W = mg$, where mass is measured in slugs, kilograms, or grams and $g = 32$ ft/s², 9.8 m/s², or 980 cm/s², respectively. As indicated in Figure 5.1.1(b), the condition of equilibrium is $mg = ks$ or $mg - ks = 0$. If the mass is displaced by an amount x from its equilibrium position, the restoring force of the spring is then $k(x + s)$. Assuming that there are no retarding forces acting on the system and assuming that the mass vibrates free of other external forces—**free motion**—we can equate Newton's second law with the net, or resultant, force of the restoring force and the weight:

$$m\frac{d^2x}{dt^2} = -k(s + x) + mg = -kx + \underbrace{mg - ks}_{zero} = -kx. \tag{1}$$

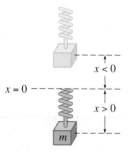

FIGURE 5.1.2   Direction below the equilibrium position is positive.

The negative sign in (1) indicates that the restoring force of the spring acts opposite to the direction of motion. Furthermore, we adopt the convention that displacements measured *below* the equilibrium position are positive. See Figure 5.1.2.

DE OF FREE UNDAMPED MOTION By dividing (1) by the mass m, we obtain the second-order differential equation $d^2x/dt^2 + (k/m)x = 0$, or

$$\frac{d^2x}{dt^2} + \omega^2 x = 0, \tag{2}$$

where $\omega^2 = k/m$. Equation (2) is said to describe **simple harmonic motion** or **free undamped motion.** Two obvious initial conditions associated with (2) are $x(0) = x_0$ and $x'(0) = x_1$, the initial displacement and initial velocity of the mass, respectively. For example, if $x_0 > 0$, $x_1 < 0$, the mass starts from a point *below* the equilibrium position with an imparted *upward* velocity. When $x'(0) = 0$, the mass is said to be released from rest. For example, if $x_0 < 0$, $x_1 = 0$, the mass is released from *rest* from a point $|x_0|$ units *above* the equilibrium position.

EQUATION OF MOTION To solve equation (2), we note that the solutions of its auxiliary equation $m^2 + \omega^2 = 0$ are the complex numbers $m_1 = \omega i$, $m_2 = -\omega i$. Thus from (8) of Section 4.3 we find the general solution of (2) to be

$$x(t) = c_1 \cos \omega t + c_2 \sin \omega t. \tag{3}$$

The **period** of motion described by (3) is $T = 2\pi/\omega$. The number T represents the time (measured in seconds) it takes the mass to execute one cycle of motion. A cycle is one complete oscillation of the mass, that is, the mass m moving from, say, the lowest point below the equilibrium position to the point highest above the equilibrium position and then back to the lowest point. From a graphical viewpoint $T = 2\pi/\omega$ seconds is the length of the time interval between two successive maxima (or minima) of $x(t)$. Keep in mind that a maximum of $x(t)$ is a positive displacement corresponding to the mass attaining its greatest distance below the equilibrium position, whereas a minimum of $x(t)$ is negative displacement corresponding to the mass attaining its greatest height above the equilibrium position. We refer to either case as an **extreme displacement** of the mass. The **frequency** of motion is $f = 1/T = \omega/2\pi$ and is the number of cycles completed each second. For example, if $x(t) = 2 \cos 3\pi t - 4 \sin 3\pi t$, then the period is $T = 2\pi/3\pi = 2/3$ s, and the frequency is $f = 3/2$ cycles/s. From a graphical view-point the graph of $x(t)$ repeats every $\frac{2}{3}$ second, that is, $x\left(t + \frac{2}{3}\right) = x(t)$, and $\frac{3}{2}$ cycles of the graph are completed each second (or, equivalently, three cycles of the graph are completed every 2 seconds). The number $\omega = \sqrt{k/m}$ (measured in radians per second) is called the **circular frequency** of the system. Depending on which text you read, both $f = \omega/2\pi$ and ω are also referred to as the **natural frequency** of the system. Finally, when the initial conditions are used to determine the constants c_1 and c_2 in (3), we say that the resulting particular solution or response is the **equation of motion.**

EXAMPLE 1 Free Undamped Motion

A mass weighing 2 pounds stretches a spring 6 inches. At $t = 0$ the mass is released from a point 8 inches below the equilibrium position with an upward velocity of $\frac{4}{3}$ ft/s. Determine the equation of motion.

SOLUTION Because we are using the engineering system of units, the measurements given in terms of inches must be converted into feet: 6 in. $= \frac{1}{2}$ ft; 8 in. $= \frac{2}{3}$ ft. In addition, we must convert the units of weight given in pounds into units of mass. From $m = W/g$ we have $m = \frac{2}{32} = \frac{1}{16}$ slug. Also, from Hooke's law, $2 = k\left(\frac{1}{2}\right)$ implies that the spring constant is $k = 4$ lb/ft. Hence (1) gives

$$\frac{1}{16}\frac{d^2x}{dt^2} = -4x \qquad \text{or} \qquad \frac{d^2x}{dt^2} + 64x = 0.$$

The initial displacement and initial velocity are $x(0) = \frac{2}{3}$, $x'(0) = -\frac{4}{3}$, where the negative sign in the last condition is a consequence of the fact that the mass is given an initial velocity in the negative, or upward, direction.

Now $\omega^2 = 64$ or $\omega = 8$, so the general solution of the differential equation is

$$x(t) = c_1 \cos 8t + c_2 \sin 8t. \tag{4}$$

Applying the initial conditions to $x(t)$ and $x'(t)$ gives $c_1 = \frac{2}{3}$ and $c_2 = -\frac{1}{6}$. Thus the equation of motion is

$$x(t) = \frac{2}{3} \cos 8t - \frac{1}{6} \sin 8t. \tag{5} \quad \blacksquare$$

ALTERNATIVE FORM OF $X(t)$ When $c_1 \neq 0$ and $c_2 \neq 0$, the actual **amplitude** A of free vibrations is not obvious from inspection of equation (3). For example, although the mass in Example 1 is initially displaced $\frac{2}{3}$ foot beyond the equilibrium position, the amplitude of vibrations is a number larger than $\frac{2}{3}$. Hence it is often convenient to convert a solution of form (3) to the simpler form

$$x(t) = A \sin(\omega t + \phi), \tag{6}$$

where $A = \sqrt{c_1^2 + c_2^2}$ and ϕ is a **phase angle** defined by

$$\left. \begin{array}{l} \sin \phi = \dfrac{c_1}{A} \\[2mm] \cos \phi = \dfrac{c_2}{A} \end{array} \right\} \tan \phi = \dfrac{c_1}{c_2}. \tag{7}$$

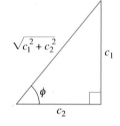

FIGURE 5.1.3   A relationship between $c_1 > 0$, $c_2 > 0$ and phase angle ϕ

To verify this, we expand (6) by the addition formula for the sine function:

$$A \sin \omega t \cos \phi + A \cos \omega t \sin \phi = (A \sin \phi) \cos \omega t + (A \cos \phi) \sin \omega t. \tag{8}$$

It follows from Figure 5.1.3 that if ϕ is defined by

$$\sin \phi = \frac{c_1}{\sqrt{c_1^2 + c_2^2}} = \frac{c_1}{A}, \qquad \cos \phi = \frac{c_2}{\sqrt{c_1^2 + c_2^2}} = \frac{c_2}{A},$$

then (8) becomes

$$A \frac{c_1}{A} \cos \omega t + A \frac{c_2}{A} \sin \omega t = c_1 \cos \omega t + c_2 \sin \omega t = x(t).$$

EXAMPLE 2   Alternative Form of Solution (5)

In view of the foregoing discussion we can write solution (5) in the alternative form $x(t) = A \sin(8t + \phi)$. Computation of the amplitude is straightforward, $A = \sqrt{(\frac{2}{3})^2 + (-\frac{1}{6})^2} = \sqrt{\frac{17}{36}} \approx 0.69$ ft, but some care should be exercised in computing the phase angle ϕ defined by (7). With $c_1 = \frac{2}{3}$ and $c_2 = -\frac{1}{6}$ we find $\tan \phi = -4$, and a calculator then gives $\tan^{-1}(-4) = -1.326$ rad. This is *not* the phase angle, since $\tan^{-1}(-4)$ is located in the *fourth quadrant* and therefore contradicts the fact that $\sin \phi > 0$ and $\cos \phi < 0$ because $c_1 > 0$ and $c_2 < 0$. Hence we must take ϕ to be the *second-quadrant* angle $\phi = \pi + (-1.326) = 1.816$ rad. Thus (5) is the same as

$$x(t) = \frac{\sqrt{17}}{6} \sin(8t + 1.816). \tag{9}$$

The period of this function is $T = 2\pi/8 = \pi/4$ s. $\quad \blacksquare$

Figure 5.1.4(a) illustrates the mass in Example 2 going through approximately two complete cycles of motion. Reading from left to right, the first five positions (marked with black dots) correspond to the initial position of the mass below the equilibrium position $\left(x = \frac{2}{3}\right)$, the mass passing through the equilibrium position

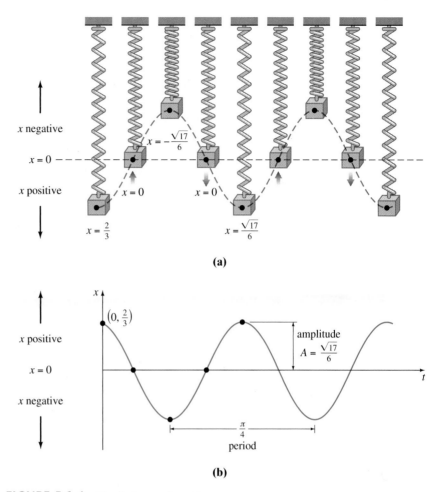

(a)

(b)

FIGURE 5.1.4 Simple harmonic motion

for the first time heading upward ($x = 0$), the mass at its extreme displacement above the equilibrium position ($x = -\sqrt{17}/6$), the mass at the equilibrium position for the second time heading downward ($x = 0$), and the mass at its extreme displacement below the equilibrium position ($x = \sqrt{17}/6$). The black dots on the graph of (9), given in Figure 5.1.4(b), also agree with the five positions just given. Note, however, that in Figure 5.1.4(b) the positive direction in the tx-plane is the usual upward direction and so is opposite to the positive direction indicated in Figure 5.1.4(a). Hence the solid blue graph representing the motion of the mass in Figure 5.1.4(b) is the reflection through the t-axis of the blue dashed curve in Figure 5.1.4(a).

Form (6) is very useful because it is easy to find values of time for which the graph of $x(t)$ crosses the positive t-axis (the line $x = 0$). We observe that $\sin(\omega t + \phi) = 0$ when $\omega t + \phi = n\pi$, where n is a nonnegative integer.

SYSTEMS WITH VARIABLE SPRING CONSTANTS In the model discussed above we assumed an ideal world—a world in which the physical characteristics of the spring do not change over time. In the nonideal world, however, it seems reasonable to expect that when a spring/mass system is in motion for a long period, the spring will weaken; in other words, the "spring constant" will vary—or, more specifically, decay—with time. In one model for the **aging spring** the spring constant k in (1) is replaced by the decreasing function $K(t) = ke^{-\alpha t}$, $k > 0$, $\alpha > 0$. The linear differential equation $mx'' + ke^{-\alpha t}x = 0$ cannot be solved by the methods that were considered in Chapter 4. Nevertheless, we can obtain two linearly independent solutions using the methods in Chapter 6. See Problem 15 in Exercises 5.1, Example 4 in Section 6.3, and Problems 33 and 39 in Exercises 6.3.

When a spring/mass system is subjected to an environment in which the temperature is rapidly decreasing, it might make sense to replace the constant k with $K(t) = kt$, $k > 0$, a function that increases with time. The resulting model, $mx'' + ktx = 0$, is a form of **Airy's differential equation.** Like the equation for an aging spring, Airy's equation can be solved by the methods of Chapter 6. See Problem 16 in Exercises 5.1, Example 3 in Section 6.1, and Problems 34, 35, and 40 in Exercises 6.3.

5.1.2 SPRING/MASS SYSTEMS: FREE DAMPED MOTION

The concept of free harmonic motion is somewhat unrealistic, since the motion described by equation (1) assumes that there are no retarding forces acting on the moving mass. Unless the mass is suspended in a perfect vacuum, there will be at least a resisting force due to the surrounding medium. As Figure 5.1.5 shows, the mass could be suspended in a viscous medium or connected to a dashpot damping device.

(a)

(b)

FIGURE 5.1.5 Damping devices

DE OF FREE DAMPED MOTION In the study of mechanics, damping forces acting on a body are considered to be proportional to a power of the instantaneous velocity. In particular, we shall assume throughout the subsequent discussion that this force is given by a constant multiple of dx/dt. When no other external forces are impressed on the system, it follows from Newton's second law that

$$m\frac{d^2x}{dt^2} = -kx - \beta\frac{dx}{dt},\tag{10}$$

where β is a positive *damping constant* and the negative sign is a consequence of the fact that the damping force acts in a direction opposite to the motion.

Dividing (10) by the mass m, we find that the differential equation of **free damped motion** is $d^2x/dt^2 + (\beta/m)dx/dt + (k/m)x = 0$ or

$$\frac{d^2x}{dt^2} + 2\lambda\frac{dx}{dt} + \omega^2 x = 0,\tag{11}$$

where

$$2\lambda = \frac{\beta}{m}, \qquad \omega^2 = \frac{k}{m}.\tag{12}$$

The symbol 2λ is used only for algebraic convenience because the auxiliary equation is $m^2 + 2\lambda m + \omega^2 = 0$, and the corresponding roots are then

$$m_1 = -\lambda + \sqrt{\lambda^2 - \omega^2}, \qquad m_2 = -\lambda - \sqrt{\lambda^2 - \omega^2}.$$

We can now distinguish three possible cases depending on the algebraic sign of $\lambda^2 - \omega^2$. Since each solution contains the *damping factor* $e^{-\lambda t}$, $\lambda > 0$, the displacements of the mass become negligible as time t increases.

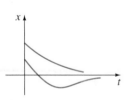

FIGURE 5.1.6 Motion of an overdamped system

CASE I: $\lambda^2 - \omega^2 > 0$ In this situation the system is said to be **overdamped** because the damping coefficient β is large when compared to the spring constant k. The corresponding solution of (11) is $x(t) = c_1 e^{m_1 t} + c_2 e^{m_2 t}$ or

$$x(t) = e^{-\lambda t}\left(c_1 e^{\sqrt{\lambda^2 - \omega^2}\,t} + c_2 e^{-\sqrt{\lambda^2 - \omega^2}\,t}\right).\tag{13}$$

This equation represents a smooth and nonoscillatory motion. Figure 5.1.6 shows two possible graphs of $x(t)$.

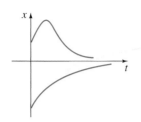

FIGURE 5.1.7 Motion of a critically damped system

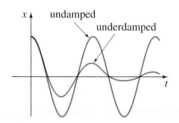

FIGURE 5.1.8 Motion of an underdamped system

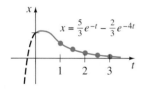

(a)

t	$x(t)$
1	0.601
1.5	0.370
2	0.225
2.5	0.137
3	0.083

(b)

FIGURE 5.1.9 Overdamped system

CASE II: $\lambda^2 - \omega^2 = 0$ The system is said to be **critically damped** because any slight decrease in the damping force would result in oscillatory motion. The general solution of (11) is $x(t) = c_1 e^{m_1 t} + c_2 t e^{m_1 t}$ or

$$x(t) = e^{-\lambda t}(c_1 + c_2 t). \tag{14}$$

Some graphs of typical motion are given in Figure 5.1.7. Notice that the motion is quite similar to that of an overdamped system. It is also apparent from (14) that the mass can pass through the equilibrium position at most one time.

CASE III: $\lambda^2 - \omega^2 < 0$ In this case the system is said to be **underdamped,** since the damping coefficient is small in comparison to the spring constant. The roots m_1 and m_2 are now complex:

$$m_1 = -\lambda + \sqrt{\omega^2 - \lambda^2}\,i, \qquad m_2 = -\lambda - \sqrt{\omega^2 - \lambda^2}\,i.$$

Thus the general solution of equation (11) is

$$x(t) = e^{-\lambda t}\left(c_1 \cos \sqrt{\omega^2 - \lambda^2}\,t + c_2 \sin \sqrt{\omega^2 - \lambda^2}\,t\right). \tag{15}$$

As indicated in Figure 5.1.8, the motion described by (15) is oscillatory; but because of the coefficient $e^{-\lambda t}$, the amplitudes of vibration $\to 0$ as $t \to \infty$.

EXAMPLE 3 Overdamped Motion

It is readily verified that the solution of the initial-value problem

$$\frac{d^2 x}{dt^2} + 5\frac{dx}{dt} + 4x = 0, \quad x(0) = 1, \quad x'(0) = 1$$

is

$$x(t) = \frac{5}{3} e^{-t} - \frac{2}{3} e^{-4t}. \tag{16}$$

The problem can be interpreted as representing the overdamped motion of a mass on a spring. The mass is initially released from a position 1 unit *below* the equilibrium position with a *downward* velocity of 1 ft/s.

To graph $x(t)$, we find the value of t for which the function has an extremum—that is, the value of time for which the first derivative (velocity) is zero. Differentiating (16) gives $x'(t) = -\frac{5}{3} e^{-t} + \frac{8}{3} e^{-4t}$, so $x'(t) = 0$ implies that $e^{3t} = \frac{8}{5}$ or $t = \frac{1}{3} \ln \frac{8}{5} = 0.157$. It follows from the first derivative test, as well as our physical intuition, that $x(0.157) = 1.069$ ft is actually a maximum. In other words, the mass attains an extreme displacement of 1.069 feet below the equilibrium position.

We should also check to see whether the graph crosses the t-axis—that is, whether the mass passes through the equilibrium position. This cannot happen in this instance because the equation $x(t) = 0$, or $e^{3t} = \frac{2}{5}$, has the physically irrelevant solution $t = \frac{1}{3} \ln \frac{2}{5} = -0.305$.

The graph of $x(t)$, along with some other pertinent data, is given in Figure 5.1.9. ∎

EXAMPLE 4 Critically Damped Motion

A mass weighing 8 pounds stretches a spring 2 feet. Assuming that a damping force numerically equal to 2 times the instantaneous velocity acts on the system, determine the equation of motion if the mass is initially released from the equilibrium position with an upward velocity of 3 ft/s.

SOLUTION From Hooke's law we see that $8 = k(2)$ gives $k = 4$ lb/ft and that $W = mg$ gives $m = \frac{8}{32} = \frac{1}{4}$ slug. The differential equation of motion is then

$$\frac{1}{4}\frac{d^2x}{dt^2} = -4x - 2\frac{dx}{dt} \quad \text{or} \quad \frac{d^2x}{dt^2} + 8\frac{dx}{dt} + 16x = 0. \quad (17)$$

The auxiliary equation for (17) is $m^2 + 8m + 16 = (m + 4)^2 = 0$, so $m_1 = m_2 = -4$. Hence the system is critically damped, and

$$x(t) = c_1 e^{-4t} + c_2 t e^{-4t}. \quad (18)$$

Applying the initial conditions $x(0) = 0$ and $x'(0) = -3$, we find, in turn, that $c_1 = 0$ and $c_2 = -3$. Thus the equation of motion is

$$x(t) = -3te^{-4t}. \quad (19)$$

To graph $x(t)$, we proceed as in Example 3. From $x'(t) = -3e^{-4t}(1 - 4t)$ we see that $x'(t) = 0$ when $t = \frac{1}{4}$. The corresponding extreme displacement is $x(\frac{1}{4}) = -3(\frac{1}{4})e^{-1} = -0.276$ ft. As shown in Figure 5.1.10, we interpret this value to mean that the mass reaches a maximum height of 0.276 foot above the equilibrium position. ∎

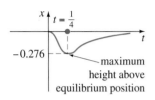

FIGURE 5.1.10 Critically damped system

EXAMPLE 5 Underdamped Motion

A mass weighing 16 pounds is attached to a 5-foot-long spring. At equilibrium the spring measures 8.2 feet. If the mass is initially released from rest at a point 2 feet above the equilibrium position, find the displacements $x(t)$ if it is further known that the surrounding medium offers a resistance numerically equal to the instantaneous velocity.

SOLUTION The elongation of the spring after the mass is attached is $8.2 - 5 = 3.2$ ft, so it follows from Hooke's law that $16 = k(3.2)$ or $k = 5$ lb/ft. In addition, $m = \frac{16}{32} = \frac{1}{2}$ slug, so the differential equation is given by

$$\frac{1}{2}\frac{d^2x}{dt^2} = -5x - \frac{dx}{dt} \quad \text{or} \quad \frac{d^2x}{dt^2} + 2\frac{dx}{dt} + 10x = 0. \quad (20)$$

Proceeding, we find that the roots of $m^2 + 2m + 10 = 0$ are $m_1 = -1 + 3i$ and $m_2 = -1 - 3i$, which then implies that the system is underdamped, and

$$x(t) = e^{-t}(c_1 \cos 3t + c_2 \sin 3t). \quad (21)$$

Finally, the initial conditions $x(0) = -2$ and $x'(0) = 0$ yield $c_1 = -2$ and $c_2 = -\frac{2}{3}$, so the equation of motion is

$$x(t) = e^{-t}\left(-2 \cos 3t - \frac{2}{3} \sin 3t\right). \quad (22) \quad ∎$$

ALTERNATIVE FORM OF $x(t)$ In a manner identical to the procedure used on page 184, we can write any solution

$$x(t) = e^{-\lambda t}\left(c_1 \cos \sqrt{\omega^2 - \lambda^2}\,t + c_2 \sin \sqrt{\omega^2 - \lambda^2}\,t\right)$$

in the alternative form

$$x(t) = Ae^{-\lambda t} \sin\left(\sqrt{\omega^2 - \lambda^2}\,t + \phi\right), \quad (23)$$

where $A = \sqrt{c_1^2 + c_2^2}$ and the phase angle ϕ is determined from the equations

$$\sin \phi = \frac{c_1}{A}, \quad \cos \phi = \frac{c_2}{A}, \quad \tan \phi = \frac{c_1}{c_2}.$$

The coefficient $Ae^{-\lambda t}$ is sometimes called the **damped amplitude** of vibrations. Because (23) is not a periodic function, the number $2\pi/\sqrt{\omega^2 - \lambda^2}$ is called the **quasi period** and $\sqrt{\omega^2 - \lambda^2}/2\pi$ is the **quasi frequency.** The quasi period is the time interval between two successive maxima of $x(t)$. You should verify, for the equation of motion in Example 5, that $A = 2\sqrt{10}/3$ and $\phi = 4.391$. Therefore an equivalent form of (22) is

$$x(t) = \frac{2\sqrt{10}}{3} e^{-t} \sin(3t + 4.391).$$

5.1.3   SPRING/MASS SYSTEMS: DRIVEN MOTION

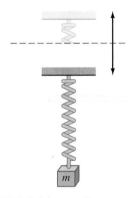

FIGURE 5.1.11   Oscillatory vertical motion of the support

DE OF DRIVEN MOTION WITH DAMPING   Suppose we now take into consideration an external force $f(t)$ acting on a vibrating mass on a spring. For example, $f(t)$ could represent a driving force causing an oscillatory vertical motion of the support of the spring. See Figure 5.1.11. The inclusion of $f(t)$ in the formulation of Newton's second law gives the differential equation of **driven** or **forced motion:**

$$m\frac{d^2x}{dt^2} = -kx - \beta\frac{dx}{dt} + f(t). \tag{24}$$

Dividing (24) by m gives

$$\frac{d^2x}{dt^2} + 2\lambda\frac{dx}{dt} + \omega^2 x = F(t), \tag{25}$$

where $F(t) = f(t)/m$ and, as in the preceding section, $2\lambda = \beta/m$, $\omega^2 = k/m$. To solve the latter nonhomogeneous equation, we can use either the method of undetermined coefficients or variation of parameters.

EXAMPLE 6   **Interpretation of an Initial-Value Problem**

Interpret and solve the initial-value problem

$$\frac{1}{5}\frac{d^2x}{dt^2} + 1.2\frac{dx}{dt} + 2x = 5\cos 4t, \quad x(0) = \frac{1}{2}, \quad x'(0) = 0. \tag{26}$$

SOLUTION   We can interpret the problem to represent a vibrational system consisting of a mass ($m = \frac{1}{5}$ slug or kilogram) attached to a spring ($k = 2$ lb/ft or N/m). The mass is initially released from rest $\frac{1}{2}$ unit (foot or meter) below the equilibrium position. The motion is damped ($\beta = 1.2$) and is being driven by an external periodic ($T = \pi/2$ s) force beginning at $t = 0$. Intuitively, we would expect that even with damping, the system would remain in motion until such time as the forcing function was "turned off," in which case the amplitudes would diminish. However, as the problem is given, $f(t) = 5\cos 4t$ will remain "on" forever.

We first multiply the differential equation in (26) by 5 and solve

$$\frac{dx^2}{dt^2} + 6\frac{dx}{dt} + 10x = 0$$

by the usual methods. Because $m_1 = -3 + i$, $m_2 = -3 - i$, it follows that $x_c(t) = e^{-3t}(c_1\cos t + c_2\sin t)$. Using the method of undetermined coefficients, we assume a particular solution of the form $x_p(t) = A\cos 4t + B\sin 4t$. Differentiating $x_p(t)$ and substituting into the DE gives

$$x_p'' + 6x_p' + 10x_p = (-6A + 24B)\cos 4t + (-24A - 6B)\sin 4t = 25\cos 4t.$$

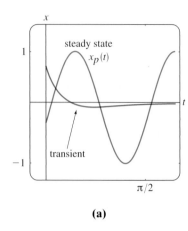

(a)

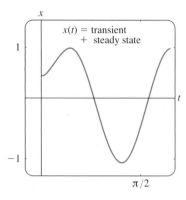

(b)

FIGURE 5.1.12 Graph of solution given in (28)

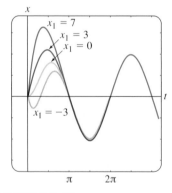

FIGURE 5.1.13 Graph of solution in Example 7 for various x_1

The resulting system of equations

$$-6A + 24B = 25, \qquad -24A - 6B = 0$$

yields $A = -\frac{25}{102}$ and $B = \frac{50}{51}$. It follows that

$$x(t) = e^{-3t}(c_1 \cos t + c_2 \sin t) - \frac{25}{102} \cos 4t + \frac{50}{51} \sin 4t. \qquad (27)$$

When we set $t = 0$ in the above equation, we obtain $c_1 = \frac{38}{51}$. By differentiating the expression and then setting $t = 0$, we also find that $c_2 = -\frac{86}{51}$. Therefore the equation of motion is

$$x(t) = e^{-3t}\left(\frac{38}{51} \cos t - \frac{86}{51} \sin t\right) - \frac{25}{102} \cos 4t + \frac{50}{51} \sin 4t. \qquad (28) \quad \blacksquare$$

TRANSIENT AND STEADY-STATE TERMS When F is a periodic function, such as $F(t) = F_0 \sin \gamma t$ or $F(t) = F_0 \cos \gamma t$, the general solution of (25) for $\lambda > 0$ is the sum of a nonperiodic function $x_c(t)$ and a periodic function $x_p(t)$. Moreover, $x_c(t)$ dies off as time increases—that is, $\lim_{t \to \infty} x_c(t) = 0$. Thus for large values of time, the displacements of the mass are closely approximated by the particular solution $x_p(t)$. The complementary function $x_c(t)$ is said to be a **transient term** or **transient solution,** and the function $x_p(t)$, the part of the solution that remains after an interval of time, is called a **steady-state term** or **steady-state solution.** Note therefore that the effect of the initial conditions on a spring/mass system driven by F is transient. In the particular solution (28), $e^{-3t}\left(\frac{38}{51} \cos t - \frac{86}{51} \sin t\right)$ is a transient term, and $x_p(t) = -\frac{25}{102} \cos 4t + \frac{50}{51} \sin 4t$ is a steady-state term. The graphs of these two terms and the solution (28) are given in Figures 5.1.12(a) and 5.1.12(b), respectively.

EXAMPLE 7   **Transient/Steady-State Solutions**

The solution of the initial-value problem

$$\frac{d^2x}{dt^2} + 2\frac{dx}{dt} + 2x = 4 \cos t + 2 \sin t, \quad x(0) = 0, \quad x'(0) = x_1,$$

where x_1 is constant, is given by

$$x(t) = \underbrace{(x_1 - 2) e^{-t} \sin t}_{\text{transient}} + \underbrace{2 \sin t}_{\text{steady-state}}.$$

Solution curves for selected values of the initial velocity x_1 are shown in Figure 5.1.13. The graphs show that the influence of the transient term is negligible for about $t > 3\pi/2$. $\blacksquare$

DE OF DRIVEN MOTION WITHOUT DAMPING With a periodic impressed force and no damping force, there is no transient term in the solution of a problem. Also, we shall see that a periodic impressed force with a frequency near or the same as the frequency of free undamped vibrations can cause a severe problem in any oscillatory mechanical system.

EXAMPLE 8   **Undamped Forced Motion**

Solve the initial-value problem

$$\frac{d^2x}{dt^2} + \omega^2 x = F_0 \sin \gamma t, \quad x(0) = 0, \quad x'(0) = 0, \qquad (29)$$

where F_0 is a constant and $\gamma \neq \omega$.

SOLUTION The complementary function is $x_c(t) = c_1 \cos \omega t + c_2 \sin \omega t$. To obtain a particular solution, we assume $x_p(t) = A \cos \gamma t + B \sin \gamma t$ so that

$$x_p'' + \omega^2 x_p = A(\omega^2 - \gamma^2) \cos \gamma t + B(\omega^2 - \gamma^2) \sin \gamma t = F_0 \sin \gamma t.$$

Equating coefficients immediately gives $A = 0$ and $B = F_0/(\omega^2 - \gamma^2)$. Therefore

$$x_p(t) = \frac{F_0}{\omega^2 - \gamma^2} \sin \gamma t.$$

Applying the given initial conditions to the general solution

$$x(t) = c_1 \cos \omega t + c_2 \sin \omega t + \frac{F_0}{\omega^2 - \gamma^2} \sin \gamma t$$

yields $c_1 = 0$ and $c_2 = -\gamma F_0/\omega(\omega^2 - \gamma^2)$. Thus the solution is

$$x(t) = \frac{F_0}{\omega(\omega^2 - \gamma^2)} (-\gamma \sin \omega t + \omega \sin \gamma t), \qquad \gamma \neq \omega. \qquad (30) \quad \blacksquare$$

PURE RESONANCE Although equation (30) is not defined for $\gamma = \omega$, it is interesting to observe that its limiting value as $\gamma \to \omega$ can be obtained by applying L'Hôpital's Rule. This limiting process is analogous to "tuning in" the frequency of the driving force ($\gamma/2\pi$) to the frequency of free vibrations ($\omega/2\pi$). Intuitively, we expect that over a length of time we should be able to substantially increase the amplitudes of vibration. For $\gamma = \omega$ we define the solution to be

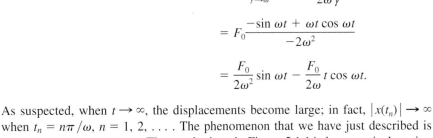

$$x(t) = \lim_{\gamma \to \omega} F_0 \frac{-\gamma \sin \omega t + \omega \sin \gamma t}{\omega(\omega^2 - \gamma^2)} = F_0 \lim_{\gamma \to \omega} \frac{\dfrac{d}{d\gamma}(-\gamma \sin \omega t + \omega \sin \gamma t)}{\dfrac{d}{d\gamma}(\omega^3 - \omega\gamma^2)}$$

$$= F_0 \lim_{\gamma \to \omega} \frac{-\sin \omega t + \omega t \cos \gamma t}{-2\omega\gamma} \qquad (31)$$

$$= F_0 \frac{-\sin \omega t + \omega t \cos \omega t}{-2\omega^2}$$

$$= \frac{F_0}{2\omega^2} \sin \omega t - \frac{F_0}{2\omega} t \cos \omega t.$$

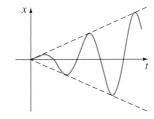

FIGURE 5.1.14 Pure resonance

As suspected, when $t \to \infty$, the displacements become large; in fact, $|x(t_n)| \to \infty$ when $t_n = n\pi/\omega$, $n = 1, 2, \ldots$. The phenomenon that we have just described is known as **pure resonance**. The graph given in Figure 5.1.14 shows typical motion in this case.

In conclusion it should be noted that there is no actual need to use a limiting process on (30) to obtain the solution for $\gamma = \omega$. Alternatively, equation (31) follows by solving the initial-value problem

$$\frac{d^2x}{dt^2} + \omega^2 x = F_0 \sin \omega t, \quad x(0) = 0, \quad x'(0) = 0$$

directly by conventional methods.

If the displacements of a spring/mass system were actually described by a function such as (31), the system would necessarily fail. Large oscillations of the mass would eventually force the spring beyond its elastic limit. One might argue too that the resonating model presented in Figure 5.1.14 is completely unrealistic because it ignores the retarding effects of ever-present damping forces. Although it is true that pure resonance cannot occur when the smallest amount of damping is taken into consideration, large and equally destructive amplitudes of vibration (although bounded as $t \to \infty$) can occur. See Problem 43 in Exercises 5.1.

5.1.4 SERIES CIRCUIT ANALOGUE

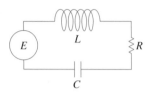

FIGURE 5.1.15 *LRC* series circuit

***LRC* SERIES CIRCUITS**   As was mentioned in the introduction to this chapter, many different physical systems can be described by a linear second-order differential equation similar to the differential equation of forced motion with damping:

$$m\frac{d^2x}{dt^2} + \beta\frac{dx}{dt} + kx = f(t). \tag{32}$$

If $i(t)$ denotes current in the ***LRC* series electrical circuit** shown in Figure 5.1.15, then the voltage drops across the inductor, resistor, and capacitor are as shown in Figure 1.3.3. By Kirchhoff's second law the sum of these voltages equals the voltage $E(t)$ impressed on the circuit; that is,

$$L\frac{di}{dt} + Ri + \frac{1}{C}q = E(t). \tag{33}$$

But the charge $q(t)$ on the capacitor is related to the current $i(t)$ by $i = dq/dt$, so (33) becomes the linear second-order differential equation

$$L\frac{d^2q}{dt^2} + R\frac{dq}{dt} + \frac{1}{C}q = E(t). \tag{34}$$

The nomenclature used in the analysis of circuits is similar to that used to describe spring/mass systems.

If $E(t) = 0$, the **electrical vibrations** of the circuit are said to be **free.** Because the auxiliary equation for (34) is $Lm^2 + Rm + 1/C = 0$, there will be three forms of the solution with $R \neq 0$, depending on the value of the discriminant $R^2 - 4L/C$. We say that the circuit is

overdamped if $R^2 - 4L/C > 0$,

critically damped if $R^2 - 4L/C = 0$,

and   **underdamped** if $R^2 - 4L/C < 0$.

In each of these three cases the general solution of (34) contains the factor $e^{-Rt/2L}$, so $q(t) \to 0$ as $t \to \infty$. In the underdamped case when $q(0) = q_0$, the charge on the capacitor oscillates as it decays; in other words, the capacitor is charging and discharging as $t \to \infty$. When $E(t) = 0$ and $R = 0$, the circuit is said to be undamped, and the electrical vibrations do not approach zero as t increases without bound; the response of the circuit is **simple harmonic.**

EXAMPLE 9   **Underdamped Series Circuit**

Find the charge $q(t)$ on the capacitor in an *LRC* series circuit when $L = 0.25$ henry (h), $R = 10$ ohms (Ω), $C = 0.001$ farad (f), $E(t) = 0$, $q(0) = q_0$ coulombs (C), and $i(0) = 0$.

SOLUTION   Since $1/C = 1000$, equation (34) becomes

$$\frac{1}{4}q'' + 10q' + 1000q = 0 \quad \text{or} \quad q'' + 40q' + 4000q = 0.$$

Solving this homogeneous equation in the usual manner, we find that the circuit is underdamped and $q(t) = e^{-20t}(c_1 \cos 60t + c_2 \sin 60t)$. Applying the initial conditions, we find $c_1 = q_0$ and $c_2 = \frac{1}{3}q_0$. Thus

$$q(t) = q_0 e^{-20t}\left(\cos 60t + \frac{1}{3}\sin 60t\right).$$

Using (23), we can write the foregoing solution as

$$q(t) = \frac{q_0 \sqrt{10}}{3} e^{-20t} \sin(60t + 1.249).$$ ∎

When there is an impressed voltage $E(t)$ on the circuit, the electrical vibrations are said to be **forced.** In the case when $R \neq 0$, the complementary function $q_c(t)$ of (34) is called a **transient solution.** If $E(t)$ is periodic or a constant, then the particular solution $q_p(t)$ of (34) is a **steady-state solution.**

EXAMPLE 10 **Steady-State Current**

Find the steady-state solution $q_p(t)$ and the **steady-state current** in an LRC series circuit when the impressed voltage is $E(t) = E_0 \sin \gamma t$.

SOLUTION The steady-state solution $q_p(t)$ is a particular solution of the differential equation

$$L \frac{d^2q}{dt^2} + R \frac{dq}{dt} + \frac{1}{C} q = E_0 \sin \gamma t.$$

Using the method of undetermined coefficients, we assume a particular solution of the form $q_p(t) = A \sin \gamma t + B \cos \gamma t$. Substituting this expression into the differential equation, simplifying, and equating coefficients gives

$$A = \frac{E_0 \left(L\gamma - \dfrac{1}{C\gamma} \right)}{-\gamma \left(L^2\gamma^2 - \dfrac{2L}{C} + \dfrac{1}{C^2\gamma^2} + R^2 \right)}, \qquad B = \frac{E_0 R}{-\gamma \left(L^2\gamma^2 - \dfrac{2L}{C} + \dfrac{1}{C^2\gamma^2} + R^2 \right)}.$$

It is convenient to express A and B in terms of some new symbols.

If $X = L\gamma - \dfrac{1}{C\gamma}$,   then $X^2 = L^2\gamma^2 - \dfrac{2L}{C} + \dfrac{1}{C^2\gamma^2}$.

If $Z = \sqrt{X^2 + R^2}$,   then $Z^2 = L^2\gamma^2 - \dfrac{2L}{C} + \dfrac{1}{C^2\gamma^2} + R^2$.

Therefore $A = E_0 X / (-\gamma Z^2)$ and $B = E_0 R / (-\gamma Z^2)$, so the steady-state charge is

$$q_p(t) = -\frac{E_0 X}{\gamma Z^2} \sin \gamma t - \frac{E_0 R}{\gamma Z^2} \cos \gamma t.$$

Now the steady-state current is given by $i_p(t) = q_p'(t)$:

$$i_p(t) = \frac{E_0}{Z} \left(\frac{R}{Z} \sin \gamma t - \frac{X}{Z} \cos \gamma t \right). \qquad (35)$$ ∎

The quantities $X = L\gamma - 1/C\gamma$ and $Z = \sqrt{X^2 + R^2}$ defined in Example 11 are called the **reactance** and **impedance,** respectively, of the circuit. Both the reactance and the impedance are measured in ohms.

EXERCISES 5.1

Answers to selected odd-numbered problems begin on page ANS-7.

5.1.1 SPRING/MASS SYSTEMS: FREE UNDAMPED MOTION

1. A mass weighing 4 pounds is attached to a spring whose spring constant is 16 lb/ft. What is the period of simple harmonic motion?

2. A 20-kilogram mass is attached to a spring. If the frequency of simple harmonic motion is $2/\pi$ cycles/s, what is the spring constant k? What is the frequency of simple harmonic motion if the original mass is replaced with an 80-kilogram mass?

3. A mass weighing 24 pounds, attached to the end of a spring, stretches it 4 inches. Initially, the mass is released from rest from a point 3 inches above the equilibrium position. Find the equation of motion.

4. Determine the equation of motion if the mass in Problem 3 is initially released from the equilibrium position with a downward velocity of 2 ft/s.

5. A mass weighing 20 pounds stretches a spring 6 inches. The mass is initially released from rest from a point 6 inches below the equilibrium position.

   (a) Find the position of the mass at the times $t = \pi/12$, $\pi/8$, $\pi/6$, $\pi/4$, and $9\pi/32$ s.

   (b) What is the velocity of the mass when $t = 3\pi/16$ s? In which direction is the mass heading at this instant?

   (c) At what times does the mass pass through the equilibrium position?

6. A force of 400 newtons stretches a spring 2 meters. A mass of 50 kilograms is attached to the end of the spring and is initially released from the equilibrium position with an upward velocity of 10 m/s. Find the equation of motion.

7. Another spring whose constant is 20 N/m is suspended from the same rigid support but parallel to the spring/mass system in Problem 6. A mass of 20 kilograms is attached to the second spring, and both masses are initially released from the equilibrium position with an upward velocity of 10 m/s.

   (a) Which mass exhibits the greater amplitude of motion?

   (b) Which mass is moving faster at $t = \pi/4$ s? At $\pi/2$ s?

   (c) At what times are the two masses in the same position? Where are the masses at these times? In which directions are the masses moving?

8. A mass weighing 32 pounds stretches a spring 2 feet. Determine the amplitude and period of motion if the mass is initially released from a point 1 foot above the equilibrium position with an upward velocity of 2 ft/s. How many complete cycles will the mass have completed at the end of 4π seconds?

9. A mass weighing 8 pounds is attached to a spring. When set in motion, the spring/mass system exhibits simple harmonic motion. Determine the equation of motion if the spring constant is 1 lb/ft and the mass is initially released from a point 6 inches below the equilibrium position with a downward velocity of $\frac{3}{2}$ ft/s. Express the equation of motion in the form given in (6).

10. A mass weighing 10 pounds stretches a spring $\frac{1}{4}$ foot. This mass is removed and replaced with a mass of 1.6 slugs, which is initially released from a point $\frac{1}{3}$ foot above the equilibrium position with a downward velocity of $\frac{5}{4}$ ft/s. Express the equation of motion in the form given in (6). At what times does the mass attain a displacement below the equilibrium position numerically equal to $\frac{1}{2}$ the amplitude?

11. A mass weighing 64 pounds stretches a spring 0.32 foot. The mass is initially released from a point 8 inches above the equilibrium position with a downward velocity of 5 ft/s.

    (a) Find the equation of motion.

    (b) What are the amplitude and period of motion?

    (c) How many complete cycles will the mass have completed at the end of 3π seconds?

    (d) At what time does the mass pass through the equilibrium position heading downward for the second time?

    (e) At what times does the mass attain its extreme displacements on either side of the equilibrium position?

    (f) What is the position of the mass at $t = 3$ s?

    (g) What is the instantaneous velocity at $t = 3$ s?

    (h) What is the acceleration at $t = 3$ s?

    (i) What is the instantaneous velocity at the times when the mass passes through the equilibrium position?

    (j) At what times is the mass 5 inches below the equilibrium position?

    (k) At what times is the mass 5 inches below the equilibrium position heading in the upward direction?

12. A mass of 1 slug is suspended from a spring whose spring constant is 9 lb/ft. The mass is initially released from a point 1 foot above the equilibrium position with an upward velocity of $\sqrt{3}$ ft/s. Find the times at which the mass is heading downward at a velocity of 3 ft/s.

13. Under some circumstances when two parallel springs, with constants k_1 and k_2, support a single mass, the

effective spring constant of the system is given by $k = 4k_1k_2/(k_1 + k_2)$. A mass weighing 20 pounds stretches one spring 6 inches and another spring 2 inches. The springs are attached to a common rigid support and then to a metal plate. As shown in Figure 5.1.16, the mass is attached to the center of the plate in the double-spring arrangement. Determine the effective spring constant of this system. Find the equation of motion if the mass is initially released from the equilibrium position with a downward velocity of 2 ft/s.

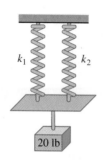

FIGURE 5.1.16 Double-spring system in Problem 13

14. A certain mass stretches one spring $\frac{1}{3}$ foot and another spring $\frac{1}{2}$ foot. The two springs are attached to a common rigid support in the manner described in Problem 13 and Figure 5.1.16. The first mass is set aside, a mass weighing 8 pounds is attached to the double-spring arrangement, and the system is set in motion. If the period of motion is $\pi/15$ second, determine how much the first mass weighs.

15. A model of a spring/mass system is $4x'' + e^{-0.1t}x = 0$. By inspection of the differential equation only, discuss the behavior of the system over a long period of time.

16. A model of a spring/mass system is $4x'' + tx = 0$. By inspection of the differential equation only, discuss the behavior of the system over a long period of time.

5.1.2 SPRING/MASS SYSTEMS: FREE DAMPED MOTION

In Problems 17–20 the given figure represents the graph of an equation of motion for a damped spring/mass system. Use the graph to determine

(a) whether the initial displacement is above or below the equilibrium position and

(b) whether the mass is initially released from rest, heading downward, or heading upward.

17.

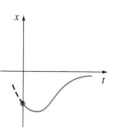

FIGURE 5.1.17 Graph for Problem 17

18.

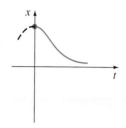

FIGURE 5.1.18 Graph for Problem 18

19.

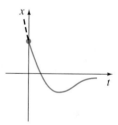

FIGURE 5.1.19 Graph for Problem 19

20.

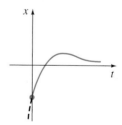

FIGURE 5.1.20 Graph for Problem 20

21. A mass weighing 4 pounds is attached to a spring whose constant is 2 lb/ft. The medium offers a damping force that is numerically equal to the instantaneous velocity. The mass is initially released from a point 1 foot above the equilibrium position with a downward velocity of 8 ft/s. Determine the time at which the mass passes through the equilibrium position. Find the time at which the mass attains its extreme displacement from the equilibrium position. What is the position of the mass at this instant?

22. A 4-foot spring measures 8 feet long after a mass weighing 8 pounds is attached to it. The medium through which the mass moves offers a damping force numerically equal to $\sqrt{2}$ times the instantaneous velocity. Find the equation of motion if the mass is initially released from the equilibrium position with a downward velocity of 5 ft/s. Find the time at which the mass attains its extreme displacement from the equilibrium position. What is the position of the mass at this instant?

23. A 1-kilogram mass is attached to a spring whose constant is 16 N/m, and the entire system is then submerged in a liquid that imparts a damping force numerically equal to 10 times the instantaneous velocity. Determine the equations of motion if

   (a) the mass is initially released from rest from a point 1 meter below the equilibrium position, and then

   (b) the mass is initially released from a point 1 meter below the equilibrium position with an upward velocity of 12 m/s.

24. In parts (a) and (b) of Problem 23 determine whether the mass passes through the equilibrium position. In each case find the time at which the mass attains its extreme displacement from the equilibrium position. What is the position of the mass at this instant?

25. A force of 2 pounds stretches a spring 1 foot. A mass weighing 3.2 pounds is attached to the spring, and the system is then immersed in a medium that offers a damping force that is numerically equal to 0.4 times the instantaneous velocity.

   (a) Find the equation of motion if the mass is initially released from rest from a point 1 foot above the equilibrium position.

   (b) Express the equation of motion in the form given in (23).

   (c) Find the first time at which the mass passes through the equilibrium position heading upward.

26. After a mass weighing 10 pounds is attached to a 5-foot spring, the spring measures 7 feet. This mass is removed and replaced with another mass that weighs 8 pounds. The entire system is placed in a medium that offers a damping force that is numerically equal to the instantaneous velocity.

   (a) Find the equation of motion if the mass is initially released from a point $\frac{1}{2}$ foot below the equilibrium position with a downward velocity of 1 ft/s.

   (b) Express the equation of motion in the form given in (23).

   (c) Find the times at which the mass passes through the equilibrium position heading downward.

   (d) Graph the equation of motion.

27. A mass weighing 10 pounds stretches a spring 2 feet. The mass is attached to a dashpot device that offers a damping force numerically equal to β ($\beta > 0$) times the instantaneous velocity. Determine the values of the damping constant β so that the subsequent motion is **(a)** overdamped, **(b)** critically damped, and **(c)** underdamped.

28. A mass weighing 24 pounds stretches a spring 4 feet. The subsequent motion takes place in medium that offers a damping force numerically equal to β ($\beta > 0$) times the instantaneous velocity. If the mass is initially released from the equilibrium position with an upward velocity of 2 ft/s, show that when $\beta > 3\sqrt{2}$ the equation of motion is

$$x(t) = \frac{-3}{\sqrt{\beta^2 - 18}}\, e^{-2\beta t/3}\, \sinh \frac{2}{3}\sqrt{\beta^2 - 18}\,t.$$

5.1.3 SPRING/MASS SYSTEMS: DRIVEN MOTION

29. A mass weighing 16 pounds stretches a spring $\frac{8}{3}$ feet. The mass is initially released from rest from a point 2 feet below the equilibrium position, and the subsequent motion takes place in a medium that offers a damping force that is numerically equal to $\frac{1}{2}$ the instantaneous velocity. Find the equation of motion if the mass is driven by an external force equal to $f(t) = 10 \cos 3t$.

30. A mass of 1 slug is attached to a spring whose constant is 5 lb/ft. Initially, the mass is released 1 foot below the equilibrium position with a downward velocity of 5 ft/s, and the subsequent motion takes place in a medium that offers a damping force that is numerically equal to 2 times the instantaneous velocity.

   (a) Find the equation of motion if the mass is driven by an external force equal to $f(t) = 12 \cos 2t + 3 \sin 2t$.

   (b) Graph the transient and steady-state solutions on the same coordinate axes.

   (c) Graph the equation of motion.

31. A mass of 1 slug, when attached to a spring, stretches it 2 feet and then comes to rest in the equilibrium position. Starting at $t = 0$, an external force equal to $f(t) = 8 \sin 4t$ is applied to the system. Find the equation of motion if the surrounding medium offers a damping force that is numerically equal to 8 times the instantaneous velocity.

32. In Problem 31 determine the equation of motion if the external force is $f(t) = e^{-t} \sin 4t$. Analyze the displacements for $t \to \infty$.

33. When a mass of 2 kilograms is attached to a spring whose constant is 32 N/m, it comes to rest in the equilibrium position. Starting at $t = 0$, a force equal to $f(t) = 68e^{-2t} \cos 4t$ is applied to the system. Find the equation of motion in the absence of damping.

34. In Problem 33 write the equation of motion in the form $x(t) = A\sin(\omega t + \phi) + Be^{-2t}\sin(4t + \theta)$. What is the amplitude of vibrations after a very long time?

35. A mass m is attached to the end of a spring whose constant is k. After the mass reaches equilibrium, its support begins to oscillate vertically about a horizontal line L according to a formula $h(t)$. The value of h represents the distance in feet measured from L. See Figure 5.1.21.

(a) Determine the differential equation of motion if the entire system moves through a medium offering a damping force that is numerically equal to $\beta(dx/dt)$.

(b) Solve the differential equation in part (a) if the spring is stretched 4 feet by a mass weighing 16 pounds and $\beta = 2$, $h(t) = 5 \cos t$, $x(0) = x'(0) = 0$.

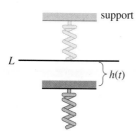

FIGURE 5.1.21 Oscillating support in Problem 35

36. A mass of 100 grams is attached to a spring whose constant is 1600 dynes/cm. After the mass reaches equilibrium, its support oscillates according to the formula $h(t) = \sin 8t$, where h represents displacement from its original position. See Problem 35 and Figure 5.1.21.

(a) In the absence of damping, determine the equation of motion if the mass starts from rest from the equilibrium position.

(b) At what times does the mass pass through the equilibrium position?

(c) At what times does the mass attain its extreme displacements?

(d) What are the maximum and minimum displacements?

(e) Graph the equation of motion.

In Problems 37 and 38 solve the given initial-value problem.

37. $\dfrac{d^2x}{dt^2} + 4x = -5 \sin 2t + 3 \cos 2t$,

$x(0) = -1$, $\quad x'(0) = 1$

38. $\dfrac{d^2x}{dt^2} + 9x = 5 \sin 3t$, $\quad x(0) = 2$, $\quad x'(0) = 0$

39. (a) Show that the solution of the initial-value problem

$$\frac{d^2x}{dt^2} + \omega^2 x = F_0 \cos \gamma t, \quad x(0) = 0, \quad x'(0) = 0$$

is $\quad x(t) = \dfrac{F_0}{\omega^2 - \gamma^2} (\cos \gamma t - \cos \omega t)$.

(b) Evaluate $\displaystyle\lim_{\gamma \to \omega} \dfrac{F_0}{\omega^2 - \gamma^2} (\cos \gamma t - \cos \omega t)$.

40. Compare the result obtained in part (b) of Problem 39 with the solution obtained using variation of parameters when the external force is $F_0 \cos \omega t$.

41. (a) Show that $x(t)$ given in part (a) of Problem 39 can be written in the form

$$x(t) = \frac{-2F_0}{\omega^2 - \gamma^2} \sin \frac{1}{2}(\gamma - \omega)t \sin \frac{1}{2}(\gamma + \omega)t.$$

(b) If we define $\varepsilon = \frac{1}{2}(\gamma - \omega)$, show that when ε is small an approximate solution is

$$x(t) = \frac{F_0}{2\varepsilon\gamma} \sin \varepsilon t \sin \gamma t.$$

When ε is small, the frequency $\gamma/2\pi$ of the impressed force is close to the frequency $\omega/2\pi$ of free vibrations. When this occurs, the motion is as indicated in Figure 5.1.22. Oscillations of this kind are called **beats** and are due to the fact that the frequency of $\sin \varepsilon t$ is quite small in comparison to the frequency of $\sin \gamma t$. The dashed curves, or envelope of the graph of $x(t)$, are obtained from the graphs of $\pm(F_0/2\varepsilon\gamma) \sin \varepsilon t$. Use a graphing utility with various values of F_0, ε, and γ to verify the graph in Figure 5.1.22.

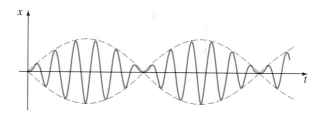

FIGURE 5.1.22 Beats phenomenon in Problem 41

Computer Lab Assignments

42. Can there be beats when a damping force is added to the model in part (a) of Problem 39? Defend your position with graphs obtained either from the explicit solution of the problem

$$\frac{d^2x}{dt^2} + 2\lambda\frac{dx}{dt} + \omega^2 x = F_0 \cos \gamma t, \quad x(0) = 0, \quad x'(0) = 0$$

or from solution curves obtained using a numerical solver.

43. (a) Show that the general solution of

$$\frac{d^2x}{dt^2} + 2\lambda\frac{dx}{dt} + \omega^2 x = F_0 \sin \gamma t$$

is

$$x(t) = Ae^{-\lambda t}\sin\left(\sqrt{\omega^2 - \lambda^2}\,t + \phi\right)$$

$$+ \frac{F_0}{\sqrt{(\omega^2 - \gamma^2)^2 + 4\lambda^2\gamma^2}}\sin(\gamma t + \theta),$$

where $A = \sqrt{c_1^2 + c_2^2}$ and the phase angles ϕ and θ are, respectively, defined by $\sin\phi = c_1/A$, $\cos\phi = c_2/A$ and

$$\sin\theta = \frac{-2\lambda\gamma}{\sqrt{(\omega^2 - \gamma^2)^2 + 4\lambda^2\gamma^2}},$$

$$\cos\theta = \frac{\omega^2 - \gamma^2}{\sqrt{(\omega^2 - \gamma^2)^2 + 4\lambda^2\gamma^2}}.$$

(b) The solution in part (a) has the form $x(t) = x_c(t) + x_p(t)$. Inspection shows that $x_c(t)$ is transient, and hence for large values of time, the solution is approximated by $x_p(t) = g(\gamma)\sin(\gamma t + \theta)$, where

$$g(\gamma) = \frac{F_0}{\sqrt{(\omega^2 - \gamma^2)^2 + 4\lambda^2\gamma^2}}.$$

Although the amplitude $g(\gamma)$ of $x_p(t)$ is bounded as $t \to \infty$, show that the maximum oscillations will occur at the value $\gamma_1 = \sqrt{\omega^2 - 2\lambda^2}$. What is the maximum value of g? The number $\sqrt{\omega^2 - 2\lambda^2}/2\pi$ is said to be the **resonance frequency** of the system.

(c) When $F_0 = 2$, $m = 1$, and $k = 4$, g becomes

$$g(\gamma) = \frac{2}{\sqrt{(4 - \gamma^2)^2 + \beta^2\gamma^2}}.$$

Construct a table of the values of γ_1 and $g(\gamma_1)$ corresponding to the damping coefficients $\beta = 2$, $\beta = 1$, $\beta = \frac{3}{4}$, $\beta = \frac{1}{2}$, and $\beta = \frac{1}{4}$. Use a graphing utility to obtain the graphs of g corresponding to these damping coefficients. Use the same coordinate axes. This family of graphs is called the **resonance curve** or **frequency response curve** of the system. What is γ_1 approaching as $\beta \to 0$? What is happening to the resonance curve as $\beta \to 0$?

44. Consider a driven undamped spring/mass system described by the initial-value problem

$$\frac{d^2x}{dt^2} + \omega^2 x = F_0\sin^n\gamma t, \quad x(0) = 0, \quad x'(0) = 0.$$

(a) For $n = 2$, discuss why there is a single frequency $\gamma_1/2\pi$ at which the system is in pure resonance.

(b) For $n = 3$, discuss why there are two frequencies $\gamma_1/2\pi$ and $\gamma_2/2\pi$ at which the system is in pure resonance.

(c) Suppose $\omega = 1$ and $F_0 = 1$. Use a numerical solver to obtain the graph of the solution of the initial-value problem for $n = 2$ and $\gamma = \gamma_1$ in part (a). Obtain the graph of the solution of the initial-value problem for $n = 3$ corresponding, in turn, to $\gamma = \gamma_1$ and $\gamma = \gamma_2$ in part (b).

5.1.4 SERIES CIRCUIT ANALOGUE

45. Find the charge on the capacitor in an LRC series circuit at $t = 0.01$ s when $L = 0.05$ h, $R = 2\,\Omega$, $C = 0.01$ f, $E(t) = 0$ V, $q(0) = 5$ C, and $i(0) = 0$ A. Determine the first time at which the charge on the capacitor is equal to zero.

46. Find the charge on the capacitor in an LRC series circuit when $L = \frac{1}{4}$ h, $R = 20\,\Omega$, $C = \frac{1}{300}$ f, $E(t) = 0$ V, $q(0) = 4$ C, and $i(0) = 0$ A. Is the charge on the capacitor ever equal to zero?

In Problems 47 and 48 find the charge on the capacitor and the current in the given LRC series circuit. Find the maximum charge on the capacitor.

47. $L = \frac{5}{3}$ h, $R = 10\,\Omega$, $C = \frac{1}{30}$ f, $E(t) = 300$ V, $q(0) = 0$ C, $i(0) = 0$ A

48. $L = 1$ h, $R = 100\,\Omega$, $C = 0.0004$ f, $E(t) = 30$ V, $q(0) = 0$ C, $i(0) = 2$ A

49. Find the steady-state charge and the steady-state current in an LRC series circuit when $L = 1$ h, $R = 2\,\Omega$, $C = 0.25$ f, and $E(t) = 50\cos t$ V.

50. Show that the amplitude of the steady-state current in the LRC series circuit in Example 10 is given by E_0/Z, where Z is the impedance of the circuit.

51. Use Problem 50 to show that the steady-state current in an LRC series circuit when $L = \frac{1}{2}$ h, $R = 20\,\Omega$, $C = 0.001$ f, and $E(t) = 100\sin 60t$ V, is given by $i_p(t) = 4.160\sin(60t - 0.588)$.

52. Find the steady-state current in an LRC series circuit when $L = \frac{1}{2}$ h, $R = 20\,\Omega$, $C = 0.001$ f, and $E(t) = 100\sin 60t + 200\cos 40t$ V.

53. Find the charge on the capacitor in an LRC series circuit when $L = \frac{1}{2}$ h, $R = 10\,\Omega$, $C = 0.01$ f, $E(t) = 150$ V, $q(0) = 1$ C, and $i(0) = 0$ A. What is the charge on the capacitor after a long time?

54. Show that if L, R, C, and E_0 are constant, then the amplitude of the steady-state current in Example 10 is a maximum when $\gamma = 1/\sqrt{LC}$. What is the maximum amplitude?

55. Show that if L, R, E_0, and γ are constant, then the amplitude of the steady-state current in Example 10 is a maximum when the capacitance is $C = 1/L\gamma^2$.

56. Find the charge on the capacitor and the current in an LC circuit when $L = 0.1$ h, $C = 0.1$ f, $E(t) = 100\sin\gamma t$ V, $q(0) = 0$ C, and $i(0) = 0$ A.

57. Find the charge on the capacitor and the current in an LC circuit when $E(t) = E_0\cos\gamma t$ V, $q(0) = q_0$ C, and $i(0) = i_0$ A.

58. In Problem 57 find the current when the circuit is in resonance.

5.2 LINEAR MODELS: BOUNDARY-VALUE PROBLEMS

REVIEW MATERIAL

- Problems 37–40 in Exercises 4.3
- Problems 37–40 in Exercises 4.4

INTRODUCTION The preceding section was devoted to systems in which a second-order mathematical model was accompanied by initial conditions—that is, side conditions that are specified on the unknown function and its first derivative at a single point. But often the mathematical description of a physical system demands that we solve a homogeneous linear differential equation subject to boundary conditions—that is, conditions specified on the unknown function, or on one of its derivatives, or even on a linear combination of the unknown function and one of its derivatives at two (or more) different points.

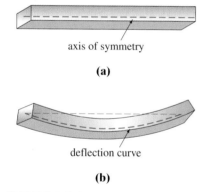

axis of symmetry

(a)

deflection curve

(b)

FIGURE 5.2.1 Deflection of a homogeneous beam

DEFLECTION OF A BEAM Many structures are constructed by using girders or beams, and these beams deflect or distort under their own weight or under the influence of some external force. As we shall now see, this deflection $y(x)$ is governed by a relatively simple linear fourth-order differential equation.

To begin, let us assume that a beam of length L is homogeneous and has uniform cross sections along its length. In the absence of any load on the beam (including its weight), a curve joining the centroids of all its cross sections is a straight line called the **axis of symmetry.** See Figure 5.2.1(a). If a load is applied to the beam in a vertical plane containing the axis of symmetry, the beam, as shown in Figure 5.2.1(b), undergoes a distortion, and the curve connecting the centroids of all cross sections is called the **deflection curve** or **elastic curve.** The deflection curve approximates the shape of the beam. Now suppose that the x-axis coincides with the axis of symmetry and that the deflection $y(x)$, measured from this axis, is positive if downward. In the theory of elasticity it is shown that the bending moment $M(x)$ at a point x along the beam is related to the load per unit length $w(x)$ by the equation

$$\frac{d^2M}{dx^2} = w(x). \tag{1}$$

In addition, the bending moment $M(x)$ is proportional to the curvature κ of the elastic curve

$$M(x) = EI\kappa, \tag{2}$$

where E and I are constants; E is Young's modulus of elasticity of the material of the beam, and I is the moment of inertia of a cross section of the beam (about an axis known as the neutral axis). The product EI is called the **flexural rigidity** of the beam.

Now, from calculus, curvature is given by $\kappa = y''/[1 + (y')^2]^{3/2}$. When the deflection $y(x)$ is small, the slope $y' \approx 0$, and so $[1 + (y')^2]^{3/2} \approx 1$. If we let $\kappa \approx y''$, equation (2) becomes $M = EI\,y''$. The second derivative of this last expression is

$$\frac{d^2M}{dx^2} = EI\frac{d^2}{dx^2}\,y'' = EI\frac{d^4y}{dx^4}. \tag{3}$$

Using the given result in (1) to replace d^2M/dx^2 in (3), we see that the deflection $y(x)$ satisfies the fourth-order differential equation

$$EI\frac{d^4y}{dx^4} = w(x). \tag{4}$$

$x = 0$ $x = L$

(a) embedded at both ends

$x = 0$ $x = L$

(b) cantilever beam: embedded at the left end, free at the right end

$x = 0$ $x = L$

(c) simply supported at both ends

FIGURE 5.2.2 Beams with various end conditions

TABLE 5.1

Ends of the Beam	Boundary Conditions
embedded	$y = 0, \quad y' = 0$
free	$y'' = 0, \quad y''' = 0$
simply supported or hinged	$y = 0, \quad y'' = 0$

Boundary conditions associated with equation (4) depend on how the ends of the beam are supported. A cantilever beam is **embedded** or **clamped** at one end and **free** at the other. A diving board, an outstretched arm, an airplane wing, and a balcony are common examples of such beams, but even trees, flagpoles, skyscrapers, and the George Washington Monument can act as cantilever beams because they are embedded at one end and are subject to the bending force of the wind. For a cantilever beam the deflection $y(x)$ must satisfy the following two conditions at the embedded end $x = 0$:

- $y(0) = 0$ because there is no deflection, and
- $y'(0) = 0$ because the deflection curve is tangent to the x-axis (in other words, the slope of the deflection curve is zero at this point).

At $x = L$ the free-end conditions are

- $y''(L) = 0$ because the bending moment is zero, and
- $y'''(L) = 0$ because the shear force is zero.

The function $F(x) = dM/dx = EI\, d^3y/dx^3$ is called the shear force. If an end of a beam is **simply supported** or **hinged** (also called **pin supported** and **fulcrum supported**) then we must have $y = 0$ and $y'' = 0$ at that end. Table 5.1 summarizes the boundary conditions that are associated with (4). See Figure 5.2.2.

EXAMPLE 1   **An Embedded Beam**

A beam of length L is embedded at both ends. Find the deflection of the beam if a constant load w_0 is uniformly distributed along its length—that is, $w(x) = w_0,\ 0 < x < L$.

SOLUTION From (4) we see that the deflection $y(x)$ satisfies

$$EI\frac{d^4y}{dx^4} = w_0.$$

Because the beam is embedded at both its left end ($x = 0$) and its right end ($x = L$), there is no vertical deflection and the line of deflection is horizontal at these points. Thus the boundary conditions are

$$y(0) = 0, \qquad y'(0) = 0, \qquad y(L) = 0, \qquad y'(L) = 0.$$

We can solve the nonhomogeneous differential equation in the usual manner (find y_c by observing that $m = 0$ is root of multiplicity four of the auxiliary equation $m^4 = 0$ and then find a particular solution y_p by undetermined coefficients), or we can simply integrate the equation $d^4y/dx^4 = w_0/EI$ four times in succession. Either way, we find the general solution of the equation $y = y_c + y_p$ to be

$$y(x) = c_1 + c_2 x + c_3 x^2 + c_4 x^3 + \frac{w_0}{24EI}x^4.$$

Now the conditions $y(0) = 0$ and $y'(0) = 0$ give, in turn, $c_1 = 0$ and $c_2 = 0$, whereas the remaining conditions $y(L) = 0$ and $y'(L) = 0$ applied to $y(x) = c_3 x^2 + c_4 x^3 + \frac{w_0}{24EI}x^4$ yield the simultaneous equations

$$c_3 L^2 + c_4 L^3 + \frac{w_0}{24EI}L^4 = 0$$

$$2c_3 L + 3c_4 L^2 + \frac{w_0}{6EI}L^3 = 0.$$

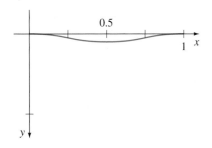

FIGURE 5.2.3 Deflection curve for Example 1

Solving this system gives $c_3 = w_0 L^2/24EI$ and $c_4 = -w_0 L/12EI$. Thus the deflection is

$$y(x) = \frac{w_0 L^2}{24EI} x^2 - \frac{w_0 L}{12EI} x^3 + \frac{w_0}{24EI} x^4$$

or $y(x) = \dfrac{w_0}{24EI} x^2 (x - L)^2$. By choosing $w_0 = 24EI$, and $L = 1$, we obtain the deflection curve in Figure 5.2.3. ∎

EIGENVALUES AND EIGENFUNCTIONS Many applied problems demand that we solve a two-point boundary-value problem (BVP) involving a linear differential equation that contains a parameter λ. We seek the values of λ for which the boundary-value problem has *nontrivial*, that is, *nonzero*, solutions.

EXAMPLE 2   **Nontrivial Solutions of a BVP**

Solve the boundary-value problem

$$y'' + \lambda y = 0, \quad y(0) = 0, \quad y(L) = 0.$$

SOLUTION   We shall consider three cases: $\lambda = 0$, $\lambda < 0$, and $\lambda > 0$.

CASE I: For $\lambda = 0$ the solution of $y'' = 0$ is $y = c_1 x + c_2$. The conditions $y(0) = 0$ and $y(L) = 0$ applied to this solution imply, in turn, $c_2 = 0$ and $c_1 = 0$. Hence for $\lambda = 0$ the only solution of the boundary-value problem is the trivial solution $y = 0$.

CASE II: For $\lambda < 0$ it is convenient to write $\lambda = -\alpha^2$, where α denotes a positive number. With this notation the roots of the auxiliary equation $m^2 - \alpha^2 = 0$ are $m_1 = \alpha$ and $m_2 = -\alpha$. Since the interval on which we are working is finite, we choose to write the general solution of $y'' - \alpha^2 y = 0$ as $y = c_1 \cosh \alpha x + c_2 \sinh \alpha x$. Now $y(0)$ is

$$y(0) = c_1 \cosh 0 + c_2 \sinh 0 = c_1 \cdot 1 + c_2 \cdot 0 = c_1,$$

■ Note that we use hyperbolic functions here. Reread "Two Equations Worth Knowing" on page 135.

and so $y(0) = 0$ implies that $c_1 = 0$. Thus $y = c_2 \sinh \alpha x$. The second condition, $y(L) = 0$, demands that $c_2 \sinh \alpha L = 0$. For $\alpha \neq 0$, $\sinh \alpha L \neq 0$; consequently, we are forced to choose $c_2 = 0$. Again the only solution of the BVP is the trivial solution $y = 0$.

CASE III: For $\lambda > 0$ we write $\lambda = \alpha^2$, where α is a positive number. Because the auxiliary equation $m^2 + \alpha^2 = 0$ has complex roots $m_1 = i\alpha$ and $m_2 = -i\alpha$, the general solution of $y'' + \alpha^2 y = 0$ is $y = c_1 \cos \alpha x + c_2 \sin \alpha x$. As before, $y(0) = 0$ yields $c_1 = 0$, and so $y = c_2 \sin \alpha x$. Now the last condition $y(L) = 0$, or

$$c_2 \sin \alpha L = 0,$$

is satisfied by choosing $c_2 = 0$. But this means that $y = 0$. If we require $c_2 \neq 0$, then $\sin \alpha L = 0$ is satisfied whenever αL is an integer multiple of π.

$$\alpha L = n\pi \quad \text{or} \quad \alpha = \frac{n\pi}{L} \quad \text{or} \quad \lambda_n = \alpha_n^2 = \left(\frac{n\pi}{L}\right)^2, \quad n = 1, 2, 3, \ldots.$$

Therefore for any real nonzero c_2, $y = c_2 \sin(n\pi x/L)$ is a solution of the problem for each n. Because the differential equation is homogeneous, any constant multiple of a solution is also a solution, so we may, if desired, simply take $c_2 = 1$. In other words, for each number in the sequence

$$\lambda_1 = \frac{\pi^2}{L^2}, \quad \lambda_2 = \frac{4\pi^2}{L^2}, \quad \lambda_3 = \frac{9\pi^2}{L^2}, \cdots,$$

the *corresponding* function in the sequence

$$y_1 = \sin\frac{\pi}{L}x, \quad y_2 = \sin\frac{2\pi}{L}x, \quad y_3 = \sin\frac{3\pi}{L}x, \cdots,$$

is a nontrivial solution of the original problem. ∎

The numbers $\lambda_n = n^2\pi^2/L^2$, $n = 1, 2, 3, \ldots$ for which the boundary-value problem in Example 2 possesses nontrivial solutions are known as **eigenvalues.** The nontrivial solutions that depend on these values of λ_n, $y_n = c_2 \sin(n\pi x/L)$ or simply $y_n = \sin(n\pi x/L)$, are called **eigenfunctions.**

BUCKLING OF A THIN VERTICAL COLUMN In the eighteenth century Leonhard Euler was one of the first mathematicians to study an eigenvalue problem in analyzing how a thin elastic column buckles under a compressive axial force.

Consider a long, slender vertical column of uniform cross section and length L. Let $y(x)$ denote the deflection of the column when a constant vertical compressive force, or load, P is applied to its top, as shown in Figure 5.2.4. By comparing bending moments at any point along the column, we obtain

$$EI\frac{d^2y}{dx^2} = -Py \quad \text{or} \quad EI\frac{d^2y}{dx^2} + Py = 0, \tag{5}$$

where E is Young's modulus of elasticity and I is the moment of inertia of a cross section about a vertical line through its centroid.

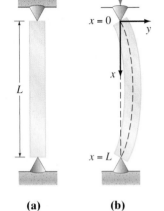

FIGURE 5.2.4 Elastic column buckling under a compressive force

EXAMPLE 3 The Euler Load

Find the deflection of a thin vertical homogeneous column of length L subjected to a constant axial load P if the column is hinged at both ends.

SOLUTION The boundary-value problem to be solved is

$$EI\frac{d^2y}{dx^2} + Py = 0, \quad y(0) = 0, \quad y(L) = 0.$$

First note that $y = 0$ is a perfectly good solution of this problem. This solution has a simple intuitive interpretation: If the load P is not great enough, there is no deflection. The question then is this: For what values of P will the column bend? In mathematical terms: For what values of P does the given boundary-value problem possess nontrivial solutions?

By writing $\lambda = P/EI$, we see that

$$y'' + \lambda y = 0, \quad y(0) = 0, \quad y(L) = 0$$

is identical to the problem in Example 2. From Case III of that discussion we see that the deflections are $y_n(x) = c_2 \sin(n\pi x/L)$ corresponding to the eigenvalues $\lambda_n = P_n/EI = n^2\pi^2/L^2$, $n = 1, 2, 3, \ldots$. Physically, this means that the column will buckle or deflect only when the compressive force is one of the values $P_n = n^2\pi^2EI/L^2$, $n = 1, 2, 3, \ldots$. These different forces are called **critical loads.** The deflection corresponding to the smallest critical load $P_1 = \pi^2EI/L^2$, called the **Euler load,** is $y_1(x) = c_2 \sin(\pi x/L)$ and is known as the **first buckling mode.** ∎

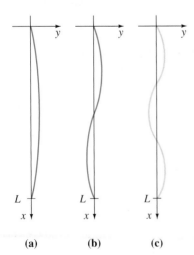

FIGURE 5.2.5 Deflection curves corresponding to compressive forces P_1, P_2, P_3

The deflection curves in Example 3 corresponding to $n = 1$, $n = 2$, and $n = 3$ are shown in Figure 5.2.5. Note that if the original column has some sort of physical restraint put on it at $x = L/2$, then the smallest critical load will be $P_2 = 4\pi^2EI/L^2$, and the deflection curve will be as shown in Figure 5.2.5(b). If restraints are put on the column at $x = L/3$ and at $x = 2L/3$, then the column will not buckle until the critical load $P_3 = 9\pi^2 EI/L^2$ is applied, and the deflection curve will be as shown in Figure 5.2.5(c). See Problem 23 in Exercises 5.2.

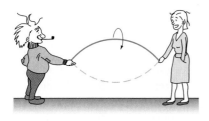

(a)

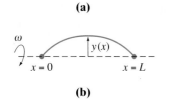

(b)

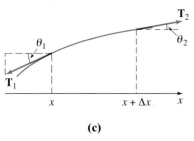

(c)

FIGURE 5.2.6 Rotating string and forces acting on it

ROTATING STRING The simple linear second-order differential equation

$$y'' + \lambda y = 0 \qquad (6)$$

occurs again and again as a mathematical model. In Section 5.1 we saw (6) in the forms $d^2x/dt^2 + (k/m)x = 0$ and $d^2q/dt^2 + (1/LC)q = 0$ as models for, respectively, the simple harmonic motion of a spring/mass system and the simple harmonic response of a series circuit. It is apparent when the model for the deflection of a thin column in (5) is written as $d^2y/dx^2 + (P/EI)y = 0$ that it is the same as (6). We encounter the basic equation (6) one more time in this section: as a model that defines the deflection curve or the shape $y(x)$ assumed by a rotating string. The physical situation is analogous to when two people hold a jump rope and twirl it in a synchronous manner. See Figures 5.2.6(a) and 5.2.6(b).

Suppose a string of length L with constant linear density ρ (mass per unit length) is stretched along the x-axis and fixed at $x = 0$ and $x = L$. Suppose the string is then rotated about that axis at a constant angular speed ω. Consider a portion of the string on the interval $[x, x + \Delta x]$, where Δx is small. If the magnitude T of the tension $\mathbf{T}$, acting tangential to the string, is constant along the string, then the desired differential equation can be obtained by equating two different formulations of the net force acting on the string on the interval $[x, x + \Delta x]$. First, we see from Figure 5.2.6(c) that the net vertical force is

$$F = T \sin \theta_2 - T \sin \theta_1. \qquad (7)$$

When angles θ_1 and θ_2 (measured in radians) are small, we have $\sin \theta_2 \approx \tan \theta_2$ and $\sin \theta_1 \approx \tan \theta_1$. Moreover, since $\tan \theta_2$ and $\tan \theta_1$ are, in turn, slopes of the lines containing the vectors $\mathbf{T}_2$ and $\mathbf{T}_1$, we can also write

$$\tan \theta_2 = y'(x + \Delta x) \qquad \text{and} \qquad \tan \theta_1 = y'(x).$$

Thus (7) becomes

$$F \approx T[y'(x + \Delta x) - y'(x)]. \qquad (8)$$

Second, we can obtain a different form of this same net force using Newton's second law, $F = ma$. Here the mass of the string on the interval is $m = \rho \, \Delta x$; the centripetal acceleration of a body rotating with angular speed ω in a circle of radius r is $a = r\omega^2$. With Δx small we take $r = y$. Thus the net vertical force is also approximated by

$$F \approx -(\rho \, \Delta x) y \omega^2, \qquad (9)$$

where the minus sign comes from the fact that the acceleration points in the direction opposite to the positive y-direction. Now by equating (8) and (9), we have

$$T[y'(x + \Delta x) - y'(x)] = -(\rho \Delta x) y \omega^2 \qquad \text{or} \qquad T \overbrace{\frac{y'(x + \Delta x) - y'(x)}{\Delta x}}^{\text{difference quotient}} + \rho \omega^2 y = 0. \qquad (10)$$

For Δx close to zero the difference quotient in (10) is approximately the second derivative d^2y/dx^2. Finally, we arrive at the model

$$T \frac{d^2 y}{dx^2} + \rho \omega^2 y = 0. \qquad (11)$$

Since the string is anchored at its ends $x = 0$ and $x = L$, we expect that the solution $y(x)$ of equation (11) should also satisfy the boundary conditions $y(0) = 0$ and $y(L) = 0$.

> **REMARKS**
>
> (*i*) Eigenvalues are not always easily found, as they were in Example 2; you might have to approximate roots of equations such as $\tan x = -x$ or $\cos x \cosh x = 1$. See Problems 34–38 in Exercises 5.2.
>
> (*ii*) Boundary conditions applied to a general solution of a linear differential equation can lead to a homogeneous algebraic system of linear equations in which the unknowns are the coefficients c_i in the general solution. A homogeneous algebraic system of linear equations is always consistent because it possesses at least a trivial solution. But a homogeneous system of n linear equations in n unknowns has a nontrivial solution if and only if the determinant of the coefficients equals zero. You might need to use this last fact in Problems 19 and 20 in Exercises 5.2.

EXERCISES 5.2

Answers to selected odd-numbered problems begin on page ANS-8.

Deflection of a Beam

In Problems 1–5 solve equation (4) subject to the appropriate boundary conditions. The beam is of length L, and w_0 is a constant.

1. (a) The beam is embedded at its left end and free at its right end, and $w(x) = w_0, 0 < x < L$.

   (b) Use a graphing utility to graph the deflection curve when $w_0 = 24EI$ and $L = 1$.

2. (a) The beam is simply supported at both ends, and $w(x) = w_0, 0 < x < L$.

   (b) Use a graphing utility to graph the deflection curve when $w_0 = 24EI$ and $L = 1$.

3. (a) The beam is embedded at its left end and simply supported at its right end, and $w(x) = w_0, 0 < x < L$.

   (b) Use a graphing utility to graph the deflection curve when $w_0 = 48EI$ and $L = 1$.

4. (a) The beam is embedded at its left end and simply supported at its right end, and $w(x) = w_0 \sin(\pi x/L)$, $0 < x < L$.

   (b) Use a graphing utility to graph the deflection curve when $w_0 = 2\pi^3 EI$ and $L = 1$.

   (c) Use a root-finding application of a CAS (or a graphic calculator) to approximate the point in the graph in part (b) at which the maximum deflection occurs. What is the maximum deflection?

5. (a) The beam is simply supported at both ends, and $w(x) = w_0 x, 0 < x < L$.

   (b) Use a graphing utility to graph the deflection curve when $w_0 = 36EI$ and $L = 1$.

   (c) Use a root-finding application of a CAS (or a graphic calculator) to approximate the point in the graph in part (b) at which the maximum deflection occurs. What is the maximum deflection?

6. (a) Find the maximum deflection of the cantilever beam in Problem 1.

   (b) How does the maximum deflection of a beam that is half as long compare with the value in part (a)?

   (c) Find the maximum deflection of the simply supported beam in Problem 2.

   (d) How does the maximum deflection of the simply supported beam in part (c) compare with the value of maximum deflection of the embedded beam in Example 1?

7. A cantilever beam of length L is embedded at its right end, and a horizontal tensile force of P pounds is applied to its free left end. When the origin is taken at its free end, as shown in Figure 5.2.7, the deflection $y(x)$ of the beam can be shown to satisfy the differential equation

$$EIy'' = Py - w(x)\frac{x}{2}.$$

Find the deflection of the cantilever beam if $w(x) = w_0 x, 0 < x < L$, and $y(0) = 0, y'(L) = 0$.

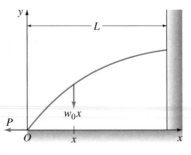

FIGURE 5.2.7 Deflection of cantilever beam in Problem 7

8. When a compressive instead of a tensile force is applied at the free end of the beam in Problem 7, the differential equation of the deflection is

$$EIy'' = -Py - w(x)\frac{x}{2}.$$

Solve this equation if $w(x) = w_0 x$, $0 < x < L$, and $y(0) = 0$, $y'(L) = 0$.

Eigenvalues and Eigenfunctions

In Problems 9–18 find the eigenvalues and eigenfunctions for the given boundary-value problem.

9. $y'' + \lambda y = 0$, $y(0) = 0$, $y(\pi) = 0$

10. $y'' + \lambda y = 0$, $y(0) = 0$, $y(\pi/4) = 0$

11. $y'' + \lambda y = 0$, $y'(0) = 0$, $y(L) = 0$

12. $y'' + \lambda y = 0$, $y(0) = 0$, $y'(\pi/2) = 0$

13. $y'' + \lambda y = 0$, $y'(0) = 0$, $y'(\pi) = 0$

14. $y'' + \lambda y = 0$, $y(-\pi) = 0$, $y(\pi) = 0$

15. $y'' + 2y' + (\lambda + 1)y = 0$, $y(0) = 0$, $y(5) = 0$

16. $y'' + (\lambda + 1)y = 0$, $y'(0) = 0$, $y'(1) = 0$

17. $x^2 y'' + xy' + \lambda y = 0$, $y(1) = 0$, $y(e^\pi) = 0$

18. $x^2 y'' + xy' + \lambda y = 0$, $y'(e^{-1}) = 0$, $y(1) = 0$

In Problems 19 and 20 find the eigenvalues and eigenfunctions for the given boundary-value problem. Consider only the case $\lambda = \alpha^4$, $\alpha > 0$.

19. $y^{(4)} - \lambda y = 0$, $y(0) = 0$, $y''(0) = 0$, $y(1) = 0$, $y''(1) = 0$

20. $y^{(4)} - \lambda y = 0$, $y'(0) = 0$, $y'''(0) = 0$, $y(\pi) = 0$, $y''(\pi) = 0$

Buckling of a Thin Column

21. Consider Figure 5.2.5. Where should physical restraints be placed on the column if we want the critical load to be P_4? Sketch the deflection curve corresponding to this load.

22. The critical loads of thin columns depend on the end conditions of the column. The value of the Euler load P_1 in Example 3 was derived under the assumption that the column was hinged at both ends. Suppose that a thin vertical homogeneous column is embedded at its base $(x = 0)$ and free at its top $(x = L)$ and that a constant axial load P is applied to its free end. This load either causes a small deflection δ as shown in Figure 5.2.8 or does not cause such a deflection. In either case the differential equation for the deflection $y(x)$ is

$$EI\frac{d^2y}{dx^2} + Py = P\delta.$$

FIGURE 5.2.8 Deflection of vertical column in Problem 22

(a) What is the predicted deflection when $\delta = 0$?

(b) When $\delta \neq 0$, show that the Euler load for this column is one-fourth of the Euler load for the hinged column in Example 3.

23. As was mentioned in Problem 22, the differential equation (5) that governs the deflection $y(x)$ of a thin elastic column subject to a constant compressive axial force P is valid only when the ends of the column are hinged. In general, the differential equation governing the deflection of the column is given by

$$\frac{d^2}{dx^2}\left(EI\frac{d^2y}{dx^2}\right) + P\frac{d^2y}{dx^2} = 0.$$

Assume that the column is uniform (EI is a constant) and that the ends of the column are hinged. Show that the solution of this fourth-order differential equation subject to the boundary conditions $y(0) = 0$, $y''(0) = 0$, $y(L) = 0$, $y''(L) = 0$ is equivalent to the analysis in Example 3.

24. Suppose that a uniform thin elastic column is hinged at the end $x = 0$ and embedded at the end $x = L$.

(a) Use the fourth-order differential equation given in Problem 23 to find the eigenvalues λ_n, the critical loads P_n, the Euler load P_1, and the deflections $y_n(x)$.

(b) Use a graphing utility to graph the first buckling mode.

Rotating String

25. Consider the boundary-value problem introduced in the construction of the mathematical model for the shape of a rotating string:

$$T\frac{d^2y}{dx^2} + \rho\omega^2 y = 0, \quad y(0) = 0, \quad y(L) = 0.$$

For constant T and ρ, define the critical speeds of angular rotation ω_n as the values of ω for which the boundary-value problem has nontrivial solutions. Find the critical speeds ω_n and the corresponding deflections $y_n(x)$.

26. When the magnitude of tension T is not constant, then a model for the deflection curve or shape $y(x)$ assumed by a rotating string is given by

$$\frac{d}{dx}\left[T(x)\frac{dy}{dx}\right] + \rho\omega^2 y = 0.$$

Suppose that $1 < x < e$ and that $T(x) = x^2$.

(a) If $y(1) = 0$, $y(e) = 0$, and $\rho\omega^2 > 0.25$, show that the critical speeds of angular rotation are $\omega_n = \frac{1}{2}\sqrt{(4n^2\pi^2 + 1)/\rho}$ and the corresponding deflections are

$$y_n(x) = c_2 x^{-1/2}\sin(n\pi \ln x), \quad n = 1, 2, 3, \dots.$$

(b) Use a graphing utility to graph the deflection curves on the interval $[1, e]$ for $n = 1, 2, 3$. Choose $c_2 = 1$.

Miscellaneous Boundary-Value Problems

27. Temperature in a Sphere Consider two concentric spheres of radius $r = a$ and $r = b$, $a < b$. See Figure 5.2.9. The temperature $u(r)$ in the region between the spheres is determined from the boundary-value problem

$$r\frac{d^2u}{dr^2} + 2\frac{du}{dr} = 0, \quad u(a) = u_0, \quad u(b) = u_1,$$

where u_0 and u_1 are constants. Solve for $u(r)$.

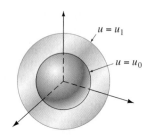

FIGURE 5.2.9 Concentric spheres in Problem 27

28. Temperature in a Ring The temperature $u(r)$ in the circular ring shown in Figure 5.2.10 is determined from the boundary-value problem

$$r\frac{d^2u}{dr^2} + \frac{du}{dr} = 0, \quad u(a) = u_0, \quad u(b) = u_1,$$

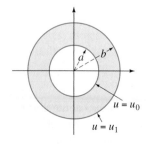

FIGURE 5.2.10 Circular ring in Problem 28

where u_0 and u_1 are constants. Show that

$$u(r) = \frac{u_0\ln(r/b) - u_1\ln(r/a)}{\ln(a/b)}.$$

Discussion Problems

29. Simple Harmonic Motion The model $mx'' + kx = 0$ for simple harmonic motion, discussed in Section 5.1, can be related to Example 2 of this section.

Consider a free undamped spring/mass system for which the spring constant is, say, $k = 10$ lb/ft. Determine those masses m_n that can be attached to the spring so that when each mass is released at the equilibrium position at $t = 0$ with a nonzero velocity v_0, it will then pass through the equilibrium position at $t = 1$ second. How many times will each mass m_n pass through the equilibrium position in the time interval $0 < t < 1$?

30. Damped Motion Assume that the model for the spring/mass system in Problem 29 is replaced by $mx'' + 2x' + kx = 0$. In other words, the system is free but is subjected to damping numerically equal to 2 times the instantaneous velocity. With the same initial conditions and spring constant as in Problem 29, investigate whether a mass m can be found that will pass through the equilibrium position at $t = 1$ second.

In Problems 31 and 32 determine whether it is possible to find values y_0 and y_1 (Problem 31) and values of $L > 0$ (Problem 32) so that the given boundary-value problem has **(a)** precisely one nontrivial solution, **(b)** more than one solution, **(c)** no solution, **(d)** the trivial solution.

31. $y'' + 16y = 0$, $y(0) = y_0$, $y(\pi/2) = y_1$

32. $y'' + 16y = 0$, $y(0) = 1$, $y(L) = 1$

33. Consider the boundary-value problem

$$y'' + \lambda y = 0, \quad y(-\pi) = y(\pi), \quad y'(-\pi) = y'(\pi).$$

(a) The type of boundary conditions specified are called **periodic boundary conditions.** Give a geometric interpretation of these conditions.

(b) Find the eigenvalues and eigenfunctions of the problem.

(c) Use a graphing utility to graph some of the eigenfunctions. Verify your geometric interpretation of the boundary conditions given in part (a).

34. Show that the eigenvalues and eigenfunctions of the boundary-value problem

$$y'' + \lambda y = 0, \quad y(0) = 0, \quad y(1) + y'(1) = 0$$

are $\lambda_n = \alpha_n^2$ and $y_n = \sin\alpha_n x$, respectively, where α_n, $n = 1, 2, 3, \dots$ are the consecutive positive roots of the equation $\tan\alpha = -\alpha$.

Computer Lab Assignments

35. Use a CAS to plot graphs to convince yourself that the equation $\tan \alpha = -\alpha$ in Problem 34 has an infinite number of roots. Explain why the negative roots of the equation can be ignored. Explain why $\lambda = 0$ is not an eigenvalue even though $\alpha = 0$ is an obvious solution of the equation $\tan \alpha = -\alpha$.

36. Use a root-finding application of a CAS to approximate the first four eigenvalues λ_1, λ_2, λ_3, and λ_4 for the BVP in Problem 34.

In Problems 37 and 38 find the eigenvalues and eigenfunctions of the given boundary-value problem. Use a CAS to approximate the first four eigenvalues λ_1, λ_2, λ_3, and λ_4.

37. $y'' + \lambda y = 0$, $\quad y(0) = 0$, $\quad y(1) - \frac{1}{2} y'(1) = 0$

38. $y^{(4)} - \lambda y = 0$, $y(0) = 0$, $y'(0) = 0$, $y(1) = 0$, $y'(1) = 0$
[*Hint*: Consider only $\lambda = \alpha^4$, $\alpha > 0$.]

5.3	**NONLINEAR MODELS**

REVIEW MATERIAL

- Section 4.9

INTRODUCTION In this section we examine some nonlinear higher-order mathematical models. We are able to solve some of these models using the substitution method (leading to reduction of the order of the DE) introduced on page 174. In some cases in which the model cannot be solved, we show how a nonlinear DE can be replaced by a linear DE through a process called *linearization*.

NONLINEAR SPRINGS The mathematical model in (1) of Section 5.1 has the form

$$m \frac{d^2 x}{dt^2} + F(x) = 0, \tag{1}$$

where $F(x) = kx$. Because x denotes the displacement of the mass from its equilibrium position, $F(x) = kx$ is Hooke's law—that is, the force exerted by the spring that tends to restore the mass to the equilibrium position. A spring acting under a linear restoring force $F(x) = kx$ is naturally referred to as a **linear spring.** But springs are seldom perfectly linear. Depending on how it is constructed and the material that is used, a spring can range from "mushy," or soft, to "stiff," or hard, so its restorative force may vary from something below to something above that given by the linear law. In the case of free motion, if we assume that a nonaging spring has some nonlinear characteristics, then it might be reasonable to assume that the restorative force of a spring—that is, $F(x)$ in (1)—is proportional to, say, the cube of the displacement x of the mass beyond its equilibrium position or that $F(x)$ is a linear combination of powers of the displacement such as that given by the nonlinear function $F(x) = kx + k_1 x^3$. A spring whose mathematical model incorporates a nonlinear restorative force, such as

$$m \frac{d^2 x}{dt^2} + kx^3 = 0 \quad \text{or} \quad m \frac{d^2 x}{dt^2} + kx + k_1 x^3 = 0, \tag{2}$$

is called a **nonlinear spring.** In addition, we examined mathematical models in which damping imparted to the motion was proportional to the instantaneous velocity dx/dt and the restoring force of a spring was given by the linear function $F(x) = kx$. But these were simply assumptions; in more realistic situations damping could be proportional to some power of the instantaneous velocity dx/dt. The nonlinear differential equation

$$m \frac{d^2 x}{dt^2} + \beta \left| \frac{dx}{dt} \right| \frac{dx}{dt} + kx = 0 \tag{3}$$

is one model of a free spring/mass system in which the damping force is proportional to the square of the velocity. One can then envision other kinds of models: linear damping and nonlinear restoring force, nonlinear damping and nonlinear restoring force, and so on. The point is that nonlinear characteristics of a physical system lead to a mathematical model that is nonlinear.

Notice in (2) that both $F(x) = kx^3$ and $F(x) = kx + k_1x^3$ are odd functions of x. To see why a polynomial function containing only odd powers of x provides a reasonable model for the restoring force, let us express F as a power series centered at the equilibrium position $x = 0$:

$$F(x) = c_0 + c_1x + c_2x^2 + c_3x^3 + \cdots.$$

When the displacements x are small, the values of x^n are negligible for n sufficiently large. If we truncate the power series with, say, the fourth term, then $F(x) = c_0 + c_1x + c_2x^2 + c_3x^3$. For the force at $x > 0$,

$$F(x) = c_0 + c_1x + c_2x^2 + c_3x^3,$$

and for the force at $-x < 0$,

$$F(-x) = c_0 - c_1x + c_2x^2 - c_3x^3$$

to have the same magnitude but act in the opposite direction, we must have $F(-x) = -F(x)$. Because this means that F is an odd function, we must have $c_0 = 0$ and $c_2 = 0$, and so $F(x) = c_1x + c_3x^3$. Had we used only the first two terms in the series, the same argument yields the linear function $F(x) = c_1x$. A restoring force with mixed powers, such as $F(x) = c_1x + c_2x^2$, and the corresponding vibrations are said to be unsymmetrical. In the next discussion we shall write $c_1 = k$ and $c_3 = k_1$.

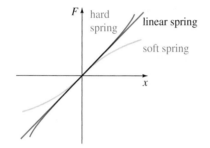

FIGURE 5.3.1 Hard and soft springs

HARD AND SOFT SPRINGS Let us take a closer look at the equation in (1) in the case in which the restoring force is given by $F(x) = kx + k_1x^3$, $k > 0$. The spring is said to be **hard** if $k_1 > 0$ and **soft** if $k_1 < 0$. Graphs of three types of restoring forces are illustrated in Figure 5.3.1. The next example illustrates these two special cases of the differential equation $m\, d^2x/dt^2 + kx + k_1x^3 = 0$, $m > 0$, $k > 0$.

EXAMPLE 1   Comparison of Hard and Soft Springs

The differential equations

$$\frac{d^2x}{dt^2} + x + x^3 = 0 \tag{4}$$

and

$$\frac{d^2x}{dt^2} + x - x^3 = 0 \tag{5}$$

are special cases of the second equation in (2) and are models of a hard spring and a soft spring, respectively. Figure 5.3.2(a) shows two solutions of (4) and Figure 5.3.2(b) shows two solutions of (5) obtained from a numerical solver. The curves shown in red are solutions that satisfy the initial conditions $x(0) = 2$, $x'(0) = -3$; the two curves in blue are solutions that satisfy $x(0) = 2$, $x'(0) = 0$. These solution curves certainly suggest that the motion of a mass on the hard spring is oscillatory, whereas motion of a mass on the soft spring appears to be nonoscillatory. But we must be careful about drawing conclusions based on a couple of numerical solution curves. A more complete picture of the nature of the solutions of both of these equations can be obtained from the qualitative analysis discussed in Chapter 10. ∎

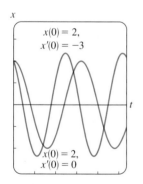

(a) hard spring

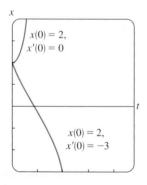

(b) soft spring

FIGURE 5.3.2 Numerical solution curves

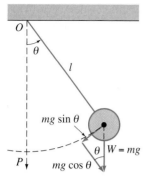

FIGURE 5.3.3 Simple pendulum

NONLINEAR PENDULUM Any object that swings back and forth is called a **physical pendulum.** The **simple pendulum** is a special case of the physical pendulum and consists of a rod of length l to which a mass m is attached at one end. In describing the motion of a simple pendulum in a vertical plane, we make the simplifying assumptions that the mass of the rod is negligible and that no external damping or driving forces act on the system. The displacement angle θ of the pendulum, measured from the vertical as shown in Figure 5.3.3, is considered positive when measured to the right of OP and negative to the left of OP. Now recall the arc s of a circle of radius l is related to the central angle θ by the formula $s = l\theta$. Hence angular acceleration is

$$a = \frac{d^2s}{dt^2} = l\,\frac{d^2\theta}{dt^2}.$$

From Newton's second law we then have

$$F = ma = ml\,\frac{d^2\theta}{dt^2}.$$

From Figure 5.3.3 we see that the magnitude of the tangential component of the force due to the weight W is $mg \sin \theta$. In direction this force is $-mg \sin \theta$ because it points to the left for $\theta > 0$ and to the right for $\theta < 0$. We equate the two different versions of the tangential force to obtain $ml\, d^2\theta/dt^2 = -mg \sin \theta$, or

$$\frac{d^2\theta}{dt^2} + \frac{g}{l}\sin \theta = 0. \tag{6}$$

LINEARIZATION Because of the presence of $\sin \theta$, the model in (6) is nonlinear. In an attempt to understand the behavior of the solutions of nonlinear higher-order differential equations, one sometimes tries to simplify the problem by replacing nonlinear terms by certain approximations. For example, the Maclaurin series for $\sin \theta$ is given by

$$\sin \theta = \theta - \frac{\theta^3}{3!} + \frac{\theta^5}{5!} - \cdots$$

so if we use the approximation $\sin \theta \approx \theta - \theta^3/6$, equation (6) becomes $d^2\theta/dt^2 + (g/l)\theta - (g/6l)\theta^3 = 0$. Observe that this last equation is the same as the second nonlinear equation in (2) with $m = 1$, $k = g/l$, and $k_1 = -g/6l$. However, if we assume that the displacements θ are small enough to justify using the replacement $\sin \theta \approx \theta$, then (6) becomes

$$\frac{d^2\theta}{dt^2} + \frac{g}{l}\theta = 0. \tag{7}$$

See Problem 22 in Exercises 5.3. If we set $\omega^2 = g/l$, we recognize (7) as the differential equation (2) of Section 5.1 that is a model for the free undamped vibrations of a linear spring/mass system. In other words, (7) is again the basic linear equation $y'' + \lambda y = 0$ discussed on page 201 of Section 5.2. As a consequence we say that equation (7) is a **linearization** of equation (6). Because the general solution of (7) is $\theta(t) = c_1 \cos \omega t + c_2 \sin \omega t$, this linearization suggests that for initial conditions amenable to small oscillations the motion of the pendulum described by (6) will be periodic.

$\theta(0) = \frac{1}{2}, \ \theta'(0) = 2$

$\theta(0) = \frac{1}{2}, \ \theta'(0) = \frac{1}{2}$

(a)

(b) $\theta(0) = \frac{1}{2}$, $\theta'(0) = \frac{1}{2}$

(c) $\theta(0) = \frac{1}{2}$, $\theta'(0) = 2$

FIGURE 5.3.4 Oscillating pendulum in (b); whirling pendulum in (c)

EXAMPLE 2 Two Initial-Value Problems

The graphs in Figure 5.3.4(a) were obtained with the aid of a numerical solver and represent solution curves of (6) when $\omega^2 = 1$. The blue curve depicts the solution of (6) that satisfies the initial conditions $\theta(0) = \frac{1}{2}, \theta'(0) = \frac{1}{2}$, whereas the red curve is the solution of (6) that satisfies $\theta(0) = \frac{1}{2}, \ \theta'(0) = 2$. The blue curve represents a periodic solution—the pendulum oscillating back and forth as shown in Figure 5.3.4(b) with an apparent amplitude $A \le 1$. The red curve shows that θ increases without bound as time increases—the pendulum, starting from the same initial displacement, is given an initial velocity of magnitude great enough to send it over the top; in other words, the pendulum is whirling about its pivot as shown in Figure 5.3.4(c). In the absence of damping, the motion in each case is continued indefinitely. ∎

TELEPHONE WIRES The first-order differential equation $dy/dx = W/T_1$ is equation (17) of Section 1.3. This differential equation, established with the aid of Figure 1.3.7 on page 25, serves as a mathematical model for the shape of a flexible cable suspended between two vertical supports when the cable is carrying a vertical load. In Section 2.2 we solved this simple DE under the assumption that the vertical load carried by the cables of a suspension bridge was the weight of a horizontal roadbed distributed evenly along the x-axis. With $W = \rho x$, ρ the weight per unit length of the roadbed, the shape of each cable between the vertical supports turned out to be parabolic. We are now in a position to determine the shape of a uniform flexible cable hanging only under its own weight, such as a wire strung between two telephone posts. The vertical load is now the wire itself, and so if ρ is the linear density of the wire (measured, say, in pounds per feet) and s is the length of the segment P_1P_2 in Figure 1.3.7 then $W = \rho s$. Hence

$$\frac{dy}{dx} = \frac{\rho s}{T_1}. \tag{8}$$

Since the arc length between points P_1 and P_2 is given by

$$s = \int_0^x \sqrt{1 + \left(\frac{dy}{dx}\right)^2}\, dx, \tag{9}$$

it follows from the fundamental theorem of calculus that the derivative of (9) is

$$\frac{ds}{dx} = \sqrt{1 + \left(\frac{dy}{dx}\right)^2}. \tag{10}$$

Differentiating (8) with respect to x and using (10) lead to the second-order equation

$$\frac{d^2y}{dx^2} = \frac{\rho}{T_1}\frac{ds}{dx} \quad \text{or} \quad \frac{d^2y}{dx^2} = \frac{\rho}{T_1}\sqrt{1 + \left(\frac{dy}{dx}\right)^2}. \tag{11}$$

In the example that follows we solve (11) and show that the curve assumed by the suspended cable is a **catenary.** Before proceeding, observe that the nonlinear second-order differential equation (11) is one of those equations having the form $F(x, y', y'') = 0$ discussed in Section 4.9. Recall that we have a chance of solving an equation of this type by reducing the order of the equation by means of the substitution $u = y'$.

EXAMPLE 3 **An Initial-Value Problem**

From the position of the y-axis in Figure 1.3.7 it is apparent that initial conditions associated with the second differential equation in (11) are $y(0) = a$ and $y'(0) = 0$. If we substitute $u = y'$, then the equation in (11) becomes $\dfrac{du}{dx} = \dfrac{\rho}{T_1}\sqrt{1 + u^2}$. Separating variables, we find that

$$\int \frac{du}{\sqrt{1 + u^2}} = \frac{\rho}{T_1}\int dx \quad \text{gives} \quad \sinh^{-1}u = \frac{\rho}{T_1}x + c_1.$$

Now, $y'(0) = 0$ is equivalent to $u(0) = 0$. Since $\sinh^{-1} 0 = 0$, $c_1 = 0$, so $u = \sinh(\rho x/T_1)$. Finally, by integrating both sides of

$$\frac{dy}{dx} = \sinh \frac{\rho}{T_1} x, \qquad \text{we get} \qquad y = \frac{T_1}{\rho} \cosh \frac{\rho}{T_1} x + c_2.$$

Using $y(0) = a$, $\cosh 0 = 1$, the last equation implies that $c_2 = a - T_1/\rho$. Thus we see that the shape of the hanging wire is given by $y = (T_1/\rho) \cosh(\rho x/T_1) + a - T_1/\rho$. ∎

In Example 3, had we been clever enough at the start to choose $a = T_1/\rho$, then the solution of the problem would have been simply the hyperbolic cosine $y = (T_1/\rho) \cosh(\rho x/T_1)$.

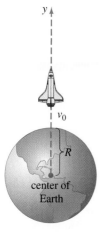

FIGURE 5.3.5 Distance to rocket is large compared to R.

ROCKET MOTION In Section 1.3 we saw that the differential equation of a free-falling body of mass m near the surface of the Earth is given by

$$m \frac{d^2 s}{dt^2} = -mg, \qquad \text{or simply} \qquad \frac{d^2 s}{dt^2} = -g,$$

where s represents the distance from the surface of the Earth to the object and the positive direction is considered to be upward. In other words, the underlying assumption here is that the distance s to the object is small when compared with the radius R of the Earth; put yet another way, the distance y from the center of the Earth to the object is approximately the same as R. If, on the other hand, the distance y to the object, such as a rocket or a space probe, is large when compared to R, then we combine Newton's second law of motion and his universal law of gravitation to derive a differential equation in the variable y.

Suppose a rocket is launched vertically upward from the ground as shown in Figure 5.3.5. If the positive direction is upward and air resistance is ignored, then the differential equation of motion after fuel burnout is

$$m \frac{d^2 y}{dt^2} = -k \frac{Mm}{y^2} \qquad \text{or} \qquad \frac{d^2 y}{dt^2} = -k \frac{M}{y^2}, \qquad (12)$$

where k is a constant of proportionality, y is the distance from the center of the Earth to the rocket, M is the mass of the Earth, and m is the mass of the rocket. To determine the constant k, we use the fact that when $y = R$, $kMm/R^2 = mg$ or $k = gR^2/M$. Thus the last equation in (12) becomes

$$\frac{d^2 y}{dt^2} = -g \frac{R^2}{y^2}. \qquad (13)$$

See Problem 14 in Exercises 5.3.

VARIABLE MASS Notice in the preceding discussion that we described the motion of the rocket after it has burned all its fuel, when presumably its mass m is constant. Of course, during its powered ascent the total mass of the rocket varies as its fuel is being expended. The second law of motion, as originally advanced by Newton, states that when a body of mass m moves through a force field with velocity v, the time rate of change of the momentum mv of the body is equal to applied or net force F acting on the body:

$$F = \frac{d}{dt}(mv). \qquad (14)$$

If m is constant, then (14) yields the more familiar form $F = m \, dv/dt = ma$, where a is acceleration. We use the form of Newton's second law given in (14) in the next example, in which the mass m of the body is variable.

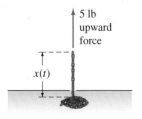

FIGURE 5.3.6 Chain pulled upward by a constant force

EXAMPLE 4   Chain Pulled Upward by a Constant Force

A uniform 10-foot-long chain is coiled loosely on the ground. One end of the chain is pulled vertically upward by means of constant force of 5 pounds. The chain weighs 1 pound per foot. Determine the height of the end above ground level at time t. See Figure 5.3.6.

SOLUTION   Let us suppose that $x = x(t)$ denotes the height of the end of the chain in the air at time t, $v = dx/dt$, and the positive direction is upward. For the portion of the chain that is in the air at time t we have the following variable quantities:

$$
\begin{aligned}
weight\text{:} \quad & W = (x \text{ ft}) \cdot (1 \text{ lb/ft}) = x, \\
mass\text{:} \quad & m = W/g = x/32, \\
net\ force\text{:} \quad & F = 5 - W = 5 - x.
\end{aligned}
$$

Thus from (14) we have

$$
\underset{\text{Product Rule}}{\downarrow}
$$

$$
\frac{d}{dt}\left(\frac{x}{32}v\right) = 5 - x \quad \text{or} \quad x\frac{dv}{dt} + v\frac{dx}{dt} = 160 - 32x. \tag{15}
$$

Because $v = dx/dt$, the last equation becomes

$$
x\frac{d^2x}{dt^2} + \left(\frac{dx}{dt}\right)^2 + 32x = 160. \tag{16}
$$

The nonlinear second-order differential equation (16) has the form $F(x, x', x'') = 0$, which is the second of the two forms considered in Section 4.9 that can possibly be solved by reduction of order. To solve (16), we revert back to (15) and use $v = x'$ along with the Chain Rule. From $\dfrac{dv}{dt} = \dfrac{dv}{dx}\dfrac{dx}{dt} = v\dfrac{dv}{dx}$ the second equation in (15) can be rewritten as

$$
xv\frac{dv}{dx} + v^2 = 160 - 32x. \tag{17}
$$

On inspection (17) might appear intractable, since it cannot be characterized as any of the first-order equations that were solved in Chapter 2. However, by rewriting (17) in differential form $M(x,v)dx + N(x,v)dv = 0$, we observe that although the equation

$$
(v^2 + 32x - 160)dx + xv\, dv = 0 \tag{18}
$$

is not exact, it can be transformed into an exact equation by multiplying it by an integrating factor. From $(M_v - N_x)/N = 1/x$ we see from (13) of Section 2.4 that an integrating factor is $e^{\int dx/x} = e^{\ln x} = x$. When (18) is multiplied by $\mu(x) = x$, the resulting equation is exact (verify). By identifying $\partial f/\partial x = xv^2 + 32x^2 - 160x$, $\partial f/\partial v = x^2 v$ and then proceeding as in Section 2.4, we obtain

$$
\frac{1}{2}x^2v^2 + \frac{32}{3}x^3 - 80x^2 = c_1. \tag{19}
$$

Since we have assumed that all of the chain is on the floor initially, we have $x(0) = 0$. This last condition applied to (19) yields $c_1 = 0$. By solving the algebraic equation $\frac{1}{2}x^2v^2 + \frac{32}{3}x^3 - 80x^2 = 0$ for $v = dx/dt > 0$, we get another first-order differential equation,

$$
\frac{dx}{dt} = \sqrt{160 - \frac{64}{3}x}.
$$

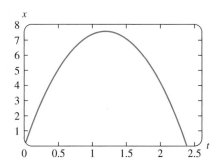

FIGURE 5.3.7 Graph of (21) for $x(t) \geq 0$

The last equation can be solved by separation of variables. You should verify that

$$-\frac{3}{32}\left(160 - \frac{64}{3}x\right)^{1/2} = t + c_2. \tag{20}$$

This time the initial condition $x(0) = 0$ implies that $c_2 = -3\sqrt{10}/8$. Finally, by squaring both sides of (20) and solving for x, we arrive at the desired result,

$$x(t) = \frac{15}{2} - \frac{15}{2}\left(1 - \frac{4\sqrt{10}}{15}t\right)^2. \tag{21}$$

The graph of (21) given in Figure 5.3.7 should not, on physical grounds, be taken at face value. See Problem 15 in Exercises 5.3. ■

EXERCISES 5.3

Answers to selected odd-numbered problems begin on page ANS-8.

To the Instructor In addition to Problems 24 and 25, all or portions of Problems 1–6, 8–13, 15, 20, and 21 could serve as Computer Lab Assignments.

Nonlinear Springs

In Problems 1–4, the given differential equation is model of an undamped spring/mass system in which the restoring force $F(x)$ in (1) is nonlinear. For each equation use a numerical solver to plot the solution curves that satisfy the given initial conditions. If the solutions appear to be periodic use the solution curve to estimate the period T of oscillations.

1. $\dfrac{d^2x}{dt^2} + x^3 = 0,$

$x(0) = 1, x'(0) = 1; \quad x(0) = \frac{1}{2}, x'(0) = -1$

2. $\dfrac{d^2x}{dt^2} + 4x - 16x^3 = 0,$

$x(0) = 1, x'(0) = 1; \quad x(0) = -2, x'(0) = 2$

3. $\dfrac{d^2x}{dt^2} + 2x - x^2 = 0,$

$x(0) = 1, x'(0) = 1; \quad x(0) = \frac{3}{2}, x'(0) = -1$

4. $\dfrac{d^2x}{dt^2} + xe^{0.01x} = 0,$

$x(0) = 1, x'(0) = 1; \quad x(0) = 3, x'(0) = -1$

5. In Problem 3, suppose the mass is released from the initial position $x(0) = 1$ with an initial velocity $x'(0) = x_1$. Use a numerical solver to estimate the smallest value of $|x_1|$ at which the motion of the mass is nonperiodic.

6. In Problem 3, suppose the mass is released from an initial position $x(0) = x_0$ with the initial velocity $x'(0) = 1$. Use a numerical solver to estimate an interval $a \leq x_0 \leq b$ for which the motion is oscillatory.

7. Find a linearization of the differential equation in Problem 4.

8. Consider the model of an undamped nonlinear spring/mass system given by $x'' + 8x - 6x^3 + x^5 = 0$. Use a numerical solver to discuss the nature of the oscillations of the system corresponding to the initial conditions:

$x(0) = 1, x'(0) = 1; \quad x(0) = -2, x'(0) = \frac{1}{2};$

$x(0) = \sqrt{2}, x'(0) = 1; \quad x(0) = 2, x'(0) = \frac{1}{2};$

$x(0) = 2, x'(0) = 0; \quad x(0) = -\sqrt{2}, x'(0) = -1.$

In Problems 9 and 10 the given differential equation is a model of a damped nonlinear spring/mass system. Predict the behavior of each system as $t \to \infty$. For each equation use a numerical solver to obtain the solution curves satisfying the given initial conditions.

9. $\dfrac{d^2x}{dt^2} + \dfrac{dx}{dt} + x + x^3 = 0,$

$x(0) = -3, x'(0) = 4; \quad x(0) = 0, x'(0) = -8$

10. $\dfrac{d^2x}{dt^2} + \dfrac{dx}{dt} + x - x^3 = 0,$

$x(0) = 0, x'(0) = \frac{3}{2}; \quad x(0) = -1, x'(0) = 1$

11. The model $mx'' + kx + k_1x^3 = F_0\cos\omega t$ of an undamped periodically driven spring/mass system is called **Duffing's differential equation.** Consider the initial-value problem $x'' + x + k_1x^3 = 5\cos t, x(0) = 1, x'(0) = 0$. Use a numerical solver to investigate the behavior of the system for values of $k_1 > 0$ ranging from $k_1 = 0.01$ to $k_1 = 100$. State your conclusions.

12. (a) Find values of $k_1 < 0$ for which the system in Problem 11 is oscillatory.

(b) Consider the initial-value problem

$$x'' + x + k_1x^3 = \cos\tfrac{3}{2}t, \quad x(0) = 0, \quad x'(0) = 0.$$

Find values for $k_1 < 0$ for which the system is oscillatory.

Nonlinear Pendulum

13. Consider the model of the free damped nonlinear pendulum given by

$$\frac{d^2\theta}{dt^2} + 2\lambda \frac{d\theta}{dt} + \omega^2 \sin\theta = 0.$$

Use a numerical solver to investigate whether the motion in the two cases $\lambda^2 - \omega^2 > 0$ and $\lambda^2 - \omega^2 < 0$ corresponds, respectively, to the overdamped and underdamped cases discussed in Section 5.1 for spring/mass systems. Choose appropriate initial conditions and values of λ and ω.

Rocket Motion

14. (a) Use the substitution $v = dy/dt$ to solve (13) for v in terms of y. Assuming that the velocity of the rocket at burnout is $v = v_0$ and $y \approx R$ at that instant, show that the approximate value of the constant c of integration is $c = -gR + \frac{1}{2}v_0^2$.

(b) Use the solution for v in part (a) to show that the escape velocity of the rocket is given by $v_0 = \sqrt{2gR}$. [*Hint:* Take $y \to \infty$ and assume $v > 0$ for all time t.]

(c) The result in part (b) holds for any body in the solar system. Use the values $g = 32$ ft/s² and $R = 4000$ mi to show that the escape velocity from the Earth is (approximately) $v_0 = 25,000$ mi/h.

(d) Find the escape velocity from the Moon if the acceleration of gravity is $0.165g$ and $R = 1080$ mi.

Variable Mass

15. (a) In Example 4, how much of the chain would you intuitively expect the constant 5-pound force to be able to lift?

(b) What is the initial velocity of the chain?

(c) Why is the time interval corresponding to $x(t) \geq 0$ given in Figure 5.3.7 not the interval I of definition of the solution (21)? Determine the interval I. How much chain is actually lifted? Explain any difference between this answer and your prediction in part (a).

(d) Why would you expect $x(t)$ to be a periodic solution?

16. A uniform chain of length L, measured in feet, is held vertically so that the lower end just touches the floor. The chain weighs 2 lb/ft. The upper end that is held is released from rest at $t = 0$ and the chain falls straight down. If $x(t)$ denotes the length of the chain on the floor at time t, air resistance is ignored, and the positive direction is taken to be downward, then

$$(L - x)\frac{d^2x}{dt^2} - \left(\frac{dx}{dt}\right)^2 = Lg.$$

(a) Solve for v in terms of x. Solve for x in terms of t. Express v in terms of t.

(b) Determine how long it takes for the chain to fall completely to the ground.

(c) What velocity does the model in part (a) predict for the upper end of the chain as it hits the ground?

Miscellaneous Mathematical Models

17. Pursuit Curve In a naval exercise a ship S_1 is pursued by a submarine S_2 as shown in Figure 5.3.8. Ship S_1 departs point $(0, 0)$ at $t = 0$ and proceeds along a straight-line course (the y-axis) at a constant speed v_1. The submarine S_2 keeps ship S_1 in visual contact, indicated by the straight dashed line L in the figure, while traveling at a constant speed v_2 along a curve C. Assume that ship S_2 starts at the point $(a, 0)$, $a > 0$, at $t = 0$ and that L is tangent to C.

(a) Determine a mathematical model that describes the curve C.

(b) Find an explicit solution of the differential equation. For convenience define $r = v_1/v_2$.

(c) Determine whether the paths of S_1 and S_2 will ever intersect by considering the cases $r > 1$, $r < 1$, and $r = 1$.

[*Hint:* $\dfrac{dt}{dx} = \dfrac{dt}{ds}\dfrac{ds}{dx}$, where s is arc length measured along C.]

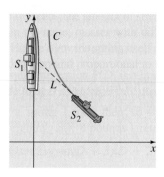

FIGURE 5.3.8 Pursuit curve in Problem 17

18. Pursuit Curve In another naval exercise a destroyer S_1 pursues a submerged submarine S_2. Suppose that S_1 at $(9, 0)$ on the x-axis detects S_2 at $(0, 0)$ and that S_2 simultaneously detects S_1. The captain of the destroyer S_1 assumes that the submarine will take immediate evasive action and conjectures that its likely new course is the straight line indicated in Figure 5.3.9. When S_1 is at $(3, 0)$, it changes from its straight-line course toward the origin to a pursuit curve C. Assume that the speed of the destroyer is, at all times, a constant 30 mi/h and that the submarine's speed is a constant 15 mi/h.

(a) Explain why the captain waits until S_1 reaches $(3, 0)$ before ordering a course change to C.

(b) Using polar coordinates, find an equation $r = f(\theta)$ for the curve C.

(c) Let T denote the time, measured from the initial detection, at which the destroyer intercepts the submarine. Find an upper bound for T.

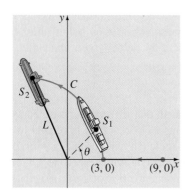

FIGURE 5.3.9   Pursuit curve in Problem 18

Discussion Problems

19. Discuss why the damping term in equation (3) is written as

$$\beta \left| \frac{dx}{dt} \right| \frac{dx}{dt} \quad \text{instead of} \quad \beta \left(\frac{dx}{dt} \right)^2.$$

20. (a) Experiment with a calculator to find an interval $0 \le \theta < \theta_1$, where θ is measured in radians, for which you think $\sin \theta \approx \theta$ is a fairly good estimate. Then use a graphing utility to plot the graphs of $y = x$ and $y = \sin x$ on the same coordinate axes for $0 \le x \le \pi/2$. Do the graphs confirm your observations with the calculator?

(b) Use a numerical solver to plot the solution curves of the initial-value problems

$$\frac{d^2\theta}{dt^2} + \sin \theta = 0, \quad \theta(0) = \theta_0, \quad \theta'(0) = 0$$

and $\dfrac{d^2\theta}{dt^2} + \theta = 0, \qquad \theta(0) = \theta_0, \quad \theta'(0) = 0$

for several values of θ_0 in the interval $0 \le \theta < \theta_1$ found in part (a). Then plot solution curves of the initial-value problems for several values of θ_0 for which $\theta_0 > \theta_1$.

21. (a) Consider the nonlinear pendulum whose oscillations are defined by (6). Use a numerical solver as an aid to determine whether a pendulum of length l will oscillate faster on the Earth or on the Moon. Use the same initial conditions, but choose these initial conditions so that the pendulum oscillates back and forth.

(b) For which location in part (a) does the pendulum have greater amplitude?

(c) Are the conclusions in parts (a) and (b) the same when the linear model (7) is used?

Computer Lab Assignments

22. Consider the initial-value problem

$$\frac{d^2\theta}{dt^2} + \sin \theta = 0, \quad \theta(0) = \frac{\pi}{12}, \quad \theta'(0) = -\frac{1}{3}$$

for a nonlinear pendulum. Since we cannot solve the differential equation, we can find no explicit solution of

this problem. But suppose we wish to determine the first time $t_1 > 0$ for which the pendulum in Figure 5.3.3, starting from its initial position to the right, reaches the position OP—that is, the first positive root of $\theta(t) = 0$. In this problem and the next we examine several ways to proceed.

(a) Approximate t_1 by solving the linear problem $d^2\theta/dt^2 + \theta = 0, \theta(0) = \pi/12, \theta'(0) = -\frac{1}{3}$.

(b) Use the method illustrated in Example 3 of Section 4.9 to find the first four nonzero terms of a Taylor series solution $\theta(t)$ centered at 0 for the nonlinear initial-value problem. Give the exact values of all coefficients.

(c) Use the first two terms of the Taylor series in part (b) to approximate t_1.

(d) Use the first three terms of the Taylor series in part (b) to approximate t_1.

(e) Use a root-finding application of a CAS (or a graphic calculator) and the first four terms of the Taylor series in part (b) to approximate t_1.

(f) In this part of the problem you are led through the commands in *Mathematica* that enable you to approximate the root t_1. The procedure is easily modified so that any root of $\theta(t) = 0$ can be approximated. (*If you do not have Mathematica, adapt the given procedure by finding the corresponding syntax for the CAS you have on hand.*) Precisely reproduce and then, in turn, execute each line in the given sequence of commands.

```
sol = NDSolve[{y″[t] + Sin[y[t]] == 0,
            y[0] == Pi/12, y′[0] == −1/3},
            y, {t, 0, 5}]//Flatten
solution = y[t]/.sol
Clear[y]
y[t_]: = Evaluate[solution]
y[t]
gr1 = Plot[y[t], {t, 0, 5}]
root = FindRoot[y[t] == 0, {t, 1}]
```

(g) Appropriately modify the syntax in part (f) and find the next two positive roots of $\theta(t) = 0$.

23. Consider a pendulum that is released from rest from an initial displacement of θ_0 radians. Solving the linear model (7) subject to the initial conditions $\theta(0) = \theta_0$, $\theta'(0) = 0$ gives $\theta(t) = \theta_0 \cos \sqrt{g/l}\,t$. The period of oscillations predicted by this model is given by the familiar formula $T = 2\pi/\sqrt{g/l} = 2\pi \sqrt{l/g}$. The interesting thing about this formula for T is that it does not depend on the magnitude of the initial displacement θ_0. In other words, the linear model predicts that the time it would take the pendulum to swing from an initial displacement of, say, $\theta_0 = \pi/2 \,(= 90°)$ to $-\pi/2$ and back again would be exactly the same as the time it would take to cycle from, say, $\theta_0 = \pi/360 \,(= 0.5°)$ to $-\pi/360$. This is intuitively unreasonable; the actual period must depend on θ_0.

If we assume that $g = 32$ ft/s^2 and $l = 32$ ft, then the period of oscillation of the linear model is $T = 2\pi$ s. Let us compare this last number with the period predicted by the nonlinear model when $\theta_0 = \pi/4$. Using a numerical solver that is capable of generating hard data, approximate the solution of

$$\frac{d^2\theta}{dt^2} + \sin\theta = 0, \quad \theta(0) = \frac{\pi}{4}, \quad \theta'(0) = 0$$

on the interval $0 \leq t \leq 2$. As in Problem 22, if t_1 denotes the first time the pendulum reaches the position OP in Figure 5.3.3, then the period of the nonlinear pendulum is $4t_1$. Here is another way of solving the equation $\theta(t) = 0$. Experiment with small step sizes and advance the time, starting at $t = 0$ and ending at $t = 2$. From your hard data observe the time t_1 when $\theta(t)$ changes, for the first time, from positive to negative. Use the value t_1 to determine the true value of the period of the nonlinear pendulum. Compute the percentage relative error in the period estimated by $T = 2\pi$.

Contributed Problem

> Warren S. Wright
> Professor
> Mathematics Department
> Loyola Marymount University

24. The Ballistic Pendulum
Historically, to maintain quality control over munitions (bullets) produced by an assembly line, the manufacturer would use a **ballistic pendulum** to determine the muzzle velocity of a gun, that is, the speed of a bullet as it leaves the barrel. The ballistic pendulum (invented in 1742) is simply a plane pendulum consisting of a rod of negligible mass to which a block of wood of mass m_w is attached. The system is set in motion by the impact of a bullet that is moving horizontally at the unknown velocity v_b; at the time of the impact, which we take as $t = 0$, the combined mass is $m_w + m_b$, where m_b is the mass of the bullet imbedded in the wood. In (7) we saw that in the case of small oscillations, the angular displacement $\theta(t)$ of a plane pendulum shown in Figure 5.3.3 is given by the linear DE $\theta'' + (g/l)\theta = 0$, where $\theta > 0$ corresponds to motion to the right of vertical. The velocity v_b can be found by measuring the height h of the mass $m_w + m_b$ at the maximum displacement angle θ_{max} shown in Figure 5.3.10.

Intuitively, the horizontal velocity V of the combined mass (wood plus bullet) after impact is only a fraction of the velocity v_b of the bullet, that is,

$$V = \left(\frac{m_b}{m_w + m_b}\right)v_b.$$

Now, recall that a distance s traveled by a particle moving along a circular path is related to the radius l and central angle θ by the formula $s = l\theta$. By differentiating the last formula with respect to time t, it follows that the angular velocity ω of the mass and its linear velocity v are related by $v = l\omega$. Thus the initial angular velocity ω_0 at the time t at which the bullet impacts the wood block is related to V by $V = l\omega_0$ or

$$\omega_0 = \left(\frac{m_b}{m_w + m_b}\right)\frac{v_b}{l}.$$

(a) Solve the initial-value problem

$$\frac{d^2\theta}{dt^2} + \frac{g}{l}\theta = 0, \quad \theta(0) = 0, \quad \theta'(0) = \omega_0.$$

(b) Use the result from part (a) to show that

$$v_b = \left(\frac{m_w + m_b}{m_b}\right)\sqrt{lg}\,\theta_{max}.$$

(c) Use Figure 5.3.10 to express $\cos\theta_{max}$ in terms of l and h. Then use the first two terms of the Maclaurin series for $\cos\theta$ to express θ_{max} in terms of l and h. Finally, show that v_b is given (approximately) by

$$v_b = \left(\frac{m_w + m_b}{m_b}\right)\sqrt{2gh}.$$

(d) Use the result in part (c) to find v_b when $m_b = 5$ g, $m_w = 1$ kg, and $h = 6$ cm.

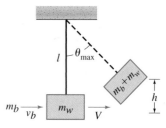

FIGURE 5.3.10 Ballistic pendulum

CHAPTER 5 IN REVIEW

Answers to selected odd-numbered problems begin on page ANS-8.

Answer Problems 1–8 without referring back to the text. Fill in the blank or answer true/false.

1. If a mass weighing 10 pounds stretches a spring 2.5 feet, a mass weighing 32 pounds will stretch it _____ feet.

2. The period of simple harmonic motion of mass weighing 8 pounds attached to a spring whose constant is 6.25 lb/ft is _____ seconds.

3. The differential equation of a spring/mass system is $x'' + 16x = 0$. If the mass is initially released from a point 1 meter above the equilibrium position with a downward velocity of 3 m/s, the amplitude of vibrations is _____ meters.

4. Pure resonance cannot take place in the presence of a damping force. _____

5. In the presence of a damping force, the displacements of a mass on a spring will always approach zero as $t \rightarrow \infty$. _____

6. A mass on a spring whose motion is critically damped can possibly pass through the equilibrium position twice. _____

7. At critical damping any increase in damping will result in an _____ system.

8. If simple harmonic motion is described by $x = (\sqrt{2}/2)\sin(2t + \phi)$, the phase angle ϕ is _____ when the initial conditions are $x(0) = -\frac{1}{2}$ and $x'(0) = 1$.

In Problems 9 and 10 the eigenvalues and eigenfunctions of the boundary-value problem $y'' + \lambda y = 0$, $y'(0) = 0$, $y'(\pi) = 0$ are $\lambda_n = n^2$, $n = 0, 1, 2, \ldots$, and $y = \cos nx$, respectively. Fill in the blanks.

9. A solution of the BVP when $\lambda = 8$ is $y =$ _____ because _____.

10. A solution of the BVP when $\lambda = 36$ is $y =$ _____ because _____.

11. A free undamped spring/mass system oscillates with a period of 3 seconds. When 8 pounds are removed from the spring, the system has a period of 2 seconds. What was the weight of the original mass on the spring?

12. A mass weighing 12 pounds stretches a spring 2 feet. The mass is initially released from a point 1 foot below the equilibrium position with an upward velocity of 4 ft/s.

(a) Find the equation of motion.

(b) What are the amplitude, period, and frequency of the simple harmonic motion?

(c) At what times does the mass return to the point 1 foot below the equilibrium position?

(d) At what times does the mass pass through the equilibrium position moving upward? Moving downward?

(e) What is the velocity of the mass at $t = 3\pi/16$ s?

(f) At what times is the velocity zero?

13. A force of 2 pounds stretches a spring 1 foot. With one end held fixed, a mass weighing 8 pounds is attached to the other end. The system lies on a table that imparts a frictional force numerically equal to $\frac{3}{2}$ times the instantaneous velocity. Initially, the mass is displaced 4 inches above the equilibrium position and released from rest. Find the equation of motion if the motion takes place along a horizontal straight line that is taken as the x-axis.

14. A mass weighing 32 pounds stretches a spring 6 inches. The mass moves through a medium offering a damping force that is numerically equal to β times the instantaneous velocity. Determine the values of $\beta > 0$ for which the spring/mass system will exhibit oscillatory motion.

15. A spring with constant $k = 2$ is suspended in a liquid that offers a damping force numerically equal to 4 times the instantaneous velocity. If a mass m is suspended from the spring, determine the values of m for which the subsequent free motion is nonoscillatory.

16. The vertical motion of a mass attached to a spring is described by the IVP $\frac{1}{4}x'' + x' + x = 0$, $x(0) = 4$, $x'(0) = 2$. Determine the maximum vertical displacement of the mass.

17. A mass weighing 4 pounds stretches a spring 18 inches. A periodic force equal to $f(t) = \cos \gamma t + \sin \gamma t$ is impressed on the system starting at $t = 0$. In the absence of a damping force, for what value of γ will the system be in a state of pure resonance?

18. Find a particular solution for $x'' + 2\lambda x' + \omega^2 x = A$, where A is a constant force.

19. A mass weighing 4 pounds is suspended from a spring whose constant is 3 lb/ft. The entire system is immersed in a fluid offering a damping force numerically equal to the instantaneous velocity. Beginning at $t = 0$, an external force equal to $f(t) = e^{-t}$ is impressed on the system. Determine the equation of motion if the mass is initially released from rest at a point 2 feet below the equilibrium position.

20. (a) Two springs are attached in series as shown in Figure 5.R.1. If the mass of each spring is ignored, show that the effective spring constant k of the system is defined by $1/k = 1/k_1 + 1/k_2$.

(b) A mass weighing W pounds stretches a spring $\frac{1}{2}$ foot and stretches a different spring $\frac{1}{4}$ foot. The two springs are attached, and the mass is then attached to the double spring as shown in Figure 5.R.1. Assume that the motion is free and that there is no damping force present. Determine the equation of motion if the mass is initially released at a point 1 foot below the equilibrium position with a downward velocity of $\frac{2}{3}$ ft/s.

(c) Show that the maximum speed of the mass is $\frac{2}{3}\sqrt{3g + 1}$.

FIGURE 5.R.1 Attached springs in Problem 20

21. A series circuit contains an inductance of $L = 1$ h, a capacitance of $C = 10^{-4}$ f, and an electromotive force of $E(t) = 100 \sin 50t$ V. Initially, the charge q and current i are zero.

(a) Determine the charge $q(t)$.

(b) Determine the current $i(t)$.

(c) Find the times for which the charge on the capacitor is zero.

22. (a) Show that the current $i(t)$ in an *LRC* series circuit satisfies $L \dfrac{d^2 i}{dt^2} + R \dfrac{di}{dt} + \dfrac{1}{C} i = E'(t)$, where $E'(t)$ denotes the derivative of $E(t)$.

(b) Two initial conditions $i(0)$ and $i'(0)$ can be specified for the DE in part (a). If $i(0) = i_0$ and $q(0) = q_0$, what is $i'(0)$?

23. Consider the boundary-value problem

$$y'' + \lambda y = 0, \quad y(0) = y(2\pi), \quad y'(0) = y'(2\pi).$$

Show that except for the case $\lambda = 0$, there are two independent eigenfunctions corresponding to each eigenvalue.

24. A bead is constrained to slide along a frictionless rod of length L. The rod is rotating in a vertical plane with a constant angular velocity ω about a pivot P fixed at the midpoint of the rod, but the design of the pivot allows the bead to move along the entire length of the rod. Let $r(t)$ denote the position of the bead relative to this rotating coordinate system as shown in Figure 5.R.2. To apply Newton's second law of motion to this rotating frame of reference, it is necessary to use the fact that the net force acting on the bead is the sum of the real forces (in this case, the force due to gravity) and the inertial forces (coriolis, transverse, and centrifugal). The mathematics is a little complicated, so we just give the resulting differential equation for r:

$$m \frac{d^2 r}{dt^2} = m\omega^2 r - mg \sin \omega t.$$

(a) Solve the foregoing DE subject to the initial conditions $r(0) = r_0$, $r'(0) = v_0$.

(b) Determine the initial conditions for which the bead exhibits simple harmonic motion. What is the minimum length L of the rod for which it can accommodate simple harmonic motion of the bead?

(c) For initial conditions other than those obtained in part (b), the bead must eventually fly off the rod. Explain using the solution $r(t)$ in part (a).

(d) Suppose $\omega = 1$ rad/s. Use a graphing utility to graph the solution $r(t)$ for the initial conditions $r(0) = 0$, $r'(0) = v_0$, where v_0 is 0, 10, 15, 16, 16.1, and 17.

(e) Suppose the length of the rod is $L = 40$ ft. For each pair of initial conditions in part (d), use a root-finding application to find the total time that the bead stays on the rod.

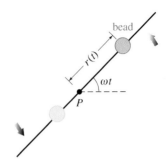

FIGURE 5.R.2 Rotating rod in Problem 24

25. Suppose a mass m lying on a flat, dry, frictionless surface is attached to the free end of a spring whose constant is k. In Figure 5.R.3(a) the mass is shown at the equilibrium position $x = 0$, that is, the spring is neither stretched nor compressed. As shown in Figure 5.R.3(b), the displacement $x(t)$ of the mass to the right of the equilibrium position is positive and negative to the left. Derive a differential equation for the free horizontal (sliding) motion of the mass. Discuss the difference between the derivation of this DE and the analysis leading to (1) of Section 5.1.

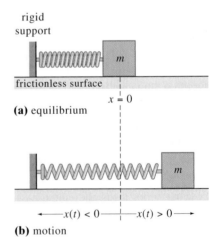

(a) equilibrium

(b) motion

FIGURE 5.R.3 Sliding spring/mass system in Problem 25

26. What is the differential equation of motion in Problem 25 if kinetic friction (but no other damping forces) acts on the sliding mass? [*Hint*: Assume that the magnitude of the force of kinetic friction is $f_k = \mu mg$, where mg is the weight of the mass and the constant $\mu > 0$ is the coefficient of kinetic friction. Then consider two cases, $x' > 0$ and $x' < 0$. Interpret these cases physically.]

6 SERIES SOLUTIONS OF LINEAR EQUATIONS

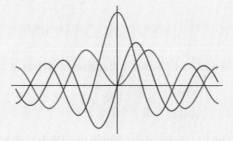

Up to now we have primarily solved linear differential equations of order two or higher when the equation had constant coefficients. The only exception was the Cauchy-Euler equation studied in Section 4.7. In applications, higher-order linear equations with variable coefficients are just as important as, if not more important than, differential equations with constant coefficients. As pointed out in Section 4.7, even a simple linear second-order equation with variable coefficients such as $y'' + xy = 0$ does not possess solutions that are elementary functions. But we can find two linearly independent solutions of $y'' + xy = 0$; we shall see in Sections 6.1 and 6.3 that the solutions of this equation are defined by infinite series.

In this chapter we shall study two infinite-series methods for finding solutions of homogeneous linear second-order DEs $a_2(x)y'' + a_1(x)y' + a_0(x)y = 0$ where the variable coefficients $a_2(x)$, $a_1(x)$, and $a_0(x)$ are, for the most part, simple polynomials.

| 6.1 | SOLUTIONS ABOUT ORDINARY POINTS |

REVIEW MATERIAL

- Power Series (see any Calculus Text)

INTRODUCTION In Section 4.3 we saw that solving a homogeneous linear DE with *constant coefficients* was essentially a problem in algebra. By finding the roots of the auxiliary equation, we could write a general solution of the DE as a linear combination of the elementary functions x^k, $x^k e^{\alpha x}$, $x^k e^{\alpha x} \cos \beta x$, and $x^k e^{\alpha x} \sin \beta x$, where k is a nonnegative integer. But as was pointed out in the introduction to Section 4.7, *most* linear higher-order DEs with *variable coefficients* cannot be solved in terms of elementary functions. A usual course of action for equations of this sort is to assume a solution in the form of infinite series and proceed in a manner similar to the method of undetermined coefficients (Section 4.4). In this section we consider linear second-order DEs with variable coefficients that possess solutions in the form of *power series*.

We begin with a brief review of some of the important facts about power series. For a more comprehensive treatment of the subject you should consult a calculus text.

6.1.1 REVIEW OF POWER SERIES

Recall from calculus that a power series in $x - a$ is an infinite series of the form

$$\sum_{n=0}^{\infty} c_n(x - a)^n = c_0 + c_1(x - a) + c_2(x - a)^2 + \cdots.$$

Such a series is also said to be a **power series centered at a.** For example, the power series $\sum_{n=0}^{\infty}(x + 1)^n$ is centered at $a = -1$. In this section we are concerned mainly with power series in x, in other words, power series such as $\sum_{n=1}^{\infty} 2^{n-1}x^n = x + 2x^2 + 4x^3 + \cdots$ that are centered at $a = 0$. The following list summarizes some important facts about power series.

- **Convergence** A power series $\sum_{n=0}^{\infty} c_n(x - a)^n$ is convergent at a specified value of x if its sequence of partial sums $\{S_N(x)\}$ converges—that is, $\lim_{N \to \infty} S_N(x) = \lim_{N \to \infty} \sum_{n=0}^{N} c_n(x - a)^n$ exists. If the limit does not exist at x, then the series is said to be divergent.

- **Interval of Convergence** Every power series has an interval of convergence. The interval of convergence is the set of all real numbers x for which the series converges.

- **Radius of Convergence** Every power series has a radius of convergence R. If $R > 0$, then the power series $\sum_{n=0}^{\infty} c_n(x - a)^n$ converges for $|x - a| < R$ and diverges for $|x - a| > R$. If the series converges only at its center a, then $R = 0$. If the series converges for all x, then we write $R = \infty$. Recall that the absolute-value inequality $|x - a| < R$ is equivalent to the simultaneous inequality $a - R < x < a + R$. A power series might or might not converge at the endpoints $a - R$ and $a + R$ of this interval.

- **Absolute Convergence** Within its interval of convergence a power series converges absolutely. In other words, if x is a number in the interval of convergence and is not an endpoint of the interval, then the series of absolute values $\sum_{n=0}^{\infty} |c_n(x - a)^n|$ converges. See Figure 6.1.1.

- **Ratio Test** Convergence of a power series can often be determined by the ratio test. Suppose that $c_n \neq 0$ for all n and that

$$\lim_{n \to \infty} \left| \frac{c_{n+1}(x - a)^{n+1}}{c_n(x - a)^n} \right| = |x - a| \lim_{n \to \infty} \left| \frac{c_{n+1}}{c_n} \right| = L.$$

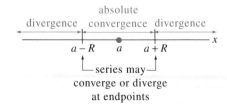

FIGURE 6.1.1 Absolute convergence within the interval of convergence and divergence outside of this interval

If $L < 1$, the series converges absolutely; if $L > 1$, the series diverges; and if $L = 1$, the test is inconclusive. For example, for the power series $\sum_{n=1}^{\infty}(x - 3)^n/2^n n$ the ratio test gives

$$\lim_{n\to\infty}\left|\frac{\dfrac{(x - 3)^{n+1}}{2^{n+1}(n + 1)}}{\dfrac{(x - 3)^n}{2^n n}}\right| = |x - 3| \lim_{n\to\infty} \frac{n}{2(n + 1)} = \frac{1}{2}|x - 3|;$$

the series converges absolutely for $\frac{1}{2}|x - 3| < 1$ or $|x - 3| < 2$ or $1 < x < 5$. This last inequality defines the *open* interval of convergence. The series diverges for $|x - 3| > 2$, that is, for $x > 5$ or $x < 1$. At the left endpoint $x = 1$ of the open interval of convergence, the series of constants $\sum_{n=1}^{\infty}((-1)^n/n)$ is convergent by the alternating series test. At the right endpoint $x = 5$, the series $\sum_{n=1}^{\infty}(1/n)$ is the divergent harmonic series. The interval of convergence of the series is $[1, 5)$, and the radius of convergence is $R = 2$.

- **A Power Series Defines a Function**   A power series defines a function $f(x) = \sum_{n=0}^{\infty} c_n(x - a)^n$ whose domain is the interval of convergence of the series. If the radius of convergence is $R > 0$, then f is continuous, differentiable, and integrable on the interval $(a - R, a + R)$. Moreover, $f'(x)$ and $\int f(x)dx$ can be found by term-by-term differentiation and integration. Convergence at an endpoint may be either lost by differentiation or gained through integration. If $y = \sum_{n=0}^{\infty} c_n x^n$ is a power series in x, then the first two derivatives are $y' = \sum_{n=0}^{\infty} nx^{n-1}$ and $y'' = \sum_{n=0}^{\infty} n(n - 1)x^{n-2}$. Notice that the first term in the first derivative and the first two terms in the second derivative are zero. We omit these zero terms and write

$$y' = \sum_{n=1}^{\infty} c_n nx^{n-1} \qquad \text{and} \qquad y'' = \sum_{n=2}^{\infty} c_n n(n - 1)x^{n-2}. \qquad (1)$$

These results are important and will be used shortly.

- **Identity Property**   If $\sum_{n=0}^{\infty} c_n(x - a)^n = 0, R > 0$ for all numbers x in the interval of convergence, then $c_n = 0$ for all n.

- **Analytic at a Point**   A function f is analytic at a point a if it can be represented by a power series in $x - a$ with a positive or infinite radius of convergence. In calculus it is seen that functions such as e^x, $\cos x$, $\sin x$, $\ln(1 - x)$, and so on can be represented by Taylor series. Recall, for example, that

$$e^x = 1 + \frac{x}{1!} + \frac{x^2}{2!} + \cdots, \qquad \sin x = x - \frac{x^3}{3!} + \frac{x^5}{5!} - \cdots, \qquad \cos x = 1 - \frac{x^2}{2!} + \frac{x^4}{4!} - \frac{x^6}{6!} + \cdots \qquad (2)$$

for $|x| < \infty$. These Taylor series centered at 0, called Maclaurin series, show that e^x, $\sin x$, and $\cos x$ are analytic at $x = 0$.

- **Arithmetic of Power Series**   Power series can be combined through the operations of addition, multiplication, and division. The procedures for power series are similar to those by which two polynomials are added, multiplied, and divided—that is, we add coefficients of like powers of x, use the distributive law and collect like terms, and perform long division. For example, using the series in (2), we have

$$e^x \sin x = \left(1 + x + \frac{x^2}{2} + \frac{x^3}{6} + \frac{x^4}{24} + \cdots\right)\left(x - \frac{x^3}{6} + \frac{x^5}{120} - \frac{x^7}{5040} + \cdots\right)$$

$$= (1)x + (1)x^2 + \left(-\frac{1}{6} + \frac{1}{2}\right)x^3 + \left(-\frac{1}{6} + \frac{1}{6}\right)x^4 + \left(\frac{1}{120} - \frac{1}{12} + \frac{1}{24}\right)x^5 + \cdots$$

$$= x + x^2 + \frac{x^3}{3} - \frac{x^5}{30} - \cdots.$$

Since the power series for e^x and $\sin x$ converge for $|x| < \infty$, the product series converges on the same interval. Problems involving multiplication or division of power series can be done with minimal fuss by using a CAS.

SHIFTING THE SUMMATION INDEX For the remainder of this section, as well as this chapter, it is important that you become adept at simplifying the sum of two or more power series, each expressed in summation (sigma) notation, to an expression with a single Σ. As the next example illustrates, combining two or more summations as a single summation often requires a reindexing — that is, a shift in the index of summation.

EXAMPLE 1   Adding Two Power Series

Write $\sum_{n=2}^{\infty} n(n-1)c_n x^{n-2} + \sum_{n=0}^{\infty} c_n x^{n+1}$ as a single power series whose general term involves x^k.

SOLUTION To add the two series, it is necessary that both summation indices start with the same number and that the powers of x in each series be "in phase"; that is, if one series starts with a multiple of, say, x to the first power, then we want the other series to start with the same power. Note that in the given problem the first series starts with x^0, whereas the second series starts with x^1. By writing the first term of the first series outside the summation notation,

$$\sum_{n=2}^{\infty} n(n-1)c_n x^{n-2} + \sum_{n=0}^{\infty} c_n x^{n+1} = 2 \cdot 1 c_2 x^0 + \overset{\substack{\text{series starts} \\ \text{with } x \\ \text{for } n = 3 \downarrow}}{\sum_{n=3}^{\infty}} n(n-1)c_n x^{n-2} + \overset{\substack{\text{series starts} \\ \text{with } x \\ \text{for } n = 0 \downarrow}}{\sum_{n=0}^{\infty}} c_n x^{n+1},$$

we see that both series on the right-hand side start with the same power of x — namely, x^1. Now to get the same summation index, we are inspired by the exponents of x; we let $k = n - 2$ in the first series and at the same time let $k = n + 1$ in the second series. The right-hand side becomes

$$2c_2 + \sum_{k=1}^{\infty} (k+2)(k+1)c_{k+2} x^k + \sum_{k=1}^{\infty} c_{k-1} x^k. \tag{3}$$

Remember that the summation index is a "dummy" variable; the fact that $k = n - 1$ in one case and $k = n + 1$ in the other should cause no confusion if you keep in mind that it is the *value* of the summation index that is important. In both cases k takes on the same successive values $k = 1, 2, 3, \ldots$ when n takes on the values $n = 2, 3, 4, \ldots$ for $k = n - 1$ and $n = 0, 1, 2, \ldots$ for $k = n + 1$. We are now in a position to add the series in (3) term by term:

$$\sum_{n=2}^{\infty} n(n-1)c_n x^{n-2} + \sum_{n=0}^{\infty} c_n x^{n+1} = 2c_2 + \sum_{k=1}^{\infty} [(k+2)(k+1)c_{k+2} + c_{k-1}]x^k. \tag{4} \quad \blacksquare$$

If you are not convinced of the result in (4), then write out a few terms on both sides of the equality.

6.1.2 POWER SERIES SOLUTIONS

A DEFINITION Suppose the linear second-order differential equation

$$a_2(x)y'' + a_1(x)y' + a_0(x)y = 0 \qquad (5)$$

is put into standard form

$$y'' + P(x)y' + Q(x)y = 0 \qquad (6)$$

by dividing by the leading coefficient $a_2(x)$. We have the following definition.

DEFINITION 6.1.1 **Ordinary and Singular Points**

A point x_0 is said to be an **ordinary point** of the differential equation (5) if both $P(x)$ and $Q(x)$ in the standard form (6) are analytic at x_0. A point that is not an ordinary point is said to be a **singular point** of the equation.

Every finite value of x is an ordinary point of the differential equation $y'' + (e^x)y' + (\sin x)y = 0$. In particular, $x = 0$ is an ordinary point because, as we have already seen in (2), both e^x and $\sin x$ are analytic at this point. The negation in the second sentence of Definition 6.1.1 stipulates that if at least one of the functions $P(x)$ and $Q(x)$ in (6) fails to be analytic at x_0, then x_0 is a singular point. Note that $x = 0$ is a singular point of the differential equation $y'' + (e^x)y' + (\ln x)y = 0$ because $Q(x) = \ln x$ is discontinuous at $x = 0$ and so cannot be represented by a power series in x.

POLYNOMIAL COEFFICIENTS We shall be interested primarily in the case when (5) has polynomial coefficients. A polynomial is analytic at any value x, and a rational function is analytic *except* at points where its denominator is zero. Thus if $a_2(x)$, $a_1(x)$, and $a_0(x)$ are *polynomials* with no common factors, then both rational functions $P(x) = a_1(x)/a_2(x)$ and $Q(x) = a_0(x)/a_2(x)$ are analytic except where $a_2(x) = 0$. It follows, then, that:

$x = x_0$ is an ordinary point of (5) if $a_2(x_0) \neq 0$ whereas $x = x_0$ is a singular point of (5) if $a_2(x_0) = 0$.

For example, the only singular points of the equation $(x^2 - 1)y'' + 2xy' + 6y = 0$ are solutions of $x^2 - 1 = 0$ or $x = \pm 1$. All other finite values[*] of x are ordinary points. Inspection of the Cauchy-Euler equation $ax^2y'' + bxy' + cy = 0$ shows that it has a singular point at $x = 0$. Singular points need not be real numbers. The equation $(x^2 + 1)y'' + xy' - y = 0$ has singular points at the solutions of $x^2 + 1 = 0$—namely, $x = \pm i$. All other values of x, real or complex, are ordinary points.

We state the following theorem about the existence of power series solutions without proof.

THEOREM 6.1.1 **Existence of Power Series Solutions**

If $x = x_0$ is an ordinary point of the differential equation (5), we can always find two linearly independent solutions in the form of a power series centered at x_0, that is, $y = \sum_{n=0}^{\infty} c_n(x - x_0)^n$. A series solution converges at least on some interval defined by $|x - x_0| < R$, where R is the distance from x_0 to the closest singular point.

---

[*]For our purposes, ordinary points and singular points will always be finite points. It is possible for an ODE to have, say, a singular point at infinity.

A solution of the form $y = \sum_{n=0}^{\infty} c_n(x - x_0)^n$ is said to be a **solution about the ordinary point x_0.** The distance R in Theorem 6.1.1 is the *minimum value* or the *lower bound* for the radius of convergence of series solutions of the differential equation about x_0.

In the next example we use the fact that in the complex plane the distance between two complex numbers $a + bi$ and $c + di$ is just the distance between the two points (a, b) and (c, d).

EXAMPLE 2   **Lower Bound for Radius of Convergence**

The complex numbers $1 \pm 2i$ are singular points of the differential equation $(x^2 - 2x + 5)y'' + xy' - y = 0$. Because $x = 0$ is an ordinary point of the equation, Theorem 6.1.1 guarantees that we can find two power series solutions about 0, that is, solutions that look like $y = \sum_{n=0}^{\infty} c_n x^n$. Without actually finding these solutions, we know that *each* series must converge *at least* for $|x| < \sqrt{5}$ because $R = \sqrt{5}$ is the distance in the complex plane from 0 (the point $(0, 0)$) to either of the numbers $1 + 2i$ (the point $(1, 2)$) or $1 - 2i$ (the point $(1, -2)$). However, one of these two solutions is valid on an interval much larger than $-\sqrt{5} < x < \sqrt{5}$; in actual fact this solution is valid on $(-\infty, \infty)$ because it can be shown that one of the two power series solutions about 0 reduces to a polynomial. Therefore we also say that $\sqrt{5}$ is the lower bound for the radius of convergence of series solutions of the differential equation about 0.

If we seek solutions of the given DE about a different ordinary point, say, $x = -1$, then each series $y = \sum_{n=0}^{\infty} c_n(x + 1)^n$ converges at least for $|x| < 2\sqrt{2}$ because the distance from -1 to either $1 + 2i$ or $1 - 2i$ is $R = \sqrt{8} = 2\sqrt{2}$. ∎

NOTE   In the examples that follow, as well as in Exercises 6.1, we shall, for the sake of simplicity, find power series solutions only about the ordinary point $x = 0$. If it is necessary to find a power series solution of a linear DE about an ordinary point $x_0 \neq 0$, we can simply make the change of variable $t = x - x_0$ in the equation (this translates $x = x_0$ to $t = 0$), find solutions of the new equation of the form $y = \sum_{n=0}^{\infty} c_n t^n$, and then resubstitute $t = x - x_0$.

FINDING A POWER SERIES SOLUTION   The actual determination of a power series solution of a homogeneous linear second-order DE is quite analogous to what we did in Section 4.4 in finding particular solutions of nonhomogeneous DEs by the method of undetermined coefficients. Indeed, the power series method of solving a linear DE with variable coefficients is often described as "the method of undetermined *series* coefficients." In brief, here is the idea: We substitute $y = \sum_{n=0}^{\infty} c_n x^n$ into the differential equation, combine series as we did in Example 1, and then equate all coefficients to the right-hand side of the equation to determine the coefficients c_n. But because the right-hand side is zero, the last step requires, by the identity property in the preceding bulleted list, that all coefficients of x must be equated to zero. No, this does *not* mean that all coefficients *are* zero; this would not make sense—after all, Theorem 6.1.1 guarantees that we can find two solutions. Example 3 illustrates how the single assumption that $y = \sum_{n=0}^{\infty} c_n x^n = c_0 + c_1 x + c_2 x^2 + \cdots$ leads to two sets of coefficients, so we have two distinct power series $y_1(x)$ and $y_2(x)$, both expanded about the ordinary point $x = 0$. The general solution of the differential equation is $y = C_1 y_1(x) + C_2 y_2(x)$; indeed, it can be shown that $C_1 = c_0$ and $C_2 = c_1$.

EXAMPLE 3   **Power Series Solutions**

Solve $y'' + xy = 0$.

SOLUTION   Since there are no finite singular points, Theorem 6.1.1 guarantees two power series solutions centered at 0, convergent for $|x| < \infty$. Substituting

$y = \sum_{n=0}^{\infty} c_n x^n$ and the second derivative $y'' = \sum_{n=2}^{\infty} n(n-1)c_n x^{n-2}$ (see (1)) into the differential equation gives

$$y'' + xy = \sum_{n=2}^{\infty} c_n n(n-1)x^{n-2} + x\sum_{n=0}^{\infty} c_n x^n = \sum_{n=2}^{\infty} c_n n(n-1)x^{n-2} + \sum_{n=0}^{\infty} c_n x^{n+1}. \quad (7)$$

In Example 1 we already added the last two series on the right-hand side of the equality in (7) by shifting the summation index. From the result given in (4),

$$y'' + xy = 2c_2 + \sum_{k=1}^{\infty} [(k+1)(k+2)c_{k+2} + c_{k-1}]x^k = 0. \quad (8)$$

At this point we invoke the identity property. Since (8) is identically zero, it is necessary that the coefficient of each power of x be set equal to zero—that is, $2c_2 = 0$ (it is the coefficient of x^0), and

$$(k+1)(k+2)c_{k+2} + c_{k-1} = 0, \qquad k = 1, 2, 3, \ldots. \quad (9)$$

Now $2c_2 = 0$ obviously dictates that $c_2 = 0$. But the expression in (9), called a **recurrence relation,** determines the c_k in such a manner that we can choose a certain subset of the set of coefficients to be *nonzero*. Since $(k+1)(k+2) \neq 0$ for all values of k, we can solve (9) for c_{k+2} in terms of c_{k-1}:

$$c_{k+2} = -\frac{c_{k-1}}{(k+1)(k+2)}, \qquad k = 1, 2, 3, \ldots. \quad (10)$$

This relation generates consecutive coefficients of the assumed solution one at a time as we let k take on the successive integers indicated in (10):

$$k = 1, \qquad c_3 = -\frac{c_0}{2 \cdot 3}$$

$$k = 2, \qquad c_4 = -\frac{c_1}{3 \cdot 4}$$

$$k = 3, \qquad c_5 = -\frac{c_2}{4 \cdot 5} = 0 \qquad\qquad \leftarrow c_2 \text{ is zero}$$

$$k = 4, \qquad c_6 = -\frac{c_3}{5 \cdot 6} = \frac{1}{2 \cdot 3 \cdot 5 \cdot 6} c_0$$

$$k = 5, \qquad c_7 = -\frac{c_4}{6 \cdot 7} = \frac{1}{3 \cdot 4 \cdot 6 \cdot 7} c_1$$

$$k = 6, \qquad c_8 = -\frac{c_5}{7 \cdot 8} = 0 \qquad\qquad \leftarrow c_5 \text{ is zero}$$

$$k = 7, \qquad c_9 = -\frac{c_6}{8 \cdot 9} = \frac{1}{2 \cdot 3 \cdot 5 \cdot 6 \cdot 8 \cdot 9} c_0$$

$$k = 8, \qquad c_{10} = -\frac{c_7}{9 \cdot 10} = \frac{1}{3 \cdot 4 \cdot 6 \cdot 7 \cdot 9 \cdot 10} c_1$$

$$k = 9, \qquad c_{11} = -\frac{c_8}{10 \cdot 11} = 0 \qquad\qquad \leftarrow c_8 \text{ is zero}$$

and so on. Now substituting the coefficients just obtained into the original assumption

$$y = c_0 + c_1 x + c_2 x^2 + c_3 x^3 + c_4 x^4 + c_5 x^5 + c_6 x^6 + c_7 x^7 + c_8 x^8 + c_9 x^9 + c_{10}x^{10} + c_{11}x^{11} + \cdots,$$

we get

$$y = c_0 + c_1 x + 0 - \frac{c_0}{2 \cdot 3}x^3 - \frac{c_1}{3 \cdot 4}x^4 + 0 + \frac{c_0}{2 \cdot 3 \cdot 5 \cdot 6}x^6$$

$$+ \frac{c_1}{3 \cdot 4 \cdot 6 \cdot 7}x^7 + 0 - \frac{c_0}{2 \cdot 3 \cdot 5 \cdot 6 \cdot 8 \cdot 9}x^9 - \frac{c_1}{3 \cdot 4 \cdot 6 \cdot 7 \cdot 9 \cdot 10}x^{10} + 0 + \cdots.$$

After grouping the terms containing c_0 and the terms containing c_1, we obtain $y = c_0 y_1(x) + c_1 y_2(x)$, where

$$y_1(x) = 1 - \frac{1}{2 \cdot 3}x^3 + \frac{1}{2 \cdot 3 \cdot 5 \cdot 6}x^6 - \frac{1}{2 \cdot 3 \cdot 5 \cdot 6 \cdot 8 \cdot 9}x^9 + \cdots = 1 + \sum_{k=1}^{\infty} \frac{(-1)^k}{2 \cdot 3 \cdots (3k-1)(3k)}x^{3k}$$

$$y_2(x) = x - \frac{1}{3 \cdot 4}x^4 + \frac{1}{3 \cdot 4 \cdot 6 \cdot 7}x^7 - \frac{1}{3 \cdot 4 \cdot 6 \cdot 7 \cdot 9 \cdot 10}x^{10} + \cdots = x + \sum_{k=1}^{\infty} \frac{(-1)^k}{3 \cdot 4 \cdots (3k)(3k+1)}x^{3k+1}.$$

Because the recursive use of (10) leaves c_0 and c_1 completely undetermined, they can be chosen arbitrarily. As was mentioned prior to this example, the linear combination $y = c_0 y_1(x) + c_1 y_2(x)$ actually represents the general solution of the differential equation. Although we know from Theorem 6.1.1 that each series solution converges for $|x| < \infty$, this fact can also be verified by the ratio test. ∎

The differential equation in Example 3 is called **Airy's equation** and is encountered in the study of diffraction of light, diffraction of radio waves around the surface of the Earth, aerodynamics, and the deflection of a uniform thin vertical column that bends under its own weight. Other common forms of Airy's equation are $y'' - xy = 0$ and $y'' + \alpha^2 xy = 0$. See Problem 41 in Exercises 6.3 for an application of the last equation.

EXAMPLE 4 Power Series Solution

Solve $(x^2 + 1)y'' + xy' - y = 0$.

SOLUTION As we have already seen on page 223, the given differential equation has singular points at $x = \pm i$, and so a power series solution centered at 0 will converge at least for $|x| < 1$, where 1 is the distance in the complex plane from 0 to either i or $-i$. The assumption $y = \sum_{n=0}^{\infty} c_n x^n$ and its first two derivatives (see (1)) lead to

$$(x^2 + 1) \sum_{n=2}^{\infty} n(n-1)c_n x^{n-2} + x \sum_{n=1}^{\infty} nc_n x^{n-1} - \sum_{n=0}^{\infty} c_n x^n$$

$$= \sum_{n=2}^{\infty} n(n-1)c_n x^n + \sum_{n=2}^{\infty} n(n-1)c_n x^{n-2} + \sum_{n=1}^{\infty} nc_n x^n - \sum_{n=0}^{\infty} c_n x^n$$

$$= 2c_2 x^0 - c_0 x^0 + 6c_3 x + c_1 x - c_1 x + \underbrace{\sum_{n=2}^{\infty} n(n-1)c_n x^n}_{k=n}$$

$$+ \underbrace{\sum_{n=4}^{\infty} n(n-1)c_n x^{n-2}}_{k=n-2} + \underbrace{\sum_{n=2}^{\infty} nc_n x^n}_{k=n} - \underbrace{\sum_{n=2}^{\infty} c_n x^n}_{k=n}$$

$$= 2c_2 - c_0 + 6c_3 x + \sum_{k=2}^{\infty} [k(k-1)c_k + (k+2)(k+1)c_{k+2} + kc_k - c_k]x^k$$

$$= 2c_2 - c_0 + 6c_3 x + \sum_{k=2}^{\infty} [(k+1)(k-1)c_k + (k+2)(k+1)c_{k+2}]x^k = 0.$$

From this identity we conclude that $2c_2 - c_0 = 0, 6c_3 = 0$, and

$$(k + 1)(k - 1)c_k + (k + 2)(k + 1)c_{k+2} = 0.$$

Thus
$$c_2 = \frac{1}{2} c_0$$

$$c_3 = 0$$

$$c_{k+2} = \frac{1-k}{k+2} c_k, \qquad k = 2, 3, 4, \ldots .$$

Substituting $k = 2, 3, 4, \ldots$ into the last formula gives

$$c_4 = -\frac{1}{4} c_2 = -\frac{1}{2 \cdot 4} c_0 = -\frac{1}{2^2 2!} c_0$$

$$c_5 = -\frac{2}{5} c_3 = 0 \qquad \leftarrow c_3 \text{ is zero}$$

$$c_6 = -\frac{3}{6} c_4 = \frac{3}{2 \cdot 4 \cdot 6} c_0 = \frac{1 \cdot 3}{2^3 3!} c_0$$

$$c_7 = -\frac{4}{7} c_5 = 0 \qquad \leftarrow c_5 \text{ is zero}$$

$$c_8 = -\frac{5}{8} c_6 = -\frac{3 \cdot 5}{2 \cdot 4 \cdot 6 \cdot 8} c_0 = -\frac{1 \cdot 3 \cdot 5}{2^4 4!} c_0$$

$$c_9 = -\frac{6}{9} c_7 = 0, \qquad \leftarrow c_7 \text{ is zero}$$

$$c_{10} = -\frac{7}{10} c_8 = \frac{3 \cdot 5 \cdot 7}{2 \cdot 4 \cdot 6 \cdot 8 \cdot 10} c_0 = \frac{1 \cdot 3 \cdot 5 \cdot 7}{2^5 5!} c_0,$$

and so on. Therefore

$$y = c_0 + c_1 x + c_2 x^2 + c_3 x^3 + c_4 x^4 + c_5 x^5 + c_6 x^6 + c_7 x^7 + c_8 x^8 + c_9 x^9 + c_{10} x^{10} + \cdots$$

$$= c_0 \left[1 + \frac{1}{2} x^2 - \frac{1}{2^2 2!} x^4 + \frac{1 \cdot 3}{2^3 3!} x^6 - \frac{1 \cdot 3 \cdot 5}{2^4 4!} x^8 + \frac{1 \cdot 3 \cdot 5 \cdot 7}{2^5 5!} x^{10} - \cdots \right] + c_1 x$$

$$= c_0 y_1(x) + c_1 y_2(x).$$

The solutions are the polynomial $y_2(x) = x$ and the power series

$$y_1(x) = 1 + \frac{1}{2} x^2 + \sum_{n=2}^{\infty} (-1)^{n-1} \frac{1 \cdot 3 \cdot 5 \cdots (2n - 3)}{2^n n!} x^{2n}, \qquad |x| < 1. \quad \blacksquare$$

EXAMPLE 5 Three-Term Recurrence Relation

If we seek a power series solution $y = \sum_{n=0}^{\infty} c_n x^n$ for the differential equation

$$y'' - (1 + x)y = 0,$$

we obtain $c_2 = \frac{1}{2} c_0$ and the three-term recurrence relation

$$c_{k+2} = \frac{c_k + c_{k-1}}{(k + 1)(k + 2)}, \qquad k = 1, 2, 3, \ldots .$$

It follows from these two results that all coefficients c_n, for $n \geq 3$, are expressed in terms of *both* c_0 and c_1. To simplify life, we can first choose $c_0 \neq 0, c_1 = 0$; this yields coefficients for one solution expressed entirely in terms of c_0. Next, if we choose $c_0 = 0$, $c_1 \neq 0$, then coefficients for the other solution are expressed in terms of c_1. Using $c_2 = \frac{1}{2}c_0$ in both cases, the recurrence relation for $k = 1, 2, 3, \ldots$ gives

$c_0 \neq 0, c_1 = 0$	$c_0 = 0, c_1 \neq 0$
$c_2 = \dfrac{1}{2}c_0$	$c_2 = \dfrac{1}{2}c_0 = 0$
$c_3 = \dfrac{c_1 + c_0}{2 \cdot 3} = \dfrac{c_0}{2 \cdot 3} = \dfrac{c_0}{6}$	$c_3 = \dfrac{c_1 + c_0}{2 \cdot 3} = \dfrac{c_1}{2 \cdot 3} = \dfrac{c_1}{6}$
$c_4 = \dfrac{c_2 + c_1}{3 \cdot 4} = \dfrac{c_0}{2 \cdot 3 \cdot 4} = \dfrac{c_0}{24}$	$c_4 = \dfrac{c_2 + c_1}{3 \cdot 4} = \dfrac{c_1}{3 \cdot 4} = \dfrac{c_1}{12}$
$c_5 = \dfrac{c_3 + c_2}{4 \cdot 5} = \dfrac{c_0}{4 \cdot 5}\left[\dfrac{1}{6} + \dfrac{1}{2}\right] = \dfrac{c_0}{30}$	$c_5 = \dfrac{c_3 + c_2}{4 \cdot 5} = \dfrac{c_1}{4 \cdot 5 \cdot 6} = \dfrac{c_1}{120}$

and so on. Finally, we see that the general solution of the equation is $y = c_0 y_1(x) + c_1 y_2(x)$, where

$$y_1(x) = 1 + \frac{1}{2}x^2 + \frac{1}{6}x^3 + \frac{1}{24}x^4 + \frac{1}{30}x^5 + \cdots$$

and

$$y_2(x) = x + \frac{1}{6}x^3 + \frac{1}{12}x^4 + \frac{1}{120}x^5 + \cdots.$$

Each series converges for all finite values of x. ∎

NONPOLYNOMIAL COEFFICIENTS The next example illustrates how to find a power series solution about the ordinary point $x_0 = 0$ of a differential equation when its coefficients are not polynomials. In this example we see an application of the multiplication of two power series.

EXAMPLE 6 **DE with Nonpolynomial Coefficients**

Solve $y'' + (\cos x)y = 0$.

SOLUTION We see that $x = 0$ is an ordinary point of the equation because, as we have already seen, $\cos x$ is analytic at that point. Using the Maclaurin series for $\cos x$ given in (2), along with the usual assumption $y = \sum_{n=0}^{\infty} c_n x^n$ and the results in (1), we find

$$y'' + (\cos x)y = \sum_{n=2}^{\infty} n(n-1)c_n x^{n-2} + \left(1 - \frac{x^2}{2!} + \frac{x^4}{4!} - \frac{x^6}{6!} + \cdots\right)\sum_{n=0}^{\infty} c_n x^n$$

$$= 2c_2 + 6c_3 x + 12c_4 x^2 + 20c_5 x^3 + \cdots + \left(1 - \frac{x^2}{2!} + \frac{x^4}{4!} + \cdots\right)(c_0 + c_1 x + c_2 x^2 + c_3 x^3 + \cdots)$$

$$= 2c_2 + c_0 + (6c_3 + c_1)x + \left(12c_4 + c_2 - \frac{1}{2}c_0\right)x^2 + \left(20c_5 + c_3 - \frac{1}{2}c_1\right)x^3 + \cdots = 0.$$

It follows that

$$2c_2 + c_0 = 0, \qquad 6c_3 + c_1 = 0, \qquad 12c_4 + c_2 - \frac{1}{2}c_0 = 0, \qquad 20c_5 + c_3 - \frac{1}{2}c_1 = 0,$$

and so on. This gives $c_2 = -\frac{1}{2}c_0$, $c_3 = -\frac{1}{6}c_1$, $c_4 = \frac{1}{12}c_0$, $c_5 = \frac{1}{30}c_1$, ... By grouping terms, we arrive at the general solution $y = c_0 y_1(x) + c_1 y_2(x)$, where

$$y_1(x) = 1 - \frac{1}{2}x^2 + \frac{1}{12}x^4 - \cdots \qquad \text{and} \qquad y_2(x) = x - \frac{1}{6}x^3 + \frac{1}{30}x^5 - \cdots.$$

Because the differential equation has no finite singular points, both power series converge for $|x| < \infty$. ∎

SOLUTION CURVES The approximate graph of a power series solution $y(x) = \sum_{n=0}^{\infty} c_n x^n$ can be obtained in several ways. We can always resort to graphing the terms in the sequence of partial sums of the series — in other words, the graphs of the polynomials $S_N(x) = \sum_{n=0}^{N} c_n x^n$. For large values of N, $S_N(x)$ should give us an indication of the behavior of $y(x)$ near the ordinary point $x = 0$. We can also obtain an approximate or numerical solution curve by using a solver as we did in Section 4.9. For example, if you carefully scrutinize the series solutions of Airy's equation in Example 3, you should see that $y_1(x)$ and $y_2(x)$ are, in turn, the solutions of the initial-value problems

$$\begin{aligned} y'' + xy &= 0, \quad y(0) = 1, \quad y'(0) = 0, \\ y'' + xy &= 0, \quad y(0) = 0, \quad y'(0) = 1. \end{aligned} \tag{11}$$

The specified initial conditions "pick out" the solutions $y_1(x)$ and $y_2(x)$ from $y = c_0 y_1(x) + c_1 y_2(x)$, since it should be apparent from our basic series assumption $y = \sum_{n=0}^{\infty} c_n x^n$ that $y(0) = c_0$ and $y'(0) = c_1$. Now if your numerical solver requires a system of equations, the substitution $y' = u$ in $y'' + xy = 0$ gives $y'' = u' = -xy$, and so a system of two first-order equations equivalent to Airy's equation is

$$\begin{aligned} y' &= u \\ u' &= -xy. \end{aligned} \tag{12}$$

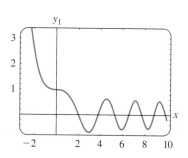

(a) plot of $y_1(x)$ vs. x

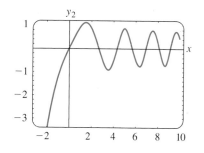

(b) plot of $y_2(x)$ vs. x

FIGURE 6.1.2 Numerical solution curves for Airy's DE

Initial conditions for the system in (12) are the two sets of initial conditions in (11) rewritten as $y(0) = 1$, $u(0) = 0$, and $y(0) = 0$, $u(0) = 1$. The graphs of $y_1(x)$ and $y_2(x)$ shown in Figure 6.1.2 were obtained with the aid of a numerical solver. The fact that the numerical solution curves appear to be oscillatory is consistent with the fact that Airy's equation appeared in Section 5.1 (page 186) in the form $mx'' + ktx = 0$ as a model of a spring whose "spring constant" $K(t) = kt$ increases with time.

REMARKS

(*i*) In the problems that follow, do not expect to be able to write a solution in terms of summation notation in each case. Even though we can generate as many terms as desired in a series solution $y = \sum_{n=0}^{\infty} c_n x^n$ either through the use of a recurrence relation or, as in Example 6, by multiplication, it might not be possible to deduce any general term for the coefficients c_n. We might have to settle, as we did in Examples 5 and 6, for just writing out the first few terms of the series.

(*ii*) A point x_0 is an ordinary point of a *nonhomogeneous* linear second-order DE $y'' + P(x)y' + Q(x)y = f(x)$ if $P(x)$, $Q(x)$, and $f(x)$ are analytic at x_0. Moreover, Theorem 6.1.1 extends to such DEs; in other words, we can find power series solutions $y = \sum_{n=0}^{\infty} c_n (x - x_0)^n$ of nonhomogeneous linear DEs in the same manner as in Examples 3–6. See Problem 36 in Exercises 6.1.

EXERCISES 6.1

Answers to selected odd-numbered problems begin on page ANS-8.

6.1.1 REVIEW OF POWER SERIES

In Problems 1–4 find the radius of convergence and interval of convergence for the given power series.

1. $\displaystyle\sum_{n=1}^{\infty} \frac{2^n}{n} x^n$

2. $\displaystyle\sum_{n=0}^{\infty} \frac{(100)^n}{n!}(x + 7)^n$

3. $\displaystyle\sum_{k=1}^{\infty} \frac{(-1)^k}{10^k}(x - 5)^k$

4. $\displaystyle\sum_{k=0}^{\infty} k!(x - 1)^k$

In Problems 5 and 6 the given function is analytic at $x = 0$. Find the first four terms of a power series in x. Perform the multiplication by hand or use a CAS, as instructed.

5. $\sin x \cos x$

6. $e^{-x} \cos x$

In Problems 7 and 8 the given function is analytic at $x = 0$. Find the first four terms of a power series in x. Perform the long division by hand or use a CAS, as instructed. Give the open interval of convergence.

7. $\dfrac{1}{\cos x}$

8. $\dfrac{1 - x}{2 + x}$

In Problems 9 and 10 rewrite the given power series so that its general term involves x^k.

9. $\displaystyle\sum_{n=1}^{\infty} nc_n x^{n+2}$

10. $\displaystyle\sum_{n=3}^{\infty} (2n - 1)c_n x^{n-3}$

In Problems 11 and 12 rewrite the given expression as a single power series whose general term involves x^k.

11. $\displaystyle\sum_{n=1}^{\infty} 2nc_n x^{n-1} + \sum_{n=0}^{\infty} 6c_n x^{n+1}$

12. $\displaystyle\sum_{n=2}^{\infty} n(n - 1)c_n x^n + 2\sum_{n=2}^{\infty} n(n - 1)c_n x^{n-2} + 3\sum_{n=1}^{\infty} nc_n x^n$

In Problems 13 and 14 verify by direct substitution that the given power series is a particular solution of the indicated differential equation.

13. $\displaystyle y = \sum_{n=1}^{\infty} \frac{(-1)^{n+1}}{n} x^n, \quad (x + 1)y'' + y' = 0$

14. $\displaystyle y = \sum_{n=0}^{\infty} \frac{(-1)^n}{2^{2n}(n!)^2} x^{2n}, \quad xy'' + y' + xy = 0$

6.1.2 POWER SERIES SOLUTIONS

In Problems 15 and 16 without actually solving the given differential equation, find a lower bound for the radius of convergence of power series solutions about the ordinary point $x = 0$. About the ordinary point $x = 1$.

15. $(x^2 - 25)y'' + 2xy' + y = 0$

16. $(x^2 - 2x + 10)y'' + xy' - 4y = 0$

In Problems 17–28 find two power series solutions of the given differential equation about the ordinary point $x = 0$.

17. $y'' - xy = 0$

18. $y'' + x^2 y = 0$

19. $y'' - 2xy' + y = 0$

20. $y'' - xy' + 2y = 0$

21. $y'' + x^2 y' + xy = 0$

22. $y'' + 2xy' + 2y = 0$

23. $(x - 1)y'' + y' = 0$

24. $(x + 2)y'' + xy' - y = 0$

25. $y'' - (x + 1)y' - y = 0$

26. $(x^2 + 1)y'' - 6y = 0$

27. $(x^2 + 2)y'' + 3xy' - y = 0$

28. $(x^2 - 1)y'' + xy' - y = 0$

In Problems 29–32 use the power series method to solve the given initial-value problem.

29. $(x - 1)y'' - xy' + y = 0, \quad y(0) = -2, y'(0) = 6$

30. $(x + 1)y'' - (2 - x)y' + y = 0, \quad y(0) = 2, y'(0) = -1$

31. $y'' - 2xy' + 8y = 0, \quad y(0) = 3, y'(0) = 0$

32. $(x^2 + 1)y'' + 2xy' = 0, \quad y(0) = 0, y'(0) = 1$

In Problems 33 and 34 use the procedure in Example 6 to find two power series solutions of the given differential equation about the ordinary point $x = 0$.

33. $y'' + (\sin x)y = 0$

34. $y'' + e^x y' - y = 0$

Discussion Problems

35. Without actually solving the differential equation $(\cos x)y'' + y' + 5y = 0$, find a lower bound for the radius of convergence of power series solutions about $x = 0$. About $x = 1$.

36. How can the method described in this section be used to find a power series solution of the *nonhomogeneous* equation $y'' - xy = 1$ about the ordinary point $x = 0$? Of $y'' - 4xy' - 4y = e^x$? Carry out your ideas by solving both DEs.

37. Is $x = 0$ an ordinary or a singular point of the differential equation $xy'' + (\sin x)y = 0$? Defend your answer with sound mathematics.

38. For purposes of this problem, ignore the graphs given in Figure 6.1.2. If Airy's DE is written as $y'' = -xy$, what can we say about the shape of a solution curve if $x > 0$ and $y > 0$? If $x > 0$ and $y < 0$?

Computer Lab Assignments

39. (a) Find two power series solutions for $y'' + xy' + y = 0$ and express the solutions $y_1(x)$ and $y_2(x)$ in terms of summation notation.

(b) Use a CAS to graph the partial sums $S_N(x)$ for $y_1(x)$. Use $N = 2, 3, 5, 6, 8, 10$. Repeat using the partial sums $S_N(x)$ for $y_2(x)$.

(c) Compare the graphs obtained in part (b) with the curve obtained by using a numerical solver. Use the initial-conditions $y_1(0) = 1$, $y_1'(0) = 0$, and $y_2(0) = 0$, $y_2'(0) = 1$.

(d) Reexamine the solution $y_1(x)$ in part (a). Express this series as an elementary function. Then use (5) of Section 4.2 to find a second solution of the equation. Verify that this second solution is the same as the power series solution $y_2(x)$.

40. (a) Find one more nonzero term for each of the solutions $y_1(x)$ and $y_2(x)$ in Example 6.

(b) Find a series solution $y(x)$ of the initial-value problem $y'' + (\cos x)y = 0$, $y(0) = 1$, $y'(0) = 1$.

(c) Use a CAS to graph the partial sums $S_N(x)$ for the solution $y(x)$ in part (b). Use $N = 2, 3, 4, 5, 6, 7$.

(d) Compare the graphs obtained in part (c) with the curve obtained using a numerical solver for the initial-value problem in part (b).

6.2 SOLUTIONS ABOUT SINGULAR POINTS

REVIEW MATERIAL

• Section 4.2 (especially (5) of that section)

INTRODUCTION The two differential equations

$$y'' + xy = 0 \qquad \text{and} \qquad xy'' + y = 0$$

are similar only in that they are both examples of simple linear second-order DEs with variable coefficients. That is all they have in common. Since $x = 0$ is an *ordinary point* of $y'' + xy = 0$, we saw in Section 6.1 that there was no problem in finding two distinct power series solutions centered at that point. In contrast, because $x = 0$ is a *singular point* of $xy'' + y = 0$, finding two infinite series—notice that we did not say *power series*—solutions of the equation about that point becomes a more difficult task.

The solution method that is discussed in this section does not always yield two infinite series solutions. When only one solution is found, we can use the formula given in (5) of Section 4.2 to find a second solution.

A DEFINITION A singular point x_0 of a linear differential equation

$$a_2(x)y'' + a_1(x)y' + a_0(x)y = 0 \tag{1}$$

is further classified as either regular or irregular. The classification again depends on the functions P and Q in the standard form

$$y'' + P(x)y' + Q(x)y = 0. \tag{2}$$

DEFINITION 6.2.1   Regular and Irregular Singular Points

A singular point x_0 is said to be a **regular singular point** of the differential equation (1) if the functions $p(x) = (x - x_0) P(x)$ and $q(x) = (x - x_0)^2 Q(x)$ are both analytic at x_0. A singular point that is not regular is said to be an **irregular singular point** of the equation.

The second sentence in Definition 6.2.1 indicates that if one or both of the functions $p(x) = (x - x_0) P(x)$ and $q(x) = (x - x_0)^2 Q(x)$ fail to be analytic at x_0, then x_0 is an irregular singular point.

POLYNOMIAL COEFFICIENTS   As in Section 6.1, we are mainly interested in linear equations (1) where the coefficients $a_2(x)$, $a_1(x)$, and $a_0(x)$ are polynomials with no common factors. We have already seen that if $a_2(x_0) = 0$, then $x = x_0$ is a singular point of (1), since at least one of the rational functions $P(x) = a_1(x)/a_2(x)$ and $Q(x) = a_0(x)/a_2(x)$ in the standard form (2) fails to be analytic at that point. But since $a_2(x)$ is a polynomial and x_0 is one of its zeros, it follows from the Factor Theorem of algebra that $x - x_0$ is a factor of $a_2(x)$. This means that after $a_1(x)/a_2(x)$ and $a_0(x)/a_2(x)$ are reduced to lowest terms, the factor $x - x_0$ must remain, to some positive integer power, in one or both denominators. Now suppose that $x = x_0$ is a singular point of (1) but both the functions defined by the products $p(x) = (x - x_0) P(x)$ and $q(x) = (x - x_0)^2 Q(x)$ are analytic at x_0. We are led to the conclusion that multiplying $P(x)$ by $x - x_0$ and $Q(x)$ by $(x - x_0)^2$ has the effect (through cancellation) that $x - x_0$ no longer appears in either denominator. We can now determine whether x_0 is regular by a quick visual check of denominators:

> If $x - x_0$ appears *at most* to the first power in the denominator of $P(x)$ and *at most* to the second power in the denominator of $Q(x)$, then $x = x_0$ is a regular singular point.

Moreover, observe that if $x = x_0$ is a regular singular point and we multiply (2) by $(x - x_0)^2$, then the original DE can be put into the form

$$(x - x_0)^2 y'' + (x - x_0) p(x) y' + q(x) y = 0, \tag{3}$$

where p and q are analytic at $x = x_0$.

EXAMPLE 1   **Classification of Singular Points**

It should be clear that $x = 2$ and $x = -2$ are singular points of

$$(x^2 - 4)^2 y'' + 3(x - 2) y' + 5y = 0.$$

After dividing the equation by $(x^2 - 4)^2 = (x - 2)^2(x + 2)^2$ and reducing the coefficients to lowest terms, we find that

$$P(x) = \frac{3}{(x - 2)(x + 2)^2} \qquad \text{and} \qquad Q(x) = \frac{5}{(x - 2)^2(x + 2)^2}.$$

We now test $P(x)$ and $Q(x)$ at each singular point.

For $x = 2$ to be a regular singular point, the factor $x - 2$ can appear at most to the first power in the denominator of $P(x)$ and at most to the second power in the denominator of $Q(x)$. A check of the denominators of $P(x)$ and $Q(x)$ shows that both these conditions are satisfied, so $x = 2$ is a regular singular point. Alternatively, we are led to the same conclusion by noting that both rational functions

$$p(x) = (x - 2) P(x) = \frac{3}{(x + 2)^2} \qquad \text{and} \qquad q(x) = (x - 2)^2 Q(x) = \frac{5}{(x + 2)^2}$$

are analytic at $x = 2$.

Now since the factor $x - (-2) = x + 2$ appears to the second power in the denominator of $P(x)$, we can conclude immediately that $x = -2$ is an irregular singular point of the equation. This also follows from the fact that

$$p(x) = (x + 2) P(x) = \frac{3}{(x - 2)(x + 2)}$$

is not analytic at $x = -2$. ∎

In Example 1, notice that since $x = 2$ is a regular singular point, the original equation can be written as

$$\begin{array}{cc} p(x) \text{ analytic} & q(x) \text{ analytic} \\ \downarrow \text{at } x = 2 & \downarrow \text{at } x = 2 \end{array}$$

$$(x - 2)^2 y'' + (x - 2) \, \frac{3}{(x + 2)^2} y' + \frac{5}{(x + 2)^2} y = 0.$$

As another example, we can see that $x = 0$ is an irregular singular point of $x^3 y'' - 2xy' + 8y = 0$ by inspection of the denominators of $P(x) = -2/x^2$ and $Q(x) = 8/x^3$. On the other hand, $x = 0$ is a regular singular point of $xy'' - 2xy' + 8y = 0$, since $x - 0$ and $(x - 0)^2$ do not even appear in the respective denominators of $P(x) = -2$ and $Q(x) = 8/x$. For a singular point $x = x_0$ any nonnegative power of $x - x_0$ less than one (namely, zero) and any nonnegative power less than two (namely, zero and one) in the denominators of $P(x)$ and $Q(x)$, respectively, imply that x_0 is a regular singular point. A singular point can be a complex number. You should verify that $x = 3i$ and $x = -3i$ are two regular singular points of $(x^2 + 9)y'' - 3xy' + (1 - x)y = 0$.

Any second-order Cauchy-Euler equation $ax^2 y'' + bxy' + cy = 0$, where a, b, and c are real constants, has a regular singular point at $x = 0$. You should verify that two solutions of the Cauchy-Euler equation $x^2 y'' - 3xy' + 4y = 0$ on the interval $(0, \infty)$ are $y_1 = x^2$ and $y_2 = x^2 \ln x$. If we attempted to find a power series solution about the regular singular point $x = 0$ (namely, $y = \sum_{n=0}^{\infty} c_n x^n$), we would succeed in obtaining only the polynomial solution $y_1 = x^2$. The fact that we would not obtain the second solution is not surprising because $\ln x$ (and consequently $y_2 = x^2 \ln x$) is not analytic at $x = 0$ — that is, y_2 does not possess a Taylor series expansion centered at $x = 0$.

METHOD OF FROBENIUS To solve a differential equation (1) about a regular singular point, we employ the following theorem due to Frobenius.

THEOREM 6.2.1 Frobenius' Theorem

If $x = x_0$ is a regular singular point of the differential equation (1), then there exists at least one solution of the form

$$y = (x - x_0)^r \sum_{n=0}^{\infty} c_n (x - x_0)^n = \sum_{n=0}^{\infty} c_n (x - x_0)^{n+r}, \qquad (4)$$

where the number r is a constant to be determined. The series will converge at least on some interval $0 < x - x_0 < R$.

Notice the words *at least* in the first sentence of Theorem 6.2.1. This means that in contrast to Theorem 6.1.1, Theorem 6.2.1 gives us no assurance that *two* series solutions of the type indicated in (4) can be found. The **method of Frobenius,** finding series solutions about a regular singular point x_0, is similar to the method of undetermined series coefficients of the preceding section in that we substitute $y = \sum_{n=0}^{\infty} c_n (x - x_0)^{n+r}$ into the given differential equation and determine the unknown coefficients c_n by a recurrence relation. However, we have an additional task in this procedure: Before determining the coefficients, we must find the unknown exponent r. If r is found to be a number that is not a nonnegative integer, then the corresponding solution $y = \sum_{n=0}^{\infty} c_n (x - x_0)^{n+r}$ is not a power series.

As we did in the discussion of solutions about ordinary points, we shall always assume, for the sake of simplicity in solving differential equations, that the regular singular point is $x = 0$.

EXAMPLE 2   Two Series Solutions

Because $x = 0$ is a regular singular point of the differential equation

$$3xy'' + y' - y = 0, \tag{5}$$

we try to find a solution of the form $y = \sum_{n=0}^{\infty} c_n x^{n+r}$. Now

$$y' = \sum_{n=0}^{\infty} (n + r)c_n x^{n+r-1} \quad \text{and} \quad y'' = \sum_{n=0}^{\infty} (n + r)(n + r - 1)c_n x^{n+r-2},$$

so

$$3xy'' + y' - y = 3\sum_{n=0}^{\infty} (n + r)(n + r - 1)c_n x^{n+r-1} + \sum_{n=0}^{\infty} (n + r)c_n x^{n+r-1} - \sum_{n=0}^{\infty} c_n x^{n+r}$$

$$= \sum_{n=0}^{\infty} (n + r)(3n + 3r - 2)c_n x^{n+r-1} - \sum_{n=0}^{\infty} c_n x^{n+r}$$

$$= x^r \left[r(3r - 2)c_0 x^{-1} + \underbrace{\sum_{n=1}^{\infty} (n + r)(3n + 3r - 2)c_n x^{n-1}}_{k = n-1} - \underbrace{\sum_{n=0}^{\infty} c_n x^n}_{k = n} \right]$$

$$= x^r \left[r(3r - 2)c_0 x^{-1} + \sum_{k=0}^{\infty} [(k + r + 1)(3k + 3r + 1)c_{k+1} - c_k]x^k \right] = 0,$$

which implies that

$$r(3r - 2)c_0 = 0$$

and

$$(k + r + 1)(3k + 3r + 1)c_{k+1} - c_k = 0, \qquad k = 0, 1, 2, \ldots.$$

Because nothing is gained by taking $c_0 = 0$, we must then have

$$r(3r - 2) = 0 \tag{6}$$

and

$$c_{k+1} = \frac{c_k}{(k + r + 1)(3k + 3r + 1)}, \qquad k = 0, 1, 2, \ldots. \tag{7}$$

When substituted in (7), the two values of r that satisfy the quadratic equation (6), $r_1 = \frac{2}{3}$ and $r_2 = 0$, give two different recurrence relations:

$$r_1 = \tfrac{2}{3}, \qquad c_{k+1} = \frac{c_k}{(3k + 5)(k + 1)}, \qquad k = 0, 1, 2, \ldots \tag{8}$$

$$r_2 = 0, \qquad c_{k+1} = \frac{c_k}{(k + 1)(3k + 1)}, \qquad k = 0, 1, 2, \ldots. \tag{9}$$

From (8) we find

$$c_1 = \frac{c_0}{5 \cdot 1}$$

$$c_2 = \frac{c_1}{8 \cdot 2} = \frac{c_0}{2!5 \cdot 8}$$

$$c_3 = \frac{c_2}{11 \cdot 3} = \frac{c_0}{3!5 \cdot 8 \cdot 11}$$

$$c_4 = \frac{c_3}{14 \cdot 4} = \frac{c_0}{4!5 \cdot 8 \cdot 11 \cdot 14}$$

$$\vdots$$

$$c_n = \frac{c_0}{n!5 \cdot 8 \cdot 11 \cdots (3n + 2)}.$$

From (9) we find

$$c_1 = \frac{c_0}{1 \cdot 1}$$

$$c_2 = \frac{c_1}{2 \cdot 4} = \frac{c_0}{2!1 \cdot 4}$$

$$c_3 = \frac{c_2}{3 \cdot 7} = \frac{c_0}{3!1 \cdot 4 \cdot 7}$$

$$c_4 = \frac{c_3}{4 \cdot 10} = \frac{c_0}{4!1 \cdot 4 \cdot 7 \cdot 10}$$

$$\vdots$$

$$c_n = \frac{c_0}{n!1 \cdot 4 \cdot 7 \cdots (3n - 2)}.$$

Here we encounter something that did not happen when we obtained solutions about an ordinary point; we have what looks to be two different sets of coefficients, but each set contains the *same* multiple c_0. If we omit this term, the series solutions are

$$y_1(x) = x^{2/3}\left[1 + \sum_{n=1}^{\infty} \frac{1}{n!5 \cdot 8 \cdot 11 \cdots (3n + 2)} x^n\right] \qquad (10)$$

$$y_2(x) = x^0\left[1 + \sum_{n=1}^{\infty} \frac{1}{n!1 \cdot 4 \cdot 7 \cdots (3n - 2)} x^n\right]. \qquad (11)$$

By the ratio test it can be demonstrated that both (10) and (11) converge for all values of x—that is, $|x| < \infty$. Also, it should be apparent from the form of these solutions that neither series is a constant multiple of the other, and therefore $y_1(x)$ and $y_2(x)$ are linearly independent on the entire x-axis. Hence by the superposition principle, $y = C_1 y_1(x) + C_2 y_2(x)$ is another solution of (5). On any interval that does not contain the origin, such as $(0, \infty)$, this linear combination represents the general solution of the differential equation. ∎

INDICIAL EQUATION   Equation (6) is called the **indicial equation** of the problem, and the values $r_1 = \frac{2}{3}$ and $r_2 = 0$ are called the **indicial roots,** or **exponents,** of the singularity $x = 0$. In general, after substituting $y = \sum_{n=0}^{\infty} c_n x^{n+r}$ into the given differential equation and simplifying, the indicial equation is a quadratic equation in r that results from equating the *total coefficient of the lowest power of x to zero.* We solve for the two values of r and substitute these values into a recurrence relation such as (7). Theorem 6.2.1 guarantees that at least one solution of the assumed series form can be found.

It is possible to obtain the indicial equation in advance of substituting $y = \sum_{n=0}^{\infty} c_n x^{n+r}$ into the differential equation. If $x = 0$ is a regular singular point of (1), then by Definition 6.2.1 both functions $p(x) = xP(x)$ and $q(x) = x^2 Q(x)$, where P and Q are defined by the standard form (2), are analytic at $x = 0$; that is, the power series expansions

$$p(x) = xP(x) = a_0 + a_1 x + a_2 x^2 + \cdots \qquad \text{and} \qquad q(x) = x^2 Q(x) = b_0 + b_1 x + b_2 x^2 + \cdots \qquad (12)$$

are valid on intervals that have a positive radius of convergence. By multiplying (2) by x^2, we get the form given in (3):

$$x^2 y'' + x[xP(x)]y' + [x^2 Q(x)]y = 0. \qquad (13)$$

After substituting $y = \sum_{n=0}^{\infty} c_n x^{n+r}$ and the two series in (12) into (13) and carrying out the multiplication of series, we find the general indicial equation to be

$$r(r - 1) + a_0 r + b_0 = 0, \qquad (14)$$

where a_0 and b_0 are as defined in (12). See Problems 13 and 14 in Exercises 6.2.

EXAMPLE 3   **Two Series Solutions**

Solve $2xy'' + (1 + x)y' + y = 0$.

SOLUTION   Substituting $y = \sum_{n=0}^{\infty} c_n x^{n+r}$ gives

$$2xy'' + (1 + x)y' + y = 2\sum_{n=0}^{\infty}(n+r)(n+r-1)c_nx^{n+r-1} + \sum_{n=0}^{\infty}(n+r)c_nx^{n+r-1}$$

$$+ \sum_{n=0}^{\infty}(n+r)c_nx^{n+r} + \sum_{n=0}^{\infty}c_nx^{n+r}$$

$$= \sum_{n=0}^{\infty}(n+r)(2n+2r-1)c_nx^{n+r-1} + \sum_{n=0}^{\infty}(n+r+1)c_nx^{n+r}$$

$$= x^r\left[r(2r-1)c_0x^{-1} + \underbrace{\sum_{n=1}^{\infty}(n+r)(2n+2r-1)c_nx^{n-1}}_{k=n-1} + \underbrace{\sum_{n=0}^{\infty}(n+r+1)c_nx^{n}}_{k=n}\right]$$

$$= x^r\left[r(2r-1)c_0x^{-1} + \sum_{k=0}^{\infty}[(k+r+1)(2k+2r+1)c_{k+1} + (k+r+1)c_k]x^k\right],$$

which implies that $$r(2r-1) = 0 \qquad (15)$$

and $$(k+r+1)(2k+2r+1)c_{k+1} + (k+r+1)c_k = 0, \qquad (16)$$

$k = 0, 1, 2, \ldots$. From (15) we see that the indicial roots are $r_1 = \frac{1}{2}$ and $r_2 = 0$.
For $r_1 = \frac{1}{2}$ we can divide by $k + \frac{3}{2}$ in (16) to obtain

$$c_{k+1} = \frac{-c_k}{2(k+1)}, \qquad k = 0, 1, 2, \ldots, \qquad (17)$$

whereas for $r_2 = 0$, (16) becomes

$$c_{k+1} = \frac{-c_k}{2k+1}, \qquad k = 0, 1, 2, \ldots. \qquad (18)$$

From (17) we find

$$c_1 = \frac{-c_0}{2 \cdot 1}$$

$$c_2 = \frac{-c_1}{2 \cdot 2} = \frac{c_0}{2^2 \cdot 2!}$$

$$c_3 = \frac{-c_2}{2 \cdot 3} = \frac{-c_0}{2^3 \cdot 3!}$$

$$c_4 = \frac{-c_3}{2 \cdot 4} = \frac{c_0}{2^4 \cdot 4!}$$

$$\vdots$$

$$c_n = \frac{(-1)^n c_0}{2^n n!}.$$

From (18) we find

$$c_1 = \frac{-c_0}{1}$$

$$c_2 = \frac{-c_1}{3} = \frac{c_0}{1 \cdot 3}$$

$$c_3 = \frac{-c_2}{5} = \frac{-c_0}{1 \cdot 3 \cdot 5}$$

$$c_4 = \frac{-c_3}{7} = \frac{c_0}{1 \cdot 3 \cdot 5 \cdot 7}$$

$$\vdots$$

$$c_n = \frac{(-1)^n c_0}{1 \cdot 3 \cdot 5 \cdot 7 \cdots (2n-1)}.$$

Thus for the indicial root $r_1 = \frac{1}{2}$ we obtain the solution

$$y_1(x) = x^{1/2}\left[1 + \sum_{n=1}^{\infty}\frac{(-1)^n}{2^n n!}x^n\right] = \sum_{n=0}^{\infty}\frac{(-1)^n}{2^n n!}x^{n+1/2},$$

where we have again omitted c_0. The series converges for $x \geq 0$; as given, the series is not defined for negative values of x because of the presence of $x^{1/2}$. For $r_2 = 0$ a second solution is

$$y_2(x) = 1 + \sum_{n=1}^{\infty}\frac{(-1)^n}{1 \cdot 3 \cdot 5 \cdot 7 \cdots (2n-1)}x^n, \qquad |x| < \infty.$$

On the interval $(0, \infty)$ the general solution is $y = C_1y_1(x) + C_2y_2(x)$. ∎

EXAMPLE 4 Only One Series Solution

Solve $xy'' + y = 0$.

SOLUTION From $xP(x) = 0$, $x^2Q(x) = x$ and the fact that 0 and x are their own power series centered at 0 we conclude that $a_0 = 0$ and $b_0 = 0$, so from (14) the indicial equation is $r(r - 1) = 0$. You should verify that the two recurrence relations corresponding to the indicial roots $r_1 = 1$ and $r_2 = 0$ yield exactly the same set of coefficients. In other words, in this case the method of Frobenius produces only a single series solution

$$y_1(x) = \sum_{n=0}^{\infty} \frac{(-1)^n}{n!(n + 1)!} x^{n+1} = x - \frac{1}{2} x^2 + \frac{1}{12} x^3 - \frac{1}{144} x^4 + \cdots. \qquad \blacksquare$$

THREE CASES For the sake of discussion let us again suppose that $x = 0$ is a regular singular point of equation (1) and that the indicial roots r_1 and r_2 of the singularity are real. When using the method of Frobenius, we distinguish three cases corresponding to the nature of the indicial roots r_1 and r_2. In the first two cases the symbol r_1 denotes the largest of two distinct roots, that is, $r_1 > r_2$. In the last case $r_1 = r_2$.

CASE I: If r_1 and r_2 are distinct and the difference $r_1 - r_2$ is not a positive integer, then there exist two linearly independent solutions of equation (1) of the form

$$y_1(x) = \sum_{n=0}^{\infty} c_n x^{n+r_1}, \quad c_0 \neq 0, \qquad y_2(x) = \sum_{n=0}^{\infty} b_n x^{n+r_2}, \quad b_0 \neq 0.$$

This is the case illustrated in Examples 2 and 3.

Next we assume that the difference of the roots is N, where N is a positive integer. In this case the second solution *may* contain a logarithm.

CASE II: If r_1 and r_2 are distinct and the difference $r_1 - r_2$ is a positive integer, then there exist two linearly independent solutions of equation (1) of the form

$$y_1(x) = \sum_{n=0}^{\infty} c_n x^{n+r_1}, \qquad c_0 \neq 0, \tag{19}$$

$$y_2(x) = C y_1(x) \ln x + \sum_{n=0}^{\infty} b_n x^{n+r_2}, \qquad b_0 \neq 0, \tag{20}$$

where C is a constant that could be zero.

Finally, in the last case, the case when $r_1 = r_2$, a second solution will *always* contain a logarithm. The situation is analogous to the solution of a Cauchy-Euler equation when the roots of the auxiliary equation are equal.

CASE III: If r_1 and r_2 are equal, then there always exist two linearly independent solutions of equation (1) of the form

$$y_1(x) = \sum_{n=0}^{\infty} c_n x^{n+r_1}, \qquad c_0 \neq 0, \tag{21}$$

$$y_2(x) = y_1(x) \ln x + \sum_{n=1}^{\infty} b_n x^{n+r_1}. \tag{22}$$

FINDING A SECOND SOLUTION When the difference $r_1 - r_2$ is a positive integer (Case II), we *may* or *may not* be able to find two solutions having the form $y = \sum_{n=0}^{\infty} c_n x^{n+r}$. This is something that we do not know in advance but is determined after we have found the indicial roots and have carefully examined the recurrence relation that defines the coefficients c_n. We just may be lucky enough to find two solutions that involve only powers of x, that is, $y_1(x) = \sum_{n=0}^{\infty} c_n x^{n+r_1}$ (equation (19)) and $y_2(x) = \sum_{n=0}^{\infty} b_n x^{n+r_2}$ (equation (20) with $C = 0$). See Problem 31 in Exercises 6.2. On the other hand, in Example 4 we see that the difference of the indicial roots is a positive integer ($r_1 - r_2 = 1$) and the method of Frobenius failed to give a second series solution. In this situation equation (20), with $C \neq 0$, indicates what the second solution looks like. Finally, when the difference $r_1 - r_2$ is a zero (Case III), the method of Frobenius fails to give a second series solution; the second solution (22) always contains a logarithm and can be shown to be equivalent to (20) with $C = 1$. One way to obtain the second solution with the logarithmic term is to use the fact that

$$y_2(x) = y_1(x) \int \frac{e^{-\int P(x)dx}}{y_1^2(x)} \, dx \qquad (23)$$

is also a solution of $y'' + P(x)y' + Q(x)y = 0$ whenever $y_1(x)$ is a known solution. We illustrate how to use (23) in the next example.

EXAMPLE 5 Example 4 Revisited Using a CAS

Find the general solution of $xy'' + y = 0$.

SOLUTION From the known solution given in Example 4,

$$y_1(x) = x - \frac{1}{2}x^2 + \frac{1}{12}x^3 - \frac{1}{144}x^4 + \cdots,$$

we can construct a second solution $y_2(x)$ using formula (23). Those with the time, energy, and patience can carry out the drudgery of squaring a series, long division, and integration of the quotient by hand. But all these operations can be done with relative ease with the help of a CAS. We give the results:

$$y_2(x) = y_1(x) \int \frac{e^{-\int 0 dx}}{[y_1(x)]^2} \, dx = y_1(x) \int \frac{dx}{\left[x - \dfrac{1}{2}x^2 + \dfrac{1}{12}x^3 - \dfrac{1}{144}x^4 + \cdots \right]^2}$$

$$= y_1(x) \int \frac{dx}{\left[x^2 - x^3 + \dfrac{5}{12}x^4 - \dfrac{7}{72}x^5 + \cdots \right]} \qquad \leftarrow \text{after squaring}$$

$$= y_1(x) \int \left[\frac{1}{x^2} + \frac{1}{x} + \frac{7}{12} + \frac{19}{72}x + \cdots \right] dx \qquad \leftarrow \text{after long division}$$

$$= y_1(x) \left[-\frac{1}{x} + \ln x + \frac{7}{12}x + \frac{19}{144}x^2 + \cdots \right] \qquad \leftarrow \text{after integrating}$$

$$= y_1(x) \ln x + y_1(x) \left[-\frac{1}{x} + \frac{7}{12}x + \frac{19}{144}x^2 + \cdots \right],$$

or $\quad y_2(x) = y_1(x) \ln x + \left[-1 - \frac{1}{2}x + \frac{1}{2}x^2 + \cdots \right]. \qquad \leftarrow \text{after multiplying out}$

On the interval $(0, \infty)$ the general solution is $y = C_1 y_1(x) + C_2 y_2(x)$. ∎

Note that the final form of y_2 in Example 5 matches (20) with $C = 1$; the series in the brackets corresponds to the summation in (20) with $r_2 = 0$.

REMARKS

(*i*) The three different forms of a linear second-order differential equation in (1), (2), and (3) were used to discuss various theoretical concepts. But on a practical level, when it comes to actually solving a differential equation using the method of Frobenius, it is advisable to work with the form of the DE given in (1).

(*ii*) When the difference of indicial roots $r_1 - r_2$ is a positive integer $(r_1 > r_2)$, it sometimes pays to iterate the recurrence relation using the smaller root r_2 first. See Problems 31 and 32 in Exercises 6.2.

(*iii*) Because an indicial root r is a solution of a quadratic equation, it could be complex. We shall not, however, investigate this case.

(*iv*) If $x = 0$ is an irregular singular point, then we might not be able to find *any* solution of the DE of form $y = \sum_{n=0}^{\infty} c_n x^{n+r}$.

EXERCISES 6.2

Answers to selected odd-numbered problems begin on page ANS-9.

In Problems 1–10 determine the singular points of the given differential equation. Classify each singular point as regular or irregular.

1. $x^3 y'' + 4x^2 y' + 3y = 0$

2. $x(x + 3)^2 y'' - y = 0$

3. $(x^2 - 9)^2 y'' + (x + 3)y' + 2y = 0$

4. $y'' - \dfrac{1}{x} y' + \dfrac{1}{(x - 1)^3} y = 0$

5. $(x^3 + 4x)y'' - 2xy' + 6y = 0$

6. $x^2(x - 5)^2 y'' + 4xy' + (x^2 - 25)y = 0$

7. $(x^2 + x - 6)y'' + (x + 3)y' + (x - 2)y = 0$

8. $x(x^2 + 1)^2 y'' + y = 0$

9. $x^3(x^2 - 25)(x - 2)^2 y'' + 3x(x - 2)y' + 7(x + 5)y = 0$

10. $(x^3 - 2x^2 + 3x)^2 y'' + x(x - 3)^2 y' - (x + 1)y = 0$

In Problems 11 and 12 put the given differential equation into form (3) for each regular singular point of the equation. Identify the functions $p(x)$ and $q(x)$.

11. $(x^2 - 1)y'' + 5(x + 1)y' + (x^2 - x)y = 0$

12. $xy'' + (x + 3)y' + 7x^2 y = 0$

In Problems 13 and 14, $x = 0$ is a regular singular point of the given differential equation. Use the general form of the indicial equation in (14) to find the indicial roots of the singularity. Without solving, discuss the number of series solutions you would expect to find using the method of Frobenius.

13. $x^2 y'' + \left(\frac{5}{3} x + x^2 \right) y' - \frac{1}{3} y = 0$

14. $xy'' + y' + 10y = 0$

In Problems 15–24, $x = 0$ is a regular singular point of the given differential equation. Show that the indicial roots of the singularity do not differ by an integer. Use the method of Frobenius to obtain two linearly independent series solutions about $x = 0$. Form the general solution on $(0, \infty)$.

15. $2xy'' - y' + 2y = 0$

16. $2xy'' + 5y' + xy = 0$

17. $4xy'' + \frac{1}{2} y' + y = 0$

18. $2x^2 y'' - xy' + (x^2 + 1)y = 0$

19. $3xy'' + (2 - x)y' - y = 0$

20. $x^2 y'' - \left(x - \frac{2}{9} \right) y = 0$

21. $2xy'' - (3 + 2x)y' + y = 0$

22. $x^2 y'' + xy' + \left(x^2 - \frac{4}{9} \right) y = 0$

23. $9x^2 y'' + 9x^2 y' + 2y = 0$

24. $2x^2 y'' + 3xy' + (2x - 1)y = 0$

In Problems 25–30, $x = 0$ is a regular singular point of the given differential equation. Show that the indicial roots of the singularity differ by an integer. Use the method of Frobenius to obtain at least one series solution about $x = 0$. Use (23) where necessary and a CAS, if instructed, to find a second solution. Form the general solution on $(0, \infty)$.

25. $xy'' + 2y' - xy = 0$

26. $x^2y'' + xy' + \left(x^2 - \frac{1}{4}\right)y = 0$

27. $xy'' - xy' + y = 0$ **28.** $y'' + \dfrac{3}{x}y' - 2y = 0$

29. $xy'' + (1 - x)y' - y = 0$ **30.** $xy'' + y' + y = 0$

In Problems 31 and 32, $x = 0$ is a regular singular point of the given differential equation. Show that the indicial roots of the singularity differ by an integer. Use the recurrence relation found by the method of Frobenius first with the larger root r_1. How many solutions did you find? Next use the recurrence relation with the smaller root r_2. How many solutions did you find?

31. $xy'' + (x - 6)y' - 3y = 0$

32. $x(x - 1)y'' + 3y' - 2y = 0$

33. (a) The differential equation $x^4y'' + \lambda y = 0$ has an irregular singular point at $x = 0$. Show that the substitution $t = 1/x$ yields the DE

$$\frac{d^2y}{dt^2} + \frac{2}{t}\frac{dy}{dt} + \lambda y = 0,$$

which now has a regular singular point at $t = 0$.

(b) Use the method of this section to find two series solutions of the second equation in part (a) about the regular singular point $t = 0$.

(c) Express each series solution of the original equation in terms of elementary functions.

Mathematical Model

34. Buckling of a Tapered Column In Example 3 of Section 5.2 we saw that when a constant vertical compressive force or load P was applied to a thin column of uniform cross section, the deflection $y(x)$ was a solution of the boundary-value problem

$$EI\frac{d^2y}{dx^2} + Py = 0, \quad y(0) = 0, \quad y(L) = 0. \quad (24)$$

The assumption here is that the column is hinged at both ends. The column will buckle or deflect only when the compressive force is a critical load P_n.

(a) In this problem let us assume that the column is of length L, is hinged at both ends, has circular cross sections, and is tapered as shown in Figure 6.2.1(a). If the column, a truncated cone, has a linear taper

$y = cx$ as shown in cross section in Figure 6.2.1(b), the moment of inertia of a cross section with respect to an axis perpendicular to the xy-plane is $I = \frac{1}{4}\pi r^4$, where $r = y$ and $y = cx$. Hence we can write $I(x) = I_0(x/b)^4$, where $I_0 = I(b) = \frac{1}{4}\pi(cb)^4$. Substituting $I(x)$ into the differential equation in (24), we see that the deflection in this case is determined from the BVP

$$x^4\frac{d^2y}{dx^2} + \lambda y = 0, \quad y(a) = 0, \quad y(b) = 0,$$

where $\lambda = Pb^4/EI_0$. Use the results of Problem 33 to find the critical loads P_n for the tapered column. Use an appropriate identity to express the buckling modes $y_n(x)$ as a single function.

(b) Use a CAS to plot the graph of the first buckling mode $y_1(x)$ corresponding to the Euler load P_1 when $b = 11$ and $a = 1$.

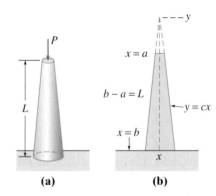

FIGURE 6.2.1 Tapered column in Problem 34

Discussion Problems

35. Discuss how you would define a regular singular point for the linear third-order differential equation

$$a_3(x)y''' + a_2(x)y'' + a_1(x)y' + a_0(x)y = 0.$$

36. Each of the differential equations

$$x^3y'' + y = 0 \quad \text{and} \quad x^2y'' + (3x - 1)y' + y = 0$$

has an irregular singular point at $x = 0$. Determine whether the method of Frobenius yields a series solution of each differential equation about $x = 0$. Discuss and explain your findings.

37. We have seen that $x = 0$ is a regular singular point of any Cauchy-Euler equation $ax^2y'' + bxy' + cy = 0$. Are the indicial equation (14) for a Cauchy-Euler equation and its auxiliary equation related? Discuss.

6.3 SPECIAL FUNCTIONS

REVIEW MATERIAL

- Sections 6.1 and 6.2

INTRODUCTION   The two differential equations

$$x^2 y'' + xy' + (x^2 - \nu^2)y = 0 \tag{1}$$

$$(1 - x^2)y'' - 2xy' + n(n + 1)y = 0 \tag{2}$$

occur in advanced studies in applied mathematics, physics, and engineering. They are called **Bessel's equation of order ν** and **Legendre's equation of order n**, respectively. When we solve (1) we shall assume that $\nu \geq 0$, whereas in (2) we shall consider only the case when n is a nonnegative integer.

6.3.1   BESSEL'S EQUATION

THE SOLUTION   Because $x = 0$ is a regular singular point of Bessel's equation, we know that there exists at least one solution of the form $y = \sum_{n=0}^{\infty} c_n x^{n+r}$. Substituting the last expression into (1) gives

$$x^2 y'' + xy' + (x^2 - \nu^2)y = \sum_{n=0}^{\infty} c_n(n + r)(n + r - 1)x^{n+r} + \sum_{n=0}^{\infty} c_n(n + r)x^{n+r} + \sum_{n=0}^{\infty} c_n x^{n+r+2} - \nu^2 \sum_{n=0}^{\infty} c_n x^{n+r}$$

$$= c_0(r^2 - r + r - \nu^2)x^r + x^r \sum_{n=1}^{\infty} c_n[(n + r)(n + r - 1) + (n + r) - \nu^2]x^n + x^r \sum_{n=0}^{\infty} c_n x^{n+2}$$

$$= c_0(r^2 - \nu^2)x^r + x^r \sum_{n=1}^{\infty} c_n[(n + r)^2 - \nu^2]x^n + x^r \sum_{n=0}^{\infty} c_n x^{n+2}. \tag{3}$$

From (3) we see that the indicial equation is $r^2 - \nu^2 = 0$, so the indicial roots are $r_1 = \nu$ and $r_2 = -\nu$. When $r_1 = \nu$, (3) becomes

$$x^\nu \sum_{n=1}^{\infty} c_n n(n + 2\nu)x^n + x^\nu \sum_{n=0}^{\infty} c_n x^{n+2}$$

$$= x^\nu \left[(1 + 2\nu)c_1 x + \underbrace{\sum_{n=2}^{\infty} c_n n(n + 2\nu)x^n}_{k = n - 2} + \underbrace{\sum_{n=0}^{\infty} c_n x^{n+2}}_{k = n} \right]$$

$$= x^\nu \left[(1 + 2\nu)c_1 x + \sum_{k=0}^{\infty} [(k + 2)(k + 2 + 2\nu)c_{k+2} + c_k]x^{k+2} \right] = 0.$$

Therefore by the usual argument we can write $(1 + 2\nu)c_1 = 0$ and

$$(k + 2)(k + 2 + 2\nu)c_{k+2} + c_k = 0$$

or

$$c_{k+2} = \frac{-c_k}{(k + 2)(k + 2 + 2\nu)}, \qquad k = 0, 1, 2, \ldots. \tag{4}$$

The choice $c_1 = 0$ in (4) implies that $c_3 = c_5 = c_7 = \cdots = 0$, so for $k = 0, 2, 4, \ldots$ we find, after letting $k + 2 = 2n$, $n = 1, 2, 3, \ldots$, that

$$c_{2n} = -\frac{c_{2n-2}}{2^2 n(n + \nu)}. \tag{5}$$

Thus $\quad c_2 = -\dfrac{c_0}{2^2 \cdot 1 \cdot (1 + \nu)}$

$$c_4 = -\frac{c_2}{2^2 \cdot 2(2 + \nu)} = \frac{c_0}{2^4 \cdot 1 \cdot 2(1 + \nu)(2 + \nu)}$$

$$c_6 = -\frac{c_4}{2^2 \cdot 3(3 + \nu)} = -\frac{c_0}{2^6 \cdot 1 \cdot 2 \cdot 3(1 + \nu)(2 + \nu)(3 + \nu)}$$

$$\vdots$$

$$c_{2n} = \frac{(-1)^n c_0}{2^{2n} n! (1 + \nu)(2 + \nu) \cdots (n + \nu)}, \qquad n = 1, 2, 3, \ldots. \qquad (6)$$

It is standard practice to choose c_0 to be a specific value, namely,

$$c_0 = \frac{1}{2^\nu \Gamma(1 + \nu)},$$

where $\Gamma(1 + \nu)$ is the gamma function. See Appendix I. Since this latter function possesses the convenient property $\Gamma(1 + \alpha) = \alpha \Gamma(\alpha)$, we can reduce the indicated product in the denominator of (6) to one term. For example,

$$\Gamma(1 + \nu + 1) = (1 + \nu)\Gamma(1 + \nu)$$

$$\Gamma(1 + \nu + 2) = (2 + \nu)\Gamma(2 + \nu) = (2 + \nu)(1 + \nu)\Gamma(1 + \nu).$$

Hence we can write (6) as

$$c_{2n} = \frac{(-1)^n}{2^{2n+\nu} n! (1 + \nu)(2 + \nu) \cdots (n + \nu)\Gamma(1 + \nu)} = \frac{(-1)^n}{2^{2n+\nu} n! \Gamma(1 + \nu + n)}$$

for $n = 0, 1, 2, \ldots$.

BESSEL FUNCTIONS OF THE FIRST KIND Using the coefficients c_{2n} just obtained and $r = \nu$, a series solution of (1) is $y = \sum_{n=0}^{\infty} c_{2n} x^{2n+\nu}$. This solution is usually denoted by $J_\nu(x)$:

$$J_\nu(x) = \sum_{n=0}^{\infty} \frac{(-1)^n}{n! \Gamma(1 + \nu + n)} \left(\frac{x}{2}\right)^{2n+\nu}. \qquad (7)$$

If $\nu \geq 0$, the series converges at least on the interval $[0, \infty)$. Also, for the second exponent $r_2 = -\nu$ we obtain, in exactly the same manner,

$$J_{-\nu}(x) = \sum_{n=0}^{\infty} \frac{(-1)^n}{n! \Gamma(1 - \nu + n)} \left(\frac{x}{2}\right)^{2n-\nu}. \qquad (8)$$

The functions $J_\nu(x)$ and $J_{-\nu}(x)$ are called **Bessel functions of the first kind** of order ν and $-\nu$, respectively. Depending on the value of ν, (8) may contain negative powers of x and hence converges on $(0, \infty)$.[*]

Now some care must be taken in writing the general solution of (1). When $\nu = 0$, it is apparent that (7) and (8) are the same. If $\nu > 0$ and $r_1 - r_2 = \nu - (-\nu) = 2\nu$ is not a positive integer, it follows from Case I of Section 6.2 that $J_\nu(x)$ and $J_{-\nu}(x)$ are linearly independent solutions of (1) on $(0, \infty)$, and so the general solution on the interval is $y = c_1 J_\nu(x) + c_2 J_{-\nu}(x)$. But we also know from Case II of Section 6.2 that when $r_1 - r_2 = 2\nu$ is a positive integer, a second series solution of (1) *may* exist. In this second case we distinguish two possibilities. When $\nu = m = $ positive integer, $J_{-m}(x)$ defined by (8) and $J_m(x)$ are not linearly independent solutions. It can be shown that J_{-m} is a constant multiple of J_m (see Property (*i*) on page 245). In addition, $r_1 - r_2 = 2\nu$ can be a positive integer when ν is half an odd positive integer. It can be shown in this

---

[*]When we replace x by $|x|$, the series given in (7) and (8) converge for $0 < |x| < \infty$.

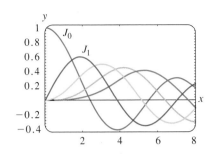

FIGURE 6.3.1 Bessel functions of the first kind for $n = 0, 1, 2, 3, 4$

latter event that $J_\nu(x)$ and $J_{-\nu}(x)$ are linearly independent. In other words, the general solution of (1) on $(0, \infty)$ is

$$y = c_1 J_\nu(x) + c_2 J_{-\nu}(x), \qquad \nu \neq \text{integer.} \tag{9}$$

The graphs of $y = J_0(x)$ and $y = J_1(x)$ are given in Figure 6.3.1.

EXAMPLE 1 Bessel's Equation of Order $\frac{1}{2}$

By identifying $\nu^2 = \frac{1}{4}$ and $\nu = \frac{1}{2}$, we can see from (9) that the general solution of the equation $x^2 y'' + xy' + \left(x^2 - \frac{1}{4}\right)y = 0$ on $(0, \infty)$ is $y = c_1 J_{1/2}(x) + c_2 J_{-1/2}(x)$. ∎

BESSEL FUNCTIONS OF THE SECOND KIND If $\nu \neq$ integer, the function defined by the linear combination

$$Y_\nu(x) = \frac{\cos \nu \pi J_\nu(x) - J_{-\nu}(x)}{\sin \nu \pi} \tag{10}$$

and the function $J_\nu(x)$ are linearly independent solutions of (1). Thus another form of the general solution of (1) is $y = c_1 J_\nu(x) + c_2 Y_\nu(x)$, provided that $\nu \neq$ integer. As $\nu \to m$, m an integer, (10) has the indeterminate form $0/0$. However, it can be shown by L'Hôpital's Rule that $\lim_{\nu \to m} Y_\nu(x)$ exists. Moreover, the function

$$Y_m(x) = \lim_{\nu \to m} Y_\nu(x)$$

and $J_m(x)$ are linearly independent solutions of $x^2 y'' + xy' + (x^2 - m^2)y = 0$. Hence for *any* value of ν the general solution of (1) on $(0, \infty)$ can be written as

$$y = c_1 J_\nu(x) + c_2 Y_\nu(x). \tag{11}$$

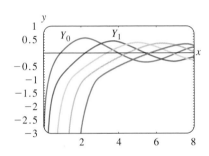

FIGURE 6.3.2 Bessel functions of the second kind for $n = 0, 1, 2, 3, 4$

$Y_\nu(x)$ is called the **Bessel function of the second kind** of order ν. Figure 6.3.2 shows the graphs of $Y_0(x)$ and $Y_1(x)$.

EXAMPLE 2 Bessel's Equation of Order 3

By identifying $\nu^2 = 9$ and $\nu = 3$, we see from (11) that the general solution of the equation $x^2 y'' + xy' + (x^2 - 9)y = 0$ on $(0, \infty)$ is $y = c_1 J_3(x) + c_2 Y_3(x)$. ∎

DEs SOLVABLE IN TERMS OF BESSEL FUNCTIONS Sometimes it is possible to transform a differential equation into equation (1) by means of a change of variable. We can then express the solution of the original equation in terms of Bessel functions. For example, if we let $t = \alpha x$, $\alpha > 0$, in

$$x^2 y'' + xy' + (\alpha^2 x^2 - \nu^2)y = 0, \tag{12}$$

then by the Chain Rule,

$$\frac{dy}{dx} = \frac{dy}{dt}\frac{dt}{dx} = \alpha \frac{dy}{dt} \qquad \text{and} \qquad \frac{d^2 y}{dx^2} = \frac{d}{dt}\left(\frac{dy}{dx}\right)\frac{dt}{dx} = \alpha^2 \frac{d^2 y}{dt^2}.$$

Accordingly, (12) becomes

$$\left(\frac{t}{\alpha}\right)^2 \alpha^2 \frac{d^2 y}{dt^2} + \left(\frac{t}{\alpha}\right)\alpha \frac{dy}{dt} + (t^2 - \nu^2)y = 0 \qquad \text{or} \qquad t^2 \frac{d^2 y}{dt^2} + t\frac{dy}{dt} + (t^2 - \nu^2)y = 0.$$

The last equation is Bessel's equation of order ν with solution $y = c_1 J_\nu(t) + c_2 Y_\nu(t)$. By resubstituting $t = \alpha x$ in the last expression, we find that the general solution of (12) is

$$y = c_1 J_\nu(\alpha x) + c_2 Y_\nu(\alpha x). \tag{13}$$

Equation (12), called the **parametric Bessel equation of order ν,** and its general solution (13) are very important in the study of certain boundary-value problems involving partial differential equations that are expressed in cylindrical coordinates.

Another equation that bears a resemblance to (1) is the **modified Bessel equation of order ν,**

$$x^2 y'' + xy' - (x^2 + \nu^2)y = 0. \tag{14}$$

This DE can be solved in the manner just illustrated for (12). This time if we let $t = ix$, where $i^2 = -1$, then (14) becomes

$$t^2 \frac{d^2 y}{dt^2} + t \frac{dy}{dt} + (t^2 - \nu^2)y = 0.$$

Because solutions of the last DE are $J_\nu(t)$ and $Y_\nu(t)$, *complex-valued* solutions of (14) are $J_\nu(ix)$ and $Y_\nu(ix)$. A real-valued solution, called the **modified Bessel function of the first kind** of order ν, is defined in terms of $J_\nu(ix)$:

$$I_\nu(x) = i^{-\nu} J_\nu(ix). \tag{15}$$

See Problem 21 in Exercises 6.3. Analogous to (10), the **modified Bessel function of the second kind** of order $\nu \neq$ integer is defined to be

$$K_\nu(x) = \frac{\pi}{2} \frac{I_{-\nu}(x) - I_\nu(x)}{\sin \nu \pi}, \tag{16}$$

and for integer $\nu = n$,

$$K_n(x) = \lim_{\nu \to n} K_\nu(x).$$

Because I_ν and K_ν are linearly independent on the interval $(0, \infty)$ for any value of v, the general solution of (14) is

$$y = c_1 I_\nu(x) + c_2 K_\nu(x). \tag{17}$$

Yet another equation, important because many DEs fit into its form by appropriate choices of the parameters, is

$$y'' + \frac{1 - 2a}{x} y' + \left(b^2 c^2 x^{2c-2} + \frac{a^2 - p^2 c^2}{x^2} \right) y = 0, \qquad p \geq 0. \tag{18}$$

Although we shall not supply the details, the general solution of (18),

$$y = x^a \left[c_1 J_p(bx^c) + c_2 Y_p(bx^c) \right], \tag{19}$$

can be found by means of a change in both the independent and the dependent variables: $z = bx^c$, $y(x) = \left(\dfrac{z}{b} \right)^{a/c} w(z)$. If p is not an integer, then Y_p in (19) can be replaced by J_{-p}.

EXAMPLE 3 Using (18)

Find the general solution of $xy'' + 3y' + 9y = 0$ on $(0, \infty)$.

SOLUTION By writing the given DE as

$$y'' + \frac{3}{x} y' + \frac{9}{x} y = 0,$$

we can make the following identifications with (18):

$$1 - 2a = 3, \qquad b^2 c^2 = 9, \qquad 2c - 2 = -1, \qquad \text{and} \qquad a^2 - p^2 c^2 = 0.$$

The first and third equations imply that $a = -1$ and $c = \frac{1}{2}$. With these values the second and fourth equations are satisfied by taking $b = 6$ and $p = 2$. From (19)

we find that the general solution of the given DE on the interval $(0, \infty)$ is
$y = x^{-1}[c_1 J_2(6x^{1/2}) + c_2 Y_2(6x^{1/2})]$. ∎

EXAMPLE 4   The Aging Spring Revisited

Recall that in Section 5.1 we saw that one mathematical model for the free undamped motion of a mass on an aging spring is given by $mx'' + ke^{-\alpha t}x = 0$, $\alpha > 0$. We are now in a position to find the general solution of the equation. It is left as a problem to show that the change of variables $s = \dfrac{2}{\alpha}\sqrt{\dfrac{k}{m}}\, e^{-\alpha t/2}$ transforms the differential equation of the aging spring into

$$s^2 \frac{d^2x}{ds^2} + s \frac{dx}{ds} + s^2 x = 0.$$

The last equation is recognized as (1) with $\nu = 0$ and where the symbols x and s play the roles of y and x, respectively. The general solution of the new equation is $x = c_1 J_0(s) + c_2 Y_0(s)$. If we resubstitute s, then the general solution of $mx'' + ke^{-\alpha t}x = 0$ is seen to be

$$x(t) = c_1 J_0\!\left(\frac{2}{\alpha}\sqrt{\frac{k}{m}}\, e^{-\alpha t/2}\right) + c_2 Y_0\!\left(\frac{2}{\alpha}\sqrt{\frac{k}{m}}\, e^{-\alpha t/2}\right).$$

See Problems 33 and 39 in Exercises 6.3. ∎

The other model that was discussed in Section 5.1 of a spring whose characteristics change with time was $mx'' + ktx = 0$. By dividing through by m, we see that the equation $x'' + \dfrac{k}{m}tx = 0$ is Airy's equation $y'' + \alpha^2 xy = 0$. See Example 3 in Section 6.1. The general solution of Airy's differential equation can also be written in terms of Bessel functions. See Problems 34, 35, and 40 in Exercises 6.3.

PROPERTIES   We list below a few of the more useful properties of Bessel functions of order m, $m = 0, 1, 2, \ldots$:

$$(i)\ \ J_{-m}(x) = (-1)^m J_m(x), \qquad (ii)\ \ J_m(-x) = (-1)^m J_m(x),$$

$$(iii)\ \ J_m(0) = \begin{cases} 0, & m > 0 \\ 1, & m = 0, \end{cases} \qquad (iv)\ \ \lim_{x\to 0^+} Y_m(x) = -\infty.$$

Note that Property (ii) indicates that $J_m(x)$ is an even function if m is an even integer and an odd function if m is an odd integer. The graphs of $Y_0(x)$ and $Y_1(x)$ in Figure 6.3.2 illustrate Property (iv), namely, $Y_m(x)$ is unbounded at the origin. This last fact is not obvious from (10). The solutions of the Bessel equation of order 0 can be obtained by using the solutions $y_1(x)$ in (21) and $y_2(x)$ in (22) of Section 6.2. It can be shown that (21) of Section 6.2 is $y_1(x) = J_0(x)$, whereas (22) of that section is

$$y_2(x) = J_0(x)\ln x - \sum_{k=1}^{\infty} \frac{(-1)^k}{(k!)^2}\left(1 + \frac{1}{2} + \cdots + \frac{1}{k}\right)\!\left(\frac{x}{2}\right)^{2k}.$$

The Bessel function of the second kind of order 0, $Y_0(x)$, is then defined to be the linear combination $Y_0(x) = \dfrac{2}{\pi}(\gamma - \ln 2)y_1(x) + \dfrac{2}{\pi}y_2(x)$ for $x > 0$. That is,

$$Y_0(x) = \frac{2}{\pi}J_0(x)\left[\gamma + \ln\frac{x}{2}\right] - \frac{2}{\pi}\sum_{k=1}^{\infty} \frac{(-1)^k}{(k!)^2}\left(1 + \frac{1}{2} + \cdots + \frac{1}{k}\right)\!\left(\frac{x}{2}\right)^{2k},$$

where $\gamma = 0.57721566\ldots$ is **Euler's constant.** Because of the presence of the logarithmic term, it is apparent that $Y_0(x)$ is discontinuous at $x = 0$.

NUMERICAL VALUES The first five nonnegative zeros of $J_0(x)$, $J_1(x)$, $Y_0(x)$, and $Y_1(x)$ are given in Table 6.1. Some additional function values of these four functions are given in Table 6.2.

TABLE 6.1 Zeros of J_0, J_1, Y_0, and Y_1

$J_0(x)$	$J_1(x)$	$Y_0(x)$	$Y_1(x)$
2.4048	0.0000	0.8936	2.1971
5.5201	3.8317	3.9577	5.4297
8.6537	7.0156	7.0861	8.5960
11.7915	10.1735	10.2223	11.7492
14.9309	13.3237	13.3611	14.8974

TABLE 6.2 Numerical Values of J_0, J_1, Y_0, and Y_1

x	$J_0(x)$	$J_1(x)$	$Y_0(x)$	$Y_1(x)$
0	1.0000	0.0000	—	—
1	0.7652	0.4401	0.0883	−0.7812
2	0.2239	0.5767	0.5104	−0.1070
3	−0.2601	0.3391	0.3769	0.3247
4	−0.3971	−0.0660	−0.0169	0.3979
5	−0.1776	−0.3276	−0.3085	0.1479
6	0.1506	−0.2767	−0.2882	−0.1750
7	0.3001	−0.0047	−0.0259	−0.3027
8	0.1717	0.2346	0.2235	−0.1581
9	−0.0903	0.2453	0.2499	0.1043
10	−0.2459	0.0435	0.0557	0.2490
11	−0.1712	−0.1768	−0.1688	0.1637
12	0.0477	−0.2234	−0.2252	−0.0571
13	0.2069	−0.0703	−0.0782	−0.2101
14	0.1711	0.1334	0.1272	−0.1666
15	−0.0142	0.2051	0.2055	0.0211

DIFFERENTIAL RECURRENCE RELATION Recurrence formulas that relate Bessel functions of different orders are important in theory and in applications. In the next example we derive a **differential recurrence relation.**

EXAMPLE 5   **Derivation Using the Series Definition**

Derive the formula $xJ_\nu'(x) = \nu J_\nu(x) - xJ_{\nu+1}(x)$.

SOLUTION It follows from (7) that

$$xJ_\nu'(x) = \sum_{n=0}^{\infty} \frac{(-1)^n(2n + \nu)}{n!\,\Gamma(1 + \nu + n)} \left(\frac{x}{2}\right)^{2n+\nu}$$

$$= \nu \sum_{n=0}^{\infty} \frac{(-1)^n}{n!\,\Gamma(1 + \nu + n)} \left(\frac{x}{2}\right)^{2n+\nu} + 2 \sum_{n=0}^{\infty} \frac{(-1)^n n}{n!\,\Gamma(1 + \nu + n)} \left(\frac{x}{2}\right)^{2n+\nu}$$

$$= \nu J_\nu(x) + x \underbrace{\sum_{n=1}^{\infty} \frac{(-1)^n}{(n - 1)!\,\Gamma(1 + \nu + n)} \left(\frac{x}{2}\right)^{2n+\nu-1}}_{k = n - 1}$$

$$= \nu J_\nu(x) - x \sum_{k=0}^{\infty} \frac{(-1)^k}{k!\,\Gamma(2 + \nu + k)} \left(\frac{x}{2}\right)^{2k+\nu+1} = \nu J_\nu(x) - xJ_{\nu+1}(x). \qquad \blacksquare$$

The result in Example 5 can be written in an alternative form. Dividing $xJ_\nu'(x) - \nu J_\nu(x) = -xJ_{\nu+1}(x)$ by x gives

$$J_\nu'(x) - \frac{\nu}{x} J_\nu(x) = -J_{\nu+1}(x).$$

This last expression is recognized as a linear first-order differential equation in $J_\nu(x)$. Multiplying both sides of the equality by the integrating factor $x^{-\nu}$ then yields

$$\frac{d}{dx}[x^{-\nu}J_\nu(x)] = -x^{-\nu}J_{\nu+1}(x). \tag{20}$$

It can be shown in a similar manner that

$$\frac{d}{dx}[x^\nu J_\nu(x)] = x^\nu J_{\nu-1}(x). \tag{21}$$

See Problem 27 in Exercises 6.3. The differential recurrence relations (20) and (21) are also valid for the Bessel function of the second kind $Y_\nu(x)$. Observe that when $\nu = 0$, it follows from (20) that

$$J_0'(x) = -J_1(x) \qquad \text{and} \qquad Y_0'(x) = -Y_1(x). \tag{22}$$

An application of these results is given in Problem 39 of Exercises 6.3.

SPHERICAL BESSEL FUNCTIONS When the order ν is half an odd integer, that is, $\pm\frac{1}{2}, \pm\frac{3}{2}, \pm\frac{5}{2}, \ldots$, the Bessel functions of the first kind $J_\nu(x)$ can be expressed in terms of the elementary functions $\sin x$, $\cos x$, and powers of x. Such Bessel functions are called **spherical Bessel functions.** Let's consider the case when $\nu = \frac{1}{2}$. From (7),

$$J_{1/2}(x) = \sum_{n=0}^{\infty} \frac{(-1)^n}{n!\,\Gamma(1 + \frac{1}{2} + n)} \left(\frac{x}{2}\right)^{2n+1/2}.$$

In view of the property $\Gamma(1 + \alpha) = \alpha\Gamma(\alpha)$ and the fact that $\Gamma(\frac{1}{2}) = \sqrt{\pi}$ the values of $\Gamma(1 + \frac{1}{2} + n)$ for $n = 0$, $n = 1$, $n = 2$, and $n = 3$ are, respectively,

$$\Gamma\left(\tfrac{3}{2}\right) = \Gamma\left(1 + \tfrac{1}{2}\right) = \tfrac{1}{2}\Gamma\left(\tfrac{1}{2}\right) = \tfrac{1}{2}\sqrt{\pi}$$

$$\Gamma\left(\tfrac{5}{2}\right) = \Gamma\left(1 + \tfrac{3}{2}\right) = \tfrac{3}{2}\Gamma\left(\tfrac{3}{2}\right) = \frac{3}{2^2}\sqrt{\pi}$$

$$\Gamma\left(\tfrac{7}{2}\right) = \Gamma\left(1 + \tfrac{5}{2}\right) = \tfrac{5}{2}\Gamma\left(\tfrac{5}{2}\right) = \frac{5 \cdot 3}{2^3}\sqrt{\pi} = \frac{5 \cdot 4 \cdot 3 \cdot 2 \cdot 1}{2^3 4 \cdot 2}\sqrt{\pi} = \frac{5!}{2^5 2!}\sqrt{\pi}$$

$$\Gamma\left(\tfrac{9}{2}\right) = \Gamma\left(1 + \tfrac{7}{2}\right) = \tfrac{7}{2}\Gamma\left(\tfrac{7}{2}\right) = \frac{7 \cdot 5}{2^6 \cdot 2!}\sqrt{\pi} = \frac{7 \cdot 6 \cdot 5!}{2^6 \cdot 6 \cdot 2!}\sqrt{\pi} = \frac{7!}{2^7 3!}\sqrt{\pi}.$$

In general,

$$\Gamma\left(1 + \frac{1}{2} + n\right) = \frac{(2n + 1)!}{2^{2n+1}n!}\sqrt{\pi}.$$

Hence
$$J_{1/2}(x) = \sum_{n=0}^{\infty} \frac{(-1)^n}{n!\dfrac{(2n + 1)!}{2^{2n+1}n!}\sqrt{\pi}} \left(\frac{x}{2}\right)^{2n+1/2} = \sqrt{\frac{2}{\pi x}} \sum_{n=0}^{\infty} \frac{(-1)^n}{(2n + 1)!}x^{2n+1}.$$

Since the infinite series in the last line is the Maclaurin series for $\sin x$, we have shown that

$$J_{1/2}(x) = \sqrt{\frac{2}{\pi x}} \sin x. \tag{23}$$

It is left as an exercise to show that

$$J_{-1/2}(x) = \sqrt{\frac{2}{\pi x}} \cos x. \tag{24}$$

See Problems 31 and 32 in Exercises 6.3.

6.3.2 LEGENDRE'S EQUATION

THE SOLUTION Since $x = 0$ is an ordinary point of Legendre's equation (2), we substitute the series $y = \sum_{k=0}^{\infty} c_k x^k$, shift summation indices, and combine series to get

$$(1 - x^2)y'' - 2xy' + n(n + 1)y = [n(n + 1)c_0 + 2c_2] + [(n - 1)(n + 2)c_1 + 6c_3]x$$

$$+ \sum_{j=2}^{\infty} [(j + 2)(j + 1)c_{j+2} + (n - j)(n + j + 1)c_j]x^j = 0$$

which implies that

$$n(n + 1)c_0 + 2c_2 = 0$$

$$(n - 1)(n + 2)c_1 + 6c_3 = 0$$

$$(j + 2)(j + 1)c_{j+2} + (n - j)(n + j + 1)c_j = 0$$

or

$$c_2 = -\frac{n(n + 1)}{2!}c_0$$

$$c_3 = -\frac{(n - 1)(n + 2)}{3!}c_1$$

$$c_{j+2} = -\frac{(n - j)(n + j + 1)}{(j + 2)(j + 1)}c_j, \qquad j = 2, 3, 4, \ldots. \tag{25}$$

If we let j take on the values $2, 3, 4, \ldots$, the recurrence relation (25) yields

$$c_4 = -\frac{(n - 2)(n + 3)}{4 \cdot 3}c_2 = \frac{(n - 2)n(n + 1)(n + 3)}{4!}c_0$$

$$c_5 = -\frac{(n - 3)(n + 4)}{5 \cdot 4}c_3 = \frac{(n - 3)(n - 1)(n + 2)(n + 4)}{5!}c_1$$

$$c_6 = -\frac{(n - 4)(n + 5)}{6 \cdot 5}c_4 = -\frac{(n - 4)(n - 2)n(n + 1)(n + 3)(n + 5)}{6!}c_0$$

$$c_7 = -\frac{(n - 5)(n + 6)}{7 \cdot 6}c_5 = -\frac{(n - 5)(n - 3)(n - 1)(n + 2)(n + 4)(n + 6)}{7!}c_1$$

and so on. Thus for at least $|x| < 1$ we obtain two linearly independent power series solutions:

$$y_1(x) = c_0\left[1 - \frac{n(n + 1)}{2!}x^2 + \frac{(n - 2)n(n + 1)(n + 3)}{4!}x^4\right.$$

$$\left. - \frac{(n - 4)(n - 2)n(n + 1)(n + 3)(n + 5)}{6!}x^6 + \cdots\right]$$

$$y_2(x) = c_1\left[x - \frac{(n - 1)(n + 2)}{3!}x^3 + \frac{(n - 3)(n - 1)(n + 2)(n + 4)}{5!}x^5\right.$$

$$\left. - \frac{(n - 5)(n - 3)(n - 1)(n + 2)(n + 4)(n + 6)}{7!}x^7 + \cdots\right].$$

$$\tag{26}$$

Notice that if n is an even integer, the first series terminates, whereas $y_2(x)$ is an infinite series. For example, if $n = 4$, then

$$y_1(x) = c_0\left[1 - \frac{4 \cdot 5}{2!}x^2 + \frac{2 \cdot 4 \cdot 5 \cdot 7}{4!}x^4\right] = c_0\left[1 - 10x^2 + \frac{35}{3}x^4\right].$$

Similarly, when n is an odd integer, the series for $y_2(x)$ terminates with x^n; that is, *when n is a nonnegative integer, we obtain an nth-degree polynomial solution* of Legendre's equation.

Because we know that a constant multiple of a solution of Legendre's equation is also a solution, it is traditional to choose specific values for c_0 or c_1, depending on whether n is an even or odd positive integer, respectively. For $n = 0$ we choose $c_0 = 1$, and for $n = 2, 4, 6, \ldots$

$$c_0 = (-1)^{n/2} \frac{1 \cdot 3 \cdots (n-1)}{2 \cdot 4 \cdots n},$$

whereas for $n = 1$ we choose $c_1 = 1$, and for $n = 3, 5, 7, \ldots$

$$c_1 = (-1)^{(n-1)/2} \frac{1 \cdot 3 \cdots n}{2 \cdot 4 \cdots (n-1)}.$$

For example, when $n = 4$, we have

$$y_1(x) = (-1)^{4/2} \frac{1 \cdot 3}{2 \cdot 4} \left[1 - 10x^2 + \frac{35}{3} x^4 \right] = \frac{1}{8} (35x^4 - 30x^2 + 3).$$

LEGENDRE POLYNOMIALS These specific nth-degree polynomial solutions are called **Legendre polynomials** and are denoted by $P_n(x)$. From the series for $y_1(x)$ and $y_2(x)$ and from the above choices of c_0 and c_1 we find that the first several Legendre polynomials are

$$P_0(x) = 1, \qquad\qquad P_1(x) = x,$$

$$P_2(x) = \frac{1}{2}(3x^2 - 1), \qquad P_3(x) = \frac{1}{2}(5x^3 - 3x), \qquad (27)$$

$$P_4(x) = \frac{1}{8}(35x^4 - 30x^2 + 3), \qquad P_5(x) = \frac{1}{8}(63x^5 - 70x^3 + 15x).$$

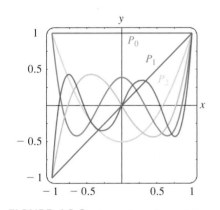

FIGURE 6.3.3 Legendre polynomials for $n = 0, 1, 2, 3, 4, 5$

Remember, $P_0(x)$, $P_1(x)$, $P_2(x)$, $P_3(x)$, $\ldots$ are, in turn, particular solutions of the differential equations

$$
\begin{array}{ll}
n = 0: & (1 - x^2)y'' - 2xy' = 0, \\
n = 1: & (1 - x^2)y'' - 2xy' + 2y = 0, \\
n = 2: & (1 - x^2)y'' - 2xy' + 6y = 0, \\
n = 3: & (1 - x^2)y'' - 2xy' + 12y = 0, \\
\vdots & \vdots
\end{array}
\qquad (28)
$$

The graphs, on the interval $[-1, 1]$, of the six Legendre polynomials in (27) are given in Figure 6.3.3.

PROPERTIES You are encouraged to verify the following properties using the Legendre polynomials in (27).

$$(i)\ \ P_n(-x) = (-1)^n P_n(x)$$

$$(ii)\ \ P_n(1) = 1 \qquad\qquad (iii)\ \ P_n(-1) = (-1)^n$$

$$(iv)\ \ P_n(0) = 0, \quad n \text{ odd} \qquad (v)\ \ P_n'(0) = 0, \quad n \text{ even}$$

Property (i) indicates, as is apparent in Figure 6.3.3, that $P_n(x)$ is an even or odd function according to whether n is even or odd.

RECURRENCE RELATION Recurrence relations that relate Legendre polynomials of different degrees are also important in some aspects of their applications. We state, without proof, the three-term recurrence relation

$$(k + 1)P_{k+1}(x) - (2k + 1)xP_k(x) + kP_{k-1}(x) = 0, \qquad (29)$$

which is valid for $k = 1, 2, 3, \ldots$. In (27) we listed the first six Legendre polynomials. If, say, we wish to find $P_6(x)$, we can use (29) with $k = 5$. This relation expresses $P_6(x)$ in terms of the known $P_4(x)$ and $P_5(x)$. See Problem 45 in Exercises 6.3.

Another formula, although not a recurrence relation, can generate the Legendre polynomials by differentiation. **Rodrigues' formula** for these polynomials is

$$P_n(x) = \frac{1}{2^n n!} \frac{d^n}{dx^n} (x^2 - 1)^n, \qquad n = 0, 1, 2, \ldots . \tag{30}$$

See Problem 48 in Exercises 6.3.

REMARKS

(*i*) Although we have assumed that the parameter n in Legendre's differential equation $(1 - x^2)y'' - 2xy' + n(n + 1)y = 0$, represented a nonnegative integer, in a more general setting n can represent any real number. Any solution of Legendre's equation is called a **Legendre function**. If n is *not* a nonnegative integer, then both Legendre functions $y_1(x)$ and $y_2(x)$ given in (26) are infinite series convergent on the open interval $(-1, 1)$ and divergent (unbounded) at $x = \pm 1$. If n is a nonnegative integer, then as we have just seen one of the Legendre functions in (26) is a polynomial and the other is an infinite series convergent for $-1 < x < 1$. You should be aware of the fact that Legendre's equation possesses solutions that are bounded on the *closed* interval $[-1, 1]$ only in the case when $n = 0, 1, 2, \ldots$. More to the point, the only Legendre functions that are bounded on the closed interval $[-1, 1]$ are the Legendre polynomials $P_n(x)$ or constant multiples of these polynomials. See Problem 47 in Exercises 6.3 and Problem 24 in Chapter 6 in Review.

(*ii*) In the *Remarks* at the end of Section 2.3 we mentioned the branch of mathematics called **special functions**. Perhaps a better appellation for this field of applied mathematics might be *named functions*, since many of the functions studied bear proper names: Bessel functions, Legendre functions, Airy functions, Chebyshev polynomials, Gauss's hypergeometric function, Hermite polynomials, Jacobi polynomials, Laguerre polynomials, Mathieu functions, Weber functions, and so on. Historically, special functions were the by-product of necessity; someone needed a solution of a very specialized differential equation that arose from an attempt to solve a physical problem.

EXERCISES 6.3

Answers to selected odd-numbered problems begin on page ANS-10.

6.3.1 BESSEL'S EQUATION

In Problems 1–6 use (1) to find the general solution of the given differential equation on $(0, \infty)$.

1. $x^2y'' + xy' + \left(x^2 - \frac{1}{9}\right)y = 0$

2. $x^2y'' + xy' + (x^2 - 1)y = 0$

3. $4x^2y'' + 4xy' + (4x^2 - 25)y = 0$

4. $16x^2y'' + 16xy' + (16x^2 - 1)y = 0$

5. $xy'' + y' + xy = 0$

6. $\dfrac{d}{dx}[xy'] + \left(x - \dfrac{4}{x}\right)y = 0$

In Problems 7–10 use (12) to find the general solution of the given differential equation on $(0, \infty)$.

7. $x^2y'' + xy' + (9x^2 - 4)y = 0$

8. $x^2y'' + xy' + \left(36x^2 - \frac{1}{4}\right)y = 0$

9. $x^2y'' + xy' + \left(25x^2 - \frac{4}{9}\right)y = 0$

10. $x^2y'' + xy' + (2x^2 - 64)y = 0$

In Problems 11 and 12 use the indicated change of variable to find the general solution of the given differential equation on $(0, \infty)$.

11. $x^2y'' + 2xy' + \alpha^2 x^2 y = 0; \quad y = x^{-1/2}v(x)$

12. $x^2y'' + \left(\alpha^2 x^2 - \nu^2 + \frac{1}{4}\right)y = 0; \quad y = \sqrt{x}\,v(x)$

In Problems 13–20 use (18) to find the general solution of the given differential equation on $(0, \infty)$.

13. $xy'' + 2y' + 4y = 0$ **14.** $xy'' + 3y' + xy = 0$

15. $xy'' - y' + xy = 0$ **16.** $xy'' - 5y' + xy = 0$

17. $x^2y'' + (x^2 - 2)y = 0$

18. $4x^2y'' + (16x^2 + 1)y = 0$

19. $xy'' + 3y' + x^3y = 0$

20. $9x^2y'' + 9xy' + (x^6 - 36)y = 0$

21. Use the series in (7) to verify that $I_\nu(x) = i^{-\nu}J_\nu(ix)$ is a real function.

22. Assume that b in equation (18) can be pure imaginary, that is, $b = \beta i, \beta > 0, i^2 = -1$. Use this assumption to express the general solution of the given differential equation in terms the modified Bessel functions I_n and K_n.

(a) $y'' - x^2y = 0$ (b) $xy'' + y' - 7x^3y = 0$

In Problems 23–26 first use (18) to express the general solution of the given differential equation in terms of Bessel functions. Then use (23) and (24) to express the general solution in terms of elementary functions.

23. $y'' + y = 0$

24. $x^2y'' + 4xy' + (x^2 + 2)y = 0$

25. $16x^2y'' + 32xy' + (x^4 - 12)y = 0$

26. $4x^2y'' - 4xy' + (16x^2 + 3)y = 0$

27. (a) Proceed as in Example 5 to show that

$$xJ_\nu'(x) = -\nu J_\nu(x) + xJ_{\nu-1}(x).$$

[*Hint*: Write $2n + \nu = 2(n + \nu) - \nu$.]

(b) Use the result in part (a) to derive (21).

28. Use the formula obtained in Example 5 along with part (a) of Problem 27 to derive the recurrence relation

$$2\nu J_\nu(x) = xJ_{\nu+1}(x) + xJ_{\nu-1}(x).$$

In Problems 29 and 30 use (20) or (21) to obtain the given result.

29. $\displaystyle\int_0^x rJ_0(r)\,dr = xJ_1(x)$ **30.** $J_0'(x) = J_{-1}(x) = -J_1(x)$

31. Proceed as on page 247 to derive the elementary form of $J_{-1/2}(x)$ given in (24).

32. (a) Use the recurrence relation in Problem 28 along with (23) and (24) to express $J_{3/2}(x)$, $J_{-3/2}(x)$, and $J_{5/2}(x)$ in terms of $\sin x$, $\cos x$, and powers of x.

(b) Use a graphing utility to graph $J_{1/2}(x)$, $J_{-1/2}(x)$, $J_{3/2}(x)$, $J_{-3/2}(x)$, and $J_{5/2}(x)$.

33. Use the change of variables $s = \dfrac{2}{\alpha}\sqrt{\dfrac{k}{m}}\,e^{-\alpha t/2}$ to show that the differential equation of the aging spring $mx'' + ke^{-\alpha t}x = 0, \alpha > 0$, becomes

$$s^2\frac{d^2x}{ds^2} + s\frac{dx}{ds} + s^2x = 0.$$

34. Show that $y = x^{1/2}w\left(\frac{2}{3}\alpha x^{3/2}\right)$ is a solution of Airy's differential equation $y'' + \alpha^2xy = 0, x > 0$, whenever w is a solution of Bessel's equation of order $\frac{1}{3}$, that is, $t^2w'' + tw' + \left(t^2 - \frac{1}{9}\right)w = 0, t > 0$. [*Hint*: After differentiating, substituting, and simplifying, then let $t = \frac{2}{3}\alpha x^{3/2}$.]

35. (a) Use the result of Problem 34 to express the general solution of Airy's differential equation for $x > 0$ in terms of Bessel functions.

(b) Verify the results in part (a) using (18).

36. Use the Table 6.1 to find the first three positive eigenvalues and corresponding eigenfunctions of the boundary-value problem

$$xy'' + y' + \lambda xy = 0,$$

$$y(x), y'(x) \text{ bounded as } x \to 0^+, \quad y(2) = 0.$$

[*Hint*: By identifying $\lambda = \alpha^2$, the DE is the parametric Bessel equation of order zero.]

37. (a) Use (18) to show that the general solution of the differential equation $xy'' + \lambda y = 0$ on the interval $(0, \infty)$ is

$$y = c_1\sqrt{x}J_1\left(2\sqrt{\lambda x}\right) + c_2\sqrt{x}Y_1\left(2\sqrt{\lambda x}\right).$$

(b) Verify by direct substitution that $y = \sqrt{x}J_1(2\sqrt{x})$ is a particular solution of the DE in the case $\lambda = 1$.

Computer Lab Assignments

38. Use a CAS to graph the modified Bessel functions $I_0(x)$, $I_1(x)$, $I_2(x)$ and $K_0(x)$, $K_1(x)$, $K_2(x)$. Compare these graphs with those shown in Figures 6.3.1 and 6.3.2. What major difference is apparent between Bessel functions and the modified Bessel functions?

39. (a) Use the general solution given in Example 4 to solve the IVP

$$4x'' + e^{-0.1t}x = 0, \quad x(0) = 1, \quad x'(0) = -\tfrac{1}{2}.$$

Also use $J_0'(x) = -J_1(x)$ and $Y_0'(x) = -Y_1(x)$ along with Table 6.1 or a CAS to evaluate coefficients.

(b) Use a CAS to graph the solution obtained in part (a) for $0 \le t \le \infty$.

40. (a) Use the general solution obtained in Problem 35 to solve the IVP

$$4x'' + tx = 0, \quad x(0.1) = 1, \quad x'(0.1) = -\tfrac{1}{2}.$$

Use a CAS to evaluate coefficients.

(b) Use a CAS to graph the solution obtained in part (a) for $0 \le t \le 200$.

41. Column Bending Under Its Own Weight A uniform thin column of length L, positioned vertically with one end embedded in the ground, will deflect, or bend away, from the vertical under the influence of its own weight when its length or height exceeds a certain critical value. It can be shown that the angular deflection $\theta(x)$ of the column from the vertical at a point $P(x)$ is a solution of the boundary-value problem:

$$EI\frac{d^2\theta}{dx^2} + \delta g(L - x)\theta = 0, \quad \theta(0) = 0, \quad \theta'(L) = 0,$$

where E is Young's modulus, I is the cross-sectional moment of inertia, δ is the constant linear density, and x is the distance along the column measured from its base. See Figure 6.3.4. The column will bend only for those values of L for which the boundary-value problem has a nontrivial solution.

(a) Restate the boundary-value problem by making the change of variables $t = L - x$. Then use the results of a problem earlier in this exercise set to express the general solution of the differential equation in terms of Bessel functions.

(b) Use the general solution found in part (a) to find a solution of the BVP and an equation which defines the critical length L, that is, the smallest value of L for which the column will start to bend.

(c) With the aid of a CAS, find the critical length L of a solid steel rod of radius $r = 0.05$ in., $\delta g = 0.28\,A$ lb/in., $E = 2.6 \times 10^7$ lb/in.^{2}, $A = \pi r^2$, and $I = \tfrac{1}{4}\pi r^4$.

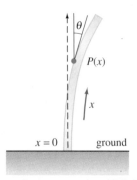

FIGURE 6.3.4 Beam in Problem 41

42. Buckling of a Thin Vertical Column In Example 3 of Section 5.2 we saw that when a constant vertical compressive force, or load, P was applied to a thin

column of uniform cross section and hinged at both ends, the deflection $y(x)$ is a solution of the BVP:

$$EI\frac{d^2y}{dx^2} + Py = 0, \quad y(0) = 0, \quad y(L) = 0.$$

(a) If the bending stiffness factor EI is proportional to x, then $EI(x) = kx$, where k is a constant of proportionality. If $EI(L) = kL = M$ is the maximum stiffness factor, then $k = M/L$ and so $EI(x) = Mx/L$. Use the information in Problem 37 to find a solution of

$$M\frac{x}{L}\frac{d^2y}{dx^2} + Py = 0, \quad y(0) = 0, \quad y(L) = 0$$

if it is known that $\sqrt{x}\,Y_1(2\sqrt{\lambda x})$ is *not* zero at $x = 0$.

(b) Use Table 6.1 to find the Euler load P_1 for the column.

(c) Use a CAS to graph the first buckling mode $y_1(x)$ corresponding to the Euler load P_1. For simplicity assume that $c_1 = 1$ and $L = 1$.

43. Pendulum of Varying Length For the simple pendulum described on page 209 of Section 5.3, suppose that the rod holding the mass m at one end is replaced by a flexible wire or string and that the wire is strung over a pulley at the point of support O in Figure 5.3.3. In this manner, while it is in motion in a vertical plane, the mass m can be raised or lowered. In other words, the length $l(t)$ of the pendulum varies with time. Under the same assumptions leading to equation (6) in Section 5.3, it can be shown* that the differential equation for the displacement angle θ is now

$$l\theta'' + 2l'\theta' + g\sin\theta = 0.$$

(a) If l increases at constant rate v and if $l(0) = l_0$, show that a linearization of the foregoing DE is

$$(l_0 + vt)\theta'' + 2v\theta' + g\theta = 0. \tag{31}$$

(b) Make the change of variables $x = (l_0 + vt)/v$ and show that (31) becomes

$$\frac{d^2\theta}{dx^2} + \frac{2}{x}\frac{d\theta}{dx} + \frac{g}{vx}\theta = 0.$$

(c) Use part (b) and (18) to express the general solution of equation (31) in terms of Bessel functions.

(d) Use the general solution obtained in part (c) to solve the initial-value problem consisting of equation (31) and the initial conditions $\theta(0) = \theta_0$, $\theta'(0) = 0$. [*Hints*: To simplify calculations, use a further change of variable $u = \dfrac{2}{v}\sqrt{g(l_0 + vt)} = 2\sqrt{\dfrac{g}{v}}\,x^{1/2}.$

*See *Mathematical Methods in Physical Sciences*, Mary Boas, John Wiley & Sons, Inc., 1966. Also see the article by Borelli, Coleman, and Hobson in *Mathematics Magazine*, vol. 58, no. 2, March 1985.

Also, recall that (20) holds for both $J_1(u)$ and $Y_1(u)$. Finally, the identity

$$J_1(u)Y_2(u) - J_2(u)Y_1(u) = -\frac{2}{\pi u} \text{ will be helpful.}]$$

(e) Use a CAS to graph the solution $\theta(t)$ of the IVP in part (d) when $l_0 = 1$ ft, $\theta_0 = \frac{1}{10}$ radian, and $v = \frac{1}{60}$ ft/s. Experiment with the graph using different time intervals such as [0, 10], [0, 30], and so on.

(f) What do the graphs indicate about the displacement angle $\theta(t)$ as the length l of the wire increases with time?

6.3.2 LEGENDRE'S EQUATION

44. (a) Use the explicit solutions $y_1(x)$ and $y_2(x)$ of Legendre's equation given in (26) and the appropriate choice of c_0 and c_1 to find the Legendre polynomials $P_6(x)$ and $P_7(x)$.

(b) Write the differential equations for which $P_6(x)$ and $P_7(x)$ are particular solutions.

45. Use the recurrence relation (29) and $P_0(x) = 1$, $P_1(x) = x$, to generate the next six Legendre polynomials.

46. Show that the differential equation

$$\sin\theta\,\frac{d^2y}{d\theta^2} + \cos\theta\,\frac{dy}{d\theta} + n(n+1)(\sin\theta)y = 0$$

can be transformed into Legendre's equation by means of the substitution $x = \cos\theta$.

47. Find the first three positive values of λ for which the problem

$$(1 - x^2)y'' - 2xy' + \lambda y = 0,$$

$$y(0) = 0, \quad y(x), y'(x) \text{ bounded on } [-1,1]$$

has nontrivial solutions.

Computer Lab Assignments

48. For purposes of this problem ignore the list of Legendre polynomials given on page 249 and the graphs given in Figure 6.3.3. Use Rodrigues' formula (30) to generate the Legendre polynomials $P_1(x), P_2(x), \ldots, P_7(x)$. Use a CAS to carry out the differentiations and simplifications.

49. Use a CAS to graph $P_1(x), P_2(x), \ldots, P_7(x)$ on the interval $[-1, 1]$.

50. Use a root-finding application to find the zeros of $P_1(x), P_2(x), \ldots, P_7(x)$. If the Legendre polynomials are built-in functions of your CAS, find zeros of Legendre polynomials of higher degree. Form a conjecture about the location of the zeros of any Legendre polynomial $P_n(x)$, and then investigate to see whether it is true.

CHAPTER 6 IN REVIEW

Answers to selected odd-numbered problems begin on page ANS-10.

In Problems 1 and 2 answer true or false without referring back to the text.

1. The general solution of $x^2y'' + xy' + (x^2 - 1)y = 0$ is $y = c_1J_1(x) + c_2J_{-1}(x)$. _____

2. Because $x = 0$ is an irregular singular point of $x^3y'' - xy' + y = 0$, the DE possesses no solution that is analytic at $x = 0$. _____

3. Both power series solutions of $y'' + \ln(x+1)y' + y = 0$ centered at the ordinary point $x = 0$ are guaranteed to converge for all x in which *one* of the following intervals?

(a) $(-\infty, \infty)$ (b) $(-1, \infty)$
(c) $[-\frac{1}{2}, \frac{1}{2}]$ (d) $[-1, 1]$

4. $x = 0$ is an ordinary point of a certain linear differential equation. After the assumed solution $y = \sum_{n=0}^{\infty} c_n x^n$ is

substituted into the DE, the following algebraic system is obtained by equating the coefficients of x^0, x^1, x^2, and x^3 to zero:

$$2c_2 + 2c_1 + c_0 = 0$$

$$6c_3 + 4c_2 + c_1 = 0$$

$$12c_4 + 6c_3 + c_2 - \tfrac{1}{3}c_1 = 0$$

$$20c_5 + 8c_4 + c_3 - \tfrac{2}{3}c_2 = 0.$$

Bearing in mind that c_0 and c_1 are arbitrary, write down the first five terms of two power series solutions of the differential equation.

5. Suppose the power series $\sum_{k=0}^{\infty} c_k(x-4)^k$ is known to converge at -2 and diverge at 13. Discuss whether the series converges at -7, 0, 7, 10, and 11. Possible answers are *does, does not, might*.

6. Use the Maclaurin series for $\sin x$ and $\cos x$ along with long division to find the first three nonzero terms of a power series in x for the function $f(x) = \dfrac{\sin x}{\cos x}$.

In Problems 7 and 8 construct a linear second-order differential equation that has the given properties.

7. A regular singular point at $x = 1$ and an irregular singular point at $x = 0$

8. Regular singular points at $x = 1$ and at $x = -3$

In Problems 9–14 use an appropriate infinite series method about $x = 0$ to find two solutions of the given differential equation.

9. $2xy'' + y' + y = 0$

10. $y'' - xy' - y = 0$

11. $(x - 1)y'' + 3y = 0$

12. $y'' - x^2 y' + xy = 0$

13. $xy'' - (x + 2)y' + 2y = 0$

14. $(\cos x)y'' + y = 0$

In Problems 15 and 16 solve the given initial-value problem.

15. $y'' + xy' + 2y = 0$, $y(0) = 3$, $y'(0) = -2$

16. $(x + 2)y'' + 3y = 0$, $y(0) = 0$, $y'(0) = 1$

17. Without actually solving the differential equation $(1 - 2\sin x)y'' + xy = 0$, find a lower bound for the radius of convergence of power series solutions about the ordinary point $x = 0$.

18. Even though $x = 0$ is an ordinary point of the differential equation, explain why it is not a good idea to try to find a solution of the IVP

$$y'' + xy' + y = 0, \quad y(1) = -6, \quad y'(1) = 3$$

of the form $y = \sum_{n=0}^{\infty} c_n x^n$. Using power series, find a better way to solve the problem.

In Problems 19 and 20 investigate whether $x = 0$ is an ordinary point, singular point, or irregular singular point of the given differential equation. [*Hint*: Recall the Maclaurin series for $\cos x$ and e^x.]

19. $xy'' + (1 - \cos x)y' + x^2 y = 0$

20. $(e^x - 1 - x)y'' + xy = 0$

21. Note that $x = 0$ is an ordinary point of the differential equation $y'' + x^2 y' + 2xy = 5 - 2x + 10x^3$. Use the assumption $y = \sum_{n=0}^{\infty} c_n x^n$ to find the general solution $y = y_c + y_p$ that consists of three power series centered at $x = 0$.

22. The first-order differential equation $dy/dx = x^2 + y^2$ cannot be solved in terms of elementary functions. However, a solution can be expressed in terms of Bessel functions.

(a) Show that the substitution $y = -\dfrac{1}{u}\dfrac{du}{dx}$ leads to the equation $u'' + x^2 u = 0$.

(b) Use (18) in Section 6.3 to find the general solution of $u'' + x^2 u = 0$.

(c) Use (20) and (21) in Section 6.3 in the forms

$$J_\nu'(x) = \frac{\nu}{x} J_\nu(x) - J_{\nu+1}(x)$$

and $$J_\nu'(x) = -\frac{\nu}{x} J_\nu(x) + J_{\nu-1}(x)$$

as an aid to show that a one-parameter family of solutions of $dy/dx = x^2 + y^2$ is given by

$$y = x \frac{J_{3/4}\left(\frac{1}{2}x^2\right) - cJ_{-3/4}\left(\frac{1}{2}x^2\right)}{cJ_{1/4}\left(\frac{1}{2}x^2\right) + J_{-1/4}\left(\frac{1}{2}x^2\right)}.$$

23. (a) Use (23) and (24) of Section 6.3 to show that

$$Y_{1/2}(x) = -\sqrt{\frac{2}{\pi x}}\cos x.$$

(b) Use (15) of Section 6.3 to show that

$$I_{1/2}(x) = \sqrt{\frac{2}{\pi x}}\sinh x \quad \text{and} \quad I_{-1/2}(x) = \sqrt{\frac{2}{\pi x}}\cosh x.$$

(c) Use part (b) to show that

$$K_{1/2}(x) = \sqrt{\frac{\pi}{2x}}\, e^{-x}.$$

24. (a) From (27) and (28) of Section 6.3 we know that when $n = 0$, Legendre's differential equation $(1 - x^2)y'' - 2xy' = 0$ has the polynomial solution $y = P_0(x) = 1$. Use (5) of Section 4.2 to show that a second Legendre function satisfying the DE for $-1 < x < 1$ is

$$y = \frac{1}{2}\ln\left(\frac{1 + x}{1 - x}\right).$$

(b) We also know from (27) and (28) of Section 6.3 that when $n = 1$, Legendre's differential equation $(1 - x^2)y'' - 2xy' + 2y = 0$ possesses the polynomial solution $y = P_1(x) = x$. Use (5) of Section 4.2 to show that a second Legendre function satisfying the DE for $-1 < x < 1$ is

$$y = \frac{x}{2}\ln\left(\frac{1 + x}{1 - x}\right) - 1.$$

(c) Use a graphing utility to graph the logarithmic Legendre functions given in parts (a) and (b).

25. (a) Use binomial series to formally show that

$$(1 - 2xt + t^2)^{-1/2} = \sum_{n=0}^{\infty} P_n(x)t^n.$$

(b) Use the result obtained in part (a) to show that $P_n(1) = 1$ and $P_n(-1) = (-1)^n$. See Properties (*ii*) and (*iii*) on page 249.

7 THE LAPLACE TRANSFORM

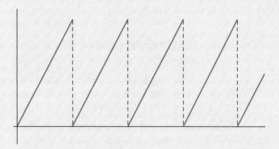

In the linear mathematical models for a physical system such as a spring/mass system or a series electrical circuit, the right-hand member, or input, of the differential equations

$$m\frac{d^2x}{dt^2} + \beta\frac{dx}{dt} + kx = f(t) \qquad \text{or} \qquad L\frac{d^2q}{dt^2} + R\frac{dq}{dt} + \frac{1}{C}q = E(t)$$

is a driving function and represents either an external force $f(t)$ or an impressed voltage $E(t)$. In Section 5.1 we considered problems in which the functions f and E were continuous. However, discontinuous driving functions are not uncommon. For example, the impressed voltage on a circuit could be piecewise continuous and periodic such as the "sawtooth" function shown above. Solving the differential equation of the circuit in this case is difficult using the techniques of Chapter 4. The Laplace transform studied in this chapter is an invaluable tool that simplifies the solution of problems such as these.

7.1 DEFINITION OF THE LAPLACE TRANSFORM

REVIEW MATERIAL

- Improper integrals with infinite limits of integration
- Partial fraction decomposition

INTRODUCTION In elementary calculus you learned that differentiation and integration are *transforms*; this means, roughly speaking, that these operations transform a function into another function. For example, the function $f(x) = x^2$ is transformed, in turn, into a linear function and a family of cubic polynomial functions by the operations of differentiation and integration:

$$\frac{d}{dx}x^2 = 2x \quad \text{and} \quad \int x^2 \, dx = \frac{1}{3}x^3 + c.$$

Moreover, these two transforms possess the **linearity property** that the transform of a linear combination of functions is a linear combination of the transforms. For α and β constants

$$\frac{d}{dx}[\alpha f(x) + \beta g(x)] = \alpha f'(x) + \beta g'(x)$$

and

$$\int [\alpha f(x) + \beta g(x)] \, dx = \alpha \int f(x) \, dx + \beta \int g(x) \, dx$$

provided that each derivative and integral exists. In this section we will examine a special type of integral transform called the **Laplace transform.** In addition to possessing the linearity property the Laplace transform has many other interesting properties that make it very useful in solving linear initial-value problems.

INTEGRAL TRANSFORM If $f(x, y)$ is a function of two variables, then a definite integral of f with respect to one of the variables leads to a function of the other variable. For example, by holding y constant, we see that $\int_1^2 2xy^2 \, dx = 3y^2$. Similarly, a definite integral such as $\int_a^b K(s, t) f(t) \, dt$ transforms a function f of the variable t into a function F of the variable s. We are particularly interested in an **integral transform,** where the interval of integration is the unbounded interval $[0, \infty)$. If $f(t)$ is defined for $t \geq 0$, then the improper integral $\int_0^\infty K(s, t) f(t) \, dt$ is defined as a limit:

$$\int_0^\infty K(s, t) f(t) \, dt = \lim_{b \to \infty} \int_0^b K(s, t) f(t) \, dt. \tag{1}$$

If the limit in (1) exists, then we say that the integral exists or is **convergent;** if the limit does not exist, the integral does not exist and is **divergent.** The limit in (1) will, in general, exist for only certain values of the variable s.

A DEFINITION The function $K(s, t)$ in (1) is called the **kernel** of the transform. The choice $K(s, t) = e^{-st}$ as the kernel gives us an especially important integral transform.

DEFINITION 7.1.1 **Laplace Transform**

Let f be a function defined for $t \geq 0$. Then the integral

$$\mathscr{L}\{f(t)\} = \int_0^\infty e^{-st} f(t) \, dt \tag{2}$$

is said to be the **Laplace transform** of f, provided that the integral converges.

When the defining integral (2) converges, the result is a function of s. In general discussion we shall use a lowercase letter to denote the function being transformed and the corresponding capital letter to denote its Laplace transform—for example,

$$\mathscr{L}\{f(t)\} = F(s), \qquad \mathscr{L}\{g(t)\} = G(s), \qquad \mathscr{L}\{y(t)\} = Y(s).$$

EXAMPLE 1 Applying Definition 7.1.1

Evaluate $\mathscr{L}\{1\}$.

SOLUTION From (2),

$$\mathscr{L}\{1\} = \int_0^\infty e^{-st}(1)\, dt = \lim_{b\to\infty} \int_0^b e^{-st}\, dt$$

$$= \lim_{b\to\infty} \frac{-e^{-st}}{s}\Big|_0^b = \lim_{b\to\infty} \frac{-e^{-sb}+1}{s} = \frac{1}{s}$$

provided that $s > 0$. In other words, when $s > 0$, the exponent $-sb$ is negative, and $e^{-sb} \to 0$ as $b \to \infty$. The integral diverges for $s < 0$. ∎

The use of the limit sign becomes somewhat tedious, so we shall adopt the notation $\big|_0^\infty$ as a shorthand for writing $\lim_{b\to\infty} (\ )\big|_0^b$. For example,

$$\mathscr{L}\{1\} = \int_0^\infty e^{-st}(1)\, dt = \frac{-e^{-st}}{s}\Big|_0^\infty = \frac{1}{s}, \qquad s > 0.$$

At the upper limit, it is understood that we mean $e^{-st} \to 0$ as $t \to \infty$ for $s > 0$.

EXAMPLE 2 Applying Definition 7.1.1

Evaluate $\mathscr{L}\{t\}$.

SOLUTION From Definition 7.1.1 we have $\mathscr{L}\{t\} = \int_0^\infty e^{-st} t\, dt$. Integrating by parts and using $\lim_{t\to\infty} te^{-st} = 0$, $s > 0$, along with the result from Example 1, we obtain

$$\mathscr{L}\{t\} = \frac{-te^{-st}}{s}\Big|_0^\infty + \frac{1}{s}\int_0^\infty e^{-st}\, dt = \frac{1}{s}\mathscr{L}\{1\} = \frac{1}{s}\left(\frac{1}{s}\right) = \frac{1}{s^2}. \qquad ∎$$

EXAMPLE 3 Applying Definition 7.1.1

Evaluate $\mathscr{L}\{e^{-3t}\}$.

SOLUTION From Definition 7.1.1 we have

$$\mathscr{L}\{e^{-3t}\} = \int_0^\infty e^{-st}e^{-3t}\, dt = \int_0^\infty e^{-(s+3)t}\, dt$$

$$= \frac{-e^{-(s+3)t}}{s+3}\Big|_0^\infty$$

$$= \frac{1}{s+3}, \qquad s > -3.$$

The result follows from the fact that $\lim_{t\to\infty} e^{-(s+3)t} = 0$ for $s+3 > 0$ or $s > -3$. ∎

EXAMPLE 4 Applying Definition 7.1.1

Evaluate $\mathcal{L}\{\sin 2t\}$.

SOLUTION From Definition 7.1.1 and integration by parts we have

$$\mathcal{L}\{\sin 2t\} = \int_0^\infty e^{-st} \sin 2t \, dt = \frac{-e^{-st} \sin 2t}{s} \bigg|_0^\infty + \frac{2}{s} \int_0^\infty e^{-st} \cos 2t \, dt$$

$$= \frac{2}{s} \int_0^\infty e^{-st} \cos 2t \, dt, \qquad s > 0$$

$$\overset{\lim\limits_{t \to \infty} e^{-st} \cos 2t = 0,\, s > 0 \qquad \qquad \text{Laplace transform of } \sin 2t}{= \frac{2}{s}\left[\frac{-e^{-st} \cos 2t}{s} \bigg|_0^\infty - \frac{2}{s} \int_0^\infty e^{-st} \sin 2t \, dt \right]}$$

$$= \frac{2}{s^2} - \frac{4}{s^2} \mathcal{L}\{\sin 2t\}.$$

At this point we have an equation with $\mathcal{L}\{\sin 2t\}$ on both sides of the equality. Solving for that quantity yields the result

$$\mathcal{L}\{\sin 2t\} = \frac{2}{s^2 + 4}, \qquad s > 0.$$ ∎

$\mathcal{L}$ IS A LINEAR TRANSFORM For a linear combination of functions we can write

$$\int_0^\infty e^{-st} [\alpha f(t) + \beta g(t)] \, dt = \alpha \int_0^\infty e^{-st} f(t) \, dt + \beta \int_0^\infty e^{-st} g(t) \, dt$$

whenever both integrals converge for $s > c$. Hence it follows that

$$\mathcal{L}\{\alpha f(t) + \beta g(t)\} = \alpha \mathcal{L}\{f(t)\} + \beta \mathcal{L}\{g(t)\} = \alpha F(s) + \beta G(s). \qquad (3)$$

Because of the property given in (3), $\mathcal{L}$ is said to be a **linear transform.** For example, from Examples 1 and 2

$$\mathcal{L}\{1 + 5t\} = \mathcal{L}\{1\} + 5\mathcal{L}\{t\} = \frac{1}{s} + \frac{5}{s^2},$$

and from Examples 3 and 4

$$\mathcal{L}\{4e^{-3t} - 10 \sin 2t\} = 4\mathcal{L}\{e^{-3t}\} - 10\mathcal{L}\{\sin 2t\} = \frac{4}{s + 3} - \frac{20}{s^2 + 4}.$$

We state the generalization of some of the preceding examples by means of the next theorem. From this point on we shall also refrain from stating any restrictions on s; it is understood that s is sufficiently restricted to guarantee the convergence of the appropriate Laplace transform.

THEOREM 7.1.1 Transforms of Some Basic Functions

(a) $\mathcal{L}\{1\} = \dfrac{1}{s}$

(b) $\mathcal{L}\{t^n\} = \dfrac{n!}{s^{n+1}}, \quad n = 1, 2, 3, \ldots$ **(c)** $\mathcal{L}\{e^{at}\} = \dfrac{1}{s - a}$

(d) $\mathcal{L}\{\sin kt\} = \dfrac{k}{s^2 + k^2}$ **(e)** $\mathcal{L}\{\cos kt\} = \dfrac{s}{s^2 + k^2}$

(f) $\mathcal{L}\{\sinh kt\} = \dfrac{k}{s^2 - k^2}$ **(g)** $\mathcal{L}\{\cosh kt\} = \dfrac{s}{s^2 - k^2}$

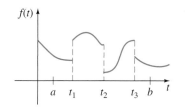

FIGURE 7.1.1 Piecewise continuous function

SUFFICIENT CONDITIONS FOR EXISTENCE OF $\mathscr{L}\{f(t)\}$ The integral that defines the Laplace transform does not have to converge. For example, neither $\mathscr{L}\{1/t\}$ nor $\mathscr{L}\{e^{t^2}\}$ exists. Sufficient conditions guaranteeing the existence of $\mathscr{L}\{f(t)\}$ are that f be piecewise continuous on $[0, \infty)$ and that f be of exponential order for $t > T$. Recall that a function f is **piecewise continuous** on $[0, \infty)$ if, in any interval $0 \le a \le t \le b$, there are at most a finite number of points t_k, $k = 1, 2, \ldots, n$ ($t_{k-1} < t_k$) at which f has finite discontinuities and is continuous on each open interval (t_{k-1}, t_k). See Figure 7.1.1. The concept of **exponential order** is defined in the following manner.

DEFINITION 7.1.2 Exponential Order

A function f is said to be of **exponential order** c if there exist constants c, $M > 0$, and $T > 0$ such that $|f(t)| \le Me^{ct}$ for all $t > T$.

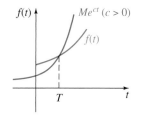

FIGURE 7.1.2 f is of exponential order c.

If f is an *increasing* function, then the condition $|f(t)| \le Me^{ct}$, $t > T$, simply states that the graph of f on the interval (T, ∞) does not grow faster than the graph of the exponential function Me^{ct}, where c is a positive constant. See Figure 7.1.2. The functions $f(t) = t$, $f(t) = e^{-t}$, and $f(t) = 2 \cos t$ are all of exponential order $c = 1$ for $t > 0$, since we have, respectively,

$$|t| \le e^t, \quad |e^{-t}| \le e^t, \quad \text{and} \quad |2 \cos t| \le 2e^t.$$

A comparison of the graphs on the interval $(0, \infty)$ is given in Figure 7.1.3.

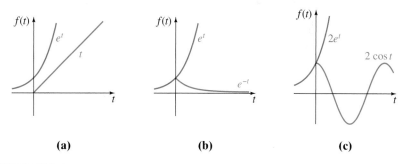

(a)   **(b)**   **(c)**

FIGURE 7.1.3 Three functions of exponential order $c = 1$

A function such as $f(t) = e^{t^2}$ is not of exponential order, since, as shown in Figure 7.1.4, its graph grows faster than any positive linear power of e for $t > c > 0$.

A positive integral power of t is always of exponential order, since, for $c > 0$,

$$|t^n| \le Me^{ct} \quad \text{or} \quad \left|\frac{t^n}{e^{ct}}\right| \le M \quad \text{for } t > T$$

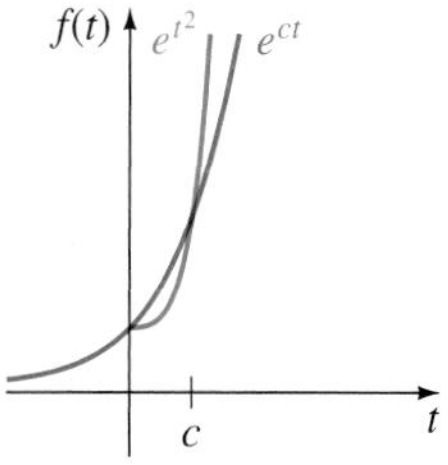

FIGURE 7.1.4 e^{t^2} is not of exponential order

is equivalent to showing that $\lim_{t \to \infty} t^n/e^{ct}$ is finite for $n = 1, 2, 3, \ldots$. The result follows by n applications of L'Hôpital's Rule.

THEOREM 7.1.2   Sufficient Conditions for Existence

If f is piecewise continuous on $[0, \infty)$ and of exponential order c, then $\mathscr{L}\{f(t)\}$ exists for $s > c$.

PROOF By the additive interval property of definite integrals we can write

$$\mathscr{L}\{f(t)\} = \int_0^T e^{-st} f(t) \, dt + \int_T^\infty e^{-st} f(t) \, dt = I_1 + I_2.$$

The integral I_1 exists because it can be written as a sum of integrals over intervals on which $e^{-st} f(t)$ is continuous. Now since f is of exponential order, there exist constants c, $M > 0$, $T > 0$ so that $|f(t)| \le Me^{ct}$ for $t > T$. We can then write

$$|I_2| \le \int_T^\infty |e^{-st} f(t)| \, dt \le M \int_T^\infty e^{-st} e^{ct} \, dt = M \int_T^\infty e^{-(s-c)t} \, dt = M \frac{e^{-(s-c)T}}{s-c}$$

for $s > c$. Since $\int_T^\infty Me^{-(s-c)t} \, dt$ converges, the integral $\int_T^\infty |e^{-st} f(t)| \, dt$ converges by the comparison test for improper integrals. This, in turn, implies that I_2 exists for $s > c$. The existence of I_1 and I_2 implies that $\mathscr{L}\{f(t)\} = \int_0^\infty e^{-st} f(t) \, dt$ exists for $s > c$. ∎

EXAMPLE 5 **Transform of a Piecewise Continuous Function**

Evaluate $\mathscr{L}\{f(t)\}$ where $f(t) = \begin{cases} 0, & 0 \le t < 3 \\ 2, & t \ge 3. \end{cases}$

SOLUTION The function f, shown in Figure 7.1.5, is piecewise continuous and of exponential order for $t > 0$. Since f is defined in two pieces, $\mathscr{L}\{f(t)\}$ is expressed as the sum of two integrals:

$$\mathscr{L}\{f(t)\} = \int_0^\infty e^{-st} f(t) \, dt = \int_0^3 e^{-st} (0) \, dt + \int_3^\infty e^{-st} (2) \, dt$$

$$= 0 + \frac{2e^{-st}}{-s} \Big|_3^\infty$$

$$= \frac{2e^{-3s}}{s}, \qquad s > 0. \qquad ∎$$

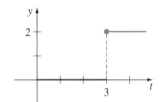

FIGURE 7.1.5 Piecewise continuous function

We conclude this section with an additional bit of theory related to the types of functions of s that we will, generally, be working with. The next theorem indicates that not every arbitrary function of s is a Laplace transform of a piecewise continuous function of exponential order.

THEOREM 7.1.3 **Behavior of $F(s)$ as $s \to \infty$**

If f is piecewise continuous on $(0, \infty)$ and of exponential order and $F(s) = \mathscr{L}\{f(t)\}$, then $\lim_{s \to \infty} F(s) = 0$.

PROOF Since f is of exponential order, there exist constants γ, $M_1 > 0$, and $T > 0$ so that $|f(t)| \le M_1 e^{\gamma t}$ for $t > T$. Also, since f is piecewise continuous for $0 \le t \le T$, it is necessarily bounded on the interval; that is, $|f(t)| \le M_2 = M_2 e^{0t}$. If M denotes the maximum of the set $\{M_1, M_2\}$ and c denotes the maximum of $\{0, \gamma\}$, then

$$|F(s)| \le \int_0^\infty e^{-st} |f(t)| \, dt \le M \int_0^\infty e^{-st} e^{ct} \, dt = M \int_0^\infty e^{-(s-c)t} \, dt = \frac{M}{s-c}$$

for $s > c$. As $s \to \infty$, we have $|F(s)| \to 0$, and so $F(s) = \mathscr{L}\{f(t)\} \to 0$. ∎

REMARKS

(*i*) Throughout this chapter we shall be concerned primarily with functions that are both piecewise continuous and of exponential order. We note, however, that these two conditions are sufficient but not necessary for the existence of a Laplace transform. The function $f(t) = t^{-1/2}$ is not piecewise continuous on the interval $[0, \infty)$, but its Laplace transform exists. See Problem 42 in Exercises 7.1.

(*ii*) As a consequence of Theorem 7.1.3 we can say that functions of s such as $F_1(s) = 1$ and $F_2(s) = s/(s + 1)$ are not the Laplace transforms of piecewise continuous functions of exponential order, since $F_1(s) \nrightarrow 0$ and $F_2(s) \nrightarrow 0$ as $s \rightarrow \infty$. But you should not conclude from this that $F_1(s)$ and $F_2(s)$ are *not* Laplace transforms. There are other kinds of functions.

EXERCISES 7.1

Answers to selected odd-numbered problems begin on page ANS-10.

In Problems 1–18 use Definition 7.1.1 to find $\mathcal{L}\{f(t)\}$.

1. $f(t) = \begin{cases} -1, & 0 \le t < 1 \\ 1, & t \ge 1 \end{cases}$

2. $f(t) = \begin{cases} 4, & 0 \le t < 2 \\ 0, & t \ge 2 \end{cases}$

3. $f(t) = \begin{cases} t, & 0 \le t < 1 \\ 1, & t \ge 1 \end{cases}$

4. $f(t) = \begin{cases} 2t + 1, & 0 \le t < 1 \\ 0, & t \ge 1 \end{cases}$

5. $f(t) = \begin{cases} \sin t, & 0 \le t < \pi \\ 0, & t \ge \pi \end{cases}$

6. $f(t) = \begin{cases} 0, & 0 \le t < \pi/2 \\ \cos t, & t \ge \pi/2 \end{cases}$

7.

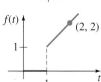

FIGURE 7.1.6   Graph for Problem 7

8.

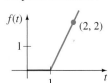

FIGURE 7.1.7   Graph for Problem 8

9.

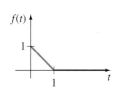

FIGURE 7.1.8   Graph for Problem 9

10.

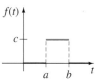

FIGURE 7.1.9   Graph for Problem 10

11. $f(t) = e^{t+7}$

12. $f(t) = e^{-2t-5}$

13. $f(t) = te^{4t}$

14. $f(t) = t^2 e^{-2t}$

15. $f(t) = e^{-t} \sin t$

16. $f(t) = e^t \cos t$

17. $f(t) = t \cos t$

18. $f(t) = t \sin t$

In Problems 19–36 use Theorem 7.1.1 to find $\mathcal{L}\{f(t)\}$.

19. $f(t) = 2t^4$

20. $f(t) = t^5$

21. $f(t) = 4t - 10$

22. $f(t) = 7t + 3$

23. $f(t) = t^2 + 6t - 3$

24. $f(t) = -4t^2 + 16t + 9$

25. $f(t) = (t + 1)^3$

26. $f(t) = (2t - 1)^3$

27. $f(t) = 1 + e^{4t}$

28. $f(t) = t^2 - e^{-9t} + 5$

29. $f(t) = (1 + e^{2t})^2$

30. $f(t) = (e^t - e^{-t})^2$

31. $f(t) = 4t^2 - 5 \sin 3t$

32. $f(t) = \cos 5t + \sin 2t$

33. $f(t) = \sinh kt$

34. $f(t) = \cosh kt$

35. $f(t) = e^t \sinh t$

36. $f(t) = e^{-t} \cosh t$

In Problems 37–40 find $\mathcal{L}\{f(t)\}$ by first using a trigonometric identity.

37. $f(t) = \sin 2t \cos 2t$

38. $f(t) = \cos^2 t$

39. $f(t) = \sin(4t + 5)$

40. $f(t) = 10 \cos\left(t - \dfrac{\pi}{6}\right)$

41. One definition of the **gamma function** is given by the improper integral $\Gamma(\alpha) = \int_0^\infty t^{\alpha-1} e^{-t} dt, \ \alpha > 0$.

(a) Show that $\Gamma(\alpha + 1) = \alpha\Gamma(\alpha)$.

(b) Show that $\mathscr{L}\{t^{\alpha}\} = \dfrac{\Gamma(\alpha + 1)}{s^{\alpha+1}}, \quad \alpha > -1$.

42. Use the fact that $\Gamma\left(\frac{1}{2}\right) = \sqrt{\pi}$ and Problem 41 to find the Laplace transform of

(a) $f(t) = t^{-1/2}$ **(b)** $f(t) = t^{1/2}$ **(c)** $f(t) = t^{3/2}$.

Discussion Problems

43. Make up a function $F(t)$ that is of exponential order but where $f(t) = F'(t)$ is not of exponential order. Make up a function f that is not of exponential order but whose Laplace transform exists.

44. Suppose that $\mathscr{L}\{f_1(t)\} = F_1(s)$ for $s > c_1$ and that $\mathscr{L}\{f_2(t)\} = F_2(s)$ for $s > c_2$. When does

$$\mathscr{L}\{f_1(t) + f_2(t)\} = F_1(s) + F_2(s)?$$

45. Figure 7.1.4 suggests, but does not prove, that the function $f(t) = e^{t^2}$ is not of exponential order. How does the observation that $t^2 > \ln M + ct$, for $M > 0$ and t sufficiently large, show that $e^{t^2} > Me^{ct}$ for any c?

46. Use part (c) of Theorem 7.1.1 to show that

$$\mathscr{L}\{e^{(a+ib)t}\} = \frac{s - a + ib}{(s - a)^2 + b^2}, \text{ where } a \text{ and } b \text{ are real}$$

and $i^2 = -1$. Show how Euler's formula (page 134) can then be used to deduce the results

$$\mathscr{L}\{e^{at}\cos bt\} = \frac{s - a}{(s - a)^2 + b^2}$$

$$\mathscr{L}\{e^{at}\sin bt\} = \frac{b}{(s - a)^2 + b^2}.$$

47. Under what conditions is a linear function $f(x) = mx + b, m \neq 0$, a linear transform?

48. The proof of part (b) of Theorem 7.1.1 requires the use of mathematical induction. Show that if $\mathscr{L}\{t^{n-1}\} = (n - 1)!/s^n$ is *assumed* to be true, then $\mathscr{L}\{t^n\} = n!/s^{n+1}$ follows.

7.2 INVERSE TRANSFORMS AND TRANSFORMS OF DERIVATIVES

REVIEW MATERIAL

- Partial fraction decomposition
- See the *Student Resource and Solutions Manual*

INTRODUCTION   In this section we take a few small steps into an investigation of how the Laplace transform can be used to solve certain types of equations for an unknown function. We begin the discussion with the concept of the inverse Laplace transform or, more precisely, the inverse of a Laplace transform $F(s)$. After some important preliminary background material on the Laplace transform of derivatives $f'(t), f''(t), \ldots$, we then illustrate how both the Laplace transform and the inverse Laplace transform come into play in solving some simple ordinary differential equations.

7.2.1   INVERSE TRANSFORMS

THE INVERSE PROBLEM   If $F(s)$ represents the Laplace transform of a function $f(t)$, that is, $\mathscr{L}\{f(t)\} = F(s)$, we then say $f(t)$ is the **inverse Laplace transform** of $F(s)$ and write $f(t) = \mathscr{L}^{-1}\{F(s)\}$. For example, from Examples 1, 2, and 3 of Section 7.1 we have, respectively,

Transform	Inverse Transform
$\mathscr{L}\{1\} = \dfrac{1}{s}$	$1 = \mathscr{L}^{-1}\left\{\dfrac{1}{s}\right\}$
$\mathscr{L}\{t\} = \dfrac{1}{s^2}$	$t = \mathscr{L}^{-1}\left\{\dfrac{1}{s^2}\right\}$
$\mathscr{L}\{e^{-3t}\} = \dfrac{1}{s + 3}$	$e^{-3t} = \mathscr{L}^{-1}\left\{\dfrac{1}{s + 3}\right\}$

We shall see shortly that in the application of the Laplace transform to equations we are not able to determine an unknown function $f(t)$ directly; rather, we are able to solve for the Laplace transform $F(s)$ of $f(t)$; but from that knowledge we ascertain f by computing $f(t) = \mathscr{L}^{-1}\{F(s)\}$. The idea is simply this: Suppose $F(s) = \dfrac{-2s + 6}{s^2 + 4}$ is a Laplace transform; find a function $f(t)$ such that $\mathscr{L}\{f(t)\} = F(s)$.

We shall show how to solve this last problem in Example 2.

For future reference the analogue of Theorem 7.1.1 for the inverse transform is presented as our next theorem.

THEOREM 7.2.1   Some Inverse Transforms

$$\textbf{(a)} \ \ 1 = \mathscr{L}^{-1}\left\{\frac{1}{s}\right\}$$

$$\textbf{(b)} \ \ t^n = \mathscr{L}^{-1}\left\{\frac{n!}{s^{n+1}}\right\}, \quad n = 1, 2, 3, \ldots \qquad \textbf{(c)} \ \ e^{at} = \mathscr{L}^{-1}\left\{\frac{1}{s - a}\right\}$$

$$\textbf{(d)} \ \ \sin kt = \mathscr{L}^{-1}\left\{\frac{k}{s^2 + k^2}\right\} \qquad\qquad \textbf{(e)} \ \ \cos kt = \mathscr{L}^{-1}\left\{\frac{s}{s^2 + k^2}\right\}$$

$$\textbf{(f)} \ \ \sinh kt = \mathscr{L}^{-1}\left\{\frac{k}{s^2 - k^2}\right\} \qquad\qquad \textbf{(g)} \ \ \cosh kt = \mathscr{L}^{-1}\left\{\frac{s}{s^2 - k^2}\right\}$$

In evaluating inverse transforms, it often happens that a function of s under consideration does not match *exactly* the form of a Laplace transform $F(s)$ given in a table. It may be necessary to "fix up" the function of s by multiplying and dividing by an appropriate constant.

EXAMPLE 1   Applying Theorem 7.2.1

Evaluate   **(a)** $\mathscr{L}^{-1}\left\{\dfrac{1}{s^5}\right\}$ **(b)** $\mathscr{L}^{-1}\left\{\dfrac{1}{s^2 + 7}\right\}$.

SOLUTION   (a) To match the form given in part (b) of Theorem 7.2.1, we identify $n + 1 = 5$ or $n = 4$ and then multiply and divide by $4!$:

$$\mathscr{L}^{-1}\left\{\frac{1}{s^5}\right\} = \frac{1}{4!}\mathscr{L}^{-1}\left\{\frac{4!}{s^5}\right\} = \frac{1}{24}t^4.$$

(b) To match the form given in part (d) of Theorem 7.2.1, we identify $k^2 = 7$, so $k = \sqrt{7}$. We fix up the expression by multiplying and dividing by $\sqrt{7}$:

$$\mathscr{L}^{-1}\left\{\frac{1}{s^2 + 7}\right\} = \frac{1}{\sqrt{7}}\mathscr{L}^{-1}\left\{\frac{\sqrt{7}}{s^2 + 7}\right\} = \frac{1}{\sqrt{7}}\sin\sqrt{7}t. \qquad \blacksquare$$

$\mathscr{L}^{-1}$ IS A LINEAR TRANSFORM   The inverse Laplace transform is also a linear transform; that is, for constants α and β

$$\mathscr{L}^{-1}\{\alpha F(s) + \beta G(s)\} = \alpha\mathscr{L}^{-1}\{F(s)\} + \beta\mathscr{L}^{-1}\{G(s)\}, \qquad (1)$$

where F and G are the transforms of some functions f and g. Like (2) of Section 7.1, (1) extends to any finite linear combination of Laplace transforms.

| **EXAMPLE 2** **Termwise Division and Linearity** |

Evaluate $\mathcal{L}^{-1}\left\{\dfrac{-2s+6}{s^2+4}\right\}$.

SOLUTION We first rewrite the given function of s as two expressions by means of termwise division and then use (1):

$$
\mathcal{L}^{-1}\left\{\frac{-2s+6}{s^2+4}\right\} \overset{\substack{\text{termwise}\\ \text{division }\downarrow}}{=} \mathcal{L}^{-1}\left\{\frac{-2s}{s^2+4}+\frac{6}{s^2+4}\right\} \overset{\substack{\text{linearity and fixing}\\ \text{up constants }\downarrow}}{=} -2\mathcal{L}^{-1}\left\{\frac{s}{s^2+4}\right\} + \frac{6}{2}\,\mathcal{L}^{-1}\left\{\frac{2}{s^2+4}\right\} \quad (2)
$$

$$= -2\cos 2t + 3\sin 2t. \quad \leftarrow \text{parts (e) and (d)}$$
$$\quad \text{of Theorem 7.2.1 with } k = 2 \qquad \blacksquare$$

PARTIAL FRACTIONS Partial fractions play an important role in finding inverse Laplace transforms. The decomposition of a rational expression into component fractions can be done quickly by means of a single command on most computer algebra systems. Indeed, some CASs have packages that implement Laplace transform and inverse Laplace transform commands. But for those of you without access to such software, we will review in this and subsequent sections some of the basic algebra in the important cases in which the denominator of a Laplace transform $F(s)$ contains distinct linear factors, repeated linear factors, and quadratic polynomials with no real factors. Although we shall examine each of these cases as this chapter develops, it still might be a good idea for you to consult either a calculus text or a current precalculus text for a more comprehensive review of this theory.

The following example illustrates partial fraction decomposition in the case when the denominator of $F(s)$ is factorable into *distinct linear factors*.

| **EXAMPLE 3** **Partial Fractions: Distinct Linear Factors** |

Evaluate $\mathcal{L}^{-1}\left\{\dfrac{s^2+6s+9}{(s-1)(s-2)(s+4)}\right\}$.

SOLUTION There exist unique real constants A, B, and C so that

$$
\frac{s^2+6s+9}{(s-1)(s-2)(s+4)} = \frac{A}{s-1}+\frac{B}{s-2}+\frac{C}{s+4}
$$

$$
= \frac{A(s-2)(s+4)+B(s-1)(s+4)+C(s-1)(s-2)}{(s-1)(s-2)(s+4)}.
$$

Since the denominators are identical, the numerators are identical:

$$s^2+6s+9 = A(s-2)(s+4)+B(s-1)(s+4)+C(s-1)(s-2). \quad (3)$$

By comparing coefficients of powers of s on both sides of the equality, we know that (3) is equivalent to a system of three equations in the three unknowns A, B, and C. However, there is a shortcut for determining these unknowns. If we set $s = 1$, $s = 2$, and $s = -4$ in (3), we obtain, respectively,

$$16 = A(-1)(5), \qquad 25 = B(1)(6), \qquad \text{and} \qquad 1 = C(-5)(-6),$$

and so $A = -\frac{16}{5}$, $B = \frac{25}{6}$, and $C = \frac{1}{30}$. Hence the partial fraction decomposition is

$$
\frac{s^2+6s+9}{(s-1)(s-2)(s+4)} = -\frac{16/5}{s-1}+\frac{25/6}{s-2}+\frac{1/30}{s+4}, \quad (4)
$$

and thus, from the linearity of $\mathcal{L}^{-1}$ and part (c) of Theorem 7.2.1,

$$\mathcal{L}^{-1}\left\{\frac{s^2 + 6s + 9}{(s - 1)(s - 2)(s + 4)}\right\} = -\frac{16}{5}\mathcal{L}^{-1}\left\{\frac{1}{s - 1}\right\} + \frac{25}{6}\mathcal{L}^{-1}\left\{\frac{1}{s - 2}\right\} + \frac{1}{30}\mathcal{L}^{-1}\left\{\frac{1}{s + 4}\right\}$$

$$= -\frac{16}{5}e^t + \frac{25}{6}e^{2t} + \frac{1}{30}e^{-4t}. \tag{5} \blacksquare$$

7.2.2 TRANSFORMS OF DERIVATIVES

TRANSFORM A DERIVATIVE As was pointed out in the introduction to this chapter, our immediate goal is to use the Laplace transform to solve differential equations. To that end we need to evaluate quantities such as $\mathcal{L}\{dy/dt\}$ and $\mathcal{L}\{d^2y/dt^2\}$. For example, if f' is continuous for $t \geq 0$, then integration by parts gives

$$\mathcal{L}\{f'(t)\} = \int_0^\infty e^{-st}f'(t)\,dt = e^{-st}f(t)\Big|_0^\infty + s\int_0^\infty e^{-st}f(t)\,dt$$

$$= -f(0) + s\mathcal{L}\{f(t)\}$$

or $\qquad \mathcal{L}\{f'(t)\} = sF(s) - f(0). \tag{6}$

Here we have assumed that $e^{-st}f(t) \to 0$ as $t \to \infty$. Similarly, with the aid of (6),

$$\mathcal{L}\{f''(t)\} = \int_0^\infty e^{-st}f''(t)\,dt = e^{-st}f'(t)\Big|_0^\infty + s\int_0^\infty e^{-st}f'(t)\,dt$$

$$= -f'(0) + s\mathcal{L}\{f'(t)\}$$

$$= s[sF(s) - f(0)] - f'(0) \qquad \leftarrow \text{from (6)}$$

or $\qquad \mathcal{L}\{f''(t)\} = s^2F(s) - sf(0) - f'(0). \tag{7}$

In like manner it can be shown that

$$\mathcal{L}\{f'''(t)\} = s^3F(s) - s^2f(0) - sf'(0) - f''(0). \tag{8}$$

The recursive nature of the Laplace transform of the derivatives of a function f should be apparent from the results in (6), (7), and (8). The next theorem gives the Laplace transform of the nth derivative of f. The proof is omitted.

THEOREM 7.2.2 **Transform of a Derivative**

If $f, f', \ldots, f^{(n-1)}$ are continuous on $[0, \infty)$ and are of exponential order and if $f^{(n)}(t)$ is piecewise continuous on $[0, \infty)$, then

$$\mathcal{L}\{f^{(n)}(t)\} = s^nF(s) - s^{n-1}f(0) - s^{n-2}f'(0) - \cdots - f^{(n-1)}(0),$$

where $F(s) = \mathcal{L}\{f(t)\}$.

SOLVING LINEAR ODEs It is apparent from the general result given in Theorem 7.2.2 that $\mathcal{L}\{d^n y/dt^n\}$ depends on $Y(s) = \mathcal{L}\{y(t)\}$ and the $n - 1$ derivatives of $y(t)$ evaluated at $t = 0$. This property makes the Laplace transform ideally suited for solving linear initial-value problems in which the differential equation has *constant coefficients*. Such a differential equation is simply a linear combination of terms $y, y', y'', \ldots, y^{(n)}$:

$$a_n\frac{d^n y}{dt^n} + a_{n-1}\frac{d^{n-1}y}{dt^{n-1}} + \cdots + a_0 y = g(t),$$

$$y(0) = y_0, y'(0) = y_1, \ldots, y^{(n-1)}(0) = y_{n-1},$$

where the a_i, $i = 0, 1, \ldots, n$ and $y_0, y_1, \ldots, y_{n-1}$ are constants. By the linearity property the Laplace transform of this linear combination is a linear combination of Laplace transforms:

$$a_n \mathcal{L}\left\{\frac{d^n y}{dt^n}\right\} + a_{n-1} \mathcal{L}\left\{\frac{d^{n-1} y}{dt^{n-1}}\right\} + \cdots + a_0 \mathcal{L}\{y\} = \mathcal{L}\{g(t)\}. \qquad (9)$$

From Theorem 7.2.2, (9) becomes

$$a_n[s^n Y(s) - s^{n-1} y(0) - \cdots - y^{(n-1)}(0)]$$
$$+ a_{n-1}[s^{n-1} Y(s) - s^{n-2} y(0) - \cdots - y^{(n-2)}(0)] + \cdots + a_0 Y(s) = G(s), \qquad (10)$$

where $\mathcal{L}\{y(t)\} = Y(s)$ and $\mathcal{L}\{g(t)\} = G(s)$. In other words, *the Laplace transform of a linear differential equation with constant coefficients becomes an algebraic equation in $Y(s)$.* If we solve the general transformed equation (10) for the symbol $Y(s)$, we first obtain $P(s)Y(s) = Q(s) + G(s)$ and then write

$$Y(s) = \frac{Q(s)}{P(s)} + \frac{G(s)}{P(s)}, \qquad (11)$$

where $P(s) = a_n s^n + a_{n-1} s^{n-1} + \cdots + a_0$, $Q(s)$ is a polynomial in s of degree less than or equal to $n - 1$ consisting of the various products of the coefficients a_i, $i = 1, \ldots, n$ and the prescribed initial conditions $y_0, y_1, \ldots, y_{n-1}$, and $G(s)$ is the Laplace transform of $g(t)$.[*] Typically, we put the two terms in (11) over the least common denominator and then decompose the expression into two or more partial fractions. Finally, the solution $y(t)$ of the original initial-value problem is $y(t) = \mathcal{L}^{-1}\{Y(s)\}$, where the inverse transform is done term by term.

The procedure is summarized in the following diagram.

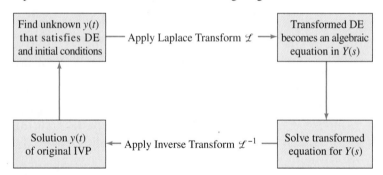

The next example illustrates the foregoing method of solving DEs, as well as partial fraction decomposition in the case when the denominator of $Y(s)$ contains a *quadratic polynomial with no real factors.*

EXAMPLE 4   Solving a First-Order IVP

Use the Laplace transform to solve the initial-value problem

$$\frac{dy}{dt} + 3y = 13 \sin 2t, \quad y(0) = 6.$$

SOLUTION We first take the transform of each member of the differential equation:

$$\mathcal{L}\left\{\frac{dy}{dt}\right\} + 3\mathcal{L}\{y\} = 13\mathcal{L}\{\sin 2t\}. \qquad (12)$$

---

[*]The polynomial $P(s)$ is the same as the nth-degree auxiliary polynomial in (12) in Section 4.3 with the usual symbol m replaced by s.

From (6), $\mathcal{L}\{dy/dt\} = sY(s) - y(0) = sY(s) - 6$, and from part (d) of Theorem 7.1.1, $\mathcal{L}\{\sin 2t\} = 2/(s^2 + 4)$, so (12) is the same as

$$sY(s) - 6 + 3Y(s) = \frac{26}{s^2 + 4} \quad \text{or} \quad (s + 3)Y(s) = 6 + \frac{26}{s^2 + 4}.$$

Solving the last equation for $Y(s)$, we get

$$Y(s) = \frac{6}{s + 3} + \frac{26}{(s + 3)(s^2 + 4)} = \frac{6s^2 + 50}{(s + 3)(s^2 + 4)}. \tag{13}$$

Since the quadratic polynomial $s^2 + 4$ does not factor using real numbers, its assumed numerator in the partial fraction decomposition is a linear polynomial in s:

$$\frac{6s^2 + 50}{(s + 3)(s^2 + 4)} = \frac{A}{s + 3} + \frac{Bs + C}{s^2 + 4}.$$

Putting the right-hand side of the equality over a common denominator and equating numerators gives $6s^2 + 50 = A(s^2 + 4) + (Bs + C)(s + 3)$. Setting $s = -3$ then immediately yields $A = 8$. Since the denominator has no more real zeros, we equate the coefficients of s^2 and s: $6 = A + B$ and $0 = 3B + C$. Using the value of A in the first equation gives $B = -2$, and then using this last value in the second equation gives $C = 6$. Thus

$$Y(s) = \frac{6s^2 + 50}{(s + 3)(s^2 + 4)} = \frac{8}{s + 3} + \frac{-2s + 6}{s^2 + 4}.$$

We are not quite finished because the last rational expression still has to be written as two fractions. This was done by termwise division in Example 2. From (2) of that example,

$$y(t) = 8\mathcal{L}^{-1}\left\{\frac{1}{s + 3}\right\} - 2\mathcal{L}^{-1}\left\{\frac{s}{s^2 + 4}\right\} + 3\mathcal{L}^{-1}\left\{\frac{2}{s^2 + 4}\right\}.$$

It follows from parts (c), (d), and (e) of Theorem 7.2.1 that the solution of the initial-value problem is $y(t) = 8e^{-3t} - 2\cos 2t + 3\sin 2t$. ∎

EXAMPLE 5 Solving a Second-Order IVP

Solve $y'' - 3y' + 2y = e^{-4t}, \quad y(0) = 1, \quad y'(0) = 5$.

SOLUTION Proceeding as in Example 4, we transform the DE. We take the sum of the transforms of each term, use (6) and (7), use the given initial conditions, use (c) of Theorem 7.1.1, and then solve for $Y(s)$:

$$\mathcal{L}\left\{\frac{d^2y}{dt^2}\right\} - 3\mathcal{L}\left\{\frac{dy}{dt}\right\} + 2\mathcal{L}\{y\} = \mathcal{L}\{e^{-4t}\}$$

$$s^2Y(s) - sy(0) - y'(0) - 3[sY(s) - y(0)] + 2Y(s) = \frac{1}{s + 4}$$

$$(s^2 - 3s + 2)Y(s) = s + 2 + \frac{1}{s + 4}$$

$$Y(s) = \frac{s + 2}{s^2 - 3s + 2} + \frac{1}{(s^2 - 3s + 2)(s + 4)} = \frac{s^2 + 6s + 9}{(s - 1)(s - 2)(s + 4)}. \tag{14}$$

The details of the partial fraction decomposition of $Y(s)$ have already been carried out in Example 3. In view of the results in (4) and (5) we have the solution of the initial-value problem

$$y(t) = \mathcal{L}^{-1}\{Y(s)\} = -\frac{16}{5}e^t + \frac{25}{6}e^{2t} + \frac{1}{30}e^{-4t}. \quad ■$$

Examples 4 and 5 illustrate the basic procedure for using the Laplace transform to solve a linear initial-value problem, but these examples may appear to demonstrate a method that is not much better than the approach to such problems outlined in Sections 2.3 and 4.3–4.6. Don't draw any negative conclusions from only two examples. Yes, there is a lot of algebra inherent in the use of the Laplace transform, *but* observe that we do not have to use variation of parameters or worry about the cases and algebra in the method of undetermined coefficients. Moreover, since the method incorporates the prescribed initial conditions directly into the solution, there is no need for the separate operation of applying the initial conditions to the general solution $y = c_1 y_1 + c_2 y_2 + \cdots + c_n y_n + y_p$ of the DE to find specific constants in a particular solution of the IVP.

The Laplace transform has many operational properties. In the sections that follow we will examine some of these properties and see how they enable us to solve problems of greater complexity.

REMARKS

(*i*) The inverse Laplace transform of a function $F(s)$ may not be unique; in other words, it is possible that $\mathscr{L}\{f_1(t)\} = \mathscr{L}\{f_2(t)\}$ and yet $f_1 \neq f_2$. For our purposes this is not anything to be concerned about. If f_1 and f_2 are piecewise continuous on $[0, \infty)$ and of exponential order, then f_1 and f_2 are *essentially* the same. See Problem 44 in Exercises 7.2. However, if f_1 and f_2 are continuous on $[0, \infty)$ and $\mathscr{L}\{f_1(t)\} = \mathscr{L}\{f_2(t)\}$, then $f_1 = f_2$ on the interval.

(*ii*) This remark is for those of you who will be required to do partial fraction decompositions by hand. There is another way of determining the coefficients in a partial fraction decomposition in the special case when $\mathscr{L}\{f(t)\} = F(s)$ is a rational function of s and the denominator of F is a product of *distinct* linear factors. Let us illustrate by reexamining Example 3. Suppose we multiply both sides of the assumed decomposition

$$\frac{s^2 + 6s + 9}{(s - 1)(s - 2)(s + 4)} = \frac{A}{s - 1} + \frac{B}{s - 2} + \frac{C}{s + 4} \tag{15}$$

by, say, $s - 1$, simplify, and then set $s = 1$. Since the coefficients of B and C on the right-hand side of the equality are zero, we get

$$\left. \frac{s^2 + 6s + 9}{(s - 2)(s + 4)} \right|_{s=1} = A \quad \text{or} \quad A = -\frac{16}{5}.$$

Written another way,

$$\left. \frac{s^2 + 6s + 9}{\boxed{(s - 1)}(s - 2)(s + 4)} \right|_{s=1} = -\frac{16}{5} = A,$$

where we have shaded, or *covered up*, the factor that canceled when the left-hand side was multiplied by $s - 1$. Now to obtain B and C, we simply evaluate the left-hand side of (15) while covering up, in turn, $s - 2$ and $s + 4$:

$$\left. \frac{s^2 + 6s + 9}{(s - 1)\boxed{(s - 2)}(s + 4)} \right|_{s=2} = \frac{25}{6} = B$$

and $$\left. \frac{s^2 + 6s + 9}{(s - 1)(s - 2)\boxed{(s + 4)}} \right|_{s=-4} = \frac{1}{30} = C.$$

The desired decomposition (15) is given in (4). This special technique for determining coefficients is naturally known as the **cover-up method.**

(*iii*) In this remark we continue our introduction to the terminology of dynamical systems. Because of (9) and (10) the Laplace transform is well adapted to *linear* dynamical systems. The polynomial $P(s) = a_n s^n + a_{n-1} s^{n-1} + \cdots + a_0$ in (11) is the total coefficient of $Y(s)$ in (10) and is simply the left-hand side of the DE with the derivatives $d^k y/dt^k$ replaced by powers s^k, $k = 0, 1, \ldots, n$. It is usual practice to call the reciprocal of $P(s)$—namely, $W(s) = 1/P(s)$—the **transfer function** of the system and write (11) as

$$Y(s) = W(s)Q(s) + W(s)G(s). \tag{16}$$

In this manner we have separated, in an additive sense, the effects on the response that are due to the initial conditions (that is, $W(s)Q(s)$) from those due to the input function g (that is, $W(s)G(s)$). See (13) and (14). Hence the response $y(t)$ of the system is a superposition of two responses:

$$y(t) = \mathcal{L}^{-1}\{W(s)Q(s)\} + \mathcal{L}^{-1}\{W(s)G(s)\} = y_0(t) + y_1(t).$$

If the input is $g(t) = 0$, then the solution of the problem is $y_0(t) = \mathcal{L}^{-1}\{W(s)Q(s)\}$. This solution is called the **zero-input response** of the system. On the other hand, the function $y_1(t) = \mathcal{L}^{-1}\{W(s)G(s)\}$ is the output due to the input $g(t)$. Now if the initial state of the system is the zero state (all the initial conditions are zero), then $Q(s) = 0$, and so the only solution of the initial-value problem is $y_1(t)$. The latter solution is called the **zero-state response** of the system. Both $y_0(t)$ and $y_1(t)$ are particular solutions: $y_0(t)$ is a solution of the IVP consisting of the associated homogeneous equation with the given initial conditions, and $y_1(t)$ is a solution of the IVP consisting of the nonhomogeneous equation with zero initial conditions. In Example 5 we see from (14) that the transfer function is $W(s) = 1/(s^2 - 3s + 2)$, the zero-input response is

$$y_0(t) = \mathcal{L}^{-1}\left\{\frac{s + 2}{(s - 1)(s - 2)}\right\} = -3e^t + 4e^{2t},$$

and the zero-state response is

$$y_1(t) = \mathcal{L}^{-1}\left\{\frac{1}{(s - 1)(s - 2)(s + 4)}\right\} = -\frac{1}{5}e^t + \frac{1}{6}e^{2t} + \frac{1}{30}e^{-4t}.$$

Verify that the sum of $y_0(t)$ and $y_1(t)$ is the solution $y(t)$ in Example 5 and that $y_0(0) = 1$, $y_0'(0) = 5$, whereas $y_1(0) = 0$, $y_1'(0) = 0$.

EXERCISES 7.2

Answers to selected odd-numbered problems begin on page ANS-10.

7.2.1 INVERSE TRANSFORMS

In Problems 1–30 use appropriate algebra and Theorem 7.2.1 to find the given inverse Laplace transform.

1. $\mathcal{L}^{-1}\left\{\dfrac{1}{s^3}\right\}$

2. $\mathcal{L}^{-1}\left\{\dfrac{1}{s^4}\right\}$

3. $\mathcal{L}^{-1}\left\{\dfrac{1}{s^2} - \dfrac{48}{s^5}\right\}$

4. $\mathcal{L}^{-1}\left\{\left(\dfrac{2}{s} - \dfrac{1}{s^3}\right)^2\right\}$

5. $\mathcal{L}^{-1}\left\{\dfrac{(s + 1)^3}{s^4}\right\}$

6. $\mathcal{L}^{-1}\left\{\dfrac{(s + 2)^2}{s^3}\right\}$

7. $\mathcal{L}^{-1}\left\{\dfrac{1}{s^2} - \dfrac{1}{s} + \dfrac{1}{s - 2}\right\}$

8. $\mathcal{L}^{-1}\left\{\dfrac{4}{s} + \dfrac{6}{s^5} - \dfrac{1}{s + 8}\right\}$

9. $\mathcal{L}^{-1}\left\{\dfrac{1}{4s + 1}\right\}$

10. $\mathcal{L}^{-1}\left\{\dfrac{1}{5s - 2}\right\}$

11. $\mathcal{L}^{-1}\left\{\dfrac{5}{s^2 + 49}\right\}$

12. $\mathcal{L}^{-1}\left\{\dfrac{10s}{s^2 + 16}\right\}$

13. $\mathcal{L}^{-1}\left\{\dfrac{4s}{4s^2 + 1}\right\}$

14. $\mathcal{L}^{-1}\left\{\dfrac{1}{4s^2 + 1}\right\}$

15. $\mathcal{L}^{-1}\left\{\dfrac{2s - 6}{s^2 + 9}\right\}$

16. $\mathcal{L}^{-1}\left\{\dfrac{s + 1}{s^2 + 2}\right\}$

17. $\mathscr{L}^{-1}\left\{\dfrac{1}{s^2 + 3s}\right\}$

18. $\mathscr{L}^{-1}\left\{\dfrac{s + 1}{s^2 - 4s}\right\}$

19. $\mathscr{L}^{-1}\left\{\dfrac{s}{s^2 + 2s - 3}\right\}$

20. $\mathscr{L}^{-1}\left\{\dfrac{1}{s^2 + s - 20}\right\}$

21. $\mathscr{L}^{-1}\left\{\dfrac{0.9s}{(s - 0.1)(s + 0.2)}\right\}$

22. $\mathscr{L}^{-1}\left\{\dfrac{s - 3}{(s - \sqrt{3})(s + \sqrt{3})}\right\}$

23. $\mathscr{L}^{-1}\left\{\dfrac{s}{(s - 2)(s - 3)(s - 6)}\right\}$

24. $\mathscr{L}^{-1}\left\{\dfrac{s^2 + 1}{s(s - 1)(s + 1)(s - 2)}\right\}$

25. $\mathscr{L}^{-1}\left\{\dfrac{1}{s^3 + 5s}\right\}$

26. $\mathscr{L}^{-1}\left\{\dfrac{s}{(s + 2)(s^2 + 4)}\right\}$

27. $\mathscr{L}^{-1}\left\{\dfrac{2s - 4}{(s^2 + s)(s^2 + 1)}\right\}$

28. $\mathscr{L}^{-1}\left\{\dfrac{1}{s^4 - 9}\right\}$

29. $\mathscr{L}^{-1}\left\{\dfrac{1}{(s^2 + 1)(s^2 + 4)}\right\}$

30. $\mathscr{L}^{-1}\left\{\dfrac{6s + 3}{s^4 + 5s^2 + 4}\right\}$

7.2.2 TRANSFORMS OF DERIVATIVES

In Problems 31–40 use the Laplace transform to solve the given initial-value problem.

31. $\dfrac{dy}{dt} - y = 1, \quad y(0) = 0$

32. $2\dfrac{dy}{dt} + y = 0, \quad y(0) = -3$

33. $y' + 6y = e^{4t}, \quad y(0) = 2$

34. $y' - y = 2\cos 5t, \quad y(0) = 0$

35. $y'' + 5y' + 4y = 0, \quad y(0) = 1, \quad y'(0) = 0$

36. $y'' - 4y' = 6e^{3t} - 3e^{-t}, \quad y(0) = 1, \quad y'(0) = -1$

37. $y'' + y = \sqrt{2}\sin\sqrt{2}t, \quad y(0) = 10, \quad y'(0) = 0$

38. $y'' + 9y = e^t, \quad y(0) = 0, \quad y'(0) = 0$

39. $2y''' + 3y'' - 3y' - 2y = e^{-t}, \quad y(0) = 0, \quad y'(0) = 0,$
$y''(0) = 1$

40. $y''' + 2y'' - y' - 2y = \sin 3t, \quad y(0) = 0, \quad y'(0) = 0,$
$y''(0) = 1$

The inverse forms of the results in Problem 46 in Exercises 7.1 are

$$\mathscr{L}^{-1}\left\{\frac{s - a}{(s - a)^2 + b^2}\right\} = e^{at}\cos bt$$

$$\mathscr{L}^{-1}\left\{\frac{b}{(s - a)^2 + b^2}\right\} = e^{at}\sin bt.$$

In Problems 41 and 42 use the Laplace transform and these inverses to solve the given initial-value problem.

41. $y' + y = e^{-3t}\cos 2t, \quad y(0) = 0$

42. $y'' - 2y' + 5y = 0, \quad y(0) = 1, \quad y'(0) = 3$

Discussion Problems

43. (a) With a slight change in notation the transform in (6) is the same as

$$\mathscr{L}\{f'(t)\} = s\mathscr{L}\{f(t)\} - f(0).$$

With $f(t) = te^{at}$, discuss how this result in conjunction with (c) of Theorem 7.1.1 can be used to evaluate $\mathscr{L}\{te^{at}\}$.

(b) Proceed as in part (a), but this time discuss how to use (7) with $f(t) = t\sin kt$ in conjunction with (d) and (e) of Theorem 7.1.1 to evaluate $\mathscr{L}\{t\sin kt\}$.

44. Make up two functions f_1 and f_2 that have the same Laplace transform. Do not think profound thoughts.

45. Reread *Remark (iii)* on page 269. Find the zero-input and the zero-state response for the IVP in Problem 36.

46. Suppose $f(t)$ is a function for which $f'(t)$ is piecewise continuous and of exponential order c. Use results in this section and Section 7.1 to justify

$$f(0) = \lim_{s \to \infty} sF(s),$$

where $F(s) = \mathscr{L}\{f(t)\}$. Verify this result with $f(t) = \cos kt$.

7.3	OPERATIONAL PROPERTIES I

REVIEW MATERIAL
- Keep practicing partial fraction decomposition
- Completion of the square

INTRODUCTION It is not convenient to use Definition 7.1.1 each time we wish to find the Laplace transform of a function $f(t)$. For example, the integration by parts involved in evaluating, say, $\mathscr{L}\{e^t t^2 \sin 3t\}$ is formidable, to say the least. In this section and the next we present several labor-saving operational properties of the Laplace transform that enable us to build up a more extensive list of transforms (see the table in Appendix III) without having to resort to the basic definition and integration.

7.3.1 TRANSLATION ON THE *s*-AXIS

A TRANSLATION Evaluating transforms such as $\mathscr{L}\{e^{5t}t^3\}$ and $\mathscr{L}\{e^{-2t}\cos 4t\}$ is straightforward provided that we know (and we do) $\mathscr{L}\{t^3\}$ and $\mathscr{L}\{\cos 4t\}$. In general, if we know the Laplace transform of a function f, $\mathscr{L}\{f(t)\} = F(s)$, it is possible to compute the Laplace transform of an exponential multiple of f, that is, $\mathscr{L}\{e^{at}f(t)\}$, with no additional effort other than *translating*, or *shifting*, the transform $F(s)$ to $F(s - a)$. This result is known as the **first translation theorem** or **first shifting theorem**.

THEOREM 7.3.1   **First Translation Theorem**

If $\mathscr{L}\{f(t)\} = F(s)$ and a is any real number, then

$$\mathscr{L}\{e^{at}f(t)\} = F(s - a).$$

PROOF   The proof is immediate, since by Definition 7.1.1

$$\mathscr{L}\{e^{at}f(t)\} = \int_0^\infty e^{-st}e^{at}f(t)\,dt = \int_0^\infty e^{-(s-a)t}f(t)\,dt = F(s - a). \qquad \blacksquare$$

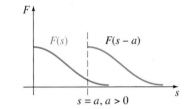

If we consider s a real variable, then the graph of $F(s - a)$ is the graph of $F(s)$ shifted on the s-axis by the amount $|a|$. If $a > 0$, the graph of $F(s)$ is shifted a units to the right, whereas if $a < 0$, the graph is shifted $|a|$ units to the left. See Figure 7.3.1.

FIGURE 7.3.1   Shift on s-axis

For emphasis it is sometimes useful to use the symbolism

$$\mathscr{L}\{e^{at}f(t)\} = \mathscr{L}\{f(t)\}\big|_{s \to s-a},$$

where $s \to s - a$ means that in the Laplace transform $F(s)$ of $f(t)$ we replace the symbol s wherever it appears by $s - a$.

EXAMPLE 1   **Using the First Translation Theorem**

Evaluate   **(a)** $\mathscr{L}\{e^{5t}t^3\}$ **(b)** $\mathscr{L}\{e^{-2t}\cos 4t\}$.

SOLUTION   The results follow from Theorems 7.1.1 and 7.3.1.

(a) $\mathscr{L}\{e^{5t}t^3\} = \mathscr{L}\{t^3\}\big|_{s \to s-5} = \dfrac{3!}{s^4}\bigg|_{s \to s-5} = \dfrac{6}{(s - 5)^4}$

(b) $\mathscr{L}\{e^{-2t}\cos 4t\} = \mathscr{L}\{\cos 4t\}\big|_{s \to s-(-2)} = \dfrac{s}{s^2 + 16}\bigg|_{s \to s+2} = \dfrac{s + 2}{(s + 2)^2 + 16}$ $\blacksquare$

INVERSE FORM OF THEOREM 7.3.1   To compute the inverse of $F(s - a)$, we must recognize $F(s)$, find $f(t)$ by taking the inverse Laplace transform of $F(s)$, and then multiply $f(t)$ by the exponential function e^{at}. This procedure can be summarized symbolically in the following manner:

$$\mathscr{L}^{-1}\{F(s - a)\} = \mathscr{L}^{-1}\{F(s)\big|_{s \to s-a}\} = e^{at}f(t), \qquad (1)$$

where $f(t) = \mathscr{L}^{-1}\{F(s)\}$.

The first part of the next example illustrates partial fraction decomposition in the case when the denominator of $Y(s)$ contains *repeated linear factors*.

> **EXAMPLE 2   Partial Fractions: Repeated Linear Factors**

Evaluate   **(a)** $\mathscr{L}^{-1}\left\{\dfrac{2s+5}{(s-3)^2}\right\}$ **(b)** $\mathscr{L}^{-1}\left\{\dfrac{s/2+5/3}{s^2+4s+6}\right\}$.

SOLUTION   (a) A repeated linear factor is a term $(s-a)^n$, where a is a real number and n is a positive integer ≥ 2. Recall that if $(s-a)^n$ appears in the denominator of a rational expression, then the assumed decomposition contains n partial fractions with constant numerators and denominators $s-a$, $(s-a)^2$, ..., $(s-a)^n$. Hence with $a=3$ and $n=2$ we write

$$\frac{2s+5}{(s-3)^2} = \frac{A}{s-3} + \frac{B}{(s-3)^2}.$$

By putting the two terms on the right-hand side over a common denominator, we obtain the numerator $2s+5 = A(s-3)+B$, and this identity yields $A=2$ and $B=11$. Therefore

$$\frac{2s+5}{(s-3)^2} = \frac{2}{s-3} + \frac{11}{(s-3)^2} \tag{2}$$

and

$$\mathscr{L}^{-1}\left\{\frac{2s+5}{(s-3)^2}\right\} = 2\mathscr{L}^{-1}\left\{\frac{1}{s-3}\right\} + 11\mathscr{L}^{-1}\left\{\frac{1}{(s-3)^2}\right\}. \tag{3}$$

Now $1/(s-3)^2$ is $F(s) = 1/s^2$ shifted three units to the right. Since $\mathscr{L}^{-1}\{1/s^2\} = t$, it follows from (1) that

$$\mathscr{L}^{-1}\left\{\frac{1}{(s-3)^2}\right\} = \mathscr{L}^{-1}\left\{\frac{1}{s^2}\Big|_{s\to s-3}\right\} = e^{3t}t.$$

Finally, (3) is

$$\mathscr{L}^{-1}\left\{\frac{2s+5}{(s-3)^2}\right\} = 2e^{3t} + 11e^{3t}t. \tag{4}$$

(b) To start, observe that the quadratic polynomial s^2+4s+6 has no real zeros and so has no real linear factors. In this situation we *complete the square*:

$$\frac{s/2+5/3}{s^2+4s+6} = \frac{s/2+5/3}{(s+2)^2+2}. \tag{5}$$

Our goal here is to recognize the expression on the right-hand side as some Laplace transform $F(s)$ in which s has been replaced throughout by $s+2$. What we are trying to do is analogous to working part (b) of Example 1 backwards. The denominator in (5) is already in the correct form—that is, s^2+2 with s replaced by $s+2$. However, we must fix up the numerator by manipulating the constants: $\frac{1}{2}s + \frac{5}{3} = \frac{1}{2}(s+2) + \frac{5}{3} - \frac{2}{2} = \frac{1}{2}(s+2) + \frac{2}{3}$.

Now by termwise division, the linearity of $\mathscr{L}^{-1}$, parts (e) and (d) of Theorem 7.2.1, and finally (1),

$$\frac{s/2+5/3}{(s+2)^2+2} = \frac{\frac{1}{2}(s+2)+\frac{2}{3}}{(s+2)^2+2} = \frac{1}{2}\frac{s+2}{(s+2)^2+2} + \frac{2}{3}\frac{1}{(s+2)^2+2}$$

$$\mathscr{L}^{-1}\left\{\frac{s/2+5/3}{s^2+4s+6}\right\} = \frac{1}{2}\mathscr{L}^{-1}\left\{\frac{s+2}{(s+2)^2+2}\right\} + \frac{2}{3}\mathscr{L}^{-1}\left\{\frac{1}{(s+2)^2+2}\right\}$$

$$= \frac{1}{2}\mathscr{L}^{-1}\left\{\frac{s}{s^2+2}\Big|_{s\to s+2}\right\} + \frac{2}{3\sqrt{2}}\mathscr{L}^{-1}\left\{\frac{\sqrt{2}}{s^2+2}\Big|_{s\to s+2}\right\} \tag{6}$$

$$= \frac{1}{2}e^{-2t}\cos\sqrt{2}t + \frac{\sqrt{2}}{3}e^{-2t}\sin\sqrt{2}t. \tag{7} \qquad \blacksquare$$

EXAMPLE 3   An Initial-Value Problem

Solve $y'' - 6y' + 9y = t^2 e^{3t}$, $y(0) = 2$, $y'(0) = 17$.

SOLUTION   Before transforming the DE, note that its right-hand side is similar to the function in part (a) of Example 1. After using linearity, Theorem 7.3.1, and the initial conditions, we simplify and then solve for $Y(s) = \mathscr{L}\{f(t)\}$:

$$\mathscr{L}\{y''\} - 6\mathscr{L}\{y'\} + 9\mathscr{L}\{y\} = \mathscr{L}\{t^2 e^{3t}\}$$

$$s^2 Y(s) - sy(0) - y'(0) - 6[sY(s) - y(0)] + 9Y(s) = \frac{2}{(s-3)^3}$$

$$(s^2 - 6s + 9)Y(s) = 2s + 5 + \frac{2}{(s-3)^3}$$

$$(s - 3)^2 Y(s) = 2s + 5 + \frac{2}{(s-3)^3}$$

$$Y(s) = \frac{2s+5}{(s-3)^2} + \frac{2}{(s-3)^5}.$$

The first term on the right-hand side was already decomposed into individual partial fractions in (2) in part (a) of Example 2:

$$Y(s) = \frac{2}{s-3} + \frac{11}{(s-3)^2} + \frac{2}{(s-3)^5}.$$

Thus $$y(t) = 2\mathscr{L}^{-1}\left\{\frac{1}{s-3}\right\} + 11\mathscr{L}^{-1}\left\{\frac{1}{(s-3)^2}\right\} + \frac{2}{4!}\mathscr{L}^{-1}\left\{\frac{4!}{(s-3)^5}\right\}. \qquad (8)$$

From the inverse form (1) of Theorem 7.3.1, the last two terms in (8) are

$$\mathscr{L}^{-1}\left\{\frac{1}{s^2}\bigg|_{s \to s-3}\right\} = te^{3t} \qquad \text{and} \qquad \mathscr{L}^{-1}\left\{\frac{4!}{s^5}\bigg|_{s \to s-3}\right\} = t^4 e^{3t}.$$

Thus (8) is $y(t) = 2e^{3t} + 11te^{3t} + \frac{1}{12}t^4 e^{3t}$.   ∎

EXAMPLE 4   An Initial-Value Problem

Solve $y'' + 4y' + 6y = 1 + e^{-t}$, $y(0) = 0$, $y'(0) = 0$.

SOLUTION $$\mathscr{L}\{y''\} + 4\mathscr{L}\{y'\} + 6\mathscr{L}\{y\} = \mathscr{L}\{1\} + \mathscr{L}\{e^{-t}\}$$

$$s^2 Y(s) - sy(0) - y'(0) + 4[sY(s) - y(0)] + 6Y(s) = \frac{1}{s} + \frac{1}{s+1}$$

$$(s^2 + 4s + 6)Y(s) = \frac{2s+1}{s(s+1)}$$

$$Y(s) = \frac{2s+1}{s(s+1)(s^2+4s+6)}.$$

Since the quadratic term in the denominator does not factor into real linear factors, the partial fraction decomposition for $Y(s)$ is found to be

$$Y(s) = \frac{1/6}{s} + \frac{1/3}{s+1} - \frac{s/2 + 5/3}{s^2 + 4s + 6}.$$

Moreover, in preparation for taking the inverse transform we already manipulated the last term into the necessary form in part (b) of Example 2. So in view of the results in (6) and (7) we have the solution

$$y(t) = \frac{1}{6}\mathscr{L}^{-1}\left\{\frac{1}{s}\right\} + \frac{1}{3}\mathscr{L}^{-1}\left\{\frac{1}{s+1}\right\} - \frac{1}{2}\mathscr{L}^{-1}\left\{\frac{s+2}{(s+2)^2+2}\right\} - \frac{2}{3\sqrt{2}}\mathscr{L}^{-1}\left\{\frac{\sqrt{2}}{(s+2)^2+2}\right\}$$

$$= \frac{1}{6} + \frac{1}{3}e^{-t} - \frac{1}{2}e^{-2t}\cos\sqrt{2}t - \frac{\sqrt{2}}{3}e^{-2t}\sin\sqrt{2}t. \qquad \blacksquare$$

7.3.2 TRANSLATION ON THE *t*-AXIS

UNIT STEP FUNCTION   In engineering, one frequently encounters functions that are either "off" or "on." For example, an external force acting on a mechanical system or a voltage impressed on a circuit can be turned off after a period of time. It is convenient, then, to define a special function that is the number 0 (off) up to a certain time $t = a$ and then the number 1 (on) after that time. This function is called the **unit step function** or the **Heaviside function.**

DEFINITION 7.3.1   Unit Step Function

The **unit step function** $\mathscr{U}(t - a)$ is defined to be

$$\mathscr{U}(t - a) = \begin{cases} 0, & 0 \le t < a \\ 1, & t \ge a. \end{cases}$$

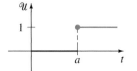

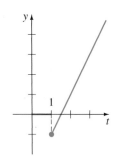

FIGURE 7.3.2   Graph of unit step function

Notice that we define $\mathscr{U}(t - a)$ only on the nonnegative *t*-axis, since this is all that we are concerned with in the study of the Laplace transform. In a broader sense $\mathscr{U}(t - a) = 0$ for $t < a$. The graph of $\mathscr{U}(t - a)$ is given in Figure 7.3.2.

When a function f defined for $t \ge 0$ is multiplied by $\mathscr{U}(t - a)$, the unit step function "turns off" a portion of the graph of that function. For example, consider the function $f(t) = 2t - 3$. To "turn off" the portion of the graph of f for $0 \le t < 1$, we simply form the product $(2t - 3)\,\mathscr{U}(t - 1)$. See Figure 7.3.3. In general, the graph of $f(t)\,\mathscr{U}(t - a)$ is 0 (off) for $0 \le t < a$ and is the portion of the graph of f (on) for $t \ge a$.

The unit step function can also be used to write piecewise-defined functions in a compact form. For example, if we consider $0 \le t < 2$, $2 \le t < 3$, and $t \ge 3$ and the corresponding values of $\mathscr{U}(t - 2)$ and $\mathscr{U}(t - 3)$, it should be apparent that the piecewise-defined function shown in Figure 7.3.4 is the same as $f(t) = 2 - 3\,\mathscr{U}(t - 2) + \mathscr{U}(t - 3)$. Also, a general piecewise-defined function of the type

$$f(t) = \begin{cases} g(t), & 0 \le t < a \\ h(t), & t \ge a \end{cases} \qquad (9)$$

FIGURE 7.3.3   Function is $f(t) = (2t - 3)\,\mathscr{U}(t - 1)$

is the same as

$$f(t) = g(t) - g(t)\,\mathscr{U}(t - a) + h(t)\,\mathscr{U}(t - a). \qquad (10)$$

Similarly, a function of the type

$$f(t) = \begin{cases} 0, & 0 \le t < a \\ g(t), & a \le t < b \\ 0, & t \ge b \end{cases} \qquad (11)$$

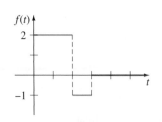

FIGURE 7.3.4   Function is $f(t) = 2 - 3\,\mathscr{U}(t - 2) + \mathscr{U}(t - 3)$

can be written

$$f(t) = g(t)[\mathscr{U}(t - a) - \mathscr{U}(t - b)]. \qquad (12)$$

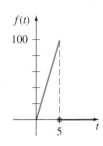

FIGURE 7.3.5 Function is $f(t) = 20t - 20t\,\mathcal{U}(t - 5)$

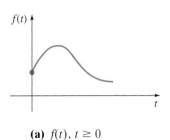

(a) $f(t)$, $t \geq 0$

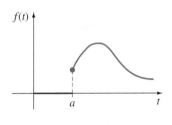

(b) $f(t - a)\,\mathcal{U}(t - a)$

FIGURE 7.3.6 Shift on t-axis

EXAMPLE 5   A Piecewise-Defined Function

Express $f(t) = \begin{cases} 20t, & 0 \leq t < 5 \\ 0, & t \geq 5 \end{cases}$ in terms of unit step functions. Graph.

SOLUTION The graph of f is given in Figure 7.3.5. Now from (9) and (10) with $a = 5$, $g(t) = 20t$, and $h(t) = 0$ we get $f(t) = 20t - 20t\,\mathcal{U}(t - 5)$. ∎

Consider a general function $y = f(t)$ defined for $t \geq 0$. The piecewise-defined function

$$f(t - a)\,\mathcal{U}(t - a) = \begin{cases} 0, & 0 \leq t < a \\ f(t - a), & t \geq a \end{cases} \tag{13}$$

plays a significant role in the discussion that follows. As shown in Figure 7.3.6, for $a > 0$ the graph of the function $y = f(t - a)\,\mathcal{U}(t - a)$ coincides with the graph of $y = f(t - a)$ for $t \geq a$ (which is the *entire* graph of $y = f(t)$, $t \geq 0$ shifted a units to the right on the t-axis), but is identically zero for $0 \leq t < a$.

We saw in Theorem 7.3.1 that an exponential multiple of $f(t)$ results in a translation of the transform $F(s)$ on the s-axis. As a consequence of the next theorem we see that whenever $F(s)$ is multiplied by an exponential function e^{-as}, $a > 0$, the inverse transform of the product $e^{-as}F(s)$ is the function f shifted along the t-axis in the manner illustrated in Figure 7.3.6(b). This result, presented next in its direct transform version, is called the **second translation theorem** or **second shifting theorem.**

THEOREM 7.3.2   Second Translation Theorem

If $F(s) = \mathcal{L}\{f(t)\}$ and $a > 0$, then

$$\mathcal{L}\{f(t - a)\,\mathcal{U}(t - a)\} = e^{-as}F(s).$$

PROOF By the additive interval property of integrals,

$$\int_0^\infty e^{-st}f(t - a)\,\mathcal{U}(t - a)\,dt$$

can be written as two integrals:

$$\mathcal{L}\{f(t - a)\,\mathcal{U}(t - a)\} = \int_0^a e^{-st}f(t - a)\,\underbrace{\mathcal{U}(t - a)}_{\substack{\text{zero for} \\ 0 \leq t < a}}\,dt + \int_a^\infty e^{-st}f(t - a)\,\underbrace{\mathcal{U}(t - a)}_{\substack{\text{one for} \\ t \geq a}}\,dt = \int_a^\infty e^{-st}f(t - a)\,dt.$$

Now if we let $v = t - a$, $dv = dt$ in the last integral, then

$$\mathcal{L}\{f(t - a)\,\mathcal{U}(t - a)\} = \int_0^\infty e^{-s(v + a)}f(v)\,dv = e^{-as}\int_0^\infty e^{-sv}f(v)\,dv = e^{-as}\mathcal{L}\{f(t)\}. \quad ∎$$

We often wish to find the Laplace transform of just a unit step function. This can be from either Definition 7.1.1 or Theorem 7.3.2. If we identify $f(t) = 1$ in Theorem 7.3.2, then $f(t - a) = 1$, $F(s) = \mathcal{L}\{1\} = 1/s$, and so

$$\mathcal{L}\{\mathcal{U}(t - a)\} = \frac{e^{-as}}{s}. \tag{14}$$

For example, by using (14), the Laplace transform of the function in Figure 7.3.4 is

$$\mathcal{L}\{f(t)\} = 2\mathcal{L}\{1\} - 3\mathcal{L}\{\mathcal{U}(t - 2)\} + \mathcal{L}\{\mathcal{U}(t - 3)\}$$

$$= 2\frac{1}{s} - 3\frac{e^{-2s}}{s} + \frac{e^{-3s}}{s}.$$

INVERSE FORM OF THEOREM 7.3.2   If $f(t) = \mathcal{L}^{-1}\{F(s)\}$, the inverse form of Theorem 7.3.2, $a > 0$, is

$$\mathcal{L}^{-1}\{e^{-as}F(s)\} = f(t - a)\,\mathcal{U}(t - a). \tag{15}$$

EXAMPLE 6   Using Formula (15)

Evaluate   **(a)** $\mathcal{L}^{-1}\left\{\dfrac{1}{s - 4}e^{-2s}\right\}$ **(b)** $\mathcal{L}^{-1}\left\{\dfrac{s}{s^2 + 9}e^{-\pi s/2}\right\}$.

SOLUTION (a) With   the   identifications $a = 2$, $F(s) = 1/(s - 4)$,   and $\mathcal{L}^{-1}\{F(s)\} = e^{4t}$, we have from (15)

$$\mathcal{L}^{-1}\left\{\frac{1}{s - 4}e^{-2s}\right\} = e^{4(t-2)}\,\mathcal{U}(t - 2).$$

(b) With $a = \pi/2$, $F(s) = s/(s^2 + 9)$, and $\mathcal{L}^{-1}\{F(s)\} = \cos 3t$, (15) yields

$$\mathcal{L}^{-1}\left\{\frac{s}{s^2 + 9}e^{-\pi s/2}\right\} = \cos 3\left(t - \frac{\pi}{2}\right)\mathcal{U}\left(t - \frac{\pi}{2}\right).$$

The last expression can be simplified somewhat by using the addition formula for the cosine. Verify that the result is the same as $-\sin 3t\,\mathcal{U}\left(t - \dfrac{\pi}{2}\right)$. ∎

ALTERNATIVE FORM OF THEOREM 7.3.2   We are frequently confronted with the problem of finding the Laplace transform of a product of a function g and a unit step function $\mathcal{U}(t - a)$ where the function g lacks the precise shifted form $f(t - a)$ in Theorem 7.3.2. To find the Laplace transform of $g(t)\mathcal{U}(t - a)$, it is possible to fix up $g(t)$ into the required form $f(t - a)$ by algebraic manipulations. For example, if we wanted to use Theorem 7.3.2 to find the Laplace transform of $t^2\,\mathcal{U}(t - 2)$, we would have to force $g(t) = t^2$ into the form $f(t - 2)$. You should work through the details and verify that $t^2 = (t - 2)^2 + 4(t - 2) + 4$ is an identity. Therefore

$$\mathcal{L}\{t^2\,\mathcal{U}(t - 2)\} = \mathcal{L}\{(t - 2)^2\,\mathcal{U}(t - 2) + 4(t - 2)\,\mathcal{U}(t - 2) + 4\,\mathcal{U}(t - 2)\},$$

where each term on the right-hand side can now be evaluated by Theorem 7.3.2. But since these manipulations are time consuming and often not obvious, it is simpler to devise an alternative version of Theorem 7.3.2. Using Definition 7.1.1, the definition of $\mathcal{U}(t - a)$, and the substitution $u = t - a$, we obtain

$$\mathcal{L}\{g(t)\,\mathcal{U}(t - a)\} = \int_a^\infty e^{-st}g(t)\,dt = \int_0^\infty e^{-s(u+a)}\,g(u + a)\,du.$$

That is, $\mathcal{L}\{g(t)\,\mathcal{U}(t - a)\} = e^{-as}\,\mathcal{L}\{g(t + a)\}. \tag{16}$

EXAMPLE 7   Second Translation Theorem—Alternative Form

Evaluate $\mathcal{L}\{\cos t\,\mathcal{U}(t - \pi)\}$.

SOLUTION   With $g(t) = \cos t$ and $a = \pi$, then $g(t + \pi) = \cos(t + \pi) = -\cos t$ by the addition formula for the cosine function. Hence by (16),

$$\mathcal{L}\{\cos t\,\mathcal{U}(t - \pi)\} = -e^{-\pi s}\,\mathcal{L}\{\cos t\} = -\frac{s}{s^2 + 1}e^{-\pi s}.$$ ∎

EXAMPLE 8   An Initial-Value Problem

Solve $y' + y = f(t)$, $y(0) = 5$,   where $f(t) = \begin{cases} 0, & 0 \le t < \pi \\ 3\cos t, & t \ge \pi. \end{cases}$

SOLUTION   The function f can be written as $f(t) = 3\cos t \, \mathcal{U}(t - \pi)$, so by linearity, the results of Example 7, and the usual partial fractions, we have

$$\mathcal{L}\{y'\} + \mathcal{L}\{y\} = 3\mathcal{L}\{\cos t \, \mathcal{U}(t - \pi)\}$$

$$sY(s) - y(0) + Y(s) = -3\frac{s}{s^2 + 1}e^{-\pi s}$$

$$(s + 1)Y(s) = 5 - \frac{3s}{s^2 + 1}e^{-\pi s}$$

$$Y(s) = \frac{5}{s + 1} - \frac{3}{2}\left[-\frac{1}{s + 1}e^{-\pi s} + \frac{1}{s^2 + 1}e^{-\pi s} + \frac{s}{s^2 + 1}e^{-\pi s}\right]. \quad (17)$$

Now proceeding as we did in Example 6, it follows from (15) with $a = \pi$ that the inverses of the terms inside the brackets are

$$\mathcal{L}^{-1}\left\{\frac{1}{s + 1}e^{-\pi s}\right\} = e^{-(t - \pi)}\mathcal{U}(t - \pi), \qquad \mathcal{L}^{-1}\left\{\frac{1}{s^2 + 1}e^{-\pi s}\right\} = \sin(t - \pi)\mathcal{U}(t - \pi),$$

and $$\mathcal{L}^{-1}\left\{\frac{s}{s^2 + 1}e^{-\pi s}\right\} = \cos(t - \pi)\mathcal{U}(t - \pi).$$

Thus the inverse of (17) is

$$y(t) = 5e^{-t} + \frac{3}{2}e^{-(t - \pi)}\mathcal{U}(t - \pi) - \frac{3}{2}\sin(t - \pi)\mathcal{U}(t - \pi) - \frac{3}{2}\cos(t - \pi)\mathcal{U}(t - \pi)$$

$$= 5e^{-t} + \frac{3}{2}[e^{-(t - \pi)} + \sin t + \cos t]\,\mathcal{U}(t - \pi) \qquad \leftarrow \text{trigonometric identities}$$

$$= \begin{cases} 5e^{-t}, & 0 \le t < \pi \\ 5e^{-t} + \frac{3}{2}e^{-(t - \pi)} + \frac{3}{2}\sin t + \frac{3}{2}\cos t, & t \ge \pi. \end{cases} \quad (18)$$

We obtained the graph of (18) shown in Figure 7.3.7 by using a graphing utility. ∎

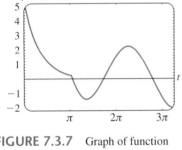

FIGURE 7.3.7   Graph of function in (18)

BEAMS   In Section 5.2 we saw that the static deflection $y(x)$ of a uniform beam of length L carrying load $w(x)$ per unit length is found from the linear fourth-order differential equation

$$EI\frac{d^4y}{dx^4} = w(x), \quad (19)$$

where E is Young's modulus of elasticity and I is a moment of inertia of a cross section of the beam. The Laplace transform is particularly useful in solving (19) when $w(x)$ is piecewise-defined. However, to use the Laplace transform, we must tacitly assume that $y(x)$ and $w(x)$ are defined on $(0, \infty)$ rather than on $(0, L)$. Note, too, that the next example is a boundary-value problem rather than an initial-value problem.

EXAMPLE 9   A Boundary-Value Problem

A beam of length L is embedded at both ends, as shown in Figure 7.3.8. Find the deflection of the beam when the load is given by

$$w(x) = \begin{cases} w_0\left(1 - \dfrac{2}{L}x\right), & 0 < x < L/2 \\ 0, & L/2 < x < L. \end{cases}$$

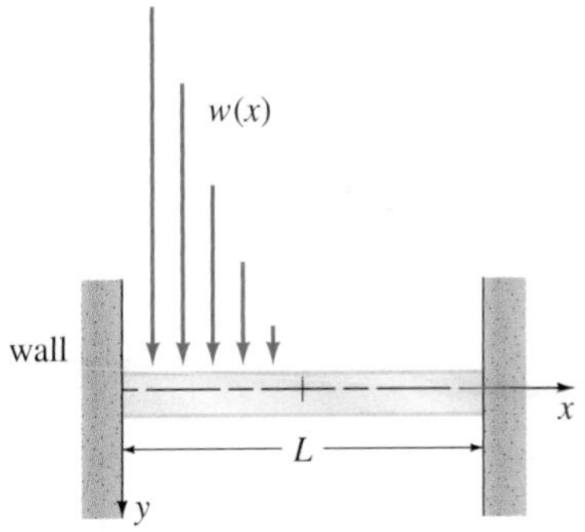

FIGURE 7.3.8   Embedded beam with variable load

SOLUTION Recall that because the beam is embedded at both ends, the boundary conditions are $y(0) = 0$, $y'(0) = 0$, $y(L) = 0$, $y'(L) = 0$. Now by (10) we can express $w(x)$ in terms of the unit step function:

$$w(x) = w_0\left(1 - \frac{2}{L}x\right) - w_0\left(1 - \frac{2}{L}x\right)\mathcal{U}\left(x - \frac{L}{2}\right)$$

$$= \frac{2w_0}{L}\left[\frac{L}{2} - x + \left(x - \frac{L}{2}\right)\mathcal{U}\left(x - \frac{L}{2}\right)\right].$$

Transforming (19) with respect to the variable x gives

$$EI(s^4Y(s) - s^3y(0) - s^2y'(0) - sy''(0) - y'''(0)) = \frac{2w_0}{L}\left[\frac{L/2}{s} - \frac{1}{s^2} + \frac{1}{s^2}e^{-Ls/2}\right]$$

or

$$s^4Y(s) - sy''(0) - y'''(0) = \frac{2w_0}{EIL}\left[\frac{L/2}{s} - \frac{1}{s^2} + \frac{1}{s^2}e^{-Ls/2}\right].$$

If we let $c_1 = y''(0)$ and $c_2 = y'''(0)$, then

$$Y(s) = \frac{c_1}{s^3} + \frac{c_2}{s^4} + \frac{2w_0}{EIL}\left[\frac{L/2}{s^5} - \frac{1}{s^6} + \frac{1}{s^6}e^{-Ls/2}\right],$$

and consequently

$$y(x) = \frac{c_1}{2!}\mathcal{L}^{-1}\left\{\frac{2!}{s^3}\right\} + \frac{c_2}{3!}\mathcal{L}^{-1}\left\{\frac{3!}{s^4}\right\} + \frac{2w_0}{EIL}\left[\frac{L/2}{4!}\mathcal{L}^{-1}\left\{\frac{4!}{s^5}\right\} - \frac{1}{5!}\mathcal{L}^{-1}\left\{\frac{5!}{s^6}\right\} + \frac{1}{5!}\mathcal{L}^{-1}\left\{\frac{5!}{s^6}e^{-Ls/2}\right\}\right]$$

$$= \frac{c_1}{2}x^2 + \frac{c_2}{6}x^3 + \frac{w_0}{60\,EIL}\left[\frac{5L}{2}x^4 - x^5 + \left(x - \frac{L}{2}\right)^5\mathcal{U}\left(x - \frac{L}{2}\right)\right].$$

Applying the conditions $y(L) = 0$ and $y'(L) = 0$ to the last result yields a system of equations for c_1 and c_2:

$$c_1\frac{L^2}{2} + c_2\frac{L^3}{6} + \frac{49w_0L^4}{1920EI} = 0$$

$$c_1L + c_2\frac{L^2}{2} + \frac{85w_0L^3}{960EI} = 0.$$

Solving, we find $c_1 = 23w_0L^2/(960EI)$ and $c_2 = -9w_0L/(40EI)$. Thus the deflection is given by

$$y(x) = \frac{23w_0L^2}{1920EI}x^2 - \frac{3w_0L}{80EI}x^3 + \frac{w_0}{60EIL}\left[\frac{5L}{2}x^4 - x^5 + \left(x - \frac{L}{2}\right)^5\mathcal{U}\left(x - \frac{L}{2}\right)\right]. \blacksquare$$

EXERCISES 7.3

Answers to selected odd-numbered problems begin on page ANS-11.

7.3.1 TRANSLATION ON THE s-AXIS

In Problems 1–20 find either $F(s)$ or $f(t)$, as indicated.

1. $\mathcal{L}\{te^{10t}\}$

2. $\mathcal{L}\{te^{-6t}\}$

3. $\mathcal{L}\{t^3e^{-2t}\}$

4. $\mathcal{L}\{t^{10}e^{-7t}\}$

5. $\mathcal{L}\{t(e^t + e^{2t})^2\}$

6. $\mathcal{L}\{e^{2t}(t - 1)^2\}$

7. $\mathcal{L}\{e^t \sin 3t\}$

8. $\mathcal{L}\{e^{-2t} \cos 4t\}$

9. $\mathcal{L}\{(1 - e^t + 3e^{-4t}) \cos 5t\}$

10. $\mathcal{L}\left\{e^{3t}\left(9 - 4t + 10\sin\frac{t}{2}\right)\right\}$

11. $\mathcal{L}^{-1}\left\{\frac{1}{(s + 2)^3}\right\}$

12. $\mathcal{L}^{-1}\left\{\frac{1}{(s - 1)^4}\right\}$

13. $\mathcal{L}^{-1}\left\{\frac{1}{s^2 - 6s + 10}\right\}$

14. $\mathcal{L}^{-1}\left\{\frac{1}{s^2 + 2s + 5}\right\}$

15. $\mathcal{L}^{-1}\left\{\frac{s}{s^2 + 4s + 5}\right\}$

16. $\mathcal{L}^{-1}\left\{\frac{2s + 5}{s^2 + 6s + 34}\right\}$

17. $\mathcal{L}^{-1}\left\{\frac{s}{(s + 1)^2}\right\}$

18. $\mathcal{L}^{-1}\left\{\frac{5s}{(s - 2)^2}\right\}$

19. $\mathcal{L}^{-1}\left\{\frac{2s - 1}{s^2(s + 1)^3}\right\}$

20. $\mathcal{L}^{-1}\left\{\frac{(s + 1)^2}{(s + 2)^4}\right\}$

In Problems 21–30 use the Laplace transform to solve the given initial-value problem.

21. $y' + 4y = e^{-4t}, \quad y(0) = 2$

22. $y' - y = 1 + te^t, \quad y(0) = 0$

23. $y'' + 2y' + y = 0, \quad y(0) = 1, y'(0) = 1$

24. $y'' - 4y' + 4y = t^3 e^{2t}, \quad y(0) = 0, y'(0) = 0$

25. $y'' - 6y' + 9y = t, \quad y(0) = 0, y'(0) = 1$

26. $y'' - 4y' + 4y = t^3, \quad y(0) = 1, y'(0) = 0$

27. $y'' - 6y' + 13y = 0, \quad y(0) = 0, y'(0) = -3$

28. $2y'' + 20y' + 51y = 0, \quad y(0) = 2, y'(0) = 0$

29. $y'' - y' = e^t \cos t, \quad y(0) = 0, y'(0) = 0$

30. $y'' - 2y' + 5y = 1 + t, \quad y(0) = 0, y'(0) = 4$

In Problems 31 and 32 use the Laplace transform and the procedure outlined in Example 9 to solve the given boundary-value problem.

31. $y'' + 2y' + y = 0, \quad y'(0) = 2, y(1) = 2$

32. $y'' + 8y' + 20y = 0, \quad y(0) = 0, y'(\pi) = 0$

33. A 4-pound weight stretches a spring 2 feet. The weight is released from rest 18 inches above the equilibrium position, and the resulting motion takes place in a medium offering a damping force numerically equal to $\frac{7}{8}$ times the instantaneous velocity. Use the Laplace transform to find the equation of motion $x(t)$.

34. Recall that the differential equation for the instantaneous charge $q(t)$ on the capacitor in an *LRC* series circuit is given by

$$L\frac{d^2q}{dt^2} + R\frac{dq}{dt} + \frac{1}{C}q = E(t). \tag{20}$$

See Section 5.1. Use the Laplace transform to find $q(t)$ when $L = 1$ h, $R = 20$ Ω, $C = 0.005$ f, $E(t) = 150$ V, $t > 0$, $q(0) = 0$, and $i(0) = 0$. What is the current $i(t)$?

35. Consider a battery of constant voltage E_0 that charges the capacitor shown in Figure 7.3.9. Divide equation (20) by L and define $2\lambda = R/L$ and $\omega^2 = 1/LC$. Use the Laplace transform to show that the solution $q(t)$ of $q'' + 2\lambda q' + \omega^2 q = E_0/L$ subject to $q(0) = 0$, $i(0) = 0$ is

$$q(t) = \begin{cases} E_0 C\left[1 - e^{-\lambda t}\left(\cosh\sqrt{\lambda^2 - \omega^2}t \right. \right. \\ \qquad \left. \left. + \frac{\lambda}{\sqrt{\lambda^2 - \omega^2}}\sinh\sqrt{\lambda^2 - \omega^2}t\right)\right], \quad \lambda > \omega, \\ E_0 C[1 - e^{-\lambda t}(1 + \lambda t)], \qquad\qquad \lambda = \omega, \\ E_0 C\left[1 - e^{-\lambda t}\left(\cos\sqrt{\omega^2 - \lambda^2}t \right. \right. \\ \qquad \left. \left. + \frac{\lambda}{\sqrt{\omega^2 - \lambda^2}}\sin\sqrt{\omega^2 - \lambda^2}t\right)\right], \quad \lambda < \omega. \end{cases}$$

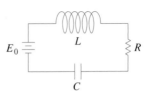

FIGURE 7.3.9 Series circuit in Problem 35

36. Use the Laplace transform to find the charge $q(t)$ in an *RC* series circuit when $q(0) = 0$ and $E(t) = E_0 e^{-kt}$, $k > 0$. Consider two cases: $k \neq 1/RC$ and $k = 1/RC$.

7.3.2 TRANSLATION ON THE *t*-AXIS

In Problems 37–48 find either $F(s)$ or $f(t)$, as indicated.

37. $\mathcal{L}\{(t-1)\,\mathcal{U}(t-1)\}$

38. $\mathcal{L}\{e^{2-t}\,\mathcal{U}(t-2)\}$

39. $\mathcal{L}\{t\,\mathcal{U}(t-2)\}$

40. $\mathcal{L}\{(3t+1)\,\mathcal{U}(t-1)\}$

41. $\mathcal{L}\{\cos 2t\,\mathcal{U}(t-\pi)\}$

42. $\mathcal{L}\left\{\sin t\,\mathcal{U}\left(t-\frac{\pi}{2}\right)\right\}$

43. $\mathcal{L}^{-1}\left\{\dfrac{e^{-2s}}{s^3}\right\}$

44. $\mathcal{L}^{-1}\left\{\dfrac{(1+e^{-2s})^2}{s+2}\right\}$

45. $\mathcal{L}^{-1}\left\{\dfrac{e^{-\pi s}}{s^2+1}\right\}$

46. $\mathcal{L}^{-1}\left\{\dfrac{se^{-\pi s/2}}{s^2+4}\right\}$

47. $\mathcal{L}^{-1}\left\{\dfrac{e^{-s}}{s(s+1)}\right\}$

48. $\mathcal{L}^{-1}\left\{\dfrac{e^{-2s}}{s^2(s-1)}\right\}$

In Problems 49–54 match the given graph with one of the functions in (a)–(f). The graph of $f(t)$ is given in Figure 7.3.10.

(a) $f(t) - f(t)\,\mathcal{U}(t-a)$

(b) $f(t-b)\,\mathcal{U}(t-b)$

(c) $f(t)\,\mathcal{U}(t-a)$

(d) $f(t) - f(t)\,\mathcal{U}(t-b)$

(e) $f(t)\,\mathcal{U}(t-a) - f(t)\,\mathcal{U}(t-b)$

(f) $f(t-a)\,\mathcal{U}(t-a) - f(t-a)\,\mathcal{U}(t-b)$

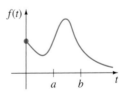

FIGURE 7.3.10 Graph for Problems 49–54

49.

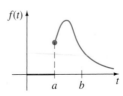

FIGURE 7.3.11 Graph for Problem 49

50.

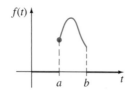

FIGURE 7.3.12   Graph for Problem 50

51.

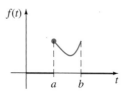

FIGURE 7.3.13   Graph for Problem 51

52.

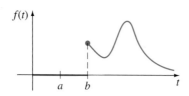

FIGURE 7.3.14   Graph for Problem 52

53.

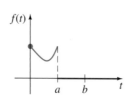

FIGURE 7.3.15   Graph for Problem 53

54.

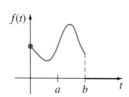

FIGURE 7.3.16   Graph for Problem 54

In Problems 55–62 write each function in terms of unit step functions. Find the Laplace transform of the given function.

55. $f(t) = \begin{cases} 2, & 0 \le t < 3 \\ -2, & t \ge 3 \end{cases}$

56. $f(t) = \begin{cases} 1, & 0 \le t < 4 \\ 0, & 4 \le t < 5 \\ 1, & t \ge 5 \end{cases}$

57. $f(t) = \begin{cases} 0, & 0 \le t < 1 \\ t^2, & t \ge 1 \end{cases}$

58. $f(t) = \begin{cases} 0, & 0 \le t < 3\pi/2 \\ \sin t, & t \ge 3\pi/2 \end{cases}$

59. $f(t) = \begin{cases} t, & 0 \le t < 2 \\ 0, & t \ge 2 \end{cases}$

60. $f(t) = \begin{cases} \sin t, & 0 \le t < 2\pi \\ 0, & t \ge 2\pi \end{cases}$

61.

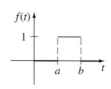

rectangular pulse

FIGURE 7.3.17   Graph for Problem 61

62.

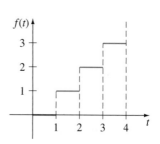

staircase function

FIGURE 7.3.18   Graph for Problem 62

In Problems 63–70 use the Laplace transform to solve the given initial-value problem.

63. $y' + y = f(t)$, $y(0) = 0$, where $f(t) = \begin{cases} 0, & 0 \le t < 1 \\ 5, & t \ge 1 \end{cases}$

64. $y' + y = f(t)$, $y(0) = 0$, where

$$f(t) = \begin{cases} 1, & 0 \le t < 1 \\ -1, & t \ge 1 \end{cases}$$

65. $y' + 2y = f(t)$, $y(0) = 0$, where

$$f(t) = \begin{cases} t, & 0 \le t < 1 \\ 0, & t \ge 1 \end{cases}$$

66. $y'' + 4y = f(t)$, $y(0) = 0, y'(0) = -1$, where

$$f(t) = \begin{cases} 1, & 0 \le t < 1 \\ 0, & t \ge 1 \end{cases}$$

67. $y'' + 4y = \sin t \, \mathcal{U}(t - 2\pi)$, $y(0) = 1, y'(0) = 0$

68. $y'' - 5y' + 6y = \mathcal{U}(t - 1)$, $y(0) = 0, y'(0) = 1$

69. $y'' + y = f(t)$, $y(0) = 0, y'(0) = 1$, where

$$f(t) = \begin{cases} 0, & 0 \le t < \pi \\ 1, & \pi \le t < 2\pi \\ 0, & t \ge 2\pi \end{cases}$$

70. $y'' + 4y' + 3y = 1 - \mathcal{U}(t - 2) - \mathcal{U}(t - 4) + \mathcal{U}(t - 6)$, $y(0) = 0, y'(0) = 0$

71. Suppose a 32-pound weight stretches a spring 2 feet. If the weight is released from rest at the equilibrium position, find the equation of motion $x(t)$ if an impressed force $f(t) = 20t$ acts on the system for $0 \leq t < 5$ and is then removed (see Example 5). Ignore any damping forces. Use a graphing utility to graph $x(t)$ on the interval $[0, 10]$.

72. Solve Problem 71 if the impressed force $f(t) = \sin t$ acts on the system for $0 \leq t < 2\pi$ and is then removed.

In Problems 73 and 74 use the Laplace transform to find the charge $q(t)$ on the capacitor in an *RC* series circuit subject to the given conditions.

73. $q(0) = 0$, $R = 2.5 \,\Omega$, $C = 0.08$ f, $E(t)$ given in Figure 7.3.19

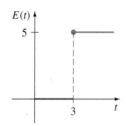

FIGURE 7.3.19 $E(t)$ in Problem 73

74. $q(0) = q_0$, $R = 10 \,\Omega$, $C = 0.1$ f, $E(t)$ given in Figure 7.3.20

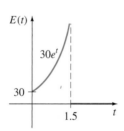

FIGURE 7.3.20 $E(t)$ in Problem 74

75. (a) Use the Laplace transform to find the current $i(t)$ in a single-loop *LR* series circuit when $i(0) = 0, L = 1$ h, $R = 10 \,\Omega$, and $E(t)$ is as given in Figure 7.3.21.

(b) Use a computer graphing program to graph $i(t)$ for $0 \leq t \leq 6$. Use the graph to estimate i_{max} and i_{min}, the maximum and minimum values of the current.

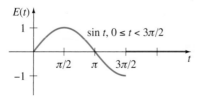

FIGURE 7.3.21 $E(t)$ in Problem 75

76. (a) Use the Laplace transform to find the charge $q(t)$ on the capacitor in an *RC* series circuit when $q(0) = 0$, $R = 50 \,\Omega$, $C = 0.01$ f, and $E(t)$ is as given in Figure 7.3.22.

(b) Assume that $E_0 = 100$ V. Use a computer graphing program to graph $q(t)$ for $0 \leq t \leq 6$. Use the graph to estimate q_{max}, the maximum value of the charge.

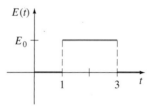

FIGURE 7.3.22 $E(t)$ in Problem 76

77. A cantilever beam is embedded at its left end and free at its right end. Use the Laplace transform to find the deflection $y(x)$ when the load is given by

$$w(x) = \begin{cases} w_0, & 0 < x < L/2 \\ 0, & L/2 \leq x < L. \end{cases}$$

78. Solve Problem 77 when the load is given by

$$w(x) = \begin{cases} 0, & 0 < x < L/3 \\ w_0, & L/3 < x < 2L/3 \\ 0, & 2L/3 < x < L. \end{cases}$$

79. Find the deflection $y(x)$ of a cantilever beam embedded at its left end and free at its right end when the load is as given in Example 9.

80. A beam is embedded at its left end and simply supported at its right end. Find the deflection $y(x)$ when the load is as given in Problem 77.

Mathematical Model

81. Cake Inside an Oven Reread Example 4 in Section 3.1 on the cooling of a cake that is taken out of an oven.

(a) Devise a mathematical model for the temperature of a cake while it is *inside* the oven based on the following assumptions: At $t = 0$ the cake mixture is at the room temperature of 70°; the oven is not preheated, so at $t = 0$, when the cake mixture is placed into the oven, the temperature inside the oven is also 70°; the temperature of the oven increases linearly until $t = 4$ minutes, when the desired temperature of 300° is attained; the oven temperature is a constant 300° for $t \geq 4$.

(b) Use the Laplace transform to solve the initial-value problem in part (a).

Discussion Problems

82. Discuss how you would fix up each of the following functions so that Theorem 7.3.2 could be used directly to find the given Laplace transform. Check your answers using (16) of this section.

(a) $\mathscr{L}\{(2t + 1)\,\mathscr{U}(t - 1)\}$ **(b)** $\mathscr{L}\{e^t\,\mathscr{U}(t - 5)\}$

(c) $\mathscr{L}\{\cos t\,\mathscr{U}(t - \pi)\}$ **(d)** $\mathscr{L}\{(t^2 - 3t)\,\mathscr{U}(t - 2)\}$

83. (a) Assume that Theorem 7.3.1 holds when the symbol a is replaced by ki, where k is a real number and $i^2 = -1$. Show that $\mathscr{L}\{te^{kti}\}$ can be used to deduce

$$\mathscr{L}\{t \cos kt\} = \frac{s^2 - k^2}{(s^2 + k^2)^2}$$

$$\mathscr{L}\{t \sin kt\} = \frac{2ks}{(s^2 + k^2)^2}.$$

(b) Now use the Laplace transform to solve the initial-value problem $x'' + \omega^2 x = \cos \omega t$, $x(0) = 0$, $x'(0) = 0$.

7.4	**OPERATIONAL PROPERTIES II**

REVIEW MATERIAL

- Definition 7.1.1
- Theorems 7.3.1 and 7.3.2

INTRODUCTION In this section we develop several more operational properties of the Laplace transform. Specifically, we shall see how to find the transform of a function $f(t)$ that is multiplied by a monomial t^n, the transform of a special type of integral, and the transform of a periodic function. The last two transform properties allow us to solve some equations that we have not encountered up to this point: Volterra integral equations, integrodifferential equations, and ordinary differential equations in which the input function is a periodic piecewise-defined function.

7.4.1 DERIVATIVES OF A TRANSFORM

MULTIPLYING A FUNCTION BY t^n The Laplace transform of the product of a function $f(t)$ with t can be found by differentiating the Laplace transform of $f(t)$. To motivate this result, let us assume that $F(s) = \mathscr{L}\{f(t)\}$ exists and that it is possible to interchange the order of differentiation and integration. Then

$$\frac{d}{ds}F(s) = \frac{d}{ds}\int_0^\infty e^{-st}f(t)\,dt = \int_0^\infty \frac{\partial}{\partial s}[e^{-st}f(t)]\,dt = -\int_0^\infty e^{-st}tf(t)\,dt = -\mathscr{L}\{tf(t)\};$$

that is,

$$\mathscr{L}\{tf(t)\} = -\frac{d}{ds}\mathscr{L}\{f(t)\}.$$

We can use the last result to find the Laplace transform of $t^2 f(t)$:

$$\mathscr{L}\{t^2 f(t)\} = \mathscr{L}\{t \cdot tf(t)\} = -\frac{d}{ds}\mathscr{L}\{tf(t)\} = -\frac{d}{ds}\left(-\frac{d}{ds}\mathscr{L}\{f(t)\}\right) = \frac{d^2}{ds^2}\mathscr{L}\{f(t)\}.$$

The preceding two cases suggest the general result for $\mathscr{L}\{t^n f(t)\}$.

THEOREM 7.4.1   Derivatives of Transforms

If $F(s) = \mathscr{L}\{f(t)\}$ and $n = 1, 2, 3, \ldots$, then

$$\mathscr{L}\{t^n f(t)\} = (-1)^n \frac{d^n}{ds^n} F(s).$$

EXAMPLE 1   Using Theorem 7.4.1

Evaluate $\mathscr{L}\{t \sin kt\}$.

SOLUTION   With $f(t) = \sin kt$, $F(s) = k/(s^2 + k^2)$, and $n = 1$, Theorem 7.4.1 gives

$$\mathscr{L}\{t \sin kt\} = -\frac{d}{ds}\mathscr{L}\{\sin kt\} = -\frac{d}{ds}\left(\frac{k}{s^2 + k^2}\right) = \frac{2ks}{(s^2 + k^2)^2}. \quad \blacksquare$$

If we want to evaluate $\mathscr{L}\{t^2 \sin kt\}$ and $\mathscr{L}\{t^3 \sin kt\}$, all we need do, in turn, is take the negative of the derivative with respect to s of the result in Example 1 and then take the negative of the derivative with respect to s of $\mathscr{L}\{t^2 \sin kt\}$.

NOTE   To find transforms of functions $t^n e^{at}$ we can use either Theorem 7.3.1 or Theorem 7.4.1. For example,

Theorem 7.3.1: $\mathscr{L}\{te^{3t}\} = \mathscr{L}\{t\}_{s \to s-3} = \left.\frac{1}{s^2}\right|_{s \to s-3} = \frac{1}{(s - 3)^2}.$

Theorem 7.4.1: $\mathscr{L}\{te^{3t}\} = -\frac{d}{ds}\mathscr{L}\{e^{3t}\} = -\frac{d}{ds}\frac{1}{s - 3} = (s - 3)^{-2} = \frac{1}{(s - 3)^2}.$

EXAMPLE 2   An Initial-Value Problem

Solve $x'' + 16x = \cos 4t$, $x(0) = 0$, $x'(0) = 1$.

SOLUTION   The initial-value problem could describe the forced, undamped, and resonant motion of a mass on a spring. The mass starts with an initial velocity of 1 ft/s in the downward direction from the equilibrium position.

Transforming the differential equation gives

$$(s^2 + 16)X(s) = 1 + \frac{s}{s^2 + 16} \quad \text{or} \quad X(s) = \frac{1}{s^2 + 16} + \frac{s}{(s^2 + 16)^2}.$$

Now we just saw in Example 1 that

$$\mathscr{L}^{-1}\left\{\frac{2ks}{(s^2 + k^2)^2}\right\} = t \sin kt, \tag{1}$$

and so with the identification $k = 4$ in (1) and in part (d) of Theorem 7.2.1, we obtain

$$x(t) = \frac{1}{4}\mathscr{L}^{-1}\left\{\frac{4}{s^2 + 16}\right\} + \frac{1}{8}\mathscr{L}^{-1}\left\{\frac{8s}{(s^2 + 16)^2}\right\}$$

$$= \frac{1}{4}\sin 4t + \frac{1}{8}t \sin 4t. \quad \blacksquare$$

7.4.2   TRANSFORMS OF INTEGRALS

CONVOLUTION   If functions f and g are piecewise continuous on the interval $[0, \infty)$, then a special product, denoted by $f * g$, is defined by the integral

$$f * g = \int_0^t f(\tau)\, g(t - \tau)\, d\tau \tag{2}$$

and is called the **convolution** of f and g. The convolution $f * g$ is a function of t. For example,

$$e^t * \sin t = \int_0^t e^\tau \sin(t - \tau)\, d\tau = \frac{1}{2}(-\sin t - \cos t + e^t). \tag{3}$$

It is left as an exercise to show that

$$\int_0^t f(\tau)\, g(t - \tau)\, d\tau = \int_0^t f(t - \tau)\, g(\tau)\, d\tau;$$

that is, $f * g = g * f$. This means that the convolution of two functions is commutative. It is *not* true that the integral of a product of functions is the product of the integrals. However, it *is* true that the Laplace transform of the special product (2) is the product of the Laplace transform of f and g. This means that it is possible to find the Laplace transform of the convolution of two functions without actually evaluating the integral as we did in (3). The result that follows is known as the **convolution theorem.**

THEOREM 7.4.2 **Convolution Theorem**

If $f(t)$ and $g(t)$ are piecewise continuous on $[0, \infty)$ and of exponential order, then

$$\mathcal{L}\{f * g\} = \mathcal{L}\{f(t)\}\, \mathcal{L}\{g(t)\} = F(s)\,G(s).$$

PROOF Let

$$F(s) = \mathcal{L}\{f(t)\} = \int_0^\infty e^{-s\tau} f(\tau)\, d\tau$$

and

$$G(s) = \mathcal{L}\{g(t)\} = \int_0^\infty e^{-s\beta} g(\beta)\, d\beta.$$

Proceeding formally, we have

$$F(s)G(s) = \left(\int_0^\infty e^{-s\tau} f(\tau)\, d\tau \right) \left(\int_0^\infty e^{-s\beta} g(\beta)\, d\beta \right)$$

$$= \int_0^\infty \int_0^\infty e^{-s(\tau + \beta)} f(\tau) g(\beta)\, d\tau\, d\beta$$

$$= \int_0^\infty f(\tau)\, d\tau \int_0^\infty e^{-s(\tau + \beta)} g(\beta)\, d\beta.$$

Holding τ fixed, we let $t = \tau + \beta$, $dt = d\beta$, so that

$$F(s)G(s) = \int_0^\infty f(\tau)\, d\tau \int_\tau^\infty e^{-st} g(t - \tau)\, dt.$$

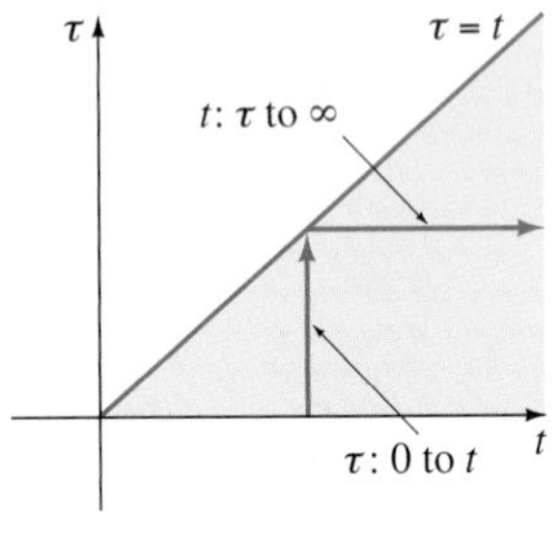

FIGURE 7.4.1 Changing order of integration from t first to τ first

In the $t\tau$-plane we are integrating over the shaded region in Figure 7.4.1. Since f and g are piecewise continuous on $[0, \infty)$ and of exponential order, it is possible to interchange the order of integration:

$$F(s)\,G(s) = \int_0^\infty e^{-st}\, dt \int_0^t f(\tau)g(t - \tau)\, d\tau = \int_0^\infty e^{-st} \left\{ \int_0^t f(\tau)\, g(t - \tau)\, d\tau \right\} dt = \mathcal{L}\{f * g\}. \quad \blacksquare$$

EXAMPLE 3 **Transform of a Convolution**

Evaluate $\displaystyle \mathcal{L}\left\{ \int_0^t e^\tau \sin(t - \tau)\, d\tau \right\}$.

SOLUTION With $f(t) = e^t$ and $g(t) = \sin t$, the convolution theorem states that the Laplace transform of the convolution of f and g is the product of their Laplace transforms:

$$\mathcal{L}\left\{ \int_0^t e^\tau \sin(t - \tau)\, d\tau \right\} = \mathcal{L}\{e^t\} \cdot \mathcal{L}\{\sin t\} = \frac{1}{s - 1} \cdot \frac{1}{s^2 + 1} = \frac{1}{(s - 1)(s^2 + 1)}. \quad \blacksquare$$

INVERSE FORM OF THEOREM 7.4.2 The convolution theorem is sometimes useful in finding the inverse Laplace transform of the product of two Laplace transforms. From Theorem 7.4.2 we have

$$\mathscr{L}^{-1}\{F(s)G(s)\} = f * g. \tag{4}$$

Many of the results in the table of Laplace transforms in Appendix III can be derived using (4). For example, in the next example we obtain entry 25 of the table:

$$\mathscr{L}\{\sin kt - kt \cos kt\} = \frac{2k^3}{(s^2 + k^2)^2}. \tag{5}$$

EXAMPLE 4 **Inverse Transform as a Convolution**

Evaluate $\mathscr{L}^{-1}\left\{\dfrac{1}{(s^2 + k^2)^2}\right\}$.

SOLUTION Let $F(s) = G(s) = \dfrac{1}{s^2 + k^2}$ so that

$$f(t) = g(t) = \frac{1}{k}\mathscr{L}^{-1}\left\{\frac{k}{s^2 + k^2}\right\} = \frac{1}{k}\sin kt.$$

In this case (4) gives

$$\mathscr{L}^{-1}\left\{\frac{1}{(s^2 + k^2)^2}\right\} = \frac{1}{k^2}\int_0^t \sin k\tau \sin k(t - \tau)\, d\tau. \tag{6}$$

With the aid of the trigonometric identity

$$\sin A \cos B = \frac{1}{2}[\cos(A - B) - \cos(A + B)]$$

and the substitutions $A = k\tau$ and $B = k(t - \tau)$ we can carry out the integration in (6):

$$\mathscr{L}^{-1}\left\{\frac{1}{(s^2 + k^2)^2}\right\} = \frac{1}{2k^2}\int_0^t [\cos k(2\tau - t) - \cos kt]\, d\tau$$

$$= \frac{1}{2k^2}\left[\frac{1}{2k}\sin k(2\tau - t) - \tau \cos kt\right]_0^t$$

$$= \frac{\sin kt - kt \cos kt}{2k^3}.$$

Multiplying both sides by $2k^3$ gives the inverse form of (5). ∎

TRANSFORM OF AN INTEGRAL When $g(t) = 1$ and $\mathscr{L}\{g(t)\} = G(s) = 1/s$, the convolution theorem implies that the Laplace transform of the integral of f is

$$\mathscr{L}\left\{\int_0^t f(\tau)\, d\tau\right\} = \frac{F(s)}{s}. \tag{7}$$

The inverse form of (7),

$$\int_0^t f(\tau)\, d\tau = \mathscr{L}^{-1}\left\{\frac{F(s)}{s}\right\}, \tag{8}$$

can be used in lieu of partial fractions when s^n is a factor of the denominator and $f(t) = \mathscr{L}^{-1}\{F(s)\}$ is easy to integrate. For example, we know for $f(t) = \sin t$ that $F(s) = 1/(s^2 + 1)$, and so by (8)

$$\mathscr{L}^{-1}\left\{\frac{1}{s(s^2 + 1)}\right\} = \int_0^t \sin \tau\, d\tau = 1 - \cos t$$

$$\mathscr{L}^{-1}\left\{\frac{1}{s^2(s^2 + 1)}\right\} = \int_0^t (1 - \cos \tau)\, d\tau = t - \sin t$$

$$\mathscr{L}^{-1}\left\{\frac{1}{s^3(s^2+1)}\right\} = \int_0^t (\tau - \sin\tau)\,d\tau = \frac{1}{2}t^2 - 1 + \cos t$$

and so on.

VOLTERRA INTEGRAL EQUATION The convolution theorem and the result in (7) are useful in solving other types of equations in which an unknown function appears under an integral sign. In the next example we solve a **Volterra integral equation** for $f(t)$,

$$f(t) = g(t) + \int_0^t f(\tau)\,h(t-\tau)\,d\tau. \tag{9}$$

The functions $g(t)$ and $h(t)$ are known. Notice that the integral in (9) has the convolution form (2) with the symbol h playing the part of g.

EXAMPLE 5 An Integral Equation

Solve $f(t) = 3t^2 - e^{-t} - \displaystyle\int_0^t f(\tau)\,e^{t-\tau}\,d\tau$ for $f(t)$.

SOLUTION In the integral we identify $h(t-\tau) = e^{t-\tau}$ so that $h(t) = e^t$. We take the Laplace transform of each term; in particular, by Theorem 7.4.2 the transform of the integral is the product of $\mathscr{L}\{f(t)\} = F(s)$ and $\mathscr{L}\{e^t\} = 1/(s-1)$:

$$F(s) = 3 \cdot \frac{2}{s^3} - \frac{1}{s+1} - F(s) \cdot \frac{1}{s-1}.$$

After solving the last equation for $F(s)$ and carrying out the partial fraction decomposition, we find

$$F(s) = \frac{6}{s^3} - \frac{6}{s^4} + \frac{1}{s} - \frac{2}{s+1}.$$

The inverse transform then gives

$$f(t) = 3\mathscr{L}^{-1}\left\{\frac{2!}{s^3}\right\} - \mathscr{L}^{-1}\left\{\frac{3!}{s^4}\right\} + \mathscr{L}^{-1}\left\{\frac{1}{s}\right\} - 2\mathscr{L}^{-1}\left\{\frac{1}{s+1}\right\}$$

$$= 3t^2 - t^3 + 1 - 2e^{-t}. \qquad\blacksquare$$

SERIES CIRCUITS In a single-loop or series circuit, Kirchhoff's second law states that the sum of the voltage drops across an inductor, resistor, and capacitor is equal to the impressed voltage $E(t)$. Now it is known that the voltage drops across an inductor, resistor, and capacitor are, respectively,

$$L\frac{di}{dt}, \qquad Ri(t), \qquad \text{and} \qquad \frac{1}{C}\int_0^t i(\tau)\,d\tau,$$

where $i(t)$ is the current and L, R, and C are constants. It follows that the current in a circuit, such as that shown in Figure 7.4.2, is governed by the **integrodifferential equation**

$$L\frac{di}{dt} + Ri(t) + \frac{1}{C}\int_0^t i(\tau)\,d\tau = E(t). \tag{10}$$

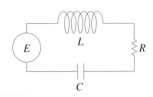

FIGURE 7.4.2 *LRC* series circuit

EXAMPLE 6 **An Integrodifferential Equation**

Determine the current $i(t)$ in a single-loop *LRC* circuit when $L = 0.1$ h, $R = 2\ \Omega$, $C = 0.1$ f, $i(0) = 0$, and the impressed voltage is

$$E(t) = 120t - 120t\ \mathcal{U}(t - 1).$$

SOLUTION With the given data equation (10) becomes

$$0.1\frac{di}{dt} + 2i + 10\int_0^t i(\tau)\,d\tau = 120t - 120t\ \mathcal{U}(t - 1).$$

Now by (7), $\mathcal{L}\left\{\int_0^t i(\tau)\,d\tau\right\} = I(s)/s$, where $I(s) = \mathcal{L}\{i(t)\}$. Thus the Laplace transform of the integrodifferential equation is

$$0.1sI(s) + 2I(s) + 10\frac{I(s)}{s} = 120\left[\frac{1}{s^2} - \frac{1}{s^2}e^{-s} - \frac{1}{s}e^{-s}\right].\quad \leftarrow \text{by (16) of Section 7.3}$$

Multiplying this equation by $10s$, using $s^2 + 20s + 100 = (s + 10)^2$, and then solving for $I(s)$ gives

$$I(s) = 1200\left[\frac{1}{s(s + 10)^2} - \frac{1}{s(s + 10)^2}e^{-s} - \frac{1}{(s + 10)^2}e^{-s}\right].$$

By partial fractions,

$$I(s) = 1200\left[\frac{1/100}{s} - \frac{1/100}{s + 10} - \frac{1/10}{(s + 10)^2} - \frac{1/100}{s}e^{-s}\right.$$
$$\left. + \frac{1/100}{s + 10}e^{-s} + \frac{1/10}{(s + 10)^2}e^{-s} - \frac{1}{(s + 10)^2}e^{-s}\right].$$

From the inverse form of the second translation theorem, (15) of Section 7.3, we finally obtain

$$i(t) = 12[1 - \mathcal{U}(t - 1)] - 12[e^{-10t} - e^{-10(t - 1)}\mathcal{U}(t - 1)]$$
$$- 120te^{-10t} - 1080(t - 1)e^{-10(t - 1)}\mathcal{U}(t - 1).$$

Written as a piecewise-defined function, the current is

$$i(t) = \begin{cases} 12 - 12e^{-10t} - 120te^{-10t}, & 0 \le t < 1 \\ -12e^{-10t} + 12e^{-10(t - 1)} - 120te^{-10t} - 1080(t - 1)e^{-10(t - 1)}, & t \ge 1. \end{cases}$$

Using this last expression and a CAS, we graph $i(t)$ on each of the two intervals and then combine the graphs. Note in Figure 7.4.3 that even though the input $E(t)$ is discontinuous, the output or response $i(t)$ is a continuous function. ∎

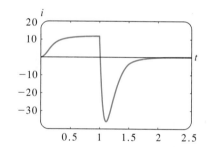

FIGURE 7.4.3 Graph of current $i(t)$ in Example 6

7.4.3 TRANSFORM OF A PERIODIC FUNCTION

PERIODIC FUNCTION If a periodic function has period T, $T > 0$, then $f(t + T) = f(t)$. The next theorem shows that the Laplace transform of a periodic function can be obtained by integration over one period.

THEOREM 7.4.3 **Transform of a Periodic Function**

If $f(t)$ is piecewise continuous on $[0, \infty)$, of exponential order, and periodic with period T, then

$$\mathcal{L}\{f(t)\} = \frac{1}{1 - e^{-sT}}\int_0^T e^{-st}f(t)\,dt.$$

PROOF Write the Laplace transform of *f* as two integrals:

$$\mathcal{L}\{f(t)\} = \int_0^T e^{-st} f(t)\, dt + \int_T^\infty e^{-st} f(t)\, dt.$$

When we let $t = u + T$, the last integral becomes

$$\int_T^\infty e^{-st} f(t)\, dt = \int_0^\infty e^{-s(u+T)} f(u + T)\, du = e^{-sT} \int_0^\infty e^{-su} f(u)\, du = e^{-sT} \mathcal{L}\{f(t)\}.$$

Therefore

$$\mathcal{L}\{f(t)\} = \int_0^T e^{-st} f(t)\, dt + e^{-sT} \mathcal{L}\{f(t)\}.$$

Solving the equation in the last line for $\mathcal{L}\{f(t)\}$ proves the theorem. ∎

EXAMPLE 7   Transform of a Periodic Function

Find the Laplace transform of the periodic function shown in Figure 7.4.4.

SOLUTION   The function $E(t)$ is called a square wave and has period $T = 2$. For $0 \le t < 2$, $E(t)$ can be defined by

$$E(t) = \begin{cases} 1, & 0 \le t < 1 \\ 0, & 1 \le t < 2 \end{cases}$$

and outside the interval by $f(t + 2) = f(t)$. Now from Theorem 7.4.3

$$\mathcal{L}\{E(t)\} = \frac{1}{1 - e^{-2s}} \int_0^2 e^{-st} E(t)\, dt = \frac{1}{1 - e^{-2s}} \left[\int_0^1 e^{-st} \cdot 1\, dt + \int_1^2 e^{-st} \cdot 0\, dt \right]$$

$$= \frac{1}{1 - e^{-2s}} \frac{1 - e^{-s}}{s} \qquad \leftarrow 1 - e^{-2s} = (1 + e^{-s})(1 - e^{-s})$$

$$= \frac{1}{s(1 + e^{-s})}. \tag{11} \quad\blacksquare$$

$E(t)$

FIGURE 7.4.4   Square wave

EXAMPLE 8   A Periodic Impressed Voltage

The differential equation for the current $i(t)$ in a single-loop *LR* series circuit is

$$L\frac{di}{dt} + Ri = E(t). \tag{12}$$

Determine the current $i(t)$ when $i(0) = 0$ and $E(t)$ is the square wave function shown in Figure 7.4.4.

SOLUTION   If we use the result in (11) of the preceding example, the Laplace transform of the DE is

$$LsI(s) + RI(s) = \frac{1}{s(1 + e^{-s})} \qquad \text{or} \qquad I(s) = \frac{1/L}{s(s + R/L)} \cdot \frac{1}{1 + e^{-s}}. \tag{13}$$

To find the inverse Laplace transform of the last function, we first make use of geometric series. With the identification $x = e^{-s}$, $s > 0$, the geometric series

$$\frac{1}{1 + x} = 1 - x + x^2 - x^3 + \cdots \qquad \text{becomes} \qquad \frac{1}{1 + e^{-s}} = 1 - e^{-s} + e^{-2s} - e^{-3s} + \cdots.$$

From

$$\frac{1}{s(s + R/L)} = \frac{L/R}{s} - \frac{L/R}{s + R/L}$$

we can then rewrite (13) as

$$I(s) = \frac{1}{R}\left(\frac{1}{s} - \frac{1}{s + R/L}\right)(1 - e^{-s} + e^{-2s} - e^{-3s} + \cdots)$$

$$= \frac{1}{R}\left(\frac{1}{s} - \frac{e^{-s}}{s} + \frac{e^{-2s}}{s} - \frac{e^{-3s}}{s} + \cdots\right) - \frac{1}{R}\left(\frac{1}{s + R/L} - \frac{1}{s + R/L}e^{-s} + \frac{e^{-2s}}{s + R/L} - \frac{e^{-3s}}{s + R/L} + \cdots\right).$$

By applying the form of the second translation theorem to each term of both series, we obtain

$$i(t) = \frac{1}{R}(1 - \mathcal{U}(t - 1) + \mathcal{U}(t - 2) - \mathcal{U}(t - 3) + \cdots)$$

$$- \frac{1}{R}(e^{-Rt/L} - e^{-R(t-1)/L}\mathcal{U}(t - 1) + e^{-R(t-2)/L}\mathcal{U}(t - 2) - e^{-R(t-3)/L}\mathcal{U}(t - 3) + \cdots)$$

or, equivalently,

$$i(t) = \frac{1}{R}(1 - e^{-Rt/L}) + \frac{1}{R}\sum_{n=1}^{\infty}(-1)^n(1 - e^{-R(t-n)/L})\,\mathcal{U}(t - n).$$

To interpret the solution, let us assume for the sake of illustration that $R = 1$, $L = 1$, and $0 \leq t < 4$. In this case

$$i(t) = 1 - e^{-t} - (1 - e^{t-1})\mathcal{U}(t - 1) + (1 - e^{-(t-2)})\mathcal{U}(t - 2) - (1 - e^{-(t-3)})\mathcal{U}(t - 3);$$

in other words,

$$i(t) = \begin{cases} 1 - e^{-t}, & 0 \leq t < 1 \\ -e^{-t} + e^{-(t-1)}, & 1 \leq t < 2 \\ 1 - e^{-t} + e^{-(t-1)} - e^{-(t-2)}, & 2 \leq t < 3 \\ -e^{-t} + e^{-(t-1)} - e^{-(t-2)} + e^{-(t-3)}, & 3 \leq t < 4. \end{cases}$$

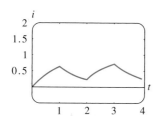

FIGURE 7.4.5 Graph of current $i(t)$ in Example 8

The graph of $i(t)$ for $0 \leq t < 4$, given in Figure 7.4.5, was obtained with the help of a CAS. ∎

EXERCISES 7.4

Answers to selected odd-numbered problems begin on page ANS-11.

7.4.1 DERIVATIVES OF A TRANSFORM

In Problems 1–8 use Theorem 7.4.1 to evaluate the given Laplace transform.

1. $\mathcal{L}\{te^{-10t}\}$

2. $\mathcal{L}\{t^3e^t\}$

3. $\mathcal{L}\{t\cos 2t\}$

4. $\mathcal{L}\{t\sinh 3t\}$

5. $\mathcal{L}\{t^2\sinh t\}$

6. $\mathcal{L}\{t^2\cos t\}$

7. $\mathcal{L}\{te^{2t}\sin 6t\}$

8. $\mathcal{L}\{te^{-3t}\cos 3t\}$

In Problems 9–14 use the Laplace transform to solve the given initial-value problem. Use the table of Laplace transforms in Appendix III as needed.

9. $y' + y = t\sin t$, $y(0) = 0$

10. $y' - y = te^t\sin t$, $y(0) = 0$

11. $y'' + 9y = \cos 3t$, $y(0) = 2$, $y'(0) = 5$

12. $y'' + y = \sin t$, $y(0) = 1$, $y'(0) = -1$

13. $y'' + 16y = f(t)$, $y(0) = 0$, $y'(0) = 1$, where

$$f(t) = \begin{cases} \cos 4t, & 0 \leq t < \pi \\ 0, & t \geq \pi \end{cases}$$

14. $y'' + y = f(t)$, $y(0) = 1$, $y'(0) = 0$, where

$$f(t) = \begin{cases} 1, & 0 \leq t < \pi/2 \\ \sin t, & t \geq \pi/2 \end{cases}$$

In Problems 15 and 16 use a graphing utility to graph the indicated solution.

15. $y(t)$ of Problem 13 for $0 \leq t < 2\pi$

16. $y(t)$ of Problem 14 for $0 \leq t < 3\pi$

In some instances the Laplace transform can be used to solve linear differential equations with variable monomial coefficients. In Problems 17 and 18 use Theorem 7.4.1 to reduce the given differential equation to a linear first-order DE in the transformed function $Y(s) = \mathscr{L}\{y(t)\}$. Solve the first-order DE for $Y(s)$ and then find $y(t) = \mathscr{L}^{-1}\{Y(s)\}$.

17. $ty'' - y' = 2t^2$, $y(0) = 0$

18. $2y'' + ty' - 2y = 10$, $y(0) = y'(0) = 0$

7.4.2 TRANSFORMS OF INTEGRALS

In Problems 19–30 use Theorem 7.4.2 to evaluate the given Laplace transform. Do not evaluate the integral before transforming.

19. $\mathscr{L}\{1 * t^3\}$

20. $\mathscr{L}\{t^2 * te^t\}$

21. $\mathscr{L}\{e^{-t} * e^t \cos t\}$

22. $\mathscr{L}\{e^{2t} * \sin t\}$

23. $\mathscr{L}\left\{\displaystyle\int_0^t e^\tau \, d\tau\right\}$

24. $\mathscr{L}\left\{\displaystyle\int_0^t \cos \tau \, d\tau\right\}$

25. $\mathscr{L}\left\{\displaystyle\int_0^t e^{-\tau}\cos \tau \, d\tau\right\}$

26. $\mathscr{L}\left\{\displaystyle\int_0^t \tau \sin \tau \, d\tau\right\}$

27. $\mathscr{L}\left\{\displaystyle\int_0^t \tau e^{t-\tau} \, d\tau\right\}$

28. $\mathscr{L}\left\{\displaystyle\int_0^t \sin \tau \cos (t - \tau) \, d\tau\right\}$

29. $\mathscr{L}\left\{t\displaystyle\int_0^t \sin \tau \, d\tau\right\}$

30. $\mathscr{L}\left\{t\displaystyle\int_0^t \tau e^{-\tau} \, d\tau\right\}$

In Problems 31–34 use (8) to evaluate the given inverse transform.

31. $\mathscr{L}^{-1}\left\{\dfrac{1}{s(s - 1)}\right\}$

32. $\mathscr{L}^{-1}\left\{\dfrac{1}{s^2(s - 1)}\right\}$

33. $\mathscr{L}^{-1}\left\{\dfrac{1}{s^3(s - 1)}\right\}$

34. $\mathscr{L}^{-1}\left\{\dfrac{1}{s(s - a)^2}\right\}$

35. The table in Appendix III does not contain an entry for

$$\mathscr{L}^{-1}\left\{\dfrac{8k^3 s}{(s^2 + k^2)^3}\right\}.$$

(a) Use (4) along with the results in (5) to evaluate this inverse transform. Use a CAS as an aid in evaluating the convolution integral.

(b) Reexamine your answer to part (a). Could you have obtained the result in a different manner?

36. Use the Laplace transform and the results of Problem 35 to solve the initial-value problem

$$y'' + y = \sin t + t \sin t, \quad y(0) = 0, \quad y'(0) = 0.$$

Use a graphing utility to graph the solution.

In Problems 37–46 use the Laplace transform to solve the given integral equation or integrodifferential equation.

37. $f(t) + \displaystyle\int_0^t (t - \tau) f(\tau) \, d\tau = t$

38. $f(t) = 2t - 4\displaystyle\int_0^t \sin \tau f(t - \tau) \, d\tau$

39. $f(t) = te^t + \displaystyle\int_0^t \tau f(t - \tau) \, d\tau$

40. $f(t) + 2\displaystyle\int_0^t f(\tau) \cos (t - \tau) \, d\tau = 4e^{-t} + \sin t$

41. $f(t) + \displaystyle\int_0^t f(\tau) \, d\tau = 1$

42. $f(t) = \cos t + \displaystyle\int_0^t e^{-\tau} f(t - \tau) \, d\tau$

43. $f(t) = 1 + t - \dfrac{8}{3}\displaystyle\int_0^t (\tau - t)^3 f(\tau) \, d\tau$

44. $t - 2f(t) = \displaystyle\int_0^t (e^\tau - e^{-\tau}) f(t - \tau) \, d\tau$

45. $y'(t) = 1 - \sin t - \displaystyle\int_0^t y(\tau) \, d\tau, \quad y(0) = 0$

46. $\dfrac{dy}{dt} + 6y(t) + 9\displaystyle\int_0^t y(\tau) \, d\tau = 1, \quad y(0) = 0$

In Problems 47 and 48 solve equation (10) subject to $i(0) = 0$ with L, R, C, and $E(t)$ as given. Use a graphing utility to graph the solution for $0 \le t \le 3$.

47. $L = 0.1$ h, $R = 3\ \Omega$, $C = 0.05$ f,
  $E(t) = 100[\mathscr{U}(t - 1) - \mathscr{U}(t - 2)]$

48. $L = 0.005$ h, $R = 1\ \Omega$, $C = 0.02$ f,
  $E(t) = 100[t - (t - 1)\mathscr{U}(t - 1)]$

7.4.3 TRANSFORM OF A PERIODIC FUNCTION

In Problems 49–54 use Theorem 7.4.3 to find the Laplace transform of the given periodic function.

49.

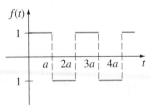

meander function

FIGURE 7.4.6 Graph for Problem 49

50.

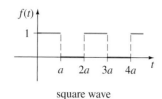

square wave

FIGURE 7.4.7 Graph for Problem 50

51.

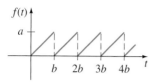

sawtooth function

FIGURE 7.4.8 Graph for Problem 51

52.

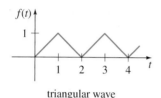

triangular wave

FIGURE 7.4.9 Graph for Problem 52

53.

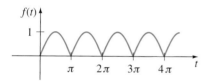

full-wave rectification of sin t

FIGURE 7.4.10 Graph for Problem 53

54.

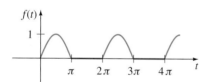

half-wave rectification of sin t

FIGURE 7.4.11 Graph for Problem 54

In Problems 55 and 56 solve equation (12) subject to $i(0) = 0$ with $E(t)$ as given. Use a graphing utility to graph the solution for $0 \le t < 4$ in the case when $L = 1$ and $R = 1$.

55. $E(t)$ is the meander function in Problem 49 with amplitude 1 and $a = 1$.

56. $E(t)$ is the sawtooth function in Problem 51 with amplitude 1 and $b = 1$.

In Problems 57 and 58 solve the model for a driven spring/mass system with damping

$$m\frac{d^2x}{dt^2} + \beta\frac{dx}{dt} + kx = f(t), \quad x(0) = 0, \quad x'(0) = 0,$$

where the driving function f is as specified. Use a graphing utility to graph $x(t)$ for the indicated values of t.

57. $m = \frac{1}{2}$, $\beta = 1$, $k = 5$, f is the meander function in Problem 49 with amplitude 10, and $a = \pi$, $0 \le t < 2\pi$.

58. $m = 1$, $\beta = 2$, $k = 1$, f is the square wave in Problem 50 with amplitude 5, and $a = \pi$, $0 \le t < 4\pi$.

Discussion Problems

59. Discuss how Theorem 7.4.1 can be used to find

$$\mathscr{L}^{-1}\left\{\ln\frac{s-3}{s+1}\right\}.$$

60. In Section 6.3 we saw that $ty'' + y' + ty = 0$ is Bessel's equation of order $\nu = 0$. In view of (22) of that section and Table 6.1 a solution of the initial-value problem $ty'' + y' + ty = 0$, $y(0) = 1$, $y'(0) = 0$, is $y = J_0(t)$. Use this result and the procedure outlined in the instructions to Problems 17 and 18 to show that

$$\mathscr{L}\{J_0(t)\} = \frac{1}{\sqrt{s^2 + 1}}.$$

[*Hint*: You might need to use Problem 46 in Exercises 7.2.]

61. (a) Laguerre's differential equation

$$ty'' + (1 - t)y' + ny = 0$$

is known to possess polynomial solutions when n is a nonnegative integer. These solutions are naturally called **Laguerre polynomials** and are denoted by $L_n(t)$. Find $y = L_n(t)$, for $n = 0, 1, 2, 3, 4$ if it is known that $L_n(0) = 1$.

(b) Show that

$$\mathscr{L}\left\{\frac{e^t}{n!}\frac{d^n}{dt^n}t^n e^{-t}\right\} = Y(s),$$

where $Y(s) = \mathscr{L}\{y\}$ and $y = L_n(t)$ is a polynomial solution of the DE in part (a). Conclude that

$$L_n(t) = \frac{e^t}{n!}\frac{d^n}{dt^n}t^n e^{-t}, \qquad n = 0, 1, 2, \ldots.$$

This last relation for generating the Laguerre polynomials is the analogue of Rodrigues' formula for the Legendre polynomials. See (30) in Section 6.3.

Computer Lab Assignments

62. In this problem you are led through the commands in *Mathematica* that enable you to obtain the symbolic Laplace transform of a differential equation and the solution of the initial-value problem by finding the inverse transform. In *Mathematica* the Laplace transform of a function $y(t)$ is obtained using **LaplaceTransform [y[t], t, s]**. In line two of the syntax we replace **LaplaceTransform [y[t], t, s]** by the symbol **Y**. (*If you do not have* Mathematica, *then adapt the given procedure by finding the corresponding syntax for the CAS you have on hand.*)

Consider the initial-value problem

$$y'' + 6y' + 9y = t \sin t, \quad y(0) = 2, \quad y'(0) = -1.$$

Load the Laplace transform package. Precisely reproduce and then, in turn, execute each line in the following sequence of commands. Either copy the output by hand or print out the results.

diffequat = y″[t] + 6y′[t] + 9y[t] == t Sin[t]
transformdeq = LaplaceTransform [diffequat, t, s] /.
  {y[0] − > 2, y′[0] − > −1,
  LaplaceTransform [y[t], t, s] − > Y}
soln = Solve[transformdeq, Y]//Flatten
Y = Y/.soln
InverseLaplaceTransform[Y, s, t]

63. Appropriately modify the procedure of Problem 62 to find a solution of

$$y''' + 3y' - 4y = 0,$$
$$y(0) = 0, \quad y'(0) = 0, \quad y''(0) = 1.$$

64. The charge $q(t)$ on a capacitor in an LC series circuit is given by

$$\frac{d^2q}{dt^2} + q = 1 - 4\,\mathcal{U}(t - \pi) + 6\,\mathcal{U}(t - 3\pi),$$
$$q(0) = 0, \quad q'(0) = 0.$$

Appropriately modify the procedure of Problem 62 to find $q(t)$. Graph your solution.

7.5   THE DIRAC DELTA FUNCTION

INTRODUCTION   In the last paragraph on page 261, we indicated that as an immediate consequence of Theorem 7.1.3, $F(s) = 1$ cannot be the Laplace transform of a function f that is piecewise continuous on $[0, \infty)$ and of exponential order. In the discussion that follows we are going to introduce a function that is very different from the kinds that you have studied in previous courses. We shall see that there does indeed exist a function—or, more precisely, a *generalized function*—whose Laplace transform is $F(s) = 1$.

UNIT IMPULSE   Mechanical systems are often acted on by an external force (or electromotive force in an electrical circuit) of large magnitude that acts only for a very short period of time. For example, a vibrating airplane wing could be struck by lightning, a mass on a spring could be given a sharp blow by a ball peen hammer, and a ball (baseball, golf ball, tennis ball) could be sent soaring when struck violently by some kind of club (baseball bat, golf club, tennis racket). See Figure 7.5.1. The graph of the piecewise-defined function

$$\delta_a(t - t_0) = \begin{cases} 0, & 0 \le t < t_0 - a \\ \dfrac{1}{2a}, & t_0 - a \le t < t_0 + a \\ 0, & t \ge t_0 + a, \end{cases} \tag{1}$$

$a > 0$, $t_0 > 0$, shown in Figure 7.5.2(a), could serve as a model for such a force. For a small value of a, $\delta_a(t - t_0)$ is essentially a constant function of large magnitude that is "on" for just a very short period of time, around t_0. The behavior of $\delta_a(t - t_0)$ as $a \to 0$ is illustrated in Figure 7.5.2(b). The function $\delta_a(t - t_0)$ is called a **unit impulse**, because it possesses the integration property $\int_0^\infty \delta_a(t - t_0)\, dt = 1$.

FIGURE 7.5.1   A golf club applies a force of large magnitude on the ball for a very short period of time

DIRAC DELTA FUNCTION   In practice it is convenient to work with another type of unit impulse, a "function" that approximates $\delta_a(t - t_0)$ and is defined by the limit

$$\delta(t - t_0) = \lim_{a \to 0} \delta_a(t - t_0). \tag{2}$$

The latter expression, which is not a function at all, can be characterized by the two properties

$$(i)\ \delta(t - t_0) = \begin{cases} \infty, & t = t_0 \\ 0, & t \neq t_0 \end{cases} \quad \text{and} \quad (ii)\ \int_0^\infty \delta(t - t_0)\,dt = 1.$$

The unit impulse $\delta(t - t_0)$ is called the **Dirac delta function.**

It is possible to obtain the Laplace transform of the Dirac delta function by the formal assumption that $\mathscr{L}\{\delta(t - t_0)\} = \lim_{a \to 0} \mathscr{L}\{\delta_a(t - t_0)\}$.

THEOREM 7.5.1 **Transform of the Dirac Delta Function**

For $t_0 > 0$, $$\mathscr{L}\{\delta(t - t_0)\} = e^{-st_0}. \tag{3}$$

PROOF To begin, we can write $\delta_a(t - t_0)$ in terms of the unit step function by virtue of (11) and (12) of Section 7.3:

$$\delta_a(t - t_0) = \frac{1}{2a}[\mathscr{U}(t - (t_0 - a)) - \mathscr{U}(t - (t_0 + a))].$$

By linearity and (14) of Section 7.3 the Laplace transform of this last expression is

$$\mathscr{L}\{\delta_a(t - t_0)\} = \frac{1}{2a}\left[\frac{e^{-s(t_0 - a)}}{s} - \frac{e^{-s(t_0 + a)}}{s}\right] = e^{-st_0}\left(\frac{e^{sa} - e^{-sa}}{2sa}\right). \tag{4}$$

Since (4) has the indeterminate form $0/0$ as $a \to 0$, we apply L'Hôpital's Rule:

$$\mathscr{L}\{\delta(t - t_0)\} = \lim_{a \to 0} \mathscr{L}\{\delta_a(t - t_0)\} = e^{-st_0} \lim_{a \to 0}\left(\frac{e^{sa} - e^{-sa}}{2sa}\right) = e^{-st_0}. \quad \blacksquare$$

Now when $t_0 = 0$, it seems plausible to conclude from (3) that

$$\mathscr{L}\{\delta(t)\} = 1.$$

The last result emphasizes the fact that $\delta(t)$ is not the usual type of function that we have been considering, since we expect from Theorem 7.1.3 that $\mathscr{L}\{f(t)\} \to 0$ as $s \to \infty$.

EXAMPLE 1 **Two Initial-Value Problems**

Solve $y'' + y = 4\delta(t - 2\pi)$ subject to

(a) $y(0) = 1$, $y'(0) = 0$ **(b)** $y(0) = 0$, $y'(0) = 0$.

The two initial-value problems could serve as models for describing the motion of a mass on a spring moving in a medium in which damping is negligible. At $t = 2\pi$ the mass is given a sharp blow. In (a) the mass is released from rest 1 unit below the equilibrium position. In (b) the mass is at rest in the equilibrium position.

SOLUTION **(a)** From (3) the Laplace transform of the differential equation is

$$s^2 Y(s) - s + Y(s) = 4e^{-2\pi s} \quad \text{or} \quad Y(s) = \frac{s}{s^2 + 1} + \frac{4e^{-2\pi s}}{s^2 + 1}.$$

Using the inverse form of the second translation theorem, we find

$$y(t) = \cos t + 4 \sin(t - 2\pi)\,\mathscr{U}(t - 2\pi).$$

Since $\sin(t - 2\pi) = \sin t$, the foregoing solution can be written as

$$y(t) = \begin{cases} \cos t, & 0 \leq t < 2\pi \\ \cos t + 4 \sin t, & t \geq 2\pi. \end{cases} \tag{5}$$

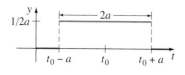

(a) graph of $\delta_a(t - t_0)$

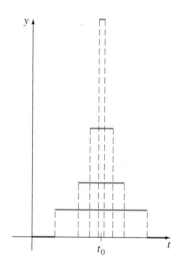

(b) behavior of δ_a as $a \to 0$

FIGURE 7.5.2 Unit impulse

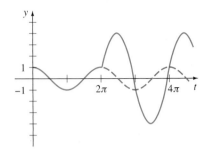

FIGURE 7.5.3 Mass is struck at $t = 2\pi$

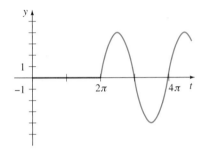

FIGURE 7.5.4 No motion until mass is struck at $t = 2\pi$

In Figure 7.5.3 we see from the graph of (5) that the mass is exhibiting simple harmonic motion until it is struck at $t = 2\pi$. The influence of the unit impulse is to increase the amplitude of vibration to $\sqrt{17}$ for $t > 2\pi$.

(b) In this case the transform of the equation is simply

$$Y(s) = \frac{4e^{-2\pi s}}{s^2 + 1},$$

and so
$$y(t) = 4\sin(t - 2\pi)\,\mathcal{U}(t - 2\pi)$$

$$= \begin{cases} 0, & 0 \le t < 2\pi \\ 4\sin t, & t \ge 2\pi. \end{cases} \tag{6}$$

The graph of (6) in Figure 7.5.4 shows, as we would expect from the initial conditions that the mass exhibits no motion until it is struck at $t = 2\pi$. ∎

REMARKS

(i) If $\delta(t - t_0)$ were a function in the usual sense, then property *(i)* on page 293 would imply $\int_0^\infty \delta(t - t_0)\,dt = 0$ rather than $\int_0^\infty \delta(t - t_0)\,dt = 1$. Because the Dirac delta function did not "behave" like an ordinary function, even though its users produced correct results, it was met initially with great scorn by mathematicians. However, in the 1940s Dirac's controversial function was put on a rigorous footing by the French mathematician Laurent Schwartz in his book *La Théorie de distribution*, and this, in turn, led to an entirely new branch of mathematics known as the **theory of distributions** or **generalized functions.** In this theory (2) is not an accepted definition of $\delta(t - t_0)$, nor does one speak of a function whose values are either ∞ or 0. Although we shall not pursue this topic any further, suffice it to say that the Dirac delta function is best characterized by its effect on other functions. If f is a continuous function, then

$$\int_0^\infty f(t)\,\delta(t - t_0)\,dt = f(t_0) \tag{7}$$

can be taken as the *definition* of $\delta(t - t_0)$. This result is known as the **sifting property,** since $\delta(t - t_0)$ has the effect of sifting the value $f(t_0)$ out of the set of values of f on $[0, \infty)$. Note that property *(ii)* (with $f(t) = 1$) and (3) (with $f(t) = e^{-st}$) are consistent with (7).

(ii) The *Remarks* in Section 7.2 indicated that the transfer function of a general linear nth-order differential equation with constant coefficients is $W(s) = 1/P(s)$, where $P(s) = a_n s^n + a_{n-1}s^{n-1} + \cdots + a_0$. The transfer function is the Laplace transform of function $w(t)$, called the **weight function** of a linear system. But $w(t)$ can also be characterized in terms of the discussion at hand. For simplicity let us consider a second-order linear system in which the input is a unit impulse at $t = 0$:

$$a_2 y'' + a_1 y' + a_0 y = \delta(t), \quad y(0) = 0, \quad y'(0) = 0.$$

Applying the Laplace transform and using $\mathcal{L}\{\delta(t)\} = 1$ shows that the transform of the response y in this case is the transfer function

$$Y(s) = \frac{1}{a_2 s^2 + a_1 s + a_0} = \frac{1}{P(s)} = W(s) \quad \text{and} \quad \text{so} \quad y = \mathcal{L}^{-1}\left\{\frac{1}{P(s)}\right\} = w(t).$$

From this we can see, in general, that the weight function $y = w(t)$ of an nth-order linear system is the zero-state response of the system to a unit impulse. For this reason $w(t)$ is also called the **impulse response** of the system.

EXERCISES 7.5

Answers to selected odd-numbered problems begin on page ANS-12.

In Problems 1–12 use the Laplace transform to solve the given initial-value problem.

1. $y' - 3y = \delta(t - 2), \quad y(0) = 0$

2. $y' + y = \delta(t - 1), \quad y(0) = 2$

3. $y'' + y = \delta(t - 2\pi), \quad y(0) = 0, y'(0) = 1$

4. $y'' + 16y = \delta(t - 2\pi), \quad y(0) = 0, y'(0) = 0$

5. $y'' + y = \delta\left(t - \frac{1}{2}\pi\right) + \delta\left(t - \frac{3}{2}\pi\right),$
$y(0) = 0, y'(0) = 0$

6. $y'' + y = \delta(t - 2\pi) + \delta(t - 4\pi), \quad y(0) = 1, y'(0) = 0$

7. $y'' + 2y' = \delta(t - 1), \quad y(0) = 0, y'(0) = 1$

8. $y'' - 2y' = 1 + \delta(t - 2), \quad y(0) = 0, y'(0) = 1$

9. $y'' + 4y' + 5y = \delta(t - 2\pi), \quad y(0) = 0, y'(0) = 0$

10. $y'' + 2y' + y = \delta(t - 1), \quad y(0) = 0, y'(0) = 0$

11. $y'' + 4y' + 13y = \delta(t - \pi) + \delta(t - 3\pi),$
$y(0) = 1, y'(0) = 0$

12. $y'' - 7y' + 6y = e^t + \delta(t - 2) + \delta(t - 4),$
$y(0) = 0, y'(0) = 0$

13. A uniform beam of length L carries a concentrated load w_0 at $x = \frac{1}{2}L$. The beam is embedded at its left end and is free at its right end. Use the Laplace transform to determine the deflection $y(x)$ from

$$EI\frac{d^4y}{dx^4} = w_0\,\delta\left(x - \tfrac{1}{2}L\right),$$

where $y(0) = 0$, $y'(0) = 0$, $y''(L) = 0$, and $y'''(L) = 0$.

14. Solve the differential equation in Problem 13 subject to $y(0) = 0$, $y'(0) = 0$, $y(L) = 0$, $y'(L) = 0$. In this case the beam is embedded at both ends. See Figure 7.5.5.

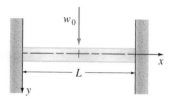

FIGURE 7.5.5 Beam in Problem 14

Discussion Problems

15. Someone tells you that the solutions of the two IVPs

$$y'' + 2y' + 10y = 0, \qquad y(0) = 0, \quad y'(0) = 1$$
$$y'' + 2y' + 10y = \delta(t), \qquad y(0) = 0, \quad y'(0) = 0$$

are exactly the same. Do you agree or disagree? Defend your answer.

7.6 SYSTEMS OF LINEAR DIFFERENTIAL EQUATIONS

REVIEW MATERIAL
- Solving systems of two equations in two unknowns

INTRODUCTION   When initial conditions are specified, the Laplace transform of each equation in a system of linear differential equations with constant coefficients reduces the system of DEs to a set of simultaneous algebraic equations in the transformed functions. We solve the system of algebraic equations for each of the transformed functions and then find the inverse Laplace transforms in the usual manner.

COUPLED SPRINGS   Two masses m_1 and m_2 are connected to two springs A and B of negligible mass having spring constants k_1 and k_2, respectively. In turn the two springs are attached as shown in Figure 7.6.1. Let $x_1(t)$ and $x_2(t)$ denote the vertical displacements of the masses from their equilibrium positions. When the system is in motion, spring B is subject to both an elongation and a compression; hence its net elongation is $x_2 - x_1$. Therefore it follows from Hooke's law that springs A and B exert forces $-k_1x_1$ and $k_2(x_2 - x_1)$, respectively, on m_1. If no external force is impressed on the system and if no damping force is present, then the net force on m_1 is $-k_1x_1 + k_2(x_2 - x_1)$. By Newton's second law we can write

$$m_1\frac{d^2x_1}{dt^2} = -k_1x_1 + k_2(x_2 - x_1).$$

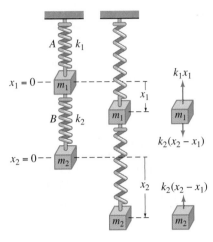

$x_1 = 0$ m_1

B k_2

$x_2 = 0$ m_2

A k_1

$k_1 x_1$

x_1

m_1

m_1

$k_2(x_2 - x_1)$

x_2 $k_2(x_2 - x_1)$

m_2

m_2

(a) equilibrium (b) motion (c) forces

FIGURE 7.6.1 Coupled spring/mass system

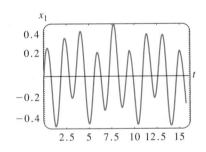

(a) plot of $x_1(t)$ vs. t

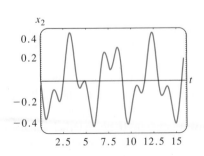

(b) plot of $x_2(t)$ vs. t

FIGURE 7.6.2 Displacements of the two masses

Similarly, the net force exerted on mass m_2 is due solely to the net elongation of B; that is, $-k_2(x_2 - x_1)$. Hence we have

$$m_2 \frac{d^2 x_2}{dt^2} = -k_2(x_2 - x_1).$$

In other words, the motion of the coupled system is represented by the system of simultaneous second-order differential equations

$$\begin{aligned} m_1 x_1'' &= -k_1 x_1 + k_2(x_2 - x_1) \\ m_2 x_2'' &= -k_2(x_2 - x_1). \end{aligned} \tag{1}$$

In the next example we solve (1) under the assumptions that $k_1 = 6$, $k_2 = 4$, $m_1 = 1$, $m_2 = 1$, and that the masses start from their equilibrium positions with opposite unit velocities.

EXAMPLE 1 Coupled Springs

Solve
$$\begin{aligned} x_1'' + 10x_1 \quad - 4x_2 &= 0 \\ -4x_1 + x_2'' + 4x_2 &= 0 \end{aligned} \tag{2}$$

subject to $x_1(0) = 0$, $x_1'(0) = 1$, $x_2(0) = 0$, $x_2'(0) = -1$.

SOLUTION The Laplace transform of each equation is

$$s^2 X_1(s) - s x_1(0) - x_1'(0) + 10 X_1(s) - 4X_2(s) = 0$$
$$-4X_1(s) + s^2 X_2(s) - s x_2(0) - x_2'(0) + 4X_2(s) = 0,$$

where $X_1(s) = \mathscr{L}\{x_1(t)\}$ and $X_2(s) = \mathscr{L}\{x_2(t)\}$. The preceding system is the same as

$$\begin{aligned} (s^2 + 10) X_1(s) - \quad 4X_2(s) &= 1 \\ -4 X_1(s) + (s^2 + 4) X_2(s) &= -1. \end{aligned} \tag{3}$$

Solving (3) for $X_1(s)$ and using partial fractions on the result yields

$$X_1(s) = \frac{s^2}{(s^2 + 2)(s^2 + 12)} = -\frac{1/5}{s^2 + 2} + \frac{6/5}{s^2 + 12},$$

and therefore

$$x_1(t) = -\frac{1}{5\sqrt{2}} \mathscr{L}^{-1}\left\{\frac{\sqrt{2}}{s^2 + 2}\right\} + \frac{6}{5\sqrt{12}} \mathscr{L}^{-1}\left\{\frac{\sqrt{12}}{s^2 + 12}\right\}$$

$$= -\frac{\sqrt{2}}{10} \sin \sqrt{2}t + \frac{\sqrt{3}}{5} \sin 2\sqrt{3}t.$$

Substituting the expression for $X_1(s)$ into the first equation of (3) gives

$$X_2(s) = -\frac{s^2 + 6}{(s^2 + 2)(s^2 + 12)} = -\frac{2/5}{s^2 + 2} - \frac{3/5}{s^2 + 12}$$

and

$$x_2(t) = -\frac{2}{5\sqrt{2}} \mathscr{L}^{-1}\left\{\frac{\sqrt{2}}{s^2 + 2}\right\} - \frac{3}{5\sqrt{12}} \mathscr{L}^{-1}\left\{\frac{\sqrt{12}}{s^2 + 12}\right\}$$

$$= -\frac{\sqrt{2}}{5} \sin \sqrt{2}t - \frac{\sqrt{3}}{10} \sin 2\sqrt{3}t.$$

Finally, the solution to the given system (2) is

$$x_1(t) = -\frac{\sqrt{2}}{10} \sin \sqrt{2}t + \frac{\sqrt{3}}{5} \sin 2\sqrt{3}t$$

$$x_2(t) = -\frac{\sqrt{2}}{5} \sin \sqrt{2}t - \frac{\sqrt{3}}{10} \sin 2\sqrt{3}t.$$

(4)

The graphs of x_1 and x_2 in Figure 7.6.2 reveal the complicated oscillatory motion of each mass. ■

NETWORKS   In (18) of Section 3.3 we saw the currents $i_1(t)$ and $i_2(t)$ in the network shown in Figure 7.6.3, containing an inductor, a resistor, and a capacitor, were governed by the system of first-order differential equations

$$L\frac{di_1}{dt} + Ri_2 = E(t)$$

$$RC\frac{di_2}{dt} + i_2 - i_1 = 0.$$

(5)

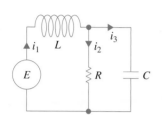

FIGURE 7.6.3   Electrical network

We solve this system by the Laplace transform in the next example.

EXAMPLE 2   An Electrical Network

Solve the system in (5) under the conditions $E(t) = 60$ V, $L = 1$ h, $R = 50$ Ω, $C = 10^{-4}$ f, and the currents i_1 and i_2 are initially zero.

SOLUTION   We must solve

$$\frac{di_1}{dt} + 50i_2 = 60$$

$$50(10^{-4})\frac{di_2}{dt} + i_2 - i_1 = 0$$

subject to $i_1(0) = 0$, $i_2(0) = 0$.

Applying the Laplace transform to each equation of the system and simplifying gives

$$sI_1(s) + 50I_2(s) = \frac{60}{s}$$

$$-200I_1(s) + (s + 200)I_2(s) = 0,$$

where $I_1(s) = \mathscr{L}\{i_1(t)\}$ and $I_2(s) = \mathscr{L}\{i_2(t)\}$. Solving the system for I_1 and I_2 and decomposing the results into partial fractions gives

$$I_1(s) = \frac{60s + 12,000}{s(s + 100)^2} = \frac{6/5}{s} - \frac{6/5}{s + 100} - \frac{60}{(s + 100)^2}$$

$$I_2(s) = \frac{12,000}{s(s + 100)^2} = \frac{6/5}{s} - \frac{6/5}{s + 100} - \frac{120}{(s + 100)^2}.$$

Taking the inverse Laplace transform, we find the currents to be

$$i_1(t) = \frac{6}{5} - \frac{6}{5}e^{-100t} - 60te^{-100t}$$

$$i_2(t) = \frac{6}{5} - \frac{6}{5}e^{-100t} - 120te^{-100t}.$$

■

Note that both $i_1(t)$ and $i_2(t)$ in Example 2 tend toward the value $E/R = \frac{6}{5}$ as $t \to \infty$. Furthermore, since the current through the capacitor is $i_3(t) = i_1(t) - i_2(t) = 60te^{-100t}$, we observe that $i_3(t) \to 0$ as $t \to \infty$.

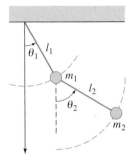

FIGURE 7.6.4 Double pendulum

DOUBLE PENDULUM Consider the double-pendulum system consisting of a pendulum attached to a pendulum shown in Figure 7.6.4. We assume that the system oscillates in a vertical plane under the influence of gravity, that the mass of each rod is negligible, and that no damping forces act on the system. Figure 7.6.4 also shows that the displacement angle θ_1 is measured (in radians) from a vertical line extending downward from the pivot of the system and that θ_2 is measured from a vertical line extending downward from the center of mass m_1. The positive direction is to the right; the negative direction is to the left. As we might expect from the analysis leading to equation (6) of Section 5.3, the system of differential equations describing the motion is nonlinear:

$$(m_1 + m_2)l_1^2\theta_1'' + m_2l_1l_2\theta_2'' \cos(\theta_1 - \theta_2) + m_2l_1l_2(\theta_2')^2 \sin(\theta_1 - \theta_2) + (m_1 + m_2)l_1g \sin\theta_1 = 0 \qquad (6)$$
$$m_2l_2^2\theta_2'' + m_2l_1l_2\theta_1'' \cos(\theta_1 - \theta_2) - m_2l_1l_2(\theta_1')^2 \sin(\theta_1 - \theta_2) + m_2l_2g \sin\theta_2 = 0.$$

But if the displacements $\theta_1(t)$ and $\theta_2(t)$ are assumed to be small, then the approximations $\cos(\theta_1 - \theta_2) \approx 1$, $\sin(\theta_1 - \theta_2) \approx 0$, $\sin\theta_1 \approx \theta_1$, $\sin\theta_2 \approx \theta_2$ enable us to replace system (6) by the linearization

$$(m_1 + m_2)l_1^2\theta_1'' + m_2l_1l_2\theta_2'' + (m_1 + m_2)l_1g\theta_1 = 0$$
$$m_2l_2^2\theta_2'' + m_2l_1l_2\theta_1'' + m_2l_2g\theta_2 = 0. \qquad (7)$$

EXAMPLE 3 Double Pendulum

It is left as an exercise to fill in the details of using the Laplace transform to solve system (7) when $m_1 = 3$, $m_2 = 1$, $l_1 = l_2 = 16$, $\theta_1(0) = 1$, $\theta_2(0) = -1$, $\theta_1'(0) = 0$, and $\theta_2'(0) = 0$. You should find that

$$\theta_1(t) = \frac{1}{4}\cos\frac{2}{\sqrt{3}}t + \frac{3}{4}\cos 2t$$
$$\theta_2(t) = \frac{1}{2}\cos\frac{2}{\sqrt{3}}t - \frac{3}{2}\cos 2t. \qquad (8)$$

With the aid of a CAS the positions of the two masses at $t = 0$ and at subsequent times are shown in Figure 7.6.5. See Problem 21 in Exercises 7.6.

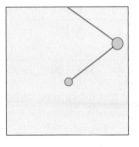
(a) $t = 0$

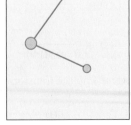
(b) $t = 1.4$

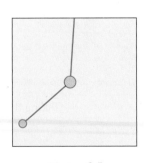
(c) $t = 2.5$

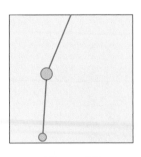
(d) $t = 8.5$

FIGURE 7.6.5 Positions of masses on double pendulum at various times

EXERCISES 7.6

Answers to selected odd-numbered problems begin on page ANS-12.

In Problems 1–12 use the Laplace transform to solve the given system of differential equations.

1. $\dfrac{dx}{dt} = -x + y$

$\dfrac{dy}{dt} = 2x$

$x(0) = 0, \quad y(0) = 1$

2. $\dfrac{dx}{dt} = 2y + e^t$

$\dfrac{dy}{dt} = 8x - t$

$x(0) = 1, \quad y(0) = 1$

3. $\dfrac{dx}{dt} = x - 2y$

$\dfrac{dy}{dt} = 5x - y$

$x(0) = -1, \quad y(0) = 2$

4. $\dfrac{dx}{dt} + 3x + \dfrac{dy}{dt} = 1$

$\dfrac{dx}{dt} - x + \dfrac{dy}{dt} - y = e^t$

$x(0) = 0, \quad y(0) = 0$

5. $2\dfrac{dx}{dt} + \dfrac{dy}{dt} - 2x = 1$

$\dfrac{dx}{dt} + \dfrac{dy}{dt} - 3x - 3y = 2$

$x(0) = 0, \quad y(0) = 0$

6. $\dfrac{dx}{dt} + x - \dfrac{dy}{dt} + y = 0$

$\dfrac{dx}{dt} + \dfrac{dy}{dt} + 2y = 0$

$x(0) = 0, \quad y(0) = 1$

7. $\dfrac{d^2x}{dt^2} + x - y = 0$

$\dfrac{d^2y}{dt^2} + y - x = 0$

$x(0) = 0, \quad x'(0) = -2,$

$y(0) = 0, \quad y'(0) = 1$

8. $\dfrac{d^2x}{dt^2} + \dfrac{dx}{dt} + \dfrac{dy}{dt} = 0$

$\dfrac{d^2y}{dt^2} + \dfrac{dy}{dt} - 4\dfrac{dx}{dt} = 0$

$x(0) = 1, \quad x'(0) = 0,$

$y(0) = -1, \quad y'(0) = 5$

9. $\dfrac{d^2x}{dt^2} + \dfrac{d^2y}{dt^2} = t^2$

$\dfrac{d^2x}{dt^2} - \dfrac{d^2y}{dt^2} = 4t$

$x(0) = 8, \quad x'(0) = 0,$

$y(0) = 0, \quad y'(0) = 0$

10. $\dfrac{dx}{dt} - 4x + \dfrac{d^3y}{dt^3} = 6\sin t$

$\dfrac{dx}{dt} + 2x - 2\dfrac{d^3y}{dt^3} = 0$

$x(0) = 0, \quad y(0) = 0,$

$y'(0) = 0, \quad y''(0) = 0$

11. $\dfrac{d^2x}{dt^2} + 3\dfrac{dy}{dt} + 3y = 0$

$\dfrac{d^2x}{dt^2} + 3y = te^{-t}$

$x(0) = 0, \quad x'(0) = 2, \quad y(0) = 0$

12. $\dfrac{dx}{dt} = 4x - 2y + 2\,\mathscr{U}(t - 1)$

$\dfrac{dy}{dt} = 3x - y + \mathscr{U}(t - 1)$

$x(0) = 0, \quad y(0) = \tfrac{1}{2}$

13. Solve system (1) when $k_1 = 3, k_2 = 2, m_1 = 1, m_2 = 1$ and $x_1(0) = 0, x_1'(0) = 1, x_2(0) = 1, x_2'(0) = 0$.

14. Derive the system of differential equations describing the straight-line vertical motion of the coupled springs shown in Figure 7.6.6. Use the Laplace transform to solve the system when $k_1 = 1, k_2 = 1, k_3 = 1, m_1 = 1, m_2 = 1$ and $x_1(0) = 0, x_1'(0) = -1, x_2(0) = 0, x_2'(0) = 1$.

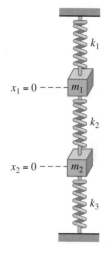

FIGURE 7.6.6 Coupled springs in Problem 14

15. (a) Show that the system of differential equations for the currents $i_2(t)$ and $i_3(t)$ in the electrical network shown in Figure 7.6.7 is

$$L_1\dfrac{di_2}{dt} + Ri_2 + Ri_3 = E(t)$$

$$L_2\dfrac{di_3}{dt} + Ri_2 + Ri_3 = E(t).$$

(b) Solve the system in part (a) if $R = 5\ \Omega, L_1 = 0.01$ h, $L_2 = 0.0125$ h, $E = 100$ V, $i_2(0) = 0$, and $i_3(0) = 0$.

(c) Determine the current $i_1(t)$.

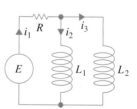

FIGURE 7.6.7 Network in Problem 15

16. (a) In Problem 12 in Exercises 3.3 you were asked to show that the currents $i_2(t)$ and $i_3(t)$ in the electrical network shown in Figure 7.6.8 satisfy

$$L\dfrac{di_2}{dt} + L\dfrac{di_3}{dt} + R_1i_2 = E(t)$$

$$-R_1\dfrac{di_2}{dt} + R_2\dfrac{di_3}{dt} + \dfrac{1}{C}i_3 = 0.$$

Solve the system if $R_1 = 10\ \Omega$, $R_2 = 5\ \Omega$, $L = 1$ h, $C = 0.2$ f,

$$E(t) = \begin{cases} 120, & 0 \le t < 2 \\ 0, & t \ge 2, \end{cases}$$

$i_2(0) = 0$, and $i_3(0) = 0$.

(b) Determine the current $i_1(t)$.

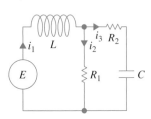

FIGURE 7.6.8 Network in Problem 16

17. Solve the system given in (17) of Section 3.3 when $R_1 = 6\ \Omega$, $R_2 = 5\ \Omega$, $L_1 = 1$ h, $L_2 = 1$ h, $E(t) = 50 \sin t$ V, $i_2(0) = 0$, and $i_3(0) = 0$.

18. Solve (5) when $E = 60$ V, $L = \frac{1}{2}$ h, $R = 50\ \Omega$, $C = 10^{-4}$ f, $i_1(0) = 0$, and $i_2(0) = 0$.

19. Solve (5) when $E = 60$ V, $L = 2$ h, $R = 50\ \Omega$, $C = 10^{-4}$ f, $i_1(0) = 0$, and $i_2(0) = 0$.

20. (a) Show that the system of differential equations for the charge on the capacitor $q(t)$ and the current $i_3(t)$ in the electrical network shown in Figure 7.6.9 is

$$R_1 \frac{dq}{dt} + \frac{1}{C} q + R_1 i_3 = E(t)$$

$$L \frac{di_3}{dt} + R_2 i_3 - \frac{1}{C} q = 0.$$

(b) Find the charge on the capacitor when $L = 1$ h, $R_1 = 1\ \Omega$, $R_2 = 1\ \Omega$, $C = 1$ f,

$$E(t) = \begin{cases} 0, & 0 < t < 1 \\ 50e^{-t}, & t \ge 1, \end{cases}$$

$i_3(0) = 0$, and $q(0) = 0$.

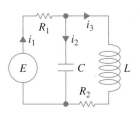

FIGURE 7.6.9 Network in Problem 20

Computer Lab Assignments

21. (a) Use the Laplace transform and the information given in Example 3 to obtain the solution (8) of the system given in (7).

(b) Use a graphing utility to graph $\theta_1(t)$ and $\theta_2(t)$ in the $t\theta$-plane. Which mass has extreme displacements of greater magnitude? Use the graphs to estimate the first time that each mass passes through its equilibrium position. Discuss whether the motion of the pendulums is periodic.

(c) Graph $\theta_1(t)$ and $\theta_2(t)$ in the $\theta_1\theta_2$-plane as parametric equations. The curve defined by these parametric equations is called a **Lissajous curve.**

(d) The positions of the masses at $t = 0$ are given in Figure 7.6.5(a). Note that we have used 1 radian $\approx 57.3°$. Use a calculator or a table application in a CAS to construct a table of values of the angles θ_1 and θ_2 for $t = 1, 2, \ldots, 10$ s. Then plot the positions of the two masses at these times.

(e) Use a CAS to find the first time that $\theta_1(t) = \theta_2(t)$ and compute the corresponding angular value. Plot the positions of the two masses at these times.

(f) Utilize the CAS to draw appropriate lines to simulate the pendulum rods, as in Figure 7.6.5. Use the animation capability of your CAS to make a "movie" of the motion of the double pendulum from $t = 0$ to $t = 10$ using a time increment of 0.1. [*Hint*: Express the coordinates $(x_1(t), y_1(t))$ and $(x_2(t), y_2(t))$ of the masses m_1 and m_2, respectively, in terms of $\theta_1(t)$ and $\theta_2(t)$.]

CHAPTER 7 IN REVIEW

Answers to selected odd-numbered problems begin on page ANS-12.

In Problems 1 and 2 use the definition of the Laplace transform to find $\mathscr{L}\{f(t)\}$.

1. $f(t) = \begin{cases} t, & 0 \le t < 1 \\ 2 - t, & t \ge 1 \end{cases}$

2. $f(t) = \begin{cases} 0, & 0 \le t < 2 \\ 1, & 2 \le t < 4 \\ 0, & t \ge 4 \end{cases}$

In Problems 3–24 fill in the blanks or answer true or false.

3. If f is not piecewise continuous on $[0, \infty)$, then $\mathscr{L}\{f(t)\}$ will not exist. _____

4. The function $f(t) = (e^t)^{10}$ is not of exponential order. _____

5. $F(s) = s^2/(s^2 + 4)$ is not the Laplace transform of a function that is piecewise continuous and of exponential order. _____

6. If $\mathscr{L}\{f(t)\} = F(s)$ and $\mathscr{L}\{g(t)\} = G(s)$, then
$\mathscr{L}^{-1}\{F(s)G(s)\} = f(t)g(t)$. _____

7. $\mathscr{L}\{e^{-7t}\} =$ _____   **8.** $\mathscr{L}\{te^{-7t}\} =$ _____

9. $\mathscr{L}\{\sin 2t\} =$ _____   **10.** $\mathscr{L}\{e^{-3t}\sin 2t\} =$ _____

11. $\mathscr{L}\{t\sin 2t\} =$ _____

12. $\mathscr{L}\{\sin 2t\, \mathscr{U}(t - \pi)\} =$ _____

13. $\mathscr{L}^{-1}\left\{\dfrac{20}{s^6}\right\} =$ _____

14. $\mathscr{L}^{-1}\left\{\dfrac{1}{3s - 1}\right\} =$ _____

15. $\mathscr{L}^{-1}\left\{\dfrac{1}{(s - 5)^3}\right\} =$ _____

16. $\mathscr{L}^{-1}\left\{\dfrac{1}{s^2 - 5}\right\} =$ _____

17. $\mathscr{L}^{-1}\left\{\dfrac{s}{s^2 - 10s + 29}\right\} =$ _____

18. $\mathscr{L}^{-1}\left\{\dfrac{e^{-5s}}{s^2}\right\} =$ _____

19. $\mathscr{L}^{-1}\left\{\dfrac{s + \pi}{s^2 + \pi^2}e^{-s}\right\} =$ _____

20. $\mathscr{L}^{-1}\left\{\dfrac{1}{L^2s^2 + n^2\pi^2}\right\} =$ _____

21. $\mathscr{L}\{e^{-5t}\}$ exists for $s >$ _____.

22. If $\mathscr{L}\{f(t)\} = F(s)$, then $\mathscr{L}\{te^{8t}f(t)\} =$ _____.

23. If $\mathscr{L}\{f(t)\} = F(s)$ and $k > 0$, then
$\mathscr{L}\{e^{at}f(t - k)\mathscr{U}(t - k)\} =$ _____.

24. $\mathscr{L}\{\int_0^t e^{a\tau}f(\tau)\,d\tau\} =$ _____ whereas
$\mathscr{L}\{e^{at}\int_0^t f(\tau)\,d\tau\} =$ _____.

In Problems 25–28 use the unit step function to find an equation for each graph in terms of the function $y = f(t)$, whose graph is given in Figure 7.R.1.

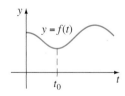

FIGURE 7.R.1   Graph for Problems 25–28

25.

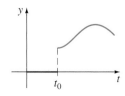

FIGURE 7.R.2   Graph for Problem 25

26.

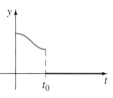

FIGURE 7.R.3   Graph for Problem 26

27.

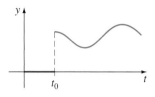

FIGURE 7.R.4   Graph for Problem 27

28.

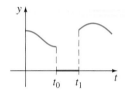

FIGURE 7.R.5   Graph for Problem 28

In Problems 29–32 express f in terms of unit step functions. Find $\mathscr{L}\{f(t)\}$ and $\mathscr{L}\{e^t f(t)\}$.

29.

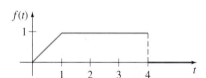

FIGURE 7.R.6   Graph for Problem 29

30.

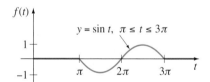

FIGURE 7.R.7   Graph for Problem 30

31.

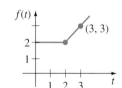

FIGURE 7.R.8   Graph for Problem 31

32.

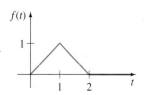

FIGURE 7.R.9   Graph for Problem 32

In Problems 33–38 use the Laplace transform to solve the given equation.

33. $y'' - 2y' + y = e^t$, $y(0) = 0$, $y'(0) = 5$

34. $y'' - 8y' + 20y = te^t$, $y(0) = 0$, $y'(0) = 0$

35. $y'' + 6y' + 5y = t - t\,\mathcal{U}(t - 2)$, $y(0) = 1$, $y'(0) = 0$

36. $y' - 5y = f(t)$, where

$$f(t) = \begin{cases} t^2, & 0 \le t < 1 \\ 0, & t \ge 1 \end{cases}, \quad y(0) = 1$$

37. $y'(t) = \cos t + \displaystyle\int_0^t y(\tau)\cos(t - \tau)\,d\tau$, $y(0) = 1$

38. $\displaystyle\int_0^t f(\tau)f(t - \tau)\,d\tau = 6t^3$

In Problems 39 and 40 use the Laplace transform to solve each system.

39. $\begin{aligned} x' + y &= t \\ 4x + y' &= 0 \\ x(0) &= 1, \quad y(0) = 2 \end{aligned}$

40. $\begin{aligned} x'' + y'' &= e^{2t} \\ 2x' + y'' &= -e^{2t} \\ x(0) &= 0, \quad y(0) = 0, \\ x'(0) &= 0, \quad y'(0) = 0 \end{aligned}$

41. The current $i(t)$ in an RC series circuit can be determined from the integral equation

$$Ri + \frac{1}{C}\int_0^t i(\tau)\,d\tau = E(t),$$

where $E(t)$ is the impressed voltage. Determine $i(t)$ when $R = 10\ \Omega$, $C = 0.5$ f, and $E(t) = 2(t^2 + t)$.

42. A series circuit contains an inductor, a resistor, and a capacitor for which $L = \frac{1}{2}$ h, $R = 10\ \Omega$, and $C = 0.01$ f, respectively. The voltage

$$E(t) = \begin{cases} 10, & 0 \le t < 5 \\ 0, & t \ge 5 \end{cases}$$

is applied to the circuit. Determine the instantaneous charge $q(t)$ on the capacitor for $t > 0$ if $q(0) = 0$ and $q'(0) = 0$.

43. A uniform cantilever beam of length L is embedded at its left end ($x = 0$) and free at its right end. Find the deflection $y(x)$ if the load per unit length is given by

$$w(x) = \frac{2w_0}{L}\left[\frac{L}{2} - x + \left(x - \frac{L}{2}\right)\mathcal{U}\left(x - \frac{L}{2}\right)\right].$$

44. When a uniform beam is supported by an elastic foundation, the differential equation for its deflection $y(x)$ is

$$EI\frac{d^4y}{dx^4} + ky = w(x),$$

where k is the modulus of the foundation and $-ky$ is the restoring force of the foundation that acts in the direction opposite to that of the load $w(x)$. See Figure 7.R.10. For

algebraic convenience suppose that the differential equation is written as

$$\frac{d^4y}{dx^4} + 4a^4y = \frac{w(x)}{EI},$$

where $a = (k/4EI)^{1/4}$. Assume $L = \pi$ and $a = 1$. Find the deflection $y(x)$ of a beam that is supported on an elastic foundation when

(a) the beam is simply supported at both ends and a constant load w_0 is uniformly distributed along its length,

(b) the beam is embedded at both ends and $w(x)$ is a concentrated load w_0 applied at $x = \pi/2$.

[*Hint*: In both parts of this problem use entries 35 and 36 in the table of Laplace transforms in Appendix III.]

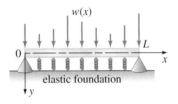

FIGURE 7.R.10 Beam on elastic foundation in Problem 44

45. (a) Suppose two identical pendulums are coupled by means of a spring with constant k. See Figure 7.R.11. Under the same assumptions made in the discussion preceding Example 3 in Section 7.6, it can be shown that when the displacement angles $\theta_1(t)$ and $\theta_2(t)$ are small, the system of linear differential equations describing the motion is

$$\theta_1'' + \frac{g}{l}\theta_1 = -\frac{k}{m}(\theta_1 - \theta_2)$$

$$\theta_2'' + \frac{g}{l}\theta_2 = \frac{k}{m}(\theta_1 - \theta_2).$$

Use the Laplace transform to solve the system when $\theta_1(0) = \theta_0$, $\theta_1'(0) = 0$, $\theta_2(0) = \psi_0$, $\theta_2'(0) = 0$, where θ_0 and ψ_0 constants. For convenience let $\omega^2 = g/l$, $K = k/m$.

(b) Use the solution in part (a) to discuss the motion of the coupled pendulums in the special case when the initial conditions are $\theta_1(0) = \theta_0$, $\theta_1'(0) = 0$, $\theta_2(0) = \theta_0$, $\theta_2'(0) = 0$. When the initial conditions are $\theta_1(0) = \theta_0$, $\theta_1'(0) = 0$, $\theta_2(0) = -\theta_0$, $\theta_2'(0) = 0$.

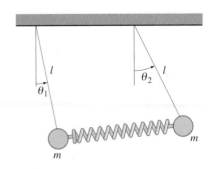

FIGURE 7.R.11 Coupled pendulums in Problem 45

8 SYSTEMS OF LINEAR FIRST-ORDER DIFFERENTIAL EQUATIONS

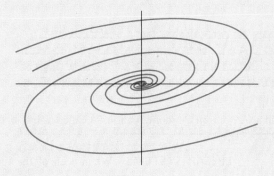

We encountered systems of differential equations in Sections 3.3, 4.8, and 7.6 and were able to solve some of these systems by means of either systematic elimination or the Laplace transform. In this chapter we are going to concentrate only on *systems of linear first-order differential equations.* Although most of the systems that are considered could be solved using elimination or the Laplace transform, we are going to develop a general theory for these kinds of systems and, in the case of systems with constant coefficients, a method of solution that utilizes some basic concepts from the algebra of matrices. We will see that this general theory and solution procedure is similar to that of linear high-order differential equations considered in Chapter 4. This material is fundamental to the analysis of nonlinear first-order equations.

8.1 PRELIMINARY THEORY—LINEAR SYSTEMS

REVIEW MATERIAL

- Matrix notation and properties are used extensively throughout this chapter. It is imperative that you review either Appendix II or a linear algebra text if you unfamiliar with these concepts.

INTRODUCTION Recall that in Section 4.8 we illustrated how to solve systems of n linear differential equations in n unknowns of the form

$$
\begin{aligned}
P_{11}(D)x_1 + P_{12}(D)x_2 + \cdots + P_{1n}(D)x_n &= b_1(t) \\
P_{21}(D)x_1 + P_{22}(D)x_2 + \cdots + P_{2n}(D)x_n &= b_2(t) \\
&\vdots \\
P_{n1}(D)x_1 + P_{n2}(D)x_2 + \cdots + P_{nn}(D)x_n &= b_n(t),
\end{aligned}
\tag{1}
$$

where the P_{ij} were polynomials of various degrees in the differential operator D. In this chapter we confine our study to systems of first-order DEs that are special cases of systems that have the normal form

$$
\begin{aligned}
\frac{dx_1}{dt} &= g_1(t, x_1, x_2, \ldots, x_n) \\
\frac{dx_2}{dt} &= g_2(t, x_1, x_2, \ldots, x_n) \\
&\vdots \\
\frac{dx_n}{dt} &= g_n(t, x_1, x_2, \ldots, x_n).
\end{aligned}
\tag{2}
$$

A system such as (2) of n first-order equations is called a **first-order system.**

LINEAR SYSTEMS When each of the functions $g_1, g_2, \ldots, g_n$ in (2) is linear in the dependent variables $x_1, x_2, \ldots, x_n$, we get the **normal form** of a first-order system of linear equations:

$$
\begin{aligned}
\frac{dx_1}{dt} &= a_{11}(t)x_1 + a_{12}(t)x_2 + \cdots + a_{1n}(t)x_n + f_1(t) \\
\frac{dx_2}{dt} &= a_{21}(t)x_1 + a_{22}(t)x_2 + \cdots + a_{2n}(t)x_n + f_2(t) \\
&\vdots \\
\frac{dx_n}{dt} &= a_{n1}(t)x_1 + a_{n2}(t)x_2 + \cdots + a_{nn}(t)x_n + f_n(t).
\end{aligned}
\tag{3}
$$

We refer to a system of the form given in (3) simply as a **linear system.** We assume that the coefficients a_{ij} as well as the functions f_i are continuous on a common interval I. When $f_i(t) = 0$, $i = 1, 2, \ldots, n$, the linear system (3) is said to be **homogeneous;** otherwise, it is **nonhomogeneous.**

MATRIX FORM OF A LINEAR SYSTEM If $\mathbf{X}$, $\mathbf{A}(t)$, and $\mathbf{F}(t)$ denote the respective matrices

$$
\mathbf{X} = \begin{pmatrix} x_1(t) \\ x_2(t) \\ \vdots \\ x_n(t) \end{pmatrix}, \qquad
\mathbf{A}(t) = \begin{pmatrix} a_{11}(t) & a_{12}(t) & \cdots & a_{1n}(t) \\ a_{21}(t) & a_{22}(t) & \cdots & a_{2n}(t) \\ \vdots & & & \vdots \\ a_{n1}(t) & a_{n2}(t) & \cdots & a_{nn}(t) \end{pmatrix}, \qquad
\mathbf{F}(t) = \begin{pmatrix} f_1(t) \\ f_2(t) \\ \vdots \\ f_n(t) \end{pmatrix},
$$

then the system of linear first-order differential equations (3) can be written as

$$\frac{d}{dt} \begin{pmatrix} x_1 \\ x_2 \\ \vdots \\ x_n \end{pmatrix} = \begin{pmatrix} a_{11}(t) & a_{12}(t) & \cdots & a_{1n}(t) \\ a_{21}(t) & a_{22}(t) & \cdots & a_{2n}(t) \\ \vdots & & & \vdots \\ a_{n1}(t) & a_{n2}(t) & \cdots & a_{nn}(t) \end{pmatrix} \begin{pmatrix} x_1 \\ x_2 \\ \vdots \\ x_n \end{pmatrix} + \begin{pmatrix} f_1(t) \\ f_2(t) \\ \vdots \\ f_n(t) \end{pmatrix}$$

or simply
$$\mathbf{X}' = \mathbf{AX} + \mathbf{F}. \tag{4}$$

If the system is homogeneous, its matrix form is then

$$\mathbf{X}' = \mathbf{AX}. \tag{5}$$

EXAMPLE 1 Systems Written in Matrix Notation

(a) If $\mathbf{X} = \begin{pmatrix} x \\ y \end{pmatrix}$, then the matrix form of the homogeneous system

$$\begin{aligned} \frac{dx}{dt} &= 3x + 4y \\ \frac{dy}{dt} &= 5x - 7y \end{aligned} \quad \text{is} \quad \mathbf{X}' = \begin{pmatrix} 3 & 4 \\ 5 & -7 \end{pmatrix} \mathbf{X}.$$

(b) If $\mathbf{X} = \begin{pmatrix} x \\ y \\ z \end{pmatrix}$, then the matrix form of the nonhomogeneous system

$$\begin{aligned} \frac{dx}{dt} &= 6x + y + z + t \\ \frac{dy}{dt} &= 8x + 7y - z + 10t \\ \frac{dz}{dt} &= 2x + 9y - z + 6t \end{aligned} \quad \text{is} \quad \mathbf{X}' = \begin{pmatrix} 6 & 1 & 1 \\ 8 & 7 & -1 \\ 2 & 9 & -1 \end{pmatrix} \mathbf{X} + \begin{pmatrix} t \\ 10t \\ 6t \end{pmatrix}.$$

∎

DEFINITION 8.1.1 Solution Vector

A **solution vector** on an interval I is any column matrix

$$\mathbf{X} = \begin{pmatrix} x_1(t) \\ x_2(t) \\ \vdots \\ x_n(t) \end{pmatrix}$$

whose entries are differentiable functions satisfying the system (4) on the interval.

A solution vector of (4) is, of course, equivalent to n scalar equations $x_1 = \phi_1(t), x_2 = \phi_2(t), \ldots, x_n = \phi_n(t)$ and can be interpreted geometrically as a set of parametric equations of a space curve. In the important case $n = 2$ the equations $x_1 = \phi_1(t), x_2 = \phi_2(t)$ represent a curve in the x_1x_2-plane. It is common practice to call a curve in the plane a **trajectory** and to call the x_1x_2-plane the **phase plane.** We will come back to these concepts and illustrate them in the next section.

EXAMPLE 2 Verification of Solutions

Verify that on the interval $(-\infty, \infty)$

$$\mathbf{X}_1 = \begin{pmatrix} 1 \\ -1 \end{pmatrix} e^{-2t} = \begin{pmatrix} e^{-2t} \\ -e^{-2t} \end{pmatrix} \quad \text{and} \quad \mathbf{X}_2 = \begin{pmatrix} 3 \\ 5 \end{pmatrix} e^{6t} = \begin{pmatrix} 3e^{6t} \\ 5e^{6t} \end{pmatrix}$$

are solutions of
$$\mathbf{X}' = \begin{pmatrix} 1 & 3 \\ 5 & 3 \end{pmatrix} \mathbf{X}. \tag{6}$$

SOLUTION From $\mathbf{X}_1' = \begin{pmatrix} -2e^{-2t} \\ 2e^{-2t} \end{pmatrix}$ and $\mathbf{X}_2' = \begin{pmatrix} 18e^{6t} \\ 30e^{6t} \end{pmatrix}$ we see that

$$\mathbf{A}\mathbf{X}_1 = \begin{pmatrix} 1 & 3 \\ 5 & 3 \end{pmatrix} \begin{pmatrix} e^{-2t} \\ -e^{-2t} \end{pmatrix} = \begin{pmatrix} e^{-2t} - 3e^{-2t} \\ 5e^{-2t} - 3e^{-2t} \end{pmatrix} = \begin{pmatrix} -2e^{-2t} \\ 2e^{-2t} \end{pmatrix} = \mathbf{X}_1',$$

and
$$\mathbf{A}\mathbf{X}_2 = \begin{pmatrix} 1 & 3 \\ 5 & 3 \end{pmatrix} \begin{pmatrix} 3e^{6t} \\ 5e^{6t} \end{pmatrix} = \begin{pmatrix} 3e^{6t} + 15e^{6t} \\ 15e^{6t} + 15e^{6t} \end{pmatrix} = \begin{pmatrix} 18e^{6t} \\ 30e^{6t} \end{pmatrix} = \mathbf{X}_2'. \quad ■$$

Much of the theory of systems of n linear first-order differential equations is similar to that of linear nth-order differential equations.

INITIAL-VALUE PROBLEM Let t_0 denote a point on an interval I and

$$\mathbf{X}(t_0) = \begin{pmatrix} x_1(t_0) \\ x_2(t_0) \\ . \\ . \\ . \\ x_n(t_0) \end{pmatrix} \quad \text{and} \quad \mathbf{X}_0 = \begin{pmatrix} \gamma_1 \\ \gamma_2 \\ . \\ . \\ . \\ \gamma_n \end{pmatrix},$$

where the γ_i, $i = 1, 2, \ldots, n$ are given constants. Then the problem

$$\begin{array}{ll} \textit{Solve:} & \mathbf{X}' = \mathbf{A}(t)\mathbf{X} + \mathbf{F}(t) \\ \textit{Subject to:} & \mathbf{X}(t_0) = \mathbf{X}_0 \end{array} \tag{7}$$

is an **initial-value problem** on the interval.

THEOREM 8.1.1 **Existence of a Unique Solution**

Let the entries of the matrices $\mathbf{A}(t)$ and $\mathbf{F}(t)$ be functions continuous on a common interval I that contains the point t_0. Then there exists a unique solution of the initial-value problem (7) on the interval.

HOMOGENEOUS SYSTEMS In the next several definitions and theorems we are concerned only with homogeneous systems. Without stating it, we shall always assume that the a_{ij} and the f_i are continuous functions of t on some common interval I.

SUPERPOSITION PRINCIPLE The following result is a **superposition principle** for solutions of linear systems.

THEOREM 8.1.2 **Superposition Principle**

Let $\mathbf{X}_1, \mathbf{X}_2, \ldots, \mathbf{X}_k$ be a set of solution vectors of the homogeneous system (5) on an interval I. Then the linear combination

$$\mathbf{X} = c_1\mathbf{X}_1 + c_2\mathbf{X}_2 + \cdots + c_k\mathbf{X}_k,$$

where the c_i, $i = 1, 2, \ldots, k$ are arbitrary constants, is also a solution on the interval.

It follows from Theorem 8.1.2 that a constant multiple of any solution vector of a homogeneous system of linear first-order differential equations is also a solution.

EXAMPLE 3 Using the Superposition Principle

You should practice by verifying that the two vectors

$$\mathbf{X}_1 = \begin{pmatrix} \cos t \\ -\frac{1}{2}\cos t + \frac{1}{2}\sin t \\ -\cos t - \sin t \end{pmatrix} \quad \text{and} \quad \mathbf{X}_2 = \begin{pmatrix} 0 \\ e^t \\ 0 \end{pmatrix}$$

are solutions of the system

$$\mathbf{X}' = \begin{pmatrix} 1 & 0 & 1 \\ 1 & 1 & 0 \\ -2 & 0 & -1 \end{pmatrix} \mathbf{X}. \tag{8}$$

By the superposition principle the linear combination

$$\mathbf{X} = c_1\mathbf{X}_1 + c_2\mathbf{X}_2 = c_1\begin{pmatrix} \cos t \\ -\frac{1}{2}\cos t + \frac{1}{2}\sin t \\ -\cos t - \sin t \end{pmatrix} + c_2\begin{pmatrix} 0 \\ e^t \\ 0 \end{pmatrix}$$

is yet another solution of the system. ■

LINEAR DEPENDENCE AND LINEAR INDEPENDENCE We are primarily interested in linearly independent solutions of the homogeneous system (5).

DEFINITION 8.1.2 Linear Dependence/Independence

Let $\mathbf{X}_1, \mathbf{X}_2, \ldots, \mathbf{X}_k$ be a set of solution vectors of the homogeneous system (5) on an interval I. We say that the set is **linearly dependent** on the interval if there exist constants $c_1, c_2, \ldots, c_k$, not all zero, such that

$$c_1\mathbf{X}_1 + c_2\mathbf{X}_2 + \cdots + c_k\mathbf{X}_k = \mathbf{0}$$

for every t in the interval. If the set of vectors is not linearly dependent on the interval, it is said to be **linearly independent.**

The case when $k = 2$ should be clear; two solution vectors $\mathbf{X}_1$ and $\mathbf{X}_2$ are linearly dependent if one is a constant multiple of the other, and conversely. For $k > 2$ a set of solution vectors is linearly dependent if we can express at least one solution vector as a linear combination of the remaining vectors.

WRONSKIAN As in our earlier consideration of the theory of a single ordinary differential equation, we can introduce the concept of the **Wronskian** determinant as a test for linear independence. We state the following theorem without proof.

THEOREM 8.1.3 Criterion for Linearly Independent Solutions

Let $\quad \mathbf{X}_1 = \begin{pmatrix} x_{11} \\ x_{21} \\ \vdots \\ x_{n1} \end{pmatrix}, \quad \mathbf{X}_2 = \begin{pmatrix} x_{12} \\ x_{22} \\ \vdots \\ x_{n2} \end{pmatrix}, \quad \ldots, \quad \mathbf{X}_n = \begin{pmatrix} x_{1n} \\ x_{2n} \\ \vdots \\ x_{nn} \end{pmatrix}$

be n solution vectors of the homogeneous system (5) on an interval I. Then the set of solution vectors is linearly independent on I if and only if the **Wronskian**

$$W(\mathbf{X}_1, \mathbf{X}_2, \ldots, \mathbf{X}_n) = \begin{vmatrix} x_{11} & x_{12} & \cdots & x_{1n} \\ x_{21} & x_{22} & \cdots & x_{2n} \\ \vdots & & & \vdots \\ x_{n1} & x_{n2} & \cdots & x_{nn} \end{vmatrix} \neq 0 \tag{9}$$

for every t in the interval.

It can be shown that if $\mathbf{X}_1, \mathbf{X}_2, \ldots, \mathbf{X}_n$ are solution vectors of (5), then for every t in I either $W(\mathbf{X}_1, \mathbf{X}_2, \ldots, \mathbf{X}_n) \neq 0$ or $W(\mathbf{X}_1, \mathbf{X}_2, \ldots, \mathbf{X}_n) = 0$. Thus if we can show that $W \neq 0$ for some t_0 in I, then $W \neq 0$ for every t, and hence the solutions are linearly independent on the interval.

Notice that, unlike our definition of the Wronskian in Section 4.1, here the definition of the determinant (9) does not involve differentiation.

■ **EXAMPLE 4** **Linearly Independent Solutions**

In Example 2 we saw that $\mathbf{X}_1 = \begin{pmatrix} 1 \\ -1 \end{pmatrix} e^{-2t}$ and $\mathbf{X}_2 = \begin{pmatrix} 3 \\ 5 \end{pmatrix} e^{6t}$ are solutions of system (6). Clearly, $\mathbf{X}_1$ and $\mathbf{X}_2$ are linearly independent on the interval $(-\infty, \infty)$, since neither vector is a constant multiple of the other. In addition, we have

$$W(\mathbf{X}_1, \mathbf{X}_2) = \begin{vmatrix} e^{-2t} & 3e^{6t} \\ -e^{-2t} & 5e^{6t} \end{vmatrix} = 8e^{4t} \neq 0$$

for all real values of t.   ∎

DEFINITION 8.1.3 **Fundamental Set of Solutions**

Any set $\mathbf{X}_1, \mathbf{X}_2, \ldots, \mathbf{X}_n$ of n linearly independent solution vectors of the homogeneous system (5) on an interval I is said to be a **fundamental set of solutions** on the interval.

THEOREM 8.1.4 **Existence of a Fundamental Set**

There exists a fundamental set of solutions for the homogeneous system (5) on an interval I.

The next two theorems are the linear system equivalents of Theorems 4.1.5 and 4.1.6.

THEOREM 8.1.5 **General Solution—Homogeneous Systems**

Let $\mathbf{X}_1, \mathbf{X}_2, \ldots, \mathbf{X}_n$ be a fundamental set of solutions of the homogeneous system (5) on an interval I. Then the **general solution** of the system on the interval is

$$\mathbf{X} = c_1\mathbf{X}_1 + c_2\mathbf{X}_2 + \cdots + c_n\mathbf{X}_n,$$

where the c_i, $i = 1, 2, \ldots, n$ are arbitrary constants.

EXAMPLE 5 General Solution of System (6)

From Example 2 we know that $\mathbf{X}_1 = \begin{pmatrix} 1 \\ -1 \end{pmatrix} e^{-2t}$ and $\mathbf{X}_2 = \begin{pmatrix} 3 \\ 5 \end{pmatrix} e^{6t}$ are linearly independent solutions of (6) on $(-\infty, \infty)$. Hence $\mathbf{X}_1$ and $\mathbf{X}_2$ form a fundamental set of solutions on the interval. The general solution of the system on the interval is then

$$\mathbf{X} = c_1 \mathbf{X}_1 + c_2 \mathbf{X}_2 = c_1 \begin{pmatrix} 1 \\ -1 \end{pmatrix} e^{-2t} + c_2 \begin{pmatrix} 3 \\ 5 \end{pmatrix} e^{6t}. \qquad (10) \quad \blacksquare$$

EXAMPLE 6 General Solution of System (8)

The vectors

$$\mathbf{X}_1 = \begin{pmatrix} \cos t \\ -\frac{1}{2}\cos t + \frac{1}{2}\sin t \\ -\cos t - \sin t \end{pmatrix}, \qquad \mathbf{X}_2 = \begin{pmatrix} 0 \\ 1 \\ 0 \end{pmatrix} e^t, \qquad \mathbf{X}_3 = \begin{pmatrix} \sin t \\ -\frac{1}{2}\sin t - \frac{1}{2}\cos t \\ -\sin t + \cos t \end{pmatrix}$$

are solutions of the system (8) in Example 3 (see Problem 16 in Exercises 8.1). Now

$$W(\mathbf{X}_1, \mathbf{X}_2, \mathbf{X}_3) = \begin{vmatrix} \cos t & 0 & \sin t \\ -\frac{1}{2}\cos t + \frac{1}{2}\sin t & e^t & -\frac{1}{2}\sin t - \frac{1}{2}\cos t \\ -\cos t - \sin t & 0 & -\sin t + \cos t \end{vmatrix} = e^t \neq 0$$

for all real values of t. We conclude that $\mathbf{X}_1$, $\mathbf{X}_2$, and $\mathbf{X}_3$ form a fundamental set of solutions on $(-\infty, \infty)$. Thus the general solution of the system on the interval is the linear combination $\mathbf{X} = c_1 \mathbf{X}_1 + c_2 \mathbf{X}_2 + c_3 \mathbf{X}_3$; that is,

$$\mathbf{X} = c_1 \begin{pmatrix} \cos t \\ -\frac{1}{2}\cos t + \frac{1}{2}\sin t \\ -\cos t - \sin t \end{pmatrix} + c_2 \begin{pmatrix} 0 \\ 1 \\ 0 \end{pmatrix} e^t + c_3 \begin{pmatrix} \sin t \\ -\frac{1}{2}\sin t - \frac{1}{2}\cos t \\ -\sin t + \cos t \end{pmatrix}. \qquad \blacksquare$$

NONHOMOGENEOUS SYSTEMS For nonhomogeneous systems a **particular solution** $\mathbf{X}_p$ on an interval I is any vector, free of arbitrary parameters, whose entries are functions that satisfy the system (4).

THEOREM 8.1.6 General Solution—Nonhomogeneous Systems

Let $\mathbf{X}_p$ be a given solution of the nonhomogeneous system (4) on an interval I and let

$$\mathbf{X}_c = c_1 \mathbf{X}_1 + c_2 \mathbf{X}_2 + \cdots + c_n \mathbf{X}_n$$

denote the general solution on the same interval of the associated homogeneous system (5). Then the **general solution** of the nonhomogeneous system on the interval is

$$\mathbf{X} = \mathbf{X}_c + \mathbf{X}_p.$$

The general solution $\mathbf{X}_c$ of the associated homogeneous system (5) is called the **complementary function** of the nonhomogeneous system (4).

| EXAMPLE 7 | General Solution—Nonhomogeneous System |

The vector $\mathbf{X}_p = \begin{pmatrix} 3t - 4 \\ -5t + 6 \end{pmatrix}$ is a particular solution of the nonhomogeneous system

$$\mathbf{X}' = \begin{pmatrix} 1 & 3 \\ 5 & 3 \end{pmatrix}\mathbf{X} + \begin{pmatrix} 12t - 11 \\ -3 \end{pmatrix} \tag{11}$$

on the interval $(-\infty, \infty)$. (Verify this.) The complementary function of (11) on the same interval, or the general solution of $\mathbf{X}' = \begin{pmatrix} 1 & 3 \\ 5 & 3 \end{pmatrix}\mathbf{X}$, was seen in (10) of Example 5 to be $\mathbf{X}_c = c_1\begin{pmatrix} 1 \\ -1 \end{pmatrix}e^{-2t} + c_2\begin{pmatrix} 3 \\ 5 \end{pmatrix}e^{6t}$. Hence by Theorem 8.1.6

$$\mathbf{X} = \mathbf{X}_c + \mathbf{X}_p = c_1\begin{pmatrix} 1 \\ -1 \end{pmatrix}e^{-2t} + c_2\begin{pmatrix} 3 \\ 5 \end{pmatrix}e^{6t} + \begin{pmatrix} 3t - 4 \\ -5t + 6 \end{pmatrix}$$

is the general solution of (11) on $(-\infty, \infty)$. ∎

EXERCISES 8.1

Answers to selected odd-numbered problems begin on page ANS-13.

In Problems 1–6 write the linear system in matrix form.

1. $\dfrac{dx}{dt} = 3x - 5y$

$\dfrac{dy}{dt} = 4x + 8y$

2. $\dfrac{dx}{dt} = 4x - 7y$

$\dfrac{dy}{dt} = 5x$

3. $\dfrac{dx}{dt} = -3x + 4y - 9z$

$\dfrac{dy}{dt} = 6x - y$

$\dfrac{dz}{dt} = 10x + 4y + 3z$

4. $\dfrac{dx}{dt} = x - y$

$\dfrac{dy}{dt} = x + 2z$

$\dfrac{dz}{dt} = -x + z$

5. $\dfrac{dx}{dt} = x - y + z + t - 1$

$\dfrac{dy}{dt} = 2x + y - z - 3t^2$

$\dfrac{dz}{dt} = x + y + z + t^2 - t + 2$

6. $\dfrac{dx}{dt} = -3x + 4y + e^{-t}\sin 2t$

$\dfrac{dy}{dt} = 5x + 9z + 4e^{-t}\cos 2t$

$\dfrac{dz}{dt} = y + 6z - e^{-t}$

In Problems 7–10 write the given system without the use of matrices.

7. $\mathbf{X}' = \begin{pmatrix} 4 & 2 \\ -1 & 3 \end{pmatrix}\mathbf{X} + \begin{pmatrix} 1 \\ -1 \end{pmatrix}e^t$

8. $\mathbf{X}' = \begin{pmatrix} 7 & 5 & -9 \\ 4 & 1 & 1 \\ 0 & -2 & 3 \end{pmatrix}\mathbf{X} + \begin{pmatrix} 0 \\ 2 \\ 1 \end{pmatrix}e^{5t} - \begin{pmatrix} 8 \\ 0 \\ 3 \end{pmatrix}e^{-2t}$

9. $\dfrac{d}{dt}\begin{pmatrix} x \\ y \\ z \end{pmatrix} = \begin{pmatrix} 1 & -1 & 2 \\ 3 & -4 & 1 \\ -2 & 5 & 6 \end{pmatrix}\begin{pmatrix} x \\ y \\ z \end{pmatrix} + \begin{pmatrix} 1 \\ 2 \\ 2 \end{pmatrix}e^{-t} - \begin{pmatrix} 3 \\ -1 \\ 1 \end{pmatrix}t$

10. $\dfrac{d}{dt}\begin{pmatrix} x \\ y \end{pmatrix} = \begin{pmatrix} 3 & -7 \\ 1 & 1 \end{pmatrix}\begin{pmatrix} x \\ y \end{pmatrix} + \begin{pmatrix} 4 \\ 8 \end{pmatrix}\sin t + \begin{pmatrix} t - 4 \\ 2t + 1 \end{pmatrix}e^{4t}$

In Problems 11–16 verify that the vector $\mathbf{X}$ is a solution of the given system.

11. $\dfrac{dx}{dt} = 3x - 4y$

$\dfrac{dy}{dt} = 4x - 7y; \quad \mathbf{X} = \begin{pmatrix} 1 \\ 2 \end{pmatrix}e^{-5t}$

12. $\dfrac{dx}{dt} = -2x + 5y$

$\dfrac{dy}{dt} = -2x + 4y; \quad \mathbf{X} = \begin{pmatrix} 5\cos t \\ 3\cos t - \sin t \end{pmatrix}e^t$

13. $\mathbf{X}' = \begin{pmatrix} -1 & \frac{1}{4} \\ 1 & -1 \end{pmatrix}\mathbf{X}; \quad \mathbf{X} = \begin{pmatrix} -1 \\ 2 \end{pmatrix}e^{-3t/2}$

14. $\mathbf{X}' = \begin{pmatrix} 2 & 1 \\ -1 & 0 \end{pmatrix}\mathbf{X}; \quad \mathbf{X} = \begin{pmatrix} 1 \\ 3 \end{pmatrix}e^t + \begin{pmatrix} 4 \\ -4 \end{pmatrix}te^t$

15. $\mathbf{X}' = \begin{pmatrix} 1 & 2 & 1 \\ 6 & -1 & 0 \\ -1 & -2 & -1 \end{pmatrix} \mathbf{X}; \quad \mathbf{X} = \begin{pmatrix} 1 \\ 6 \\ -13 \end{pmatrix}$

16. $\mathbf{X}' = \begin{pmatrix} 1 & 0 & 1 \\ 1 & 1 & 0 \\ -2 & 0 & -1 \end{pmatrix} \mathbf{X}; \quad \mathbf{X} = \begin{pmatrix} \sin t \\ -\frac{1}{2}\sin t - \frac{1}{2}\cos t \\ -\sin t + \cos t \end{pmatrix}$

In Problems 17–20 the given vectors are solutions of a system $\mathbf{X}' = \mathbf{AX}$. Determine whether the vectors form a fundamental set on the interval $(-\infty, \infty)$.

17. $\mathbf{X}_1 = \begin{pmatrix} 1 \\ 1 \end{pmatrix} e^{-2t}, \quad \mathbf{X}_2 = \begin{pmatrix} 1 \\ -1 \end{pmatrix} e^{-6t}$

18. $\mathbf{X}_1 = \begin{pmatrix} 1 \\ -1 \end{pmatrix} e^{t}, \quad \mathbf{X}_2 = \begin{pmatrix} 2 \\ 6 \end{pmatrix} e^{t} + \begin{pmatrix} 8 \\ -8 \end{pmatrix} te^{t}$

19. $\mathbf{X}_1 = \begin{pmatrix} 1 \\ -2 \\ 4 \end{pmatrix} + t\begin{pmatrix} 1 \\ 2 \\ 2 \end{pmatrix}, \quad \mathbf{X}_2 = \begin{pmatrix} 1 \\ -2 \\ 4 \end{pmatrix},$

$\mathbf{X}_3 = \begin{pmatrix} 3 \\ -6 \\ 12 \end{pmatrix} + t\begin{pmatrix} 2 \\ 4 \\ 4 \end{pmatrix}$

20. $\mathbf{X}_1 = \begin{pmatrix} 1 \\ 6 \\ -13 \end{pmatrix}, \quad \mathbf{X}_2 = \begin{pmatrix} 1 \\ -2 \\ -1 \end{pmatrix} e^{-4t}, \quad \mathbf{X}_3 = \begin{pmatrix} 2 \\ 3 \\ -2 \end{pmatrix} e^{3t}$

In Problems 21–24 verify that the vector $\mathbf{X}_p$ is a particular solution of the given system.

21. $\dfrac{dx}{dt} = x + 4y + 2t - 7$

$\dfrac{dy}{dt} = 3x + 2y - 4t - 18; \quad \mathbf{X}_p = \begin{pmatrix} 2 \\ -1 \end{pmatrix} t + \begin{pmatrix} 5 \\ 1 \end{pmatrix}$

22. $\mathbf{X}' = \begin{pmatrix} 2 & 1 \\ 1 & -1 \end{pmatrix} \mathbf{X} + \begin{pmatrix} -5 \\ 2 \end{pmatrix}; \quad \mathbf{X}_p = \begin{pmatrix} 1 \\ 3 \end{pmatrix}$

23. $\mathbf{X}' = \begin{pmatrix} 2 & 1 \\ 3 & 4 \end{pmatrix} \mathbf{X} - \begin{pmatrix} 1 \\ 7 \end{pmatrix} e^{t}; \quad \mathbf{X}_p = \begin{pmatrix} 1 \\ 1 \end{pmatrix} e^{t} + \begin{pmatrix} 1 \\ -1 \end{pmatrix} te^{t}$

24. $\mathbf{X}' = \begin{pmatrix} 1 & 2 & 3 \\ -4 & 2 & 0 \\ -6 & 1 & 0 \end{pmatrix} \mathbf{X} + \begin{pmatrix} -1 \\ 4 \\ 3 \end{pmatrix} \sin 3t; \quad \mathbf{X}_p = \begin{pmatrix} \sin 3t \\ 0 \\ \cos 3t \end{pmatrix}$

25. Prove that the general solution of

$$\mathbf{X}' = \begin{pmatrix} 0 & 6 & 0 \\ 1 & 0 & 1 \\ 1 & 1 & 0 \end{pmatrix} \mathbf{X}$$

on the interval $(-\infty, \infty)$ is

$$\mathbf{X} = c_1 \begin{pmatrix} 6 \\ -1 \\ -5 \end{pmatrix} e^{-t} + c_2 \begin{pmatrix} -3 \\ 1 \\ 1 \end{pmatrix} e^{-2t} + c_3 \begin{pmatrix} 2 \\ 1 \\ 1 \end{pmatrix} e^{3t}.$$

26. Prove that the general solution of

$$\mathbf{X}' = \begin{pmatrix} -1 & -1 \\ -1 & 1 \end{pmatrix} \mathbf{X} + \begin{pmatrix} 1 \\ 1 \end{pmatrix} t^2 + \begin{pmatrix} 4 \\ -6 \end{pmatrix} t + \begin{pmatrix} -1 \\ 5 \end{pmatrix}$$

on the interval $(-\infty, \infty)$ is

$$\mathbf{X} = c_1 \begin{pmatrix} 1 \\ -1 - \sqrt{2} \end{pmatrix} e^{\sqrt{2}t} + c_2 \begin{pmatrix} 1 \\ -1 + \sqrt{2} \end{pmatrix} e^{-\sqrt{2}t}$$

$$+ \begin{pmatrix} 1 \\ 0 \end{pmatrix} t^2 + \begin{pmatrix} -2 \\ 4 \end{pmatrix} t + \begin{pmatrix} 1 \\ 0 \end{pmatrix}.$$

8.2 HOMOGENEOUS LINEAR SYSTEMS

REVIEW MATERIAL

- Section II.3 of Appendix II
- Also the *Student Resource and Solutions Manual*

INTRODUCTION We saw in Example 5 of Section 8.1 that the general solution of the homogeneous system $\mathbf{X}' = \begin{pmatrix} 1 & 3 \\ 5 & 3 \end{pmatrix} \mathbf{X}$ is

$$\mathbf{X} = c_1 \mathbf{X}_1 + c_2 \mathbf{X}_2 = c_1 \begin{pmatrix} 1 \\ -1 \end{pmatrix} e^{-2t} + c_2 \begin{pmatrix} 3 \\ 5 \end{pmatrix} e^{6t}.$$

Because the solution vectors $\mathbf{X}_1$ and $\mathbf{X}_2$ have the form

$$\mathbf{X}_i = \begin{pmatrix} k_1 \\ k_2 \end{pmatrix} e^{\lambda_i t}, \qquad i = 1, 2,$$

where k_1, k_2, λ_1, and λ_2 are constants, we are prompted to ask whether we can always find a solution of the form

$$\mathbf{X} = \begin{pmatrix} k_1 \\ k_2 \\ \cdot \\ \cdot \\ \cdot \\ k_n \end{pmatrix} e^{\lambda t} = \mathbf{K} e^{\lambda t} \tag{1}$$

for the general homogeneous linear first-order system

$$\mathbf{X}' = \mathbf{A}\mathbf{X}, \tag{2}$$

where $\mathbf{A}$ is an $n \times n$ matrix of constants.

EIGENVALUES AND EIGENVECTORS If (1) is to be a solution vector of the homogeneous linear system (2), then $\mathbf{X}' = \mathbf{K}\lambda e^{\lambda t}$, so the system becomes $\mathbf{K}\lambda e^{\lambda t} = \mathbf{A}\mathbf{K}e^{\lambda t}$. After dividing out $e^{\lambda t}$ and rearranging, we obtain $\mathbf{A}\mathbf{K} = \lambda\mathbf{K}$ or $\mathbf{A}\mathbf{K} - \lambda\mathbf{K} = \mathbf{0}$. Since $\mathbf{K} = \mathbf{I}\mathbf{K}$, the last equation is the same as

$$(\mathbf{A} - \lambda\mathbf{I})\mathbf{K} = \mathbf{0}. \tag{3}$$

The matrix equation (3) is equivalent to the simultaneous algebraic equations

$$\begin{aligned} (a_{11} - \lambda)k_1 + \quad a_{12}k_2 + \cdots + \quad a_{1n}k_n &= 0 \\ a_{21}k_1 + (a_{22} - \lambda)k_2 + \cdots + \quad a_{2n}k_n &= 0 \\ \vdots \qquad\qquad \vdots \\ a_{n1}k_1 + \quad a_{n2}k_2 + \cdots + (a_{nn} - \lambda)k_n &= 0. \end{aligned}$$

Thus to find a nontrivial solution $\mathbf{X}$ of (2), we must first find a nontrivial solution of the foregoing system; in other words, we must find a nontrivial vector $\mathbf{K}$ that satisfies (3). But for (3) to have solutions other than the obvious solution $k_1 = k_2 = \cdots = k_n = 0$, we must have

$$\det(\mathbf{A} - \lambda\mathbf{I}) = 0.$$

This polynomial equation in λ is called the **characteristic equation** of the matrix $\mathbf{A}$; its solutions are the **eigenvalues** of $\mathbf{A}$. A solution $\mathbf{K} \neq \mathbf{0}$ of (3) corresponding to an eigenvalue λ is called an **eigenvector** of $\mathbf{A}$. A solution of the homogeneous system (2) is then $\mathbf{X} = \mathbf{K}e^{\lambda t}$.

In the discussion that follows we examine three cases: real and distinct eigenvalues (that is, no eigenvalues are equal), repeated eigenvalues, and, finally, complex eigenvalues.

8.2.1 DISTINCT REAL EIGENVALUES

When the $n \times n$ matrix $\mathbf{A}$ possesses n distinct real eigenvalues $\lambda_1, \lambda_2, \ldots, \lambda_n$, then a set of n linearly independent eigenvectors $\mathbf{K}_1, \mathbf{K}_2, \ldots, \mathbf{K}_n$ can always be found, and

$$\mathbf{X}_1 = \mathbf{K}_1 e^{\lambda_1 t}, \qquad \mathbf{X}_2 = \mathbf{K}_2 e^{\lambda_2 t}, \qquad \ldots, \qquad \mathbf{X}_n = \mathbf{K}_n e^{\lambda_n t}$$

is a fundamental set of solutions of (2) on the interval $(-\infty, \infty)$.

THEOREM 8.2.1   **General Solution—Homogeneous Systems**

Let $\lambda_1, \lambda_2, \ldots, \lambda_n$ be n distinct real eigenvalues of the coefficient matrix $\mathbf{A}$ of the homogeneous system (2) and let $\mathbf{K}_1, \mathbf{K}_2, \ldots, \mathbf{K}_n$ be the corresponding eigenvectors. Then the **general solution** of (2) on the interval $(-\infty, \infty)$ is given by

$$\mathbf{X} = c_1\mathbf{K}_1 e^{\lambda_1 t} + c_2\mathbf{K}_2 e^{\lambda_2 t} + \cdots + c_n\mathbf{K}_n e^{\lambda_n t}.$$

EXAMPLE 1 Distinct Eigenvalues

Solve

$$\frac{dx}{dt} = 2x + 3y$$

$$\frac{dy}{dt} = 2x + y. \tag{4}$$

SOLUTION We first find the eigenvalues and eigenvectors of the matrix of coefficients.

From the characteristic equation

$$\det(\mathbf{A} - \lambda\mathbf{I}) = \begin{vmatrix} 2 - \lambda & 3 \\ 2 & 1 - \lambda \end{vmatrix} = \lambda^2 - 3\lambda - 4 = (\lambda + 1)(\lambda - 4) = 0$$

we see that the eigenvalues are $\lambda_1 = -1$ and $\lambda_2 = 4$.

Now for $\lambda_1 = -1$, (3) is equivalent to

$$3k_1 + 3k_2 = 0$$

$$2k_1 + 2k_2 = 0.$$

Thus $k_1 = -k_2$. When $k_2 = -1$, the related eigenvector is

$$\mathbf{K}_1 = \begin{pmatrix} 1 \\ -1 \end{pmatrix}.$$

For $\lambda_2 = 4$ we have

$$-2k_1 + 3k_2 = 0$$

$$2k_1 - 3k_2 = 0$$

so $k_1 = \frac{3}{2}k_2$; therefore with $k_2 = 2$ the corresponding eigenvector is

$$\mathbf{K}_2 = \begin{pmatrix} 3 \\ 2 \end{pmatrix}.$$

Since the matrix of coefficients $\mathbf{A}$ is a 2×2 matrix and since we have found two linearly independent solutions of (4),

$$\mathbf{X}_1 = \begin{pmatrix} 1 \\ -1 \end{pmatrix} e^{-t} \quad \text{and} \quad \mathbf{X}_2 = \begin{pmatrix} 3 \\ 2 \end{pmatrix} e^{4t},$$

we conclude that the general solution of the system is

$$\mathbf{X} = c_1 \mathbf{X}_1 + c_2 \mathbf{X}_2 = c_1 \begin{pmatrix} 1 \\ -1 \end{pmatrix} e^{-t} + c_2 \begin{pmatrix} 3 \\ 2 \end{pmatrix} e^{4t}. \tag{5} \blacksquare$$

PHASE PORTRAIT You should keep firmly in mind that writing a solution of a system of linear first-order differential equations in terms of matrices is simply an alternative to the method that we employed in Section 4.8, that is, listing the individual functions and the relationship between the constants. If we add the vectors on the right-hand side of (5) and then equate the entries with the corresponding entries in the vector on the left-hand side, we obtain the more familiar statement

$$x = c_1 e^{-t} + 3c_2 e^{4t}, \qquad y = -c_1 e^{-t} + 2c_2 e^{4t}.$$

As was pointed out in Section 8.1, we can interpret these equations as parametric equations of curves in the xy-plane or **phase plane.** Each curve, corresponding to specific choices for c_1 and c_2, is called a **trajectory.** For the choice of constants $c_1 = c_2 = 1$ in the solution (5) we see in Figure 8.2.1 the graph of $x(t)$ in the tx-plane, the graph of $y(t)$ in the ty-plane, and the trajectory consisting of the points

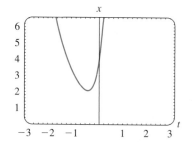

(a) graph of $x = e^{-t} + 3e^{4t}$

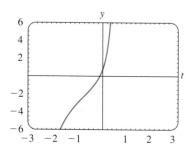

(b) graph of $y = -e^{-t} + 2e^{4t}$

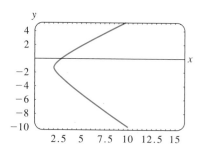

(c) trajectory defined by $x = e^{-t} + 3e^{4t}$, $y = -e^{-t} + 2e^{4t}$ in the phase plane

FIGURE 8.2.1 A particular solution from (5) yields three different curves in three different planes

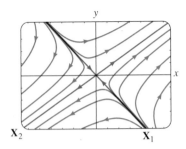

$\mathbf{X}_2$ $\mathbf{X}_1$

FIGURE 8.2.2 A phase portrait of system (4)

$(x(t), y(t))$ in the phase plane. A collection of representative trajectories in the phase plane, as shown in Figure 8.2.2, is said to be a **phase portrait** of the given linear system. What appears to be *two* red lines in Figure 8.2.2 are actually *four* red half-lines defined parametrically in the first, second, third, and fourth quadrants by the solutions $\mathbf{X}_2$, $-\mathbf{X}_1$, $-\mathbf{X}_2$, and $\mathbf{X}_1$, respectively. For example, the Cartesian equations $y = \frac{2}{3}x$, $x > 0$, and $y = -x$, $x > 0$, of the half-lines in the first and fourth quadrants were obtained by eliminating the parameter t in the solutions $x = 3e^{4t}$, $y = 2e^{4t}$, and $x = e^{-t}$, $y = -e^{-t}$, respectively. Moreover, each eigenvector can be visualized as a two-dimensional vector lying along one of these half-lines. The eigenvector $\mathbf{K}_2 = \begin{pmatrix} 3 \\ 2 \end{pmatrix}$ lies along $y = \frac{2}{3}x$ in the first quadrant, and $\mathbf{K}_1 = \begin{pmatrix} 1 \\ -1 \end{pmatrix}$ lies along $y = -x$ in the fourth quadrant. Each vector starts at the origin; $\mathbf{K}_2$ terminates at the point $(2, 3)$, and $\mathbf{K}_1$ terminates at $(1, -1)$.

The origin is not only a constant solution $x = 0$, $y = 0$ of every 2×2 homogeneous linear system $\mathbf{X}' = \mathbf{AX}$, but also an important point in the qualitative study of such systems. If we think in physical terms, the arrowheads on each trajectory in Figure 8.2.2 indicate the direction that a particle with coordinates $(x(t), y(t))$ on that trajectory at time t moves as time increases. Observe that the arrowheads, with the exception of only those on the half-lines in the second and fourth quadrants, indicate that a particle moves away from the origin as time t increases. If we imagine time ranging from $-\infty$ to ∞, then inspection of the solution $x = c_1 e^{-t} + 3c_2 e^{4t}$, $y = -c_1 e^{-t} + 2c_2 e^{4t}$, $c_1 \neq 0$, $c_2 \neq 0$ shows that a trajectory, or moving particle, "starts" asymptotic to one of the half-lines defined by $\mathbf{X}_1$ or $-\mathbf{X}_1$ (since e^{4t} is negligible for $t \to -\infty$) and "finishes" asymptotic to one of the half-lines defined by $\mathbf{X}_2$ and $-\mathbf{X}_2$ (since e^{-t} is negligible for $t \to \infty$).

We note in passing that Figure 8.2.2 represents a phase portrait that is typical of *all* 2×2 homogeneous linear systems $\mathbf{X}' = \mathbf{AX}$ with real eigenvalues of opposite signs. See Problem 17 in Exercises 8.2. Moreover, phase portraits in the two cases when distinct real eigenvalues have the same algebraic sign are typical of all such 2×2 linear systems; the only difference is that the arrowheads indicate that a particle moves away from the origin on any trajectory as $t \to \infty$ when both λ_1 and λ_2 are positive and moves toward the origin on any trajectory when both λ_1 and λ_2 are negative. Consequently, we call the origin a **repeller** in the case $\lambda_1 > 0$, $\lambda_2 > 0$ and an **attractor** in the case $\lambda_1 < 0$, $\lambda_2 < 0$. See Problem 18 in Exercises 8.2. The origin in Figure 8.2.2 is neither a repeller nor an attractor. Investigation of the remaining case when $\lambda = 0$ is an eigenvalue of a 2×2 homogeneous linear system is left as an exercise. See Problem 49 in Exercises 8.2.

| **EXAMPLE 2** | **Distinct Eigenvalues** |

Solve

$$\frac{dx}{dt} = -4x + y + z$$

$$\frac{dy}{dt} = x + 5y - z \qquad (6)$$

$$\frac{dz}{dt} = y - 3z.$$

SOLUTION Using the cofactors of the third row, we find

$$\det(\mathbf{A} - \lambda\mathbf{I}) = \begin{vmatrix} -4 - \lambda & 1 & 1 \\ 1 & 5 - \lambda & -1 \\ 0 & 1 & -3 - \lambda \end{vmatrix} = -(\lambda + 3)(\lambda + 4)(\lambda - 5) = 0,$$

and so the eigenvalues are $\lambda_1 = -3$, $\lambda_2 = -4$, and $\lambda_3 = 5$.

For $\lambda_1 = -3$ Gauss-Jordan elimination gives

$$(\mathbf{A} + 3\mathbf{I}|\mathbf{0}) = \begin{pmatrix} -1 & 1 & 1 & | & 0 \\ 1 & 8 & -1 & | & 0 \\ 0 & 1 & 0 & | & 0 \end{pmatrix} \xrightarrow[\text{operations}]{\text{row}} \begin{pmatrix} 1 & 0 & -1 & | & 0 \\ 0 & 1 & 0 & | & 0 \\ 0 & 0 & 0 & | & 0 \end{pmatrix}.$$

Therefore $k_1 = k_3$ and $k_2 = 0$. The choice $k_3 = 1$ gives an eigenvector and corresponding solution vector

$$\mathbf{K}_1 = \begin{pmatrix} 1 \\ 0 \\ 1 \end{pmatrix}, \qquad \mathbf{X}_1 = \begin{pmatrix} 1 \\ 0 \\ 1 \end{pmatrix} e^{-3t}. \tag{7}$$

Similarly, for $\lambda_2 = -4$

$$(\mathbf{A} + 4\mathbf{I}|\mathbf{0}) = \begin{pmatrix} 0 & 1 & 1 & | & 0 \\ 1 & 9 & -1 & | & 0 \\ 0 & 1 & 1 & | & 0 \end{pmatrix} \xrightarrow[\text{operations}]{\text{row}} \begin{pmatrix} 1 & 0 & -10 & | & 0 \\ 0 & 1 & 1 & | & 0 \\ 0 & 0 & 0 & | & 0 \end{pmatrix}$$

implies that $k_1 = 10k_3$ and $k_2 = -k_3$. Choosing $k_3 = 1$, we get a second eigenvector and solution vector

$$\mathbf{K}_2 = \begin{pmatrix} 10 \\ -1 \\ 1 \end{pmatrix}, \qquad \mathbf{X}_2 = \begin{pmatrix} 10 \\ -1 \\ 1 \end{pmatrix} e^{-4t}. \tag{8}$$

Finally, when $\lambda_3 = 5$, the augmented matrices

$$(\mathbf{A} + 5\mathbf{I}|\mathbf{0}) = \begin{pmatrix} -9 & 1 & 1 & | & 0 \\ 1 & 0 & -1 & | & 0 \\ 0 & 1 & -8 & | & 0 \end{pmatrix} \xrightarrow[\text{operations}]{\text{row}} \begin{pmatrix} 1 & 0 & -1 & | & 0 \\ 0 & 1 & -8 & | & 0 \\ 0 & 0 & 0 & | & 0 \end{pmatrix}$$

yield

$$\mathbf{K}_3 = \begin{pmatrix} 1 \\ 8 \\ 1 \end{pmatrix}, \qquad \mathbf{X}_3 = \begin{pmatrix} 1 \\ 8 \\ 1 \end{pmatrix} e^{5t}. \tag{9}$$

The general solution of (6) is a linear combination of the solution vectors in (7), (8), and (9):

$$\mathbf{X} = c_1 \begin{pmatrix} 1 \\ 0 \\ 1 \end{pmatrix} e^{-3t} + c_2 \begin{pmatrix} 10 \\ -1 \\ 1 \end{pmatrix} e^{-4t} + c_3 \begin{pmatrix} 1 \\ 8 \\ 1 \end{pmatrix} e^{5t}. \qquad ■$$

USE OF COMPUTERS Software packages such as MATLAB, *Mathematica, Maple,* and DERIVE can be real time savers in finding eigenvalues and eigenvectors of a matrix $\mathbf{A}$.

8.2.2 REPEATED EIGENVALUES

Of course, not all of the n eigenvalues $\lambda_1, \lambda_2, \ldots, \lambda_n$ of an $n \times n$ matrix $\mathbf{A}$ need be distinct; that is, some of the eigenvalues may be repeated. For example, the characteristic equation of the coefficient matrix in the system

$$\mathbf{X}' = \begin{pmatrix} 3 & -18 \\ 2 & -9 \end{pmatrix} \mathbf{X} \tag{10}$$

is readily shown to be $(\lambda + 3)^2 = 0$, and therefore $\lambda_1 = \lambda_2 = -3$ is a root of *multiplicity two*. For this value we find the single eigenvector

$$\mathbf{K}_1 = \begin{pmatrix} 3 \\ 1 \end{pmatrix}, \qquad \text{so} \qquad \mathbf{X}_1 = \begin{pmatrix} 3 \\ 1 \end{pmatrix} e^{-3t} \tag{11}$$

is one solution of (10). But since we are obviously interested in forming the general solution of the system, we need to pursue the question of finding a second solution.

In general, if m is a positive integer and $(\lambda - \lambda_1)^m$ is a factor of the characteristic equation while $(\lambda - \lambda_1)^{m+1}$ is not a factor, then λ_1 is said to be an **eigenvalue of multiplicity m.** The next three examples illustrate the following cases:

(*i*) For some $n \times n$ matrices $\mathbf{A}$ it may be possible to find m linearly independent eigenvectors $\mathbf{K}_1, \mathbf{K}_2, \ldots, \mathbf{K}_m$ corresponding to an eigenvalue λ_1 of multiplicity $m \leq n$. In this case the general solution of the system contains the linear combination

$$c_1 \mathbf{K}_1 e^{\lambda_1 t} + c_2 \mathbf{K}_2 e^{\lambda_1 t} + \cdots + c_m \mathbf{K}_m e^{\lambda_1 t}.$$

(*ii*) If there is only one eigenvector corresponding to the eigenvalue λ_1 of multiplicity m, then m linearly independent solutions of the form

$$\mathbf{X}_1 = \mathbf{K}_{11} e^{\lambda_1 t}$$
$$\mathbf{X}_2 = \mathbf{K}_{21} t e^{\lambda_1 t} + \mathbf{K}_{22} e^{\lambda_1 t}$$
$$\vdots$$
$$\mathbf{X}_m = \mathbf{K}_{m1} \frac{t^{m-1}}{(m-1)!} e^{\lambda_1 t} + \mathbf{K}_{m2} \frac{t^{m-2}}{(m-2)!} e^{\lambda_1 t} + \cdots + \mathbf{K}_{mm} e^{\lambda_1 t},$$

where $\mathbf{K}_{ij}$ are column vectors, can always be found.

EIGENVALUE OF MULTIPLICITY TWO We begin by considering eigenvalues of multiplicity two. In the first example we illustrate a matrix for which we can find two distinct eigenvectors corresponding to a double eigenvalue.

EXAMPLE 3 Repeated Eigenvalues

Solve $\mathbf{X}' = \begin{pmatrix} 1 & -2 & 2 \\ -2 & 1 & -2 \\ 2 & -2 & 1 \end{pmatrix} \mathbf{X}$.

SOLUTION Expanding the determinant in the characteristic equation

$$\det(\mathbf{A} - \lambda\mathbf{I}) = \begin{vmatrix} 1 - \lambda & -2 & 2 \\ -2 & 1 - \lambda & -2 \\ 2 & -2 & 1 - \lambda \end{vmatrix} = 0$$

yields $-(\lambda + 1)^2(\lambda - 5) = 0$. We see that $\lambda_1 = \lambda_2 = -1$ and $\lambda_3 = 5$.

For $\lambda_1 = -1$ Gauss-Jordan elimination immediately gives

$$(\mathbf{A} + \mathbf{I} | \mathbf{0}) = \begin{pmatrix} 2 & -2 & 2 & | & 0 \\ -2 & 2 & -2 & | & 0 \\ 2 & -2 & 2 & | & 0 \end{pmatrix} \xrightarrow[\text{operations}]{\text{row}} \begin{pmatrix} 1 & -1 & 1 & | & 0 \\ 0 & 0 & 0 & | & 0 \\ 0 & 0 & 0 & | & 0 \end{pmatrix}.$$

The first row of the last matrix means $k_1 - k_2 + k_3 = 0$ or $k_1 = k_2 - k_3$. The choices $k_2 = 1$, $k_3 = 0$ and $k_2 = 1$, $k_3 = 1$ yield, in turn, $k_1 = 1$ and $k_1 = 0$. Thus two eigenvectors corresponding to $\lambda_1 = -1$ are

$$\mathbf{K}_1 = \begin{pmatrix} 1 \\ 1 \\ 0 \end{pmatrix} \quad \text{and} \quad \mathbf{K}_2 = \begin{pmatrix} 0 \\ 1 \\ 1 \end{pmatrix}.$$

Since neither eigenvector is a constant multiple of the other, we have found two linearly independent solutions,

$$\mathbf{X}_1 = \begin{pmatrix} 1 \\ 1 \\ 0 \end{pmatrix} e^{-t} \quad \text{and} \quad \mathbf{X}_2 = \begin{pmatrix} 0 \\ 1 \\ 1 \end{pmatrix} e^{-t},$$

corresponding to the same eigenvalue. Last, for $\lambda_3 = 5$ the reduction

$$(\mathbf{A} + 5\mathbf{I}|\mathbf{0}) = \begin{pmatrix} -4 & -2 & 2 & | & 0 \\ -2 & -4 & -2 & | & 0 \\ 2 & -2 & -4 & | & 0 \end{pmatrix} \xrightarrow[\text{operations}]{\text{row}} \begin{pmatrix} 1 & 0 & -1 & | & 0 \\ 0 & 1 & 1 & | & 0 \\ 0 & 0 & 0 & | & 0 \end{pmatrix}$$

implies that $k_1 = k_3$ and $k_2 = -k_3$. Picking $k_3 = 1$ gives $k_1 = 1$, $k_2 = -1$; thus a third eigenvector is

$$\mathbf{K}_3 = \begin{pmatrix} 1 \\ -1 \\ 1 \end{pmatrix}.$$

We conclude that the general solution of the system is

$$\mathbf{X} = c_1 \begin{pmatrix} 1 \\ 1 \\ 0 \end{pmatrix} e^{-t} + c_2 \begin{pmatrix} 0 \\ 1 \\ 1 \end{pmatrix} e^{-t} + c_3 \begin{pmatrix} 1 \\ -1 \\ 1 \end{pmatrix} e^{5t}. \qquad \blacksquare$$

The matrix of coefficients $\mathbf{A}$ in Example 3 is a special kind of matrix known as a symmetric matrix. An $n \times n$ matrix $\mathbf{A}$ is said to be **symmetric** if its transpose $\mathbf{A}^T$ (where the rows and columns are interchanged) is the same as $\mathbf{A}$—that is, if $\mathbf{A}^T = \mathbf{A}$. It can be proved that if the matrix $\mathbf{A}$ in the system $\mathbf{X}' = \mathbf{A}\mathbf{X}$ is symmetric and has real entries, then we can always find n linearly independent eigenvectors $\mathbf{K}_1, \mathbf{K}_2, \ldots, \mathbf{K}_n$, and the general solution of such a system is as given in Theorem 8.2.1. As illustrated in Example 3, this result holds even when some of the eigenvalues are repeated.

SECOND SOLUTION Now suppose that λ_1 is an eigenvalue of multiplicity two and that there is only one eigenvector associated with this value. A second solution can be found of the form

$$\mathbf{X}_2 = \mathbf{K}te^{\lambda_1 t} + \mathbf{P}e^{\lambda_1 t}, \qquad (12)$$

where

$$\mathbf{K} = \begin{pmatrix} k_1 \\ k_2 \\ \vdots \\ k_n \end{pmatrix} \quad \text{and} \quad \mathbf{P} = \begin{pmatrix} p_1 \\ p_2 \\ \vdots \\ p_n \end{pmatrix}.$$

To see this, we substitute (12) into the system $\mathbf{X}' = \mathbf{AX}$ and simplify:

$$(\mathbf{AK} - \lambda_1\mathbf{K})te^{\lambda_1 t} + (\mathbf{AP} - \lambda_1\mathbf{P} - \mathbf{K})e^{\lambda_1 t} = \mathbf{0}.$$

Since this last equation is to hold for all values of t, we must have

$$(\mathbf{A} - \lambda_1\mathbf{I})\mathbf{K} = \mathbf{0} \tag{13}$$

and

$$(\mathbf{A} - \lambda_1\mathbf{I})\mathbf{P} = \mathbf{K}. \tag{14}$$

Equation (13) simply states that $\mathbf{K}$ must be an eigenvector of $\mathbf{A}$ associated with λ_1. By solving (13), we find one solution $\mathbf{X}_1 = \mathbf{K}e^{\lambda_1 t}$. To find the second solution $\mathbf{X}_2$, we need only solve the additional system (14) for the vector $\mathbf{P}$.

EXAMPLE 4   Repeated Eigenvalues

Find the general solution of the system given in (10).

SOLUTION From (11) we know that $\lambda_1 = -3$ and that one solution is $\mathbf{X}_1 = \begin{pmatrix} 3 \\ 1 \end{pmatrix}e^{-3t}$. Identifying $\mathbf{K} = \begin{pmatrix} 3 \\ 1 \end{pmatrix}$ and $\mathbf{P} = \begin{pmatrix} p_1 \\ p_2 \end{pmatrix}$, we find from (14) that we must now solve

$$(\mathbf{A} + 3\mathbf{I})\mathbf{P} = \mathbf{K} \qquad \text{or} \qquad \begin{array}{r} 6p_1 - 18p_2 = 3 \\ 2p_1 - 6p_2 = 1. \end{array}$$

Since this system is obviously equivalent to one equation, we have an infinite number of choices for p_1 and p_2. For example, by choosing $p_1 = 1$, we find $p_2 = \frac{1}{6}$. However, for simplicity we shall choose $p_1 = \frac{1}{2}$ so that $p_2 = 0$. Hence $\mathbf{P} = \begin{pmatrix} \frac{1}{2} \\ 0 \end{pmatrix}$. Thus from (12) we find $\mathbf{X}_2 = \begin{pmatrix} 3 \\ 1 \end{pmatrix}te^{-3t} + \begin{pmatrix} \frac{1}{2} \\ 0 \end{pmatrix}e^{-3t}$. The general solution of (10) is then $\mathbf{X} = c_1\mathbf{X}_1 + c_2\mathbf{X}_2$ or

$$\mathbf{X} = c_1 \begin{pmatrix} 3 \\ 1 \end{pmatrix}e^{-3t} + c_2\left[\begin{pmatrix} 3 \\ 1 \end{pmatrix}te^{-3t} + \begin{pmatrix} \frac{1}{2} \\ 0 \end{pmatrix}e^{-3t} \right]. \qquad \blacksquare$$

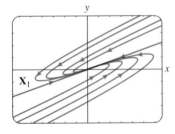

FIGURE 8.2.3   A phase portrait of system (10)

By assigning various values to c_1 and c_2 in the solution in Example 4, we can plot trajectories of the system in (10). A phase portrait of (10) is given in Figure 8.2.3. The solutions $\mathbf{X}_1$ and $-\mathbf{X}_1$ determine two half-lines $y = \frac{1}{3}x, x > 0$ and $y = \frac{1}{3}x, x < 0$, respectively, shown in red in the figure. Because the single eigenvalue is negative and $e^{-3t} \to 0$ as $t \to \infty$ on *every* trajectory, we have $(x(t), y(t)) \to (0, 0)$ as $t \to \infty$. This is why the arrowheads in Figure 8.2.3 indicate that a particle on any trajectory moves toward the origin as time increases and why the origin is an attractor in this case. Moreover, a moving particle or trajectory $x = 3c_1e^{-3t} + c_2(3te^{-3t} + \frac{1}{2}e^{-3t})$, $y = c_1e^{-3t} + c_2te^{-3t}, c_2 \neq 0$, approaches $(0, 0)$ tangentially to one of the half-lines as $t \to \infty$. In contrast, when the repeated eigenvalue is positive, the situation is reversed and the origin is a repeller. See Problem 21 in Exercises 8.2. Analogous to Figure 8.2.2, Figure 8.2.3 is typical of *all* 2×2 homogeneous linear systems $\mathbf{X}' = \mathbf{AX}$ that have two repeated negative eigenvalues. See Problem 32 in Exercises 8.2.

EIGENVALUE OF MULTIPLICITY THREE   When the coefficient matrix $\mathbf{A}$ has only one eigenvector associated with an eigenvalue λ_1 of multiplicity three, we can find a second solution of the form (12) and a third solution of the form

$$\mathbf{X}_3 = \mathbf{K}\frac{t^2}{2}e^{\lambda_1 t} + \mathbf{P}te^{\lambda_1 t} + \mathbf{Q}e^{\lambda_1 t}, \tag{15}$$

where
$$\mathbf{K} = \begin{pmatrix} k_1 \\ k_2 \\ \cdot \\ \cdot \\ \cdot \\ k_n \end{pmatrix}, \quad \mathbf{P} = \begin{pmatrix} p_1 \\ p_2 \\ \cdot \\ \cdot \\ \cdot \\ p_n \end{pmatrix}, \quad \text{and} \quad \mathbf{Q} = \begin{pmatrix} q_1 \\ q_2 \\ \cdot \\ \cdot \\ \cdot \\ q_n \end{pmatrix}.$$

By substituting (15) into the system $\mathbf{X}' = \mathbf{AX}$, we find that the column vectors $\mathbf{K}$, $\mathbf{P}$, and $\mathbf{Q}$ must satisfy

$$(\mathbf{A} - \lambda_1\mathbf{I})\mathbf{K} = \mathbf{0} \tag{16}$$

$$(\mathbf{A} - \lambda_1\mathbf{I})\mathbf{P} = \mathbf{K} \tag{17}$$

and $$(\mathbf{A} - \lambda_1\mathbf{I})\mathbf{Q} = \mathbf{P}. \tag{18}$$

Of course, the solutions of (16) and (17) can be used in forming the solutions $\mathbf{X}_1$ and $\mathbf{X}_2$.

EXAMPLE 5   Repeated Eigenvalues

Solve $\mathbf{X}' = \begin{pmatrix} 2 & 1 & 6 \\ 0 & 2 & 5 \\ 0 & 0 & 2 \end{pmatrix}\mathbf{X}$.

SOLUTION The characteristic equation $(\lambda - 2)^3 = 0$ shows that $\lambda_1 = 2$ is an eigenvalue of multiplicity three. By solving $(\mathbf{A} - 2\mathbf{I})\mathbf{K} = \mathbf{0}$, we find the single eigenvector

$$\mathbf{K} = \begin{pmatrix} 1 \\ 0 \\ 0 \end{pmatrix}.$$

We next solve the systems $(\mathbf{A} - 2\mathbf{I})\mathbf{P} = \mathbf{K}$ and $(\mathbf{A} - 2\mathbf{I})\mathbf{Q} = \mathbf{P}$ in succession and find that

$$\mathbf{P} = \begin{pmatrix} 0 \\ 1 \\ 0 \end{pmatrix} \quad \text{and} \quad \mathbf{Q} = \begin{pmatrix} 0 \\ -\frac{6}{5} \\ \frac{1}{5} \end{pmatrix}.$$

Using (12) and (15), we see that the general solution of the system is

$$\mathbf{X} = c_1 \begin{pmatrix} 1 \\ 0 \\ 0 \end{pmatrix}e^{2t} + c_2 \left[\begin{pmatrix} 1 \\ 0 \\ 0 \end{pmatrix}te^{2t} + \begin{pmatrix} 0 \\ 1 \\ 0 \end{pmatrix}e^{2t} \right] + c_3 \left[\begin{pmatrix} 1 \\ 0 \\ 0 \end{pmatrix}\frac{t^2}{2}e^{2t} + \begin{pmatrix} 0 \\ 1 \\ 0 \end{pmatrix}te^{2t} + \begin{pmatrix} 0 \\ -\frac{6}{5} \\ \frac{1}{5} \end{pmatrix}e^{2t} \right]. \quad\blacksquare$$

REMARKS

When an eigenvalue λ_1 has multiplicity m, either we can find m linearly independent eigenvectors or the number of corresponding eigenvectors is less than m. Hence the two cases listed on page 316 are not all the possibilities under which a repeated eigenvalue can occur. It can happen, say, that a 5×5 matrix has an eigenvalue of multiplicity five and there exist three corresponding linearly independent eigenvectors. See Problems 31 and 50 in Exercises 8.2.

8.2.3 COMPLEX EIGENVALUES

If $\lambda_1 = \alpha + \beta i$ and $\lambda_2 = \alpha - \beta i$, $\beta > 0$, $i^2 = -1$ are complex eigenvalues of the coefficient matrix $\mathbf{A}$, we can then certainly expect their corresponding eigenvectors to also have complex entries.[*]

For example, the characteristic equation of the system

$$\frac{dx}{dt} = 6x - y$$

$$\frac{dy}{dt} = 5x + 4y \tag{19}$$

is
$$\det(\mathbf{A} - \lambda\mathbf{I}) = \begin{vmatrix} 6 - \lambda & -1 \\ 5 & 4 - \lambda \end{vmatrix} = \lambda^2 - 10\lambda + 29 = 0.$$

From the quadratic formula we find $\lambda_1 = 5 + 2i$, $\lambda_2 = 5 - 2i$.

Now for $\lambda_1 = 5 + 2i$ we must solve

$$(1 - 2i)k_1 - \qquad k_2 = 0$$

$$5k_1 - (1 + 2i)k_2 = 0.$$

Since $k_2 = (1 - 2i)k_1$,[†] the choice $k_1 = 1$ gives the following eigenvector and corresponding solution vector:

$$\mathbf{K}_1 = \begin{pmatrix} 1 \\ 1 - 2i \end{pmatrix}, \qquad \mathbf{X}_1 = \begin{pmatrix} 1 \\ 1 - 2i \end{pmatrix} e^{(5 + 2i)t}.$$

In like manner, for $\lambda_2 = 5 - 2i$ we find

$$\mathbf{K}_2 = \begin{pmatrix} 1 \\ 1 + 2i \end{pmatrix}, \qquad \mathbf{X}_2 = \begin{pmatrix} 1 \\ 1 + 2i \end{pmatrix} e^{(5 - 2i)t}.$$

We can verify by means of the Wronskian that these solution vectors are linearly independent, and so the general solution of (19) is

$$\mathbf{X} = c_1 \begin{pmatrix} 1 \\ 1 - 2i \end{pmatrix} e^{(5+2i)t} + c_2 \begin{pmatrix} 1 \\ 1 + 2i \end{pmatrix} e^{(5-2i)t}. \tag{20}$$

Note that the entries in $\mathbf{K}_2$ corresponding to λ_2 are the conjugates of the entries in $\mathbf{K}_1$ corresponding to λ_1. The conjugate of λ_1 is, of course, λ_2. We write this as $\lambda_2 = \overline{\lambda}_1$ and $\mathbf{K}_2 = \overline{\mathbf{K}}_1$. We have illustrated the following general result.

THEOREM 8.2.2 Solutions Corresponding to a Complex Eigenvalue
Let $\mathbf{A}$ be the coefficient matrix having real entries of the homogeneous system (2), and let $\mathbf{K}_1$ be an eigenvector corresponding to the complex eigenvalue $\lambda_1 = \alpha + i\beta$, α and β real. Then $$\mathbf{K}_1 e^{\lambda_1 t} \qquad \text{and} \qquad \overline{\mathbf{K}}_1 e^{\overline{\lambda}_1 t}$$ are solutions of (2).

---

[*]When the characteristic equation has real coefficients, complex eigenvalues always appear in conjugate pairs.
[†]Note that the second equation is simply $(1 + 2i)$ times the first.

It is desirable and relatively easy to rewrite a solution such as (20) in terms of real functions. To this end we first use Euler's formula to write

$$e^{(5+2i)t} = e^{5t}e^{2ti} = e^{5t}(\cos 2t + i \sin 2t)$$

$$e^{(5-2i)t} = e^{5t}e^{-2ti} = e^{5t}(\cos 2t - i \sin 2t).$$

Then, after we multiply complex numbers, collect terms, and replace $c_1 + c_2$ by C_1 and $(c_1 - c_2)i$ by C_2, (20) becomes

$$\mathbf{X} = C_1\mathbf{X}_1 + C_2\mathbf{X}_2, \tag{21}$$

where

$$\mathbf{X}_1 = \left[\begin{pmatrix} 1 \\ 1 \end{pmatrix}\cos 2t - \begin{pmatrix} 0 \\ -2 \end{pmatrix}\sin 2t\right]e^{5t}$$

and

$$\mathbf{X}_2 = \left[\begin{pmatrix} 0 \\ -2 \end{pmatrix}\cos 2t + \begin{pmatrix} 1 \\ 1 \end{pmatrix}\sin 2t\right]e^{5t}.$$

It is now important to realize that the vectors $\mathbf{X}_1$ and $\mathbf{X}_2$ in (21) constitute a linearly independent set of *real* solutions of the original system. Consequently, we are justified in ignoring the relationship between C_1, C_2 and c_1, c_2, and we can regard C_1 and C_2 as completely arbitrary and real. In other words, the linear combination (21) is an alternative general solution of (19). Moreover, with the real form given in (21) we are able to obtain a phase portrait of the system in (19). From (21) we find $x(t)$ and $y(t)$ to be

$$x = C_1e^{5t}\cos 2t + C_2e^{5t}\sin 2t$$

$$y = (C_1 - 2C_2)e^{5t}\cos 2t + (2C_1 + C_2)e^{5t}\sin 2t.$$

By plotting the trajectories $(x(t), y(t))$ for various values of C_1 and C_2, we obtain the phase portrait of (19) shown in Figure 8.2.4. Because the real part of λ_1 is $5 > 0$, $e^{5t} \to \infty$ as $t \to \infty$. This is why the arrowheads in Figure 8.2.4 point away from the origin; a particle on any trajectory spirals away from the origin as $t \to \infty$. The origin is a repeller.

The process by which we obtained the real solutions in (21) can be generalized. Let $\mathbf{K}_1$ be an eigenvector of the coefficient matrix $\mathbf{A}$ (with real entries) corresponding to the complex eigenvalue $\lambda_1 = \alpha + i\beta$. Then the solution vectors in Theorem 8.2.2 can be written as

$$\mathbf{K}_1e^{\lambda_1 t} = \mathbf{K}_1e^{\alpha t}e^{i\beta t} = \mathbf{K}_1e^{\alpha t}(\cos \beta t + i \sin \beta t)$$

$$\overline{\mathbf{K}}_1e^{\overline{\lambda}_1 t} = \overline{\mathbf{K}}_1e^{\alpha t}e^{-i\beta t} = \overline{\mathbf{K}}_1e^{\alpha t}(\cos \beta t - i \sin \beta t).$$

By the superposition principle, Theorem 8.1.2, the following vectors are also solutions:

$$\mathbf{X}_1 = \frac{1}{2}(\mathbf{K}_1e^{\lambda_1 t} + \overline{\mathbf{K}}_1e^{\overline{\lambda}_1 t}) = \frac{1}{2}(\mathbf{K}_1 + \overline{\mathbf{K}}_1)e^{\alpha t}\cos \beta t - \frac{i}{2}(-\mathbf{K}_1 + \overline{\mathbf{K}}_1)e^{\alpha t}\sin \beta t$$

$$\mathbf{X}_2 = \frac{i}{2}(-\mathbf{K}_1e^{\lambda_1 t} + \overline{\mathbf{K}}_1e^{\overline{\lambda}_1 t}) = \frac{i}{2}(-\mathbf{K}_1 + \overline{\mathbf{K}}_1)e^{\alpha t}\cos \beta t + \frac{1}{2}(\mathbf{K}_1 + \overline{\mathbf{K}}_1)e^{\alpha t}\sin \beta t.$$

Both $\frac{1}{2}(z + \overline{z}) = a$ and $\frac{1}{2}i(-z + \overline{z}) = b$ are *real* numbers for *any* complex number $z = a + ib$. Therefore, the entries in the column vectors $\frac{1}{2}(\mathbf{K}_1 + \overline{\mathbf{K}}_1)$ and $\frac{1}{2}i(-\mathbf{K}_1 + \overline{\mathbf{K}}_1)$ are real numbers. By defining

$$\mathbf{B}_1 = \frac{1}{2}(\mathbf{K}_1 + \overline{\mathbf{K}}_1) \quad \text{and} \quad \mathbf{B}_2 = \frac{i}{2}(-\mathbf{K}_1 + \overline{\mathbf{K}}_1), \tag{22}$$

we are led to the following theorem.

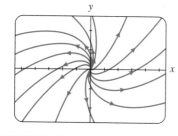

FIGURE 8.2.4 A phase portrait of system (19)

> **THEOREM 8.2.3 Real Solutions Corresponding to a Complex Eigenvalue**
>
> Let $\lambda_1 = \alpha + i\beta$ be a complex eigenvalue of the coefficient matrix $\mathbf{A}$ in the homogeneous system (2) and let $\mathbf{B}_1$ and $\mathbf{B}_2$ denote the column vectors defined in (22). Then
>
> $$\mathbf{X}_1 = [\mathbf{B}_1 \cos \beta t - \mathbf{B}_2 \sin \beta t]e^{\alpha t}$$
> $$\mathbf{X}_2 = [\mathbf{B}_2 \cos \beta t + \mathbf{B}_1 \sin \beta t]e^{\alpha t} \qquad (23)$$
>
> are linearly independent solutions of (2) on $(-\infty, \infty)$.

The matrices $\mathbf{B}_1$ and $\mathbf{B}_2$ in (22) are often denoted by

$$\mathbf{B}_1 = \text{Re}(\mathbf{K}_1) \qquad \text{and} \qquad \mathbf{B}_2 = \text{Im}(\mathbf{K}_1) \qquad (24)$$

since these vectors are, respectively, the *real* and *imaginary* parts of the eigenvector $\mathbf{K}_1$. For example, (21) follows from (23) with

$$\mathbf{K}_1 = \begin{pmatrix} 1 \\ 1 - 2i \end{pmatrix} = \begin{pmatrix} 1 \\ 1 \end{pmatrix} + i\begin{pmatrix} 0 \\ -2 \end{pmatrix},$$

$$\mathbf{B}_1 = \text{Re}(\mathbf{K}_1) = \begin{pmatrix} 1 \\ 1 \end{pmatrix} \qquad \text{and} \qquad \mathbf{B}_2 = \text{Im}(\mathbf{K}_1) = \begin{pmatrix} 0 \\ -2 \end{pmatrix}.$$

EXAMPLE 6 Complex Eigenvalues

Solve the initial-value problem

$$\mathbf{X}' = \begin{pmatrix} 2 & 8 \\ -1 & -2 \end{pmatrix}\mathbf{X}, \quad \mathbf{X}(0) = \begin{pmatrix} 2 \\ -1 \end{pmatrix}. \qquad (25)$$

SOLUTION First we obtain the eigenvalues from

$$\det(\mathbf{A} - \lambda\mathbf{I}) = \begin{vmatrix} 2 - \lambda & 8 \\ -1 & -2 - \lambda \end{vmatrix} = \lambda^2 + 4 = 0.$$

The eigenvalues are $\lambda_1 = 2i$ and $\lambda_2 = \overline{\lambda_1} = -2i$. For λ_1 the system

$$(2 - 2i)\,k_1 + \qquad\qquad 8k_2 = 0$$
$$-k_1 + (-2 - 2i)k_2 = 0$$

gives $k_1 = -(2 + 2i)k_2$. By choosing $k_2 = -1$, we get

$$\mathbf{K}_1 = \begin{pmatrix} 2 + 2i \\ -1 \end{pmatrix} = \begin{pmatrix} 2 \\ -1 \end{pmatrix} + i\begin{pmatrix} 2 \\ 0 \end{pmatrix}.$$

Now from (24) we form

$$\mathbf{B}_1 = \text{Re}(\mathbf{K}_1) = \begin{pmatrix} 2 \\ -1 \end{pmatrix} \qquad \text{and} \qquad \mathbf{B}_2 = \text{Im}(\mathbf{K}_1) = \begin{pmatrix} 2 \\ 0 \end{pmatrix}.$$

Since $\alpha = 0$, it follows from (23) that the general solution of the system is

$$\mathbf{X} = c_1\left[\begin{pmatrix} 2 \\ -1 \end{pmatrix}\cos 2t - \begin{pmatrix} 2 \\ 0 \end{pmatrix}\sin 2t\right] + c_2\left[\begin{pmatrix} 2 \\ 0 \end{pmatrix}\cos 2t + \begin{pmatrix} 2 \\ -1 \end{pmatrix}\sin 2t\right]$$

$$= c_1\begin{pmatrix} 2\cos 2t - 2\sin 2t \\ -\cos 2t \end{pmatrix} + c_2\begin{pmatrix} 2\cos 2t + 2\sin 2t \\ -\sin 2t \end{pmatrix}. \qquad (26)$$

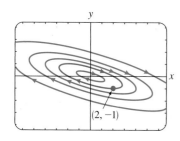

FIGURE 8.2.5 A phase portrait of system (25)

Some graphs of the curves or trajectories defined by solution (26) of the system are illustrated in the phase portrait in Figure 8.2.5. Now the initial condition $\mathbf{X}(0) = \begin{pmatrix} 2 \\ -1 \end{pmatrix}$ or, equivalently, $x(0) = 2$ and $y(0) = -1$ yields the algebraic system $2c_1 + 2c_2 = 2$, $-c_1 = -1$, whose solution is $c_1 = 1$, $c_2 = 0$. Thus the solution to the problem is $\mathbf{X} = \begin{pmatrix} 2 \cos 2t - 2 \sin 2t \\ -\cos 2t \end{pmatrix}$. The specific trajectory defined parametrically by the particular solution $x = 2 \cos 2t - 2 \sin 2t$, $y = -\cos 2t$ is the red curve in Figure 8.2.5. Note that this curve passes through $(2, -1)$. ∎

REMARKS

In this section we have examined exclusively homogeneous first-order systems of linear equations in normal form $\mathbf{X}' = \mathbf{AX}$. But often the mathematical model of a dynamical physical system is a homogeneous second-order system whose normal form is $\mathbf{X}'' = \mathbf{AX}$. For example, the model for the coupled springs in (1) of Section 7.6,

$$
\begin{aligned}
m_1 x_1'' &= -k_1 x_1 + k_2(x_2 - x_1) \\
m_2 x_2'' &= -k_2(x_2 - x_1),
\end{aligned}
\tag{27}
$$

can be written as $\qquad \mathbf{MX}'' = \mathbf{KX},$
where

$$
\mathbf{M} = \begin{pmatrix} m_1 & 0 \\ 0 & m_2 \end{pmatrix}, \quad \mathbf{K} = \begin{pmatrix} -k_1 - k_2 & k_2 \\ k_2 & -k_2 \end{pmatrix}, \quad \text{and} \quad \mathbf{X} = \begin{pmatrix} x_1(t) \\ x_2(t) \end{pmatrix}.
$$

Since $\mathbf{M}$ is nonsingular, we can solve for $\mathbf{X}''$ as $\mathbf{X}'' = \mathbf{AX}$, where $\mathbf{A} = \mathbf{M}^{-1}\mathbf{K}$. Thus (27) is equivalent to

$$
\mathbf{X}'' = \begin{pmatrix} -\dfrac{k_1}{m_1} - \dfrac{k_2}{m_1} & \dfrac{k_2}{m_1} \\ \dfrac{k_2}{m_2} & -\dfrac{k_2}{m_2} \end{pmatrix} \mathbf{X}.
\tag{28}
$$

The methods of this section can be used to solve such a system in two ways:

- First, the original system (27) can be transformed into a first-order system by means of substitutions. If we let $x_1' = x_3$ and $x_2' = x_4$, then $x_3' = x_1''$ and $x_4' = x_2''$ and so (27) is equivalent to a system of *four* linear first-order DEs:

$$
\begin{aligned}
x_1' &= x_3 \\
x_2' &= x_4 \\
x_3' &= -\left(\frac{k_1}{m_1} + \frac{k_2}{m_1}\right)x_1 + \frac{k_2}{m_1}x_2 \\
x_4' &= \frac{k_2}{m_2}x_1 - \frac{k_2}{m_2}x_2
\end{aligned}
\quad \text{or} \quad \mathbf{X}' = \begin{pmatrix} 0 & 0 & 1 & 0 \\ 0 & 0 & 0 & 1 \\ -\dfrac{k_1}{m_1} - \dfrac{k_2}{m_1} & \dfrac{k_2}{m_1} & 0 & 0 \\ \dfrac{k_2}{m_2} & -\dfrac{k_2}{m_2} & 0 & 0 \end{pmatrix} \mathbf{X}. \tag{29}
$$

By finding the eigenvalues and eigenvectors of the coefficient matrix $\mathbf{A}$ in (29), we see that the solution of this first-order system gives the complete state of the physical system—the positions of the masses relative to the equilibrium positions (x_1 and x_2) as well as the velocities of the masses (x_3 and x_4) at time t. See Problem 48(a) in Exercises 8.2.

- Second, because (27) describes free undamped motion, it can be argued that real-valued solutions of the second-order system (28) will have the form

$$\mathbf{X} = \mathbf{V} \cos \omega t \quad \text{and} \quad \mathbf{X} = \mathbf{V} \sin \omega t, \tag{30}$$

where $\mathbf{V}$ is a column matrix of constants. Substituting either of the functions in (30) into $\mathbf{X}'' = \mathbf{AX}$ yields $(\mathbf{A} + \omega^2\mathbf{I})\mathbf{V} = \mathbf{0}$. (Verify.) By identification with (3) of this section we conclude that $\lambda = -\omega^2$ represents an eigenvalue and $\mathbf{V}$ a corresponding eigenvector of $\mathbf{A}$. It can be shown that the eigenvalues $\lambda_i = -\omega_i^2$, $i = 1, 2$ of $\mathbf{A}$ are negative, and so $\omega_i = \sqrt{-\lambda_i}$ is a real number and represents a (circular) frequency of vibration (see (4) of Section 7.6). By superposition of solutions the general solution of (28) is then

$$\mathbf{X} = c_1\mathbf{V}_1 \cos \omega_1 t + c_2\mathbf{V}_1 \sin \omega_1 t + c_3\mathbf{V}_2 \cos \omega_2 t + c_4\mathbf{V}_2 \sin \omega_2 t$$
$$= (c_1 \cos \omega_1 t + c_2 \sin \omega_1 t)\mathbf{V}_1 + (c_3 \cos \omega_2 t + c_4 \sin \omega_2 t)\mathbf{V}_2, \tag{31}$$

where $\mathbf{V}_1$ and $\mathbf{V}_2$ are, in turn, real eigenvectors of $\mathbf{A}$ corresponding to λ_1 and λ_2.

The result given in (31) generalizes. If $-\omega_1^2, -\omega_2^2, \dots, -\omega_n^2$ are distinct negative eigenvalues and $\mathbf{V}_1, \mathbf{V}_2, \dots, \mathbf{V}_n$ are corresponding real eigenvectors of the $n \times n$ coefficient matrix $\mathbf{A}$, then the homogeneous second-order system $\mathbf{X}'' = \mathbf{AX}$ has the general solution

$$\mathbf{X} = \sum_{i=1}^{n} (a_i \cos \omega_i t + b_i \sin \omega_i t)\mathbf{V}_i, \tag{32}$$

where a_i and b_i represent arbitrary constants. See Problem 48(b) in Exercises 8.2.

EXERCISES 8.2

Answers to selected odd-numbered problems begin on page ANS-13.

8.2.1 DISTINCT REAL EIGENVALUES

In Problems 1–12 find the general solution of the given system.

1. $\dfrac{dx}{dt} = x + 2y$

$\dfrac{dy}{dt} = 4x + 3y$

2. $\dfrac{dx}{dt} = 2x + 2y$

$\dfrac{dy}{dt} = x + 3y$

3. $\dfrac{dx}{dt} = -4x + 2y$

$\dfrac{dy}{dt} = -\dfrac{5}{2}x + 2y$

4. $\dfrac{dx}{dt} = -\dfrac{5}{2}x + 2y$

$\dfrac{dy}{dt} = \dfrac{3}{4}x - 2y$

5. $\mathbf{X}' = \begin{pmatrix} 10 & -5 \\ 8 & -12 \end{pmatrix}\mathbf{X}$

6. $\mathbf{X}' = \begin{pmatrix} -6 & 2 \\ -3 & 1 \end{pmatrix}\mathbf{X}$

7. $\dfrac{dx}{dt} = x + y - z$

$\dfrac{dy}{dt} = 2y$

$\dfrac{dz}{dt} = y - z$

8. $\dfrac{dx}{dt} = 2x - 7y$

$\dfrac{dy}{dt} = 5x + 10y + 4z$

$\dfrac{dz}{dt} = 5y + 2z$

9. $\mathbf{X}' = \begin{pmatrix} -1 & 1 & 0 \\ 1 & 2 & 1 \\ 0 & 3 & -1 \end{pmatrix}\mathbf{X}$

10. $\mathbf{X}' = \begin{pmatrix} 1 & 0 & 1 \\ 0 & 1 & 0 \\ 1 & 0 & 1 \end{pmatrix}\mathbf{X}$

11. $\mathbf{X}' = \begin{pmatrix} -1 & -1 & 0 \\ \frac{3}{4} & -\frac{3}{2} & 3 \\ \frac{1}{8} & \frac{1}{4} & -\frac{1}{2} \end{pmatrix}\mathbf{X}$

12. $\mathbf{X}' = \begin{pmatrix} -1 & 4 & 2 \\ 4 & -1 & -2 \\ 0 & 0 & 6 \end{pmatrix}\mathbf{X}$

In Problems 13 and 14 solve the given initial-value problem.

13. $\mathbf{X}' = \begin{pmatrix} \frac{1}{2} & 0 \\ 1 & -\frac{1}{2} \end{pmatrix}\mathbf{X}, \quad \mathbf{X}(0) = \begin{pmatrix} 3 \\ 5 \end{pmatrix}$

14. $\mathbf{X}' = \begin{pmatrix} 1 & 1 & 4 \\ 0 & 2 & 0 \\ 1 & 1 & 1 \end{pmatrix}\mathbf{X}, \quad \mathbf{X}(0) = \begin{pmatrix} 1 \\ 3 \\ 0 \end{pmatrix}$

Computer Lab Assignments

In Problems 15 and 16 use a CAS or linear algebra software as an aid in finding the general solution of the given system.

15. $\mathbf{X}' = \begin{pmatrix} 0.9 & 2.1 & 3.2 \\ 0.7 & 6.5 & 4.2 \\ 1.1 & 1.7 & 3.4 \end{pmatrix} \mathbf{X}$

16. $\mathbf{X}' = \begin{pmatrix} 1 & 0 & 2 & -1.8 & 0 \\ 0 & 5.1 & 0 & -1 & 3 \\ 1 & 2 & -3 & 0 & 0 \\ 0 & 1 & -3.1 & 4 & 0 \\ -2.8 & 0 & 0 & 1.5 & 1 \end{pmatrix} \mathbf{X}$

17. (a) Use computer software to obtain the phase portrait of the system in Problem 5. If possible, include arrowheads as in Figure 8.2.2. Also include four half-lines in your phase portrait.

(b) Obtain the Cartesian equations of each of the four half-lines in part (a).

(c) Draw the eigenvectors on your phase portrait of the system.

18. Find phase portraits for the systems in Problems 2 and 4. For each system find any half-line trajectories and include these lines in your phase portrait.

8.2.2 REPEATED EIGENVALUES

In Problems 19–28 find the general solution of the given system.

19.
$$\frac{dx}{dt} = 3x - y$$
$$\frac{dy}{dt} = 9x - 3y$$

20.
$$\frac{dx}{dt} = -6x + 5y$$
$$\frac{dy}{dt} = -5x + 4y$$

21. $\mathbf{X}' = \begin{pmatrix} -1 & 3 \\ -3 & 5 \end{pmatrix} \mathbf{X}$

22. $\mathbf{X}' = \begin{pmatrix} 12 & -9 \\ 4 & 0 \end{pmatrix} \mathbf{X}$

23.
$$\frac{dx}{dt} = 3x - y - z$$
$$\frac{dy}{dt} = x + y - z$$
$$\frac{dz}{dt} = x - y + z$$

24.
$$\frac{dx}{dt} = 3x + 2y + 4z$$
$$\frac{dy}{dt} = 2x + 2z$$
$$\frac{dz}{dt} = 4x + 2y + 3z$$

25. $\mathbf{X}' = \begin{pmatrix} 5 & -4 & 0 \\ 1 & 0 & 2 \\ 0 & 2 & 5 \end{pmatrix} \mathbf{X}$

26. $\mathbf{X}' = \begin{pmatrix} 1 & 0 & 0 \\ 0 & 3 & 1 \\ 0 & -1 & 1 \end{pmatrix} \mathbf{X}$

27. $\mathbf{X}' = \begin{pmatrix} 1 & 0 & 0 \\ 2 & 2 & -1 \\ 0 & 1 & 0 \end{pmatrix} \mathbf{X}$

28. $\mathbf{X}' = \begin{pmatrix} 4 & 1 & 0 \\ 0 & 4 & 1 \\ 0 & 0 & 4 \end{pmatrix} \mathbf{X}$

In Problems 29 and 30 solve the given initial-value problem.

29. $\mathbf{X}' = \begin{pmatrix} 2 & 4 \\ -1 & 6 \end{pmatrix} \mathbf{X}, \quad \mathbf{X}(0) = \begin{pmatrix} -1 \\ 6 \end{pmatrix}$

30. $\mathbf{X}' = \begin{pmatrix} 0 & 0 & 1 \\ 0 & 1 & 0 \\ 1 & 0 & 0 \end{pmatrix} \mathbf{X}, \quad \mathbf{X}(0) = \begin{pmatrix} 1 \\ 2 \\ 5 \end{pmatrix}$

31. Show that the 5×5 matrix

$$\mathbf{A} = \begin{pmatrix} 2 & 1 & 0 & 0 & 0 \\ 0 & 2 & 0 & 0 & 0 \\ 0 & 0 & 2 & 0 & 0 \\ 0 & 0 & 0 & 2 & 1 \\ 0 & 0 & 0 & 0 & 2 \end{pmatrix}$$

has an eigenvalue λ_1 of multiplicity 5. Show that three linearly independent eigenvectors corresponding to λ_1 can be found.

Computer Lab Assignments

32. Find phase portraits for the systems in Problems 20 and 21. For each system find any half-line trajectories and include these lines in your phase portrait.

8.2.3 COMPLEX EIGENVALUES

In Problems 33–44 find the general solution of the given system.

33.
$$\frac{dx}{dt} = 6x - y$$
$$\frac{dy}{dt} = 5x + 2y$$

34.
$$\frac{dx}{dt} = x + y$$
$$\frac{dy}{dt} = -2x - y$$

35.
$$\frac{dx}{dt} = 5x + y$$
$$\frac{dy}{dt} = -2x + 3y$$

36.
$$\frac{dx}{dt} = 4x + 5y$$
$$\frac{dy}{dt} = -2x + 6y$$

37. $\mathbf{X}' = \begin{pmatrix} 4 & -5 \\ 5 & -4 \end{pmatrix} \mathbf{X}$

38. $\mathbf{X}' = \begin{pmatrix} 1 & -8 \\ 1 & -3 \end{pmatrix} \mathbf{X}$

39.
$$\frac{dx}{dt} = z$$
$$\frac{dy}{dt} = -z$$
$$\frac{dz}{dt} = y$$

40.
$$\frac{dx}{dt} = 2x + y + 2z$$
$$\frac{dy}{dt} = 3x + 6z$$
$$\frac{dz}{dt} = -4x - 3z$$

41. $\mathbf{X}' = \begin{pmatrix} 1 & -1 & 2 \\ -1 & 1 & 0 \\ -1 & 0 & 1 \end{pmatrix} \mathbf{X}$

42. $\mathbf{X}' = \begin{pmatrix} 4 & 0 & 1 \\ 0 & 6 & 0 \\ -4 & 0 & 4 \end{pmatrix} \mathbf{X}$

43. $\mathbf{X}' = \begin{pmatrix} 2 & 5 & 1 \\ -5 & -6 & 4 \\ 0 & 0 & 2 \end{pmatrix} \mathbf{X}$ **44.** $\mathbf{X}' = \begin{pmatrix} 2 & 4 & 4 \\ -1 & -2 & 0 \\ -1 & 0 & -2 \end{pmatrix} \mathbf{X}$

In Problems 45 and 46 solve the given initial-value problem.

45. $\mathbf{X}' = \begin{pmatrix} 1 & -12 & -14 \\ 1 & 2 & -3 \\ 1 & 1 & -2 \end{pmatrix} \mathbf{X}, \quad \mathbf{X}(0) = \begin{pmatrix} 4 \\ 6 \\ -7 \end{pmatrix}$

46. $\mathbf{X}' = \begin{pmatrix} 6 & -1 \\ 5 & 4 \end{pmatrix} \mathbf{X}, \quad \mathbf{X}(0) = \begin{pmatrix} -2 \\ 8 \end{pmatrix}$

Computer Lab Assignments

47. Find phase portraits for the systems in Problems 36, 37, and 38.

48. (a) Solve (2) of Section 7.6 using the first method outlined in the *Remarks* (page 323)—that is, express (2) of Section 7.6 as a first-order system of four linear equations. Use a CAS or linear algebra software as an aid in finding eigenvalues and eigenvectors of a 4 × 4 matrix. Then apply the initial conditions to your general solution to obtain (4) of Section 7.6.

   (b) Solve (2) of Section 7.6 using the second method outlined in the *Remarks*—that is, express (2) of Section 7.6 as a second-order system of two linear equations. Assume solutions of the form $\mathbf{X} = \mathbf{V} \sin \omega t$ and $\mathbf{X} = \mathbf{V} \cos \omega t$. Find the eigenvalues and eigenvectors of a 2 × 2 matrix. As in part (a), obtain (4) of Section 7.6.

Discussion Problems

49. Solve each of the following linear systems.

   (a) $\mathbf{X}' = \begin{pmatrix} 1 & 1 \\ 1 & 1 \end{pmatrix} \mathbf{X}$ **(b)** $\mathbf{X}' = \begin{pmatrix} 1 & 1 \\ -1 & -1 \end{pmatrix} \mathbf{X}$

   Find a phase portrait of each system. What is the geometric significance of the line $y = -x$ in each portrait?

50. Consider the 5 × 5 matrix given in Problem 31. Solve the system $\mathbf{X}' = \mathbf{AX}$ without the aid of matrix methods, but write the general solution using matrix notation. Use the general solution as a basis for a discussion of how the system can be solved using the matrix methods of this section. Carry out your ideas.

51. Obtain a Cartesian equation of the curve defined parametrically by the solution of the linear system in Example 6. Identify the curve passing through $(2, -1)$ in Figure 8.2.5 [*Hint*: Compute x^2, y^2, and xy.]

52. Examine your phase portraits in Problem 47. Under what conditions will the phase portrait of a 2 × 2 homogeneous linear system with complex eigenvalues consist of a family of closed curves? consist of a family of spirals? Under what conditions is the origin $(0, 0)$ a repeller? An attractor?

APPENDIX I

GAMMA FUNCTION

Euler's integral definition of the **gamma function** is

$$\Gamma(x) = \int_0^\infty t^{x-1} e^{-t}\, dt. \tag{1}$$

Convergence of the integral requires that $x - 1 > -1$ or $x > 0$. The recurrence relation

$$\Gamma(x + 1) = x\Gamma(x), \tag{2}$$

which we saw in Section 6.3, can be obtained from (1) with integration by parts. Now when $x = 1$, $\Gamma(1) = \int_0^\infty e^{-t}\, dt = 1$, and thus (2) gives

$$\Gamma(2) = 1\Gamma(1) = 1$$

$$\Gamma(3) = 2\Gamma(2) = 2 \cdot 1$$

$$\Gamma(4) = 3\Gamma(3) = 3 \cdot 2 \cdot 1$$

and so on. In this manner it is seen that when n is a positive integer, $\Gamma(n + 1) = n!$. For this reason the gamma function is often called the **generalized factorial function.**

Although the integral form (1) does not converge for $x < 0$, it can be shown by means of alternative definitions that the gamma function is defined for all real and complex numbers *except* $x = -n$, $n = 0, 1, 2, \ldots$. As a consequence, (2) is actually valid for $x \neq -n$. The graph of $\Gamma(x)$, considered as a function of a real variable x, is as given in Figure I.1. Observe that the nonpositive integers correspond to vertical asymptotes of the graph.

In Problems 31 and 32 of Exercises 6.3 we utilized the fact that $\Gamma\left(\frac{1}{2}\right) = \sqrt{\pi}$. This result can be derived from (1) by setting $x = \frac{1}{2}$:

$$\Gamma\left(\tfrac{1}{2}\right) = \int_0^\infty t^{-1/2} e^{-t}\, dt. \tag{3}$$

When we let $t = u^2$, (3) can be written as $\Gamma\left(\frac{1}{2}\right) = 2\int_0^\infty e^{-u^2}\, du$. But $\int_0^\infty e^{-u^2}\, du = \int_0^\infty e^{-v^2}\, dv$, so

$$\left[\Gamma\left(\tfrac{1}{2}\right)\right]^2 = \left(2\int_0^\infty e^{-u^2}\, du\right)\left(2\int_0^\infty e^{-v^2}\, dv\right) = 4\int_0^\infty \int_0^\infty e^{-(u^2+v^2)}\, du\, dv.$$

Switching to polar coordinates $u = r\cos\theta$, $v = r\sin\theta$ enables us to evaluate the double integral:

$$4\int_0^\infty \int_0^\infty e^{-(u^2+v^2)}\, du\, dv = 4\int_0^{\pi/2} \int_0^\infty e^{-r^2} r\, dr\, d\theta = \pi.$$

Hence

$$\left[\Gamma\left(\tfrac{1}{2}\right)\right]^2 = \pi \qquad \text{or} \qquad \Gamma\left(\tfrac{1}{2}\right) = \sqrt{\pi}. \tag{4}$$

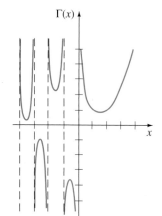

$\Gamma(x)$

FIGURE I.1 Graph of $\Gamma(x)$ for x neither 0 nor a negative integer

| EXAMPLE 1   Value of $\Gamma\left(-\frac{1}{2}\right)$

Evaluate $\Gamma\left(-\frac{1}{2}\right)$.

SOLUTION   In view of (2) and (4) it follows that, with $x = -\frac{1}{2}$,

$$\Gamma\left(\tfrac{1}{2}\right) = -\tfrac{1}{2}\Gamma\left(-\tfrac{1}{2}\right).$$

Therefore $\qquad\qquad \Gamma\left(-\tfrac{1}{2}\right) = -2\Gamma\left(\tfrac{1}{2}\right) = -2\sqrt{\pi}.$ ∎

EXERCISES FOR APPENDIX I

Answers to selected odd-numbered problems begin on page ANS-29.

1. Evaluate.
   (a) $\Gamma(5)$ (b) $\Gamma(7)$
   (c) $\Gamma\left(-\frac{3}{2}\right)$ (d) $\Gamma\left(-\frac{5}{2}\right)$

2. Use (1) and the fact that $\Gamma\left(\frac{6}{5}\right) = 0.92$ to evaluate $\displaystyle\int_0^\infty x^5 e^{-x^5}\,dx.$ [*Hint*: Let $t = x^5$.]

3. Use (1) and the fact that $\Gamma\left(\frac{5}{3}\right) = 0.89$ to evaluate $\displaystyle\int_0^\infty x^4 e^{-x^3}\,dx.$

4. Evaluate $\displaystyle\int_0^1 x^3 \left(\ln\frac{1}{x}\right)^3 dx.$ [*Hint*: Let $t = -\ln x$.]

5. Use the fact that $\Gamma(x) > \displaystyle\int_0^1 t^{x-1} e^{-t}\,dt$ to show that $\Gamma(x)$ is unbounded as $x \to 0^+$.

6. Use (1) to derive (2) for $x > 0$.

EXAMPLE 17   Eigenvalues/Eigenvectors

Find the eigenvalues and eigenvectors of $\mathbf{A} = \begin{pmatrix} 3 & 4 \\ -1 & 7 \end{pmatrix}$.

SOLUTION   From the characteristic equation

$$\det(\mathbf{A} - \lambda\mathbf{I}) = \begin{vmatrix} 3 - \lambda & 4 \\ -1 & 7 - \lambda \end{vmatrix} = (\lambda - 5)^2 = 0$$

we see that $\lambda_1 = \lambda_2 = 5$ is an eigenvalue of multiplicity two. In the case of a 2×2 matrix there is no need to use Gauss-Jordan elimination. To find the eigenvector(s) corresponding to $\lambda_1 = 5$, we resort to the system $(\mathbf{A} - 5\mathbf{I}|\mathbf{0})$ in its equivalent form

$$-2k_1 + 4k_2 = 0$$
$$-k_1 + 2k_2 = 0.$$

It is apparent from this system that $k_1 = 2k_2$. Thus if we choose $k_2 = 1$, we find the single eigenvector

$$\mathbf{K}_1 = \begin{pmatrix} 2 \\ 1 \end{pmatrix}. \qquad \blacksquare$$

EXAMPLE 18   Eigenvalues/Eigenvectors

Find the eigenvalues and eigenvectors of $\mathbf{A} = \begin{pmatrix} 9 & 1 & 1 \\ 1 & 9 & 1 \\ 1 & 1 & 9 \end{pmatrix}$.

SOLUTION   The characteristic equation

$$\det(\mathbf{A} - \lambda\mathbf{I}) = \begin{vmatrix} 9 - \lambda & 1 & 1 \\ 1 & 9 - \lambda & 1 \\ 1 & 1 & 9 - \lambda \end{vmatrix} = -(\lambda - 11)(\lambda - 8)^2 = 0$$

shows that $\lambda_1 = 11$ and that $\lambda_2 = \lambda_3 = 8$ is an eigenvalue of multiplicity two. For $\lambda_1 = 11$ Gauss-Jordan elimination gives

$$(\mathbf{A} - 11\mathbf{I}\,|\,\mathbf{0}) = \begin{pmatrix} -2 & 1 & 1 & | & 0 \\ 1 & -2 & 1 & | & 0 \\ 1 & 1 & -2 & | & 0 \end{pmatrix} \xrightarrow[\text{operations}]{\text{row}} \begin{pmatrix} 1 & 0 & -1 & | & 0 \\ 0 & 1 & -1 & | & 0 \\ 0 & 0 & 0 & | & 0 \end{pmatrix}.$$

Hence $k_1 = k_3$ and $k_2 = k_3$. If $k_3 = 1$, then

$$\mathbf{K}_1 = \begin{pmatrix} 1 \\ 1 \\ 1 \end{pmatrix}.$$

Now for $\lambda_2 = 8$ we have

$$(\mathbf{A} - 8\mathbf{I}\,|\,\mathbf{0}) = \begin{pmatrix} 1 & 1 & 1 & | & 0 \\ 1 & 1 & 1 & | & 0 \\ 1 & 1 & 1 & | & 0 \end{pmatrix} \xrightarrow[\text{operations}]{\text{row}} \begin{pmatrix} 1 & 1 & 1 & | & 0 \\ 0 & 0 & 0 & | & 0 \\ 0 & 0 & 0 & | & 0 \end{pmatrix}.$$

In the equation $k_1 + k_2 + k_3 = 0$ we are free to select two of the variables arbitrarily. Choosing, on the one hand, $k_2 = 1$, $k_3 = 0$ and, on the other, $k_2 = 0$, $k_3 = 1$, we obtain two linearly independent eigenvectors

$$\mathbf{K}_2 = \begin{pmatrix} -1 \\ 1 \\ 0 \end{pmatrix} \quad \text{and} \quad \mathbf{K}_3 = \begin{pmatrix} -1 \\ 0 \\ 1 \end{pmatrix}. \qquad \blacksquare$$

EXERCISES FOR APPENDIX II
Answers to selected odd-numbered problems begin on page ANS-29.

II.1 BASIC DEFINITIONS AND THEORY

1. If $\mathbf{A} = \begin{pmatrix} 4 & 5 \\ -6 & 9 \end{pmatrix}$ and $\mathbf{B} = \begin{pmatrix} -2 & 6 \\ 8 & -10 \end{pmatrix}$, find

(a) $\mathbf{A} + \mathbf{B}$ (b) $\mathbf{B} - \mathbf{A}$ (c) $2\mathbf{A} + 3\mathbf{B}$

2. If $\mathbf{A} = \begin{pmatrix} -2 & 0 \\ 4 & 1 \\ 7 & 3 \end{pmatrix}$ and $\mathbf{B} = \begin{pmatrix} 3 & -1 \\ 0 & 2 \\ -4 & -2 \end{pmatrix}$, find

(a) $\mathbf{A} - \mathbf{B}$ (b) $\mathbf{B} - \mathbf{A}$ (c) $2(\mathbf{A} + \mathbf{B})$

3. If $\mathbf{A} = \begin{pmatrix} 2 & -3 \\ -5 & 4 \end{pmatrix}$ and $\mathbf{B} = \begin{pmatrix} -1 & 6 \\ 3 & 2 \end{pmatrix}$, find

(a) $\mathbf{AB}$ (b) $\mathbf{BA}$ (c) $\mathbf{A}^2 = \mathbf{AA}$ (d) $\mathbf{B}^2 = \mathbf{BB}$

4. If $\mathbf{A} = \begin{pmatrix} 1 & 4 \\ 5 & 10 \\ 8 & 12 \end{pmatrix}$ and $\mathbf{B} = \begin{pmatrix} -4 & 6 & -3 \\ 1 & -3 & 2 \end{pmatrix}$, find

(a) $\mathbf{AB}$ (b) $\mathbf{BA}$

5. If $\mathbf{A} = \begin{pmatrix} 1 & -2 \\ -2 & 4 \end{pmatrix}$, $\mathbf{B} = \begin{pmatrix} 6 & 3 \\ 2 & 1 \end{pmatrix}$, and $\mathbf{C} = \begin{pmatrix} 0 & 2 \\ 3 & 4 \end{pmatrix}$, find

(a) $\mathbf{BC}$ (b) $\mathbf{A}(\mathbf{BC})$ (c) $\mathbf{C}(\mathbf{BA})$ (d) $\mathbf{A}(\mathbf{B} + \mathbf{C})$

6. If $\mathbf{A} = (5 \quad -6 \quad 7)$, $\mathbf{B} = \begin{pmatrix} 3 \\ 4 \\ -1 \end{pmatrix}$, and

$\mathbf{C} = \begin{pmatrix} 1 & 2 & 4 \\ 0 & 1 & -1 \\ 3 & 2 & 1 \end{pmatrix}$, find

(a) $\mathbf{AB}$ (b) $\mathbf{BA}$ (c) $(\mathbf{BA})\mathbf{C}$ (d) $(\mathbf{AB})\mathbf{C}$

7. If $\mathbf{A} = \begin{pmatrix} 4 \\ 8 \\ -10 \end{pmatrix}$ and $\mathbf{B} = (2 \quad 4 \quad 5)$, find

(a) $\mathbf{A}^T\mathbf{A}$ (b) $\mathbf{B}^T\mathbf{B}$ (c) $\mathbf{A} + \mathbf{B}^T$

8. If $\mathbf{A} = \begin{pmatrix} 1 & 2 \\ 2 & 4 \end{pmatrix}$ and $\mathbf{B} = \begin{pmatrix} -2 & 3 \\ 5 & 7 \end{pmatrix}$, find

(a) $\mathbf{A} + \mathbf{B}^T$ (b) $2\mathbf{A}^T - \mathbf{B}^T$ (c) $\mathbf{A}^T(\mathbf{A} - \mathbf{B})$

9. If $\mathbf{A} = \begin{pmatrix} 3 & 4 \\ 8 & 1 \end{pmatrix}$ and $\mathbf{B} = \begin{pmatrix} 5 & 10 \\ -2 & -5 \end{pmatrix}$, find

(a) $(\mathbf{AB})^T$ (b) $\mathbf{B}^T\mathbf{A}^T$

10. If $\mathbf{A} = \begin{pmatrix} 5 & 9 \\ -4 & 6 \end{pmatrix}$ and $\mathbf{B} = \begin{pmatrix} -3 & 11 \\ -7 & 2 \end{pmatrix}$, find

(a) $\mathbf{A}^T + \mathbf{B}^T$ (b) $(\mathbf{A} + \mathbf{B})^T$

In Problems 11–14 write the given sum as a single column matrix.

11. $4\begin{pmatrix} -1 \\ 2 \end{pmatrix} - 2\begin{pmatrix} 2 \\ 8 \end{pmatrix} + 3\begin{pmatrix} -2 \\ 3 \end{pmatrix}$

12. $3t\begin{pmatrix} 2 \\ t \\ -1 \end{pmatrix} + (t-1)\begin{pmatrix} -1 \\ -t \\ 3 \end{pmatrix} - 2\begin{pmatrix} 3t \\ 4 \\ -5t \end{pmatrix}$

13. $\begin{pmatrix} 2 & -3 \\ 1 & 4 \end{pmatrix}\begin{pmatrix} -2 \\ 5 \end{pmatrix} - \begin{pmatrix} -1 & 6 \\ -2 & 3 \end{pmatrix}\begin{pmatrix} -7 \\ 2 \end{pmatrix}$

14. $\begin{pmatrix} 1 & -3 & 4 \\ 2 & 5 & -1 \\ 0 & -4 & -2 \end{pmatrix}\begin{pmatrix} t \\ 2t-1 \\ -t \end{pmatrix} + \begin{pmatrix} -t \\ 1 \\ 4 \end{pmatrix} - \begin{pmatrix} 2 \\ 8 \\ -6 \end{pmatrix}$

In Problems 15–22 determine whether the given matrix is singular or nonsingular. If it is nonsingular, find $\mathbf{A}^{-1}$ using Theorem II.2.

15. $\mathbf{A} = \begin{pmatrix} -3 & 6 \\ -2 & 4 \end{pmatrix}$ **16.** $\mathbf{A} = \begin{pmatrix} 2 & 5 \\ 1 & 4 \end{pmatrix}$

17. $\mathbf{A} = \begin{pmatrix} 4 & 8 \\ -3 & -5 \end{pmatrix}$ **18.** $\mathbf{A} = \begin{pmatrix} 7 & 10 \\ 2 & 2 \end{pmatrix}$

19. $\mathbf{A} = \begin{pmatrix} 2 & 1 & 0 \\ -1 & 2 & 1 \\ 1 & 2 & 1 \end{pmatrix}$ **20.** $\mathbf{A} = \begin{pmatrix} 3 & 2 & 1 \\ 4 & 1 & 0 \\ -2 & 5 & -1 \end{pmatrix}$

21. $\mathbf{A} = \begin{pmatrix} 2 & 1 & 1 \\ 1 & -2 & -3 \\ 3 & 2 & 4 \end{pmatrix}$ **22.** $\mathbf{A} = \begin{pmatrix} 4 & 1 & -1 \\ 6 & 2 & -3 \\ -2 & -1 & 2 \end{pmatrix}$

In Problems 23 and 24 show that the given matrix is nonsingular for every real value of t. Find $\mathbf{A}^{-1}(t)$ using Theorem II.2.

23. $\mathbf{A}(t) = \begin{pmatrix} 2e^{-t} & e^{4t} \\ 4e^{-t} & 3e^{4t} \end{pmatrix}$

24. $\mathbf{A}(t) = \begin{pmatrix} 2e^t \sin t & -2e^t \cos t \\ e^t \cos t & e^t \sin t \end{pmatrix}$

In Problems 25–28 find $d\mathbf{X}/dt$.

25. $\mathbf{X} = \begin{pmatrix} 5e^{-t} \\ 2e^{-t} \\ -7e^{-t} \end{pmatrix}$ **26.** $\mathbf{X} = \begin{pmatrix} \frac{1}{2}\sin 2t - 4\cos 2t \\ -3\sin 2t + 5\cos 2t \end{pmatrix}$

27. $\mathbf{X} = 2\begin{pmatrix} 1 \\ -1 \end{pmatrix}e^{2t} + 4\begin{pmatrix} 2 \\ 1 \end{pmatrix}e^{-3t}$ **28.** $\mathbf{X} = \begin{pmatrix} 5te^{2t} \\ t\sin 3t \end{pmatrix}$

29. Let $\mathbf{A}(t) = \begin{pmatrix} e^{4t} & \cos \pi t \\ 2t & 3t^2 - 1 \end{pmatrix}$. Find

    (a) $\dfrac{d\mathbf{A}}{dt}$ **(b)** $\displaystyle\int_0^2 \mathbf{A}(t)\,dt$ **(c)** $\displaystyle\int_0^t \mathbf{A}(s)\,ds$

30. Let $\mathbf{A}(t) = \begin{pmatrix} \dfrac{1}{t^2 + 1} & 3t \\ t^2 & t \end{pmatrix}$ and $\mathbf{B}(t) = \begin{pmatrix} 6t & 2 \\ 1/t & 4t \end{pmatrix}$. Find

    (a) $\dfrac{d\mathbf{A}}{dt}$ **(b)** $\dfrac{d\mathbf{B}}{dt}$

    (c) $\displaystyle\int_0^1 \mathbf{A}(t)\,dt$ **(d)** $\displaystyle\int_1^2 \mathbf{B}(t)\,dt$

    (e) $\mathbf{A}(t)\mathbf{B}(t)$ **(f)** $\dfrac{d}{dt}\mathbf{A}(t)\mathbf{B}(t)$

    (g) $\displaystyle\int_1^t \mathbf{A}(s)\mathbf{B}(s)\,ds$

II.2 GAUSSIAN AND GAUSS-JORDAN ELIMINATION

In Problems 31–38 solve the given system of equations by either Gaussian elimination or Gauss-Jordan elimination.

31. $\begin{aligned} x + y - 2z &= 14 \\ 2x - y + z &= 0 \\ 6x + 3y + 4z &= 1 \end{aligned}$ **32.** $\begin{aligned} 5x - 2y + 4z &= 10 \\ x + y + z &= 9 \\ 4x - 3y + 3z &= 1 \end{aligned}$

33. $\begin{aligned} y + z &= -5 \\ 5x + 4y - 16z &= -10 \\ x - y - 5z &= 7 \end{aligned}$ **34.** $\begin{aligned} 3x + y + z &= 4 \\ 4x + 2y - z &= 7 \\ x + y - 3z &= 6 \end{aligned}$

35. $\begin{aligned} 2x + y + z &= 4 \\ 10x - 2y + 2z &= -1 \\ 6x - 2y + 4z &= 8 \end{aligned}$ **36.** $\begin{aligned} x + 2z &= 8 \\ x + 2y - 2z &= 4 \\ 2x + 5y - 6z &= 6 \end{aligned}$

37. $\begin{aligned} x_1 + x_2 - x_3 - x_4 &= -1 \\ x_1 + x_2 + x_3 + x_4 &= 3 \\ x_1 - x_2 + x_3 - x_4 &= 3 \\ 4x_1 + x_2 - 2x_3 + x_4 &= 0 \end{aligned}$ **38.** $\begin{aligned} 2x_1 + x_2 + x_3 &= 0 \\ x_1 + 3x_2 + x_3 &= 0 \\ 7x_1 + x_2 + 3x_3 &= 0 \end{aligned}$

In Problems 39 and 40 use Gauss-Jordan elimination to demonstrate that the given system of equations has no solution.

39. $\begin{aligned} x + 2y + 4z &= 2 \\ 2x + 4y + 3z &= 1 \\ x + 2y - z &= 7 \end{aligned}$ **40.** $\begin{aligned} x_1 + x_2 - x_3 + 3x_4 &= 1 \\ x_2 - x_3 - 4x_4 &= 0 \\ x_1 + 2x_2 - 2x_3 - x_4 &= 6 \\ 4x_1 + 7x_2 - 7x_3 &= 9 \end{aligned}$

In Problems 41–46 use Theorem II.3 to find $\mathbf{A}^{-1}$ for the given matrix or show that no inverse exists.

41. $\mathbf{A} = \begin{pmatrix} 4 & 2 & 3 \\ 2 & 1 & 0 \\ -1 & -2 & 0 \end{pmatrix}$ **42.** $\mathbf{A} = \begin{pmatrix} 2 & 4 & -2 \\ 4 & 2 & -2 \\ 8 & 10 & -6 \end{pmatrix}$

43. $\mathbf{A} = \begin{pmatrix} -1 & 3 & 0 \\ 1 & -2 & 1 \\ 0 & 1 & 2 \end{pmatrix}$ **44.** $\mathbf{A} = \begin{pmatrix} 1 & 2 & 3 \\ 0 & 1 & 4 \\ 0 & 0 & 8 \end{pmatrix}$

45. $\mathbf{A} = \begin{pmatrix} 1 & 2 & 3 & 1 \\ -1 & 0 & 2 & 1 \\ 2 & 1 & -3 & 0 \\ 1 & 1 & 2 & 1 \end{pmatrix}$ **46.** $\mathbf{A} = \begin{pmatrix} 1 & 0 & 0 & 0 \\ 0 & 0 & 1 & 0 \\ 0 & 0 & 0 & 1 \\ 0 & 1 & 0 & 0 \end{pmatrix}$

11.3 THE EIGENVALUE PROBLEM

In Problems 47–54 find the eigenvalues and eigenvectors of the given matrix.

47. $\begin{pmatrix} -1 & 2 \\ -7 & 8 \end{pmatrix}$ **48.** $\begin{pmatrix} 2 & 1 \\ 2 & 1 \end{pmatrix}$

49. $\begin{pmatrix} -8 & -1 \\ 16 & 0 \end{pmatrix}$ **50.** $\begin{pmatrix} 1 & 1 \\ \frac{1}{4} & 1 \end{pmatrix}$

51. $\begin{pmatrix} 5 & -1 & 0 \\ 0 & -5 & 9 \\ 5 & -1 & 0 \end{pmatrix}$ **52.** $\begin{pmatrix} 3 & 0 & 0 \\ 0 & 2 & 0 \\ 4 & 0 & 1 \end{pmatrix}$

53. $\begin{pmatrix} 0 & 4 & 0 \\ -1 & -4 & 0 \\ 0 & 0 & -2 \end{pmatrix}$ **54.** $\begin{pmatrix} 1 & 6 & 0 \\ 0 & 2 & 1 \\ 0 & 1 & 2 \end{pmatrix}$

In Problems 55 and 56 show that the given matrix has complex eigenvalues. Find the eigenvectors of the matrix.

55. $\begin{pmatrix} -1 & 2 \\ -5 & 1 \end{pmatrix}$ **56.** $\begin{pmatrix} 2 & -1 & 0 \\ 5 & 2 & 4 \\ 0 & 1 & 2 \end{pmatrix}$

Miscellaneous Problems

57. If $\mathbf{A}(t)$ is a 2×2 matrix of differentiable functions and $\mathbf{X}(t)$ is a 2×1 column matrix of differentiable functions, prove the product rule

$$\frac{d}{dt}[\mathbf{A}(t)\mathbf{X}(t)] = \mathbf{A}(t)\mathbf{X}'(t) + \mathbf{A}'(t)\mathbf{X}(t).$$

58. Derive formula (3). [*Hint*: Find a matrix

$$\mathbf{B} = \begin{pmatrix} b_{11} & b_{12} \\ b_{21} & b_{22} \end{pmatrix}$$

for which $\mathbf{AB} = \mathbf{I}$. Solve for b_{11}, b_{12}, b_{21}, and b_{22}. Then show that $\mathbf{BA} = \mathbf{I}$.]

59. If $\mathbf{A}$ is nonsingular and $\mathbf{AB} = \mathbf{AC}$, show that $\mathbf{B} = \mathbf{C}$.

60. If $\mathbf{A}$ and $\mathbf{B}$ are nonsingular, show that $(\mathbf{AB})^{-1} = \mathbf{B}^{-1}\mathbf{A}^{-1}$.

61. Let $\mathbf{A}$ and $\mathbf{B}$ be $n \times n$ matrices. In general, is

$$(\mathbf{A} + \mathbf{B})^2 = \mathbf{A}^2 + 2\mathbf{AB} + \mathbf{B}^2?$$

62. A square matrix $\mathbf{A}$ is said to be a **diagonal matrix** if all its entries off the main diagonal are zero—that is, $a_{ij} = 0$, $i \neq j$. The entries a_{ii} on the main diagonal may or may not be zero. The multiplicative identity matrix $\mathbf{I}$ is an example of a diagonal matrix.

(a) Find the inverse of the 2×2 diagonal matrix

$$\mathbf{A} = \begin{pmatrix} a_{11} & 0 \\ 0 & a_{22} \end{pmatrix}$$

when $a_{11} \neq 0$, $a_{22} \neq 0$.

(b) Find the inverse of a 3×3 diagonal matrix $\mathbf{A}$ whose main diagonal entries a_{ii} are all nonzero.

(c) In general, what is the inverse of an $n \times n$ diagonal matrix $\mathbf{A}$ whose main diagonal entries a_{ii} are all nonzero?

APPENDIX III

LAPLACE TRANSFORMS

$f(t)$	$\mathscr{L}\{f(t)\} = F(s)$
1. 1	$\dfrac{1}{s}$
2. t	$\dfrac{1}{s^2}$
3. t^n	$\dfrac{n!}{s^{n+1}}$, $\quad n$ a positive integer
4. $t^{-1/2}$	$\sqrt{\dfrac{\pi}{s}}$
5. $t^{1/2}$	$\dfrac{\sqrt{\pi}}{2s^{3/2}}$
6. t^{α}	$\dfrac{\Gamma(\alpha + 1)}{s^{\alpha+1}}$, $\quad \alpha > -1$
7. $\sin kt$	$\dfrac{k}{s^2 + k^2}$
8. $\cos kt$	$\dfrac{s}{s^2 + k^2}$
9. $\sin^2 kt$	$\dfrac{2k^2}{s(s^2 + 4k^2)}$
10. $\cos^2 kt$	$\dfrac{s^2 + 2k^2}{s(s^2 + 4k^2)}$
11. e^{at}	$\dfrac{1}{s - a}$
12. $\sinh kt$	$\dfrac{k}{s^2 - k^2}$
13. $\cosh kt$	$\dfrac{s}{s^2 - k^2}$
14. $\sinh^2 kt$	$\dfrac{2k^2}{s(s^2 - 4k^2)}$
15. $\cosh^2 kt$	$\dfrac{s^2 - 2k^2}{s(s^2 - 4k^2)}$
16. te^{at}	$\dfrac{1}{(s - a)^2}$
17. $t^n e^{at}$	$\dfrac{n!}{(s - a)^{n+1}}$, $\quad n$ a positive integer

$f(t)$	$\mathcal{L}\{f(t)\} = F(s)$
18. $e^{at} \sin kt$	$\dfrac{k}{(s-a)^2 + k^2}$
19. $e^{at} \cos kt$	$\dfrac{s-a}{(s-a)^2 + k^2}$
20. $e^{at} \sinh kt$	$\dfrac{k}{(s-a)^2 - k^2}$
21. $e^{at} \cosh kt$	$\dfrac{s-a}{(s-a)^2 - k^2}$
22. $t \sin kt$	$\dfrac{2ks}{(s^2 + k^2)^2}$
23. $t \cos kt$	$\dfrac{s^2 - k^2}{(s^2 + k^2)^2}$
24. $\sin kt + kt \cos kt$	$\dfrac{2ks^2}{(s^2 + k^2)^2}$
25. $\sin kt - kt \cos kt$	$\dfrac{2k^3}{(s^2 + k^2)^2}$
26. $t \sinh kt$	$\dfrac{2ks}{(s^2 - k^2)^2}$
27. $t \cosh kt$	$\dfrac{s^2 + k^2}{(s^2 - k^2)^2}$
28. $\dfrac{e^{at} - e^{bt}}{a - b}$	$\dfrac{1}{(s-a)(s-b)}$
29. $\dfrac{ae^{at} - be^{bt}}{a - b}$	$\dfrac{s}{(s-a)(s-b)}$
30. $1 - \cos kt$	$\dfrac{k^2}{s(s^2 + k^2)}$
31. $kt - \sin kt$	$\dfrac{k^3}{s^2(s^2 + k^2)}$
32. $\dfrac{a \sin bt - b \sin at}{ab(a^2 - b^2)}$	$\dfrac{1}{(s^2 + a^2)(s^2 + b^2)}$
33. $\dfrac{\cos bt - \cos at}{a^2 - b^2}$	$\dfrac{s}{(s^2 + a^2)(s^2 + b^2)}$
34. $\sin kt \sinh kt$	$\dfrac{2k^2 s}{s^4 + 4k^4}$
35. $\sin kt \cosh kt$	$\dfrac{k(s^2 + 2k^2)}{s^4 + 4k^4}$
36. $\cos kt \sinh kt$	$\dfrac{k(s^2 - 2k^2)}{s^4 + 4k^4}$
37. $\cos kt \cosh kt$	$\dfrac{s^3}{s^4 + 4k^4}$

$f(t)$	$\mathscr{L}\{f(t)\} = F(s)$
38. $J_0(kt)$	$\dfrac{1}{\sqrt{s^2 + k^2}}$
39. $\dfrac{e^{bt} - e^{at}}{t}$	$\ln\dfrac{s - a}{s - b}$
40. $\dfrac{2(1 - \cos kt)}{t}$	$\ln\dfrac{s^2 + k^2}{s^2}$
41. $\dfrac{2(1 - \cosh kt)}{t}$	$\ln\dfrac{s^2 - k^2}{s^2}$
42. $\dfrac{\sin at}{t}$	$\arctan\left(\dfrac{a}{s}\right)$
43. $\dfrac{\sin at \cos bt}{t}$	$\dfrac{1}{2}\arctan\dfrac{a + b}{s} + \dfrac{1}{2}\arctan\dfrac{a - b}{s}$
44. $\dfrac{1}{\sqrt{\pi t}}e^{-a^2/4t}$	$\dfrac{e^{-a\sqrt{s}}}{\sqrt{s}}$
45. $\dfrac{a}{2\sqrt{\pi t^3}}e^{-a^2/4t}$	$e^{-a\sqrt{s}}$
46. $\operatorname{erfc}\left(\dfrac{a}{2\sqrt{t}}\right)$	$\dfrac{e^{-a\sqrt{s}}}{s}$
47. $2\sqrt{\dfrac{t}{\pi}}e^{-a^2/4t} - a\operatorname{erfc}\left(\dfrac{a}{2\sqrt{t}}\right)$	$\dfrac{e^{-a\sqrt{s}}}{s\sqrt{s}}$
48. $e^{ab}e^{b^2 t}\operatorname{erfc}\left(b\sqrt{t} + \dfrac{a}{2\sqrt{t}}\right)$	$\dfrac{e^{-a\sqrt{s}}}{\sqrt{s}(\sqrt{s} + b)}$
49. $-e^{ab}e^{b^2 t}\operatorname{erfc}\left(b\sqrt{t} + \dfrac{a}{2\sqrt{t}}\right)$ $\quad + \operatorname{erfc}\left(\dfrac{a}{2\sqrt{t}}\right)$	$\dfrac{be^{-a\sqrt{s}}}{s(\sqrt{s} + b)}$
50. $e^{at}f(t)$	$F(s - a)$
51. $\mathscr{U}(t - a)$	$\dfrac{e^{-as}}{s}$
52. $f(t - a)\mathscr{U}(t - a)$	$e^{-as}F(s)$
53. $g(t)\mathscr{U}(t - a)$	$e^{-as}\mathscr{L}\{g(t + a)\}$
54. $f^{(n)}(t)$	$s^n F(s) - s^{(n-1)}f(0) - \cdots - f^{(n-1)}(0)$
55. $t^n f(t)$	$(-1)^n\dfrac{d^n}{ds^n}F(s)$
56. $\displaystyle\int_0^t f(\tau)g(t - \tau)\,d\tau$	$F(s)G(s)$
57. $\delta(t)$	1
58. $\delta(t - t_0)$	e^{-st_0}

1 Introduction to Differential Equations

Definitions and Terminology

1. Second order; linear

2. Third order; nonlinear because of $(dy/dx)^4$

3. Fourth order; linear

4. Second order; nonlinear because of $\cos(r+u)$

5. Second order; nonlinear because of $(dy/dx)^2$ or $\sqrt{1+(dy/dx)^2}$

6. Second order; nonlinear because of R^2

7. Third order; linear

8. Second order; nonlinear because of $\dot{x}^2$

9. Writing the differential equation in the form $x(dy/dx) + y^2 = 1$, we see that it is nonlinear in y because of y^2. However, writing it in the form $(y^2 - 1)(dx/dy) + x = 0$, we see that it is linear in x.

10. Writing the differential equation in the form $u(dv/du) + (1+u)v = ue^u$ we see that it is linear in v. However, writing it in the form $(v + uv - ue^u)(du/dv) + u = 0$, we see that it is nonlinear in u.

11. From $y = e^{-x/2}$ we obtain $y' = -\frac{1}{2}e^{-x/2}$. Then $2y' + y = -e^{-x/2} + e^{-x/2} = 0$.

12. From $y = \frac{6}{5} - \frac{6}{5}e^{-20t}$ we obtain $dy/dt = 24e^{-20t}$, so that

$$\frac{dy}{dt} + 20y = 24e^{-20t} + 20\left(\frac{6}{5} - \frac{6}{5}e^{-20t}\right) = 24.$$

13. From $y = e^{3x}\cos 2x$ we obtain $y' = 3e^{3x}\cos 2x - 2e^{3x}\sin 2x$ and $y'' = 5e^{3x}\cos 2x - 12e^{3x}\sin 2x$, so that $y'' - 6y' + 13y = 0$.

14. From $y = -\cos x\ln(\sec x + \tan x)$ we obtain $y' = -1 + \sin x\ln(\sec x + \tan x)$ and $y'' = \tan x + \cos x\ln(\sec x + \tan x)$. Then $y'' + y = \tan x$.

15. The domain of the function, found by solving $x + 2 \geq 0$, is $[-2, \infty)$. From $y' = 1 + 2(x+2)^{-1/2}$ we

1

have

$$(y - x)y' = (y - x)[1 + (2(x + 2)^{-1/2}]$$

$$= y - x + 2(y - x)(x + 2)^{-1/2}$$

$$= y - x + 2[x + 4(x + 2)^{1/2} - x](x + 2)^{-1/2}$$

$$= y - x + 8(x + 2)^{1/2}(x + 2)^{-1/2} = y - x + 8.$$

An interval of definition for the solution of the differential equation is $(-2, \infty)$ because y' is not defined at $x = -2$.

16. Since $\tan x$ is not defined for $x = \pi/2 + n\pi$, n an integer, the domain of $y = 5 \tan 5x$ is $\{x \mid 5x \neq \pi/2 + n\pi\}$ or $\{x \mid x \neq \pi/10 + n\pi/5\}$. From $y' = 25 \sec^2 5x$ we have

$$y' = 25(1 + \tan^2 5x) = 25 + 25 \tan^2 5x = 25 + y^2.$$

An interval of definition for the solution of the differential equation is $(-\pi/10, \pi/10)$. Another interval is $(\pi/10, 3\pi/10)$, and so on.

17. The domain of the function is $\{x \mid 4 - x^2 \neq 0\}$ or $\{x \mid x \neq -2 \text{ or } x \neq 2\}$. From $y' = 2x/(4 - x^2)^2$ we have

$$y' = 2x \left(\frac{1}{4 - x^2}\right)^2 = 2xy.$$

An interval of definition for the solution of the differential equation is $(-2, 2)$. Other intervals are $(-\infty, -2)$ and $(2, \infty)$.

18. The function is $y = 1/\sqrt{1 - \sin x}$, whose domain is obtained from $1 - \sin x \neq 0$ or $\sin x \neq 1$. Thus, the domain is $\{x \mid x \neq \pi/2 + 2n\pi\}$. From $y' = -\frac{1}{2}(1 - \sin x)^{-3/2}(-\cos x)$ we have

$$2y' = (1 - \sin x)^{-3/2} \cos x = [(1 - \sin x)^{-1/2}]^3 \cos x = y^3 \cos x.$$

An interval of definition for the solution of the differential equation is $(\pi/2, 5\pi/2)$. Another interval is $(5\pi/2, 9\pi/2)$ and so on.

19. Writing $\ln(2X - 1) - \ln(X - 1) = t$ and differentiating implicitly we obtain

$$\frac{2}{2X - 1} \frac{dX}{dt} - \frac{1}{X - 1} \frac{dX}{dt} = 1$$

$$\left(\frac{2}{2X - 1} - \frac{1}{X - 1}\right) \frac{dX}{dt} = 1$$

$$\frac{2X - 2 - 2X + 1}{(2X - 1)(X - 1)} \frac{dX}{dt} = 1$$

$$\frac{dX}{dt} = -(2X - 1)(X - 1) = (X - 1)(1 - 2X).$$

Exponentiating both sides of the implicit solution we obtain

$$\frac{2X - 1}{X - 1} = e^t$$

$$2X - 1 = Xe^t - e^t$$

$$(e^t - 1) = (e^t - 2)X$$

$$X = \frac{e^t - 1}{e^t - 2}.$$

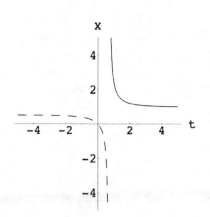

Solving $e^t - 2 = 0$ we get $t = \ln 2$. Thus, the solution is defined on $(-\infty, \ln 2)$ or on $(\ln 2, \infty)$. The graph of the solution defined on $(-\infty, \ln 2)$ is dashed, and the graph of the solution defined on $(\ln 2, \infty)$ is solid.

20. Implicitly differentiating the solution, we obtain

$$-2x^2 \frac{dy}{dx} - 4xy + 2y \frac{dy}{dx} = 0$$

$$-x^2\,dy - 2xy\,dx + y\,dy = 0$$

$$2xy\,dx + (x^2 - y)dy = 0.$$

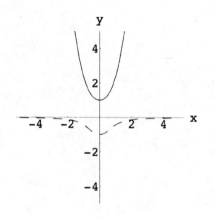

Using the quadratic formula to solve $y^2 - 2x^2y - 1 = 0$ for y, we get $y = (2x^2 \pm \sqrt{4x^4 + 4})/2 = x^2 \pm \sqrt{x^4 + 1}$. Thus, two explicit solutions are $y_1 = x^2 + \sqrt{x^4 + 1}$ and $y_2 = x^2 - \sqrt{x^4 + 1}$. Both solutions are defined on $(-\infty, \infty)$. The graph of $y_1(x)$ is solid and the graph of y_2 is dashed.

21. Differentiating $P = c_1 e^t / \left(1 + c_1 e^t\right)$ we obtain

$$\frac{dP}{dt} = \frac{\left(1 + c_1 e^t\right) c_1 e^t - c_1 e^t \cdot c_1 e^t}{(1 + c_1 e^t)^2} = \frac{c_1 e^t}{1 + c_1 e^t} \frac{\left[\left(1 + c_1 e^t\right) - c_1 e^t\right]}{1 + c_1 e^t}$$

$$= \frac{c_1 e^t}{1 + c_1 e^t}\left[1 - \frac{c_1 e^t}{1 + c_1 e^t}\right] = P(1 - P).$$

22. Differentiating $y = e^{-x^2} \int_0^x e^{t^2}\,dt + c_1 e^{-x^2}$ we obtain

$$y' = e^{-x^2}e^{x^2} - 2xe^{-x^2}\int_0^x e^{t^2}\,dt - 2c_1 xe^{-x^2} = 1 - 2xe^{-x^2}\int_0^x e^{t^2}\,dt - 2c_1 xe^{-x^2}.$$

Substituting into the differential equation, we have

$$y' + 2xy = 1 - 2xe^{-x^2}\int_0^x e^{t^2}\,dt - 2c_1 xe^{-x^2} + 2xe^{-x^2}\int_0^x e^{t^2}\,dt + 2c_1 xe^{-x^2} = 1.$$

23. From $y = c_1 e^{2x} + c_2 x e^{2x}$ we obtain $\dfrac{dy}{dx} = (2c_1 + c_2)e^{2x} + 2c_2 x e^{2x}$ and $\dfrac{d^2 y}{dx^2} = (4c_1 + 4c_2)e^{2x} + 4c_2 x e^{2x}$, so that

$$\frac{d^2 y}{dx^2} - 4\frac{dy}{dx} + 4y = (4c_1 + 4c_2 - 8c_1 - 4c_2 + 4c_1)e^{2x} + (4c_2 - 8c_2 + 4c_2)x e^{2x} = 0.$$

24. From $y = c_1 x^{-1} + c_2 x + c_3 x \ln x + 4x^2$ we obtain

$$\frac{dy}{dx} = -c_1 x^{-2} + c_2 + c_3 + c_3 \ln x + 8x,$$

$$\frac{d^2 y}{dx^2} = 2c_1 x^{-3} + c_3 x^{-1} + 8,$$

and

$$\frac{d^3 y}{dx^3} = -6c_1 x^{-4} - c_3 x^{-2},$$

so that

$$x^3 \frac{d^3 y}{dx^3} + 2x^2 \frac{d^2 y}{dx^2} - x\frac{dy}{dx} + y = (-6c_1 + 4c_1 + c_1 + c_1)x^{-1} + (-c_3 + 2c_3 - c_2 - c_3 + c_2)x$$

$$+ (-c_3 + c_3)x \ln x + (16 - 8 + 4)x^2$$

$$= 12x^2.$$

25. From $y = \begin{cases} -x^2, & x < 0 \\ x^2, & x \geq 0 \end{cases}$ we obtain $y' = \begin{cases} -2x, & x < 0 \\ 2x, & x \geq 0 \end{cases}$ so that $xy' - 2y = 0$.

26. The function $y(x)$ is not continuous at $x = 0$ since $\lim\limits_{x \to 0^-} y(x) = 5$ and $\lim\limits_{x \to 0^+} y(x) = -5$. Thus, $y'(x)$ does not exist at $x = 0$.

27. From $y = e^{mx}$ we obtain $y' = me^{mx}$. Then $y' + 2y = 0$ implies

$$me^{mx} + 2e^{mx} = (m + 2)e^{mx} = 0.$$

Since $e^{mx} > 0$ for all x, $m = -2$. Thus $y = e^{-2x}$ is a solution.

28. From $y = e^{mx}$ we obtain $y' = me^{mx}$. Then $5y' = 2y$ implies

$$5me^{mx} = 2e^{mx} \quad \text{or} \quad m = \frac{2}{5}.$$

Thus $y = e^{2x/5} > 0$ is a solution.

29. From $y = e^{mx}$ we obtain $y' = me^{mx}$ and $y'' = m^2 e^{mx}$. Then $y'' - 5y' + 6y = 0$ implies

$$m^2 e^{mx} - 5me^{mx} + 6e^{mx} = (m - 2)(m - 3)e^{mx} = 0.$$

Since $e^{mx} > 0$ for all x, $m = 2$ and $m = 3$. Thus $y = e^{2x}$ and $y = e^{3x}$ are solutions.

30. From $y = e^{mx}$ we obtain $y' = me^{mx}$ and $y'' = m^2 e^{mx}$. Then $2y'' + 7y' - 4y = 0$ implies

$$2m^2 e^{mx} + 7me^{mx} - 4e^{mx} = (2m - 1)(m + 4)e^{mx} = 0.$$

Since $e^{mx} > 0$ for all x, $m = \frac{1}{2}$ and $m = -4$. Thus $y = e^{x/2}$ and $y = e^{-4x}$ are solutions.

31. From $y = x^m$ we obtain $y' = mx^{m-1}$ and $y'' = m(m-1)x^{m-2}$. Then $xy'' + 2y' = 0$ implies

$$xm(m-1)x^{m-2} + 2mx^{m-1} = [m(m-1) + 2m]x^{m-1} = (m^2 + m)x^{m-1}$$

$$= m(m+1)x^{m-1} = 0.$$

Since $x^{m-1} > 0$ for $x > 0$, $m = 0$ and $m = -1$. Thus $y = 1$ and $y = x^{-1}$ are solutions.

32. From $y = x^m$ we obtain $y' = mx^{m-1}$ and $y'' = m(m-1)x^{m-2}$. Then $x^2y'' - 7xy' + 15y = 0$ implies

$$x^2 m(m-1)x^{m-2} - 7xmx^{m-1} + 15x^m = [m(m-1) - 7m + 15]x^m$$

$$= (m^2 - 8m + 15)x^m = (m-3)(m-5)x^m = 0.$$

Since $x^m > 0$ for $x > 0$, $m = 3$ and $m = 5$. Thus $y = x^3$ and $y = x^5$ are solutions.

In Problems 33–36 we substitute $y = c$ into the differential equations and use $y' = 0$ and $y'' = 0$

33. Solving $5c = 10$ we see that $y = 2$ is a constant solution.

34. Solving $c^2 + 2c - 3 = (c+3)(c-1) = 0$ we see that $y = -3$ and $y = 1$ are constant solutions.

35. Since $1/(c-1) = 0$ has no solutions, the differential equation has no constant solutions.

36. Solving $6c = 10$ we see that $y = 5/3$ is a constant solution.

37. From $x = e^{-2t} + 3e^{6t}$ and $y = -e^{-2t} + 5e^{6t}$ we obtain

$$\frac{dx}{dt} = -2e^{-2t} + 18e^{6t} \quad \text{and} \quad \frac{dy}{dt} = 2e^{-2t} + 30e^{6t}.$$

Then

$$x + 3y = (e^{-2t} + 3e^{6t}) + 3(-e^{-2t} + 5e^{6t}) = -2e^{-2t} + 18e^{6t} = \frac{dx}{dt}$$

and

$$5x + 3y = 5(e^{-2t} + 3e^{6t}) + 3(-e^{-2t} + 5e^{6t}) = 2e^{-2t} + 30e^{6t} = \frac{dy}{dt}.$$

38. From $x = \cos 2t + \sin 2t + \frac{1}{5}e^t$ and $y = -\cos 2t - \sin 2t - \frac{1}{5}e^t$ we obtain

$$\frac{dx}{dt} = -2\sin 2t + 2\cos 2t + \frac{1}{5}e^t \quad \text{and} \quad \frac{dy}{dt} = 2\sin 2t - 2\cos 2t - \frac{1}{5}e^t$$

and

$$\frac{d^2x}{dt^2} = -4\cos 2t - 4\sin 2t + \frac{1}{5}e^t \quad \text{and} \quad \frac{d^2y}{dt^2} = 4\cos 2t + 4\sin 2t - \frac{1}{5}e^t.$$

Then

$$4y + e^t = 4(-\cos 2t - \sin 2t - \frac{1}{5}e^t) + e^t = -4\cos 2t - 4\sin 2t + \frac{1}{5}e^t = \frac{d^2x}{dt^2}$$

and

5

$$4x - e^t = 4(\cos 2t + \sin 2t + \frac{1}{5}e^t) - e^t = 4\cos 2t + 4\sin 2t - \frac{1}{5}e^t = \frac{d^2y}{dt^2}.$$

39. $(y')^2 + 1 = 0$ has no real solutions because $(y')^2 + 1$ is positive for all functions $y = \phi(x)$.

40. The only solution of $(y')^2 + y^2 = 0$ is $y = 0$, since if $y \neq 0$, $y^2 > 0$ and $(y')^2 + y^2 \geq y^2 > 0$.

41. The first derivative of $f(x) = e^x$ is e^x. The first derivative of $f(x) = e^{kx}$ is ke^{kx}. The differential equations are $y' = y$ and $y' = ky$, respectively.

42. Any function of the form $y = ce^x$ or $y = ce^{-x}$ is its own second derivative. The corresponding differential equation is $y'' - y = 0$. Functions of the form $y = c\sin x$ or $y = c\cos x$ have second derivatives that are the negatives of themselves. The differential equation is $y'' + y = 0$.

43. We first note that $\sqrt{1 - y^2} = \sqrt{1 - \sin^2 x} = \sqrt{\cos^2 x} = |\cos x|$. This prompts us to consider values of x for which $\cos x < 0$, such as $x = \pi$. In this case

$$\frac{dy}{dx}\Big|_{x=\pi} = \frac{d}{dx}(\sin x)\Big|_{x=\pi} = \cos x\big|_{x=\pi} = \cos \pi = -1,$$

but

$$\sqrt{1 - y^2}\big|_{x=\pi} = \sqrt{1 - \sin^2 \pi} = \sqrt{1} = 1.$$

Thus, $y = \sin x$ will only be a solution of $y' = \sqrt{1 - y^2}$ when $\cos x > 0$. An interval of definition is then $(-\pi/2, \pi/2)$. Other intervals are $(3\pi/2, 5\pi/2)$, $(7\pi/2, 9\pi/2)$, and so on.

44. Since the first and second derivatives of $\sin t$ and $\cos t$ involve $\sin t$ and $\cos t$, it is plausible that a linear combination of these functions, $A\sin t + B\cos t$, could be a solution of the differential equation. Using $y' = A\cos t - B\sin t$ and $y'' = -A\sin t - B\cos t$ and substituting into the differential equation we get

$$y'' + 2y' + 4y = -A\sin t - B\cos t + 2A\cos t - 2B\sin t + 4A\sin t + 4B\cos t$$

$$= (3A - 2B)\sin t + (2A + 3B)\cos t = 5\sin t.$$

Thus $3A - 2B = 5$ and $2A + 3B = 0$. Solving these simultaneous equations we find $A = \frac{15}{13}$ and $B = -\frac{10}{13}$. A particular solution is $y = \frac{15}{13}\sin t - \frac{10}{13}\cos t$.

45. One solution is given by the upper portion of the graph with domain approximately $(0, 2.6)$. The other solution is given by the lower portion of the graph, also with domain approximately $(0, 2.6)$.

46. One solution, with domain approximately $(-\infty, 1.6)$ is the portion of the graph in the second quadrant together with the lower part of the graph in the first quadrant. A second solution, with domain approximately $(0, 1.6)$ is the upper part of the graph in the first quadrant. The third solution, with domain $(0, \infty)$, is the part of the graph in the fourth quadrant.

47. Differentiating $(x^3 + y^3)/xy = 3c$ we obtain

$$\frac{xy(3x^2 + 3y^2 y') - (x^3 + y^3)(xy' + y)}{x^2 y^2} = 0$$

$$3x^3 y + 3xy^3 y' - x^4 y' - x^3 y - xy^3 y' - y^4 = 0$$

$$(3xy^3 - x^4 - xy^3)y' = -3x^3 y + x^3 y + y^4$$

$$y' = \frac{y^4 - 2x^3 y}{2xy^3 - x^4} = \frac{y(y^3 - 2x^3)}{x(2y^3 - x^3)}.$$

48. A tangent line will be vertical where y' is undefined, or in this case, where $x(2y^3 - x^3) = 0$. This gives $x = 0$ and $2y^3 = x^3$. Substituting $y^3 = x^3/2$ into $x^3 + y^3 = 3xy$ we get

$$x^3 + \frac{1}{2}x^3 = 3x\left(\frac{1}{2^{1/3}}x\right)$$

$$\frac{3}{2}x^3 = \frac{3}{2^{1/3}}x^2$$

$$x^3 = 2^{2/3}x^2$$

$$x^2(x - 2^{2/3}) = 0.$$

Thus, there are vertical tangent lines at $x = 0$ and $x = 2^{2/3}$, or at $(0,0)$ and $(2^{2/3}, 2^{1/3})$. Since $2^{2/3} \approx 1.59$, the estimates of the domains in Problem 46 were close.

49. The derivatives of the functions are $\phi_1'(x) = -x/\sqrt{25 - x^2}$ and $\phi_2'(x) = x/\sqrt{25 - x^2}$, neither of which is defined at $x = \pm 5$.

50. To determine if a solution curve passes through $(0, 3)$ we let $t = 0$ and $P = 3$ in the equation $P = c_1 e^t/(1 + c_1 e^t)$. This gives $3 = c_1/(1 + c_1)$ or $c_1 = -\frac{3}{2}$. Thus, the solution curve

$$P = \frac{(-3/2)e^t}{1 - (3/2)e^t} = \frac{-3e^t}{2 - 3e^t}$$

passes through the point $(0, 3)$. Similarly, letting $t = 0$ and $P = 1$ in the equation for the one-parameter family of solutions gives $1 = c_1/(1 + c_1)$ or $c_1 = 1 + c_1$. Since this equation has no solution, no solution curve passes through $(0, 1)$.

51. For the first-order differential equation integrate $f(x)$. For the second-order differential equation integrate twice. In the latter case we get $y = \int(\int f(x)dx)dx + c_1 x + c_2$.

52. Solving for y' using the quadratic formula we obtain the two differential equations

$$y' = \frac{1}{x}\left(2 + 2\sqrt{1 + 3x^6}\right) \quad \text{and} \quad y' = \frac{1}{x}\left(2 - 2\sqrt{1 + 3x^6}\right),$$

so the differential equation cannot be put in the form $dy/dx = f(x, y)$.

53. The differential equation $yy' - xy = 0$ has normal form $dy/dx = x$. These are not equivalent because $y = 0$ is a solution of the first differential equation but not a solution of the second.

54. Differentiating we get $y' = c_1 + 3c_2x^2$ and $y'' = 6c_2x$. Then $c_2 = y''/6x$ and $c_1 = y' - xy''/2$, so

$$y = \left(y' - \frac{xy''}{2}\right)x + \left(\frac{y''}{6x}\right)x^3 = xy' - \frac{1}{3}x^2y''$$

and the differential equation is $x^2y'' - 3xy' + 3y = 0$.

55. **(a)** Since e^{-x^2} is positive for all values of x, $dy/dx > 0$ for all x, and a solution, $y(x)$, of the differential equation must be increasing on any interval.

(b) $\displaystyle\lim_{x \to -\infty} \frac{dy}{dx} = \lim_{x \to -\infty} e^{-x^2} = 0$ and $\displaystyle\lim_{x \to \infty} \frac{dy}{dx} = \lim_{x \to \infty} e^{-x^2} = 0$. Since dy/dx approaches 0 as x approaches $-\infty$ and ∞, the solution curve has horizontal asymptotes to the left and to the right.

(c) To test concavity we consider the second derivative

$$\frac{d^2y}{dx^2} = \frac{d}{dx}\left(\frac{dy}{dx}\right) = \frac{d}{dx}\left(e^{-x^2}\right) = -2xe^{-x^2}.$$

Since the second derivative is positive for $x < 0$ and negative for $x > 0$, the solution curve is concave up on $(-\infty, 0)$ and concave down on $(0, \infty)$. x

(d)

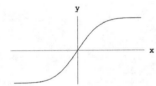

56. **(a)** The derivative of a constant solution $y = c$ is 0, so solving $5 - c = 0$ we see that $c = 5$ and so $y = 5$ is a constant solution.

(b) A solution is increasing where $dy/dx = 5 - y > 0$ or $y < 5$. A solution is decreasing where $dy/dx = 5 - y < 0$ or $y > 5$.

57. **(a)** The derivative of a constant solution is 0, so solving $y(a - by) = 0$ we see that $y = 0$ and $y = a/b$ are constant solutions.

(b) A solution is increasing where $dy/dx = y(a - by) = by(a/b - y) > 0$ or $0 < y < a/b$. A solution is decreasing where $dy/dx = by(a/b - y) < 0$ or $y < 0$ or $y > a/b$.

(c) Using implicit differentiation we compute

$$\frac{d^2y}{dx^2} = y(-by') + y'(a - by) = y'(a - 2by).$$

Solving $d^2y/dx^2 = 0$ we obtain $y = a/2b$. Since $d^2y/dx^2 > 0$ for $0 < y < a/2b$ and $d^2y/dx^2 < 0$ for $a/2b < y < a/b$, the graph of $y = \phi(x)$ has a point of inflection at $y = a/2b$.

(d)

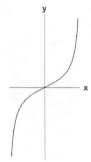

58. **(a)** If $y = c$ is a constant solution then $y' = 0$, but $c^2 + 4$ is never 0 for any real value of c.

   (b) Since $y' = y^2 + 4 > 0$ for all x where a solution $y = \phi(x)$ is defined, any solution must be increasing on any interval on which it is defined. Thus it cannot have any relative extrema.

   (c) Using implicit differentiation we compute $d^2y/dx^2 = 2yy' = 2y(y^2 + 4)$. Setting $d^2y/dx^2 = 0$ we see that $y = 0$ corresponds to the only possible point of inflection. Since $d^2y/dx^2 < 0$ for $y < 0$ and $d^2y/dx^2 > 0$ for $y > 0$, there is a point of inflection where $y = 0$.

   (d)

59. In *Mathematica* use

   Clear[y]
   y[x_]:= x Exp[5x] Cos[2x]
   y[x]
   y''''[x] − 20y'''[x] + 158y''[x] − 580y'[x] +841y[x]//Simplify

   The output will show $y(x) = e^{5x}x\cos 2x$, which verifies that the correct function was entered, and 0, which verifies that this function is a solution of the differential equation.

60. In *Mathematica* use

   Clear[y]
   y[x_]:= 20Cos[5Log[x]]/x − 3Sin[5Log[x]]/x
   y[x]
   x^3 y'''[x] + 2x^2 y''[x] + 20x y'[x] − 78y[x]//Simplify

   The output will show $y(x) = 20\cos(5\ln x)/x - 3\sin(5\ln x)/x$, which verifies that the correct function was entered, and 0, which verifies that this function is a solution of the differential equation.

Exercises 1.2 **Initial-Value Problems**

1. Solving $-1/3 = 1/(1 + c_1)$ we get $c_1 = -4$. The solution is $y = 1/(1 - 4e^{-x})$.

2. Solving $2 = 1/(1 + c_1 e)$ we get $c_1 = -(1/2)e^{-1}$. The solution is $y = 2/(2 - e^{-(x+1)})$.

3. Letting $x = 2$ and solving $1/3 = 1/(4 + c)$ we get $c = -1$. The solution is $y = 1/(x^2 - 1)$. This solution is defined on the interval $(1, \infty)$.

4. Letting $x = -2$ and solving $1/2 = 1/(4 + c)$ we get $c = -2$. The solution is $y = 1/(x^2 - 2)$. This solution is defined on the interval $(-\infty, -\sqrt{2}\,)$.

5. Letting $x = 0$ and solving $1 = 1/c$ we get $c = 1$. The solution is $y = 1/(x^2 + 1)$. This solution is defined on the interval $(-\infty, \infty)$.

6. Letting $x = 1/2$ and solving $-4 = 1/(1/4 + c)$ we get $c = -1/2$. The solution is $y = 1/(x^2 - 1/2) = 2/(2x^2 - 1)$. This solution is defined on the interval $(-1/\sqrt{2}\,, 1/\sqrt{2}\,)$.

In Problems 7–10 we use $x = c_1 \cos t + c_2 \sin t$ and $x' = -c_1 \sin t + c_2 \cos t$ to obtain a system of two equations in the two unknowns c_1 and c_2.

7. From the initial conditions we obtain the system

$$c_1 = -1$$

$$c_2 = 8.$$

The solution of the initial-value problem is $x = -\cos t + 8 \sin t$.

8. From the initial conditions we obtain the system

$$c_2 = 0$$

$$-c_1 = 1.$$

The solution of the initial-value problem is $x = -\cos t$.

9. From the initial conditions we obtain

$$\frac{\sqrt{3}}{2} c_1 + \frac{1}{2} c_2 = \frac{1}{2}$$

$$-\frac{1}{2} c_1 + \frac{\sqrt{3}}{2} c_2 = 0.$$

Solving, we find $c_1 = \sqrt{3}/4$ and $c_2 = 1/4$. The solution of the initial-value problem is $x = (\sqrt{3}/4) \cos t + (1/4) \sin t$.

10

10. From the initial conditions we obtain

$$\frac{\sqrt{2}}{2}c_1 + \frac{\sqrt{2}}{2}c_2 = \sqrt{2}$$

$$-\frac{\sqrt{2}}{2}c_1 + \frac{\sqrt{2}}{2}c_2 = 2\sqrt{2}.$$

Solving, we find $c_1 = -1$ and $c_2 = 3$. The solution of the initial-value problem is $x = -\cos t + 3\sin t$.

In Problems 11–14 we use $y = c_1 e^x + c_2 e^{-x}$ and $y' = c_1 e^x - c_2 e^{-x}$ to obtain a system of two equations in the two unknowns c_1 and c_2.

11. From the initial conditions we obtain

$$c_1 + c_2 = 1$$

$$c_1 - c_2 = 2.$$

Solving, we find $c_1 = \frac{3}{2}$ and $c_2 = -\frac{1}{2}$. The solution of the initial-value problem is $y = \frac{3}{2}e^x - \frac{1}{2}e^{-x}$.

12. From the initial conditions we obtain

$$ec_1 + e^{-1}c_2 = 0$$

$$ec_1 - e^{-1}c_2 = e.$$

Solving, we find $c_1 = \frac{1}{2}$ and $c_2 = -\frac{1}{2}e^2$. The solution of the initial-value problem is
$y = \frac{1}{2}e^x - \frac{1}{2}e^2 e^{-x} = \frac{1}{2}e^x - \frac{1}{2}e^{2-x}$.

13. From the initial conditions we obtain

$$e^{-1}c_1 + ec_2 = 5$$

$$e^{-1}c_1 - ec_2 = -5.$$

Solving, we find $c_1 = 0$ and $c_2 = 5e^{-1}$. The solution of the initial-value problem is $y = 5e^{-1}e^{-x} = 5e^{-1-x}$.

14. From the initial conditions we obtain

$$c_1 + c_2 = 0$$

$$c_1 - c_2 = 0.$$

Solving, we find $c_1 = c_2 = 0$. The solution of the initial-value problem is $y = 0$.

15. Two solutions are $y = 0$ and $y = x^3$.

16. Two solutions are $y = 0$ and $y = x^2$. (Also, any constant multiple of x^2 is a solution.)

17. For $f(x,y) = y^{2/3}$ we have $\dfrac{\partial f}{\partial y} = \dfrac{2}{3}y^{-1/3}$. Thus, the differential equation will have a unique solution in any rectangular region of the plane where $y \neq 0$.

11

18. For $f(x, y) = \sqrt{xy}$ we have $\partial f/\partial y = \frac{1}{2}\sqrt{x/y}$. Thus, the differential equation will have a unique solution in any region where $x > 0$ and $y > 0$ or where $x < 0$ and $y < 0$.

19. For $f(x, y) = \dfrac{y}{x}$ we have $\dfrac{\partial f}{\partial y} = \dfrac{1}{x}$. Thus, the differential equation will have a unique solution in any region where $x \neq 0$.

20. For $f(x, y) = x + y$ we have $\dfrac{\partial f}{\partial y} = 1$. Thus, the differential equation will have a unique solution in the entire plane.

21. For $f(x, y) = x^2/(4 - y^2)$ we have $\partial f/\partial y = 2x^2y/(4 - y^2)^2$. Thus the differential equation will have a unique solution in any region where $y < -2$, $-2 < y < 2$, or $y > 2$.

22. For $f(x, y) = \dfrac{x^2}{1 + y^3}$ we have $\dfrac{\partial f}{\partial y} = \dfrac{-3x^2y^2}{(1 + y^3)^2}$. Thus, the differential equation will have a unique solution in any region where $y \neq -1$.

23. For $f(x, y) = \dfrac{y^2}{x^2 + y^2}$ we have $\dfrac{\partial f}{\partial y} = \dfrac{2x^2y}{(x^2 + y^2)^2}$. Thus, the differential equation will have a unique solution in any region not containing $(0, 0)$.

24. For $f(x, y) = (y + x)/(y - x)$ we have $\partial f/\partial y = -2x/(y - x)^2$. Thus the differential equation will have a unique solution in any region where $y < x$ or where $y > x$.

In Problems 25–28 we identify $f(x, y) = \sqrt{y^2 - 9}$ and $\partial f/\partial y = y/\sqrt{y^2 - 9}$. We see that f and $\partial f/\partial y$ are both continuous in the regions of the plane determined by $y < -3$ and $y > 3$ with no restrictions on x.

25. Since $4 > 3$, $(1, 4)$ is in the region defined by $y > 3$ and the differential equation has a unique solution through $(1, 4)$.

26. Since $(5, 3)$ is not in either of the regions defined by $y < -3$ or $y > 3$, there is no guarantee of a unique solution through $(5, 3)$.

27. Since $(2, -3)$ is not in either of the regions defined by $y < -3$ or $y > 3$, there is no guarantee of a unique solution through $(2, -3)$.

28. Since $(-1, 1)$ is not in either of the regions defined by $y < -3$ or $y > 3$, there is no guarantee of a unique solution through $(-1, 1)$.

29. (a) A one-parameter family of solutions is $y = cx$. Since $y' = c$, $xy' = xc = y$ and $y(0) = c \cdot 0 = 0$.

    (b) Writing the equation in the form $y' = y/x$, we see that R cannot contain any point on the y-axis. Thus, any rectangular region disjoint from the y-axis and containing (x_0, y_0) will determine an

12

interval around x_0 and a unique solution through (x_0, y_0). Since $x_0 = 0$ in part (a), we are not guaranteed a unique solution through $(0, 0)$.

(c) The piecewise-defined function which satisfies $y(0) = 0$ is not a solution since it is not differentiable at $x = 0$.

30. (a) Since $\dfrac{d}{dx} \tan(x + c) = \sec^2(x + c) = 1 + \tan^2(x + c)$, we see that $y = \tan(x + c)$ satisfies the differential equation.

(b) Solving $y(0) = \tan c = 0$ we obtain $c = 0$ and $y = \tan x$. Since $\tan x$ is discontinuous at $x = \pm \pi/2$, the solution is not defined on $(-2, 2)$ because it contains $\pm \pi/2$.

(c) The largest interval on which the solution can exist is $(-\pi/2, \pi/2)$.

31. (a) Since $\dfrac{d}{dx} \left(-\dfrac{1}{x + c} \right) = \dfrac{1}{(x + c)^2} = y^2$, we see that $y = -\dfrac{1}{x + c}$ is a solution of the differential equation.

(b) Solving $y(0) = -1/c = 1$ we obtain $c = -1$ and $y = 1/(1 - x)$. Solving $y(0) = -1/c = -1$ we obtain $c = 1$ and $y = -1/(1 + x)$. Being sure to include $x = 0$, we see that the interval of existence of $y = 1/(1 - x)$ is $(-\infty, 1)$, while the interval of existence of $y = -1/(1 + x)$ is $(-1, \infty)$.

(c) By inspection we see that $y = 0$ is a solution on $(-\infty, \infty)$.

32. (a) Applying $y(1) = 1$ to $y = -1/(x + c)$ gives

$$1 = -\frac{1}{1 + c} \quad \text{or} \quad 1 + c = -1.$$

Thus $c = -2$ and

$$y = -\frac{1}{x - 2} = \frac{1}{2 - x}.$$

(b) Applying $y(3) = -1$ to $y = -1/(x + c)$ gives

$$-1 = -\frac{1}{3 + c} \quad \text{or} \quad 3 + c = 1.$$

Thus $c = -2$ and

$$y = -\frac{1}{x - 2} = \frac{1}{2 - x}.$$

(c) No, they are not the same solution. The interval I of definition for the solution in part (a) is $(-\infty, 2)$; whereas the interval I of definition for the solution in part (b) is $(2, \infty)$. See the figure.

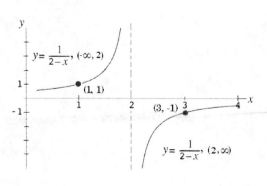

13

33. (a) Differentiating $3x^2 - y^2 = c$ we get $6x - 2yy' = 0$ or $yy' = 3x.$

(b) Solving $3x^2 - y^2 = 3$ for y we get

$$y = \phi_1(x) = \sqrt{3(x^2 - 1)}, \qquad 1 < x < \infty,$$

$$y = \phi_2(x) = -\sqrt{3(x^2 - 1)}, \qquad 1 < x < \infty,$$

$$y = \phi_3(x) = \sqrt{3(x^2 - 1)}, \qquad -\infty < x < -1,$$

$$y = \phi_4(x) = -\sqrt{3(x^2 - 1)}, \qquad -\infty < x < -1.$$

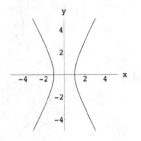

(c) Only $y = \phi_3(x)$ satisfies $y(-2) = 3.$

34. (a) Setting $x = 2$ and $y = -4$ in $3x^2 - y^2 = c$ we get $12 - 16 = -4 = c,$
so the explicit solution is

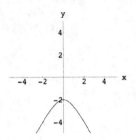

$$y = -\sqrt{3x^2 + 4}, \quad -\infty < x < \infty.$$

(b) Setting $c = 0$ we have $y = \sqrt{3}x$ and $y = -\sqrt{3}x,$ both defined on
$(-\infty, \infty).$

In Problems 35–38 we consider the points on the graphs with x-coordinates $x_0 = -1,$ $x_0 = 0,$ and $x_0 = 1.$ The slopes of the tangent lines at these points are compared with the slopes given by $y'(x_0)$ in (a) through (f).

35. The graph satisfies the conditions in (b) and (f).

36. The graph satisfies the conditions in (e).

37. The graph satisfies the conditions in (c) and (d).

38. The graph satisfies the conditions in (a).

39. Integrating $y' = 8e^{2x} + 6x$ we obtain

$$y = \int (8e^{2x} + 6x)dx = 4e^{2x} + 3x^2 + c.$$

Setting $x = 0$ and $y = 9$ we have $9 = 4 + c$ so $c = 5$ and $y = 4e^{2x} + 3x^2 + 5.$

40. Integrating $y'' = 12x - 2$ we obtain

$$y' = \int (12x - 2)dx = 6x^2 - 2x + c_1.$$

Then, integrating y' we obtain

$$y = \int (6x^2 - 2x + c_1)dx = 2x^3 - x^2 + c_1 x + c_2.$$

At $x = 1$ the y-coordinate of the point of tangency is $y = -1 + 5 = 4$. This gives the initial condition $y(1) = 4$. The slope of the tangent line at $x = 1$ is $y'(1) = -1$. From the initial conditions we obtain

$$2 - 1 + c_1 + c_2 = 4 \qquad \text{or} \qquad c_1 + c_2 = 3$$

and

$$6 - 2 + c_1 = -1 \qquad \text{or} \qquad c_1 = -5.$$

Thus, $c_1 = -5$ and $c_2 = 8$, so $y = 2x^3 - x^2 - 5x + 8$.

41. When $x = 0$ and $y = \frac{1}{2}$, $y' = -1$, so the only plausible solution curve is the one with negative slope at $(0, \frac{1}{2})$, or the black curve.

42. If the solution is tangent to the x-axis at $(x_0, 0)$, then $y' = 0$ when $x = x_0$ and $y = 0$. Substituting these values into $y' + 2y = 3x - 6$ we get $0 + 0 = 3x_0 - 6$ or $x_0 = 2$.

43. The theorem guarantees a unique (meaning single) solution through any point. Thus, there cannot be two distinct solutions through any point.

44. When $y = \frac{1}{16}x^4$, $y' = \frac{1}{4}x^3 = x(\frac{1}{4}x^2) = xy^{1/2}$, and $y(2) = \frac{1}{16}(16) = 1$. When

$$y = \begin{cases} 0, & x < 0 \\ \frac{1}{16}x^4, & x \geq 0 \end{cases}$$

we have

$$y' = \begin{cases} 0, & x < 0 \\ \frac{1}{4}x^3, & x \geq 0 \end{cases} = x \begin{cases} 0, & x < 0 \\ \frac{1}{4}x^2, & x \geq 0 \end{cases} = xy^{1/2},$$

and $y(2) = \frac{1}{16}(16) = 1$. The two different solutions are the same on the interval $(0, \infty)$, which is all that is required by Theorem 1.2.1.

45. At $t = 0$, $dP/dt = 0.15P(0) + 20 = 0.15(100) + 20 = 35$. Thus, the population is increasing at a rate of 3,500 individuals per year.

If the population is 500 at time $t = T$ then

$$\frac{dP}{dt}\bigg|_{t=T} = 0.15P(T) + 20 = 0.15(500) + 20 = 95.$$

Thus, at this time, the population is increasing at a rate of 9,500 individuals per year.

Exercises 1.3

Differential Equations as Mathematical Models

1. $\dfrac{dP}{dt} = kP + r;$ $\qquad$ $\dfrac{dP}{dt} = kP - r$

2. Let b be the rate of births and d the rate of deaths. Then $b = k_1 P$ and $d = k_2 P$. Since $dP/dt = b - d$, the differential equation is $dP/dt = k_1 P - k_2 P$.

3. Let b be the rate of births and d the rate of deaths. Then $b = k_1 P$ and $d = k_2 P^2$. Since $dP/dt = b - d$, the differential equation is $dP/dt = k_1 P - k_2 P^2$.

4. $\dfrac{dP}{dt} = k_1 P - k_2 P^2 - h, \quad h > 0$

5. From the graph in the text we estimate $T_0 = 180°$ and $T_m = 75°$. We observe that when $T = 85$, $dT/dt \approx -1$. From the differential equation we then have

$$k = \frac{dT/dt}{T - T_m} = \frac{-1}{85 - 75} = -0.1.$$

6. By inspecting the graph in the text we take T_m to be $T_m(t) = 80 - 30\cos\pi t/12$. Then the temperature of the body at time t is determined by the differential equation

$$\frac{dT}{dt} = k\left[T - \left(80 - 30\cos\frac{\pi}{12}t\right)\right], \quad t > 0.$$

7. The number of students with the flu is x and the number not infected is $1000 - x$, so $dx/dt = kx(1000 - x)$.

8. By analogy, with the differential equation modeling the spread of a disease, we assume that the rate at which the technological innovation is adopted is proportional to the number of people who have adopted the innovation and also to the number of people, $y(t)$, who have not yet adopted it. Then $x + y = n$, and assuming that initially one person has adopted the innovation, we have

$$\frac{dx}{dt} = kx(n - x), \quad x(0) = 1.$$

9. The rate at which salt is leaving the tank is

$$R_{out}\ (3\ \text{gal/min}) \cdot \left(\frac{A}{300}\ \text{lb/gal}\right) = \frac{A}{100}\ \text{lb/min}.$$

Thus $dA/dt = -A/100$ (where the minus sign is used since the amount of salt is decreasing. The initial amount is $A(0) = 50$.

10. The rate at which salt is entering the tank is

$$R_{in} = (3\ \text{gal/min}) \cdot (2\ \text{lb/gal}) = 6\ \text{lb/min}.$$

Since the solution is pumped out at a slower rate, it is accumulating at the rate of $(3-2)$gal/min $=$ 1 gal/min. After t minutes there are $300 + t$ gallons of brine in the tank. The rate at which salt is leaving is

$$R_{out} = (2 \text{ gal/min}) \cdot \left(\frac{A}{300 + t} \text{ lb/gal} \right) = \frac{2A}{300 + t} \text{ lb/min}.$$

The differential equation is

$$\frac{dA}{dt} = 6 - \frac{2A}{300 + t}.$$

11. The rate at which salt is entering the tank is

$$R_{in} = (3 \text{ gal/min}) \cdot (2 \text{ lb/gal}) = 6 \text{ lb/min}.$$

Since the tank loses liquid at the net rate of

$$3 \text{ gal/min} - 3.5 \text{ gal/min} = -0.5 \text{ gal/min},$$

after t minutes the number of gallons of brine in the tank is $300 - \frac{1}{2}t$ gallons. Thus the rate at which salt is leaving is

$$R_{out} = \left(\frac{A}{300 - t/2} \text{ lb/gal} \right) \cdot (3.5 \text{ gal/min}) = \frac{3.5A}{300 - t/2} \text{ lb/min} = \frac{7A}{600 - t} \text{ lb/min}.$$

The differential equation is

$$\frac{dA}{dt} = 6 - \frac{7A}{600 - t} \quad \text{or} \quad \frac{dA}{dt} + \frac{7}{600 - t} A = 6.$$

12. The rate at which salt is entering the tank is

$$R_{in} = (c_{in} \text{ lb/gal}) \cdot (r_{in} \text{ gal/min}) = c_{in} r_{in} \text{ lb/min}.$$

Now let $A(t)$ denote the number of pounds of salt and $N(t)$ the number of gallons of brine in the tank at time t. The concentration of salt in the tank as well as in the outflow is $c(t) = x(t)/N(t)$. But the number of gallons of brine in the tank remains steady, is increased, or is decreased depending on whether $r_{in} = r_{out}$, $r_{in} > r_{out}$, or $r_{in} < r_{out}$. In any case, the number of gallons of brine in the tank at time t is $N(t) = N_0 + (r_{in} - r_{out})t$. The output rate of salt is then

$$R_{out} = \left(\frac{A}{N_0 + (r_{in} - r_{out})t} \text{ lb/gal} \right) \cdot (r_{out} \text{ gal/min}) = r_{out} \frac{A}{N_0 + (r_{in} - r_{out})t} \text{ lb/min}.$$

The differential equation for the amount of salt, $dA/dt = R_{in} - R_{out}$, is

$$\frac{dA}{dt} = c_{in} r_{in} - r_{out} \frac{A}{N_0 + (r_{in} - r_{out})t} \quad \text{or} \quad \frac{dA}{dt} + \frac{r_{out}}{N_0 + (r_{in} - r_{out})t} A = c_{in} r_{in}.$$

13. The volume of water in the tank at time t is $V = A_w h$. The differential equation is then

$$\frac{dh}{dt} = \frac{1}{A_w} \frac{dV}{dt} = \frac{1}{A_w} \left(-cA_h \sqrt{2gh} \right) = -\frac{cA_h}{A_w} \sqrt{2gh}.$$

Using $A_h = \pi \left(\dfrac{2}{12}\right)^2 = \dfrac{\pi}{36}$, $A_w = 10^2 = 100$, and $g = 32$, this becomes

$$\frac{dh}{dt} = -\frac{c\pi/36}{100}\sqrt{64h} = -\frac{c\pi}{450}\sqrt{h}\,.$$

14. The volume of water in the tank at time t is $V = \frac{1}{3}\pi r^2 h$ where r is the radius of the tank at height h. From the figure in the text we see that $r/h = 8/20$ so that $r = \frac{2}{5}h$ and $V = \frac{1}{3}\pi \left(\frac{2}{5}h\right)^2 h = \frac{4}{75}\pi h^3$. Differentiating with respect to t we have $dV/dt = \frac{4}{25}\pi h^2\, dh/dt$ or

$$\frac{dh}{dt} = \frac{25}{4\pi h^2}\frac{dV}{dt}\,.$$

From Problem 13 we have $dV/dt = -cA_h\sqrt{2gh}$ where $c = 0.6$, $A_h = \pi \left(\frac{2}{12}\right)^2$, and $g = 32$. Thus $dV/dt = -2\pi\sqrt{h}/15$ and

$$\frac{dh}{dt} = \frac{25}{4\pi h^2}\left(-\frac{2\pi\sqrt{h}}{15}\right) = -\frac{5}{6h^{3/2}}\,.$$

15. Since $i = dq/dt$ and $L\,d^2q/dt^2 + R\,dq/dt = E(t)$, we obtain $L\,di/dt + Ri = E(t)$.

16. By Kirchhoff's second law we obtain $R\dfrac{dq}{dt} + \dfrac{1}{C}q = E(t)$.

17. From Newton's second law we obtain $m\dfrac{dv}{dt} = -kv^2 + mg$.

18. Since the barrel in Figure 1.3.16(b) in the text is submerged an additional y feet below its equilibrium position the number of cubic feet in the additional submerged portion is the volume of the circular cylinder: $\pi\times(\text{radius})^2\times\text{height}$ or $\pi(s/2)^2y$. Then we have from Archimedes' principle

upward force of water on barrel = weight of water displaced

$$= (62.4) \times (\text{volume of water displaced})$$

$$= (62.4)\pi(s/2)^2y = 15.6\pi s^2 y.$$

It then follows from Newton's second law that

$$\frac{w}{g}\frac{d^2y}{dt^2} = -15.6\pi s^2 y \qquad \text{or} \qquad \frac{d^2y}{dt^2} + \frac{15.6\pi s^2 g}{w}y = 0,$$

where $g = 32$ and w is the weight of the barrel in pounds.

19. The net force acting on the mass is

$$F = ma = m\frac{d^2x}{dt^2} = -k(s + x) + mg = -kx + mg - ks.$$

Since the condition of equilibrium is $mg = ks$, the differential equation is

$$m\frac{d^2x}{dt^2} = -kx.$$

20. From Problem 19, without a damping force, the differential equation is $m\,d^2x/dt^2 = -kx$. With a damping force proportional to velocity, the differential equation becomes

$$m\frac{d^2x}{dt^2} = -kx - \beta\frac{dx}{dt} \qquad \text{or} \qquad m\frac{d^2x}{dt^2} + \beta\frac{dx}{dt} + kx = 0.$$

21. From $g = k/R^2$ we find $k = gR^2$. Using $a = d^2r/dt^2$ and the fact that the positive direction is upward we get

$$\frac{d^2r}{dt^2} = -a = -\frac{k}{r^2} = -\frac{gR^2}{r^2} \qquad \text{or} \qquad \frac{d^2r}{dt^2} + \frac{gR^2}{r^2} = 0.$$

22. The gravitational force on m is $F = -kM_r m/r^2$. Since $M_r = 4\pi\delta r^3/3$ and $M = 4\pi\delta R^3/3$ we have $M_r = r^3 M/R^3$ and

$$F = -k\frac{M_r m}{r^2} = -k\frac{r^3 Mm/R^3}{r^2} = -k\frac{mM}{R^3}\,r.$$

Now from $F = ma = d^2r/dt^2$ we have

$$m\frac{d^2r}{dt^2} = -k\frac{mM}{R^3}\,r \qquad \text{or} \qquad \frac{d^2r}{dt^2} = -\frac{kM}{R^3}\,r.$$

23. The differential equation is $\dfrac{dA}{dt} = k(M - A)$.

24. The differential equation is $\dfrac{dA}{dt} = k_1(M - A) - k_2 A$.

25. The differential equation is $x'(t) = r - kx(t)$ where $k > 0$.

26. By the Pythagorean Theorem the slope of the tangent line is $y' = \dfrac{-y}{\sqrt{s^2 - y^2}}$.

27. We see from the figure that $2\theta + \alpha = \pi$. Thus

$$\frac{y}{-x} = \tan\alpha = \tan(\pi - 2\theta) = -\tan 2\theta = -\frac{2\tan\theta}{1 - \tan^2\theta}.$$

Since the slope of the tangent line is $y' = \tan\theta$ we have $y/x = 2y'/[1 - (y')^2]$ or $y - y(y')^2 = 2xy'$, which is the quadratic equation $y(y')^2 + 2xy' - y = 0$ in y'. Using the quadratic formula, we get

$$y' = \frac{-2x \pm \sqrt{4x^2 + 4y^2}}{2y} = \frac{-x \pm \sqrt{x^2 + y^2}}{y}.$$

Since $dy/dx > 0$, the differential equation is

$$\frac{dy}{dx} = \frac{-x + \sqrt{x^2 + y^2}}{y} \qquad \text{or} \qquad y\frac{dy}{dx} - \sqrt{x^2 + y^2} + x = 0.$$

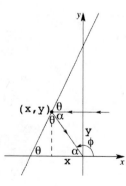

28. The differential equation is $dP/dt = kP$, so from Problem 41 in Exercises 1.1, $P = e^{kt}$, and a one-parameter family of solutions is $P = ce^{kt}$.

Exercises 1.3 Differential Equations as Mathematical Models

29. The differential equation in (3) is $dT/dt = k(T - T_m)$. When the body is cooling, $T > T_m$, so $T - T_m > 0$. Since T is decreasing, $dT/dt < 0$ and $k < 0$. When the body is warming, $T < T_m$, so $T - T_m < 0$. Since T is increasing, $dT/dt > 0$ and $k < 0$.

30. The differential equation in (8) is $dA/dt = 6 - A/100$. If $A(t)$ attains a maximum, then $dA/dt = 0$ at this time and $A = 600$. If $A(t)$ continues to increase without reaching a maximum, then $A'(t) > 0$ for $t > 0$ and A cannot exceed 600. In this case, if $A'(t)$ approaches 0 as t increases to infinity, we see that $A(t)$ approaches 600 as t increases to infinity.

31. This differential equation could describe a population that undergoes periodic fluctuations.

32. (a) As shown in Figure 1.3.22(b) in the text, the resultant of the reaction force of magnitude F and the weight of magnitude mg of the particle is the centripetal force of magnitude $m\omega^2 x$. The centripetal force points to the center of the circle of radius x on which the particle rotates about the y-axis. Comparing parts of similar triangles gives

$$F \cos\theta = mg \quad \text{and} \quad F \sin\theta = m\omega^2 x.$$

(b) Using the equations in part (a) we find

$$\tan\theta = \frac{F \sin\theta}{F \cos\theta} = \frac{m\omega^2 x}{mg} = \frac{\omega^2 x}{g} \quad \text{or} \quad \frac{dy}{dx} = \frac{\omega^2 x}{g}.$$

33. From Problem 21, $d^2r/dt^2 = -gR^2/r^2$. Since R is a constant, if $r = R + s$, then $d^2r/dt^2 = d^2s/dt^2$ and, using a Taylor series, we get

$$\frac{d^2 s}{dt^2} = -g\frac{R^2}{(R+s)^2} = -gR^2(R+s)^{-2} \approx -gR^2[R^{-2} - 2sR^{-3} + \cdots] = -g + \frac{2gs}{R^3} + \cdots.$$

Thus, for R much larger than s, the differential equation is approximated by $d^2s/dt^2 = -g$.

34. (a) If ρ is the mass density of the raindrop, then $m = \rho V$ and

$$\frac{dm}{dt} = \rho\frac{dV}{dt} = \rho\frac{d}{dt}\left[\frac{4}{3}\pi r^3\right] = \rho\left(4\pi r^2\frac{dr}{dt}\right) = \rho S\frac{dr}{dt}.$$

If dr/dt is a constant, then $dm/dt = kS$ where $\rho\, dr/dt = k$ or $dr/dt = k/\rho$. Since the radius is decreasing, $k < 0$. Solving $dr/dt = k/\rho$ we get $r = (k/\rho)t + c_0$. Since $r(0) = r_0$, $c_0 = r_0$ and $r = kt/\rho + r_0$.

(b) From Newton's second law, $\dfrac{d}{dt}[mv] = mg$, where v is the velocity of the raindrop. Then

$$m\frac{dv}{dt} + v\frac{dm}{dt} = mg \quad \text{or} \quad \rho\left(\frac{4}{3}\pi r^3\right)\frac{dv}{dt} + v(k4\pi r^2) = \rho\left(\frac{4}{3}\pi r^3\right)g.$$

Dividing by $4\rho\pi r^3/3$ we get

$$\frac{dv}{dt} + \frac{3k}{\rho r}v = g \quad \text{or} \quad \frac{dv}{dt} + \frac{3k/\rho}{kt/\rho + r_0}v = g, \quad k < 0.$$

35. We assume that the plow clears snow at a constant rate of k cubic miles per hour. Let t be the time in hours after noon, $x(t)$ the depth in miles of the snow at time t, and $y(t)$ the distance the plow has moved in t hours. Then dy/dt is the velocity of the plow and the assumption gives

$$wx\frac{dy}{dt} = k,$$

where w is the width of the plow. Each side of this equation simply represents the volume of snow plowed in one hour. Now let t_0 be the number of hours before noon when it started snowing and let s be the constant rate in miles per hour at which x increases. Then for $t > -t_0$, $x = s(t + t_0)$. The differential equation then becomes

$$\frac{dy}{dt} = \frac{k}{ws}\frac{1}{t + t_0}.$$

Integrating, we obtain

$$y = \frac{k}{ws}\left[\ln(t + t_0) + c\right]$$

where c is a constant. Now when $t = 0$, $y = 0$ so $c = -\ln t_0$ and

$$y = \frac{k}{ws}\ln\left(1 + \frac{t}{t_0}\right).$$

Finally, from the fact that when $t = 1$, $y = 2$ and when $t = 2$, $y = 3$, we obtain

$$\left(1 + \frac{2}{t_0}\right)^2 = \left(1 + \frac{1}{t_0}\right)^3.$$

Expanding and simplifying gives $t_0^2 + t_0 - 1 = 0$. Since $t_0 > 0$, we find $t_0 \approx 0.618$ hours $\approx$ 37 minutes. Thus it started snowing at about 11:23 in the morning.

36. (1): $\dfrac{dP}{dt} = kP$ is linear

(2): $\dfrac{dA}{dt} = kA$ is linear

(3): $\dfrac{dT}{dt} = k(T - T_m)$ is linear

(5): $\dfrac{dx}{dt} = kx(n + 1 - x)$ is nonlinear

(6): $\dfrac{dX}{dt} = k(\alpha - X)(\beta - X)$ is nonlinear

(8): $\dfrac{dA}{dt} = 6 - \dfrac{A}{100}$ is linear

(10): $\dfrac{dh}{dt} = -\dfrac{A_h}{A_w}\sqrt{2gh}$ is nonlinear

(11): $L\dfrac{d^2q}{dt^2} + R\dfrac{dq}{dt} + \dfrac{1}{C}q = E(t)$ is linear

(12): $\dfrac{d^2s}{dt^2} = -g$ is linear

(14): $m\dfrac{dv}{dt} = mg - kv$ is linear

(15): $m\dfrac{d^2s}{dt^2} + k\dfrac{ds}{dt} = mg$ is linear

(16): linearity or nonlinearity is determined by the manner in which W and T_1 involve x.

Chapter 1 in Review

Chapter 1 in Review

1. $\dfrac{d}{dx} c_1 e^{10x} = 10c_1 e^{10x}; \qquad \dfrac{dy}{dx} = 10y$

2. $\dfrac{d}{dx}(5 + c_1 e^{-2x}) = -2c_1 e^{-2x} = -2(5 + c_1 e^{-2x} - 5); \qquad \dfrac{dy}{dx} = -2(y - 5) \quad \text{or} \quad \dfrac{dy}{dx} = -2y + 10$

3. $\dfrac{d}{dx}(c_1 \cos kx + c_2 \sin kx) = -kc_1 \sin kx + kc_2 \cos kx;$

   $\dfrac{d^2}{dx^2}(c_1 \cos kx + c_2 \sin kx) = -k^2 c_1 \cos kx - k^2 c_2 \sin kx = -k^2(c_1 \cos kx + c_2 \sin kx);$

   $\dfrac{d^2 y}{dx^2} = -k^2 y \quad \text{or} \quad \dfrac{d^2 y}{dx^2} + k^2 y = 0$

4. $\dfrac{d}{dx}(c_1 \cosh kx + c_2 \sinh kx) = kc_1 \sinh kx + kc_2 \cosh kx;$

   $\dfrac{d^2}{dx^2}(c_1 \cosh kx + c_2 \sinh kx) = k^2 c_1 \cosh kx + k^2 c_2 \sinh kx = k^2(c_1 \cosh kx + c_2 \sinh kx);$

   $\dfrac{d^2 y}{dx^2} = k^2 y \quad \text{or} \quad \dfrac{d^2 y}{dx^2} - k^2 y = 0$

5. $y = c_1 e^x + c_2 x e^x; \qquad y' = c_1 e^x + c_2 x e^x + c_2 e^x; \qquad y'' = c_1 e^x + c_2 x e^x + 2c_2 e^x;$

   $y'' + y = 2(c_1 e^x + c_2 x e^x) + 2c_2 e^x = 2(c_1 e^x + c_2 x e^x + c_2 e^x) = 2y'; \qquad y'' - 2y' + y = 0$

6. $y' = -c_1 e^x \sin x + c_1 e^x \cos x + c_2 e^x \cos x + c_2 e^x \sin x;$

   $y'' = -c_1 e^x \cos x - c_1 e^x \sin x - c_1 e^x \sin x + c_1 e^x \cos x - c_2 e^x \sin x + c_2 e^x \cos x + c_2 e^x \cos x + c_2 e^x \sin x$

   $\qquad = -2c_1 e^x \sin x + 2c_2 e^x \cos x;$

   $y'' - 2y' = -2c_1 e^x \cos x - 2c_2 e^x \sin x = -2y; \qquad y'' - 2y' + 2y = 0$

7. a,d   8. c   9. b   10. a,c   11. b   12. a,b,d

13. A few solutions are $y = 0$, $y = c$, and $y = e^x$.

14. Easy solutions to see are $y = 0$ and $y = 3$.

15. The slope of the tangent line at (x, y) is y', so the differential equation is $y' = x^2 + y^2$.

16. The rate at which the slope changes is $dy'/dx = y''$, so the differential equation is $y'' = -y'$ or $y'' + y' = 0$.

17. (a) The domain is all real numbers.

    (b) Since $y' = 2/3x^{1/3}$, the solution $y = x^{2/3}$ is undefined at $x = 0$. This function is a solution of the differential equation on $(-\infty, 0)$ and also on $(0, \infty)$.

18. (a) Differentiating $y^2 - 2y = x^2 - x + c$ we obtain $2yy' - 2y' = 2x - 1$ or $(2y - 2)y' = 2x - 1$.

(b) Setting $x = 0$ and $y = 1$ in the solution we have $1 - 2 = 0 - 0 + c$ or $c = -1$. Thus, a solution of the initial-value problem is $y^2 - 2y = x^2 - x - 1$.

(c) Solving $y^2 - 2y - (x^2 - x - 1) = 0$ by the quadratic formula we get $y = (2 \pm \sqrt{4 + 4(x^2 - x - 1)})/2$
$= 1 \pm \sqrt{x^2 - x} = 1 \pm \sqrt{x(x - 1)}$. Since $x(x - 1) \geq 0$ for $x \leq 0$ or $x \geq 1$, we see that neither $y = 1 + \sqrt{x(x - 1)}$ nor $y = 1 - \sqrt{x(x - 1)}$ is differentiable at $x = 0$. Thus, both functions are solutions of the differential equation, but neither is a solution of the initial-value problem.

19. Setting $x = x_0$ and $y = 1$ in $y = -2/x + x$, we get

$$1 = -\frac{2}{x_0} + x_0 \qquad \text{or} \qquad x_0^2 - x_0 - 2 = (x_0 - 2)(x_0 + 1) = 0.$$

Thus, $x_0 = 2$ or $x_0 = -1$. Since $x = 0$ in $y = -2/x + x$, we see that $y = -2/x + x$ is a solution of the initial-value problem $xy' + y = 2x$, $y(-1) = 1$, on the interval $(-\infty, 0)$ and $y = -2/x + x$ is a solution of the initial-value problem $xy' + y = 2x$, $y(2) = 1$, on the interval $(0, \infty)$.

20. From the differential equation, $y'(1) = 1^2 + [y(1)]^2 = 1 + (-1)^2 = 2 > 0$, so $y(x)$ is increasing in some neighborhood of $x = 1$. From $y'' = 2x + 2yy'$ we have $y''(1) = 2(1) + 2(-1)(2) = -2 < 0$, so $y(x)$ is concave down in some neighborhood of $x = 1$.

21. (a)

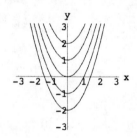 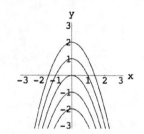

$$y = x^2 + c_1 \qquad\qquad\qquad y = -x^2 + c_2$$

(b) When $y = x^2 + c_1$, $y' = 2x$ and $(y')^2 = 4x^2$. When $y = -x^2 + c_2$, $y' = -2x$ and $(y')^2 = 4x^2$.

(c) Pasting together x^2, $x \geq 0$, and $-x^2$, $x \leq 0$, we get $y = \begin{cases} -x^2, & x \leq 0 \\ x^2, & x > 0. \end{cases}$

22. The slope of the tangent line is $y'\,|_{(-1,4)} = 6\sqrt{4} + 5(-1)^3 = 7$.

23. Differentiating $y = x\sin x + x\cos x$ we get

$$y' = x\cos x + \sin x - x\sin x + \cos x$$

and

$$y'' = -x\sin x + \cos x + \cos x - x\cos x - \sin x - \sin x$$

$$= -x\sin x - x\cos x + 2\cos x - 2\sin x.$$

Thus

$$y'' + y = -x \sin x - x \cos x + 2 \cos x - 2 \sin x + x \sin x + x \cos x = 2 \cos x - 2 \sin x.$$

An interval of definition for the solution is $(-\infty, \infty)$.

24. Differentiating $y = x \sin x + (\cos x) \ln(\cos x)$ we get

$$y' = x \cos x + \sin x + \cos x \left(\frac{-\sin x}{\cos x} \right) - (\sin x) \ln(\cos x)$$

$$= x \cos x + \sin x - \sin x - (\sin x) \ln(\cos x)$$

$$= x \cos x - (\sin x) \ln(\cos x)$$

and

$$y'' = -x \sin x + \cos x - \sin x \left(\frac{-\sin x}{\cos x} \right) - (\cos x) \ln(\cos x)$$

$$= -x \sin x + \cos x + \frac{\sin^2 x}{\cos x} - (\cos x) \ln(\cos x)$$

$$= -x \sin x + \cos x + \frac{1 - \cos^2 x}{\cos x} - (\cos x) \ln(\cos x)$$

$$= -x \sin x + \cos x + \sec x - \cos x - (\cos x) \ln(\cos x)$$

$$= -x \sin x + \sec x - (\cos x) \ln(\cos x).$$

Thus

$$y'' + y = -x \sin x + \sec x - (\cos x) \ln(\cos x) + x \sin x + (\cos x) \ln(\cos x) = \sec x.$$

To obtain an interval of definition we note that the domain of $\ln x$ is $(0, \infty)$, so we must have $\cos x > 0$. Thus, an interval of definition is $(-\pi/2, \pi/2)$.

25. Differentiating $y = \sin(\ln x)$ we obtain $y' = \cos(\ln x)/x$ and $y'' = -[\sin(\ln x) + \cos(\ln x)]/x^2$. Then

$$x^2 y'' + x y' + y = x^2 \left(-\frac{\sin(\ln x) + \cos(\ln x)}{x^2} \right) + x \frac{\cos(\ln x)}{x} + \sin(\ln x) = 0.$$

An interval of definition for the solution is $(0, \infty)$.

26. Differentiating $y = \cos(\ln x) \ln(\cos(\ln x)) + (\ln x) \sin(\ln x)$ we obtain

$$y' = \cos(\ln x) \frac{1}{\cos(\ln x)} \left(-\frac{\sin(\ln x)}{x} \right) + \ln(\cos(\ln x)) \left(-\frac{\sin(\ln x)}{x} \right) + \ln x \frac{\cos(\ln x)}{x} + \frac{\sin(\ln x)}{x}$$

$$= -\frac{\ln(\cos(\ln x)) \sin(\ln x)}{x} + \frac{(\ln x) \cos(\ln x)}{x}$$

and

$$y'' = -x\left[\ln(\cos(\ln x))\frac{\cos(\ln x)}{x} + \sin(\ln x)\frac{1}{\cos(\ln x)}\left(-\frac{\sin(\ln x)}{x}\right)\right]\frac{1}{x^2}$$

$$+ \ln(\cos(\ln x))\sin(\ln x)\frac{1}{x^2} + x\left[(\ln x)\left(-\frac{\sin(\ln x)}{x}\right) + \frac{\cos(\ln x)}{x}\right]\frac{1}{x^2} - (\ln x)\cos(\ln x)\frac{1}{x^2}$$

$$= \frac{1}{x^2}\left[-\ln(\cos(\ln x))\cos(\ln x) + \frac{\sin^2(\ln x)}{\cos(\ln x)} + \ln(\cos(\ln x))\sin(\ln x)\right.$$

$$\left. - (\ln x)\sin(\ln x) + \cos(\ln x) - (\ln x)\cos(\ln x)\right].$$

Then

$$x^2 y'' + xy' + y = -\ln(\cos(\ln x))\cos(\ln x) + \frac{\sin^2(\ln x)}{\cos(\ln x)} + \ln(\cos(\ln x))\sin(\ln x) - (\ln x)\sin(\ln x)$$

$$+ \cos(\ln x) - (\ln x)\cos(\ln x) - \ln(\cos(\ln x))\sin(\ln x)$$

$$+ (\ln x)\cos(\ln x) + \cos(\ln x)\ln(\cos(\ln x)) + (\ln x)\sin(\ln x)$$

$$= \frac{\sin^2(\ln x)}{\cos(\ln x)} + \cos(\ln x) = \frac{\sin^2(\ln x) + \cos^2(\ln x)}{\cos(\ln x)} = \frac{1}{\cos(\ln x)} = \sec(\ln x).$$

To obtain an interval of definition, we note that the domain of $\ln x$ is $(0, \infty)$, so we must have $\cos(\ln x) > 0$. Since $\cos x > 0$ when $-\pi/2 < x < \pi/2$, we require $-\pi/2 < \ln x < \pi/2$. Since e^x is an increasing function, this is equivalent to $e^{-\pi/2} < x < e^{\pi/2}$. Thus, an interval of definition is $(e^{-\pi/2}, e^{\pi/2})$. (Much of this problem is more easily done using a computer algebra system such as *Mathematica* or *Maple*.)

In Problems 27 – 30 we have $y' = 3c_1 e^{3x} - c_2 e^{-x} - 2$.

27. The initial conditions imply

$$c_1 + c_2 = 0$$

$$3c_1 - c_2 - 2 = 0,$$

so $c_1 = \frac{1}{2}$ and $c_2 = -\frac{1}{2}$. Thus $y = \frac{1}{2}e^{3x} - \frac{1}{2}e^{-x} - 2x$.

28. The initial conditions imply

$$c_1 + c_2 = 1$$

$$3c_1 - c_2 - 2 = -3,$$

so $c_1 = 0$ and $c_2 = 1$. Thus $y = e^{-x} - 2x$.

Chapter 1 in Review

29. The initial conditions imply

$$c_1 e^3 + c_2 e^{-1} - 2 = 4$$

$$3c_1 e^3 - c_2 e^{-1} - 2 = -2,$$

so $c_1 = \frac{3}{2}e^{-3}$ and $c_2 = \frac{9}{2}e$. Thus $y = \frac{3}{2}e^{3x-3} + \frac{9}{2}e^{-x+1} - 2x$.

30. The initial conditions imply

$$c_1 e^{-3} + c_2 e + 2 = 0$$

$$3c_1 e^{-3} - c_2 e - 2 = 1,$$

so $c_1 = \frac{1}{4}e^3$ and $c_2 = -\frac{9}{4}e^{-1}$. Thus $y = \frac{1}{4}e^{3x+3} - \frac{9}{4}e^{-x-1} - 2x$.

31. From the graph we see that estimates for y_0 and y_1 are $y_0 = -3$ and $y_1 = 0$.

32. The differential equation is

$$\frac{dh}{dt} = -\frac{cA_0}{A_w}\sqrt{2gh}\,.$$

Using $A_0 = \pi(1/24)^2 = \pi/576$, $A_w = \pi(2)^2 = 4\pi$, and $g = 32$, this becomes

$$\frac{dh}{dt} = -\frac{c\pi/576}{4\pi}\sqrt{64h} = \frac{c}{288}\sqrt{h}\,.$$

33. Let $P(t)$ be the number of owls present at time t. Then $dP/dt = k(P - 200 + 10t)$.

34. Setting $A'(t) = -0.002$ and solving $A'(t) = -0.0004332A(t)$ for $A(t)$, we obtain

$$A(t) = \frac{A'(t)}{-0.0004332} = \frac{-0.002}{-0.0004332} \approx 4.6 \text{ grams.}$$

2 First-Order Differential Equations

Exercises 2.1

Solution Curves Without a Solution

1.

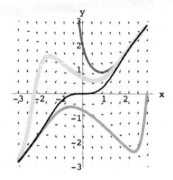

2.

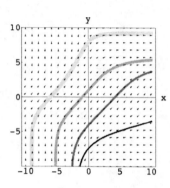

3.

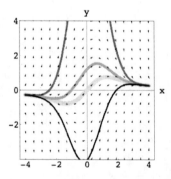

4.

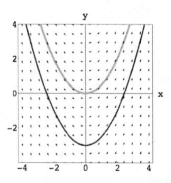

5.

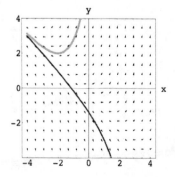

6.

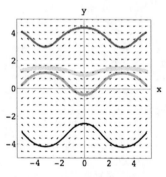

Exercises 2.1 Solution Curves Without a Solution

7.

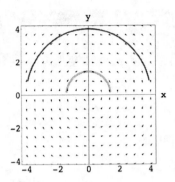

8.

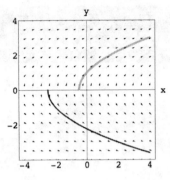

9.

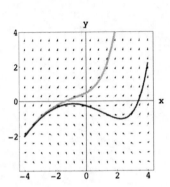

10.

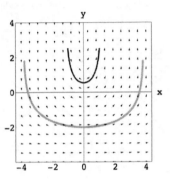

11.

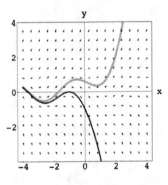

12.

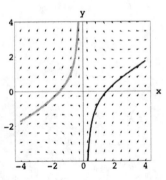

13.

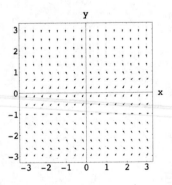

14.

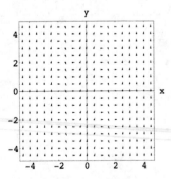

28

15. (a) The isoclines have the form $y = -x + c$, which are straight lines with slope -1.

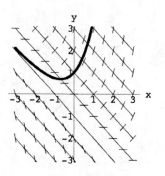

(b) The isoclines have the form $x^2 + y^2 = c$, which are circles centered at the origin.

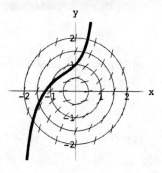

16. (a) When $x = 0$ or $y = 4$, $dy/dx = -2$ so the lineal elements have slope -2. When $y = 3$ or $y = 5$, $dy/dx = x - 2$, so the lineal elements at $(x, 3)$ and $(x, 5)$ have slopes $x - 2$.

(b) At $(0, y_0)$ the solution curve is headed down. If $y \to \infty$ as x increases, the graph must eventually turn around and head up, but while heading up it can never cross $y = 4$ where a tangent line to a solution curve must have slope -2. Thus, y cannot approach ∞ as x approaches ∞.

17. When $y < \frac{1}{2}x^2$, $y' = x^2 - 2y$ is positive and the portions of solution curves "outside" the nullcline parabola are increasing. When $y > \frac{1}{2}x^2$, $y' = x^2 - 2y$ is negative and the portions of the solution curves "inside" the nullcline parabola are decreasing.

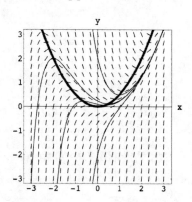

18. (a) Any horizontal lineal element should be at a point on a nullcline. In Problem 1 the nullclines are $x^2 - y^2 = 0$ or $y = \pm x$. In Problem 3 the nullclines are $1 - xy = 0$ or $y = 1/x$. In Problem 4 the nullclines are $(\sin x) \cos y = 0$ or $x = n\pi$ and $y = \pi/2 + n\pi$, where n is an integer. The graphs on the next page show the nullclines for the differential equations in Problems 1, 3, and 4 superimposed on the corresponding direction field.

Exercises 2.1 Solution Curves Without a Solution

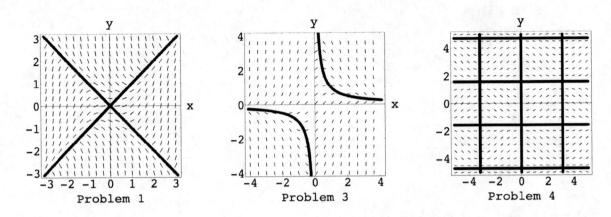

Problem 1   Problem 3   Problem 4

(b) An autonomous first-order differential equation has the form $y' = f(y)$. Nullclines have the form $y = c$ where $f(c) = 0$. These are the graphs of the equilibrium solutions of the differential equation.

19. Writing the differential equation in the form $dy/dx = y(1 - y)(1 + y)$ we see that critical points are located at $y = -1$, $y = 0$, and $y = 1$. The phase portrait is shown at the right.

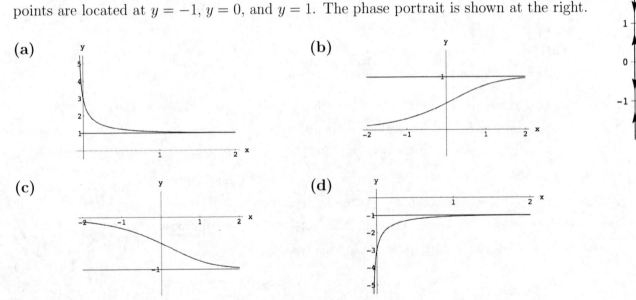

(a)

(b)

(c)

(d)

20. Writing the differential equation in the form $dy/dx = y^2(1 - y)(1 + y)$ we see that critical points are located at $y = -1$, $y = 0$, and $y = 1$. The phase portrait is shown at the right.

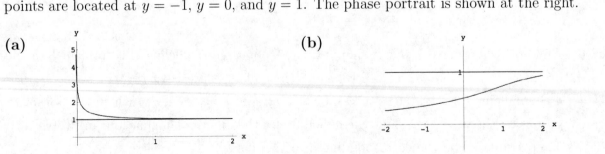

(a)

(b)

(c) 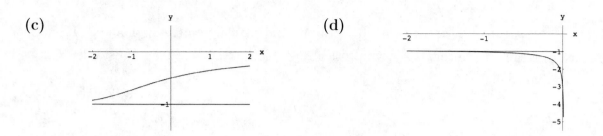 (d)

21. Solving $y^2 - 3y = y(y - 3) = 0$ we obtain the critical points 0 and 3. From the phase portrait we see that 0 is asymptotically stable (attractor) and 3 is unstable (repeller).

22. Solving $y^2 - y^3 = y^2(1 - y) = 0$ we obtain the critical points 0 and 1. From the phase portrait we see that 1 is asymptotically stable (attractor) and 0 is semi-stable.

23. Solving $(y - 2)^4 = 0$ we obtain the critical point 2. From the phase portrait we see that 2 is semi-stable.

24. Solving $10 + 3y - y^2 = (5 - y)(2 + y) = 0$ we obtain the critical points -2 and 5. From the phase portrait we see that 5 is asymptotically stable (attractor) and -2 is unstable (repeller).

25. Solving $y^2(4-y^2) = y^2(2-y)(2+y) = 0$ we obtain the critical points -2, 0, and 2. From the phase portrait we see that 2 is asymptotically stable (attractor), 0 is semi-stable, and -2 is unstable (repeller).

26. Solving $y(2-y)(4-y) = 0$ we obtain the critical points 0, 2, and 4. From the phase portrait we see that 2 is asymptotically stable (attractor) and 0 and 4 are unstable (repellers).

27. Solving $y\ln(y+2) = 0$ we obtain the critical points -1 and 0. From the phase portrait we see that -1 is asymptotically stable (attractor) and 0 is unstable (repeller).

28. Solving $ye^y - 9y = y(e^y - 9) = 0$ we obtain the critical points 0 and $\ln 9$. From the phase portrait we see that 0 is asymptotically stable (attractor) and $\ln 9$ is unstable (repeller).

29. The critical points are 0 and c because the graph of $f(y)$ is 0 at these points. Since $f(y) > 0$ for $y < 0$ and $y > c$, the graph of the solution is increasing on $(-\infty, 0)$ and (c, ∞). Since $f(y) < 0$ for $0 < y < c$, the graph of the solution is decreasing on $(0, c)$.

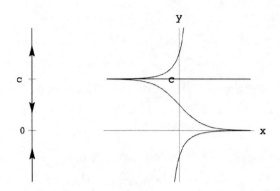

30. The critical points are approximately at $-2, 2$, 0.5, and 1.7. Since $f(y) > 0$ for $y < -2.2$ and $0.5 < y < 1.7$, the graph of the solution is increasing on $(-\infty, -2.2)$ and $(0.5, 1.7)$. Since $f(y) < 0$ for $-2.2 < y < 0.5$ and $y > 1.7$, the graph is decreasing on $(-2.2, 0.5)$ and $(1.7, \infty)$.

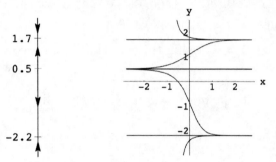

31. From the graphs of $z = \pi/2$ and $z = \sin y$ we see that $(\pi/2)y - \sin y = 0$ has only three solutions. By inspection we see that the critical points are $-\pi/2$, 0, and $\pi/2$.

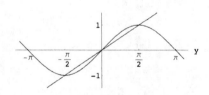

From the graph at the right we see that

$$\frac{2}{\pi}y - \sin y \begin{cases} < 0 & \text{for} \quad y < -\pi/2 \\ > 0 & \text{for} \quad y > \pi/2 \end{cases}$$

$$\frac{2}{\pi}y - \sin y \begin{cases} > 0 & \text{for} \quad -\pi/2 < y < 0 \\ < 0 & \text{for} \quad 0 < y < \pi/2. \end{cases}$$

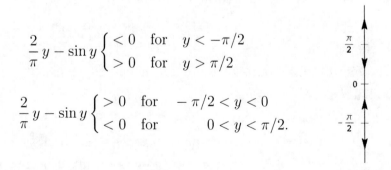

This enables us to construct the phase portrait shown at the right. From this portrait we see that $\pi/2$ and $-\pi/2$ are unstable (repellers), and 0 is asymptotically stable (attractor).

32. For $dy/dx = 0$ every real number is a critical point, and hence all critical points are nonisolated.

33. Recall that for $dy/dx = f(y)$ we are assuming that f and f' are continuous functions of y on some interval I. Now suppose that the graph of a nonconstant solution of the differential equation crosses the line $y = c$. If the point of intersection is taken as an initial condition we have two distinct solutions of the initial-value problem. This violates uniqueness, so the graph of any nonconstant solution must lie entirely on one side of any equilibrium solution. Since f is continuous it can only change signs at a point where it is 0. But this is a critical point. Thus, $f(y)$ is completely positive or completely negative in each region R_i. If $y(x)$ is oscillatory or has a relative extremum, then it must have a horizontal tangent line at some point (x_0, y_0). In this case y_0 would be a critical point of the differential equation, but we saw above that the graph of a nonconstant solution cannot intersect the graph of the equilibrium solution $y = y_0$.

34. By Problem 33, a solution $y(x)$ of $dy/dx = f(y)$ cannot have relative extrema and hence must be monotone. Since $y'(x) = f(y) > 0$, $y(x)$ is monotone increasing, and since $y(x)$ is bounded above by c_2, $\lim_{x \to \infty} y(x) = L$, where $L \leq c_2$. We want to show that $L = c_2$. Since L is a horizontal asymptote of $y(x)$, $\lim_{x \to \infty} y'(x) = 0$. Using the fact that $f(y)$ is continuous we have

$$f(L) = f(\lim_{x \to \infty} y(x)) = \lim_{x \to \infty} f(y(x)) = \lim_{x \to \infty} y'(x) = 0.$$

But then L is a critical point of f. Since $c_1 < L \leq c_2$, and f has no critical points between c_1 and c_2, $L = c_2$.

35. Assuming the existence of the second derivative, points of inflection of $y(x)$ occur where $y''(x) = 0$. From $dy/dx = f(y)$ we have $d^2y/dx^2 = f'(y) \, dy/dx$. Thus, the y-coordinate of a point of inflection can be located by solving $f'(y) = 0$. (Points where $dy/dx = 0$ correspond to constant solutions of the differential equation.)

36. Solving $y^2 - y - 6 = (y - 3)(y + 2) = 0$ we see that 3 and -2 are critical points. Now $d^2y/dx^2 = (2y - 1) \, dy/dx = (2y - 1)(y - 3)(y + 2)$, so the only possible point of inflection is at $y = \frac{1}{2}$, although the concavity of solutions can be different on either side of $y = -2$ and $y = 3$. Since $y''(x) < 0$ for $y < -2$ and $\frac{1}{2} < y < 3$, and $y''(x) > 0$ for $-2 < y < \frac{1}{2}$ and $y > 3$, we see that solution curves are concave down for $y < -2$ and $\frac{1}{2} < y < 3$ and concave up for $-2 < y < \frac{1}{2}$ and $y > 3$. Points of inflection of solutions of autonomous differential equations will have the same y-coordinates because between critical points they are horizontal translates of each other.

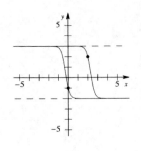

37. If (1) in the text has no critical points it has no constant solutions. The solutions have neither an upper nor lower bound. Since solutions are monotonic, every solution assumes all real values.

38. The critical points are 0 and b/a. From the phase portrait we see that 0 is an attractor and b/a is a repeller. Thus, if an initial population satisfies $P_0 > b/a$, the population becomes unbounded as t increases, most probably in finite time, i.e. $P(t) \to \infty$ as $t \to T$. If $0 < P_0 < b/a$, then the population eventually dies out, that is, $P(t) \to 0$ as $t \to \infty$. Since population $P > 0$ we do not consider the case $P_0 < 0$.

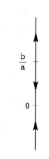

39. The only critical point of the autonomous differential equation is the positive number h/k. A phase portrait shows that this point is unstable, so h/k is a repeller. For any initial condition $P(0) = P_0 < h/k$, $dP/dt < 0$, which means $P(t)$ is monotonic decreasing and so the graph of $P(t)$ must cross the t-axis or the line $P = 0$ at some time $t_1 > 0$. But $P(t_1) = 0$ means the population is extinct at time t_1.

40. Writing the differential equation in the form

$$\frac{dv}{dt} = \frac{k}{m}\left(\frac{mg}{k} - v\right)$$

we see that a critical point is mg/k.

From the phase portrait we see that mg/k is an asymptotically stable critical point. Thus, $\lim_{t\to\infty} v = mg/k$.

41. Writing the differential equation in the form

$$\frac{dv}{dt} = \frac{k}{m}\left(\frac{mg}{k} - v^2\right) = \frac{k}{m}\left(\sqrt{\frac{mg}{k}} - v\right)\left(\sqrt{\frac{mg}{k}} + v\right)$$

we see that the only physically meaningful critical point is $\sqrt{mg/k}$.

From the phase portrait we see that $\sqrt{mg/k}$ is an asymptotically stable critical point. Thus, $\lim_{t\to\infty} v = \sqrt{mg/k}$.

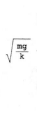

42. (a) From the phase portrait we see that critical points are α and β. Let $X(0) = X_0$. If $X_0 < \alpha$, we see that $X \to \alpha$ as $t \to \infty$. If $\alpha < X_0 < \beta$, we see that $X \to \alpha$ as $t \to \infty$. If $X_0 > \beta$, we see that $X(t)$ increases in an unbounded manner, but more specific behavior of $X(t)$ as $t \to \infty$ is not known.

(b) When $\alpha = \beta$ the phase portrait is as shown. If $X_0 < \alpha$, then $X(t) \to \alpha$ as $t \to \infty$. If $X_0 > \alpha$, then $X(t)$ increases in an unbounded manner. This could happen in a finite amount of time. That is, the phase portrait does not indicate that X becomes unbounded as $t \to \infty$.

(c) When $k = 1$ and $\alpha = \beta$ the differential equation is $dX/dt = (\alpha - X)^2$. For $X(t) = \alpha - 1/(t+c)$ we have $dX/dt = 1/(t+c)^2$ and

$$(\alpha - X)^2 = \left[\alpha - \left(\alpha - \frac{1}{t+c}\right)\right]^2 = \frac{1}{(t+c)^2} = \frac{dX}{dt}\,.$$

For $X(0) = \alpha/2$ we obtain

$$X(t) = \alpha - \frac{1}{t + 2/\alpha}\,.$$

For $X(0) = 2\alpha$ we obtain

$$X(t) = \alpha - \frac{1}{t - 1/\alpha}\,.$$

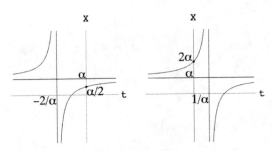

For $X_0 > \alpha$, $X(t)$ increases without bound up to $t = 1/\alpha$. For $t > 1/\alpha$, $X(t)$ increases but $X \to \alpha$ as $t \to \infty$

Exercises 2.2

Separable Variables

In many of the following problems we will encounter an expression of the form $\ln |g(y)| = f(x) + c$. To solve for $g(y)$ we exponentiate both sides of the equation. This yields $|g(y)| = e^{f(x)+c} = e^c e^{f(x)}$ which implies $g(y) = \pm e^c e^{f(x)}$. Letting $c_1 = \pm e^c$ we obtain $g(y) = c_1 e^{f(x)}$.

1. From $dy = \sin 5x \, dx$ we obtain $y = -\frac{1}{5}\cos 5x + c$.

2. From $dy = (x+1)^2 \, dx$ we obtain $y = \frac{1}{3}(x+1)^3 + c$.

3. From $dy = -e^{-3x} \, dx$ we obtain $y = \frac{1}{3}e^{-3x} + c$.

4. From $\dfrac{1}{(y-1)^2} \, dy = dx$ we obtain $-\dfrac{1}{y-1} = x + c$ or $y = 1 - \dfrac{1}{x+c}$.

5. From $\dfrac{1}{y} \, dy = \dfrac{4}{x} \, dx$ we obtain $\ln|y| = 4\ln|x| + c$ or $y = c_1 x^4$.

6. From $\dfrac{1}{y^2} \, dy = -2x \, dx$ we obtain $-\dfrac{1}{y} = -x^2 + c$ or $y = \dfrac{1}{x^2 + c_1}$.

7. From $e^{-2y} dy = e^{3x} dx$ we obtain $3e^{-2y} + 2e^{3x} = c$.

8. From $ye^y dy = \left(e^{-x} + e^{-3x}\right) dx$ we obtain $ye^y - e^y + e^{-x} + \dfrac{1}{3}e^{-3x} = c$.

9. From $\left(y + 2 + \dfrac{1}{y}\right) dy = x^2 \ln x \, dx$ we obtain $\dfrac{y^2}{2} + 2y + \ln|y| = \dfrac{x^3}{3} \ln|x| - \dfrac{1}{9}x^3 + c$.

10. From $\dfrac{1}{(2y+3)^2} \, dy = \dfrac{1}{(4x+5)^2} \, dx$ we obtain $\dfrac{2}{2y+3} = \dfrac{1}{4x+5} + c$.

11. From $\dfrac{1}{\csc y} \, dy = -\dfrac{1}{\sec^2 x} \, dx$ or $\sin y \, dy = -\cos^2 x \, dx = -\frac{1}{2}(1 + \cos 2x) \, dx$ we obtain
    $-\cos y = -\frac{1}{2}x - \frac{1}{4}\sin 2x + c$ or $4\cos y = 2x + \sin 2x + c_1$.

12. From $2y \, dy = -\dfrac{\sin 3x}{\cos^3 3x} \, dx$ or $2y \, dy = -\tan 3x \sec^2 3x \, dx$ we obtain $y^2 = -\frac{1}{6}\sec^2 3x + c$.

13. From $\dfrac{e^y}{(e^y+1)^2} \, dy = \dfrac{-e^x}{(e^x+1)^3} \, dx$ we obtain $-\left(e^y + 1\right)^{-1} = \frac{1}{2}\left(e^x + 1\right)^{-2} + c$.

14. From $\dfrac{y}{(1+y^2)^{1/2}} \, dy = \dfrac{x}{(1+x^2)^{1/2}} \, dx$ we obtain $\left(1 + y^2\right)^{1/2} = \left(1 + x^2\right)^{1/2} + c$.

15. From $\dfrac{1}{S} \, dS = k \, dr$ we obtain $S = ce^{kr}$.

16. From $\dfrac{1}{Q-70} \, dQ = k \, dt$ we obtain $\ln|Q - 70| = kt + c$ or $Q - 70 = c_1 e^{kt}$.

Exercises 2.2 Separable Variables

17. From $\dfrac{1}{P-P^2}\,dP = \left(\dfrac{1}{P} + \dfrac{1}{1-P}\right)dP = dt$ we obtain $\ln|P| - \ln|1-P| = t + c$ so that $\ln\left|\dfrac{P}{1-P}\right| =$

$t + c$ or $\dfrac{P}{1-P} = c_1 e^t$. Solving for P we have $P = \dfrac{c_1 e^t}{1 + c_1 e^t}$.

18. From $\dfrac{1}{N}\,dN = \left(te^{t+2} - 1\right)dt$ we obtain $\ln|N| = te^{t+2} - e^{t+2} - t + c$ or $N = c_1 e^{te^{t+2} - e^{t+2} - t}$.

19. From $\dfrac{y-2}{y+3}\,dy = \dfrac{x-1}{x+4}\,dx$ or $\left(1 - \dfrac{5}{y+3}\right)dy = \left(1 - \dfrac{5}{x+4}\right)dx$ we obtain $y - 5\ln|y+3| =$

$x - 5\ln|x+4| + c$ or $\left(\dfrac{x+4}{y+3}\right)^5 = c_1 e^{x-y}$.

20. From $\dfrac{y+1}{y-1}\,dy = \dfrac{x+2}{x-3}\,dx$ or $\left(1 + \dfrac{2}{y-1}\right)dy = \left(1 + \dfrac{5}{x-3}\right)dx$ we obtain $y + 2\ln|y-1| =$

$x + 5\ln|x-3| + c$ or $\dfrac{(y-1)^2}{(x-3)^5} = c_1 e^{x-y}$.

21. From $x\,dx = \dfrac{1}{\sqrt{1-y^2}}\,dy$ we obtain $\tfrac{1}{2}x^2 = \sin^{-1} y + c$ or $y = \sin\left(\dfrac{x^2}{2} + c_1\right)$.

22. From $\dfrac{1}{y^2}\,dy = \dfrac{1}{e^x + e^{-x}}\,dx = \dfrac{e^x}{(e^x)^2 + 1}\,dx$ we obtain $-\dfrac{1}{y} = \tan^{-1} e^x + c$ or $y = -\dfrac{1}{\tan^{-1} e^x + c}$.

23. From $\dfrac{1}{x^2 + 1}\,dx = 4\,dt$ we obtain $\tan^{-1} x = 4t + c$. Using $x(\pi/4) = 1$ we find $c = -3\pi/4$. The

solution of the initial-value problem is $\tan^{-1} x = 4t - \dfrac{3\pi}{4}$ or $x = \tan\left(4t - \dfrac{3\pi}{4}\right)$.

24. From $\dfrac{1}{y^2 - 1}\,dy = \dfrac{1}{x^2 - 1}\,dx$ or $\dfrac{1}{2}\left(\dfrac{1}{y-1} - \dfrac{1}{y+1}\right)dy = \dfrac{1}{2}\left(\dfrac{1}{x-1} - \dfrac{1}{x+1}\right)dx$ we obtain

$\ln|y-1| - \ln|y+1| = \ln|x-1| - \ln|x+1| + \ln c$ or $\dfrac{y-1}{y+1} = \dfrac{c(x-1)}{x+1}$. Using $y(2) = 2$ we find

$c = 1$. A solution of the initial-value problem is $\dfrac{y-1}{y+1} = \dfrac{x-1}{x+1}$ or $y = x$.

25. From $\dfrac{1}{y}\,dy = \dfrac{1-x}{x^2}\,dx = \left(\dfrac{1}{x^2} - \dfrac{1}{x}\right)dx$ we obtain $\ln|y| = -\dfrac{1}{x} - \ln|x| = c$ or $xy = c_1 e^{-1/x}$. Using

$y(-1) = -1$ we find $c_1 = e^{-1}$. The solution of the initial-value problem is $xy = e^{-1-1/x}$ or

$y = e^{-(1+1/x)}/x$.

26. From $\dfrac{1}{1-2y}\,dy = dt$ we obtain $-\tfrac{1}{2}\ln|1-2y| = t + c$ or $1 - 2y = c_1 e^{-2t}$. Using $y(0) = 5/2$ we find

$c_1 = -4$. The solution of the initial-value problem is $1 - 2y = -4e^{-2t}$ or $y = 2e^{-2t} + \tfrac{1}{2}$.

27. Separating variables and integrating we obtain

$$\dfrac{dx}{\sqrt{1-x^2}} - \dfrac{dy}{\sqrt{1-y^2}} = 0 \quad \text{and} \quad \sin^{-1} x - \sin^{-1} y = c.$$

Setting $x = 0$ and $y = \sqrt{3}/2$ we obtain $c = -\pi/3$. Thus, an implicit solution of the initial-value problem is $\sin^{-1} x - \sin^{-1} y = -\pi/3$. Solving for y and using an addition formula from trigonometry, we get

$$y = \sin\left(\sin^{-1} x + \frac{\pi}{3}\right) = x \cos \frac{\pi}{3} + \sqrt{1 - x^2} \sin \frac{\pi}{3} = \frac{x}{2} + \frac{\sqrt{3}\sqrt{1 - x^2}}{2}.$$

28. From $\dfrac{1}{1 + (2y)^2} \, dy = \dfrac{-x}{1 + (x^2)^2} \, dx$ we obtain

$$\frac{1}{2} \tan^{-1} 2y = -\frac{1}{2} \tan^{-1} x^2 + c \quad \text{or} \quad \tan^{-1} 2y + \tan^{-1} x^2 = c_1.$$

Using $y(1) = 0$ we find $c_1 = \pi/4$. Thus, an implicit solution of the initial-value problem is $\tan^{-1} 2y + \tan^{-1} x^2 = \pi/4$. Solving for y and using a trigonometric identity we get

$$2y = \tan\left(\frac{\pi}{4} - \tan^{-1} x^2\right)$$

$$y = \frac{1}{2} \tan\left(\frac{\pi}{4} - \tan^{-1} x^2\right)$$

$$= \frac{1}{2} \frac{\tan \frac{\pi}{4} - \tan(\tan^{-1} x^2)}{1 + \tan \frac{\pi}{4} \tan(\tan^{-1} x^2)}$$

$$= \frac{1}{2} \frac{1 - x^2}{1 + x^2}.$$

29. Separating variables, integrating from 4 to x, and using t as a dummy variable of integration gives

$$\int_4^x \frac{1}{y} \frac{dy}{dt} \, dt = \int_4^x e^{-t^2} \, dt$$

$$\ln y(t) \Big|_4^x = \int_4^x e^{-t^2} \, dt$$

$$\ln y(x) - \ln y(4) = \int_4^x e^{-t^2} \, dt$$

Using the initial condition we have

$$\ln y(x) = \ln y(4) + \int_4^x e^{-t^2} \, dt = \ln 1 + \int_4^x e^{-t^2} \, dt = \int_4^x e^{-t^2} \, dt.$$

Thus,

$$y(x) = e^{\int_4^x e^{-t^2} \, dt}.$$

Exercises 2.2   Separable Variables

30. Separating variables, integrating from -2 to x, and using t as a dummy variable of integration gives

$$\int_{-2}^{x} \frac{1}{y^2} \frac{dy}{dt}\, dt = \int_{-2}^{x} \sin t^2 dt$$

$$-y(t)^{-1}\Big|_{-2}^{x} = \int_{-2}^{x} \sin t^2 dt$$

$$-y(x)^{-1} + y(-2)^{-1} = \int_{-2}^{x} \sin t^2 dt$$

$$-y(x)^{-1} = -y(-2)^{-1} + \int_{-2}^{x} \sin t^2 dt$$

$$y(x)^{-1} = 3 - \int_{-2}^{x} \sin t^2 dt.$$

Thus

$$y(x) = \frac{1}{3 - \int_{-2}^{x} \sin t^2 dt}.$$

31. (a) The equilibrium solutions $y(x) = 2$ and $y(x) = -2$ satisfy the initial conditions $y(0) = 2$ and $y(0) = -2$, respectively. Setting $x = \frac{1}{4}$ and $y = 1$ in $y = 2(1 + ce^{4x})/(1 - ce^{4x})$ we obtain

$$1 = 2\frac{1 + ce}{1 - ce}, \quad 1 - ce = 2 + 2ce, \quad -1 = 3ce, \quad \text{and} \quad c = -\frac{1}{3e}.$$

The solution of the corresponding initial-value problem is

$$y = 2\frac{1 - \frac{1}{3}e^{4x-1}}{1 + \frac{1}{3}e^{4x-1}} = 2\frac{3 - e^{4x-1}}{3 + e^{4x-1}}.$$

(b) Separating variables and integrating yields

$$\frac{1}{4}\ln|y - 2| - \frac{1}{4}\ln|y + 2| + \ln c_1 = x$$

$$\ln|y - 2| - \ln|y + 2| + \ln c = 4x$$

$$\ln\left|\frac{c(y - 2)}{y + 2}\right| = 4x$$

$$c\frac{y - 2}{y + 2} = e^{4x}.$$

Solving for y we get $y = 2(c + e^{4x})/(c - e^{4x})$. The initial condition $y(0) = -2$ implies $2(c + 1)/(c - 1) = -2$ which yields $c = 0$ and $y(x) = -2$. The initial condition $y(0) = 2$ does not correspond to a value of c, and it must simply be recognized that $y(x) = 2$ is a solution of the initial-value problem. Setting $x = \frac{1}{4}$ and $y = 1$ in $y = 2(c + e^{4x})/(c - e^{4x})$ leads to $c = -3e$. Thus, a solution of the initial-value problem is

$$y = 2\frac{-3e + e^{4x}}{-3e - e^{4x}} = 2\frac{3 - e^{4x-1}}{3 + e^{4x-1}}.$$

32. Separating variables, we have

$$\frac{dy}{y^2 - y} = \frac{dx}{x} \quad \text{or} \quad \int \frac{dy}{y(y-1)} = \ln|x| + c.$$

Using partial fractions, we obtain

$$\int \left(\frac{1}{y-1} - \frac{1}{y} \right) dy = \ln|x| + c$$

$$\ln|y-1| - \ln|y| = \ln|x| + c$$

$$\ln\left| \frac{y-1}{xy} \right| = c$$

$$\frac{y-1}{xy} = e^c = c_1.$$

Solving for y we get $y = 1/(1 - c_1 x)$. We note by inspection that $y = 0$ is a singular solution of the differential equation.

(a) Setting $x = 0$ and $y = 1$ we have $1 = 1/(1 - 0)$, which is true for all values of c_1. Thus, solutions passing through $(0, 1)$ are $y = 1/(1 - c_1 x)$.

(b) Setting $x = 0$ and $y = 0$ in $y = 1/(1 - c_1 x)$ we get $0 = 1$. Thus, the only solution passing through $(0, 0)$ is $y = 0$.

(c) Setting $x = \frac{1}{2}$ and $y = \frac{1}{2}$ we have $\frac{1}{2} = 1/(1 - \frac{1}{2} c_1)$, so $c_1 = -2$ and $y = 1/(1 + 2x)$.

(d) Setting $x = 2$ and $y = \frac{1}{4}$ we have $\frac{1}{4} = 1/(1 - 2c_1)$, so $c_1 = -\frac{3}{2}$ and $y = 1/(1 + \frac{3}{2}x) = 2/(2 + 3x)$.

33. Singular solutions of $dy/dx = x\sqrt{1 - y^2}$ are $y = -1$ and $y = 1$. A singular solution of $(e^x + e^{-x})dy/dx = y^2$ is $y = 0$.

34. Differentiating $\ln(x^2 + 10) + \csc y = c$ we get

$$\frac{2x}{x^2 + 10} - \csc y \cot y \frac{dy}{dx} = 0,$$

$$\frac{2x}{x^2 + 10} - \frac{1}{\sin y} \cdot \frac{\cos y}{\sin y} \frac{dy}{dx} = 0,$$

or

$$2x \sin^2 y \, dx - (x^2 + 10) \cos y \, dy = 0.$$

Writing the differential equation in the form

$$\frac{dy}{dx} = \frac{2x \sin^2 y}{(x^2 + 10) \cos y}$$

we see that singular solutions occur when $\sin^2 y = 0$, or $y = k\pi$, where k is an integer.

35. The singular solution $y = 1$ satisfies the initial-value problem.

36. Separating variables we obtain $\dfrac{dy}{(y-1)^2} = dx$. Then

$$-\frac{1}{y-1} = x + c \quad \text{and} \quad y = \frac{x+c-1}{x+c}.$$

Setting $x = 0$ and $y = 1.01$ we obtain $c = -100$. The solution is

$$y = \frac{x - 101}{x - 100}.$$

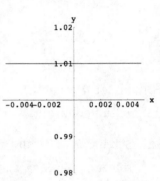

37. Separating variables we obtain $\dfrac{dy}{(y-1)^2 + 0.01} = dx$. Then

$$10 \tan^{-1} 10(y-1) = x + c \quad \text{and} \quad y = 1 + \frac{1}{10} \tan \frac{x+c}{10}.$$

Setting $x = 0$ and $y = 1$ we obtain $c = 0$. The solution is

$$y = 1 + \frac{1}{10} \tan \frac{x}{10}.$$

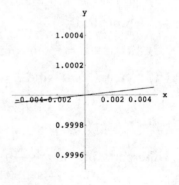

38. Separating variables we obtain $\dfrac{dy}{(y-1)^2 - 0.01} = dx$. Then, from (11) in this section of the manual with $u = y - 1$ and $a = \frac{1}{10}$, we get

$$5 \ln \left| \frac{10y - 11}{10y - 9} \right| = x + c.$$

Setting $x = 0$ and $y = 1$ we obtain $c = 5 \ln 1 = 0$. The solution is

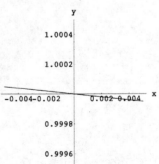

$$5 \ln \left| \frac{10y - 11}{10y - 9} \right| = x.$$

Solving for y we obtain

$$y = \frac{11 + 9e^{x/5}}{10 + 10e^{x/5}} .$$

Alternatively, we can use the fact that

$$\int \frac{dy}{(y-1)^2 - 0.01} = -\frac{1}{0.1} \tanh^{-1} \frac{y-1}{0.1} = -10 \tanh^{-1} 10(y-1).$$

(We use the inverse hyperbolic tangent because $|y - 1| < 0.1$ or $0.9 < y < 1.1$. This follows from the initial condition $y(0) = 1$.) Solving the above equation for y we get $y = 1 + 0.1 \tanh(x/10)$.

39. Separating variables, we have

$$\frac{dy}{y - y^3} = \frac{dy}{y(1 - y)(1 + y)} = \left(\frac{1}{y} + \frac{1/2}{1 - y} - \frac{1/2}{1 + y} \right) dy = dx.$$

Integrating, we get

$$\ln |y| - \frac{1}{2} \ln |1 - y| - \frac{1}{2} \ln |1 + y| = x + c.$$

When $y > 1$, this becomes

$$\ln y - \frac{1}{2} \ln(y - 1) - \frac{1}{2} \ln(y + 1) = \ln \frac{y}{\sqrt{y^2 - 1}} = x + c.$$

Letting $x = 0$ and $y = 2$ we find $c = \ln(2/\sqrt{3})$. Solving for y we get $y_1(x) = 2e^x/\sqrt{4e^{2x} - 3}$, where $x > \ln(\sqrt{3}/2)$.

When $0 < y < 1$ we have

$$\ln y - \frac{1}{2} \ln(1 - y) - \frac{1}{2} \ln(1 + y) = \ln \frac{y}{\sqrt{1 - y^2}} = x + c.$$

Letting $x = 0$ and $y = \frac{1}{2}$ we find $c = \ln(1/\sqrt{3})$. Solving for y we get $y_2(x) = e^x/\sqrt{e^{2x} + 3}$, where $-\infty < x < \infty$.

When $-1 < y < 0$ we have

$$\ln(-y) - \frac{1}{2} \ln(1 - y) - \frac{1}{2} \ln(1 + y) = \ln \frac{-y}{\sqrt{1 - y^2}} = x + c.$$

Letting $x = 0$ and $y = -\frac{1}{2}$ we find $c = \ln(1/\sqrt{3})$. Solving for y we get $y_3(x) = -e^x/\sqrt{e^{2x} + 3}$, where $-\infty < x < \infty$.

When $y < -1$ we have

$$\ln(-y) - \frac{1}{2} \ln(1 - y) - \frac{1}{2} \ln(-1 - y) = \ln \frac{-y}{\sqrt{y^2 - 1}} = x + c.$$

Letting $x = 0$ and $y = -2$ we find $c = \ln(2/\sqrt{3}\,)$. Solving for y we get $y_4(x) = -2e^x/\sqrt{4e^{2x}-3}\,$, where $x > \ln(\sqrt{3}/2)$.

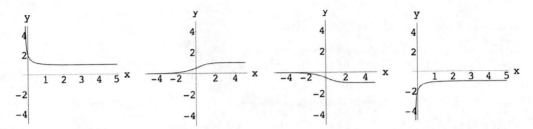

40. (a) The second derivative of y is

$$\frac{d^2y}{dx^2} = -\frac{dy/dx}{(y-1)^2} = -\frac{1/(y-3)}{(y-3)^2} = -\frac{1}{(y-3)^3}\,.$$

The solution curve is concave down when $d^2y/dx^2 < 0$ or $y > 3$, and concave up when $d^2y/dx^2 > 0$ or $y < 3$. From the phase portrait we see that the solution curve is decreasing when $y < 3$ and increasing when $y > 3$.

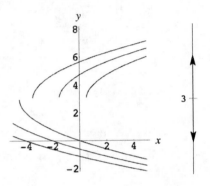

(b) Separating variables and integrating we obtain

$$(y-3)\,dy = dx$$

$$\frac{1}{2}y^2 - 3y = x + c$$

$$y^2 - 6y + 9 = 2x + c_1$$

$$(y-3)^2 = 2x + c_1$$

$$y = 3 \pm \sqrt{2x + c_1}\,.$$

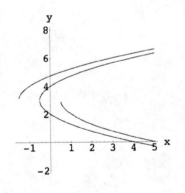

The initial condition dictates whether to use the plus or minus sign.

When $y_1(0) = 4$ we have $c_1 = 1$ and $y_1(x) = 3 + \sqrt{2x+1}\,$.

When $y_2(0) = 2$ we have $c_1 = 1$ and $y_2(x) = 3 - \sqrt{2x+1}\,$.

When $y_3(1) = 2$ we have $c_1 = -1$ and $y_3(x) = 3 - \sqrt{2x-1}\,$.

When $y_4(-1) = 4$ we have $c_1 = 3$ and $y_4(x) = 3 + \sqrt{2x+3}\,$.

41. (a) Separating variables we have $2y\,dy = (2x+1)dx$. Integrating gives $y^2 = x^2 + x + c$. When $y(-2) = -1$ we find $c = -1$, so $y^2 = x^2 + x - 1$ and $y = -\sqrt{x^2+x-1}\,$. The negative square root is chosen because of the initial condition.

(b) From the figure, the largest interval of definition appears to be approximately $(-\infty, -1.65)$.

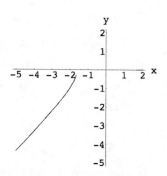

(c) Solving $x^2 + x - 1 = 0$ we get $x = -\frac{1}{2} \pm \frac{1}{2}\sqrt{5}$, so the largest interval of definition is $(-\infty, -\frac{1}{2} - \frac{1}{2}\sqrt{5})$. The right-hand endpoint of the interval is excluded because $y = -\sqrt{x^2 + x - 1}$ is not differentiable at this point.

42. (a) From Problem 7 the general solution is $3e^{-2y} + 2e^{3x} = c$. When $y(0) = 0$ we find $c = 5$, so $3e^{-2y} + 2e^{3x} = 5$. Solving for y we get $y = -\frac{1}{2} \ln \frac{1}{3}(5 - 2e^{3x})$.

(b) The interval of definition appears to be approximately $(-\infty, 0.3)$.

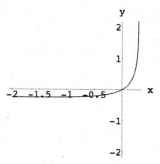

(c) Solving $\frac{1}{3}(5 - 2e^{3x}) = 0$ we get $x = \frac{1}{3}\ln(\frac{5}{2})$, so the exact interval of definition is $(-\infty, \frac{1}{3}\ln\frac{5}{2})$.

43. (a) While $y_2(x) = -\sqrt{25 - x^2}$ is defined at $x = -5$ and $x = 5$, $y_2'(x)$ is not defined at these values, and so the interval of definition is the open interval $(-5, 5)$.

(b) At any point on the x-axis the derivative of $y(x)$ is undefined, so no solution curve can cross the x-axis. Since $-x/y$ is not defined when $y = 0$, the initial-value problem has no solution.

44. (a) Separating variables and integrating we obtain $x^2 - y^2 = c$. For $c \neq 0$ the graph is a hyperbola centered at the origin. All four initial conditions imply $c = 0$ and $y = \pm x$. Since the differential equation is not defined for $y = 0$, solutions are $y = \pm x$, $x < 0$ and $y = \pm x$, $x > 0$. The solution for $y(a) = a$ is $y = x$, $x > 0$; for $y(a) = -a$ is $y = -x$; for $y(-a) = a$ is $y = -x$, $x < 0$; and for $y(-a) = -a$ is $y = x$, $x < 0$.

(b) Since x/y is not defined when $y = 0$, the initial-value problem has no solution.

(c) Setting $x = 1$ and $y = 2$ in $x^2 - y^2 = c$ we get $c = -3$, so $y^2 = x^2 + 3$ and $y(x) = \sqrt{x^2 + 3}$, where the positive square root is chosen because of the initial condition. The domain is all real numbers since $x^2 + 3 > 0$ for all x.

Exercises 2.2   Separable Variables

45. Separating variables we have $dy/(\sqrt{1+y^2}\,\sin^2 y) = dx$ which is not readily integrated (even by a CAS). We note that $dy/dx \geq 0$ for all values of x and y and that $dy/dx = 0$ when $y = 0$ and $y = \pi$, which are equilibrium solutions.

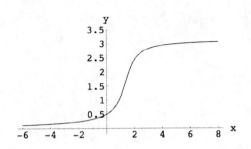

46. Separating variables we have $dy/(\sqrt{y}+y) = dx/(\sqrt{x}+x)$. To integrate $\int dx/(\sqrt{x}+x)$ we substitute $u^2 = x$ and get

$$\int \frac{2u}{u+u^2}\,du = \int \frac{.2}{1+u}\,du = 2\ln|1+u| + c = 2\ln(1+\sqrt{x}) + c.$$

Integrating the separated differential equation we have

$$2\ln(1+\sqrt{y}) = 2\ln(1+\sqrt{x}) + c \quad \text{or} \quad \ln(1+\sqrt{y}) = \ln(1+\sqrt{x}) + \ln c_1.$$

Solving for y we get $y = [c_1(1+\sqrt{x})-1]^2$.

47. We are looking for a function $y(x)$ such that

$$y^2 + \left(\frac{dy}{dx}\right)^2 = 1.$$

Using the positive square root gives

$$\frac{dy}{dx} = \sqrt{1-y^2} \implies \frac{dy}{\sqrt{1-y^2}} = dx \implies \sin^{-1} y = x + c.$$

Thus a solution is $y = \sin(x+c)$. If we use the negative square root we obtain

$$y = \sin(c-x) = -\sin(x-c) = -\sin(x+c_1).$$

Note that when $c = c_1 = 0$ and when $c = c_1 = \pi/2$ we obtain the well known particular solutions $y = \sin x$, $y = -\sin x$, $y = \cos x$, and $y = -\cos x$. Note also that $y = 1$ and $y = -1$ are singular solutions.

48. (a)

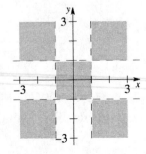

46

(b) For $|x| > 1$ and $|y| > 1$ the differential equation is $dy/dx = \sqrt{y^2 - 1}\,/\sqrt{x^2 - 1}$. Separating variables and integrating, we obtain

$$\frac{dy}{\sqrt{y^2 - 1}} = \frac{dx}{\sqrt{x^2 - 1}} \quad \text{and} \quad \cosh^{-1} y = \cosh^{-1} x + c.$$

Setting $x = 2$ and $y = 2$ we find $c = \cosh^{-1} 2 - \cosh^{-1} 2 = 0$ and $\cosh^{-1} y = \cosh^{-1} x$. An explicit solution is $y = x$.

49. Since the tension T_1 (or magnitude T_1) acts at the lowest point of the cable, we use symmetry to solve the problem on the interval $[0, L/2]$. The assumption that the roadbed is uniform (that is, weighs a constant ρ pounds per horizontal foot) implies $W = \rho x$, where x is measured in feet and $0 \le x \le L/2$. Therefore (10) in the text becomes $dy/dx = (\rho/T_1)x$. This last equation is a separable equation of the form given in (1) of Section 2.2 in the text. Integrating and using the initial condition $y(0) = a$ shows that the shape of the cable is a parabola: $y(x) = (\rho/2T_1)x^2 + a$. In terms of the sag h of the cable and the span L, we see from Figure 2.2.5 in the text that $y(L/2) = h + a$. By applying this last condition to $y(x) = (\rho/2T_1)x^2 + a$ enables us to express $\rho/2T_1$ in terms of h and L: $y(x) = (4h/L^2)x^2 + a$. Since $y(x)$ is an even function of x, the solution is valid on $-L/2 \le x \le L/2$.

50. (a) Separating variables and integrating, we have $(3y^2 + 1)dy = -(8x + 5)dx$ and $y^3 + y = -4x^2 - 5x + c$. Using a CAS we show various contours of $f(x, y) = y^3 + y + 4x^2 + 5x$. The plots shown on $[-5, 5] \times [-5, 5]$ correspond to c-values of 0, ± 5, ± 20, ± 40, ± 80, and ± 125.

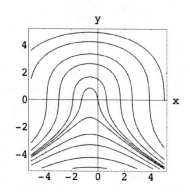

(b) The value of c corresponding to $y(0) = -1$ is $f(0, -1) = -2$; to $y(0) = 2$ is $f(0, 2) = 10$; to $y(-1) = 4$ is $f(-1, 4) = 67$; and to $y(-1) = -3$ is -31.

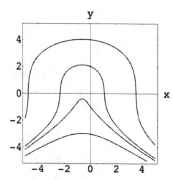

51. (a) An implicit solution of the differential equation $(2y + 2)dy - (4x^3 + 6x)dx = 0$ is

$$y^2 + 2y - x^4 - 3x^2 + c = 0.$$

The condition $y(0) = -3$ implies that $c = -3$. Therefore $y^2 + 2y - x^4 - 3x^2 - 3 = 0$.

(b) Using the quadratic formula we can solve for y in terms of x:

$$y = \frac{-2 \pm \sqrt{4 + 4(x^4 + 3x^2 + 3)}}{2}.$$

The explicit solution that satisfies the initial condition is then

$$y = -1 - \sqrt{x^4 + 3x^3 + 4}\,.$$

(c) From the graph of $f(x) = x^4 + 3x^3 + 4$ below we see that $f(x) \le 0$ on the approximate interval $-2.8 \le x \le -1.3$. Thus the approximate domain of the function

$$y = -1 - \sqrt{x^4 + 3x^3 + 4} = -1 - \sqrt{f(x)}$$

is $x \le -2.8$ or $x \ge -1.3$. The graph of this function is shown below.

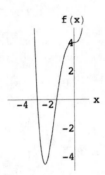

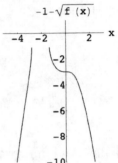

(d) Using the root finding capabilities of a CAS, the zeros of f are found to be -2.82202 and -1.3409. The domain of definition of the solution $y(x)$ is then $x > -1.3409$. The equality has been removed since the derivative dy/dx does not exist at the points where $f(x) = 0$. The graph of the solution $y = \phi(x)$ is given on the right.

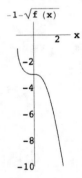

52. (a) Separating variables and integrating, we have

$$(-2y + y^2)dy = (x - x^2)dx$$

and

$$-y^2 + \frac{1}{3}y^3 = \frac{1}{2}x^2 - \frac{1}{3}x^3 + c.$$

Using a CAS we show some contours of $f(x, y) = 2y^3 - 6y^2 + 2x^3 - 3x^2$. The plots shown on $[-7, 7] \times [-5, 5]$ correspond to c-values of -450, -300, -200, -120, -60, -20, -10, -8.1, -5, -0.8, 20, 60, and 120.

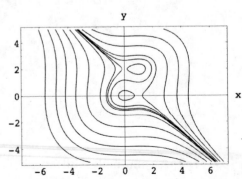

(b) The value of c corresponding to $y(0) = \frac{3}{2}$ is $f(0, \frac{3}{2}) = -\frac{27}{4}$. The portion of the graph between the dots corresponds to the solution curve satisfying the intial condition. To determine the interval of definition we find dy/dx for $2y^3 - 6y^2 + 2x^3 - 3x^2 = -\frac{27}{4}$. Using implicit differentiation we get $y' = (x - x^2)/(y^2 - 2y)$, which is infinite when $y = 0$ and $y = 2$. Letting $y = 0$ in $2y^3 - 6y^2 + 2x^3 - 3x^2 = -\frac{27}{4}$ and using a CAS to solve

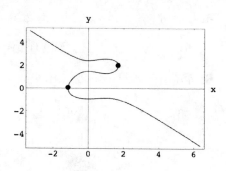

for x we get $x = -1.13232$. Similarly, letting $y = 2$, we find $x = 1.71299$. The largest interval of definition is approximately $(-1.13232, 1.71299)$.

(c) The value of c corresponding to $y(0) = -2$ is $f(0, -2) = -40$. The portion of the graph to the right of the dot corresponds to the solution curve satisfying the initial condition. To determine the interval of definition we find dy/dx for $2y^3 - 6y^2 + 2x^3 - 3x^2 = -40$. Using implicit differentiation we get $y' = (x - x^2)/(y^2 - 2y)$, which is infinite when $y = 0$ and $y = 2$. Letting $y = 0$ in $2y^3 - 6y^2 + 2x^3 - 3x^2 = -40$ and using a CAS to solve

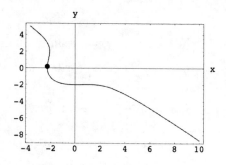

for x we get $x = -2.29551$. The largest interval of definition is approximately $(-2.29551, \infty)$.

Exercises 2.3   Linear Equations

1. For $y' - 5y = 0$ an integrating factor is $e^{-\int 5\,dx} = e^{-5x}$ so that $\dfrac{d}{dx}\left[e^{-5x}y\right] = 0$ and $y = ce^{5x}$ for $-\infty < x < \infty$. There is no transient term.

2. For $y' + 2y = 0$ an integrating factor is $e^{\int 2\,dx} = e^{2x}$ so that $\dfrac{d}{dx}\left[e^{2x}y\right] = 0$ and $y = ce^{-2x}$ for $-\infty < x < \infty$. The transient term is ce^{-2x}.

3. For $y' + y = e^{3x}$ an integrating factor is $e^{\int dx} = e^{x}$ so that $\dfrac{d}{dx}\left[e^{x}y\right] = e^{4x}$ and $y = \frac{1}{4}e^{3x} + ce^{-x}$ for $-\infty < x < \infty$. The transient term is ce^{-x}.

4. For $y' + 4y = \frac{4}{3}$ an integrating factor is $e^{\int 4\,dx} = e^{4x}$ so that $\dfrac{d}{dx}\left[e^{4x}y\right] = \frac{4}{3}e^{4x}$ and $y = \frac{1}{3} + ce^{-4x}$ for $-\infty < x < \infty$. The transient term is ce^{-4x}.

Exercises 2.3   Linear Equations

5. For $y' + 3x^2y = x^2$ an integrating factor is $e^{\int 3x^2\,dx} = e^{x^3}$ so that $\dfrac{d}{dx}\left[e^{x^3}y\right] = x^2e^{x^3}$ and $y = \frac{1}{3} + ce^{-x^3}$ for $-\infty < x < \infty$. The transient term is ce^{-x^3}.

6. For $y' + 2xy = x^3$ an integrating factor is $e^{\int 2x\,dx} = e^{x^2}$ so that $\dfrac{d}{dx}\left[e^{x^2}y\right] = x^3e^{x^2}$ and $y = \frac{1}{2}x^2 - \frac{1}{2} + ce^{-x^2}$ for $-\infty < x < \infty$. The transient term is ce^{-x^2}.

7. For $y' + \dfrac{1}{x}y = \dfrac{1}{x^2}$ an integrating factor is $e^{\int(1/x)dx} = x$ so that $\dfrac{d}{dx}[xy] = \dfrac{1}{x}$ and $y = \dfrac{1}{x}\ln x + \dfrac{c}{x}$ for $0 < x < \infty$. The entire solution is transient.

8. For $y' - 2y = x^2 + 5$ an integrating factor is $e^{-\int 2\,dx} = e^{-2x}$ so that $\dfrac{d}{dx}\left[e^{-2x}y\right] = x^2e^{-2x} + 5e^{-2x}$ and $y = -\frac{1}{2}x^2 - \frac{1}{2}x - \frac{11}{4} + ce^{2x}$ for $-\infty < x < \infty$. There is no transient term.

9. For $y' - \dfrac{1}{x}y = x\sin x$ an integrating factor is $e^{-\int(1/x)dx} = \dfrac{1}{x}$ so that $\dfrac{d}{dx}\left[\dfrac{1}{x}y\right] = \sin x$ and $y = cx - x\cos x$ for $0 < x < \infty$. There is no transient term.

10. For $y' + \dfrac{2}{x}y = \dfrac{3}{x}$ an integrating factor is $e^{\int(2/x)dx} = x^2$ so that $\dfrac{d}{dx}\left[x^2y\right] = 3x$ and $y = \frac{3}{2} + cx^{-2}$ for $0 < x < \infty$. The transient term is cx^{-2}.

11. For $y' + \dfrac{4}{x}y = x^2 - 1$ an integrating factor is $e^{\int(4/x)dx} = x^4$ so that $\dfrac{d}{dx}\left[x^4y\right] = x^6 - x^4$ and $y = \frac{1}{7}x^3 - \frac{1}{5}x + cx^{-4}$ for $0 < x < \infty$. The transient term is cx^{-4}.

12. For $y' - \dfrac{x}{(1+x)}y = x$ an integrating factor is $e^{-\int[x/(1+x)]dx} = (x+1)e^{-x}$ so that $\dfrac{d}{dx}\left[(x+1)e^{-x}y\right] = x(x+1)e^{-x}$ and $y = -x - \dfrac{2x+3}{x+1} + \dfrac{ce^x}{x+1}$ for $-1 < x < \infty$. There is no transient term.

13. For $y' + \left(1 + \dfrac{2}{x}\right)y = \dfrac{e^x}{x^2}$ an integrating factor is $e^{\int[1+(2/x)]dx} = x^2e^x$ so that $\dfrac{d}{dx}\left[x^2e^xy\right] = e^{2x}$ and $y = \dfrac{1}{2}\dfrac{e^x}{x^2} + \dfrac{ce^{-x}}{x^2}$ for $0 < x < \infty$. The transient term is $\dfrac{ce^{-x}}{x^2}$.

14. For $y' + \left(1 + \dfrac{1}{x}\right)y = \dfrac{1}{x}e^{-x}\sin 2x$ an integrating factor is $e^{\int[1+(1/x)]dx} = xe^x$ so that $\dfrac{d}{dx}[xe^xy] = \sin 2x$ and $y = -\dfrac{1}{2x}e^{-x}\cos 2x + \dfrac{ce^{-x}}{x}$ for $0 < x < \infty$. The entire solution is transient.

15. For $\dfrac{dx}{dy} - \dfrac{4}{y}x = 4y^5$ an integrating factor is $e^{-\int(4/y)dy} = e^{\ln y^{-4}} = y^{-4}$ so that $\dfrac{d}{dy}\left[y^{-4}x\right] = 4y$ and $x = 2y^6 + cy^4$ for $0 < y < \infty$. There is no transient term.

50

16. For $\dfrac{dx}{dy} + \dfrac{2}{y}x = e^y$ an integrating factor is $e^{\int(2/y)dy} = y^2$ so that $\dfrac{d}{dy}\left[y^2 x\right] = y^2 e^y$ and

$x = e^y - \dfrac{2}{y}e^y + \dfrac{2}{y^2}e^y + \dfrac{c}{y^2}$ for $0 < y < \infty$. The transient term is $\dfrac{c}{y^2}$.

17. For $y' + (\tan x)y = \sec x$ an integrating factor is $e^{\int \tan x\, dx} = \sec x$ so that $\dfrac{d}{dx}\left[(\sec x)\,y\right] = \sec^2 x$ and $y = \sin x + c\cos x$ for $-\pi/2 < x < \pi/2$. There is no transient term.

18. For $y' + (\cot x)y = \sec^2 x \csc x$ an integrating factor is $e^{\int \cot x\, dx} = e^{\ln|\sin x|} = \sin x$ so that $\dfrac{d}{dx}\left[(\sin x)\,y\right] = \sec^2 x$ and $y = \sec x + c\csc x$ for $0 < x < \pi/2$. There is no transient term.

19. For $y' + \dfrac{x+2}{x+1}y = \dfrac{2xe^{-x}}{x+1}$ an integrating factor is $e^{\int[(x+2)/(x+1)]dx} = (x+1)e^x$, so $\dfrac{d}{dx}\left[(x+1)e^x y\right] =$

$2x$ and $y = \dfrac{x^2}{x+1}e^{-x} + \dfrac{c}{x+1}e^{-x}$ for $-1 < x < \infty$. The entire solution is transient.

20. For $y' + \dfrac{4}{x+2}y = \dfrac{5}{(x+2)^2}$ an integrating factor is $e^{\int[4/(x+2)]dx} = (x+2)^4$ so that $\dfrac{d}{dx}\left[(x+2)^4 y\right] =$

$5(x+2)^2$ and $y = \dfrac{5}{3}(x+2)^{-1} + c(x+2)^{-4}$ for $-2 < x < \infty$. The entire solution is transient.

21. For $\dfrac{dr}{d\theta} + r\sec\theta = \cos\theta$ an integrating factor is $e^{\int \sec\theta\, d\theta} = e^{\ln|\sec x + \tan x|} = \sec\theta + \tan\theta$ so that

$\dfrac{d}{d\theta}\left[(\sec\theta + \tan\theta)r\right] = 1 + \sin\theta$ and $(\sec\theta + \tan\theta)r = \theta - \cos\theta + c$ for $-\pi/2 < \theta < \pi/2$.

22. For $\dfrac{dP}{dt} + (2t-1)P = 4t - 2$ an integrating factor is $e^{\int(2t-1)\,dt} = e^{t^2-t}$ so that $\dfrac{d}{dt}\left[e^{t^2-t}P\right] =$

$(4t-2)e^{t^2-t}$ and $P = 2 + ce^{t-t^2}$ for $-\infty < t < \infty$. The transient term is ce^{t-t^2}.

23. For $y' + \left(3 + \dfrac{1}{x}\right)y = \dfrac{e^{-3x}}{x}$ an integrating factor is $e^{\int[3+(1/x)]dx} = xe^{3x}$ so that $\dfrac{d}{dx}\left[xe^{3x}y\right] = 1$ and

$y = e^{-3x} + \dfrac{ce^{-3x}}{x}$ for $0 < x < \infty$. The entire solution is transient.

24. For $y' + \dfrac{2}{x^2-1}y = \dfrac{x+1}{x-1}$ an integrating factor is $e^{\int[2/(x^2-1)]dx} = \dfrac{x-1}{x+1}$ so that $\dfrac{d}{dx}\left[\dfrac{x-1}{x+1}y\right] = 1$

and $(x-1)y = x(x+1) + c(x+1)$ for $-1 < x < 1$.

25. For $y' + \dfrac{1}{x}y = \dfrac{1}{x}e^x$ an integrating factor is $e^{\int(1/x)dx} = x$ so that $\dfrac{d}{dx}\left[xy\right] = e^x$ and $y = \dfrac{1}{x}e^x + \dfrac{c}{x}$

for $0 < x < \infty$. If $y(1) = 2$ then $c = 2 - e$ and $y = \dfrac{1}{x}e^x + \dfrac{2-e}{x}$.

26. For $\dfrac{dx}{dy} - \dfrac{1}{y}x = 2y$ an integrating factor is $e^{-\int(1/y)dy} = \dfrac{1}{y}$ so that $\dfrac{d}{dy}\left[\dfrac{1}{y}x\right] = 2$ and $x = 2y^2 + cy$

for $0 < y < \infty$. If $y(1) = 5$ then $c = -49/5$ and $x = 2y^2 - \dfrac{49}{5}y$.

27. For $\dfrac{di}{dt} + \dfrac{R}{L}i = \dfrac{E}{L}$ an integrating factor is $e^{\int(R/L)\,dt} = e^{Rt/L}$ so that $\dfrac{d}{dt}\left[e^{Rt/L}\,i\right] = \dfrac{E}{L}e^{Rt/L}$ and

$i = \dfrac{E}{R} + ce^{-Rt/L}$ for $-\infty < t < \infty$. If $i(0) = i_0$ then $c = i_0 - E/R$ and $i = \dfrac{E}{R} + \left(i_0 - \dfrac{E}{R}\right)e^{-Rt/L}$.

28. For $\dfrac{dT}{dt} - kT = -T_m k$ an integrating factor is $e^{\int(-k)dt} = e^{-kt}$ so that $\dfrac{d}{dt}\left[e^{-kt}T\right] = -T_m k e^{-kt}$ and $T = T_m + ce^{kt}$ for $-\infty < t < \infty$. If $T(0) = T_0$ then $c = T_0 - T_m$ and $T = T_m + (T_0 - T_m)e^{kt}$.

29. For $y' + \dfrac{1}{x+1}y = \dfrac{\ln x}{x+1}$ an integrating factor is $e^{\int[1/(x+1)]dx} = x+1$ so that $\dfrac{d}{dx}[(x+1)y] =$

$\ln x$ and $y = \dfrac{x}{x+1}\ln x - \dfrac{x}{x+1} + \dfrac{c}{x+1}$ for $0 < x < \infty$. If $y(1) = 10$ then $c = 21$ and

$y = \dfrac{x}{x+1}\ln x - \dfrac{x}{x+1} + \dfrac{21}{x+1}$.

30. For $y' + (\tan x)y = \cos^2 x$ an integrating factor is $e^{\int \tan x \, dx} = e^{\ln|\sec x|} = \sec x$ so that $\dfrac{d}{dx}[(\sec x)\,y] =$
$\cos x$ and $y = \sin x \cos x + c \cos x$ for $-\pi/2 < x < \pi/2$. If $y(0) = -1$ then $c = -1$ and $y = \sin x \cos x - \cos x$.

31. For $y' + 2y = f(x)$ an integrating factor is e^{2x} so that
$$ye^{2x} = \begin{cases} \frac{1}{2}e^{2x} + c_1, & 0 \le x \le 3 \\ c_2, & x > 3. \end{cases}$$
If $y(0) = 0$ then $c_1 = -1/2$ and for continuity we must have $c_2 = \frac{1}{2}e^6 - \frac{1}{2}$ so that
$$y = \begin{cases} \frac{1}{2}(1 - e^{-2x}), & 0 \le x \le 3 \\ \frac{1}{2}(e^6 - 1)e^{-2x}, & x > 3. \end{cases}$$

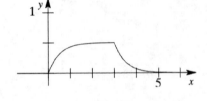

32. For $y' + y = f(x)$ an integrating factor is e^x so that
$$ye^x = \begin{cases} e^x + c_1, & 0 \le x \le 1 \\ -e^x + c_2, & x > 1. \end{cases}$$
If $y(0) = 1$ then $c_1 = 0$ and for continuity we must have $c_2 = 2e$
so that
$$y = \begin{cases} 1, & 0 \le x \le 1 \\ 2e^{1-x} - 1, & x > 1. \end{cases}$$

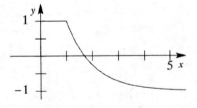

33. For $y' + 2xy = f(x)$ an integrating factor is e^{x^2} so that
$$ye^{x^2} = \begin{cases} \frac{1}{2}e^{x^2} + c_1, & 0 \le x \le 1 \\ c_2, & x > 1. \end{cases}$$
If $y(0) = 2$ then $c_1 = 3/2$ and for continuity we must have $c_2 = \frac{1}{2}e + \frac{3}{2}$ so that

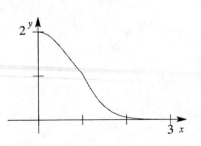

$$y = \begin{cases} \frac{1}{2} + \frac{3}{2}e^{-x^2}, & 0 \le x \le 1 \\ \left(\frac{1}{2}e + \frac{3}{2}\right)e^{-x^2}, & x > 1. \end{cases}$$

34. For

$$y' + \frac{2x}{1+x^2}\, y = \begin{cases} \dfrac{x}{1+x^2}, & 0 \le x \le 1 \\ \dfrac{-x}{1+x^2}, & x > 1, \end{cases}$$

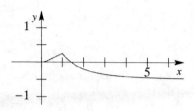

an integrating factor is $1 + x^2$ so that

$$\left(1 + x^2\right) y = \begin{cases} \frac{1}{2}x^2 + c_1, & 0 \le x \le 1 \\ -\frac{1}{2}x^2 + c_2, & x > 1. \end{cases}$$

If $y(0) = 0$ then $c_1 = 0$ and for continuity we must have $c_2 = 1$ so that

$$y = \begin{cases} \dfrac{1}{2} - \dfrac{1}{2\left(1 + x^2\right)}, & 0 \le x \le 1 \\ \dfrac{3}{2\left(1 + x^2\right)} - \dfrac{1}{2}, & x > 1. \end{cases}$$

35. We first solve the initial-value problem $y' + 2y = 4x$, $y(0) = 3$ on the interval $[0, 1]$. The integrating factor is $e^{\int 2\,dx} = e^{2x}$, so

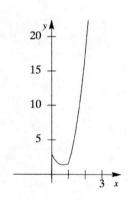

$$\frac{d}{dx}[e^{2x}y] = 4xe^{2x}$$

$$e^{2x}y = \int 4xe^{2x}dx = 2xe^{2x} - e^{2x} + c_1$$

$$y = 2x - 1 + c_1e^{-2x}.$$

Using the initial condition, we find $y(0) = -1 + c_1 = 3$, so $c_1 = 4$ and $y = 2x - 1 + 4e^{-2x}$, $0 \le x \le 1$. Now, since $y(1) = 2 - 1 + 4e^{-2} = 1 + 4e^{-2}$, we solve the initial-value problem $y' - (2/x)y = 4x$, $y(1) = 1 + 4e^{-2}$ on the interval $(1, \infty)$. The integrating factor is $e^{\int(-2/x)dx} = e^{-2\ln x} = x^{-2}$, so

$$\frac{d}{dx}[x^{-2}y] = 4xx^{-2} = \frac{4}{x}$$

$$x^{-2}y = \int \frac{4}{x}\, dx = 4\ln x + c_2$$

$$y = 4x^2 \ln x + c_2x^2.$$

(We use $\ln x$ instead of $\ln|x|$ because $x > 1$.) Using the initial condition we find $y(1) = c_2 = 1 + 4e^{-2}$, so $y = 4x^2 \ln x + (1 + 4e^{-2})x^2$, $x > 1$. Thus, the solution of the original initial-value problem is

$$y = \begin{cases} 2x - 1 + 4e^{-2x}, & 0 \leq x \leq 1 \\ 4x^2 \ln x + (1 + 4e^{-2})x^2, & x > 1. \end{cases}$$

See Problem 42 in this section.

36. For $y' + e^x y = 1$ an integrating factor is e^{e^x}. Thus

$$\frac{d}{dx}[e^{e^x} y] = e^{e^x} \quad \text{and} \quad e^{e^x} y = \int_0^x e^{e^t} dt + c.$$

From $y(0) = 1$ we get $c = e$, so $y = e^{-e^x} \int_0^x e^{e^t} dt + e^{1-e^x}$.

When $y' + e^x y = 0$ we can separate variables and integrate:

$$\frac{dy}{y} = -e^x \, dx \quad \text{and} \quad \ln|y| = -e^x + c.$$

Thus $y = c_1 e^{-e^x}$. From $y(0) = 1$ we get $c_1 = e$, so $y = e^{1-e^x}$.

When $y' + e^x y = e^x$ we can see by inspection that $y = 1$ is a solution.

37. An integrating factor for $y' - 2xy = 1$ is e^{-x^2}. Thus

$$\frac{d}{dx}[e^{-x^2} y] = e^{-x^2}$$

$$e^{-x^2} y = \int_0^x e^{-t^2} dt = \frac{\sqrt{\pi}}{2} \operatorname{erf}(x) + c$$

$$y = \frac{\sqrt{\pi}}{2} e^{x^2} \operatorname{erf}(x) + ce^{x^2}.$$

From $y(1) = (\sqrt{\pi}/2)e \operatorname{erf}(1) + ce = 1$ we get $c = e^{-1} - \frac{\sqrt{\pi}}{2}\operatorname{erf}(1)$. The solution of the initial-value problem is

$$y = \frac{\sqrt{\pi}}{2} e^{x^2} \operatorname{erf}(x) + \left(e^{-1} - \frac{\sqrt{\pi}}{2}\operatorname{erf}(1)\right)e^{x^2}$$

$$= e^{x^2-1} + \frac{\sqrt{\pi}}{2} e^{x^2}(\operatorname{erf}(x) - \operatorname{erf}(1)).$$

38. We want 4 to be a critical point, so we use $y' = 4 - y$.

39. (a) All solutions of the form $y = x^5 e^x - x^4 e^x + cx^4$ satisfy the initial condition. In this case, since $4/x$ is discontinuous at $x = 0$, the hypotheses of Theorem 1.2.1 are not satisfied and the initial-value problem does not have a unique solution.

(b) The differential equation has no solution satisfying $y(0) = y_0$, $y_0 > 0$.

(c) In this case, since $x_0 > 0$, Theorem 1.2.1 applies and the initial-value problem has a unique solution given by $y = x^5 e^x - x^4 e^x + cx^4$ where $c = y_0/x_0^4 - x_0 e^{x_0} + e^{x_0}$.

40. On the interval $(-3, 3)$ the integrating factor is

$$e^{\int x\,dx/(x^2-9)} = e^{-\int x\,dx/(9-x^2)} = e^{\frac{1}{2}\ln(9-x^2)} = \sqrt{9 - x^2}$$

and so

$$\frac{d}{dx}\left[\sqrt{9-x^2}\,y\right]=0 \quad \text{and} \quad y=\frac{c}{\sqrt{9-x^2}}.$$

41. We want the general solution to be $y=3x-5+ce^{-x}$. (Rather than e^{-x}, any function that approaches 0 as $x\to\infty$ could be used.) Differentiating we get

$$y'=3-ce^{-x}=3-(y-3x+5)=-y+3x-2,$$

so the differential equation $y'+y=3x-2$ has solutions asymptotic to the line $y=3x-5$.

42. The left-hand derivative of the function at $x=1$ is $1/e$ and the right-hand derivative at $x=1$ is $1-1/e$. Thus, y is not differentiable at $x=1$.

43. (a) Differentiating $y_c=c/x^3$ we get

$$y_c'=-\frac{3c}{x^4}=-\frac{3}{x}\frac{c}{x^3}=-\frac{3}{x}y_c$$

so a differential equation with general solution $y_c=c/x^3$ is $xy'+3y=0$. Now

$$xy_p'+3y_p=x(3x^2)+3(x^3)=6x^3$$

so a differential equation with general solution $y=c/x^3+x^3$ is $xy'+3y=6x^3$. This will be a general solution on $(0,\infty)$.

(b) Since $y(1)=1^3-1/1^3=0$, an initial condition is $y(1)=0$. Since $y(1)=1^3+2/1^3=3$, an initial condition is $y(1)=3$. In each case the interval of definition is $(0,\infty)$. The initial-value problem $xy'+3y=6x^3$, $y(0)=0$ has solution $y=x^3$ for $-\infty<x<\infty$. In the figure the lower curve is the graph of $y(x)=x^3-1/x^3$, while the upper curve is the graph of $y=x^3-2/x^3$.

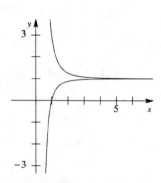

(c) The first two initial-value problems in part (b) are not unique. For example, setting $y(2)=2^3-1/2^3=63/8$, we see that $y(2)=63/8$ is also an initial condition leading to the solution $y=x^3-1/x^3$.

44. Since $e^{\int P(x)dx+c}=e^c e^{\int P(x)dx}=c_1 e^{\int P(x)dx}$, we would have

$$c_1 e^{\int P(x)dx}y=c_2+\int c_1 e^{\int P(x)dx}f(x)\,dx \quad \text{and} \quad e^{\int P(x)dx}y=c_3+\int e^{\int P(x)dx}f(x)\,dx,$$

which is the same as (6) in the text.

45. We see by inspection that $y=0$ is a solution.

46. The solution of the first equation is $x=c_1 e^{-\lambda_1 t}$. From $x(0)=x_0$ we obtain $c_1=x_0$ and so $x=x_0 e^{-\lambda_1 t}$. The second equation then becomes

$$\frac{dy}{dt}=x_0\lambda_1 e^{-\lambda_1 t}-\lambda_2 y \quad \text{or} \quad \frac{dy}{dt}+\lambda_2 y=x_0\lambda_1 e^{-\lambda_1 t}$$

which is linear. An integrating factor is $e^{\lambda_2 t}$. Thus

$$\frac{d}{dt}\left[e^{\lambda_2 t} y\right] = x_0 \lambda_1 e^{-\lambda_1 t} e^{\lambda_2 t} = x_0 \lambda_1 e^{(\lambda_2 - \lambda_1)t}$$

$$e^{\lambda_2 t} y = \frac{x_0 \lambda_1}{\lambda_2 - \lambda_1} e^{(\lambda_2 - \lambda_1)t} + c_2$$

$$y = \frac{x_0 \lambda_1}{\lambda_2 - \lambda_1} e^{-\lambda_1 t} + c_2 e^{-\lambda_2 t}.$$

From $y(0) = y_0$ we obtain $c_2 = (y_0 \lambda_2 - y_0 \lambda_1 - x_0 \lambda_1)/(\lambda_2 - \lambda_1)$. The solution is

$$y = \frac{x_0 \lambda_1}{\lambda_2 - \lambda_1} e^{-\lambda_1 t} + \frac{y_0 \lambda_2 - y_0 \lambda_1 - x_0 \lambda_1}{\lambda_2 - \lambda_1} e^{-\lambda_2 t}.$$

47. Writing the differential equation as $\dfrac{dE}{dt} + \dfrac{1}{RC} E = 0$ we see that an integrating factor is $e^{t/RC}$. Then

$$\frac{d}{dt}\left[e^{t/RC} E\right] = 0$$

$$e^{t/RC} E = c$$

$$E = c e^{-t/RC}.$$

From $E(4) = c e^{-4/RC} = E_0$ we find $c = E_0 e^{4/RC}$. Thus, the solution of the initial-value problem is

$$E = E_0 e^{4/RC} e^{-t/RC} = E_0 e^{-(t-4)/RC}.$$

48. (a) An integrating factor for $y' - 2xy = -1$ is e^{-x^2}. Thus

$$\frac{d}{dx}\left[e^{-x^2} y\right] = -e^{-x^2}$$

$$e^{-x^2} y = -\int_0^x e^{-t^2}\, dt = -\frac{\sqrt{\pi}}{2}\operatorname{erf}(x) + c.$$

From $y(0) = \sqrt{\pi}/2$, and noting that $\operatorname{erf}(0) = 0$, we get $c = \sqrt{\pi}/2$. Thus

$$y = e^{x^2}\left(-\frac{\sqrt{\pi}}{2}\operatorname{erf}(x) + \frac{\sqrt{\pi}}{2}\right) = \frac{\sqrt{\pi}}{2} e^{x^2}\left(1 - \operatorname{erf}(x)\right) = \frac{\sqrt{\pi}}{2} e^{x^2} \operatorname{erfc}(x).$$

(b) Using a CAS we find $y(2) \approx 0.226339$.

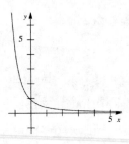

49. (a) An integrating factor for

$$y' + \frac{2}{x} y = \frac{10 \sin x}{x^3}$$

is x^2. Thus

$$\frac{d}{dx}[x^2 y] = 10\frac{\sin x}{x}$$

$$x^2 y = 10 \int_0^x \frac{\sin t}{t}\, dt + c$$

$$y = 10x^{-2}\mathrm{Si}(x) + cx^{-2}.$$

From $y(1) = 0$ we get $c = -10\mathrm{Si}(1)$. Thus

$$y = 10x^{-2}\mathrm{Si}(x) - 10x^{-2}\mathrm{Si}(1) = 10x^{-2}(\mathrm{Si}(x) - \mathrm{Si}(1)).$$

(b)

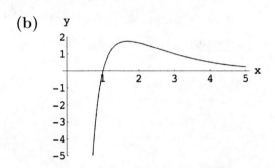

(c) From the graph in part (b) we see that the absolute maximum occurs around $x = 1.7$. Using the root-finding capability of a CAS and solving $y'(x) = 0$ for x we see that the absolute maximum is $(1.688, 1.742)$.

50. (a) The integrating factor for $y' - (\sin x^2)y = 0$ is $e^{-\int_0^x \sin t^2\, dt}$. Then

$$\frac{d}{dx}[e^{-\int_0^x \sin t^2 dt}\, y] = 0$$

$$e^{-\int_0^x \sin t^2\, dt}\, y = c_1$$

$$y = c_1 e^{\int_0^x \sin t^2 dt}.$$

Letting $t = \sqrt{\pi/2}\, u$ we have $dt = \sqrt{\pi/2}\, du$ and

$$\int_0^x \sin t^2\, dt = \sqrt{\frac{\pi}{2}} \int_0^{\sqrt{2/\pi}\, x} \sin\left(\frac{\pi}{2} u^2\right) du = \sqrt{\frac{\pi}{2}}\, S\!\left(\sqrt{\frac{2}{\pi}} x\right)$$

so $y = c_1 e^{\sqrt{\pi/2}\, S(\sqrt{2/\pi}\, x)}$. Using $S(0) = 0$ and $y(0) = c_1 = 5$ we have $y = 5 e^{\sqrt{\pi/2}\, S(\sqrt{2/\pi}\, x)}$.

Exercises 2.3 Linear Equations

(b)

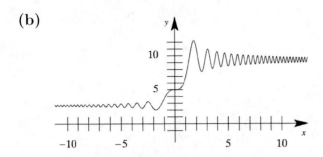

(c) From the graph we see that as $x \to \infty$, $y(x)$ oscillates with decreasing amplitudes approaching 9.35672. Since $\lim_{x\to\infty} 5S(x) = \frac{1}{2}$, $\lim_{x\to\infty} y(x) = 5e^{\sqrt{\pi/8}} \approx 9.357$, and since $\lim_{x\to-\infty} S(x) = -\frac{1}{2}$, $\lim_{x\to-\infty} y(x) = 5e^{-\sqrt{\pi/8}} \approx 2.672$.

(d) From the graph in part (b) we see that the absolute maximum occurs around $x = 1.7$ and the absolute minimum occurs around $x = -1.8$. Using the root-finding capability of a CAS and solving $y'(x) = 0$ for x, we see that the absolute maximum is $(1.772, 12.235)$ and the absolute minimum is $(-1.772, 2.044)$.

Exercises 2.4 Exact Equations

1. Let $M = 2x - 1$ and $N = 3y + 7$ so that $M_y = 0 = N_x$. From $f_x = 2x - 1$ we obtain $f = x^2 - x + h(y)$, $h'(y) = 3y + 7$, and $h(y) = \frac{3}{2}y^2 + 7y$. A solution is $x^2 - x + \frac{3}{2}y^2 + 7y = c$.

2. Let $M = 2x + y$ and $N = -x - 6y$. Then $M_y = 1$ and $N_x = -1$, so the equation is not exact.

3. Let $M = 5x + 4y$ and $N = 4x - 8y^3$ so that $M_y = 4 = N_x$. From $f_x = 5x + 4y$ we obtain $f = \frac{5}{2}x^2 + 4xy + h(y)$, $h'(y) = -8y^3$, and $h(y) = -2y^4$. A solution is $\frac{5}{2}x^2 + 4xy - 2y^4 = c$.

4. Let $M = \sin y - y \sin x$ and $N = \cos x + x \cos y - y$ so that $M_y = \cos y - \sin x = N_x$. From $f_x = \sin y - y \sin x$ we obtain $f = x \sin y + y \cos x + h(y)$, $h'(y) = -y$, and $h(y) = -\frac{1}{2}y^2$. A solution is $x \sin y + y \cos x - \frac{1}{2}y^2 = c$.

5. Let $M = 2y^2x - 3$ and $N = 2yx^2 + 4$ so that $M_y = 4xy = N_x$. From $f_x = 2y^2x - 3$ we obtain $f = x^2y^2 - 3x + h(y)$, $h'(y) = 4$, and $h(y) = 4y$. A solution is $x^2y^2 - 3x + 4y = c$.

6. Let $M = 4x^3 - 3y \sin 3x - y/x^2$ and $N = 2y - 1/x + \cos 3x$ so that $M_y = -3 \sin 3x - 1/x^2$ and $N_x = 1/x^2 - 3 \sin 3x$. The equation is not exact.

7. Let $M = x^2 - y^2$ and $N = x^2 - 2xy$ so that $M_y = -2y$ and $N_x = 2x - 2y$. The equation is not exact.

58

8. Let $M = 1 + \ln x + y/x$ and $N = -1 + \ln x$ so that $M_y = 1/x = N_x$. From $f_y = -1 + \ln x$ we obtain $f = -y + y \ln x + h(y)$, $h'(x) = 1 + \ln x$, and $h(y) = x \ln x$. A solution is $-y + y \ln x + x \ln x = c$.

9. Let $M = y^3 - y^2 \sin x - x$ and $N = 3xy^2 + 2y \cos x$ so that $M_y = 3y^2 - 2y \sin x = N_x$. From $f_x = y^3 - y^2 \sin x - x$ we obtain $f = xy^3 + y^2 \cos x - \frac{1}{2}x^2 + h(y)$, $h'(y) = 0$, and $h(y) = 0$. A solution is $xy^3 + y^2 \cos x - \frac{1}{2}x^2 = c$.

10. Let $M = x^3 + y^3$ and $N = 3xy^2$ so that $M_y = 3y^2 = N_x$. From $f_x = x^3 + y^3$ we obtain $f = \frac{1}{4}x^4 + xy^3 + h(y)$, $h'(y) = 0$, and $h(y) = 0$. A solution is $\frac{1}{4}x^4 + xy^3 = c$.

11. Let $M = y \ln y - e^{-xy}$ and $N = 1/y + x \ln y$ so that $M_y = 1 + \ln y + xe^{-xy}$ and $N_x = \ln y$. The equation is not exact.

12. Let $M = 3x^2 y + e^y$ and $N = x^3 + xe^y - 2y$ so that $M_y = 3x^2 + e^y = N_x$. From $f_x = 3x^2 y + e^y$ we obtain $f = x^3 y + xe^y + h(y)$, $h'(y) = -2y$, and $h(y) = -y^2$. A solution is $x^3 y + xe^y - y^2 = c$.

13. Let $M = y - 6x^2 - 2xe^x$ and $N = x$ so that $M_y = 1 = N_x$. From $f_x = y - 6x^2 - 2xe^x$ we obtain $f = xy - 2x^3 - 2xe^x + 2e^x + h(y)$, $h'(y) = 0$, and $h(y) = 0$. A solution is $xy - 2x^3 - 2xe^x + 2e^x = c$.

14. Let $M = 1 - 3/x + y$ and $N = 1 - 3/y + x$ so that $M_y = 1 = N_x$. From $f_x = 1 - 3/x + y$ we obtain $f = x - 3 \ln|x| + xy + h(y)$, $h'(y) = 1 - \dfrac{3}{y}$, and $h(y) = y - 3 \ln|y|$. A solution is $x + y + xy - 3 \ln|xy| = c$.

15. Let $M = x^2 y^3 - 1/(1 + 9x^2)$ and $N = x^3 y^2$ so that $M_y = 3x^2 y^2 = N_x$. From $f_x = x^2 y^3 - 1/(1 + 9x^2)$ we obtain $f = \frac{1}{3}x^3 y^3 - \frac{1}{3} \arctan(3x) + h(y)$, $h'(y) = 0$, and $h(y) = 0$. A solution is $x^3 y^3 - \arctan(3x) = c$.

16. Let $M = -2y$ and $N = 5y - 2x$ so that $M_y = -2 = N_x$. From $f_x = -2y$ we obtain $f = -2xy + h(y)$, $h'(y) = 5y$, and $h(y) = \frac{5}{2}y^2$. A solution is $-2xy + \frac{5}{2}y^2 = c$.

17. Let $M = \tan x - \sin x \sin y$ and $N = \cos x \cos y$ so that $M_y = -\sin x \cos y = N_x$. From $f_x = \tan x - \sin x \sin y$ we obtain $f = \ln|\sec x| + \cos x \sin y + h(y)$, $h'(y) = 0$, and $h(y) = 0$. A solution is $\ln|\sec x| + \cos x \sin y = c$.

18. Let $M = 2y \sin x \cos x - y + 2y^2 e^{xy^2}$ and $N = -x + \sin^2 x + 4xye^{xy^2}$ so that
$$M_y = 2 \sin x \cos x - 1 + 4xy^3 e^{xy^2} + 4ye^{xy^2} = N_x.$$
From $f_x = 2y \sin x \cos x - y + 2y^2 e^{xy^2}$ we obtain $f = y \sin^2 x - xy + 2e^{xy^2} + h(y)$, $h'(y) = 0$, and $h(y) = 0$. A solution is $y \sin^2 x - xy + 2e^{xy^2} = c$.

19. Let $M = 4t^3 y - 15t^2 - y$ and $N = t^4 + 3y^2 - t$ so that $M_y = 4t^3 - 1 = N_t$. From $f_t = 4t^3 y - 15t^2 - y$ we obtain $f = t^4 y - 5t^3 - ty + h(y)$, $h'(y) = 3y^2$, and $h(y) = y^3$. A solution is $t^4 y - 5t^3 - ty + y^3 = c$.

20. Let $M = 1/t + 1/t^2 - y/(t^2 + y^2)$ and $N = ye^y + t/(t^2 + y^2)$ so that $M_y = (y^2 - t^2)/(t^2 + y^2)^2 = N_t$. From $f_t = 1/t + 1/t^2 - y/(t^2 + y^2)$ we obtain $f = \ln|t| - \dfrac{1}{t} - \arctan\left(\dfrac{t}{y}\right) + h(y)$, $h'(y) = ye^y$,

and $h(y) = ye^y - e^y$. A solution is

$$\ln|t| - \frac{1}{t} - \arctan\left(\frac{t}{y}\right) + ye^y - e^y = c.$$

21. Let $M = x^2 + 2xy + y^2$ and $N = 2xy + x^2 - 1$ so that $M_y = 2(x+y) = N_x$. From $f_x = x^2 + 2xy + y^2$ we obtain $f = \frac{1}{3}x^3 + x^2y + xy^2 + h(y)$, $h'(y) = -1$, and $h(y) = -y$. The solution is $\frac{1}{3}x^3 + x^2y + xy^2 - y = c$. If $y(1) = 1$ then $c = 4/3$ and a solution of the initial-value problem is $\frac{1}{3}x^3 + x^2y + xy^2 - y = \frac{4}{3}$.

22. Let $M = e^x + y$ and $N = 2 + x + ye^y$ so that $M_y = 1 = N_x$. From $f_x = e^x + y$ we obtain $f = e^x + xy + h(y)$, $h'(y) = 2 + ye^y$, and $h(y) = 2y + ye^y - y$. The solution is $e^x + xy + 2y + ye^y - e^y = c$. If $y(0) = 1$ then $c = 3$ and a solution of the initial-value problem is $e^x + xy + 2y + ye^y - e^y = 3$.

23. Let $M = 4y + 2t - 5$ and $N = 6y + 4t - 1$ so that $M_y = 4 = N_t$. From $f_t = 4y + 2t - 5$ we obtain $f = 4ty + t^2 - 5t + h(y)$, $h'(y) = 6y - 1$, and $h(y) = 3y^2 - y$. The solution is $4ty + t^2 - 5t + 3y^2 - y = c$. If $y(-1) = 2$ then $c = 8$ and a solution of the initial-value problem is $4ty + t^2 - 5t + 3y^2 - y = 8$.

24. Let $M = t/2y^4$ and $N = \left(3y^2 - t^2\right)/y^5$ so that $M_y = -2t/y^5 = N_t$. From $f_t = t/2y^4$ we obtain $f = \frac{t^2}{4y^4} + h(y)$, $h'(y) = \frac{3}{y^3}$, and $h(y) = -\frac{3}{2y^2}$. The solution is $\frac{t^2}{4y^4} - \frac{3}{2y^2} = c$. If $y(1) = 1$ then $c = -5/4$ and a solution of the initial-value problem is $\frac{t^2}{4y^4} - \frac{3}{2y^2} = -\frac{5}{4}$.

25. Let $M = y^2 \cos x - 3x^2 y - 2x$ and $N = 2y \sin x - x^3 + \ln y$ so that $M_y = 2y \cos x - 3x^2 = N_x$. From $f_x = y^2 \cos x - 3x^2 y - 2x$ we obtain $f = y^2 \sin x - x^3 y - x^2 + h(y)$, $h'(y) = \ln y$, and $h(y) = y \ln y - y$. The solution is $y^2 \sin x - x^3 y - x^2 + y \ln y - y = c$. If $y(0) = e$ then $c = 0$ and a solution of the initial-value problem is $y^2 \sin x - x^3 y - x^2 + y \ln y - y = 0$.

26. Let $M = y^2 + y \sin x$ and $N = 2xy - \cos x - 1/\left(1 + y^2\right)$ so that $M_y = 2y + \sin x = N_x$. From $f_x = y^2 + y \sin x$ we obtain $f = xy^2 - y \cos x + h(y)$, $h'(y) = \frac{-1}{1 + y^2}$, and $h(y) = -\tan^{-1} y$. The solution is $xy^2 - y \cos x - \tan^{-1} y = c$. If $y(0) = 1$ then $c = -1 - \pi/4$ and a solution of the initial-value problem is $xy^2 - y \cos x - \tan^{-1} y = -1 - \frac{\pi}{4}$.

27. Equating $M_y = 3y^2 + 4kxy^3$ and $N_x = 3y^2 + 40xy^3$ we obtain $k = 10$.

28. Equating $M_y = 18xy^2 - \sin y$ and $N_x = 4kxy^2 - \sin y$ we obtain $k = 9/2$.

29. Let $M = -x^2 y^2 \sin x + 2xy^2 \cos x$ and $N = 2x^2 y \cos x$ so that $M_y = -2x^2 y \sin x + 4xy \cos x = N_x$. From $f_y = 2x^2 y \cos x$ we obtain $f = x^2 y^2 \cos x + h(y)$, $h'(y) = 0$, and $h(y) = 0$. A solution of the differential equation is $x^2 y^2 \cos x = c$.

30. Let $M = \left(x^2 + 2xy - y^2\right)/\left(x^2 + 2xy + y^2\right)$ and $N = \left(y^2 + 2xy - x^2\right)/\left(y^2 + 2xy + x^2\right)$ so that $M_y = -4xy/(x+y)^3 = N_x$. From $f_x = \left(x^2 + 2xy + y^2 - 2y^2\right)/(x+y)^2$ we obtain

$f = x + \dfrac{2y^2}{x+y} + h(y)$, $h'(y) = -1$, and $h(y) = -y$. A solution of the differential equation is $x^2 + y^2 = c(x+y)$.

31. We note that $(M_y - N_x)/N = 1/x$, so an integrating factor is $e^{\int dx/x} = x$. Let $M = 2xy^2 + 3x^2$ and $N = 2x^2y$ so that $M_y = 4xy = N_x$. From $f_x = 2xy^2 + 3x^2$ we obtain $f = x^2y^2 + x^3 + h(y)$, $h'(y) = 0$, and $h(y) = 0$. A solution of the differential equation is $x^2y^2 + x^3 = c$.

32. We note that $(M_y - N_x)/N = 1$, so an integrating factor is $e^{\int dx} = e^x$. Let $M = xye^x + y^2e^x + ye^x$ and $N = xe^x + 2ye^x$ so that $M_y = xe^x + 2ye^x + e^x = N_x$. From $f_y = xe^x + 2ye^x$ we obtain $f = xye^x + y^2e^x + h(x)$, $h'(y) = 0$, and $h(y) = 0$. A solution of the differential equation is $xye^x + y^2e^x = c$.

33. We note that $(N_x - M_y)/M = 2/y$, so an integrating factor is $e^{\int 2dy/y} = y^2$. Let $M = 6xy^3$ and $N = 4y^3 + 9x^2y^2$ so that $M_y = 18xy^2 = N_x$. From $f_x = 6xy^3$ we obtain $f = 3x^2y^3 + h(y)$, $h'(y) = 4y^3$, and $h(y) = y^4$. A solution of the differential equation is $3x^2y^3 + y^4 = c$.

34. We note that $(M_y - N_x)/N = -\cot x$, so an integrating factor is $e^{-\int \cot x\, dx} = \csc x$. Let $M = \cos x \csc x = \cot x$ and $N = (1 + 2/y)\sin x \csc x = 1 + 2/y$, so that $M_y = 0 = N_x$. From $f_x = \cot x$ we obtain $f = \ln(\sin x) + h(y)$, $h'(y) = 1 + 2/y$, and $h(y) = y + \ln y^2$. A solution of the differential equation is $\ln(\sin x) + y + \ln y^2 = c$.

35. We note that $(M_y - N_x)/N = 3$, so an integrating factor is $e^{\int 3\,dx} = e^{3x}$. Let

$$M = (10 - 6y + e^{-3x})e^{3x} = 10e^{3x} - 6ye^{3x} + 1$$

and

$$N = -2e^{3x},$$

so that $M_y = -6e^{3x} = N_x$. From $f_x = 10e^{3x} - 6ye^{3x} + 1$ we obtain $f = \frac{10}{3}e^{3x} - 2ye^{3x} + x + h(y)$, $h'(y) = 0$, and $h(y) = 0$. A solution of the differential equation is $\frac{10}{3}e^{3x} - 2ye^{3x} + x = c$.

36. We note that $(N_x - M_y)/M = -3/y$, so an integrating factor is $e^{-3\int dy/y} = 1/y^3$. Let

$$M = (y^2 + xy^3)/y^3 = 1/y + x$$

and

$$N = (5y^2 - xy + y^3 \sin y)/y^3 = 5/y - x/y^2 + \sin y,$$

so that $M_y = -1/y^2 = N_x$. From $f_x = 1/y + x$ we obtain $f = x/y + \frac{1}{2}x^2 + h(y)$, $h'(y) = 5/y + \sin y$, and $h(y) = 5\ln|y| - \cos y$. A solution of the differential equation is $x/y + \frac{1}{2}x^2 + 5\ln|y| - \cos y = c$.

37. We note that $(M_y - N_x)/N = 2x/(4+x^2)$, so an integrating factor is $e^{-2\int x\, dx/(4+x^2)} = 1/(4+x^2)$. Let $M = x/(4+x^2)$ and $N = (x^2y + 4y)/(4+x^2) = y$, so that $M_y = 0 = N_x$. From $f_x = x(4+x^2)$ we obtain $f = \frac{1}{2}\ln(4+x^2) + h(y)$, $h'(y) = y$, and $h(y) = \frac{1}{2}y^2$. A solution of the differential equation is $\frac{1}{2}\ln(4+x^2) + \frac{1}{2}y^2 = c$.

38. We note that $(M_y - N_x)/N = -3/(1+x)$, so an integrating factor is $e^{-3\int dx/(1+x)} = 1/(1+x)^3$. Let $M = (x^2+y^2-5)/(1+x)^3$ and $N = -(y+xy)/(1+x)^3 = -y/(1+x)^2$, so that $M_y = 2y/(1+x)^3 = N_x$. From $f_y = -y/(1+x)^2$ we obtain $f = -\frac{1}{2}y^2/(1+x)^2 + h(x)$, $h'(x) = (x^2-5)/(1+x)^3$, and $h(x) = 2/(1+x)^2 + 2/(1+x) + \ln|1+x|$. A solution of the differential equation is

$$-\frac{y^2}{2(1+x)^2} + \frac{2}{(1+x)^2} + \frac{2}{(1+x)} + \ln|1+x| = c.$$

39. (a) Implicitly differentiating $x^3 + 2x^2y + y^2 = c$ and solving for dy/dx we obtain

$$3x^2 + 2x^2\frac{dy}{dx} + 4xy + 2y\frac{dy}{dx} = 0 \quad \text{and} \quad \frac{dy}{dx} = -\frac{3x^2 + 4xy}{2x^2 + 2y}.$$

By writing the last equation in differential form we get $(4xy + 3x^2)dx + (2y + 2x^2)dy = 0$.

(b) Setting $x = 0$ and $y = -2$ in $x^3 + 2x^2y + y^2 = c$ we find $c = 4$, and setting $x = y = 1$ we also find $c = 4$. Thus, both initial conditions determine the same implicit solution.

(c) Solving $x^3 + 2x^2y + y^2 = 4$ for y we get

$$y_1(x) = -x^2 - \sqrt{4 - x^3 + x^4}$$

and

$$y_2(x) = -x^2 + \sqrt{4 - x^3 + x^4}\,.$$

Observe in the figure that $y_1(0) = -2$ and $y_2(1) = 1$.

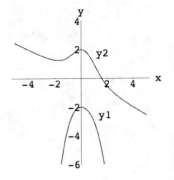

40. To see that the equations are not equivalent consider $dx = -(x/y)dy$. An integrating factor is $\mu(x, y) = y$ resulting in $y\,dx + x\,dy = 0$. A solution of the latter equation is $y = 0$, but this is not a solution of the original equation.

41. The explicit solution is $y = \sqrt{(3 + \cos^2 x)/(1 - x^2)}$. Since $3 + \cos^2 x > 0$ for all x we must have $1 - x^2 > 0$ or $-1 < x < 1$. Thus, the interval of definition is $(-1, 1)$.

42. (a) Since $f_y = N(x, y) = xe^{xy} + 2xy + 1/x$ we obtain $f = e^{xy} + xy^2 + \frac{y}{x} + h(x)$ so that $f_x = ye^{xy} + y^2 - \frac{y}{x^2} + h'(x)$. Let $M(x, y) = ye^{xy} + y^2 - \frac{y}{x^2}$.

(b) Since $f_x = M(x, y) = y^{1/2}x^{-1/2} + x\left(x^2 + y\right)^{-1}$ we obtain $f = 2y^{1/2}x^{1/2} + \frac{1}{2}\ln\left|x^2 + y\right| + g(y)$ so that $f_y = y^{-1/2}x^{1/2} + \frac{1}{2}\left(x^2 + y\right)^{-1} + g'(x)$. Let $N(x, y) = y^{-1/2}x^{1/2} + \frac{1}{2}\left(x^2 + y\right)^{-1}$.

43. First note that

$$d\left(\sqrt{x^2 + y^2}\right) = \frac{x}{\sqrt{x^2 + y^2}}\,dx + \frac{y}{\sqrt{x^2 + y^2}}\,dy.$$

Then $x\,dx + y\,dy = \sqrt{x^2 + y^2}\,dx$ becomes

$$\frac{x}{\sqrt{x^2 + y^2}}\,dx + \frac{y}{\sqrt{x^2 + y^2}}\,dy = d\left(\sqrt{x^2 + y^2}\right) = dx.$$

The left side is the total differential of $\sqrt{x^2 + y^2}$ and the right side is the total differential of $x + c$. Thus $\sqrt{x^2 + y^2} = x + c$ is a solution of the differential equation.

44. To see that the statement is true, write the separable equation as $-g(x)\,dx + dy/h(y) = 0$. Identifying $M = -g(x)$ and $N = 1/h(y)$, we see that $M_y = 0 = N_x$, so the differential equation is exact.

45. (a) In differential form we have $(v^2 - 32x)dx + xv\,dv = 0$. This is not an exact form, but $\mu(x) = x$ is an integrating factor. Multiplying by x we get $(xv^2 - 32x^2)dx + x^2v\,dv = 0$. This form is the total differential of $u = \frac{1}{2}x^2v^2 - \frac{32}{3}x^3$, so an implicit solution is $\frac{1}{2}x^2v^2 - \frac{32}{3}x^3 = c$. Letting $x = 3$ and $v = 0$ we find $c = -288$. Solving for v we get

$$v = 8\sqrt{\frac{x}{3} - \frac{9}{x^2}}\,.$$

(b) The chain leaves the platform when $x = 8$, so the velocity at this time is

$$v(8) = 8\sqrt{\frac{8}{3} - \frac{9}{64}} \approx 12.7 \text{ ft/s}.$$

46. (a) Letting

$$M(x, y) = \frac{2xy}{(x^2 + y^2)^2} \qquad \text{and} \qquad N(x, y) = 1 + \frac{y^2 - x^2}{(x^2 + y^2)^2}$$

we compute

$$M_y = \frac{2x^3 - 8xy^2}{(x^2 + y^2)^3} = N_x,$$

so the differential equation is exact. Then we have

$$\frac{\partial f}{\partial x} = M(x, y) = \frac{2xy}{(x^2 + y^2)^2} = 2xy(x^2 + y^2)^{-2}$$

$$f(x, y) = -y(x^2 + y^2)^{-1} + g(y) = -\frac{y}{x^2 + y^2} + g(y)$$

$$\frac{\partial f}{\partial y} = \frac{y^2 - x^2}{(x^2 + y^2)^2} + g'(y) = N(x, y) = 1 + \frac{y^2 - x^2}{(x^2 + y^2)^2}\,.$$

Thus, $g'(y) = 1$ and $g(y) = y$. The solution is $y - \dfrac{y}{x^2 + y^2} = c$. When $c = 0$ the solution is $x^2 + y^2 = 1$.

(b) The first graph below is obtained in *Mathematica* using $f(x, y) = y - y/(x^2 + y^2)$ and

   ContourPlot[f[x, y], {x, -3, 3}, {y, -3, 3},

$$\text{Axes->True, AxesOrigin->}\{0,\,0\},\text{ AxesLabel->}\{x,\,y\},$$
$$\text{Frame->False, PlotPoints->100, ContourShading->False,}$$
$$\text{Contours->}\{0,\,-0.2,\,0.2,\,-0.4,\,0.4,\,-0.6,\,0.6,\,-0.8,\,0.8\}]$$

The second graph uses

$$x = -\sqrt{\frac{y^3 - cy^2 - y}{c - y}} \qquad \text{and} \qquad x = \sqrt{\frac{y^3 - cy^2 - y}{c - y}}\,.$$

In this case the x-axis is vertical and the y-axis is horizontal. To obtain the third graph, we solve $y - y/(x^2 + y^2) = c$ for y in a CAS. This appears to give one real and two complex solutions. When graphed in *Mathematica* however, all three solutions contribute to the graph. This is because the solutions involve the square root of expressions containing c. For some values of c the expression is negative, causing an apparent complex solution to actually be real.

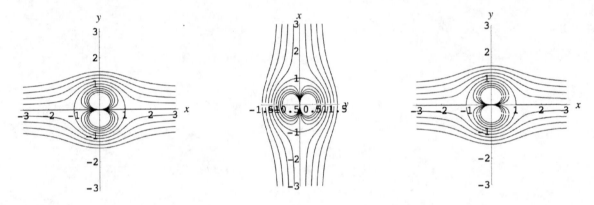

1. Letting $y = ux$ we have

$$(x - ux)\,dx + x(u\,dx + x\,du) = 0$$

$$dx + x\,du = 0$$

$$\frac{dx}{x} + du = 0$$

$$\ln|x| + u = c$$

$$x\ln|x| + y = cx.$$

2. Letting $y = ux$ we have

$$(x + ux)\,dx + x(u\,dx + x\,du) = 0$$

$$(1 + 2u)\,dx + x\,du = 0$$

$$\frac{dx}{x} + \frac{du}{1 + 2u} = 0$$

$$\ln|x| + \frac{1}{2}\ln|1 + 2u| = c$$

$$x^2\left(1 + 2\frac{y}{x}\right) = c_1$$

$$x^2 + 2xy = c_1.$$

3. Letting $x = vy$ we have

$$vy(v\,dy + y\,dv) + (y - 2vy)\,dy = 0$$

$$vy^2\,dv + y\left(v^2 - 2v + 1\right)dy = 0$$

$$\frac{v\,dv}{(v - 1)^2} + \frac{dy}{y} = 0$$

$$\ln|v - 1| - \frac{1}{v - 1} + \ln|y| = c$$

$$\ln\left|\frac{x}{y} - 1\right| - \frac{1}{x/y - 1} + \ln y = c$$

$$(x - y)\ln|x - y| - y = c(x - y).$$

4. Letting $x = vy$ we have

$$y(v\,dy + y\,dv) - 2(vy + y)\,dy = 0$$

$$y\,dv - (v + 2)\,dy = 0$$

$$\frac{dv}{v + 2} - \frac{dy}{y} = 0$$

$$\ln|v + 2| - \ln|y| = c$$

$$\ln\left|\frac{x}{y} + 2\right| - \ln|y| = c$$

$$x + 2y = c_1 y^2.$$

Exercises 2.5 Solutions by Substitutions

5. Letting $y = ux$ we have

$$\left(u^2 x^2 + ux^2\right) dx - x^2 (u\, dx + x\, du) = 0$$

$$u^2\, dx - x\, du = 0$$

$$\frac{dx}{x} - \frac{du}{u^2} = 0$$

$$\ln|x| + \frac{1}{u} = c$$

$$\ln|x| + \frac{x}{y} = c$$

$$y \ln|x| + x = cy.$$

6. Letting $y = ux$ and using partial fractions, we have

$$\left(u^2 x^2 + ux^2\right) dx + x^2 (u\, dx + x\, du) = 0$$

$$x^2 \left(u^2 + 2u\right) dx + x^3\, du = 0$$

$$\frac{dx}{x} + \frac{du}{u(u+2)} = 0$$

$$\ln|x| + \frac{1}{2} \ln|u| - \frac{1}{2} \ln|u+2| = c$$

$$\frac{x^2 u}{u+2} = c_1$$

$$x^2 \frac{y}{x} = c_1 \left(\frac{y}{x} + 2\right)$$

$$x^2 y = c_1 (y + 2x).$$

7. Letting $y = ux$ we have

$$(ux - x)\, dx - (ux + x)(u\, dx + x\, du) = 0$$

$$\left(u^2 + 1\right) dx + x(u+1)\, du = 0$$

$$\frac{dx}{x} + \frac{u+1}{u^2+1}\, du = 0$$

$$\ln|x| + \frac{1}{2} \ln\left(u^2 + 1\right) + \tan^{-1} u = c$$

$$\ln x^2 \left(\frac{y^2}{x^2} + 1\right) + 2\tan^{-1} \frac{y}{x} = c_1$$

$$\ln\left(x^2 + y^2\right) + 2\tan^{-1} \frac{y}{x} = c_1.$$

8. Letting $y = ux$ we have

$$(x + 3ux)\,dx - (3x + ux)(u\,dx + x\,du) = 0$$

$$\left(u^2 - 1\right)dx + x(u + 3)\,du = 0$$

$$\frac{dx}{x} + \frac{u + 3}{(u - 1)(u + 1)}\,du = 0$$

$$\ln|x| + 2\ln|u - 1| - \ln|u + 1| = c$$

$$\frac{x(u - 1)^2}{u + 1} = c_1$$

$$x\left(\frac{y}{x} - 1\right)^2 = c_1\left(\frac{y}{x} + 1\right)$$

$$(y - x)^2 = c_1(y + x).$$

9. Letting $y = ux$ we have

$$-ux\,dx + (x + \sqrt{u}\,x)(u\,dx + x\,du) = 0$$

$$(x^2 + x^2\sqrt{u}\,)\,du + xu^{3/2}\,dx = 0$$

$$\left(u^{-3/2} + \frac{1}{u}\right)du + \frac{dx}{x} = 0$$

$$-2u^{-1/2} + \ln|u| + \ln|x| = c$$

$$\ln|y/x| + \ln|x| = 2\sqrt{x/y} + c$$

$$y(\ln|y| - c)^2 = 4x.$$

10. Letting $y = ux$ we have

$$\left(ux + \sqrt{x^2 - (ux)^2}\,\right)dx - x(u\,dx + x\,du)\,du = 0$$

$$\sqrt{x^2 - u^2x^2}\,dx - x^2\,du = 0$$

$$x\sqrt{1 - u^2}\,dx - x^2\,du = 0, \quad (x > 0)$$

$$\frac{dx}{x} - \frac{du}{\sqrt{1 - u^2}} = 0$$

$$\ln x - \sin^{-1}u = c$$

$$\sin^{-1}u = \ln x + c_1$$

$$\sin^{-1}\frac{y}{x} = \ln x + c_2$$

$$\frac{y}{x} = \sin(\ln x + c_2)$$

$$y = x\sin(\ln x + c_2).$$

See Problem 33 in this section for an analysis of the solution.

11. Letting $y = ux$ we have

$$\left(x^3 - u^3 x^3\right)dx + u^2 x^3 (u\,dx + x\,du) = 0$$

$$dx + u^2 x\,du = 0$$

$$\frac{dx}{x} + u^2\,du = 0$$

$$\ln|x| + \frac{1}{3}u^3 = c$$

$$3x^3 \ln|x| + y^3 = c_1 x^3.$$

Using $y(1) = 2$ we find $c_1 = 8$. The solution of the initial-value problem is $3x^3 \ln|x| + y^3 = 8x^3$.

12. Letting $y = ux$ we have

$$(x^2 + 2u^2 x^2)dx - ux^2(u\,dx + x\,du) = 0$$

$$x^2(1 + u^2)dx - ux^3\,du = 0$$

$$\frac{dx}{x} - \frac{u\,du}{1 + u^2} = 0$$

$$\ln|x| - \frac{1}{2}\ln(1 + u^2) = c$$

$$\frac{x^2}{1 + u^2} = c_1$$

$$x^4 = c_1(x^2 + y^2).$$

Using $y(-1) = 1$ we find $c_1 = 1/2$. The solution of the initial-value problem is $2x^4 = y^2 + x^2$.

13. Letting $y = ux$ we have

$$(x + uxe^u)\,dx - xe^u(u\,dx + x\,du) = 0$$

$$dx - xe^u\,du = 0$$

$$\frac{dx}{x} - e^u\,du = 0$$

$$\ln|x| - e^u = c$$

$$\ln|x| - e^{y/x} = c.$$

Using $y(1) = 0$ we find $c = -1$. The solution of the initial-value problem is $\ln|x| = e^{y/x} - 1$.

14. Letting $x = vy$ we have

$$y(v\,dy + y\,dv) + vy(\ln vy - \ln y - 1)\,dy = 0$$

$$y\,dv + v\ln v\,dy = 0$$

$$\frac{dv}{v\ln v} + \frac{dy}{y} = 0$$

$$\ln|\ln|v|| + \ln|y| = c$$

$$y\ln\left|\frac{x}{y}\right| = c_1.$$

Using $y(1) = e$ we find $c_1 = -e$. The solution of the initial-value problem is $y\ln\left|\dfrac{x}{y}\right| = -e$.

15. From $y' + \dfrac{1}{x}y = \dfrac{1}{x}y^{-2}$ and $w = y^3$ we obtain $\dfrac{dw}{dx} + \dfrac{3}{x}w = \dfrac{3}{x}$. An integrating factor is x^3 so that $x^3 w = x^3 + c$ or $y^3 = 1 + cx^{-3}$.

16. From $y' - y = e^x y^2$ and $w = y^{-1}$ we obtain $\dfrac{dw}{dx} + w = -e^x$. An integrating factor is e^x so that $e^x w = -\frac{1}{2}e^{2x} + c$ or $y^{-1} = -\frac{1}{2}e^x + ce^{-x}$.

17. From $y' + y = xy^4$ and $w = y^{-3}$ we obtain $\dfrac{dw}{dx} - 3w = -3x$. An integrating factor is e^{-3x} so that $e^{-3x}w = xe^{-3x} + \frac{1}{3}e^{-3x} + c$ or $y^{-3} = x + \frac{1}{3} + ce^{3x}$.

18. From $y' - \left(1 + \dfrac{1}{x}\right)y = y^2$ and $w = y^{-1}$ we obtain $\dfrac{dw}{dx} + \left(1 + \dfrac{1}{x}\right)w = -1$. An integrating factor is xe^x so that $xe^x w = -xe^x + e^x + c$ or $y^{-1} = -1 + \dfrac{1}{x} + \dfrac{c}{x}e^{-x}$.

19. From $y' - \dfrac{1}{t}y = -\dfrac{1}{t^2}y^2$ and $w = y^{-1}$ we obtain $\dfrac{dw}{dt} + \dfrac{1}{t}w = \dfrac{1}{t^2}$. An integrating factor is t so that $tw = \ln t + c$ or $y^{-1} = \dfrac{1}{t}\ln t + \dfrac{c}{t}$. Writing this in the form $\dfrac{t}{y} = \ln t + c$, we see that the solution can also be expressed in the form $e^{t/y} = c_1 t$.

20. From $y' + \dfrac{2}{3(1+t^2)}y = \dfrac{2t}{3(1+t^2)}y^4$ and $w = y^{-3}$ we obtain $\dfrac{dw}{dt} - \dfrac{2t}{1+t^2}w = \dfrac{-2t}{1+t^2}$. An integrating factor is $\dfrac{1}{1+t^2}$ so that $\dfrac{w}{1+t^2} = \dfrac{1}{1+t^2} + c$ or $y^{-3} = 1 + c\left(1+t^2\right)$.

69

Exercises 2.5   Solutions by Substitutions

21. From $y' - \frac{2}{x}y = \frac{3}{x^2}y^4$ and $w = y^{-3}$ we obtain $\frac{dw}{dx} + \frac{6}{x}w = -\frac{9}{x^2}$. An integrating factor is x^6 so that

   $x^6 w = -\frac{9}{5}x^5 + c$ or $y^{-3} = -\frac{9}{5}x^{-1} + cx^{-6}$. If $y(1) = \frac{1}{2}$ then $c = \frac{49}{5}$ and $y^{-3} = -\frac{9}{5}x^{-1} + \frac{49}{5}x^{-6}$.

22. From $y' + y = y^{-1/2}$ and $w = y^{3/2}$ we obtain $\frac{dw}{dx} + \frac{3}{2}w = \frac{3}{2}$. An integrating factor is $e^{3x/2}$ so that

   $e^{3x/2}w = e^{3x/2} + c$ or $y^{3/2} = 1 + ce^{-3x/2}$. If $y(0) = 4$ then $c = 7$ and $y^{3/2} = 1 + 7e^{-3x/2}$.

23. Let $u = x + y + 1$ so that $du/dx = 1 + dy/dx$. Then $\frac{du}{dx} - 1 = u^2$ or $\frac{1}{1 + u^2}\,du = dx$. Thus

   $\tan^{-1} u = x + c$ or $u = \tan(x + c)$, and $x + y + 1 = \tan(x + c)$ or $y = \tan(x + c) - x - 1$.

24. Let $u = x + y$ so that $du/dx = 1 + dy/dx$. Then $\frac{du}{dx} - 1 = \frac{1 - u}{u}$ or $u\,du = dx$. Thus $\frac{1}{2}u^2 = x + c$
   or $u^2 = 2x + c_1$, and $(x + y)^2 = 2x + c_1$.

25. Let $u = x + y$ so that $du/dx = 1 + dy/dx$. Then $\frac{du}{dx} - 1 = \tan^2 u$ or $\cos^2 u\,du = dx$. Thus
   $\frac{1}{2}u + \frac{1}{4}\sin 2u = x + c$ or $2u + \sin 2u = 4x + c_1$, and $2(x+y) + \sin 2(x+y) = 4x + c_1$ or $2y + \sin 2(x+y) = 2x + c_1$.

26. Let $u = x + y$ so that $du/dx = 1 + dy/dx$. Then $\frac{du}{dx} - 1 = \sin u$ or $\frac{1}{1 + \sin u}\,du = dx$. Multiplying
   by $(1 - \sin u)/(1 - \sin u)$ we have $\frac{1 - \sin u}{\cos^2 u}\,du = dx$ or $(\sec^2 u - \sec u \tan u)\,du = dx$. Thus
   $\tan u - \sec u = x + c$ or $\tan(x + y) - \sec(x + y) = x + c$.

27. Let $u = y - 2x + 3$ so that $du/dx = dy/dx - 2$. Then $\frac{du}{dx} + 2 = 2 + \sqrt{u}$ or $\frac{1}{\sqrt{u}}\,du = dx$. Thus
   $2\sqrt{u} = x + c$ and $2\sqrt{y - 2x + 3} = x + c$.

28. Let $u = y - x + 5$ so that $du/dx = dy/dx - 1$. Then $\frac{du}{dx} + 1 = 1 + e^u$ or $e^{-u}du = dx$. Thus
   $-e^{-u} = x + c$ and $-e^{y-x+5} = x + c$.

29. Let $u = x + y$ so that $du/dx = 1 + dy/dx$. Then $\frac{du}{dx} - 1 = \cos u$ and $\frac{1}{1 + \cos u}\,du = dx$. Now

   $$\frac{1}{1 + \cos u} = \frac{1 - \cos u}{1 - \cos^2 u} = \frac{1 - \cos u}{\sin^2 u} = \csc^2 u - \csc u \cot u$$

   so we have $\int(\csc^2 u - \csc u \cot u)\,du = \int dx$ and $-\cot u + \csc u = x + c$. Thus $-\cot(x+y) + \csc(x+y) = x + c$. Setting $x = 0$ and $y = \pi/4$ we obtain $c = \sqrt{2} - 1$. The solution is

   $$\csc(x + y) - \cot(x + y) = x + \sqrt{2} - 1.$$

30. Let $u = 3x + 2y$ so that $du/dx = 3 + 2\,dy/dx$. Then $\frac{du}{dx} = 3 + \frac{2u}{u + 2} = \frac{5u + 6}{u + 2}$ and $\frac{u + 2}{5u + 6}\,du = dx$.
   Now by long division

   $$\frac{u + 2}{5u + 6} = \frac{1}{5} + \frac{4}{25u + 30}$$

70

so we have

$$\int \left(\frac{1}{5} + \frac{4}{25u + 30}\right) du = dx$$

and $\frac{1}{5}u + \frac{4}{25}\ln|25u + 30| = x + c$. Thus

$$\frac{1}{5}(3x + 2y) + \frac{4}{25}\ln|75x + 50y + 30| = x + c.$$

Setting $x = -1$ and $y = -1$ we obtain $c = \frac{4}{25}\ln 95$. The solution is

$$\frac{1}{5}(3x + 2y) + \frac{4}{25}\ln|75x + 50y + 30| = x + \frac{4}{25}\ln 95$$

or

$$5y - 5x + 2\ln|75x + 50y + 30| = 2\ln 95.$$

31. We write the differential equation $M(x, y)dx + N(x, y)dy = 0$ as $dy/dx = f(x, y)$ where

$$f(x, y) = -\frac{M(x, y)}{N(x, y)}.$$

The function $f(x, y)$ must necessarily be homogeneous of degree 0 when M and N are homogeneous of degree α. Since M is homogeneous of degree α, $M(tx, ty) = t^\alpha M(x, y)$, and letting $t = 1/x$ we have

$$M(1, y/x) = \frac{1}{x^\alpha} M(x, y) \quad \text{or} \quad M(x, y) = x^\alpha M(1, y/x).$$

Thus

$$\frac{dy}{dx} = f(x, y) = -\frac{x^\alpha M(1, y/x)}{x^\alpha N(1, y/x)} = -\frac{M(1, y/x)}{N(1, y/x)} = F\left(\frac{y}{x}\right).$$

32. Rewrite $(5x^2 - 2y^2)dx - xy\,dy = 0$ as

$$xy\frac{dy}{dx} = 5x^2 - 2y^2$$

and divide by xy, so that

$$\frac{dy}{dx} = 5\frac{x}{y} - 2\frac{y}{x}.$$

We then identify

$$F\left(\frac{y}{x}\right) = 5\left(\frac{y}{x}\right)^{-1} - 2\left(\frac{y}{x}\right).$$

33. (a) By inspection $y = x$ and $y = -x$ are solutions of the differential equation and not members of the family $y = x\sin(\ln x + c_2)$.

(b) Letting $x = 5$ and $y = 0$ in $\sin^{-1}(y/x) = \ln x + c_2$ we get $\sin^{-1} 0 = \ln 5 + c$ or $c = -\ln 5$. Then $\sin^{-1}(y/x) = \ln x - \ln 5 = \ln(x/5)$. Because the range of the arcsine function is $[-\pi/2, \pi/2]$ we

71

must have

$$-\frac{\pi}{2} \le \ln\frac{x}{5} \le \frac{\pi}{2}$$

$$e^{-\pi/2} \le \frac{x}{5} \le e^{\pi/2}$$

$$5e^{-\pi/2} \le x \le 5e^{\pi/2}.$$

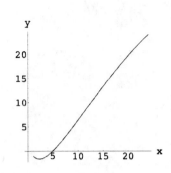

The interval of definition of the solution is approximately $[1.04, 24.05]$.

34. As $x \to -\infty$, $e^{6x} \to 0$ and $y \to 2x + 3$. Now write $(1 + ce^{6x})/(1 - ce^{6x})$ as $(e^{-6x} + c)/(e^{-6x} - c)$. Then, as $x \to \infty$, $e^{-6x} \to 0$ and $y \to 2x - 3$.

35. **(a)** The substitutions $y = y_1 + u$ and

$$\frac{dy}{dx} = \frac{dy_1}{dx} + \frac{du}{dx}$$

lead to

$$\frac{dy_1}{dx} + \frac{du}{dx} = P + Q(y_1 + u) + R(y_1 + u)^2$$

$$= P + Qy_1 + Ry_1^2 + Qu + 2y_1Ru + Ru^2$$

or

$$\frac{du}{dx} - (Q + 2y_1R)u = Ru^2.$$

This is a Bernoulli equation with $n = 2$ which can be reduced to the linear equation

$$\frac{dw}{dx} + (Q + 2y_1R)w = -R$$

by the substitution $w = u^{-1}$.

(b) Identify $P(x) = -4/x^2$, $Q(x) = -1/x$, and $R(x) = 1$. Then $\dfrac{dw}{dx} + \left(-\dfrac{1}{x} + \dfrac{4}{x}\right)w = -1$. An integrating factor is x^3 so that $x^3 w = -\frac{1}{4}x^4 + c$ or $u = \left[-\frac{1}{4}x + cx^{-3}\right]^{-1}$. Thus, $y = \dfrac{2}{x} + u$.

36. Write the differential equation in the form $x(y'/y) = \ln x + \ln y$ and let $u = \ln y$. Then $du/dx = y'/y$ and the differential equation becomes $x(du/dx) = \ln x + u$ or $du/dx - u/x = (\ln x)/x$, which is first-order and linear. An integrating factor is $e^{-\int dx/x} = 1/x$, so that (using integration by parts)

$$\frac{d}{dx}\left[\frac{1}{x}u\right] = \frac{\ln x}{x^2} \quad\text{and}\quad \frac{u}{x} = -\frac{1}{x} - \frac{\ln x}{x} + c.$$

The solution is

$$\ln y = -1 - \ln x + cx \quad\text{or}\quad y = \frac{e^{cx-1}}{x}.$$

37. Write the differential equation as

$$\frac{dv}{dx} + \frac{1}{x}v = 32v^{-1},$$

and let $u = v^2$ or $v = u^{1/2}$. Then

$$\frac{dv}{dx} = \frac{1}{2}u^{-1/2}\frac{du}{dx},$$

and substituting into the differential equation, we have

$$\frac{1}{2}u^{-1/2}\frac{du}{dx} + \frac{1}{x}u^{1/2} = 32u^{-1/2} \qquad \text{or} \qquad \frac{du}{dx} + \frac{2}{x}u = 64.$$

The latter differential equation is linear with integrating factor $e^{\int(2/x)dx} = x^2$, so

$$\frac{d}{dx}[x^2u] = 64x^2$$

and

$$x^2u = \frac{64}{3}x^3 + c \qquad \text{or} \qquad v^2 = \frac{64}{3}x + \frac{c}{x^2}.$$

38. Write the differential equation as $dP/dt - aP = -bP^2$ and let $u = P^{-1}$ or $P = u^{-1}$. Then

$$\frac{dp}{dt} = -u^{-2}\frac{du}{dt},$$

and substituting into the differential equation, we have

$$-u^{-2}\frac{du}{dt} - au^{-1} = -bu^{-2} \qquad \text{or} \qquad \frac{du}{dt} + au = b.$$

The latter differential equation is linear with integrating factor $e^{\int a\,dt} = e^{at}$, so

$$\frac{d}{dt}[e^{at}u] = be^{at}$$

and

$$e^{at}u = \frac{b}{a}e^{at} + c$$

$$e^{at}P^{-1} = \frac{b}{a}e^{at} + c$$

$$P^{-1} = \frac{b}{a} + ce^{-at}$$

$$P = \frac{1}{b/a + ce^{-at}} = \frac{a}{b + c_1e^{-at}}.$$

1. We identify $f(x, y) = 2x - 3y + 1$. Then, for $h = 0.1$,

$$y_{n+1} = y_n + 0.1(2x_n - 3y_n + 1) = 0.2x_n + 0.7y_n + 0.1,$$

and

$$y(1.1) \approx y_1 = 0.2(1) + 0.7(5) + 0.1 = 3.8$$

$$y(1.2) \approx y_2 = 0.2(1.1) + 0.7(3.8) + 0.1 = 2.98.$$

For $h = 0.05$,

$$y_{n+1} = y_n + 0.05(2x_n - 3y_n + 1) = 0.1x_n + 0.85y_n + 0.05,$$

and

$$y(1.05) \approx y_1 = 0.1(1) + 0.85(5) + 0.05 = 4.4$$

$$y(1.1) \approx y_2 = 0.1(1.05) + 0.85(4.4) + 0.05 = 3.895$$

$$y(1.15) \approx y_3 = 0.1(1.1) + 0.85(3.895) + 0.05 = 3.47075$$

$$y(1.2) \approx y_4 = 0.1(1.15) + 0.85(3.47075) + 0.05 = 3.11514.$$

2. We identify $f(x, y) = x + y^2$. Then, for $h = 0.1$,

$$y_{n+1} = y_n + 0.1(x_n + y_n^2) = 0.1x_n + y_n + 0.1y_n^2,$$

and

$$y(0.1) \approx y_1 = 0.1(0) + 0 + 0.1(0)^2 = 0$$

$$y(0.2) \approx y_2 = 0.1(0.1) + 0 + 0.1(0)^2 = 0.01.$$

For $h = 0.05$,

$$y_{n+1} = y_n + 0.05(x_n + y_n^2) = 0.05x_n + y_n + 0.05y_n^2,$$

and

$$y(0.05) \approx y_1 = 0.05(0) + 0 + 0.05(0)^2 = 0$$

$$y(0.1) \approx y_2 = 0.05(0.05) + 0 + 0.05(0)^2 = 0.0025$$

$$y(0.15) \approx y_3 = 0.05(0.1) + 0.0025 + 0.05(0.0025)^2 = 0.0075$$

$$y(0.2) \approx y_4 = 0.05(0.15) + 0.0075 + 0.05(0.0075)^2 = 0.0150.$$

3. Separating variables and integrating, we have

$$\frac{dy}{y} = dx \quad \text{and} \quad \ln|y| = x + c.$$

Thus $y = c_1 e^x$ and, using $y(0) = 1$, we find $c = 1$, so $y = e^x$ is the solution of the initial-value problem.

$h=0.1$

x_n	y_n	Actual Value	Abs. Error	% Rel. Error
0.00	1.0000	1.0000	0.0000	0.00
0.10	1.1000	1.1052	0.0052	0.47
0.20	1.2100	1.2214	0.0114	0.93
0.30	1.3310	1.3499	0.0189	1.40
0.40	1.4641	1.4918	0.0277	1.86
0.50	1.6105	1.6487	0.0382	2.32
0.60	1.7716	1.8221	0.0506	2.77
0.70	1.9487	2.0138	0.0650	3.23
0.80	2.1436	2.2255	0.0820	3.68
0.90	2.3579	2.4596	0.1017	4.13
1.00	2.5937	2.7183	0.1245	4.58

$h=0.05$

x_n	y_n	Actual Value	Abs. Error	% Rel. Error
0.00	1.0000	1.0000	0.0000	0.00
0.05	1.0500	1.0513	0.0013	0.12
0.10	1.1025	1.1052	0.0027	0.24
0.15	1.1576	1.1618	0.0042	0.36
0.20	1.2155	1.2214	0.0059	0.48
0.25	1.2763	1.2840	0.0077	0.60
0.30	1.3401	1.3499	0.0098	0.72
0.35	1.4071	1.4191	0.0120	0.84
0.40	1.4775	1.4918	0.0144	0.96
0.45	1.5513	1.5683	0.0170	1.08
0.50	1.6289	1.6487	0.0198	1.20
0.55	1.7103	1.7333	0.0229	1.32
0.60	1.7959	1.8221	0.0263	1.44
0.65	1.8856	1.9155	0.0299	1.56
0.70	1.9799	2.0138	0.0338	1.68
0.75	2.0789	2.1170	0.0381	1.80
0.80	2.1829	2.2255	0.0427	1.92
0.85	2.2920	2.3396	0.0476	2.04
0.90	2.4066	2.4596	0.0530	2.15
0.95	2.5270	2.5857	0.0588	2.27
1.00	2.6533	2.7183	0.0650	2.39

4. Separating variables and integrating, we have

$$\frac{dy}{y} = 2x\,dx \quad \text{and} \quad \ln|y| = x^2 + c.$$

Thus $y = c_1 e^{x^2}$ and, using $y(1) = 1$, we find $c = e^{-1}$, so $y = e^{x^2-1}$ is the solution of the initial-value problem.

Exercises 2.6 A Numerical Method

h=0.1

x_n	y_n	Actual Value	Abs. Error	% Rel. Error
1.00	1.0000	1.0000	0.0000	0.00
1.10	1.2000	1.2337	0.0337	2.73
1.20	1.4640	1.5527	0.0887	5.71
1.30	1.8154	1.9937	0.1784	8.95
1.40	2.2874	2.6117	0.3243	12.42
1.50	2.9278	3.4903	0.5625	16.12

h=0.05

x_n	y_n	Actual Value	Abs. Error	% Rel. Error
1.00	1.0000	1.0000	0.0000	0.00
1.05	1.1000	1.1079	0.0079	0.72
1.10	1.2155	1.2337	0.0182	1.47
1.15	1.3492	1.3806	0.0314	2.27
1.20	1.5044	1.5527	0.0483	3.11
1.25	1.6849	1.7551	0.0702	4.00
1.30	1.8955	1.9937	0.0982	4.93
1.35	2.1419	2.2762	0.1343	5.90
1.40	2.4311	2.6117	0.1806	6.92
1.45	2.7714	3.0117	0.2403	7.98
1.50	3.1733	3.4903	0.3171	9.08

5.

h=0.1

x_n	y_n
0.00	0.0000
0.10	0.1000
0.20	0.1905
0.30	0.2731
0.40	0.3492
0.50	0.4198

h=0.05

x_n	y_n
0.00	0.0000
0.05	0.0500
0.10	0.0976
0.15	0.1429
0.20	0.1863
0.25	0.2278
0.30	0.2676
0.35	0.3058
0.40	0.3427
0.45	0.3782
0.50	0.4124

6.

h=0.1

x_n	y_n
0.00	1.0000
0.10	1.1000
0.20	1.2220
0.30	1.3753
0.40	1.5735
0.50	1.8371

h=0.05

x_n	y_n
0.00	1.0000
0.05	1.0500
0.10	1.1053
0.15	1.1668
0.20	1.2360
0.25	1.3144
0.30	1.4039
0.35	1.5070
0.40	1.6267
0.45	1.7670
0.50	1.9332

7.

h=0.1

x_n	y_n
0.00	0.5000
0.10	0.5250
0.20	0.5431
0.30	0.5548
0.40	0.5613
0.50	0.5639

h=0.05

x_n	y_n
0.00	0.5000
0.05	0.5125
0.10	0.5232
0.15	0.5322
0.20	0.5395
0.25	0.5452
0.30	0.5496
0.35	0.5527
0.40	0.5547
0.45	0.5559
0.50	0.5565

8.

h=0.1

x_n	y_n
0.00	1.0000
0.10	1.1000
0.20	1.2159
0.30	1.3505
0.40	1.5072
0.50	1.6902

h=0.05

x_n	y_n
0.00	1.0000
0.05	1.0500
0.10	1.1039
0.15	1.1619
0.20	1.2245
0.25	1.2921
0.30	1.3651
0.35	1.4440
0.40	1.5293
0.45	1.6217
0.50	1.7219

9.

h=0.1

x_n	y_n
1.00	1.0000
1.10	1.0000
1.20	1.0191
1.30	1.0588
1.40	1.1231
1.50	1.2194

h=0.05

x_n	y_n
1.00	1.0000
1.05	1.0000
1.10	1.0049
1.15	1.0147
1.20	1.0298
1.25	1.0506
1.30	1.0775
1.35	1.1115
1.40	1.1538
1.45	1.2057
1.50	1.2696

10.

h=0.1

x_n	y_n
0.00	0.5000
0.10	0.5250
0.20	0.5499
0.30	0.5747
0.40	0.5991
0.50	0.6231

h=0.05

x_n	y_n
0.00	0.5000
0.05	0.5125
0.10	0.5250
0.15	0.5375
0.20	0.5499
0.25	0.5623
0.30	0.5746
0.35	0.5868
0.40	0.5989
0.45	0.6109
0.50	0.6228

11. Tables of values were computed using the Euler and RK4 methods. The resulting points were plotted and joined using **ListPlot** in *Mathematica*. A somewhat simplified version of the code used to do this is given in the *Student Resource and Solutions Manual (SRSM)* under **Use of Computers** in Section 2.6.

$h = 0.25$ $h = 0.1$ $h = 0.05$

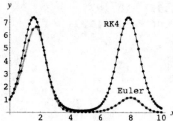
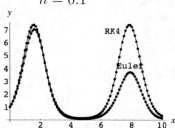
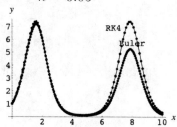

12. See the comments in Problem 11 above.

$h = 0.25$ $h = 0.1$ $h = 0.05$

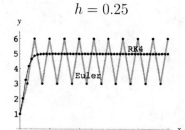
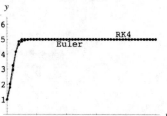
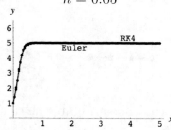

13. Tables of values, shown below, were first computed using Euler's method with $h = 0.1$ and $h = 0.05$ and then using the RK4 method with the same values of h. Using separation of variables we find that the solution of the differential equation is $y = 1/(1 - x^2)$, which is undefined at $x = 1$, where the graph has a vertical asymptote. Because the actual solution of the differential equation becomes unbounded at x approaches 1, very small changes in the inputs x will result in large changes in the corresponding outputs y. This can be expected to have a serious effect on numerical procedures.

Exercises 2.6 A Numerical Method

h=0.1 (Euler)		h=0.05 (Euler)		h=0.1 (RK4)		h=0.05 (RK4)	
x_n	y_n	x_n	y_n	x_n	y_n	x_n	y_n
0.00	1.0000	0.00	1.0000	0.00	1.0000	0.00	1.0000
0.10	1.0000	0.05	1.0000	0.10	1.0101	0.05	1.0025
0.20	1.0200	0.10	1.0050	0.20	1.0417	0.10	1.0101
0.30	1.0616	0.15	1.0151	0.30	1.0989	0.15	1.0230
0.40	1.1292	0.20	1.0306	0.40	1.1905	0.20	1.0417
0.50	1.2313	0.25	1.0518	0.50	1.3333	0.25	1.0667
0.60	1.3829	0.30	1.0795	0.60	1.5625	0.30	1.0989
0.70	1.6123	0.35	1.1144	0.70	1.9607	0.35	1.1396
0.80	1.9763	0.40	1.1579	0.80	2.7771	0.40	1.1905
0.90	2.6012	0.45	1.2115	0.90	5.2388	0.45	1.2539
1.00	3.8191	0.50	1.2776	1.00	42.9931	0.50	1.3333
		0.55	1.3592			0.55	1.4337
		0.60	1.4608			0.60	1.5625
		0.65	1.5888			0.65	1.7316
		0.70	1.7529			0.70	1.9608
		0.75	1.9679			0.75	2.2857
		0.80	2.2584			0.80	2.7777
		0.85	2.6664			0.85	3.6034
		0.90	3.2708			0.90	5.2609
		0.95	4.2336			0.95	10.1973
		1.00	5.9363			1.00	84.0132

The graphs below were obtained as described above in Problem 11.

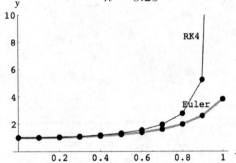

$h = 0.25$

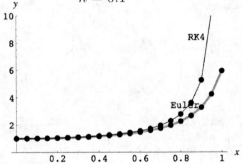

$h = 0.1$

14. (a) The graph to the right was obtained as described above
in Problem 11 using $h = 0.1$.

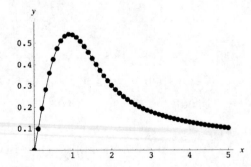

(b) Writing the differential equation in the form $y' + 2xy = 1$ we see that an integrating factor is $e^{\int 2x\,dx} = e^{x^2}$, so

$$\frac{d}{dx}[e^{x^2}y] = e^{x^2}$$

and

$$y = e^{-x^2}\int_0^x e^{t^2}\,dt + ce^{-x^2}.$$

This solution can also be expressed in terms of the inverse error function as

$$y = \frac{\sqrt{\pi}}{2}e^{-x^2}\,\mathrm{erfi}(x) + ce^{-x^2}.$$

Letting $x = 0$ and $y(0) = 0$ we find $c = 0$, so the solution of the initial-value problem is

$$y = e^{-x^2}\int_0^x e^{t^2}\,dt = \frac{\sqrt{\pi}}{2}e^{-x^2}\,\mathrm{erfi}(x).$$

(c) Using either **FindRoot** in *Mathematica* or `fsolve` in *Maple* we see that $y'(x) = 0$ when $x = 0.924139$. Since $y(0.924139) = 0.541044$, we see from the graph in part (a) that $(0.924139, 0.541044)$ is a relative maximum. Now, using the substitution $u = -t$ in the integral below, we have

$$y(-x) = e^{-(-x)^2}\int_0^{-x} e^{t^2}\,dt = e^{-x^2}\int_0^x e^{(-u)^2}(-du) = -e^{-x^2}\int_0^x e^{u^2}\,du = -y(x).$$

Thus, $y(x)$ is an odd function and $(-0.924139, -0.541044)$ is a relative minimum.

Chapter 2 in Review

1. Writing the differential equation in the form $y' = k(y + A/k)$ we see that the critical point $-A/k$ is a repeller for $k > 0$ and an attractor for $k < 0$.

2. Separating variables and integrating we have

$$\frac{dy}{y} = \frac{4}{x}\,dx$$

$$\ln y = 4\ln x + c = \ln x^4 + c$$

$$y = c_1 x^4.$$

We see that when $x = 0$, $y = 0$, so the initial-value problem has an infinite number of solutions for $k = 0$ and no solutions for $k \neq 0$.

3. True; $y = k_2/k_1$ is always a solution for $k_1 \neq 0$.

Chapter 2 in Review

4. True; writing the differential equation as $a_1(x)\,dy + a_2(x)y\,dx = 0$ and separating variables yields

$$\frac{dy}{y} = -\frac{a_2(x)}{a_1(x)}\,dx.$$

5. $\dfrac{dy}{dx} = (y-1)^2(y-3)^2$

6. $\dfrac{dy}{dx} = y(y-2)^2(y-4)$

7. When n is odd, $x^n < 0$ for $x < 0$ and $x^n > 0$ for $x > 0$. In this case 0 is unstable. When n is even, $x^n > 0$ for $x < 0$ and for $x > 0$. In this case 0 is semi-stable.

   When n is odd, $-x^n > 0$ for $x < 0$ and $-x^n < 0$ for $x > 0$. In this case 0 is asymptotically stable. When n is even, $-x^n < 0$ for $x < 0$ and for $x > 0$. In this case 0 is semi-stable.

8. Using a CAS we find that the zero of f occurs at approximately $P = 1.3214$. From the graph we observe that $dP/dt > 0$ for $P < 1.3214$ and $dP/dt < 0$ for $P > 1.3214$, so $P = 1.3214$ is an asymptotically stable critical point. Thus, $\lim_{t\to\infty} P(t) = 1.3214$.

9.

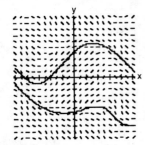

10. **(a)** linear in y, homogeneous, exact   **(b)** linear in x

    (c) separable, exact, linear in x and y **(d)** Bernoulli in x

    (e) separable   **(f)** separable, linear in x, Bernoulli

    (g) linear in x **(h)** homogeneous

    (i) Bernoulli   **(j)** homogeneous, exact, Bernoulli

    (k) linear in x and y, exact, separable, homogeneous

    (l) exact, linear in y **(m)** homogeneous

    (n) separable

11. Separating variables and using the identity $\cos^2 x = \frac{1}{2}(1 + \cos 2x)$, we have

$$\cos^2 x\,dx = \frac{y}{y^2 + 1}\,dy,$$

$$\frac{1}{2}x + \frac{1}{4}\sin 2x = \frac{1}{2}\ln\left(y^2 + 1\right) + c,$$

and

$$2x + \sin 2x = 2 \ln \left(y^2 + 1 \right) + c.$$

12. Write the differential equation in the form

$$y \ln \frac{x}{y}\, dx = \left(x \ln \frac{x}{y} - y \right) dy.$$

This is a homogeneous equation, so let $x = uy$. Then $dx = u\, dy + y\, du$ and the differential equation becomes

$$y \ln u(u\, dy + y\, du) = (uy \ln u - y)\, dy \quad \text{or} \quad y \ln u\, du = -dy.$$

Separating variables, we obtain

$$\ln u\, du = -\frac{dy}{y}$$

$$u \ln |u| - u = -\ln |y| + c$$

$$\frac{x}{y} \ln \left| \frac{x}{y} \right| - \frac{x}{y} = -\ln |y| + c$$

$$x(\ln x - \ln y) - x = -y \ln |y| + cy.$$

13. The differential equation

$$\frac{dy}{dx} + \frac{2}{6x + 1} y = -\frac{3x^2}{6x + 1} y^{-2}$$

is Bernoulli. Using $w = y^3$, we obtain the linear equation

$$\frac{dw}{dx} + \frac{6}{6x + 1} w = -\frac{9x^2}{6x + 1}.$$

An integrating factor is $6x + 1$, so

$$\frac{d}{dx}\left[(6x + 1)w \right] = -9x^2,$$

$$w = -\frac{3x^3}{6x + 1} + \frac{c}{6x + 1},$$

and

$$(6x + 1)y^3 = -3x^3 + c.$$

(Note: The differential equation is also exact.)

14. Write the differential equation in the form $(3y^2 + 2x)dx + (4y^2 + 6xy)dy = 0$. Letting $M = 3y^2 + 2x$ and $N = 4y^2 + 6xy$ we see that $M_y = 6y = N_x$, so the differential equation is exact. From $f_x = 3y^2 + 2x$ we obtain $f = 3xy^2 + x^2 + h(y)$. Then $f_y = 6xy + h'(y) = 4y^2 + 6xy$ and $h'(y) = 4y^2$ so $h(y) = \frac{4}{3}y^3$. A one-parameter family of solutions is

$$3xy^2 + x^2 + \frac{4}{3}y^3 = c.$$

Chapter 2 in Review

15. Write the equation in the form

$$\frac{dQ}{dt} + \frac{1}{t}Q = t^3 \ln t.$$

An integrating factor is $e^{\ln t} = t$, so

$$\frac{d}{dt}[tQ] = t^4 \ln t$$

$$tQ = -\frac{1}{25}t^5 + \frac{1}{5}t^5 \ln t + c$$

and

$$Q = -\frac{1}{25}t^4 + \frac{1}{5}t^4 \ln t + \frac{c}{t}.$$

16. Letting $u = 2x + y + 1$ we have

$$\frac{du}{dx} = 2 + \frac{dy}{dx},$$

and so the given differential equation is transformed into

$$u\left(\frac{du}{dx} - 2\right) = 1 \quad \text{or} \quad \frac{du}{dx} = \frac{2u+1}{u}.$$

Separating variables and integrating we get

$$\frac{u}{2u+1}\,du = dx$$

$$\left(\frac{1}{2} - \frac{1}{2}\frac{1}{2u+1}\right)du = dx$$

$$\frac{1}{2}u - \frac{1}{4}\ln|2u+1| = x + c$$

$$2u - \ln|2u+1| = 2x + c_1.$$

Resubstituting for u gives the solution

$$4x + 2y + 2 - \ln|4x + 2y + 3| = 2x + c_1$$

or

$$2x + 2y + 2 - \ln|4x + 2y + 3| = c_1.$$

17. Write the equation in the form

$$\frac{dy}{dx} + \frac{8x}{x^2+4}y = \frac{2x}{x^2+4}.$$

An integrating factor is $\left(x^2+4\right)^4$, so

$$\frac{d}{dx}\left[\left(x^2+4\right)^4 y\right] = 2x\left(x^2+4\right)^3$$

$$\left(x^2 + 4\right)^4 y = \frac{1}{4}\left(x^2 + 4\right)^4 + c$$

and

$$y = \frac{1}{4} + c\left(x^2 + 4\right)^{-4}.$$

18. Letting $M = 2r^2 \cos\theta \sin\theta + r \cos\theta$ and $N = 4r + \sin\theta - 2r\cos^2\theta$ we see that $M_r = 4r \cos\theta \sin\theta + \cos\theta = N_\theta$, so the differential equation is exact. From $f_\theta = 2r^2 \cos\theta \sin\theta + r \cos\theta$ we obtain $f = -r^2 \cos^2\theta + r\sin\theta + h(r)$. Then $f_r = -2r\cos^2\theta + \sin\theta + h'(r) = 4r + \sin\theta - 2r\cos^2\theta$ and $h'(r) = 4r$ so $h(r) = 2r^2$. The solution is

$$-r^2 \cos^2\theta + r\sin\theta + 2r^2 = c.$$

19. The differential equation has the form $(d/dx)\left[(\sin x)y\right] = 0$. Integrating, we have $(\sin x)y = c$ or $y = c/\sin x$. The initial condition implies $c = -2\sin(7\pi/6) = 1$. Thus, $y = 1/\sin x$, where the interval $\pi < x < 2\pi$ is chosen to include $x = 7\pi/6$.

20. Separating variables and integrating we have

$$\frac{dy}{y^2} = -2(t+1)\,dt$$

$$-\frac{1}{y} = -(t+1)^2 + c$$

$$y = \frac{1}{(t+1)^2 + c_1}, \qquad \text{where } -c = c_1.$$

The initial condition $y(0) = -\frac{1}{8}$ implies $c_1 = -9$, so a solution of the initial-value problem is

$$y = \frac{1}{(t+1)^2 - 9} \qquad \text{or} \qquad y = \frac{1}{t^2 + 2t - 8},$$

where $-4 < t < 2$.

21. (a) For $y < 0$, $\sqrt{y}$ is not a real number.

(b) Separating variables and integrating we have

$$\frac{dy}{\sqrt{y}} = dx \quad \text{and} \quad 2\sqrt{y} = x + c.$$

Letting $y(x_0) = y_0$ we get $c = 2\sqrt{y_0} - x_0$, so that

$$2\sqrt{y} = x + 2\sqrt{y_0} - x_0 \quad \text{and} \quad y = \frac{1}{4}(x + 2\sqrt{y_0} - x_0)^2.$$

Since $\sqrt{y} > 0$ for $y \neq 0$, we see that $dy/dx = \frac{1}{2}(x + 2\sqrt{y_0} - x_0)$ must be positive. Thus, the interval on which the solution is defined is $(x_0 - 2\sqrt{y_0}, \infty)$.

22. (a) The differential equation is homogeneous and we let $y = ux$. Then

$$(x^2 - y^2)\,dx + xy\,dy = 0$$

$$(x^2 - u^2x^2)\,dx + ux^2(u\,dx + x\,du) = 0$$

$$dx + ux\,du = 0$$

$$u\,du = -\frac{dx}{x}$$

$$\frac{1}{2}u^2 = -\ln|x| + c$$

$$\frac{y^2}{x^2} = -2\ln|x| + c_1.$$

The initial condition gives $c_1 = 2$, so an implicit solution is $y^2 = x^2(2 - 2\ln|x|)$.

(b) Solving for y in part (a) and being sure that the initial condition is still satisfied, we have $y = -\sqrt{2}\,|x|(1 - \ln|x|)^{1/2}$, where $-e \le x \le e$ so that $1 - \ln|x| \ge 0$. The graph of this function indicates that the derivative is not defined at $x = 0$ and $x = e$. Thus, the solution of the initial-value problem is $y = -\sqrt{2}\,x(1 - \ln x)^{1/2}$, for $0 < x < e$.

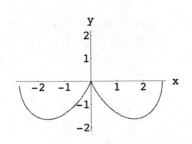

23. The graph of $y_1(x)$ is the portion of the closed black curve lying in the fourth quadrant. Its interval of definition is approximately $(0.7, 4.3)$. The graph of $y_2(x)$ is the portion of the left-hand black curve lying in the third quadrant. Its interval of definition is $(-\infty, 0)$.

24. The first step of Euler's method gives $y(1.1) \approx 9 + 0.1(1 + 3) = 9.4$. Applying Euler's method one more time gives $y(1.2) \approx 9.4 + 0.1(1 + 1.1\sqrt{9.4}) \approx 9.8373$.

25. Since the differential equation is autonomous, all lineal elements on a given horizontal line have the same slope. The direction field is then as shown in the figure at the right. It appears from the figure that the differential equation has critical points at -2 (an attractor) and at 2 (a repeller). Thus, -2 is an aymptotically stable critical point and 2 is an unstable critical point.

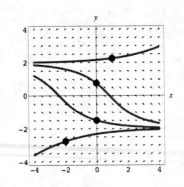

26. Since the differential equation is autonomous, all lineal elements on a given horizontal line have the same slope. The direction field is then as shown in the figure at the right. It appears from the figure that the differential equation has no critical points.

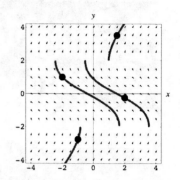

3 Modeling with First-Order Differential Equations

1. Let $P = P(t)$ be the population at time t, and P_0 the initial population. From $dP/dt = kP$ we obtain $P = P_0 e^{kt}$. Using $P(5) = 2P_0$ we find $k = \frac{1}{5}\ln 2$ and $P = P_0 e^{(\ln 2)t/5}$. Setting $P(t) = 3P_0$ we have $3 = e^{(\ln 2)t/5}$, so

$$\ln 3 = \frac{(\ln 2)t}{5} \qquad \text{and} \qquad t = \frac{5\ln 3}{\ln 2} \approx 7.9 \text{ years.}$$

Setting $P(t) = 4P_0$ we have $4 = e^{(\ln 2)t/5}$, so

$$\ln 4 = \frac{(\ln 2)t}{5} \qquad \text{and} \qquad t \approx 10 \text{ years.}$$

2. From Problem 1 the growth constant is $k = \frac{1}{5}\ln 2$. Then $P = P_0 e^{(1/5)(\ln 2)t}$ and $10{,}000 = P_0 e^{(3/5)\ln 2}$. Solving for P_0 we get $P_0 = 10{,}000 e^{-(3/5)\ln 2} = 6{,}597.5$. Now

$$P(10) = P_0 e^{(1/5)(\ln 2)(10)} = 6{,}597.5 e^{2\ln 2} = 4P_0 = 26{,}390.$$

The rate at which the population is growing is

$$P'(10) = kP(10) = \frac{1}{5}(\ln 2)26{,}390 = 3658 \text{ persons/year.}$$

3. Let $P = P(t)$ be the population at time t. Then $dP/dt = kP$ and $P = ce^{kt}$. From $P(0) = c = 500$ we see that $P = 500 e^{kt}$. Since 15% of 500 is 75, we have $P(10) = 500 e^{10k} = 575$. Solving for k, we get $k = \frac{1}{10}\ln\frac{575}{500} = \frac{1}{10}\ln 1.15$. When $t = 30$,

$$P(30) = 500 e^{(1/10)(\ln 1.15)30} = 500 e^{3\ln 1.15} = 760 \text{ years}$$

and

$$P'(30) = kP(30) = \frac{1}{10}(\ln 1.15)760 = 10.62 \text{ persons/year.}$$

4. Let $P = P(t)$ be bacteria population at time t and P_0 the initial number. From $dP/dt = kP$ we obtain $P = P_0 e^{kt}$. Using $P(3) = 400$ and $P(10) = 2000$ we find $400 = P_0 e^{3k}$ or $e^k = (400/P_0)^{1/3}$. From $P(10) = 2000$ we then have $2000 = P_0 e^{10k} = P_0(400/P_0)^{10/3}$, so

$$\frac{2000}{400^{10/3}} = P_0^{-7/3} \qquad \text{and} \qquad P_0 = \left(\frac{2000}{400^{10/3}}\right)^{-3/7} \approx 201.$$

5. Let $A = A(t)$ be the amount of lead present at time t. From $dA/dt = kA$ and $A(0) = 1$ we obtain $A = e^{kt}$. Using $A(3.3) = 1/2$ we find $k = \frac{1}{3.3}\ln(1/2)$. When 90% of the lead has decayed, 0.1 grams will remain. Setting $A(t) = 0.1$ we have $e^{t(1/3.3)\ln(1/2)} = 0.1$, so

$$\frac{t}{3.3}\ln\frac{1}{2} = \ln 0.1 \quad \text{and} \quad t = \frac{3.3\ln 0.1}{\ln(1/2)} \approx 10.96 \text{ hours.}$$

6. Let $A = A(t)$ be the amount present at time t. From $dA/dt = kA$ and $A(0) = 100$ we obtain $A = 100e^{kt}$. Using $A(6) = 97$ we find $k = \frac{1}{6}\ln 0.97$. Then $A(24) = 100e^{(1/6)(\ln 0.97)24} = 100(0.97)^4 \approx 88.5$ mg.

7. Setting $A(t) = 50$ in Problem 6 we obtain $50 = 100e^{kt}$, so

$$kt = \ln\frac{1}{2} \quad \text{and} \quad t = \frac{\ln(1/2)}{(1/6)\ln 0.97} \approx 136.5 \text{ hours.}$$

8. **(a)** The solution of $dA/dt = kA$ is $A(t) = A_0 e^{kt}$. Letting $A = \frac{1}{2}A_0$ and solving for t we obtain the half-life $T = -(\ln 2)/k$.

   (b) Since $k = -(\ln 2)/T$ we have

   $$A(t) = A_0 e^{-(\ln 2)t/T} = A_0 2^{-t/T}.$$

   (c) Writing $\frac{1}{8}A_0 = A_0 2^{-t/T}$ as $2^{-3} = 2^{-t/T}$ and solving for t we get $t = 3T$. Thus, an initial amount A_0 will decay to $\frac{1}{8}A_0$ in three half-lives.

9. Let $I = I(t)$ be the intensity, t the thickness, and $I(0) = I_0$. If $dI/dt = kI$ and $I(3) = 0.25I_0$, then $I = I_0 e^{kt}$, $k = \frac{1}{3}\ln 0.25$, and $I(15) = 0.00098I_0$.

10. From $dS/dt = rS$ we obtain $S = S_0 e^{rt}$ where $S(0) = S_0$.

    (a) If $S_0 = \$5000$ and $r = 5.75\%$ then $S(5) = \$6665.45$.

    (b) If $S(t) = \$10{,}000$ then $t = 12$ years.

    (c) $S \approx \$6651.82$

11. Assume that $A = A_0 e^{kt}$ and $k = -0.00012378$. If $A(t) = 0.145A_0$ then $t \approx 15{,}600$ years.

12. From Example 3 in the text, the amount of carbon present at time t is $A(t) = A_0 e^{-0.00012378t}$. Letting $t = 660$ and solving for A_0 we have $A(660) = A_0 e^{-0.0001237(660)} = 0.921553A_0$. Thus, approximately 92% of the original amount of C-14 remained in the cloth as of 1988.

13. Assume that $dT/dt = k(T - 10)$ so that $T = 10 + ce^{kt}$. If $T(0) = 70°$ and $T(1/2) = 50°$ then $c = 60$ and $k = 2\ln(2/3)$ so that $T(1) = 36.67°$. If $T(t) = 15°$ then $t = 3.06$ minutes.

14. Assume that $dT/dt = k(T - 5)$ so that $T = 5 + ce^{kt}$. If $T(1) = 55°$ and $T(5) = 30°$ then $k = -\frac{1}{4}\ln 2$ and $c = 59.4611$ so that $T(0) = 64.4611°$.

15. We use the fact that the boiling temperature for water is $100°$ C. Now assume that $dT/dt = k(T - 100)$ so that $T = 100 + ce^{kt}$. If $T(0) = 20°$ and $T(1) = 22°$, then $c = -80$ and $k = \ln(39/40) \approx -0.0253$. Then $T(t) = 100 - 80e^{-0.0253t}$, and when $T = 90$, $t = 82.1$ seconds. If $T(t) = 98°$ then $t = 145.7$ seconds.

16. The differential equation for the first container is $dT_1/dt = k_1(T_1 - 0) = k_1 T_1$, whose solution is $T_1(t) = c_1 e^{k_1 t}$. Since $T_1(0) = 100$ (the initial temperature of the metal bar), we have $100 = c_1$ and $T_1(t) = 100 e^{k_1 t}$. After 1 minute, $T_1(1) = 100 e^{k_1} = 90°C$, so $k_1 = \ln 0.9$ and $T_1(t) = 100 e^{t \ln 0.9}$. After 2 minutes, $T_1(2) = 100 e^{2 \ln 0.9} = 100(0.9)^2 = 81°C$.

The differential equation for the second container is $dT_2/dt = k_2(T_2 - 100)$, whose solution is $T_2(t) = 100 + c_2 e^{k_2 t}$. When the metal bar is immersed in the second container, its initial temperature is $T_2(0) = 81$, so

$$T_2(0) = 100 + c_2 e^{k_2(0)} = 100 + c_2 = 81$$

and $c_2 = -19$. Thus, $T_2(t) = 100 - 19e^{k_2 t}$. After 1 minute in the second tank, the temperature of the metal bar is $91°C$, so

$$T_2(1) = 100 - 19e^{k_2} = 91$$

$$e^{k_2} = \frac{9}{19}$$

$$k_2 = \ln \frac{9}{19}$$

and $T_2(t) = 100 - 19e^{t \ln(9/19)}$. Setting $T_2(t) = 99.9$ we have

$$100 - 19e^{t \ln(9/19)} = 99.9$$

$$e^{t \ln(9/19)} = \frac{0.1}{19}$$

$$t = \frac{\ln(0.1/19)}{\ln(9/19)} \approx 7.02.$$

Thus, from the start of the "double dipping" process, the total time until the bar reaches $99.9°C$ in the second container is approximately 9.02 minutes.

17. Using separation of variables to solve $dT/dt = k(T - T_m)$ we get $T(t) = T_m + ce^{kt}$. Using $T(0) = 70$ we find $c = 70 - T_m$, so $T(t) = T_m + (70 - T_m)e^{kt}$. Using the given observations, we obtain

$$T\left(\frac{1}{2}\right) = T_m + (70 - T_m)e^{k/2} = 110$$

$$T(1) = T_m + (70 - T_m)e^{k} = 145.$$

Then, from the first equation, $e^{k/2} = (110 - T_m)/(70 - T_m)$ and

$$e^k = (e^{k/2})^2 = \left(\frac{110 - T_m}{70 - T_m}\right)^2 = \frac{145 - T_m}{70 - T_m}$$

$$\frac{(110 - T_m)^2}{70 - T_m} = 145 - T_m$$

$$12100 - 220T_m + T_m^2 = 10150 - 215T_m + T_m^2$$

$$T_m = 390.$$

The temperature in the oven is $390°$.

18. **(a)** The initial temperature of the bath is $T_m(0) = 60°$, so in the short term the temperature of the chemical, which starts at $80°$, should decrease or cool. Over time, the temperature of the bath will increase toward $100°$ since $e^{-0.1t}$ decreases from 1 toward 0 as t increases from 0. Thus, in the long term, the temperature of the chemical should increase or warm toward $100°$.

(b) Adapting the model for Newton's law of cooling, we have

$$\frac{dT}{dt} = -0.1(T - 100 + 40e^{-0.1t}), \quad T(0) = 80.$$

Writing the differential equation in the form

$$\frac{dT}{dt} + 0.1T = 10 - 4e^{-0.1t}$$

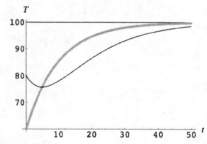

we see that it is linear with integrating factor $e^{\int 0.1\,dt} = e^{0.1t}$. Thus

$$\frac{d}{dt}[e^{0.1t}T] = 10e^{0.1t} - 4$$

$$e^{0.1t}T = 100e^{0.1t} - 4t + c$$

and

$$T(t) = 100 - 4te^{-0.1t} + ce^{-0.1t}.$$

Now $T(0) = 80$ so $100 + c = 80$, $c = -20$ and

$$T(t) = 100 - 4te^{-0.1t} - 20e^{-0.1t} = 100 - (4t + 20)e^{-0.1t}.$$

The thinner curve verifies the prediction of cooling followed by warming toward $100°$. The wider curve shows the temperature T_m of the liquid bath.

19. Identifying $T_m = 70$, the differential equation is $dT/dt = k(T - 70)$. Assuming $T(0) = 98.6$ and separating variables we find $T(t) = 70 + 28.9e^{kt}$. If $t_1 > 0$ is the time of discovery of the body, then

$$T(t_1) = 70 + 28.6e^{kt_1} = 85 \quad \text{and} \quad T(t_1 + 1) = 70 + 28.6e^{k(t_1+1)} = 80.$$

Therefore $e^{kt_1} = 15/28.6$ and $e^{k(t_1+1)} = 10/28.6$. This implies

$$e^k = \frac{10}{28.6}e^{-kt_1} = \frac{10}{28.6} \cdot \frac{28.6}{15} = \frac{2}{3},$$

so $k = \ln\frac{2}{3} \approx -0.405465108$. Therefore

$$t_1 = \frac{1}{k}\ln\frac{15}{28.6} \approx 1.5916 \approx 1.6.$$

Death took place about 1.6 hours prior to the discovery of the body.

20. Solving the differential equation $dT/dt = kS(T - T_m)$ subject to $T(0) = T_0$ gives

$$T(t) = T_m + (T_0 - T_m)e^{kSt}.$$

The temperatures of the coffee in cups A and B are, respectively,

$$T_A(t) = 70 + 80e^{kSt} \quad \text{and} \quad T_B(t) = 70 + 80e^{2kSt}.$$

Then $T_A(30) = 70 + 80e^{30kS} = 100$, which implies $e^{30kS} = \frac{3}{8}$. Hence

$$T_B(30) = 70 + 80e^{60kS} = 70 + 80\left(e^{30kS}\right)^2$$

$$= 70 + 80\left(\frac{3}{8}\right)^2 = 70 + 80\left(\frac{9}{64}\right) = 81.25°\text{F}.$$

21. From $dA/dt = 4 - A/50$ we obtain $A = 200 + ce^{-t/50}$. If $A(0) = 30$ then $c = -170$ and $A = 200 - 170e^{-t/50}$.

22. From $dA/dt = 0 - A/50$ we obtain $A = ce^{-t/50}$. If $A(0) = 30$ then $c = 30$ and $A = 30e^{-t/50}$.

23. From $dA/dt = 10 - A/100$ we obtain $A = 1000 + ce^{-t/100}$. If $A(0) = 0$ then $c = -1000$ and $A(t) = 1000 - 1000e^{-t/100}$.

24. From Problem 23 the number of pounds of salt in the tank at time t is $A(t) = 1000 - 1000e^{-t/100}$. The concentration at time t is $c(t) = A(t)/500 = 2 - 2e^{-t/100}$. Therefore $c(5) = 2 - 2e^{-1/20} = 0.0975\,\text{lb/gal}$ and $\lim_{t\to\infty} c(t) = 2$. Solving $c(t) = 1 = 2 - 2e^{-t/100}$ for t we obtain $t = 100\ln 2 \approx 69.3\,\text{min}$.

25. From

$$\frac{dA}{dt} = 10 - \frac{10A}{500 - (10-5)t} = 10 - \frac{2A}{100 - t}$$

we obtain $A = 1000 - 10t + c(100 - t)^2$. If $A(0) = 0$ then $c = -\frac{1}{10}$. The tank is empty in 100 minutes.

26. With $c_{in}(t) = 2 + \sin(t/4)\,\text{lb/gal}$, the initial-value problem is

$$\frac{dA}{dt} + \frac{1}{100}A = 6 + 3\sin\frac{t}{4}, \quad A(0) = 50.$$

The differential equation is linear with integrating factor $e^{\int dt/100} = e^{t/100}$, so

$$\frac{d}{dt}[e^{t/100}A(t)] = \left(6 + 3\sin\frac{t}{4}\right)e^{t/100}$$

$$e^{t/100}A(t) = 600e^{t/100} + \frac{150}{313}e^{t/100}\sin\frac{t}{4} - \frac{3750}{313}e^{t/100}\cos\frac{t}{4} + c,$$

and

$$A(t) = 600 + \frac{150}{313}\sin\frac{t}{4} - \frac{3750}{313}\cos\frac{t}{4} + ce^{-t/100}.$$

Letting $t = 0$ and $A = 50$ we have $600 - 3750/313 + c = 50$ and $c = -168400/313$. Then

$$A(t) = 600 + \frac{150}{313}\sin\frac{t}{4} - \frac{3750}{313}\cos\frac{t}{4} - \frac{168400}{313}e^{-t/100}.$$

The graphs on $[0, 300]$ and $[0, 600]$ below show the effect of the sine function in the input when compared with the graph in Figure 3.1.4(a) in the text.

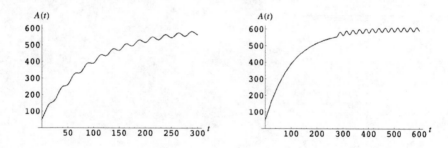

27. From

$$\frac{dA}{dt} = 3 - \frac{4A}{100 + (6 - 4)t} = 3 - \frac{2A}{50 + t}$$

we obtain $A = 50 + t + c(50 + t)^{-2}$. If $A(0) = 10$ then $c = -100{,}000$ and $A(30) = 64.38$ pounds.

28. (a) Initially the tank contains 300 gallons of solution. Since brine is pumped in at a rate of 3 gal/min and the mixture is pumped out at a rate of 2 gal/min, the net change is an increase of 1 gal/min. Thus, in 100 minutes the tank will contain its capacity of 400 gallons.

(b) The differential equation describing the amount of salt in the tank is $A'(t) = 6 - 2A/(300 + t)$ with solution

$$A(t) = 600 + 2t - (4.95 \times 10^7)(300 + t)^{-2}, \qquad 0 \le t \le 100,$$

as noted in the discussion following Example 5 in the text. Thus, the amount of salt in the tank when it overflows is

$$A(100) = 800 - (4.95 \times 10^7)(400)^{-2} = 490.625 \text{ lbs.}$$

(c) When the tank is overflowing the amount of salt in the tank is governed by the differential equation

$$\frac{dA}{dt} = (3 \text{ gal/min})(2 \text{ lb/gal}) - \left(\frac{A}{400} \text{ lb/gal}\right)(3 \text{ gal/min})$$

$$= 6 - \frac{3A}{400}, \qquad A(100) = 490.625.$$

Solving the equation, we obtain $A(t) = 800 + ce^{-3t/400}$. The initial condition yields $c = -654.947$, so that

$$A(t) = 800 - 654.947e^{-3t/400}.$$

When $t = 150$, $A(150) = 587.37$ lbs.

(d) As $t \to \infty$, the amount of salt is 800 lbs, which is to be expected since $(400 \text{ gal})(2 \text{ lb/gal}) = 800$ lbs.

(e)

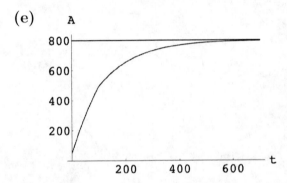

29. Assume $L\,di/dt + Ri = E(t)$, $L = 0.1$, $R = 50$, and $E(t) = 50$ so that $i = \frac{3}{5} + ce^{-500t}$. If $i(0) = 0$ then $c = -3/5$ and $\lim_{t\to\infty} i(t) = 3/5$.

30. Assume $L\,di/dt + Ri = E(t)$, $E(t) = E_0 \sin \omega t$, and $i(0) = i_0$ so that

$$i = \frac{E_0 R}{L^2\omega^2 + R^2} \sin \omega t - \frac{E_0 L\omega}{L^2\omega^2 + R^2} \cos \omega t + ce^{-Rt/L}.$$

Since $i(0) = i_0$ we obtain $c = i_0 + \dfrac{E_0 L\omega}{L^2\omega^2 + R^2}$.

31. Assume $R\,dq/dt + (1/C)q = E(t)$, $R = 200$, $C = 10^{-4}$, and $E(t) = 100$ so that $q = 1/100 + ce^{-50t}$. If $q(0) = 0$ then $c = -1/100$ and $i = \frac{1}{2}e^{-50t}$.

32. Assume $R\,dq/dt + (1/C)q = E(t)$, $R = 1000$, $C = 5 \times 10^{-6}$, and $E(t) = 200$. Then $q = \frac{1}{1000} + ce^{-200t}$ and $i = -200ce^{-200t}$. If $i(0) = 0.4$ then $c = -\frac{1}{500}$, $q(0.005) = 0.003$ coulombs, and $i(0.005) = 0.1472$ amps. We have $q \to \frac{1}{1000}$ as $t \to \infty$.

33. For $0 \le t \le 20$ the differential equation is $20\,di/dt + 2i = 120$. An integrating factor is $e^{t/10}$, so $(d/dt)[e^{t/10}i] = 6e^{t/10}$ and $i = 60 + c_1 e^{-t/10}$. If $i(0) = 0$ then $c_1 = -60$ and $i = 60 - 60e^{-t/10}$. For $t > 20$ the differential equation is $20\,di/dt + 2i = 0$ and $i = c_2 e^{-t/10}$. At $t = 20$ we want

$c_2 e^{-2} = 60 - 60 e^{-2}$ so that $c_2 = 60\left(e^2 - 1\right)$. Thus

$$i(t) = \begin{cases} 60 - 60 e^{-t/10}, & 0 \le t \le 20 \\ 60\left(e^2 - 1\right) e^{-t/10}, & t > 20. \end{cases}$$

34. Separating variables, we obtain

$$\frac{dq}{E_0 - q/C} = \frac{dt}{k_1 + k_2 t}$$

$$-C \ln\left|E_0 - \frac{q}{C}\right| = \frac{1}{k_2} \ln|k_1 + k_2 t| + c_1$$

$$\frac{(E_0 - q/C)^{-C}}{(k_1 + k_2 t)^{1/k_2}} = c_2.$$

Setting $q(0) = q_0$ we find $c_2 = (E_0 - q_0/C)^{-C}/k_1^{1/k_2}$, so

$$\frac{(E_0 - q/C)^{-C}}{(k_1 + k_2 t)^{1/k_2}} = \frac{(E_0 - q_0/C)^{-C}}{k_1^{1/k_2}}$$

$$\left(E_0 - \frac{q}{C}\right)^{-C} = \left(E_0 - \frac{q_0}{C}\right)^{-C} \left(\frac{k_1}{k + k_2 t}\right)^{-1/k_2}$$

$$E_0 - \frac{q}{C} = \left(E_0 - \frac{q_0}{C}\right) \left(\frac{k_1}{k + k_2 t}\right)^{1/Ck_2}$$

$$q = E_0 C + (q_0 - E_0 C) \left(\frac{k_1}{k + k_2 t}\right)^{1/Ck_2}.$$

35. (a) From $m \, dv/dt = mg - kv$ we obtain $v = mg/k + ce^{-kt/m}$. If $v(0) = v_0$ then $c = v_0 - mg/k$ and the solution of the initial-value problem is

$$v(t) = \frac{mg}{k} + \left(v_0 - \frac{mg}{k}\right) e^{-kt/m}.$$

(b) As $t \to \infty$ the limiting velocity is mg/k.

(c) From $ds/dt = v$ and $s(0) = 0$ we obtain

$$s(t) = \frac{mg}{k} t - \frac{m}{k}\left(v_0 - \frac{mg}{k}\right) e^{-kt/m} + \frac{m}{k}\left(v_0 - \frac{mg}{k}\right).$$

36. (a) Integrating $d^2 s/dt^2 = -g$ we get $v(t) = ds/dt = -gt + c$. From $v(0) = 300$ we find $c = 300$, and we are given $g = 32$, so the velocity is $v(t) = -32t + 300$.

(b) Integrating again and using $s(0) = 0$ we get $s(t) = -16t^2 + 300t$. The maximum height is attained when $v = 0$, that is, at $t_a = 9.375$. The maximum height will be $s(9.375) = 1406.25 \, \text{ft}$.

37. When air resistance is proportional to velocity, the model for the velocity is $m\,dv/dt = -mg - kv$ (using the fact that the positive direction is upward.) Solving the differential equation using separation of variables we obtain $v(t) = -mg/k + ce^{-kt/m}$. From $v(0) = 300$ we get

$$v(t) = -\frac{mg}{k} + \left(300 + \frac{mg}{k}\right)e^{-kt/m}.$$

Integrating and using $s(0) = 0$ we find

$$s(t) = -\frac{mg}{k}t + \frac{m}{k}\left(300 + \frac{mg}{k}\right)(1 - e^{-kt/m}).$$

Setting $k = 0.0025$, $m = 16/32 = 0.5$, and $g = 32$ we have

$$s(t) = 1{,}340{,}000 - 6{,}400t - 1{,}340{,}000e^{-0.005t}$$

and

$$v(t) = -6{,}400 + 6{,}700e^{-0.005t}.$$

The maximum height is attained when $v = 0$, that is, at $t_a = 9.162$. The maximum height will be $s(9.162) = 1363.79$ ft, which is less than the maximum height in Problem 36.

38. Assuming that the air resistance is proportional to velocity and the positive direction is downward with $s(0) = 0$, the model for the velocity is $m\,dv/dt = mg - kv$. Using separation of variables to solve this differential equation, we obtain $v(t) = mg/k + ce^{-kt/m}$. Then, using $v(0) = 0$, we get $v(t) = (mg/k)(1 - e^{-kt/m})$. Letting $k = 0.5$, $m = (125 + 35)/32 = 5$, and $g = 32$, we have $v(t) = 320(1 - e^{-0.1t})$. Integrating, we find $s(t) = 320t + 3200e^{-0.1t} + c_1$. Solving $s(0) = 0$ for c_1 we find $c_1 = -3200$, therefore $s(t) = 320t + 3200e^{-0.1t} - 3200$. At $t = 15$, when the parachute opens, $v(15) = 248.598$ and $s(15) = 2314.02$. At this time the value of k changes to $k = 10$ and the new initial velocity is $v_0 = 248.598$. With the parachute open, the skydiver's velocity is $v_p(t) = mg/k + c_2e^{-kt/m}$, where t is reset to 0 when the parachute opens. Letting $m = 5$, $g = 32$, and $k = 10$, this gives $v_p(t) = 16 + c_2e^{-2t}$. From $v(0) = 248.598$ we find $c_2 = 232.598$, so $v_p(t) = 16 + 232.598e^{-2t}$. Integrating, we get $s_p(t) = 16t - 116.299e^{-2t} + c_3$. Solving $s_p(0) = 0$ for c_3, we find $c_3 = 116.299$, so $s_p(t) = 16t - 116.299e^{-2t} + 116.299$. Twenty seconds after leaving the plane is five seconds after the parachute opens. The skydiver's velocity at this time is $v_p(5) = 16.0106$ ft/s and she has fallen a total of $s(15) + s_p(5) = 2314.02 + 196.294 = 2510.31$ ft. Her terminal velocity is $\lim_{t\to\infty} v_p(t) = 16$, so she has very nearly reached her terminal velocity five seconds after the parachute opens. When the parachute opens, the distance to the ground is $15{,}000 - s(15) = 15{,}000 - 2{,}314 = 12{,}686$ ft. Solving $s_p(t) = 12{,}686$ we get $t = 785.6$ s $= 13.1$ min. Thus, it will take her approximately 13.1 minutes to reach the ground after her parachute has opened and a total of $(785.6 + 15)/60 = 13.34$ minutes after she exits the plane.

39. (a) The differential equation is first-order and linear. Letting $b = k/\rho$, the integrating factor is

$e^{\int 3b\,dt/(bt+r_0)} = (r_0 + bt)^3$. Then

$$\frac{d}{dt}[(r_0 + bt)^3 v] = g(r_0 + bt)^3 \quad \text{and} \quad (r_0 + bt)^3 v = \frac{g}{4b}(r_0 + bt)^4 + c.$$

The solution of the differential equation is $v(t) = (g/4b)(r_0 + bt) + c(r_0 + bt)^{-3}$. Using $v(0) = 0$ we find $c = -gr_0^4/4b$, so that

$$v(t) = \frac{g}{4b}(r_0 + bt) - \frac{gr_0^4}{4b(r_0 + bt)^3} = \frac{g\rho}{4k}\left(r_0 + \frac{k}{\rho}t\right) - \frac{g\rho r_0^4}{4k(r_0 + kt/\rho)^3}.$$

(b) Integrating $dr/dt = k/\rho$ we get $r = kt/\rho + c$. Using $r(0) = r_0$ we have $c = r_0$, so $r(t) = kt/\rho + r_0$.

(c) If $r = 0.007$ ft when $t = 10$ s, then solving $r(10) = 0.007$ for k/ρ, we obtain $k/\rho = -0.0003$ and $r(t) = 0.01 - 0.0003t$. Solving $r(t) = 0$ we get $t = 33.3$, so the raindrop will have evaporated completely at 33.3 seconds.

40. Separating variables, we obtain $dP/P = k \cos t\, dt$, so

$$\ln|P| = k \sin t + c \qquad \text{and} \qquad P = c_1 e^{k \sin t}.$$

If $P(0) = P_0$, then $c_1 = P_0$ and $P = P_0 e^{k \sin t}$.

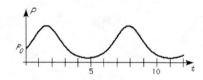

41. (a) From $dP/dt = (k_1 - k_2)P$ we obtain $P = P_0 e^{(k_1 - k_2)t}$ where $P_0 = P(0)$.

(b) If $k_1 > k_2$ then $P \to \infty$ as $t \to \infty$. If $k_1 = k_2$ then $P = P_0$ for every t. If $k_1 < k_2$ then $P \to 0$ as $t \to \infty$.

42. (a) The solution of the differential equation is $P(t) = c_1 e^{kt} + h/k$. If we let the initial population of fish be P_0 then $P(0) = P_0$ which implies that

$$c_1 = P_0 - \frac{h}{k} \quad \text{and} \quad P(t) = \left(P_0 - \frac{h}{k}\right) e^{kt} + \frac{h}{k}.$$

(b) For $P_0 > h/k$ all terms in the solution are positive. In this case $P(t)$ increases as time t increases. That is, $P(t) \to \infty$ as $t \to \infty$.

For $P_0 = h/k$ the population remains constant for all time t:

$$P(t) = \left(\frac{h}{k} - \frac{h}{k}\right) e^{kt} + \frac{h}{k} = \frac{h}{k}.$$

For $0 < P_0 < h/k$ the coefficient of the exponential function is negative and so the function decreases as time t increases.

(c) Since the function decreases and is concave down, the graph of $P(t)$ crosses the t-axis. That is, there exists a time $T > 0$ such that $P(T) = 0$. Solving

$$\left(P_0 - \frac{h}{k}\right) e^{kT} + \frac{h}{k} = 0$$

for T shows that the time of extinction is

$$T = \frac{1}{k} \ln \left(\frac{h}{h - kP_0} \right).$$

43. (a) Solving $r - kx = 0$ for x we find the equilibrium solution $x = r/k$. When $x < r/k$, $dx/dt > 0$ and when $x > r/k$, $dx/dt < 0$. From the phase portrait we see that $\lim_{t \to \infty} x(t) = r/k$.

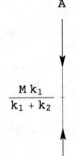

(b) From $dx/dt = r - kx$ and $x(0) = 0$ we obtain $x = r/k - (r/k)e^{-kt}$ so that $x \to r/k$ as $t \to \infty$. If $x(T) = r/2k$ then $T = (\ln 2)/k$.

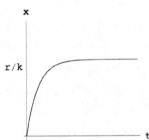

44. (a) Solving $k_1(M - A) - k_2 A = 0$ for A we find the equilibrium solution $A = k_1 M/(k_1 + k_2)$. From the phase portrait we see that $\lim_{t \to \infty} A(t) = k_1 M/(k_1 + k_2)$. Since $k_2 > 0$, the material will never be completely memorized and the larger k_2 is, the less the amount of material will be memorized over time.

(b) Write the differential equation in the form $dA/dt + (k_1 + k_2)A = k_1 M$. Then an integrating factor is $e^{(k_1 + k_2)t}$, and

$$\frac{d}{dt}\left[e^{(k_1 + k_2)t} A \right] = k_1 M e^{(k_1 + k_2)t}$$

$$e^{(k_1 + k_2)t} A = \frac{k_1 M}{k_1 + k_2} e^{(k_1 + k_2)t} + c$$

$$A = \frac{k_1 M}{k_1 + k_2} + c e^{-(k_1 + k_2)t}.$$

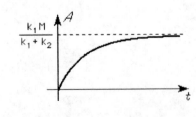

Using $A(0) = 0$ we find $c = -\dfrac{k_1 M}{k_1 + k_2}$ and $A = \dfrac{k_1 M}{k_1 + k_2}\left(1 - e^{-(k_1+k_2)t}\right)$. As $t \to \infty$,

$A \to \dfrac{k_1 M}{k_1 + k_2}$.

45. (a) For $0 \le t < 4$, $6 \le t < 10$ and $12 \le t < 16$, no voltage is applied to the heart and $E(t) = 0$. At the other times, the differential equation is $dE/dt = -E/RC$. Separating variables, integrating, and solving for e, we get $E = ke^{-t/RC}$, subject to $E(4) = E(10) = E(16) = 12$. These intitial conditions yield, respectively, $k = 12e^{4/RC}$, $k = 12e^{10/RC}$, $k = 12e^{16/RC}$, and $k = 12e^{22/RC}$. Thus

$$E(t) = \begin{cases} 0, & 0 \le t < 4, \;\; 6 \le t < 10, \;\; 12 \le t < 16 \\ 12e^{(4-t)/RC}, & 4 \le t < 6 \\ 12e^{(10-t)/RC}, & 10 \le t < 12 \\ 12e^{(16-t)/RC}, & 16 \le t < 18 \\ 12e^{(22-t)/RC}, & 22 \le t < 24. \end{cases}$$

(b)

46. (a) (i) Using Newton's second law of motion, $F = ma = m\,dv/dt$, the differential equation for the velocity v is

$$m\frac{dv}{dt} = mg\sin\theta \qquad \text{or} \qquad \frac{dv}{dt} = g\sin\theta,$$

where $mg\sin\theta$, $0 < \theta < \pi/2$, is the component of the weight along the plane in the direction of motion.

(ii) The model now becomes

$$m\frac{dv}{dt} = mg\sin\theta - \mu mg\cos\theta,$$

where $\mu mg\cos\theta$ is the component of the force of sliding friction (which acts perpendicular to the plane) along the plane. The negative sign indicates that this component of force is a retarding force which acts in the direction opposite to that of motion.

(iii) If air resistance is taken to be proportional to the instantaneous velocity of the body, the model becomes

$$m\frac{dv}{dt} = mg\sin\theta - \mu mg\cos\theta - kv,$$

where k is a constant of proportionality.

(b) (*i*) With $m = 3$ slugs, the differential equation is

$$3\frac{dv}{dt} = (96) \cdot \frac{1}{2} \qquad \text{or} \qquad \frac{dv}{dt} = 16.$$

Integrating the last equation gives $v(t) = 16t + c_1$. Since $v(0) = 0$, we have $c_1 = 0$ and so $v(t) = 16t$.

(*ii*) With $m = 3$ slugs, the differential equation is

$$3\frac{dv}{dt} = (96) \cdot \frac{1}{2} - \frac{\sqrt{3}}{4} \cdot (96) \cdot \frac{\sqrt{3}}{2} \qquad \text{or} \qquad \frac{dv}{dt} = 4.$$

In this case $v(t) = 4t$.

(*iii*) When the retarding force due to air resistance is taken into account, the differential equation for velocity v becomes

$$3\frac{dv}{dt} = (96) \cdot \frac{1}{2} - \frac{\sqrt{3}}{4} \cdot (96) \cdot \frac{\sqrt{3}}{2} - \frac{1}{4}v \qquad \text{or} \qquad 3\frac{dv}{dt} = 12 - \frac{1}{4}v.$$

The last differential equation is linear and has solution $v(t) = 48 + c_1 e^{-t/12}$. Since $v(0) = 0$, we find $c_1 = -48$, so $v(t) = 48 - 48e^{-t/12}$.

47. (a) (*i*) If $s(t)$ is distance measured down the plane from the highest point, then $ds/dt = v$. Integrating $ds/dt = 16t$ gives $s(t) = 8t^2 + c_2$. Using $s(0) = 0$ then gives $c_2 = 0$. Now the length L of the plane is $L = 50/\sin 30° = 100$ ft. The time it takes the box to slide completely down the plane is the solution of $s(t) = 100$ or $t^2 = 25/2$, so $t \approx 3.54$ s.

(*ii*) Integrating $ds/dt = 4t$ gives $s(t) = 2t^2 + c_2$. Using $s(0) = 0$ gives $c_2 = 0$, so $s(t) = 2t^2$ and the solution of $s(t) = 100$ is now $t \approx 7.07$ s.

(*iii*) Integrating $ds/dt = 48 - 48e^{-t/12}$ and using $s(0) = 0$ to determine the constant of integration, we obtain $s(t) = 48t + 576e^{-t/12} - 576$. With the aid of a CAS we find that the solution of $s(t) = 100$, or

$$100 = 48t + 576e^{-t/12} - 576 \qquad \text{or} \qquad 0 = 48t + 576e^{-t/12} - 676,$$

is now $t \approx 7.84$ s.

(b) The differential equation $m\,dv/dt = mg\sin\theta - \mu mg\cos\theta$ can be written

$$m\frac{dv}{dt} = mg\cos\theta(\tan\theta - \mu).$$

If $\tan\theta = \mu$, $dv/dt = 0$ and $v(0) = 0$ implies that $v(t) = 0$. If $\tan\theta < \mu$ and $v(0) = 0$, then integration implies $v(t) = g\cos\theta(\tan\theta - \mu)t < 0$ for all time t.

(c) Since $\tan 23° = 0.4245$ and $\mu = \sqrt{3}/4 = 0.4330$, we see that $\tan 23° < 0.4330$. The differential equation is $dv/dt = 32\cos 23°(\tan 23° - \sqrt{3}/4) = -0.251493$. Integration and the use of the initial condition gives $v(t) = -0.251493t + 1$. When the box stops, $v(t) = 0$ or $0 = -0.251493t+1$ or $t = 3.976254$ s. From $s(t) = -0.125747t^2+t$ we find $s(3.976254) = 1.988119$ ft.

(d) With $v_0 > 0$, $v(t) = -0.251493t + v_0$ and $s(t) = -0.125747t^2 + v_0t$. Because two real positive solutions of the equation $s(t) = 100$, or $0 = -0.125747t^2 + v_0t - 100$, would be physically meaningless, we use the quadratic formula and require that $b^2 - 4ac = 0$ or $v_0^2 - 50.2987 = 0$. From this last equality we find $v_0 \approx 7.092164$ ft/s. For the time it takes the box to traverse the entire inclined plane, we must have $0 = -0.125747t^2 + 7.092164t - 100$. *Mathematica* gives complex roots for the last equation: $t = 28.2001 \pm 0.0124458i$. But, for

$$0 = -0.125747t^2 + 7.092164691t - 100,$$

the roots are $t = 28.1999$ s and $t = 28.2004$ s. So if $v_0 > 7.092164$, we are guaranteed that the box will slide completely down the plane.

48. (a) We saw in part (b) of Problem 36 that the ascent time is $t_a = 9.375$. To find when the cannonball hits the ground we solve $s(t) = -16t^2 + 300t = 0$, getting a total time in flight of $t = 18.75$ s. Thus, the time of descent is $t_d = 18.75 - 9.375 = 9.375$. The impact velocity is $v_i = v(18.75) = -300$, which has the same magnitude as the initial velocity.

(b) We saw in Problem 37 that the ascent time in the case of air resistance is $t_a = 9.162$. Solving $s(t) = 1,340,000 - 6,400t - 1,340,000e^{-0.005t} = 0$ we see that the total time of flight is 18.466 s. Thus, the descent time is $t_d = 18.466 - 9.162 = 9.304$. The impact velocity is $v_i = v(18.466) = -290.91$, compared to an initial velocity of $v_0 = 300$.

Exercises 3.2

Nonlinear Models

1. (a) Solving $N(1 - 0.0005N) = 0$ for N we find the equilibrium solutions $N = 0$ and $N = 2000$. When $0 < N < 2000$, $dN/dt > 0$. From the phase portrait we see that $\lim_{t\to\infty} N(t) = 2000$. A graph of the solution is shown in part (b).

(b) Separating variables and integrating we have

$$\frac{dN}{N(1-0.0005N)} = \left(\frac{1}{N} - \frac{1}{N-2000}\right)dN = dt$$

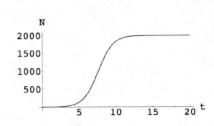

and

$$\ln N - \ln(N-2000) = t + c.$$

Solving for N we get $N(t) = 2000e^{c+t}/(1+e^{c+t}) = 2000e^c e^t/(1+e^c e^t)$. Using $N(0) = 1$ and solving for e^c we find $e^c = 1/1999$ and so $N(t) = 2000e^t/(1999+e^t)$. Then $N(10) = 1833.59$, so 1834 companies are expected to adopt the new technology when $t = 10$.

2. From $dN/dt = N(a - bN)$ and $N(0) = 500$ we obtain

$$N = \frac{500a}{500b + (a - 500b)e^{-at}}.$$

Since $\lim_{t\to\infty} N = a/b = 50{,}000$ and $N(1) = 1000$ we have $a = 0.7033$, $b = 0.00014$, and $N = 50{,}000/(1 + 99e^{-0.7033t})$.

3. From $dP/dt = P\left(10^{-1} - 10^{-7}P\right)$ and $P(0) = 5000$ we obtain $P = 500/(0.0005 + 0.0995e^{-0.1t})$ so that $P \to 1{,}000{,}000$ as $t \to \infty$. If $P(t) = 500{,}000$ then $t = 52.9$ months.

4. **(a)** We have $dP/dt = P(a - bP)$ with $P(0) = 3.929$ million. Using separation of variables we obtain

$$P(t) = \frac{3.929a}{3.929b + (a - 3.929b)e^{-at}} = \frac{a/b}{1 + (a/3.929b - 1)e^{-at}}$$

$$= \frac{c}{1 + (c/3.929 - 1)e^{-at}},$$

where $c = a/b$. At $t = 60(1850)$ the population is 23.192 million, so

$$23.192 = \frac{c}{1 + (c/3.929 - 1)e^{-60a}}$$

or $c = 23.192 + 23.192(c/3.929 - 1)e^{-60a}$. At $t = 120(1910)$,

$$91.972 = \frac{c}{1 + (c/3.929 - 1)e^{-120a}}$$

or $c = 91.972 + 91.972(c/3.929 - 1)(e^{-60a})^2$. Combining the two equations for c we get

$$\left(\frac{(c - 23.192)/23.192}{c/3.929 - 1}\right)^2 \left(\frac{c}{3.929} - 1\right) = \frac{c - 91.972}{91.972}$$

or

$$91.972(3.929)(c - 23.192)^2 = (23.192)^2(c - 91.972)(c - 3.929).$$

The solution of this quadratic equation is $c = 197.274$. This in turn gives $a = 0.0313$. Therefore,

$$P(t) = \frac{197.274}{1 + 49.21e^{-0.0313t}}.$$

(b)

Year	Census Population	Predicted Population	Error	% Error
1790	3.929	3.929	0.000	0.00
1800	5.308	5.334	-0.026	-0.49
1810	7.240	7.222	0.018	0.24
1820	9.638	9.746	-0.108	-1.12
1830	12.866	13.090	-0.224	-1.74
1840	17.069	17.475	-0.406	-2.38
1850	23.192	23.143	0.049	0.21
1860	31.433	30.341	1.092	3.47
1870	38.558	39.272	-0.714	-1.85
1880	50.156	50.044	0.112	0.22
1890	62.948	62.600	0.348	0.55
1900	75.996	76.666	-0.670	-0.88
1910	91.972	91.739	0.233	0.25
1920	105.711	107.143	-1.432	-1.35
1930	122.775	122.140	0.635	0.52
1940	131.669	136.068	-4.399	-3.34
1950	150.697	148.445	2.252	1.49

The model predicts a population of 159.0 million for 1960 and 167.8 million for 1970. The census populations for these years were 179.3 and 203.3, respectively. The percentage errors are 12.8 and 21.2, respectively.

5. (a) The differential equation is $dP/dt = P(5 - P) - 4$. Solving $P(5 - P) - 4 = 0$ for P we obtain equilibrium solutions $P = 1$ and $P = 4$. The phase portrait is shown on the right and solution curves are shown in part (b). We see that for $P_0 > 4$ and $1 < P_0 < 4$ the population approaches 4 as t increases. For $0 < P < 1$ the population decreases to 0 in finite time.

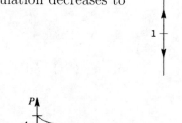

(b) The differential equation is

$$\frac{dP}{dt} = P(5 - P) - 4 = -(P^2 - 5P + 4) = -(P - 4)(P - 1).$$

Separating variables and integrating, we obtain

$$\frac{dP}{(P - 4)(P - 1)} = -dt$$

$$\left(\frac{1/3}{P - 4} - \frac{1/3}{P - 1}\right) dP = -dt$$

$$\frac{1}{3} \ln\left|\frac{P - 4}{P - 1}\right| = -t + c$$

$$\frac{P - 4}{P - 1} = c_1 e^{-3t}.$$

Setting $t = 0$ and $P = P_0$ we find $c_1 = (P_0 - 4)/(P_0 - 1)$. Solving for P we obtain

$$P(t) = \frac{4(P_0 - 1) - (P_0 - 4)e^{-3t}}{(P_0 - 1) - (P_0 - 4)e^{-3t}}.$$

101

(c) To find when the population becomes extinct in the case $0 < P_0 < 1$ we set $P = 0$ in

$$\frac{P-4}{P-1} = \frac{P_0-4}{P_0-1} e^{-3t}$$

from part (a) and solve for t. This gives the time of extinction

$$t = -\frac{1}{3} \ln \frac{4(P_0-1)}{P_0-4}.$$

6. Solving $P(5-P) - \frac{25}{4} = 0$ for P we obtain the equilibrium solution $P = \frac{5}{2}$. For $P \neq \frac{5}{2}$, $dP/dt < 0$. Thus, if $P_0 < \frac{5}{2}$, the population becomes extinct (otherwise there would be another equilibrium solution.) Using separation of variables to solve the initial-value problem, we get

$$P(t) = [4P_0 + (10P_0 - 25)t]/[4 + (4P_0 - 10)t].$$

To find when the population becomes extinct for $P_0 < \frac{5}{2}$ we solve $P(t) = 0$ for t. We see that the time of extinction is $t = 4P_0/5(5 - 2P_0)$.

7. Solving $P(5-P) - 7 = 0$ for P we obtain complex roots, so there are no equilibrium solutions. Since $dP/dt < 0$ for all values of P, the population becomes extinct for any initial condition. Using separation of variables to solve the initial-value problem, we get

$$P(t) = \frac{5}{2} + \frac{\sqrt{3}}{2} \tan\left[\tan^{-1}\left(\frac{2P_0 - 5}{\sqrt{3}}\right) - \frac{\sqrt{3}}{2}t\right].$$

Solving $P(t) = 0$ for t we see that the time of extinction is

$$t = \frac{2}{3}\left(\sqrt{3}\tan^{-1}(5/\sqrt{3}) + \sqrt{3}\tan^{-1}[(2P_0 - 5)/\sqrt{3}]\right).$$

8. (a) The differential equation is $dP/dt = P(1 - \ln P)$, which has the equilibrium solution $P = e$. When $P_0 > e$, $dP/dt < 0$, and when $P_0 < e$, $dP/dt > 0$.

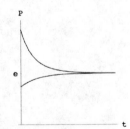

(b) The differential equation is $dP/dt = P(1 + \ln P)$, which has the equilibrium solution $P = 1/e$. When $P_0 > 1/e$, $dP/dt > 0$, and when $P_0 < 1/e$, $dP/dt < 0$.

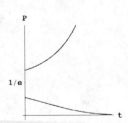

(c) From $dP/dt = P(a - b\ln P)$ we obtain $-(1/b)\ln|a - b\ln P| = t + c_1$ so that $P = e^{a/b}e^{-ce^{-bt}}$. If $P(0) = P_0$ then $c = (a/b) - \ln P_0$.

9. Let $X = X(t)$ be the amount of C at time t and $dX/dt = k(120 - 2X)(150 - X)$. If $X(0) = 0$ and $X(5) = 10$, then

$$X(t) = \frac{150 - 150e^{180kt}}{1 - 2.5e^{180kt}},$$

where $k = .0001259$ and $X(20) = 29.3$ grams. Now by L'Hôpital's rule, $X \to 60$ as $t \to \infty$, so that the amount of $A \to 0$ and the amount of $B \to 30$ as $t \to \infty$.

10. From $dX/dt = k(150 - X)^2$, $X(0) = 0$, and $X(5) = 10$ we obtain $X = 150 - 150/(150kt + 1)$ where $k = .000095238$. Then $X(20) = 33.3$ grams and $X \to 150$ as $t \to \infty$ so that the amount of $A \to 0$ and the amount of $B \to 0$ as $t \to \infty$. If $X(t) = 75$ then $t = 70$ minutes.

11. **(a)** The initial-value problem is $dh/dt = -8A_h\sqrt{h}/A_w$, $h(0) = H$. Separating variables and integrating we have

    $$\frac{dh}{\sqrt{h}} = -\frac{8A_h}{A_w}dt \quad \text{and} \quad 2\sqrt{h} = -\frac{8A_h}{A_w}t + c.$$

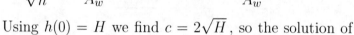

    Using $h(0) = H$ we find $c = 2\sqrt{H}$, so the solution of the initial-value problem is $\sqrt{h(t)} = (A_w\sqrt{H} - 4A_h t)/A_w$, where $A_w\sqrt{H} - 4A_h t \geq 0$. Thus,

    $$h(t) = (A_w\sqrt{H} - 4A_h t)^2/A_w^2 \quad \text{for} \quad 0 \leq t \leq A_w\sqrt{H}/4A_h.$$

    (b) Identifying $H = 10$, $A_w = 4\pi$, and $A_h = \pi/576$ we have $h(t) = t^2/331{,}776 - (\sqrt{5/2}/144)t + 10$. Solving $h(t) = 0$ we see that the tank empties in $576\sqrt{10}$ seconds or 30.36 minutes.

12. To obtain the solution of this differential equation we use $h(t)$ from Problem 13 in Exercises 1.3. Then $h(t) = (A_w\sqrt{H} - 4cA_h t)^2/A_w^2$. Solving $h(t) = 0$ with $c = 0.6$ and the values from Problem 11 we see that the tank empties in 3035.79 seconds or 50.6 minutes.

13. **(a)** Separating variables and integrating gives

    $$6h^{3/2}dh = -5dt \quad \text{and} \quad \frac{12}{5}h^{5/2} = -5t + c.$$

    Using $h(0) = 20$ we find $c = 1920\sqrt{5}$, so the solution of the initial-value problem is $h(t) = \left(800\sqrt{5} - \frac{25}{12}t\right)^{2/5}$. Solving $h(t) = 0$ we see that the tank empties in $384\sqrt{5}$ seconds or 14.31 minutes.

    (b) When the height of the water is h, the radius of the top of the water is $r = h\tan 30° = h/\sqrt{3}$ and $A_w = \pi h^2/3$. The differential equation is

    $$\frac{dh}{dt} = -c\frac{A_h}{A_w}\sqrt{2gh} = -0.6\frac{\pi(2/12)^2}{\pi h^2/3}\sqrt{64h} = -\frac{2}{5h^{3/2}}.$$

Exercises 3.2 Nonlinear Models

Separating variables and integrating gives

$$5h^{3/2}dh = -2\,dt \quad \text{and} \quad 2h^{5/2} = -2t + c.$$

Using $h(0) = 9$ we find $c = 486$, so the solution of the initial-value problem is $h(t) = (243-t)^{2/5}$. Solving $h(t) = 0$ we see that the tank empties in 243 seconds or 4.05 minutes.

14. When the height of the water is h, the radius of the top of the water is $\frac{2}{5}(20 - h)$ and $A_w = 4\pi(20 - h)^2/25$. The differential equation is

$$\frac{dh}{dt} = -c\frac{A_h}{A_w}\sqrt{2gh} = -0.6\frac{\pi(2/12)^2}{4\pi(20 - h)^2/25}\sqrt{64h} = -\frac{5}{6}\frac{\sqrt{h}}{(20 - h)^2}.$$

Separating variables and integrating we have

$$\frac{(20 - h)^2}{\sqrt{h}}\,dh = -\frac{5}{6}\,dt \quad \text{and} \quad 800\sqrt{h} - \frac{80}{3}h^{3/2} + \frac{2}{5}h^{5/2} = -\frac{5}{6}t + c.$$

Using $h(0) = 20$ we find $c = 2560\sqrt{5}/3$, so an implicit solution of the initial-value problem is

$$800\sqrt{h} - \frac{80}{3}h^{3/2} + \frac{2}{5}h^{5/2} = -\frac{5}{6}t + \frac{2560\sqrt{5}}{3}.$$

To find the time it takes the tank to empty we set $h = 0$ and solve for t. The tank empties in $1024\sqrt{5}$ seconds or 38.16 minutes. Thus, the tank empties more slowly when the base of the cone is on the bottom.

15. (a) After separating variables we obtain

$$\frac{m\,dv}{mg - kv^2} = dt$$

$$\frac{1}{g}\frac{dv}{1 - (\sqrt{k}\,v/\sqrt{mg})^2} = dt$$

$$\frac{\sqrt{mg}}{\sqrt{k}\,g}\frac{\sqrt{k/mg}\,dv}{1 - (\sqrt{k}\,v/\sqrt{mg})^2} = dt$$

$$\sqrt{\frac{m}{kg}}\tanh^{-1}\frac{\sqrt{k}\,v}{\sqrt{mg}} = t + c$$

$$\tanh^{-1}\frac{\sqrt{k}\,v}{\sqrt{mg}} = \sqrt{\frac{kg}{m}}\,t + c_1.$$

Thus the velocity at time t is

$$v(t) = \sqrt{\frac{mg}{k}}\tanh\left(\sqrt{\frac{kg}{m}}t + c_1\right).$$

Setting $t = 0$ and $v = v_0$ we find $c_1 = \tanh^{-1}(\sqrt{k}\,v_0/\sqrt{mg})$.

(b) Since $\tanh t \to 1$ as $t \to \infty$, we have $v \to \sqrt{mg/k}$ as $t \to \infty$.

(c) Integrating the expression for $v(t)$ in part (a) we obtain an integral of the form $\int du/u$:

$$s(t) = \sqrt{\frac{mg}{k}} \int \tanh\left(\sqrt{\frac{kg}{m}}t + c_1\right) dt = \frac{m}{k} \ln\left[\cosh\left(\sqrt{\frac{kg}{m}}t + c_1\right)\right] + c_2.$$

Setting $t = 0$ and $s = 0$ we find $c_2 = -(m/k)\ln(\cosh c_1)$, where c_1 is given in part (a).

16. The differential equation is $m\,dv/dt = -mg - kv^2$. Separating variables and integrating, we have

$$\frac{dv}{mg + kv^2} = -\frac{dt}{m}$$

$$\frac{1}{\sqrt{mgk}}\tan^{-1}\left(\frac{\sqrt{k}\,v}{\sqrt{mg}}\right) = -\frac{1}{m}t + c$$

$$\tan^{-1}\left(\frac{\sqrt{k}\,v}{\sqrt{mg}}\right) = -\sqrt{\frac{gk}{m}}\,t + c_1$$

$$v(t) = \sqrt{\frac{mg}{k}}\tan\left(c_1 - \sqrt{\frac{gk}{m}}\,t\right).$$

Setting $v(0) = 300$, $m = \frac{16}{32} = \frac{1}{2}$, $g = 32$, and $k = 0.0003$, we find $v(t) = 230.94\tan(c_1 - 0.138564t)$ and $c_1 = 0.914743$. Integrating

$$v(t) = 230.94\tan(0.914743 - 0.138564t)$$

we get

$$s(t) = 1666.67\ln|\cos(0.914743 - 0.138564t)| + c_2.$$

Using $s(0) = 0$ we find $c_2 = 823.843$. Solving $v(t) = 0$ we see that the maximum height is attained when $t = 6.60159$. The maximum height is $s(6.60159) = 823.843$ ft.

17. **(a)** Let ρ be the weight density of the water and V the volume of the object. Archimedes' principle states that the upward buoyant force has magnitude equal to the weight of the water displaced. Taking the positive direction to be down, the differential equation is

$$m\frac{dv}{dt} = mg - kv^2 - \rho V.$$

(b) Using separation of variables we have

$$\frac{m\,dv}{(mg - \rho V) - kv^2} = dt$$

$$\frac{m}{\sqrt{k}}\frac{\sqrt{k}\,dv}{(\sqrt{mg - \rho V})^2 - (\sqrt{k}\,v)^2} = dt$$

$$\frac{m}{\sqrt{k}}\frac{1}{\sqrt{mg - \rho V}}\tanh^{-1}\frac{\sqrt{k}\,v}{\sqrt{mg - \rho V}} = t + c.$$

Thus

$$v(t) = \sqrt{\frac{mg - \rho V}{k}} \tanh\left(\frac{\sqrt{kmg - k\rho V}}{m} t + c_1\right).$$

(c) Since $\tanh t \to 1$ as $t \to \infty$, the terminal velocity is $\sqrt{(mg - \rho V)/k}$.

18. (a) Writing the equation in the form $(x - \sqrt{x^2 + y^2})dx + y\,dy = 0$ we identify $M = x - \sqrt{x^2 + y^2}$ and $N = y$. Since M and N are both homogeneous functions of degree 1 we use the substitution $y = ux$. It follows that

$$\left(x - \sqrt{x^2 + u^2 x^2}\right)dx + ux(u\,dx + x\,du) = 0$$

$$x\left[1 - \sqrt{1 + u^2} + u^2\right]dx + x^2 u\,du = 0$$

$$-\frac{u\,du}{1 + u^2 - \sqrt{1 + u^2}} = \frac{dx}{x}$$

$$\frac{u\,du}{\sqrt{1 + u^2}\left(1 - \sqrt{1 + u^2}\right)} = \frac{dx}{x}.$$

Letting $w = 1 - \sqrt{1 + u^2}$ we have $dw = -u\,du/\sqrt{1 + u^2}$ so that

$$-\ln\left|1 - \sqrt{1 + u^2}\right| = \ln|x| + c$$

$$\frac{1}{1 - \sqrt{1 + u^2}} = c_1 x$$

$$1 - \sqrt{1 + u^2} = -\frac{c_2}{x} \qquad (-c_2 = 1/c_1)$$

$$1 + \frac{c_2}{x} = \sqrt{1 + \frac{y^2}{x^2}}$$

$$1 + \frac{2c_2}{x} + \frac{c_2^2}{x^2} = 1 + \frac{y^2}{x^2}.$$

Solving for y^2 we have

$$y^2 = 2c_2 x + c_2^2 = 4\left(\frac{c_2}{2}\right)\left(x + \frac{c_2}{2}\right)$$

which is a family of parabolas symmetric with respect to the x-axis with vertex at $(-c_2/2, 0)$ and focus at the origin.

(b) Let $u = x^2 + y^2$ so that

$$\frac{du}{dx} = 2x + 2y\frac{dy}{dx}.$$

Then

$$y\frac{dy}{dx} = \frac{1}{2}\frac{du}{dx} - x$$

and the differential equation can be written in the form

$$\frac{1}{2}\frac{du}{dx} - x = -x + \sqrt{u} \quad \text{or} \quad \frac{1}{2}\frac{du}{dx} = \sqrt{u}.$$

Separating variables and integrating gives

$$\frac{du}{2\sqrt{u}} = dx$$

$$\sqrt{u} = x + c$$

$$u = x^2 + 2cx + c^2$$

$$x^2 + y^2 = x^2 + 2cx + c^2$$

$$y^2 = 2cx + c^2.$$

19. (a) From $2W^2 - W^3 = W^2(2 - W) = 0$ we see that $W = 0$ and $W = 2$ are constant solutions.

(b) Separating variables and using a CAS to integrate we get

$$\frac{dW}{W\sqrt{4 - 2W}} = dx \quad \text{and} \quad -\tanh^{-1}\left(\frac{1}{2}\sqrt{4 - 2W}\right) = x + c.$$

Using the facts that the hyperbolic tangent is an odd function and $1 - \tanh^2 x = \operatorname{sech}^2 x$ we have

$$\frac{1}{2}\sqrt{4 - 2W} = \tanh(-x - c) = -\tanh(x + c)$$

$$\frac{1}{4}(4 - 2W) = \tanh^2(x + c)$$

$$1 - \frac{1}{2}W = \tanh^2(x + c)\text{-}$$

$$\frac{1}{2}W = 1 - \tanh^2(x + c) = \operatorname{sech}^2(x + c).$$

Thus, $W(x) = 2\operatorname{sech}^2(x + c)$.

(c) Letting $x = 0$ and $W = 2$ we find that $\operatorname{sech}^2(c) = 1$ and $c = 0$.

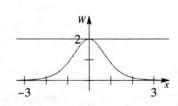

20. (a) Solving $r^2 + (10 - h)^2 = 10^2$ for r^2 we see that $r^2 = 20h - h^2$. Combining the rate of input of water, π, with the rate of output due to evaporation, $k\pi r^2 = k\pi(20h - h^2)$, we have $dV/dt =$

$\pi - k\pi(20h - h^2)$. Using $V = 10\pi h^2 - \frac{1}{3}\pi h^3$, we see also that $dV/dt = (20\pi h - \pi h^2)dh/dt$. Thus,

$$(20\pi h - \pi h^2)\frac{dh}{dt} = \pi - k\pi(20h - h^2) \quad \text{and} \quad \frac{dh}{dt} = \frac{1 - 20kh + kh^2}{20h - h^2}.$$

(b) Letting $k = 1/100$, separating variables and integrating (with the help of a CAS), we get

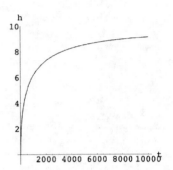

$$\frac{100h(h - 20)}{(h - 10)^2} dh = dt \quad \text{and} \quad \frac{100(h^2 - 10h + 100)}{10 - h} = t + c.$$

Using $h(0) = 0$ we find $c = 1000$, and solving for h we get $h(t) = 0.005(\sqrt{t^2 + 4000t} - t)$, where the positive square root is chosen because $h \geq 0$.

(c) The volume of the tank is $V = \frac{2}{3}\pi(10)^3$ feet, so at a rate of π cubic feet per minute, the tank will fill in $\frac{2}{3}(10)^3 \approx 666.67$ minutes ≈ 11.11 hours.

(d) At 666.67 minutes, the depth of the water is $h(666.67) = 5.486$ feet. From the graph in (b) we suspect that $\lim_{t \to \infty} h(t) = 10$, in which case the tank will never completely fill. To prove this we compute the limit of $h(t)$:

$$\lim_{t \to \infty} h(t) = 0.005 \lim_{t \to \infty} \left(\sqrt{t^2 + 4000t} - t\right) = 0.005 \lim_{t \to \infty} \frac{t^2 + 4000t - t^2}{\sqrt{t^2 + 4000t} + t}$$

$$= 0.005 \lim_{t \to \infty} \frac{4000t}{t\sqrt{1 + 4000/t} + t} = 0.005 \frac{4000}{1 + 1} = 0.005(2000) = 10.$$

21. (a)

t	P(t)	Q(t)
0	3.929	0.035
10	5.308	0.036
20	7.240	0.033
30	9.638	0.033
40	12.866	0.033
50	17.069	0.036
60	23.192	0.036
70	31.433	0.023
80	38.558	0.030
90	50.156	0.026
100	62.948	0.021
110	75.996	0.021
120	91.972	0.015
130	105.711	0.016
140	122.775	0.007
150	131.669	0.014
160	150.697	0.019
170	179.300	

(b) The regression line is $Q = 0.0348391 - 0.000168222P$.

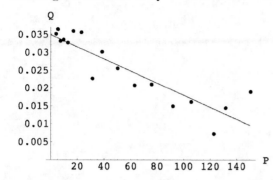

(c) The solution of the logistic equation is given in equation (5) in the text. Identifying $a = 0.0348391$ and $b = 0.000168222$ we have

$$P(t) = \frac{aP_0}{bP_0 + (a - bP_0)e^{-at}}.$$

(d) With $P_0 = 3.929$ the solution becomes

$$P(t) = \frac{0.136883}{0.000660944 + 0.0341781e^{-0.0348391t}}.$$

(e)

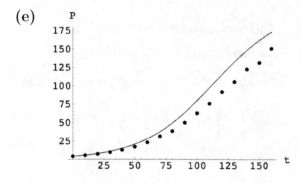

(f) We identify $t = 180$ with 1970, $t = 190$ with 1980, and $t = 200$ with 1990. The model predicts $P(180) = 188.661$, $P(190) = 193.735$, and $P(200) = 197.485$. The actual population figures for these years are 203.303, 226.542, and 248.765 millions. As $t \to \infty$, $P(t) \to a/b = 207.102$.

22. (a) Using a CAS to solve $P(1 - P) + 0.3e^{-P} = 0$ for P we see that $P = 1.09216$ is an equilibrium solution.

(b) Since $f(P) > 0$ for $0 < P < 1.09216$, the solution $P(t)$ of

$$dP/dt = P(1 - P) + 0.3e^{-P}, \quad P(0) = P_0,$$

is increasing for $P_0 < 1.09216$. Since $f(P) < 0$ for $P > 1.09216$, the solution $P(t)$ is decreasing for $P_0 > 1.09216$. Thus $P = 1.09216$ is an attractor.

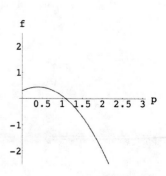

(c) The curves for the second initial-value problem are thicker. The equilibrium solution for the logic model is $P = 1$. Comparing 1.09216 and 1, we see that the percentage increase is 9.216%.

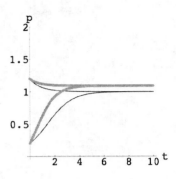

23. To find t_d we solve

$$m\frac{dv}{dt} = mg - kv^2, \qquad v(0) = 0$$

using separation of variables. This gives

$$v(t) = \sqrt{\frac{mg}{k}}\,\tanh\sqrt{\frac{kg}{m}}\,t.$$

Integrating and using $s(0) = 0$ gives

$$s(t) = \frac{m}{k}\ln\left(\cosh\sqrt{\frac{kg}{m}}\,t\right).$$

To find the time of descent we solve $s(t) = 823.84$ and find $t_d = 7.77882$. The impact velocity is $v(t_d) = 182.998$, which is positive because the positive direction is downward.

24. (a) Solving $v_t = \sqrt{mg/k}$ for k we obtain $k = mg/v_t^2$. The differential equation then becomes

$$m\frac{dv}{dt} = mg - \frac{mg}{v_t^2}v^2 \quad \text{or} \quad \frac{dv}{dt} = g\left(1 - \frac{1}{v_t^2}v^2\right).$$

Separating variables and integrating gives

$$v_t\tanh^{-1}\frac{v}{v_t} = gt + c_1.$$

The initial condition $v(0) = 0$ implies $c_1 = 0$, so

$$v(t) = v_t\tanh\frac{gt}{v_t}.$$

We find the distance by integrating:

$$s(t) = \int v_t\tanh\frac{gt}{v_t}\,dt = \frac{v_t^2}{g}\ln\left(\cosh\frac{gt}{v_t}\right) + c_2.$$

The initial condition $s(0) = 0$ implies $c_2 = 0$, so

$$s(t) = \frac{v_t^2}{g}\ln\left(\cosh\frac{gt}{v_t}\right).$$

In 25 seconds she has fallen $20{,}000 - 14{,}800 = 5{,}200$ feet. Using a CAS to solve

$$5200 = (v_t^2/32) \ln \left(\cosh \frac{32(25)}{v_t} \right)$$

for v_t gives $v_t \approx 271.711$ ft/s. Then

$$s(t) = \frac{v_t^2}{g} \ln \left(\cosh \frac{gt}{v_t} \right) = 2307.08 \ln(\cosh 0.117772t).$$

(b) At $t = 15$, $s(15) = 2{,}542.94$ ft and $v(15) = s'(15) = 256.287$ ft/sec.

25. While the object is in the air its velocity is modeled by the linear differential equation $m\,dv/dt = mg - kv$. Using $m = 160$, $k = \frac{1}{4}$, and $g = 32$, the differential equation becomes $dv/dt + (1/640)v = 32$. The integrating factor is $e^{\int dt/640} = e^{t/640}$ and the solution of the differential equation is $e^{t/640}v = \int 32e^{t/640}dt = 20{,}480e^{t/640} + c$. Using $v(0) = 0$ we see that $c = -20{,}480$ and $v(t) = 20{,}480 - 20{,}480e^{-t/640}$. Integrating we get $s(t) = 20{,}480t + 13{,}107{,}200e^{-t/640} + c$. Since $s(0) = 0$, $c = -13{,}107{,}200$ and $s(t) = -13{,}107{,}200 + 20{,}480t + 13{,}107{,}200e^{-t/640}$. To find when the object hits the liquid we solve $s(t) = 500 - 75 = 425$, obtaining $t_a = 5.16018$. The velocity at the time of impact with the liquid is $v_a = v(t_a) = 164.482$. When the object is in the liquid its velocity is modeled by the nonlinear differential equation $m\,dv/dt = mg - kv^2$. Using $m = 160$, $g = 32$, and $k = 0.1$ this becomes $dv/dt = (51{,}200 - v^2)/1600$. Separating variables and integrating we have

$$\frac{dv}{51{,}200 - v^2} = \frac{dt}{1600} \quad \text{and} \quad \frac{\sqrt{2}}{640} \ln \left| \frac{v - 160\sqrt{2}}{v + 160\sqrt{2}} \right| = \frac{1}{1600}t + c.$$

Solving $v(0) = v_a = 164.482$ we obtain $c = -0.00407537$. Then, for $v < 160\sqrt{2} = 226.274$,

$$\left| \frac{v - 160\sqrt{2}}{v + 160\sqrt{2}} \right| = e^{\sqrt{2}t/5 - 1.8443} \quad \text{or} \quad -\frac{v - 160\sqrt{2}}{v + 160\sqrt{2}} = e^{\sqrt{2}t/5 - 1.8443}.$$

Solving for v we get

$$v(t) = \frac{13964.6 - 2208.29e^{\sqrt{2}t/5}}{61.7153 + 9.75937e^{\sqrt{2}t/5}}.$$

Integrating we find

$$s(t) = 226.275t - 1600 \ln(6.3237 + e^{\sqrt{2}t/5}) + c.$$

Solving $s(0) = 0$ we see that $c = 3185.78$, so

$$s(t) = 3185.78 + 226.275t - 1600 \ln(6.3237 + e^{\sqrt{2}t/5}).$$

To find when the object hits the bottom of the tank we solve $s(t) = 75$, obtaining $t_b = 0.466273$. The time from when the object is dropped from the helicopter to when it hits the bottom of the tank is $t_a + t_b = 5.62708$ seconds.

Exercises 3.2   Nonlinear Models

26. The velocity vector of the swimmer is

$$\mathbf{v} = \mathbf{v}_s + \mathbf{v}_r = (-v_s \cos\theta, -v_s \sin\theta) + (0, v_r) = (-v_s \cos\theta, -v_s \sin\theta + v_r) = \left(\frac{dx}{dt}, \frac{dy}{dt}\right).$$

Equating components gives

$$\frac{dx}{dt} = -v_s \cos\theta \quad \text{and} \quad \frac{dy}{dt} = -v_s \sin\theta + v_r$$

so

$$\frac{dx}{dt} = -v_s \frac{x}{\sqrt{x^2 + y^2}} \quad \text{and} \quad \frac{dy}{dt} = -v_s \frac{y}{\sqrt{x^2 + y^2}} + v_r.$$

Thus,

$$\frac{dy}{dx} = \frac{dy/dt}{dx/dt} = \frac{-v_s y + v_r\sqrt{x^2 + y^2}}{-v_s x} = \frac{v_s y - v_r\sqrt{x^2 + y^2}}{v_s x}.$$

27. **(a)** With $k = v_r/v_s$,

$$\frac{dy}{dx} = \frac{y - k\sqrt{x^2 + y^2}}{x}$$

is a first-order homogeneous differential equation (see Section 2.5). Substituting $y = ux$ into the differential equation gives

$$u + x\frac{du}{dx} = u - k\sqrt{1 + u^2} \quad \text{or} \quad \frac{du}{dx} = -k\sqrt{1 + u^2}.$$

Separating variables and integrating we obtain

$$\int \frac{du}{\sqrt{1 + u^2}} = -\int k\,dx \quad \text{or} \quad \ln\left(u + \sqrt{1 + u^2}\right) = -k\ln x + \ln c.$$

This implies

$$\ln x^k\left(u + \sqrt{1 + u^2}\right) = \ln c \quad \text{or} \quad x^k\left(\frac{y}{x} + \frac{\sqrt{x^2 + y^2}}{x}\right) = c.$$

The condition $y(1) = 0$ gives $c = 1$ and so $y + \sqrt{x^2 + y^2} = x^{1-k}$. Solving for y gives

$$y(x) = \frac{1}{2}\left(x^{1-k} - x^{1+k}\right).$$

(b) If $k = 1$, then $v_s = v_r$ and $y = \frac{1}{2}(1 - x^2)$. Since $y(0) = \frac{1}{2}$, the swimmer lands on the west beach at $(0, \frac{1}{2})$. That is, $\frac{1}{2}$ mile north of $(0,0)$.

If $k > 1$, then $v_r > v_s$ and $1 - k < 0$. This means $\lim_{x\to 0+} y(x)$ becomes infinite, since $\lim_{x\to 0+} x^{1-k}$ becomes infinite. The swimmer never makes it to the west beach and is swept northward with the current.

If $0 < k < 1$, then $v_s > v_r$ and $1 - k > 0$. The value of $y(x)$ at $x = 0$ is $y(0) = 0$. The swimmer has made it to the point $(0,0)$.

28. The velocity vector of the swimmer is

$$\mathbf{v} = \mathbf{v}_s + \mathbf{v}_r = (-v_s, 0) + (0, v_r) = \left(\frac{dx}{dt}, \frac{dy}{dt}\right).$$

Equating components gives

$$\frac{dx}{dt} = -v_s \quad \text{and} \quad \frac{dy}{dt} = v_r$$

so

$$\frac{dy}{dx} = \frac{dy/dt}{dx/dt} = \frac{v_r}{-v_s} = -\frac{v_r}{v_s}.$$

29. The differential equation

$$\frac{dy}{dx} = -\frac{30x(1-x)}{2}$$

separates into $dy = 15(-x + x^2)dx$. Integration gives $y(x) = -\frac{15}{2}x^2 + 5x^3 + c$. The condition $y(1) = 0$ gives $c = \frac{5}{2}$ and so $y(x) = \frac{1}{2}(-15x^2 + 10x^3 + 5)$. Since $y(0) = \frac{5}{2}$, the swimmer has to walk 2.5 miles back down the west beach to reach $(0, 0)$.

30. This problem has a great many components, so we will consider the case in which air resistance is assumed to be proportional to the velocity. By Problem 35 in Section 3.1 the differential equation is

$$m\frac{dv}{dt} = mg - kv,$$

and the solution is

$$v(t) = \frac{mg}{k} + \left(v_0 - \frac{mg}{k}\right)e^{-kt/m}.$$

If we take the initial velocity to be 0, then the velocity at time t is

$$v(t) = \frac{mg}{k} - \frac{mg}{k}e^{-kt/m}.$$

The mass of the raindrop is about $m = 62 \times 0.000000155/32 \approx 0.0000003$ and $g = 32$, so the volocity at time t is

$$v(t) = \frac{0.0000096}{k} - \frac{0.0000096}{k}e^{-3333333kt}$$

If we let $k = 0.0000007$, then $v(100) \approx 13.7$ ft/s. In this case 100 is the time in seconds. Since 7 mph ≈ 10.3 ft/s, the assertion that the average velocity is 7 mph is not unreasonable. Of course, this assumes that the air resistance is proportional to the velocity, and, more importantly, that the constant of proportionality is 0.0000007. The assumption about the constant is particularly suspect.

31. (a) Letting $c = 0.6$, $A_h = \pi(\frac{1}{32} \cdot \frac{1}{12})^2$, $A_w = \pi \cdot 1^2 = \pi$, and $g = 32$, the differential equation in Proble 12 becomes $dh/dt = -0.00003255\sqrt{h}$. Separating variables and integrating, we get $2\sqrt{h} = -0.00003255t + c$, so $h = (c_1 - 0.00001628t)^2$. Setting $h(0) = 2$, we find $c = \sqrt{2}$, so $h(t) = (\sqrt{2} - 0.00001628t)^2$, where h is measured in feet and t in seconds.

(b) One hour is 3,600 seconds, so the hour mark should be placed at

$$h(3600) = [\sqrt{2} - 0.00001628(3600)]^2 \approx 1.838\,\text{ft} \approx 22.0525\,\text{in}.$$

up from the bottom of the tank. The remaining marks corresponding to the passage of 2, 3, 4, ..., 12 hours are placed at the values shown in the table. The marks are not evenly spaced because the water is not draining out at a uniform rate; that is, $h(t)$ is not a linear function of time.

time (seconds)	height (inches)
0	24.0000
1	22.0520
2	20.1864
3	18.4033
4	16.7026
5	15.0844
6	13.5485
7	12.0952
8	10.7242
9	9.4357
10	8.2297
11	7.1060
12	6.0648

32. (a) In this case $A_w = \pi h^2/4$ and the differential equation is

$$\frac{dh}{dt} = -\frac{1}{7680}\, h^{-3/2}.$$

Separating variables and integrating, we have

$$h^{3/2}\, dh = -\frac{1}{7680}\, dt$$

$$\frac{2}{5}\, h^{5/2} = -\frac{1}{7680}\, t + c_1.$$

Setting $h(0) = 2$ we find $c_1 = 8\sqrt{2}/5$, so that

$$\frac{2}{5}\, h^{5/2} = -\frac{1}{7680}\, t + \frac{8\sqrt{2}}{5},$$

$$h^{5/2} = 4\sqrt{2} - \frac{1}{3072}\, t,$$

and

$$h = \left(4\sqrt{2} - \frac{1}{3072}\, t\right)^{2/5}.$$

(b) In this case $h(4\ \text{hr}) = h(14{,}400\ \text{s}) = 11.8515$ inches and $h(5\ \text{hr}) = h(18{,}000\ \text{s})$ is not a real number. Using a CAS to solve $h(t) = 0$, we see that the tank runs dry at $t \approx 17{,}378\ \text{s} \approx 4.83$ hr. Thus, this particular conical water clock can only measure time intervals of less than 4.83 hours.

33. If we let r_h denote the radius of the hole and $A_w = \pi[f(h)]^2$, then the differential equation $dh/dt = -k\sqrt{h}$, where $k = cA_h\sqrt{2g}/A_w$, becomes

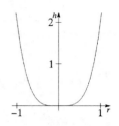

$$\frac{dh}{dt} = -\frac{c\pi r_h^2\sqrt{2g}}{\pi[f(h)]^2}\sqrt{h} = -\frac{8cr_h^2\sqrt{h}}{[f(h)]^2}.$$

For the time marks to be equally spaced, the rate of change of the height must be a constant; that is, $dh/dt = -a$. (The constant is negative because the height is decreasing.) Thus

$$-a = -\frac{8cr_h^2\sqrt{h}}{[f(h)]^2}, \qquad [f(h)]^2 = \frac{8cr_h^2\sqrt{h}}{a}, \qquad \text{and} \qquad r = f(h) = 2r_h\sqrt{\frac{2c}{a}}\,h^{1/4}.$$

Solving for h, we have

$$h = \frac{a^2}{64c^2 r_h^4}\,r^4.$$

The shape of the tank with $c = 0.6$, $a = 2$ ft/12 hr $= 1$ ft/21,600 s, and $r_h = 1/32(12) = 1/384$ is shown in the above figure.

34. (*This is a Contributed Problem and the solution has been provided by the authors of the problem.*)

(a) Answers will vary

(b) Answers will vary. This sample data is from Data from "Growth of Sunflower Seeds" by H.S. Reed and R.H. Holland, Proc. Nat. Acad. Sci., Volume 5, 1919, page 140. as quoted in http://math.arizona.edu/~dsl/bflower.htm

day	height
7	17.93
14	36.36
21	67.76
28	98.10
35	131.00
42	169.50
49	205.50
56	228.30
63	247.10
70	250.50
77	253.80
84	254.50

(c)

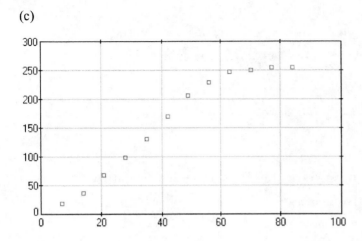

(d) In the case of the sample data, it looks more like logistic growth, with C = 255 cm. C is the height of the flower when it is fully grown.

(e) For our sample data:

day	height	dH/dt	k estimate
7	17.93	2.633	0.000619
14	36.36	3.559	0.000448
21	67.76	4.410	0.000348
28	98.10	4.517	0.000293
35	131.00	5.100	0.000314
42	169.50	5.321	0.000367
49	205.50	4.200	0.000413
56	228.30	2.971	0.000487
63	247.10	1.586	0.000812
70	250.50	0.479	0.000425
77	253.80	0.286	0.000938
84	254.50	0.100	0.000786

We average the k values to obtain $k \approx 0.000521$. An argument can be made for dropping the first two and last two estimates, to obtain $k \approx 0.000432$.

(f) The solution is $y = \dfrac{255}{1 + Ke^{-.133t}}$. We use the height of the sunflower at day 42 to obtain $y = \dfrac{255}{1 + 133.697e^{-.133t}}$.

116

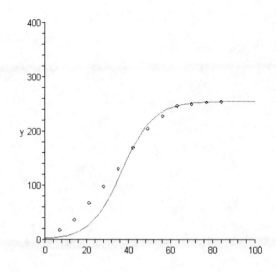

35. (*This is a Contributed Problem and the solution has been provided by the author of the problem.*)

(a) Direction field and the solution curve sketch together:

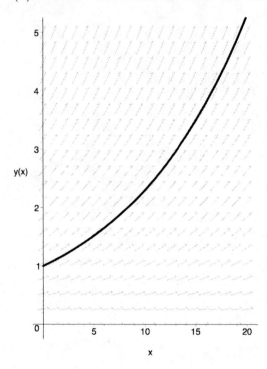

Exercises 3.2   Nonlinear Models

(b) The solution is $P(t) = e^{kt}$, $k = 1/12$, with graph:

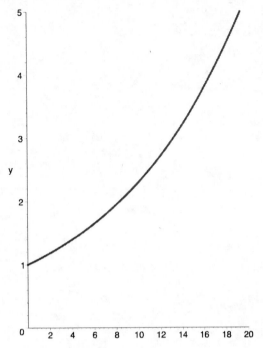

(c) the DE has the constant zero function as equilibrium.
(d) The population grows to infinity.
(e) If the initial population is P_0 then the resulting population would be
$P(t) = P_0 e^{kt}$, $k = 1/12$,
(f) The solution would change from constant to exponential.
(g) Direction field with solution sketch.

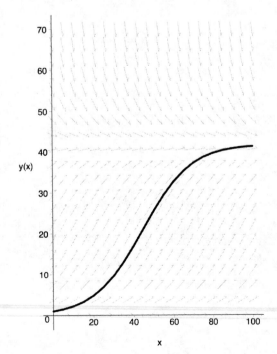

(**h**) The solution to the IVP is

$$P = \frac{125}{3 + 122e^{-t/12}}$$

and the graph is

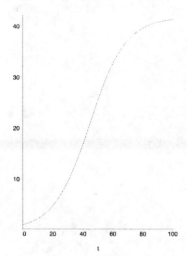

(**i**) the constant solutions to the DE are the zero function and the 125/3 function.

(**j**) solutions tend to 125/3.

(**k**) If the initial population is P_0 then the resulting population could be expressed by

$$P = \frac{125}{3 + 125Ce^{-t/12}}$$

where

$$C = \frac{1}{P_0} - \frac{3}{125}.$$

(**l**) the solution would no longer be constant but tend to 125/3.

(**m**) there would be little change...the new solution would still tend to 125/3.

(**n**) Direction field with solution sketch.

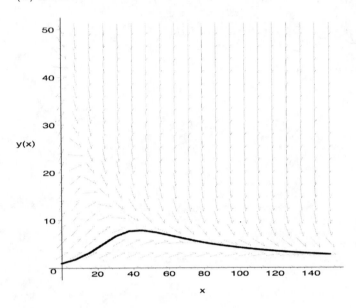

(**o**) the zero function is the only constant solution.

(**p**) The solution is slowly approaching 0; a change to $P(0)$ would still result in a solution curve which tends to 0.

Exercises 3.3

Modeling with Systems of First-Order DEs

1. The linear equation $dx/dt = -\lambda_1 x$ can be solved by either separation of variables or by an integrating factor. Integrating both sides of $dx/x = -\lambda_1 dt$ we obtain $\ln|x| = -\lambda_1 t + c$ from which we get $x = c_1 e^{-\lambda_1 t}$. Using $x(0) = x_0$ we find $c_1 = x_0$ so that $x = x_0 e^{-\lambda_1 t}$. Substituting this result into the second differential equation we have

$$\frac{dy}{dt} + \lambda_2 y = \lambda_1 x_0 e^{-\lambda_1 t}$$

which is linear. An integrating factor is $e^{\lambda_2 t}$ so that

$$\frac{d}{dt}\left[e^{\lambda_2 t} y\right] = \lambda_1 x_0 e^{(\lambda_2 - \lambda_1)t} + c_2$$

$$y = \frac{\lambda_1 x_0}{\lambda_2 - \lambda_1} e^{(\lambda_2 - \lambda_1)t} e^{-\lambda_2 t} + c_2 e^{-\lambda_2 t} = \frac{\lambda_1 x_0}{\lambda_2 - \lambda_1} e^{-\lambda_1 t} + c_2 e^{-\lambda_2 t}.$$

Using $y(0) = 0$ we find $c_2 = -\lambda_1 x_0/(\lambda_2 - \lambda_1)$. Thus

$$y = \frac{\lambda_1 x_0}{\lambda_2 - \lambda_1}\left(e^{-\lambda_1 t} - e^{-\lambda_2 t}\right).$$

Substituting this result into the third differential equation we have

$$\frac{dz}{dt} = \frac{\lambda_1 \lambda_2 x_0}{\lambda_2 - \lambda_1}\left(e^{-\lambda_1 t} - e^{-\lambda_2 t}\right).$$

Integrating we find

$$z = -\frac{\lambda_2 x_0}{\lambda_2 - \lambda_1}e^{-\lambda_1 t} + \frac{\lambda_1 x_0}{\lambda_2 - \lambda_1}e^{-\lambda_2 t} + c_3.$$

Using $z(0) = 0$ we find $c_3 = x_0$. Thus

$$z = x_0\left(1 - \frac{\lambda_2}{\lambda_2 - \lambda_1}e^{-\lambda_1 t} + \frac{\lambda_1}{\lambda_2 - \lambda_1}e^{-\lambda_2 t}\right).$$

2. We see from the graph that the half-life of A is approximately 4.7 days. To determine the half-life of B we use $t = 50$ as a base, since at this time the amount of substance A is so small that it contributes very little to substance B. Now we see from the graph that $y(50) \approx 16.2$ and $y(191) \approx 8.1$. Thus, the half-life of B is approximately 141 days.

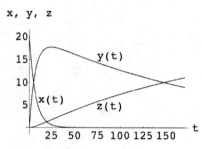

3. The amounts x and y are the same at about $t = 5$ days. The amounts x and z are the same at about $t = 20$ days. The amounts y and z are the same at about $t = 147$ days. The time when y and z are the same makes sense because most of A and half of B are gone, so half of C should have been formed.

4. Suppose that the series is described schematically by $W \Longrightarrow -\lambda_1 X \Longrightarrow -\lambda_2 Y \Longrightarrow -\lambda_3 Z$ where $-\lambda_1$, $-\lambda_2$, and $-\lambda_3$ are the decay constants for W, X and Y, respectively, and Z is a stable element. Let $w(t)$, $x(t)$, $y(t)$, and $z(t)$ denote the amounts of substances W, X, Y, and Z, respectively. A model for the radioactive series is

$$\frac{dw}{dt} = -\lambda_1 w$$

$$\frac{dx}{dt} = \lambda_1 w - \lambda_2 x$$

$$\frac{dy}{dt} = \lambda_2 x - \lambda_3 y$$

$$\frac{dz}{dt} = \lambda_3 y.$$

5. The system is

$$x_1' = 2 \cdot 3 + \frac{1}{50}x_2 - \frac{1}{50}x_1 \cdot 4 = -\frac{2}{25}x_1 + \frac{1}{50}x_2 + 6$$

$$x_2' = \frac{1}{50}x_1 \cdot 4 - \frac{1}{50}x_2 - \frac{1}{50}x_2 \cdot 3 = \frac{2}{25}x_1 - \frac{2}{25}x_2.$$

6. Let x_1, x_2, and x_3 be the amounts of salt in tanks A, B, and C, respectively, so that

$$x_1' = \frac{1}{100}x_2 \cdot 2 - \frac{1}{100}x_1 \cdot 6 = \frac{1}{50}x_2 - \frac{3}{50}x_1$$

$$x_2' = \frac{1}{100}x_1 \cdot 6 + \frac{1}{100}x_3 - \frac{1}{100}x_2 \cdot 2 - \frac{1}{100}x_2 \cdot 5 = \frac{3}{50}x_1 - \frac{7}{100}x_2 + \frac{1}{100}x_3$$

$$x_3' = \frac{1}{100}x_2 \cdot 5 - \frac{1}{100}x_3 - \frac{1}{100}x_3 \cdot 4 = \frac{1}{20}x_2 - \frac{1}{20}x_3.$$

7. (a) A model is

$$\frac{dx_1}{dt} = 3 \cdot \frac{x_2}{100 - t} - 2 \cdot \frac{x_1}{100 + t}, \qquad x_1(0) = 100$$

$$\frac{dx_2}{dt} = 2 \cdot \frac{x_1}{100 + t} - 3 \cdot \frac{x_2}{100 - t}, \qquad x_2(0) = 50.$$

(b) Since the system is closed, no salt enters or leaves the system and $x_1(t) + x_2(t) = 100 + 50 = 150$ for all time. Thus $x_1 = 150 - x_2$ and the second equation in part (a) becomes

$$\frac{dx_2}{dt} = \frac{2(150 - x_2)}{100 + t} - \frac{3x_2}{100 - t} = \frac{300}{100 + t} - \frac{2x_2}{100 + t} - \frac{3x_2}{100 - t}$$

or

$$\frac{dx_2}{dt} + \left(\frac{2}{100 + t} + \frac{3}{100 - t}\right)x_2 = \frac{300}{100 + t},$$

which is linear in x_2. An integrating factor is

$$e^{2\ln(100+t) - 3\ln(100-t)} = (100 + t)^2(100 - t)^{-3}$$

so

$$\frac{d}{dt}[(100 + t)^2(100 - t)^{-3}x_2] = 300(100 + t)(100 - t)^{-3}.$$

Using integration by parts, we obtain

$$(100 + t)^2(100 - t)^{-3}x_2 = 300\left[\frac{1}{2}(100 + t)(100 - t)^{-2} - \frac{1}{2}(100 - t)^{-1} + c\right].$$

Thus

$$x_2 = \frac{300}{(100 + t)^2}\left[c(100 - t)^3 - \frac{1}{2}(100 - t)^2 + \frac{1}{2}(100 + t)(100 - t)\right]$$

$$= \frac{300}{(100 + t)^2}[c(100 - t)^3 + t(100 - t)].$$

Using $x_2(0) = 50$ we find $c = 5/3000$. At $t = 30$, $x_2 = (300/130^2)(70^3 c + 30 \cdot 70) \approx 47.4$ lbs.

8. A model is

$$\frac{dx_1}{dt} = (4 \text{ gal/min})(0 \text{ lb/gal}) - (4 \text{ gal/min})\left(\frac{1}{200}x_1 \text{ lb/gal}\right)$$

$$\frac{dx_2}{dt} = (4 \text{ gal/min})\left(\frac{1}{200}x_1 \text{ lb/gal}\right) - (4 \text{ gal/min})\left(\frac{1}{150}x_2 \text{ lb/gal}\right)$$

$$\frac{dx_3}{dt} = (4 \text{ gal/min})\left(\frac{1}{150}x_2 \text{ lb/gal}\right) - (4 \text{ gal/min})\left(\frac{1}{100}x_3 \text{ lb/gal}\right)$$

or

$$\frac{dx_1}{dt} = -\frac{1}{50}x_1$$

$$\frac{dx_2}{dt} = \frac{1}{50}x_1 - \frac{2}{75}x_2$$

$$\frac{dx_3}{dt} = \frac{2}{75}x_2 - \frac{1}{25}x_3.$$

Over a long period of time we would expect x_1, x_2, and x_3 to approach 0 because the entering pure water should flush the salt out of all three tanks.

9. Zooming in on the graph it can be seen that the populations are first equal at about $t = 5.6$. The approximate periods of x and y are both 45.

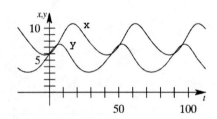

10. **(a)** The population $y(t)$ approaches 10,000, while the population $x(t)$ approaches extinction.

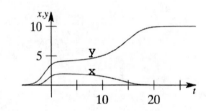

(b) The population $x(t)$ approaches 5,000, while the population $y(t)$ approaches extinction.

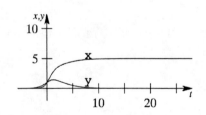

(c) The population $y(t)$ approaches 10,000, while the population $x(t)$ approaches extinction.

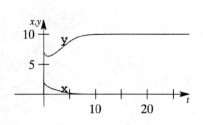

(d) The population $x(t)$ approaches 5,000, while the population $y(t)$ approaches extinction.

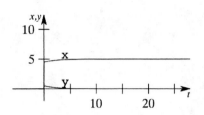

11. (a)

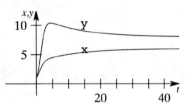

(b)

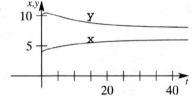

(c)

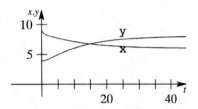

(d)

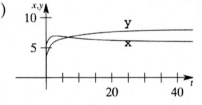

In each case the population $x(t)$ approaches 6,000, while the population $y(t)$ approaches 8,000.

12. By Kirchhoff's first law we have $i_1 = i_2 + i_3$. By Kirchhoff's second law, on each loop we have $E(t) = Li_1' + R_1 i_2$ and $E(t) = Li_1' + R_2 i_3 + q/C$ so that $q = CR_1 i_2 - CR_2 i_3$. Then $i_3 = q' = CR_1 i_2' - CR_2 i_3$ so that the system is

$$Li_2' + Li_3' + R_1 i_2 = E(t)$$

$$-R_1 i_2' + R_2 i_3' + \frac{1}{C} i_3 = 0.$$

13. By Kirchhoff's first law we have $i_1 = i_2 + i_3$. Applying Kirchhoff's second law to each loop we obtain

$$E(t) = i_1 R_1 + L_1 \frac{di_2}{dt} + i_2 R_2$$

and

$$E(t) = i_1 R_1 + L_2 \frac{di_3}{dt} + i_3 R_3.$$

Combining the three equations, we obtain the system

$$L_1 \frac{di_2}{dt} + (R_1 + R_2)i_2 + R_1 i_3 = E$$

$$L_2 \frac{di_3}{dt} + R_1 i_2 + (R_1 + R_3)i_3 = E.$$

14. By Kirchhoff's first law we have $i_1 = i_2 + i_3$. By Kirchhoff's second law, on each loop we have $E(t) = Li_1' + Ri_2$ and $E(t) = Li_1' + q/C$ so that $q = CRi_2$. Then $i_3 = q' = CRi_2'$ so that system is

$$Li' + Ri_2 = E(t)$$

$$CRi_2' + i_2 - i_1 = 0.$$

15. We first note that $s(t) + i(t) + r(t) = n$. Now the rate of change of the number of susceptible persons, $s(t)$, is proportional to the number of contacts between the number of people infected and the number who are susceptible; that is, $ds/dt = -k_1 si$. We use $-k_1 < 0$ because $s(t)$ is decreasing. Next, the rate of change of the number of persons who have recovered is proportional to the number infected; that is, $dr/dt = k_2 i$ where $k_2 > 0$ since r is increasing. Finally, to obtain di/dt we use

$$\frac{d}{dt}(s + i + r) = \frac{d}{dt} n = 0.$$

This gives

$$\frac{di}{dt} = -\frac{dr}{dt} - \frac{ds}{dt} = -k_2 i + k_1 si.$$

The system of differential equations is then

$$\frac{ds}{dt} = -k_1 si$$

$$\frac{di}{dt} = -k_2 i + k_1 si$$

$$\frac{dr}{dt} = k_2 i.$$

A reasonable set of initial conditions is $i(0) = i_0$, the number of infected people at time 0, $s(0) = n - i_0$, and $r(0) = 0$.

16. **(a)** If we know $s(t)$ and $i(t)$ then we can determine $r(t)$ from $s + i + r = n$.

(b) In this case the system is

$$\frac{ds}{dt} = -0.2si$$

$$\frac{di}{dt} = -0.7i + 0.2si.$$

We also note that when $i(0) = i_0$, $s(0) = 10 - i_0$ since $r(0) = 0$ and $i(t) + s(t) + r(t) = 0$ for all values of t. Now $k_2/k_1 = 0.7/0.2 = 3.5$, so we consider initial conditions $s(0) = 2$, $i(0) = 8$; $s(0) = 3.4$, $i(0) = 6.6$; $s(0) = 7$, $i(0) = 3$; and $s(0) = 9$, $i(0) = 1$.

125

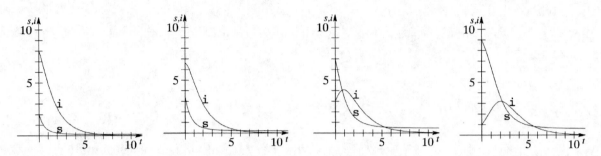

We see that an initial susceptible population greater than k_2/k_1 results in an epidemic in the sense that the number of infected persons increases to a maximum before decreasing to 0. On the other hand, when $s(0) < k_2/k_1$, the number of infected persons decreases from the start and there is no epidemic.

17. Since $x_0 > y_0 > 0$ we have $x(t) > y(t)$ and $y - x < 0$. Thus $dx/dt < 0$ and $dy/dt > 0$. We conclude that $x(t)$ is decreasing and $y(t)$ is increasing. As $t \to \infty$ we expect that $x(t) \to C$ and $y(t) \to C$, where C is a constant common equilibrium concentration.

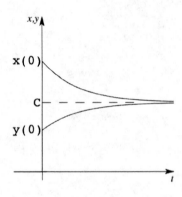

18. We write the system in the form

$$\frac{dx}{dt} = k_1(y - x)$$

$$\frac{dy}{dt} = k_2(x - y),$$

where $k_1 = \kappa/V_A$ and $k_2 = \kappa/V_B$. Letting $z(t) = x(t) - y(t)$ we have

$$\frac{dx}{dt} - \frac{dy}{dt} = k_1(y - x) - k_2(x - y)$$

$$\frac{dz}{dt} = k_1(-z) - k_2 z$$

$$\frac{dz}{dt} + (k_1 + k_2)z = 0.$$

This is a linear first-order differential equation with solution $z(t) = c_1 e^{-(k_1+k_2)t}$. Now

$$\frac{dx}{dt} = -k_1(y - x) = -k_1 z = -k_1 c_1 e^{-(k_1+k_2)t}$$

and

$$x(t) = c_1 \frac{k_1}{k_1 + k_2} e^{-(k_1+k_2)t} + c_2.$$

Since $y(t) = x(t) - z(t)$ we have

$$y(t) = -c_1 \frac{k_2}{k_1 + k_2} e^{-(k_1+k_2)t} + c_2.$$

The initial conditions $x(0) = x_0$ and $y(0) = y_0$ imply

$$c_1 = x_0 - y_0 \quad \text{and} \quad c_2 = \frac{x_0 k_2 + y_0 k_1}{k_1 + k_2}.$$

The solution of the system is

$$x(t) = \frac{(x_0 - y_0)k_1}{k_1 + k_2} e^{-(k_1+k_2)t} + \frac{x_0 k_2 + y_0 k_1}{k_1 + k_2}$$

$$y(t) = \frac{(y_0 - x_0)k_2}{k_1 + k_2} e^{-(k_1+k_2)t} + \frac{x_0 k_2 + y_0 k_1}{k_1 + k_2}.$$

As $t \to \infty$, $x(t)$ and $y(t)$ approach the common limit

$$\frac{x_0 k_2 + y_0 k_1}{k_1 + k_2} = \frac{x_0 \kappa/V_B + y_0 \kappa/V_A}{\kappa/V_A + \kappa/V_B} = \frac{x_0 V_A + y_0 V_B}{V_A + V_B}$$

$$= x_0 \frac{V_A}{V_A + V_B} + y_0 \frac{V_B}{V_A + V_B}.$$

This makes intuitive sense because the limiting concentration is seen to be a weighted average of the two initial concentrations.

19. Since there are initially 25 pounds of salt in tank A and none in tank B, and since furthermore only pure water is being pumped into tank A, we would expect that $x_1(t)$ would steadily decrease over time. On the other hand, since salt is being added to tank B from tank A, we would expect $x_2(t)$ to increase over time. However, since pure water is being added to the system at a constant rate and a mixed solution is being pumped out of the system, it makes sense that the amount of salt in both tanks would approach 0 over time.

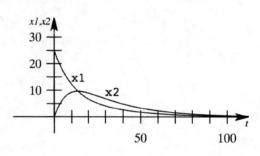

20. We assume here that the temperature, $T(t)$, of the metal bar does not affect the temperature, $T_A(t)$, of the medium in container A. By Newton's law of cooling, then, the differential equations for $T_A(t)$ and $T(t)$ are

$$\frac{dT_A}{dt} = k_A(T_A - T_B), \quad k_A < 0$$

$$\frac{dT}{dt} = k(T - T_A), \quad k < 0,$$

subject to the initial conditions $T(0) = T_0$ and $T_A(0) = T_1$. Separating variables in the first equation, we find $T_A(t) = T_B + c_1 e^{k_A t}$. Using $T_A(0) = T_1$ we find $c_1 = T_1 - T_B$, so

$$T_A(t) = T_B + (T_1 - T_B)e^{k_A t}.$$

Exercises 3.3   Modeling with Systems of First-Order DEs

Substituting into the second differential equation, we have

$$\frac{dT}{dt} = k(T - T_A) = kT - kT_A = kT - k[T_B + (T_1 - T_B)e^{k_A t}]$$

$$\frac{dT}{dt} - kT = -kT_B - k(T_1 - T_B)e^{k_A t}.$$

This is a linear differential equation with integrating factor $e^{\int -k\,dt} = e^{-kt}$. Then

$$\frac{d}{dt}[e^{-kt}T] = -kT_B e^{-kt} - k(T_1 - T_B)e^{(k_A - k)t}$$

$$e^{-kt}T = T_B e^{-kt} - \frac{k}{k_A - k}(T_1 - T_B)e^{(k_A - k)t} + c_2$$

$$T = T_B - \frac{k}{k_A - k}(T_1 - T_B)e^{k_A t} + c_2 e^{kt}.$$

Using $T(0) = T_0$ we find $c_2 = T_0 - T_B + \dfrac{k}{k_A - k}(T_1 - T_B)$, so

$$T(t) = T_B - \frac{k}{k_A - k}(T_1 - T_B)e^{k_A t} + \left[T_0 - T_B + \frac{k}{k_A - k}(T_1 - T_B)\right]e^{kt}.$$

21. (*This is a Contributed Problem and the solution has been provided by the authors of the problem.*)

(**a**) In the short term there is a mixing of an ethanol solution. In the long term, the system will contain a 20% solution of ethanol.

(**b**)

$$100P'' = \frac{1}{50}P - \frac{1}{10}Q - P'$$

(**c**) First write $Q = 50P' - 30 + P/2$ and then it's straightforward substitution into the equation in (**b**).

(**d**) From equation in (19) we find $P'(0) = 6/10 + 7/50 - 200/100 = -63/50$. The solution is

$$P(t) = \frac{-604}{19}e^{-t/400}\sin(\frac{\sqrt{95}t}{2000})\sqrt{95} - 100e^{-t/400}\cos(\frac{\sqrt{95}t}{2000}) + 100$$

(**e**) The solution is

$$Q(t) = \frac{-270}{19}e^{-t/400}\cos(\frac{\sqrt{95}t}{2000}) - \frac{130}{19}e^{-t/400}\sin(\frac{\sqrt{95}t}{2000})\sqrt{95} + 20 + \frac{23}{19}e^{-t/20}$$

(**f**) In both cases, the there is a concentration of 20% in each tank; $P(t) \to 100$ and $Q(t) \to 20$.

Chapter 3 in Review

1. The differential equation is $dP/dt = 0.15P$.

2. True. From $dA/dt = kA$, $A(0) = A_0$, we have $A(t) = A_0 e^{kt}$ and $A'(t) = kA_0 e^{kt}$, so $A'(0) = kA_0$. At $T = -(\ln 2)k$,

$$A'(-(\ln 2)/k) = kA(-(\ln 2)/k) = kA_0 e^{k[-(\ln 2)/k]} = kA_0 e^{-\ln 2} = \frac{1}{2} kA_0.$$

3. From $\dfrac{dP}{dt} = 0.018P$ and $P(0) = 4$ billion we obtain $P = 4e^{0.018t}$ so that $P(45) = 8.99$ billion.

4. Let $A = A(t)$ be the volume of CO_2 at time t. From $dA/dt = 1.2 - A/4$ and $A(0) = 16\,\text{ft}^3$ we obtain $A = 4.8 + 11.2e^{-t/4}$. Since $A(10) = 5.7\,\text{ft}^3$, the concentration is 0.017%. As $t \to \infty$ we have $A \to 4.8\,\text{ft}^3$ or 0.06%.

5. Separating variables, we have

$$\frac{\sqrt{s^2 - y^2}}{y}\, dy = -dx.$$

Substituting $y = s \sin\theta$, this becomes

$$\frac{\sqrt{s^2 - s^2 \sin^2\theta}}{s \sin\theta}(s\cos\theta)d\theta = -dx$$

$$s \int \frac{\cos^2\theta}{\sin\theta}\, d\theta = -\int dx$$

$$s \int \frac{1 - \sin^2\theta}{\sin\theta}\, d\theta = -x + c$$

$$s \int (\csc\theta - \sin\theta)d\theta = -x + c$$

$$-s \ln|\csc\theta + \cot\theta| + s\cos\theta = -x + c$$

$$-s \ln\left|\frac{s}{y} + \frac{\sqrt{s^2 - y^2}}{y}\right| + s\frac{\sqrt{s^2 - y^2}}{s} = -x + c.$$

Letting $s = 10$, this is

$$-10 \ln\left|\frac{10}{y} + \frac{\sqrt{100 - y^2}}{y}\right| + \sqrt{100 - y^2} = -x + c.$$

Chapter 3 in Review

Letting $x = 0$ and $y = 10$ we determine that $c = 0$, so the solution is

$$-10 \ln \left| \frac{10 + \sqrt{100 - y^2}}{y} \right| + \sqrt{100 - y^2} = -x$$

or

$$x = 10 \ln \left| \frac{10 + \sqrt{100 - y^2}}{y} \right| - \sqrt{100 - y^2}.$$

6. From $V \, dC/dt = kA(C_s - C)$ and $C(0) = C_0$ we obtain $C = C_s + (C_0 - C_s)e^{-kAt/V}$.

7. (a) The differential equation

$$\frac{dT}{dt} = k(T - T_m) = k[T - T_2 - B(T_1 - T)]$$

$$= k[(1 + B)T - (BT_1 + T_2)] = k(1 + B)\left(T - \frac{BT_1 + T_2}{1 + B} \right)$$

is autonomous and has the single critical point $(BT_1 + T_2)/(1 + B)$. Since $k < 0$ and $B > 0$, by phase-line analysis it is found that the critical point is an attractor and

$$\lim_{t \to \infty} T(t) = \frac{BT_1 + T_2}{1 + B}.$$

Moreover,

$$\lim_{t \to \infty} T_m(t) = \lim_{t \to \infty} [T_2 + B(T_1 - T)] = T_2 + B\left(T_1 - \frac{BT_1 + T_2}{1 + B} \right) = \frac{BT_1 + T_2}{1 + B}.$$

(b) The differential equation is

$$\frac{dT}{dt} = k(T - T_m) = k(T - T_2 - BT_1 + BT)$$

or

$$\frac{dT}{dt} - k(1 + B)T = -k(BT_1 + T_2).$$

This is linear and has integrating factor $e^{-\int k(1+B)dt} = e^{-k(1+B)t}$. Thus,

$$\frac{d}{dt}[e^{-k(1+B)t}T] = -k(BT_1 + T_2)e^{-k(1+B)t}$$

$$e^{-k(1+B)t}T = \frac{BT_1 + T_2}{1 + B} e^{-k(1+B)t} + c$$

$$T(t) = \frac{BT_1 + T_2}{1 + B} + ce^{k(1+B)t}.$$

Since k is negative, $\lim_{t \to \infty} T(t) = (BT_1 + T_2)/(1 + B)$.

(c) The temperature $T(t)$ decreases to the value $(BT_1 + T_2)/(1 + B)$, whereas $T_m(t)$ increases to $(BT_1 + T_2)/(1 + B)$ as $t \to \infty$. Thus, the temperature $(BT_1 + T_2)/(1 + B)$, (which is a weighted average

$$\frac{B}{1 + B} T_1 + \frac{1}{1 + B} T_2$$

of the two initial temperatures), can be interpreted as an equilibrium temperature. The body cannot get cooler than this value whereas the medium cannot get hotter than this value.

8. By separation of variables and partial fractions,

$$\ln\left|\frac{T - T_m}{T + T_m}\right| - 2\tan^{-1}\left(\frac{T}{T_m}\right) = 4T_m^3 kt + c.$$

Then rewrite the right-hand side of the differential equation as

$$\frac{dT}{dt} = k(T^4 - T_m^4) = [(T_m + (T - T_m))^4 - T_m^4]$$

$$= kT_m^4\left[\left(1 + \frac{T - T_m}{T_m}\right)^4 - 1\right]$$

$$= kT_m^4\left[\left(1 + 4\frac{T - T_m}{T_m} + 6\left(\frac{T - T_m}{T_m}\right)^2 \cdots\right) - 1\right] \leftarrow \text{binomial expansion}$$

When $T - T_m$ is small compared to T_m, every term in the expansion after the first two can be ignored, giving

$$\frac{dT}{dt} \approx k_1(T - T_m), \quad \text{where} \quad k_1 = 4kT_m^3.$$

9. We first solve $(1 - t/10)di/dt + 0.2i = 4$. Separating variables we obtain $di/(40 - 2i) = dt/(10 - t)$. Then

$$-\frac{1}{2}\ln|40 - 2i| = -\ln|10 - t| + c \quad \text{or} \quad \sqrt{40 - 2i} = c_1(10 - t).$$

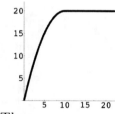

Since $i(0) = 0$ we must have $c_1 = 2/\sqrt{10}$. Solving for i we get $i(t) = 4t - \frac{1}{5}t^2$, $0 \le t < 10$. For $t \ge 10$ the equation for the current becomes $0.2i = 4$ or $i = 20$. Thus

$$i(t) = \begin{cases} 4t - \frac{1}{5}t^2, & 0 \le t < 10 \\ 20, & t \ge 10. \end{cases}$$

The graph of $i(t)$ is given in the figure.

10. From $y\left[1 + (y')^2\right] = k$ we obtain $dx = (\sqrt{y}/\sqrt{k - y})dy$. If $y = k\sin^2\theta$ then

$$dy = 2k\sin\theta\cos\theta\,d\theta, \quad dx = 2k\left(\frac{1}{2} - \frac{1}{2}\cos 2\theta\right)d\theta, \quad \text{and} \quad x = k\theta - \frac{k}{2}\sin 2\theta + c.$$

If $x = 0$ when $\theta = 0$ then $c = 0$.

11. From $dx/dt = k_1x(\alpha - x)$ we obtain

$$\left(\frac{1/\alpha}{x} + \frac{1/\alpha}{\alpha - x}\right)dx = k_1\,dt$$

so that $x = \alpha c_1 e^{\alpha k_1 t}/(1 + c_1 e^{\alpha k_1 t})$. From $dy/dt = k_2xy$ we obtain

$$\ln|y| = \frac{k_2}{k_1}\ln\left|1 + c_1 e^{\alpha k_1 t}\right| + c \quad \text{or} \quad y = c_2\left(1 + c_1 e^{\alpha k_1 t}\right)^{k_2/k_1}.$$

Chapter 3 in Review

12. In tank A the salt input is

$$\left(7 \frac{\text{gal}}{\text{min}}\right)\left(2 \frac{\text{lb}}{\text{gal}}\right) + \left(1 \frac{\text{gal}}{\text{min}}\right)\left(\frac{x_2}{100} \frac{\text{lb}}{\text{gal}}\right) = \left(14 + \frac{1}{100} x_2\right) \frac{\text{lb}}{\text{min}}.$$

The salt output is

$$\left(3 \frac{\text{gal}}{\text{min}}\right)\left(\frac{x_1}{100} \frac{\text{lb}}{\text{gal}}\right) + \left(5 \frac{\text{gal}}{\text{min}}\right)\left(\frac{x_1}{100} \frac{\text{lb}}{\text{gal}}\right) = \frac{2}{25} x_1 \frac{\text{lb}}{\text{min}}.$$

In tank B the salt input is

$$\left(5 \frac{\text{gal}}{\text{min}}\right)\left(\frac{x_1}{100} \frac{\text{lb}}{\text{gal}}\right) = \frac{1}{20} x_1 \frac{\text{lb}}{\text{min}}.$$

The salt output is

$$\left(1 \frac{\text{gal}}{\text{min}}\right)\left(\frac{x_2}{100} \frac{\text{lb}}{\text{gal}}\right) + \left(4 \frac{\text{gal}}{\text{min}}\right)\left(\frac{x_2}{100} \frac{\text{lb}}{\text{gal}}\right) = \frac{1}{20} x_2 \frac{\text{lb}}{\text{min}}.$$

The system of differential equations is then

$$\frac{dx_1}{dt} = 14 + \frac{1}{100} x_2 - \frac{2}{25} x_1$$

$$\frac{dx_2}{dt} = \frac{1}{20} x_1 - \frac{1}{20} x_2.$$

13. From $y = -x - 1 + c_1 e^x$ we obtain $y' = y + x$ so that the differential equation of the orthogonal family is

$$\frac{dy}{dx} = -\frac{1}{y + x} \qquad \text{or} \qquad \frac{dx}{dy} + x = -y.$$

This is a linear differential equation and has integrating factor $e^{\int dy} = e^y$, so

$$\frac{d}{dy}[e^y x] = -y e^y$$

$$e^y x = -y e^y + e^y + c_2$$

$$x = -y + 1 + c_2 e^{-y}.$$

14. Differentiating the family of curves, we have

$$y' = -\frac{1}{(x + c_1)^2} = -\frac{1}{y^2}.$$

The differential equation for the family of orthogonal trajectories is then $y' = y^2$. Separating variables and integrating we get

$$\frac{dy}{y^2} = dx$$

$$-\frac{1}{y} = x + c_1$$

$$y = -\frac{1}{x + c_1}.$$

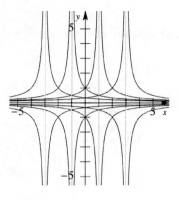

15. (*This is a Contributed Problem and the solution has been provided by the author of the problem.*)

(a) $p(x) = -\rho(x)g\left(y + \dfrac{1}{K}\displaystyle\int q(x)\,dx\right)$

(b) The ratio is increasing. The ratio is constant.

(c) $p(x) = ke^{-(\alpha g\rho/K)x}$

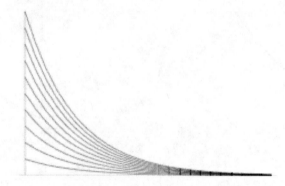

(d) When the pressure p is constant but the density ρ is a function of x then

$$\rho(x) = -\frac{Kp}{g\left(Ky + \int q(x)\,dx\right)}.$$

When the Darcy flux is proportional to the density then

$$\rho = \sqrt{\frac{Kp}{2(CKp - \beta gx)}},$$

where C is an arbitrary constant.

(e) As the density and Darcy velocity decreases, the pressure in the container initially increases but then decreases. The density change is less dramatic than the drop in the velocity and has a greater initial effect on the system. However, as the density of the fluid decreases, the effect is to decrease the pressure.

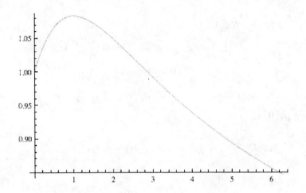

16. (*This is a Contributed Problem and the solution has been provided by the authors of the problem.*)

(a) Direction field and the solution curve sketch together: (b) The solution is $P(t) = e^{kt}, k = 1/12$, with graph:

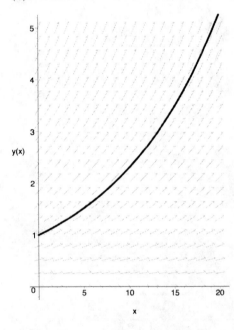

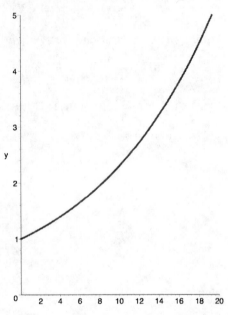

(c) the DE has the constant zero function as equilibrium.
(d) The population grows to infinity.
(e) If the initial population is P_0 then the resulting population would be
$P(t) = P_0 e^{kt}, k = 1/12,$
(f) The solution would change from constant to exponential.

(**g**) Direction field with solution sketch.

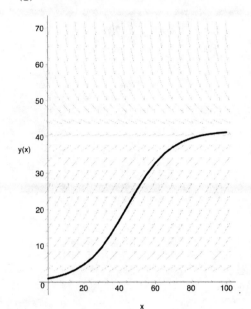

(**h**) The solution to the IVP is

$$P = \frac{125}{3 + 122e^{-t/12}}$$

and the graph is

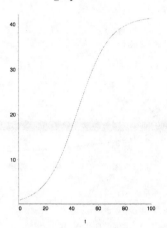

(**i**) the constant solutions to the DE are the zero function and the 125/3 function.

(**j**) solutions tend to 125/3.

(**k**) If the initial population is P_0 then the resulting population could be expressed by

$$P = \frac{125}{3 + 125Ce^{-t/12}}$$

where

$$C = \frac{1}{P_0} - \frac{3}{125}.$$

(**l**) the solution would no longer be constant but tend to 125/3.

(**m**) there would be little change...the new solution would still tend to 125/3.

Chapter 3 in Review

(**n**) Direction field with solution sketch.

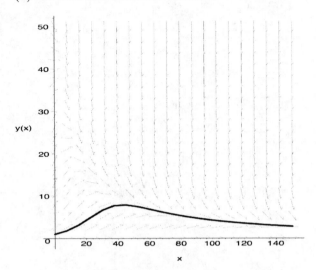

(**o**) the zero function is the only constant solution.

(**p**) The solution is slowly approaching 0; a change to $P(0)$ would still result in a solution curve which tends to 0.

4 Higher-Order Differential Equations

Exercises 4.1

Preliminary Theory—Linear Equations

1. From $y = c_1 e^x + c_2 e^{-x}$ we find $y' = c_1 e^x - c_2 e^{-x}$. Then $y(0) = c_1 + c_2 = 0$, $y'(0) = c_1 - c_2 = 1$ so that $c_1 = \frac{1}{2}$ and $c_2 = -\frac{1}{2}$. The solution is $y = \frac{1}{2}e^x - \frac{1}{2}e^{-x}$.

2. From $y = c_1 e^{4x} + c_2 e^{-x}$ we find $y' = 4c_1 e^{4x} - c_2 e^{-x}$. Then $y(0) = c_1 + c_2 = 1$, $y'(0) = 4c_1 - c_2 = 2$ so that $c_1 = \frac{3}{5}$ and $c_2 = \frac{2}{5}$. The solution is $y = \frac{3}{5}e^{4x} + \frac{2}{5}e^{-x}$.

3. From $y = c_1 x + c_2 x \ln x$ we find $y' = c_1 + c_2(1 + \ln x)$. Then $y(1) = c_1 = 3$, $y'(1) = c_1 + c_2 = -1$ so that $c_1 = 3$ and $c_2 = -4$. The solution is $y = 3x - 4x \ln x$.

4. From $y = c_1 + c_2 \cos x + c_3 \sin x$ we find $y' = -c_2 \sin x + c_3 \cos x$ and $y'' = -c_2 \cos x - c_3 \sin x$. Then $y(\pi) = c_1 - c_2 = 0$, $y'(\pi) = -c_3 = 2$, $y''(\pi) = c_2 = -1$ so that $c_1 = -1$, $c_2 = -1$, and $c_3 = -2$. The solution is $y = -1 - \cos x - 2\sin x$.

5. From $y = c_1 + c_2 x^2$ we find $y' = 2c_2 x$. Then $y(0) = c_1 = 0$, $y'(0) = 2c_2 \cdot 0 = 0$ and hence $y'(0) = 1$ is not possible. Since $a_2(x) = x$ is 0 at $x = 0$, Theorem 4.1 is not violated.

6. In this case we have $y(0) = c_1 = 0$, $y'(0) = 2c_2 \cdot 0 = 0$ so $c_1 = 0$ and c_2 is arbitrary. Two solutions are $y = x^2$ and $y = 2x^2$.

7. From $x(0) = x_0 = c_1$ we see that $x(t) = x_0 \cos \omega t + c_2 \sin \omega t$ and $x'(t) = -x_0 \sin \omega t + c_2 \omega \cos \omega t$. Then $x'(0) = x_1 = c_2 \omega$ implies $c_2 = x_1/\omega$. Thus

$$x(t) = x_0 \cos \omega t + \frac{x_1}{\omega} \sin \omega t.$$

8. Solving the system

$$x(t_0) = c_1 \cos \omega t_0 + c_2 \sin \omega t_0 = x_0$$

$$x'(t_0) = -c_1 \omega \sin \omega t_0 + c_2 \omega \cos \omega t_0 = x_1$$

for c_1 and c_2 gives

$$c_1 = \frac{\omega x_0 \cos \omega t_0 - x_1 \sin \omega t_0}{\omega} \quad \text{and} \quad c_2 = \frac{x_1 \cos \omega t_0 + \omega x_0 \sin \omega t_0}{\omega}.$$

Thus

$$x(t) = \frac{\omega x_0 \cos \omega t_0 - x_1 \sin \omega t_0}{\omega} \cos \omega t + \frac{x_1 \cos \omega t_0 + \omega x_0 \sin \omega t_0}{\omega} \sin \omega t$$

$$= x_0(\cos \omega t \cos \omega t_0 + \sin \omega t \sin \omega t_0) + \frac{x_1}{\omega}(\sin \omega t \cos \omega t_0 - \cos \omega t \sin \omega t_0)$$

$$= x_0 \cos \omega(t - t_0) + \frac{x_1}{\omega} \sin \omega(t - t_0).$$

9. Since $a_2(x) = x - 2$ and $x_0 = 0$ the problem has a unique solution for $-\infty < x < 2$.

10. Since $a_0(x) = \tan x$ and $x_0 = 0$ the problem has a unique solution for $-\pi/2 < x < \pi/2$.

11. **(a)** We have $y(0) = c_1 + c_2 = 0$, $y(1) = c_1 e + c_2 e^{-1} = 1$ so that $c_1 = e/\left(e^2 - 1\right)$ and $c_2 = -e/\left(e^2 - 1\right)$. The solution is $y = e\left(e^x - e^{-x}\right)/\left(e^2 - 1\right)$.

(b) We have $y(0) = c_3 \cosh 0 + c_4 \sinh 0 = c_3 = 0$ and $y(1) = c_3 \cosh 1 + c_4 \sinh 1 = c_4 \sinh 1 = 1$, so $c_3 = 0$ and $c_4 = 1/\sinh 1$. The solution is $y = (\sinh x)/(\sinh 1)$.

(c) Starting with the solution in part (b) we have

$$y = \frac{1}{\sinh 1} \sinh x = \frac{2}{e^1 - e^{-1}} \frac{e^x - e^{-x}}{2} = \frac{e^x - e^{-x}}{e - 1/e} = \frac{e}{e^2 - 1}(e^x - e^{-x}).$$

12. In this case we have $y(0) = c_1 = 1$, $y'(1) = 2c_2 = 6$ so that $c_1 = 1$ and $c_2 = 3$. The solution is $y = 1 + 3x^2$.

13. From $y = c_1 e^x \cos x + c_2 e^x \sin x$ we find $y' = c_1 e^x(-\sin x + \cos x) + c_2 e^x(\cos x + \sin x)$.

(a) We have $y(0) = c_1 = 1$, $y'(\pi) = -e^\pi(c_1 + c_2) = 0$ so that $c_1 = 1$ and $c_2 = -1$. The solution is $y = e^x \cos x - e^x \sin x$.

(b) We have $y(0) = c_1 = 1$, $y(\pi) = -e^\pi = -1$, which is not possible.

(c) We have $y(0) = c_1 = 1$, $y(\pi/2) = c_2 e^{\pi/2} = 1$ so that $c_1 = 1$ and $c_2 = e^{-\pi/2}$. The solution is $y = e^x \cos x + e^{-\pi/2} e^x \sin x$.

(d) We have $y(0) = c_1 = 0$, $y(\pi) = c_2 e^\pi \sin \pi = 0$ so that $c_1 = 0$ and c_2 is arbitrary. Solutions are $y = c_2 e^x \sin x$, for any real numbers c_2.

14. **(a)** We have $y(-1) = c_1 + c_2 + 3 = 0$, $y(1) = c_1 + c_2 + 3 = 4$, which is not possible.

(b) We have $y(0) = c_1 \cdot 0 + c_2 \cdot 0 + 3 = 1$, which is not possible.

(c) We have $y(0) = c_1 \cdot 0 + c_2 \cdot 0 + 3 = 3$, $y(1) = c_1 + c_2 + 3 = 0$ so that c_1 is arbitrary and $c_2 = -3 - c_1$. Solutions are $y = c_1 x^2 - (c_1 + 3)x^4 + 3$.

(d) We have $y(1) = c_1 + c_2 + 3 = 3$, $y(2) = 4c_1 + 16c_2 + 3 = 15$ so that $c_1 = -1$ and $c_2 = 1$. The solution is $y = -x^2 + x^4 + 3$.

15. Since $(-4)x + (3)x^2 + (1)(4x - 3x^2) = 0$ the set of functions is linearly dependent.

16. Since $(1)0 + (0)x + (0)e^x = 0$ the set of functions is linearly dependent. A similar argument shows that any set of functions containing $f(x) = 0$ will be linearly dependent.

17. Since $(-1/5)5 + (1)\cos^2 x + (1)\sin^2 x = 0$ the set of functions is linearly dependent.

18. Since $(1)\cos 2x + (1)1 + (-2)\cos^2 x = 0$ the set of functions is linearly dependent.

19. Since $(-4)x + (3)(x-1) + (1)(x+3) = 0$ the set of functions is linearly dependent.

20. From the graphs of $f_1(x) = 2 + x$ and $f_2(x) = 2 + |x|$ we see that the set of functions is linearly independent since they cannot be multiples of each other.

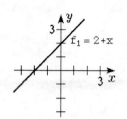 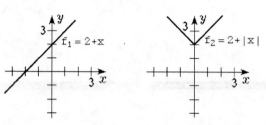

21. Suppose $c_1(1+x) + c_2 x + c_3 x^2 = 0$. Then $c_1 + (c_1 + c_2)x + c_3 x^2 = 0$ and so $c_1 = 0$, $c_1 + c_2 = 0$, and $c_3 = 0$. Since $c_1 = 0$ we also have $c_2 = 0$. Thus, the set of functions is linearly independent.

22. Since $(-1/2)e^x + (1/2)e^{-x} + (1)\sinh x = 0$ the set of functions is linearly dependent.

23. The functions satisfy the differential equation and are linearly independent since

$$W\left(e^{-3x}, e^{4x}\right) = 7e^x \neq 0$$

for $-\infty < x < \infty$. The general solution is

$$y = c_1 e^{-3x} + c_2 e^{4x}.$$

24. The functions satisfy the differential equation and are linearly independent since

$$W(\cosh 2x, \sinh 2x) = 2$$

for $-\infty < x < \infty$. The general solution is

$$y = c_1 \cosh 2x + c_2 \sinh 2x.$$

25. The functions satisfy the differential equation and are linearly independent since

$$W\left(e^x \cos 2x, e^x \sin 2x\right) = 2e^{2x} \neq 0$$

for $-\infty < x < \infty$. The general solution is $y = c_1 e^x \cos 2x + c_2 e^x \sin 2x$.

26. The functions satisfy the differential equation and are linearly independent since

$$W\left(e^{x/2}, xe^{x/2}\right) = e^x \neq 0$$

for $-\infty < x < \infty$. The general solution is

$$y = c_1 e^{x/2} + c_2 xe^{x/2}.$$

Exercises 4.1 Preliminary Theory—Linear Equations

27. The functions satisfy the differential equation and are linearly independent since
$$W\left(x^3, x^4\right) = x^6 \neq 0$$
for $0 < x < \infty$. The general solution on this interval is
$$y = c_1 x^3 + c_2 x^4.$$

28. The functions satisfy the differential equation and are linearly independent since
$$W\left(\cos(\ln x), \sin(\ln x)\right) = 1/x \neq 0$$
for $0 < x < \infty$. The general solution on this interval is
$$y = c_1 \cos(\ln x) + c_2 \sin(\ln x).$$

29. The functions satisfy the differential equation and are linearly independent since
$$W\left(x, x^{-2}, x^{-2}\ln x\right) = 9x^{-6} \neq 0$$
for $0 < x < \infty$. The general solution on this interval is
$$y = c_1 x + c_2 x^{-2} + c_3 x^{-2}\ln x.$$

30. The functions satisfy the differential equation and are linearly independent since
$$W(1, x, \cos x, \sin x) = 1$$
for $-\infty < x < \infty$. The general solution on this interval is
$$y = c_1 + c_2 x + c_3 \cos x + c_4 \sin x.$$

31. The functions $y_1 = e^{2x}$ and $y_2 = e^{5x}$ form a fundamental set of solutions of the associated homogeneous equation, and $y_p = 6e^x$ is a particular solution of the nonhomogeneous equation.

32. The functions $y_1 = \cos x$ and $y_2 = \sin x$ form a fundamental set of solutions of the associated homogeneous equation, and $y_p = x \sin x + (\cos x)\ln(\cos x)$ is a particular solution of the nonhomogeneous equation.

33. The functions $y_1 = e^{2x}$ and $y_2 = xe^{2x}$ form a fundamental set of solutions of the associated homogeneous equation, and $y_p = x^2 e^{2x} + x - 2$ is a particular solution of the nonhomogeneous equation.

34. The functions $y_1 = x^{-1/2}$ and $y_2 = x^{-1}$ form a fundamental set of solutions of the associated homogeneous equation, and $y_p = \frac{1}{15}x^2 - \frac{1}{6}x$ is a particular solution of the nonhomogeneous equation.

35. (a) We have $y'_{p_1} = 6e^{2x}$ and $y''_{p_1} = 12e^{2x}$, so
$$y''_{p_1} - 6y'_{p_1} + 5y_{p_1} = 12e^{2x} - 36e^{2x} + 15e^{2x} = -9e^{2x}.$$

Also, $y'_{p_2} = 2x + 3$ and $y''_{p_2} = 2$, so

$$y''_{p_2} - 6y'_{p_2} + 5y_{p_2} = 2 - 6(2x + 3) + 5(x^2 + 3x) = 5x^2 + 3x - 16.$$

(b) By the superposition principle for nonhomogeneous equations a particular solution of $y'' - 6y' + 5y = 5x^2 + 3x - 16 - 9e^{2x}$ is $y_p = x^2 + 3x + 3e^{2x}$. A particular solution of the second equation is

$$y_p = -2y_{p_2} - \frac{1}{9}y_{p_1} = -2x^2 - 6x - \frac{1}{3}e^{2x}.$$

36. (a) $y_{p_1} = 5$

(b) $y_{p_2} = -2x$

(c) $y_p = y_{p_1} + y_{p_2} = 5 - 2x$

(d) $y_p = \frac{1}{2}y_{p_1} - 2y_{p_2} = \frac{5}{2} + 4x$

37. (a) Since $D^2 x = 0$, x and 1 are solutions of $y'' = 0$. Since they are linearly independent, the general solution is $y = c_1 x + c_2$.

(b) Since $D^3 x^2 = 0$, x^2, x, and 1 are solutions of $y''' = 0$. Since they are linearly independent, the general solution is $y = c_1 x^2 + c_2 x + c_3$.

(c) Since $D^4 x^3 = 0$, x^3, x^2, x, and 1 are solutions of $y^{(4)} = 0$. Since they are linearly independent, the general solution is $y = c_1 x^3 + c_2 x^2 + c_3 x + c_4$.

(d) By part (a), the general solution of $y'' = 0$ is $y_c = c_1 x + c_2$. Since $D^2 x^2 = 2! = 2$, $y_p = x^2$ is a particular solution of $y'' = 2$. Thus, the general solution is $y = c_1 x + c_2 + x^2$.

(e) By part (b), the general solution of $y''' = 0$ is $y_c = c_1 x^2 + c_2 x + c_3$. Since $D^3 x^3 = 3! = 6$, $y_p = x^3$ is a particular solution of $y''' = 6$. Thus, the general solution is $y = c_1 x^2 + c_2 x + c_3 + x^3$.

(f) By part (c), the general solution of $y^{(4)} = 0$ is $y_c = c_1 x^3 + c_2 x^2 + c_3 x + c_4$. Since $D^4 x^4 = 4! = 24$, $y_p = x^4$ is a particular solution of $y^{(4)} = 24$. Thus, the general solution is $y = c_1 x^3 + c_2 x^2 + c_3 x + c_4 + x^4$.

38. By the superposition principle, if $y_1 = e^x$ and $y_2 = e^{-x}$ are both solutions of a homogeneous linear differential equation, then so are

$$\frac{1}{2}(y_1 + y_2) = \frac{e^x + e^{-x}}{2} = \cosh x \quad \text{and} \quad \frac{1}{2}(y_1 - y_2) = \frac{e^x - e^{-x}}{2} = \sinh x.$$

39. (a) From the graphs of $y_1 = x^3$ and $y_2 = |x|^3$ we see that the functions are linearly independent since they cannot be multiples of each other. It is easily shown that $y_1 = x^3$ is a solution of $x^2 y'' - 4xy' + 6y = 0$. To show that $y_2 = |x|^3$ is a solution let $y_2 = x^3$ for $x \geq 0$ and let $y_2 = -x^3$ for $x < 0$.

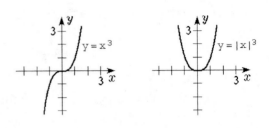

(b) If $x \geq 0$ then $y_2 = x^3$ and

$$W(y_1, y_2) = \begin{vmatrix} x^3 & x^3 \\ 3x^2 & 3x^2 \end{vmatrix} = 0.$$

If $x < 0$ then $y_2 = -x^3$ and

$$W(y_1, y_2) = \begin{vmatrix} x^3 & -x^3 \\ 3x^2 & -3x^2 \end{vmatrix} = 0.$$

This does not violate Theorem 4.1.3 since $a_2(x) = x^2$ is zero at $x = 0$.

(c) The functions $Y_1 = x^3$ and $Y_2 = x^2$ are solutions of $x^2 y'' - 4xy' + 6y = 0$. They are linearly independent since $W\left(x^3, x^2\right) = x^4 \neq 0$ for $-\infty < x < \infty$.

(d) The function $y = x^3$ satisfies $y(0) = 0$ and $y'(0) = 0$.

(e) Neither is the general solution on $(-\infty, \infty)$ since we form a general solution on an interval for which
$a_2(x) \neq 0$ for every x in the interval.

40. Since $e^{x-3} = e^{-3}e^x = (e^{-5}e^2)e^x = e^{-5}e^{x+2}$, we see that e^{x-3} is a constant multiple of e^{x+2} and the set of functions is linearly dependent.

41. Since $0y_1 + 0y_2 + \cdots + 0y_k + 1y_{k+1} = 0$, the set of solutions is linearly dependent.

42. The set of solutions is linearly dependent. Suppose n of the solutions are linearly independent (if not, then the set of $n+1$ solutions is linearly dependent). Without loss of generality, let this set be $y_1, y_2, \ldots, y_n$. Then $y = c_1 y_1 + c_2 y_2 + \cdots + c_n y_n$ is the general solution of the nth-order differential equation and for some choice, $c_1^*, c_2^*, \ldots, c_n^*$, of the coefficients $y_{n+1} = c_1^* y_1 + c_2^* y_2 + \cdots + c_n^* y_n$. But then the set $y_1, y_2, \ldots, y_n, y_{n+1}$ is linearly dependent.

In Problems 1-8 we use reduction of order to find a second solution. In Problems 9-16 we use formula (5) from the text.

1. Define $y = u(x)e^{2x}$ so

$$y' = 2ue^{2x} + u'e^{2x}, \quad y'' = e^{2x}u'' + 4e^{2x}u' + 4e^{2x}u, \quad \text{and} \quad y'' - 4y' + 4y = e^{2x}u'' = 0.$$

Therefore $u'' = 0$ and $u = c_1 x + c_2$. Taking $c_1 = 1$ and $c_2 = 0$ we see that a second solution is $y_2 = xe^{2x}$.

2. Define $y = u(x)xe^{-x}$ so

$$y' = (1 - x)e^{-x}u + xe^{-x}u', \quad y'' = xe^{-x}u'' + 2(1 - x)e^{-x}u' - (2 - x)e^{-x}u,$$

and

$$y'' + 2y' + y = e^{-x}(xu'' + 2u') = 0 \quad \text{or} \quad u'' + \frac{2}{x}u' = 0.$$

If $w = u'$ we obtain the linear first-order equation $w' + \frac{2}{x}w = 0$ which has the integrating factor $e^{2\int dx/x} = x^2$. Now

$$\frac{d}{dx}\left[x^2 w\right] = 0 \quad \text{gives} \quad x^2 w = c.$$

Therefore $w = u' = c/x^2$ and $u = c_1/x$. A second solution is $y_2 = \frac{1}{x}xe^{-x} = e^{-x}$.

3. Define $y = u(x)\cos 4x$ so

$$y' = -4u\sin 4x + u'\cos 4x, \quad y'' = u''\cos 4x - 8u'\sin 4x - 16u\cos 4x$$

and

$$y'' + 16y = (\cos 4x)u'' - 8(\sin 4x)u' = 0 \quad \text{or} \quad u'' - 8(\tan 4x)u' = 0.$$

If $w = u'$ we obtain the linear first-order equation $w' - 8(\tan 4x)w = 0$ which has the integrating factor $e^{-8\int \tan 4x\, dx} = \cos^2 4x$. Now

$$\frac{d}{dx}\left[(\cos^2 4x)w\right] = 0 \quad \text{gives} \quad (\cos^2 4x)w = c.$$

Therefore $w = u' = c\sec^2 4x$ and $u = c_1 \tan 4x$. A second solution is $y_2 = \tan 4x \cos 4x = \sin 4x$.

4. Define $y = u(x)\sin 3x$ so

$$y' = 3u\cos 3x + u'\sin 3x, \quad y'' = u''\sin 3x + 6u'\cos 3x - 9u\sin 3x,$$

143

Exercises 4.2   Reduction of Order

and

$$y'' + 9y = (\sin 3x)u'' + 6(\cos 3x)u' = 0 \quad \text{or} \quad u'' + 6(\cot 3x)u' = 0.$$

If $w = u'$ we obtain the linear first-order equation $w' + 6(\cot 3x)w = 0$ which has the integrating factor $e^{6\int \cot 3x\,dx} = \sin^2 3x$. Now

$$\frac{d}{dx}[(\sin^2 3x)w] = 0 \quad \text{gives} \quad (\sin^2 3x)w = c.$$

Therefore $w = u' = c\csc^2 3x$ and $u = c_1 \cot 3x$. A second solution is $y_2 = \cot 3x \sin 3x = \cos 3x$.

5. Define $y = u(x)\cosh x$ so

$$y' = u\sinh x + u'\cosh x, \quad y'' = u''\cosh x + 2u'\sinh x + u\cosh x$$

and

$$y'' - y = (\cosh x)u'' + 2(\sinh x)u' = 0 \quad \text{or} \quad u'' + 2(\tanh x)u' = 0.$$

If $w = u'$ we obtain the linear first-order equation $w' + 2(\tanh x)w = 0$ which has the integrating factor $e^{2\int \tanh x\,dx} = \cosh^2 x$. Now

$$\frac{d}{dx}[(\cosh^2 x)w] = 0 \quad \text{gives} \quad (\cosh^2 x)w = c.$$

Therefore $w = u' = c\,\text{sech}^2 x$ and $u = c\tanh x$. A second solution is $y_2 = \tanh x \cosh x = \sinh x$.

6. Define $y = u(x)e^{5x}$ so

$$y' = 5e^{5x}u + e^{5x}u', \quad y'' = e^{5x}u'' + 10e^{5x}u' + 25e^{5x}u$$

and

$$y'' - 25y = e^{5x}(u'' + 10u') = 0 \quad \text{or} \quad u'' + 10u' = 0.$$

If $w = u'$ we obtain the linear first-order equation $w' + 10w = 0$ which has the integrating factor $e^{10\int dx} = e^{10x}$. Now

$$\frac{d}{dx}[e^{10x}w] = 0 \quad \text{gives} \quad e^{10x}w = c.$$

Therefore $w = u' = ce^{-10x}$ and $u = c_1 e^{-10x}$. A second solution is $y_2 = e^{-10x}e^{5x} = e^{-5x}$.

7. Define $y = u(x)e^{2x/3}$ so

$$y' = \frac{2}{3}e^{2x/3}u + e^{2x/3}u', \quad y'' = e^{2x/3}u'' + \frac{4}{3}e^{2x/3}u' + \frac{4}{9}e^{2x/3}u$$

and

$$9y'' - 12y' + 4y = 9e^{2x/3}u'' = 0.$$

Therefore $u'' = 0$ and $u = c_1 x + c_2$. Taking $c_1 = 1$ and $c_2 = 0$ we see that a second solution is $y_2 = xe^{2x/3}$.

8. Define $y = u(x)e^{x/3}$ so

$$y' = \frac{1}{3}e^{x/3}u + e^{x/3}u', \quad y'' = e^{x/3}u'' + \frac{2}{3}e^{x/3}u' + \frac{1}{9}e^{x/3}u$$

144

and

$$6y'' + y' - y = e^{x/3}(6u'' + 5u') = 0 \quad \text{or} \quad u'' + \frac{5}{6}u' = 0.$$

If $w = u'$ we obtain the linear first-order equation $w' + \frac{5}{6}w = 0$ which has the integrating factor $e^{(5/6)\int dx} = e^{5x/6}$. Now

$$\frac{d}{dx}\left[e^{5x/6}w\right] = 0 \quad \text{gives} \quad e^{5x/6}w = c.$$

Therefore $w = u' = ce^{-5x/6}$ and $u = c_1 e^{-5x/6}$. A second solution is $y_2 = e^{-5x/6}e^{x/3} = e^{-x/2}$.

9. Identifying $P(x) = -7/x$ we have

$$y_2 = x^4 \int \frac{e^{-\int(-7/x)\,dx}}{x^8}\,dx = x^4 \int \frac{1}{x}\,dx = x^4 \ln|x|.$$

A second solution is $y_2 = x^4 \ln|x|$.

10. Identifying $P(x) = 2/x$ we have

$$y_2 = x^2 \int \frac{e^{-\int(2/x)\,dx}}{x^4}\,dx = x^2 \int x^{-6}\,dx = -\frac{1}{5}x^{-3}.$$

A second solution is $y_2 = x^{-3}$.

11. Identifying $P(x) = 1/x$ we have

$$y_2 = \ln x \int \frac{e^{-\int dx/x}}{(\ln x)^2}\,dx = \ln x \int \frac{dx}{x(\ln x)^2} = \ln x \left(-\frac{1}{\ln x}\right) = -1.$$

A second solution is $y_2 = 1$.

12. Identifying $P(x) = 0$ we have

$$y_2 = x^{1/2}\ln x \int \frac{e^{-\int 0\,dx}}{x(\ln x)^2}\,dx = x^{1/2}\ln x \left(-\frac{1}{\ln x}\right) = -x^{1/2}.$$

A second solution is $y_2 = x^{1/2}$.

13. Identifying $P(x) = -1/x$ we have

$$y_2 = x\sin(\ln x) \int \frac{e^{-\int -dx/x}}{x^2 \sin^2(\ln x)}\,dx = x\sin(\ln x) \int \frac{x}{x^2 \sin^2(\ln x)}\,dx$$

$$= x\sin(\ln x) \int \frac{\csc^2(\ln x)}{x}\,dx = [x\sin(\ln x)]\,[-\cot(\ln x)] = -x\cos(\ln x).$$

A second solution is $y_2 = x\cos(\ln x)$.

14. Identifying $P(x) = -3/x$ we have

$$y_2 = x^2 \cos(\ln x) \int \frac{e^{-\int -3\,dx/x}}{x^4 \cos^2(\ln x)}\,dx = x^2 \cos(\ln x) \int \frac{x^3}{x^4 \cos^2(\ln x)}\,dx$$

$$= x^2 \cos(\ln x) \int \frac{\sec^2(\ln x)}{x}\,dx = x^2 \cos(\ln x)\tan(\ln x) = x^2 \sin(\ln x).$$

Exercises 4.2   Reduction of Order

A second solution is $y_2 = x^2 \sin(\ln x)$.

15. Identifying $P(x) = 2(1+x)/\left(1 - 2x - x^2\right)$ we have

$$y_2 = (x+1) \int \frac{e^{-\int 2(1+x)dx/\left(1-2x-x^2\right)}}{(x+1)^2}\, dx = (x+1) \int \frac{e^{\ln\left(1-2x-x^2\right)}}{(x+1)^2}\, dx$$

$$= (x+1) \int \frac{1-2x-x^2}{(x+1)^2}\, dx = (x+1) \int \left[\frac{2}{(x+1)^2} - 1\right] dx$$

$$= (x+1) \left[-\frac{2}{x+1} - x\right] = -2 - x^2 - x.$$

A second solution is $y_2 = x^2 + x + 2$.

16. Identifying $P(x) = -2x/\left(1 - x^2\right)$ we have

$$y_2 = \int e^{-\int -2x\, dx/\left(1-x^2\right)}\, dx = \int e^{-\ln\left(1-x^2\right)}\, dx = \int \frac{1}{1-x^2}\, dx = \frac{1}{2}\ln\left|\frac{1+x}{1-x}\right|.$$

A second solution is $y_2 = \ln|(1+x)/(1-x)|$.

17. Define $y = u(x)e^{-2x}$ so

$$y' = -2ue^{-2x} + u'e^{-2x}, \quad y'' = u''e^{-2x} - 4u'e^{-2x} + 4ue^{-2x}$$

and

$$y'' - 4y = e^{-2x}u'' - 4e^{-2x}u' = 0 \quad\text{or}\quad u'' - 4u' = 0.$$

If $w = u'$ we obtain the linear first-order equation $w' - 4w = 0$ which has the integrating factor $e^{-4\int dx} = e^{-4x}$. Now

$$\frac{d}{dx}[e^{-4x}w] = 0 \quad\text{gives}\quad e^{-4x}w = c.$$

Therefore $w = u' = ce^{4x}$ and $u = c_1e^{4x}$. A second solution is $y_2 = e^{-2x}e^{4x} = e^{2x}$. We see by observation that a particular solution is $y_p = -1/2$. The general solution is

$$y = c_1e^{-2x} + c_2e^{2x} - \frac{1}{2}.$$

18. Define $y = u(x) \cdot 1$ so

$$y' = u', \quad y'' = u'' \quad\text{and}\quad y'' + y' = u'' + u' = 1.$$

If $w = u'$ we obtain the linear first-order equation $w' + w = 1$ which has the integrating factor $e^{\int dx} = e^x$. Now

$$\frac{d}{dx}[e^x w] = e^x \quad\text{gives}\quad e^x w = e^x + c.$$

Therefore $w = u' = 1 + ce^{-x}$ and $u = x + c_1e^{-x} + c_2$. The general solution is

$$y = u = x + c_1e^{-x} + c_2.$$

146

19. Define $y = u(x)e^x$ so

$$y' = ue^x + u'e^x, \quad y'' = u''e^x + 2u'e^x + ue^x$$

and

$$y'' - 3y' + 2y = e^x u'' - e^x u' = 5e^{3x}.$$

If $w = u'$ we obtain the linear first-order equation $w' - w = 5e^{2x}$ which has the integrating factor $e^{-\int dx} = e^{-x}$. Now

$$\frac{d}{dx}[e^{-x}w] = 5e^x \quad \text{gives} \quad e^{-x}w = 5e^x + c_1.$$

Therefore $w = u' = 5e^{2x} + c_1 e^x$ and $u = \frac{5}{2}e^{2x} + c_1 e^x + c_2$. The general solution is

$$y = ue^x = \frac{5}{2}e^{3x} + c_1 e^{2x} + c_2 e^x.$$

20. Define $y = u(x)e^x$ so

$$y' = ue^x + u'e^x, \quad y'' = u''e^x + 2u'e^x + ue^x$$

and

$$y'' - 4y' + 3y = e^x u'' - e^x u' = x.$$

If $w = u'$ we obtain the linear first-order equation $w' - 2w = xe^{-x}$ which has the integrating factor $e^{-\int 2dx} = e^{-2x}$. Now

$$\frac{d}{dx}[e^{-2x}w] = xe^{-3x} \quad \text{gives} \quad e^{-2x}w = -\frac{1}{3}xe^{-3x} - \frac{1}{9}e^{-3x} + c_1.$$

Therefore $w = u' = -\frac{1}{3}xe^{-x} - \frac{1}{9}e^{-x} + c_1 e^{2x}$ and $u = \frac{1}{3}xe^{-x} + \frac{4}{9}e^{-x} + c_2 e^{2x} + c_3$. The general solution is

$$y = ue^x = \frac{1}{3}x + \frac{4}{9} + c_2 e^{3x} + c_3 e^x.$$

21. **(a)** For m_1 constant, let $y_1 = e^{m_1 x}$. Then $y_1' = m_1 e^{m_1 x}$ and $y_1'' = m_1^2 e^{m_1 x}$. Substituting into the differential equation we obtain

$$ay_1'' + by_1' + cy_1 = am_1^2 e^{m_1 x} + bm_1 e^{m_1 x} + ce^{m_1 x}$$

$$= e^{m_1 x}(am_1^2 + bm_1 + c) = 0.$$

Thus, $y_1 = e^{m_1 x}$ will be a solution of the differential equation whenever $am_1^2 + bm_1 + c = 0$. Since a quadratic equation always has at least one real or complex root, the differential equation must have a solution of the form $y_1 = e^{m_1 x}$.

(b) Write the differential equation in the form

$$y'' + \frac{b}{a}y' + \frac{c}{a}y = 0,$$

147

and let $y_1 = e^{m_1 x}$ be a solution. Then a second solution is given by

$$y_2 = e^{m_1 x} \int \frac{e^{-bx/a}}{e^{2m_1 x}}\, dx$$

$$= e^{m_1 x} \int e^{-(b/a+2m_1)x}\, dx$$

$$= -\frac{1}{b/a + 2m_1}\, e^{m_1 x} e^{-(b/a+2m_1)x} \qquad (m_1 \neq -b/2a)$$

$$= -\frac{1}{b/a + 2m_1}\, e^{-(b/a+m_1)x}.$$

Thus, when $m_1 \neq -b/2a$, a second solution is given by $y_2 = e^{m_2 x}$ where $m_2 = -b/a - m_1$. When $m_1 = -b/2a$ a second solution is given by

$$y_2 = e^{m_1 x} \int dx = x e^{m_1 x}.$$

(c) The functions

$$\sin x = \frac{1}{2i}(e^{ix} - e^{-ix}) \qquad \cos x = \frac{1}{2}(e^{ix} + e^{-ix})$$

$$\sinh x = \frac{1}{2}(e^x - e^{-x}) \qquad \cosh x = \frac{1}{2}(e^x + e^{-x})$$

are all expressible in terms of exponential functions.

22. We have $y_1' = 1$ and $y_1'' = 0$, so $xy_1'' - xy_1' + y_1 = 0 - x + x = 0$ and $y_1(x) = x$ is a solution of the differential equation. Letting $y = u(x)y_1(x) = xu(x)$ we get

$$y' = xu'(x) + u(x) \quad \text{and} \quad y'' = xu''(x) + 2u'(x).$$

Then $xy'' - xy' + y = x^2 u'' + 2xu' - x^2 u' - xu + xu = x^2 u'' - (x^2 - 2x)u' = 0$. If we make the substitution $w = u'$, the linear first-order differential equation becomes $x^2 w' - (x^2 - x)w = 0$, which is separable:

$$\frac{dw}{dx} = \left(1 - \frac{1}{x}\right)w$$

$$\frac{dw}{w} = \left(1 - \frac{1}{x}\right)dx$$

$$\ln w = x - \ln x + c$$

$$w = c_1 \frac{e^x}{x}.$$

Then $u' = c_1 e^x/x$ and $u = c_1 \int e^x dx/x$. To integrate e^x/x we use the series representation for e^x.

Thus, a second solution is

$$y_2 = xu(x) = c_1 x \int \frac{e^x}{x}\, dx$$

$$= c_1 x \int \frac{1}{x}\left(1 + x + \frac{1}{2!}x^2 + \frac{1}{3!}x^3 + \cdots\right)dx$$

$$= c_1 x \int \left(\frac{1}{x} + 1 + \frac{1}{2!}x + \frac{1}{3!}x^2 + \cdots\right)dx$$

$$= c_1 x \left(\ln x + x + \frac{1}{2(2!)}x^2 + \frac{1}{3(3!)}x^3 + \cdots\right)$$

$$= c_1 \left(x \ln x + x^2 + \frac{1}{2(2!)}x^3 + \frac{1}{3(3!)}x^4 + \cdots\right).$$

An interval of definition is probably $(0, \infty)$ because of the $\ln x$ term.

23. (a) We have $y' = y'' = e^x$, so

$$xy'' - (x + 10)y' + 10y = xe^x - (x + 10)e^x + 10e^x = 0,$$

and $y = e^x$ is a solution of the differential equation.

(b) By (5) a second solution is

$$y_2 = y_1 \int \frac{e^{-\int P(x)\,dx}}{y_1^2}\, dx = e^x \int \frac{e^{\int \frac{x+10}{x}\,dx}}{e^{2x}}\, dx = e^x \int \frac{e^{\int (1+10/x)dx}}{e^{2x}}\, dx$$

$$= e^x \int \frac{e^{x+\ln x^{10}}}{e^{2x}}\, dx = e^x \int x^{10} e^{-x}\, dx$$

$$= e^x(-3{,}628{,}800 - 3{,}628{,}800x - 1{,}814{,}400x^2 - 604{,}800x^3 - 151{,}200x^4$$

$$\qquad - 30{,}240x^5 - 5{,}040x^6 - 720x^7 - 90x^8 - 10x^9 - x^{10})e^{-x}$$

$$= -3{,}628{,}800 - 3{,}628{,}800x - 1{,}814{,}400x^2 - 604{,}800x^3 - 151{,}200x^4$$

$$\qquad - 30{,}240x^5 - 5{,}040x^6 - 720x^7 - 90x^8 - 10x^9 - x^{10}.$$

(c) By Corollary (**A**) of Theorem 4.1.2, $-\dfrac{1}{10!}\, y_2 = \displaystyle\sum_{n=0}^{10} \frac{1}{n!}\, x^n$ is a solution.

Exercises 4.3

Homogeneous Linear Equations with Constant Coefficients

1. From $4m^2 + m = 0$ we obtain $m = 0$ and $m = -1/4$ so that $y = c_1 + c_2 e^{-x/4}$.

2. From $m^2 - 36 = 0$ we obtain $m = 6$ and $m = -6$ so that $y = c_1 e^{6x} + c_2 e^{-6x}$.

3. From $m^2 - m - 6 = 0$ we obtain $m = 3$ and $m = -2$ so that $y = c_1 e^{3x} + c_2 e^{-2x}$.

4. From $m^2 - 3m + 2 = 0$ we obtain $m = 1$ and $m = 2$ so that $y = c_1 e^x + c_2 e^{2x}$.

5. From $m^2 + 8m + 16 = 0$ we obtain $m = -4$ and $m = -4$ so that $y = c_1 e^{-4x} + c_2 x e^{-4x}$.

6. From $m^2 - 10m + 25 = 0$ we obtain $m = 5$ and $m = 5$ so that $y = c_1 e^{5x} + c_2 x e^{5x}$.

7. From $12m^2 - 5m - 2 = 0$ we obtain $m = -1/4$ and $m = 2/3$ so that $y = c_1 e^{-x/4} + c_2 e^{2x/3}$.

8. From $m^2 + 4m - 1 = 0$ we obtain $m = -2 \pm \sqrt{5}$ so that $y = c_1 e^{(-2+\sqrt{5})x} + c_2 e^{(-2-\sqrt{5})x}$.

9. From $m^2 + 9 = 0$ we obtain $m = 3i$ and $m = -3i$ so that $y = c_1 \cos 3x + c_2 \sin 3x$.

10. From $3m^2 + 1 = 0$ we obtain $m = i/\sqrt{3}$ and $m = -i/\sqrt{3}$ so that $y = c_1 \cos(x/\sqrt{3}) + c_2(\sin x/\sqrt{3})$.

11. From $m^2 - 4m + 5 = 0$ we obtain $m = 2 \pm i$ so that $y = e^{2x}(c_1 \cos x + c_2 \sin x)$.

12. From $2m^2 + 2m + 1 = 0$ we obtain $m = -1/2 \pm i/2$ so that
$$y = e^{-x/2}[c_1 \cos(x/2) + c_2 \sin(x/2)].$$

13. From $3m^2 + 2m + 1 = 0$ we obtain $m = -1/3 \pm \sqrt{2}\,i/3$ so that
$$y = e^{-x/3}[c_1 \cos(\sqrt{2}x/3) + c_2 \sin(\sqrt{2}x/3)].$$

14. From $2m^2 - 3m + 4 = 0$ we obtain $m = 3/4 \pm \sqrt{23}\,i/4$ so that
$$y = e^{3x/4}[c_1 \cos(\sqrt{23}x/4) + c_2 \sin(\sqrt{23}x/4)].$$

15. From $m^3 - 4m^2 - 5m = 0$ we obtain $m = 0$, $m = 5$, and $m = -1$ so that
$$y = c_1 + c_2 e^{5x} + c_3 e^{-x}.$$

16. From $m^3 - 1 = 0$ we obtain $m = 1$ and $m = -1/2 \pm \sqrt{3}\,i/2$ so that
$$y = c_1 e^x + e^{-x/2}[c_2 \cos(\sqrt{3}x/2) + c_3 \sin(\sqrt{3}x/2)].$$

17. From $m^3 - 5m^2 + 3m + 9 = 0$ we obtain $m = -1$, $m = 3$, and $m = 3$ so that
$$y = c_1 e^{-x} + c_2 e^{3x} + c_3 x e^{3x}.$$

18. From $m^3 + 3m^2 - 4m - 12 = 0$ we obtain $m = -2$, $m = 2$, and $m = -3$ so that
$$y = c_1 e^{-2x} + c_2 e^{2x} + c_3 e^{-3x}.$$

19. From $m^3 + m^2 - 2 = 0$ we obtain $m = 1$ and $m = -1 \pm i$ so that

$$u = c_1 e^t + e^{-t}(c_2 \cos t + c_3 \sin t).$$

20. From $m^3 - m^2 - 4 = 0$ we obtain $m = 2$ and $m = -1/2 \pm \sqrt{7}\, i/2$ so that

$$x = c_1 e^{2t} + e^{-t/2}[c_2 \cos(\sqrt{7}t/2) + c_3 \sin(\sqrt{7}t/2)].$$

21. From $m^3 + 3m^2 + 3m + 1 = 0$ we obtain $m = -1$, $m = -1$, and $m = -1$ so that

$$y = c_1 e^{-x} + c_2 x e^{-x} + c_3 x^2 e^{-x}.$$

22. From $m^3 - 6m^2 + 12m - 8 = 0$ we obtain $m = 2$, $m = 2$, and $m = 2$ so that

$$y = c_1 e^{2x} + c_2 x e^{2x} + c_3 x^2 e^{2x}.$$

23. From $m^4 + m^3 + m^2 = 0$ we obtain $m = 0$, $m = 0$, and $m = -1/2 \pm \sqrt{3}\, i/2$ so that

$$y = c_1 + c_2 x + e^{-x/2}[c_3 \cos(\sqrt{3}x/2) + c_4 \sin(\sqrt{3}x/2)].$$

24. From $m^4 - 2m^2 + 1 = 0$ we obtain $m = 1$, $m = 1$, $m = -1$, and $m = -1$ so that

$$y = c_1 e^x + c_2 x e^x + c_3 e^{-x} + c_4 x e^{-x}.$$

25. From $16m^4 + 24m^2 + 9 = 0$ we obtain $m = \pm\sqrt{3}\, i/2$ and $m = \pm\sqrt{3}\, i/2$ so that

$$y = c_1 \cos(\sqrt{3}x/2) + c_2 \sin(\sqrt{3}x/2) + c_3 x \cos(\sqrt{3}x/2) + c_4 x \sin(\sqrt{3}x/2).$$

26. From $m^4 - 7m^2 - 18 = 0$ we obtain $m = 3$, $m = -3$, and $m = \pm\sqrt{2}\, i$ so that

$$y = c_1 e^{3x} + c_2 e^{-3x} + c_3 \cos\sqrt{2}x + c_4 \sin\sqrt{2}x.$$

27. From $m^5 + 5m^4 - 2m^3 - 10m^2 + m + 5 = 0$ we obtain $m = -1$, $m = -1$, $m = 1$, and $m = 1$, and $m = -5$ so that

$$u = c_1 e^{-r} + c_2 r e^{-r} + c_3 e^r + c_4 r e^r + c_5 e^{-5r}.$$

28. From $2m^5 - 7m^4 + 12m^3 + 8m^2 = 0$ we obtain $m = 0$, $m = 0$, $m = -1/2$, and $m = 2 \pm 2i$ so that

$$x = c_1 + c_2 s + c_3 e^{-s/2} + e^{2s}(c_4 \cos 2s + c_5 \sin 2s).$$

29. From $m^2 + 16 = 0$ we obtain $m = \pm 4i$ so that $y = c_1 \cos 4x + c_2 \sin 4x$. If $y(0) = 2$ and $y'(0) = -2$ then $c_1 = 2$, $c_2 = -1/2$, and $y = 2\cos 4x - \frac{1}{2}\sin 4x$.

30. From $m^2 + 1 = 0$ we obtain $m = \pm i$ so that $y = c_1 \cos\theta + c_2 \sin\theta$. If $y(\pi/3) = 0$ and $y'(\pi/3) = 2$ then

$$\frac{1}{2}c_1 + \frac{\sqrt{3}}{2}c_2 = 0$$

$$-\frac{\sqrt{3}}{2}c_1 + \frac{1}{2}c_2 = 2,$$

so $c_1 = -\sqrt{3}$, $c_2 = 1$, and $y = -\sqrt{3}\cos\theta + \sin\theta$.

31. From $m^2 - 4m - 5 = 0$ we obtain $m = -1$ and $m = 5$, so that $y = c_1 e^{-t} + c_2 e^{5t}$. If $y(1) = 0$ and $y'(1) = 2$, then $c_1 e^{-1} + c_2 e^5 = 0$, $-c_1 e^{-1} + 5c_2 e^5 = 2$, so $c_1 = -e/3$, $c_2 = e^{-5}/3$, and $y = -\frac{1}{3}e^{1-t} + \frac{1}{3}e^{5t-5}$.

32. From $4m^2 - 4m - 3 = 0$ we obtain $m = -1/2$ and $m = 3/2$ so that $y = c_1 e^{-x/2} + c_2 e^{3x/2}$. If $y(0) = 1$ and $y'(0) = 5$ then $c_1 + c_2 = 1$, $-\frac{1}{2}c_1 + \frac{3}{2}c_2 = 5$, so $c_1 = -7/4$, $c_2 = 11/4$, and $y = -\frac{7}{4}e^{-x/2} + \frac{11}{4}e^{3x/2}$.

33. From $m^2 + m + 2 = 0$ we obtain $m = -1/2 \pm \sqrt{7}\,i/2$ so that $y = e^{-x/2}[c_1\cos(\sqrt{7}\,x/2) + c_2\sin(\sqrt{7}\,x/2)]$. If $y(0) = 0$ and $y'(0) = 0$ then $c_1 = 0$ and $c_2 = 0$ so that $y = 0$.

34. From $m^2 - 2m + 1 = 0$ we obtain $m = 1$ and $m = 1$ so that $y = c_1 e^x + c_2 x e^x$. If $y(0) = 5$ and $y'(0) = 10$ then $c_1 = 5$, $c_1 + c_2 = 10$ so $c_1 = 5$, $c_2 = 5$, and $y = 5e^x + 5xe^x$.

35. From $m^3 + 12m^2 + 36m = 0$ we obtain $m = 0$, $m = -6$, and $m = -6$ so that $y = c_1 + c_2 e^{-6x} + c_3 x e^{-6x}$. If $y(0) = 0$, $y'(0) = 1$, and $y''(0) = -7$ then

$$c_1 + c_2 = 0, \quad -6c_2 + c_3 = 1, \quad 36c_2 - 12c_3 = -7,$$

so $c_1 = 5/36$, $c_2 = -5/36$, $c_3 = 1/6$, and $y = \frac{5}{36} - \frac{5}{36}e^{-6x} + \frac{1}{6}xe^{-6x}$.

36. From $m^3 + 2m^2 - 5m - 6 = 0$ we obtain $m = -1$, $m = 2$, and $m = -3$ so that

$$y = c_1 e^{-x} + c_2 e^{2x} + c_3 e^{-3x}.$$

If $y(0) = 0$, $y'(0) = 0$, and $y''(0) = 1$ then

$$c_1 + c_2 + c_3 = 0, \quad -c_1 + 2c_2 - 3c_3 = 0, \quad c_1 + 4c_2 + 9c_3 = 1,$$

so $c_1 = -1/6$, $c_2 = 1/15$, $c_3 = 1/10$, and

$$y = -\frac{1}{6}e^{-x} + \frac{1}{15}e^{2x} + \frac{1}{10}e^{-3x}.$$

37. From $m^2 - 10m + 25 = 0$ we obtain $m = 5$ and $m = 5$ so that $y = c_1 e^{5x} + c_2 x e^{5x}$. If $y(0) = 1$ and $y(1) = 0$ then $c_1 = 1$, $c_1 e^5 + c_2 e^5 = 0$, so $c_1 = 1$, $c_2 = -1$, and $y = e^{5x} - xe^{5x}$.

38. From $m^2 + 4 = 0$ we obtain $m = \pm 2i$ so that $y = c_1\cos 2x + c_2\sin 2x$. If $y(0) = 0$ and $y(\pi) = 0$ then $c_1 = 0$ and $y = c_2\sin 2x$.

39. From $m^2 + 1 = 0$ we obtain $m = \pm i$ so that $y = c_1\cos x + c_2\sin x$ and $y' = -c_1\sin x + c_2\cos x$. From $y'(0) = c_1(0) + c_2(1) = c_2 = 0$ and $y'(\pi/2) = -c_1(1) = 0$ we find $c_1 = c_2 = 0$. A solution of the boundary-value problem is $y = 0$.

40. From $m^2 - 2m + 2 = 0$ we obtain $m = 1 \pm i$ so that $y = e^x(c_1\cos x + c_2\sin x)$. If $y(0) = 1$ and $y(\pi) = 1$ then $c_1 = 1$ and $y(\pi) = e^\pi\cos\pi = -e^\pi$. Since $-e^\pi \neq 1$, the boundary-value problem has no solution.

41. The auxiliary equation is $m^2 - 3 = 0$ which has roots $-\sqrt{3}$ and $\sqrt{3}$. By (10) the general solution is $y = c_1 e^{\sqrt{3}x} + c_2 e^{-\sqrt{3}x}$. By (11) the general solution is $y = c_1 \cosh\sqrt{3}x + c_2 \sinh\sqrt{3}x$. For $y = c_1 e^{\sqrt{3}x} + c_2 e^{-\sqrt{3}x}$ the initial conditions imply $c_1 + c_2 = 1$, $\sqrt{3}c_1 - \sqrt{3}c_2 = 5$. Solving for c_1 and c_2 we find $c_1 = \frac{1}{2}(1 + 5\sqrt{3})$ and $c_2 = \frac{1}{2}(1 - 5\sqrt{3})$ so $y = \frac{1}{2}(1 + 5\sqrt{3})e^{\sqrt{3}x} + \frac{1}{2}(1 - 5\sqrt{3})e^{-\sqrt{3}x}$. For $y = c_1 \cosh\sqrt{3}x + c_2 \sinh\sqrt{3}x$ the initial conditions imply $c_1 = 1$, $\sqrt{3}c_2 = 5$. Solving for c_1 and c_2 we find $c_1 = 1$ and $c_2 = \frac{5}{3}\sqrt{3}$ so $y = \cosh\sqrt{3}x + \frac{5}{3}\sqrt{3}\sinh\sqrt{3}x$.

42. The auxiliary equation is $m^2 - 1 = 0$ which has roots -1 and 1. By (10) the general solution is $y = c_1 e^x + c_2 e^{-x}$. By (11) the general solution is $y = c_1 \cosh x + c_2 \sinh x$. For $y = c_1 e^x + c_2 e^{-x}$ the boundary conditions imply $c_1 + c_2 = 1$, $c_1 e - c_2 e^{-1} = 0$. Solving for c_1 and c_2 we find $c_1 = 1/(1 + e^2)$ and $c_2 = e^2/(1 + e^2)$ so $y = e^x/(1 + e^2) + e^2 e^{-x}/(1 + e^2)$. For $y = c_1 \cosh x + c_2 \sinh x$ the boundary conditions imply $c_1 = 1$, $c_2 = -\tanh 1$, so $y = \cosh x - (\tanh 1)\sinh x$.

43. The auxiliary equation should have two positive roots, so that the solution has the form $y = c_1 e^{k_1 x} + c_2 e^{k_2 x}$. Thus, the differential equation is (f).

44. The auxiliary equation should have one positive and one negative root, so that the solution has the form $y = c_1 e^{k_1 x} + c_2 e^{-k_2 x}$. Thus, the differential equation is (a).

45. The auxiliary equation should have a pair of complex roots $\alpha \pm \beta i$ where $\alpha < 0$, so that the solution has the form $e^{\alpha x}(c_1 \cos\beta x + c_2 \sin\beta x)$. Thus, the differential equation is (e).

46. The auxiliary equation should have a repeated negative root, so that the solution has the form $y = c_1 e^{-x} + c_2 x e^{-x}$. Thus, the differential equation is (c).

47. The differential equation should have the form $y'' + k^2 y = 0$ where $k = 1$ so that the period of the solution is 2π. Thus, the differential equation is (d).

48. The differential equation should have the form $y'' + k^2 y = 0$ where $k = 2$ so that the period of the solution is π. Thus, the differential equation is (b).

49. Since $(m - 4)(m + 5)^2 = m^3 + 6m^2 - 15m - 100$ the differential equation is $y''' + 6y'' - 15y' - 100y = 0$. The differential equation is not unique since any constant multiple of the left-hand side of the differential equation would lead to the auxiliary roots.

50. A third root must be $m_3 = 3 - i$ and the auxiliary equation is

$$\left(m + \frac{1}{2}\right)[m - (3 + i)][m - (3 - i)] = \left(m + \frac{1}{2}\right)(m^2 - 6x + 10) = m^3 - \frac{11}{2}m^2 + 7m + 5.$$

The differential equation is

$$y''' - \frac{11}{2}y'' + 7y' + 5y = 0.$$

51. From the solution $y_1 = e^{-4x}\cos x$ we conclude that $m_1 = -4 + i$ and $m_2 = -4 - i$ are roots of the auxiliary equation. Hence another solution must be $y_2 = e^{-4x}\sin x$. Now dividing the polynomial

$m^3 + 6m^2 + m - 34$ by $[m - (-4+i)][m - (-4-i)] = m^2 + 8m + 17$ gives $m - 2$. Therefore $m_3 = 2$ is the third root of the auxiliary equation, and the general solution of the differential equation is

$$y = c_1 e^{-4x} \cos x + c_2 e^{-4x} \sin x + c_3 e^{2x}.$$

52. Factoring the difference of two squares we obtain

$$m^4 + 1 = (m^2 + 1)^2 - 2m^2 = (m^2 + 1 - \sqrt{2}\,m)(m^2 + 1 + \sqrt{2}\,m) = 0.$$

Using the quadratic formula on each factor we get $m = \pm\sqrt{2}/2 \pm \sqrt{2}\,i/2$. The solution of the differential equation is

$$y(x) = e^{\sqrt{2}\,x/2}\left(c_1 \cos \frac{\sqrt{2}}{2} x + c_2 \sin \frac{\sqrt{2}}{2} x\right) + e^{-\sqrt{2}\,x/2}\left(c_3 \cos \frac{\sqrt{2}}{2} x + c_4 \sin \frac{\sqrt{2}}{2} x\right).$$

53. Using the definition of $\sinh x$ and the formula for the cosine of the sum of two angles, we have

$$y = \sinh x - 2\cos(x + \pi/6)$$

$$= \frac{1}{2}e^x - \frac{1}{2}e^{-x} - 2\left[(\cos x)\left(\cos\frac{\pi}{6}\right) - (\sin x)\left(\sin\frac{\pi}{6}\right)\right]$$

$$= \frac{1}{2}e^x - \frac{1}{2}e^{-x} - 2\left(\frac{\sqrt{3}}{2}\cos x - \frac{1}{2}\sin x\right)$$

$$= \frac{1}{2}e^x - \frac{1}{2}e^{-x} - \sqrt{3}\cos x + \sin x.$$

This form of the solution can be obtained from the general solution $y = c_1 e^x + c_2 e^{-x} + c_3 \cos x + c_4 \sin x$ by choosing $c_1 = \frac{1}{2}$, $c_2 = -\frac{1}{2}$, $c_3 = -\sqrt{3}$, and $c_4 = 1$.

54. The auxiliary equation is $m^2 + \alpha = 0$ and we consider three cases where $\lambda = 0$, $\lambda = \alpha^2 > 0$, and $\lambda = -\alpha^2 < 0$:

Case I When $\alpha = 0$ the general solution of the differential equation is $y = c_1 + c_2 x$. The boundary conditions imply $0 = y(0) = c_1$ and $0 = y(\pi/2) = c_2\pi/2$, so that $c_1 = c_2 = 0$ and the problem possesses only the trivial solution.

Case II When $\lambda = -\alpha^2 < 0$ the general solution of the differential equation is $y = c_1 e^{\alpha x} + c_2 e^{-\alpha x}$, or alternatively, $y = c_1 \cosh \alpha x + c_2 \sinh \alpha x$. Again, $y(0) = 0$ implies $c_1 = 0$ so $y = c_2 \sinh \alpha x$. The second boundary condition implies $0 = y(\pi/2) = c_2 \sinh \alpha \pi/2$ or $c_2 = 0$. In this case also, the problem possesses only the trivial solution.

Case III When $\lambda = \alpha^2 > 0$ the general solution of the differential equation is $y = c_1 \cos \alpha x + c_2 \sin \alpha x$. In this case also, $y(0) = 0$ yields $c_1 = 0$, so that $y = c_2 \sin \alpha x$. The second boundary condition implies $0 = c_2 \sin \alpha \pi/2$. When $\alpha \pi/2$ is an integer multiple of π, that is, when $\alpha = 2k$ for k a nonzero integer, the problem will have nontrivial solutions. Thus, for $\lambda = \alpha^2 = 4k^2$ the boundary-value problem will have nontrivial solutions $y = c_2 \sin 2kx$, where k is a nonzero integer.

On the other hand, when α is not an even integer, the boundary-value problem will have only the trivial solution.

55. Using a CAS to solve the auxiliary equation $m^3 - 6m^2 + 2m + 1$ we find $m_1 = -0.270534$, $m_2 = 0.658675$, and $m_3 = 5.61186$. The general solution is

$$y = c_1 e^{-0.270534x} + c_2 e^{0.658675x} + c_3 e^{5.61186x}.$$

56. Using a CAS to solve the auxiliary equation $6.11m^3 + 8.59m^2 + 7.93m + 0.778 = 0$ we find $m_1 = -0.110241$, $m_2 = -0.647826 + 0.857532i$, and $m_3 = -0.647826 - 0.857532i$. The general solution is

$$y = c_1 e^{-0.110241x} + e^{-0.647826x}(c_2 \cos 0.857532x + c_3 \sin 0.857532x).$$

57. Using a CAS to solve the auxiliary equation $3.15m^4 - 5.34m^2 + 6.33m - 2.03 = 0$ we find $m_1 = -1.74806$, $m_2 = 0.501219$, $m_3 = 0.62342 + 0.588965i$, and $m_4 = 0.62342 - 0.588965i$. The general solution is

$$y = c_1 e^{-1.74806x} + c_2 e^{0.501219x} + e^{0.62342x}(c_3 \cos 0.588965x + c_4 \sin 0.588965x).$$

58. Using a CAS to solve the auxiliary equation $m^4 + 2m^2 - m + 2 = 0$ we find $m_1 = 1/2 + \sqrt{3}\,i/2$, $m_2 = 1/2 - \sqrt{3}\,i/2$, $m_3 = -1/2 + \sqrt{7}\,i/2$, and $m_4 = -1/2 - \sqrt{7}\,i/2$. The general solution is

$$y = e^{x/2}\left(c_1 \cos \frac{\sqrt{3}}{2}x + c_2 \sin \frac{\sqrt{3}}{2}x\right) + e^{-x/2}\left(c_3 \cos \frac{\sqrt{7}}{2}x + c_4 \sin \frac{\sqrt{7}}{2}x\right).$$

59. From $2m^4 + 3m^3 - 16m^2 + 15m - 4 = 0$ we obtain $m = -4$, $m = \frac{1}{2}$, $m = 1$, and $m = 1$, so that $y = c_1 e^{-4x} + c_2 e^{x/2} + c_3 e^x + c_4 x e^x$. If $y(0) = -2$, $y'(0) = 6$, $y''(0) = 3$, and $y'''(0) = \frac{1}{2}$, then

$$c_1 + c_2 + c_3 = -2$$

$$-4c_1 + \frac{1}{2}c_2 + c_3 + c_4 = 6$$

$$16c_1 + \frac{1}{4}c_2 + c_3 + 2c_4 = 3$$

$$-64c_1 + \frac{1}{8}c_2 + c_3 + 3c_4 = \frac{1}{2},$$

so $c_1 = -\frac{4}{75}$, $c_2 = -\frac{116}{3}$, $c_3 = \frac{918}{25}$, $c_4 = -\frac{58}{5}$, and

$$y = -\frac{4}{75}e^{-4x} - \frac{116}{3}e^{x/2} + \frac{918}{25}e^x - \frac{58}{5}xe^x.$$

60. From $m^4 - 3m^3 + 3m^2 - m = 0$ we obtain $m = 0$, $m = 1$, $m = 1$, and $m = 1$ so that $y = c_1 + c_2 e^x + c_3 x e^x + c_4 x^2 e^x$. If $y(0) = 0$, $y'(0) = 0$, $y''(0) = 1$, and $y'''(0) = 1$ then

$$c_1 + c_2 = 0, \quad c_2 + c_3 = 0, \quad c_2 + 2c_3 + 2c_4 = 1, \quad c_2 + 3c_3 + 6c_4 = 1,$$

so $c_1 = 2$, $c_2 = -2$, $c_3 = 2$, $c_4 = -1/2$, and

$$y = 2 - 2e^x + 2xe^x - \frac{1}{2}x^2 e^x.$$

Exercises 4.4

Undetermined Coefficients – Superposition Approach

1. From $m^2 + 3m + 2 = 0$ we find $m_1 = -1$ and $m_2 = -2$. Then $y_c = c_1 e^{-x} + c_2 e^{-2x}$ and we assume $y_p = A$. Substituting into the differential equation we obtain $2A = 6$. Then $A = 3$, $y_p = 3$ and

$$y = c_1 e^{-x} + c_2 e^{-2x} + 3.$$

2. From $4m^2 + 9 = 0$ we find $m_1 = -\frac{3}{2}i$ and $m_2 = \frac{3}{2}i$. Then $y_c = c_1 \cos \frac{3}{2}x + c_2 \sin \frac{3}{2}x$ and we assume $y_p = A$. Substituting into the differential equation we obtain $9A = 15$. Then $A = \frac{5}{3}$, $y_p = \frac{5}{3}$ and

$$y = c_1 \cos \frac{3}{2}x + c_2 \sin \frac{3}{2}x + \frac{5}{3}.$$

3. From $m^2 - 10m + 25 = 0$ we find $m_1 = m_2 = 5$. Then $y_c = c_1 e^{5x} + c_2 x e^{5x}$ and we assume $y_p = Ax + B$. Substituting into the differential equation we obtain $25A = 30$ and $-10A + 25B = 3$. Then $A = \frac{6}{5}$, $B = \frac{3}{5}$, $y_p = \frac{6}{5}x + \frac{3}{5}$, and

$$y = c_1 e^{5x} + c_2 x e^{5x} + \frac{6}{5}x + \frac{3}{5}.$$

4. From $m^2 + m - 6 = 0$ we find $m_1 = -3$ and $m_2 = 2$. Then $y_c = c_1 e^{-3x} + c_2 e^{2x}$ and we assume $y_p = Ax + B$. Substituting into the differential equation we obtain $-6A = 2$ and $A - 6B = 0$. Then $A = -\frac{1}{3}$, $B = -\frac{1}{18}$, $y_p = -\frac{1}{3}x - \frac{1}{18}$, and

$$y = c_1 e^{-3x} + c_2 e^{2x} - \frac{1}{3}x - \frac{1}{18}.$$

5. From $\frac{1}{4}m^2 + m + 1 = 0$ we find $m_1 = m_2 = -2$. Then $y_c = c_1 e^{-2x} + c_2 x e^{-2x}$ and we assume $y_p = Ax^2 + Bx + C$. Substituting into the differential equation we obtain $A = 1$, $2A + B = -2$, and $\frac{1}{2}A + B + C = 0$. Then $A = 1$, $B = -4$, $C = \frac{7}{2}$, $y_p = x^2 - 4x + \frac{7}{2}$, and

$$y = c_1 e^{-2x} + c_2 x e^{-2x} + x^2 - 4x + \frac{7}{2}.$$

6. From $m^2 - 8m + 20 = 0$ we find $m_1 = 4 + 2i$ and $m_2 = 4 - 2i$. Then $y_c = e^{4x}(c_1 \cos 2x + c_2 \sin 2x)$ and we assume $y_p = Ax^2 + Bx + C + (Dx + E)e^x$. Substituting into the differential equation we

obtain

$$2A - 8B + 20C = 0$$

$$-6D + 13E = 0$$

$$-16A + 20B = 0$$

$$13D = -26$$

$$20A = 100.$$

Then $A = 5$, $B = 4$, $C = \frac{11}{10}$, $D = -2$, $E = -\frac{12}{13}$, $y_p = 5x^2 + 4x + \frac{11}{10} + \left(-2x - \frac{12}{13}\right)e^x$ and

$$y = e^{4x}(c_1 \cos 2x + c_2 \sin 2x) + 5x^2 + 4x + \frac{11}{10} + \left(-2x - \frac{12}{13}\right)e^x.$$

7. From $m^2 + 3 = 0$ we find $m_1 = \sqrt{3}\,i$ and $m_2 = -\sqrt{3}\,i$. Then $y_c = c_1 \cos\sqrt{3}\,x + c_2 \sin\sqrt{3}\,x$ and we assume $y_p = (Ax^2 + Bx + C)e^{3x}$. Substituting into the differential equation we obtain $2A + 6B + 12C = 0$, $12A + 12B = 0$, and $12A = -48$. Then $A = -4$, $B = 4$, $C = -\frac{4}{3}$, $y_p = \left(-4x^2 + 4x - \frac{4}{3}\right)e^{3x}$ and

$$y = c_1 \cos\sqrt{3}\,x + c_2 \sin\sqrt{3}\,x + \left(-4x^2 + 4x - \frac{4}{3}\right)e^{3x}.$$

8. From $4m^2 - 4m - 3 = 0$ we find $m_1 = \frac{3}{2}$ and $m_2 = -\frac{1}{2}$. Then $y_c = c_1 e^{3x/2} + c_2 e^{-x/2}$ and we assume $y_p = A\cos 2x + B\sin 2x$. Substituting into the differential equation we obtain $-19 - 8B = 1$ and $8A - 19B = 0$. Then $A = -\frac{19}{425}$, $B = -\frac{8}{425}$, $y_p = -\frac{19}{425}\cos 2x - \frac{8}{425}\sin 2x$, and

$$y = c_1 e^{3x/2} + c_2 e^{-x/2} - \frac{19}{425}\cos 2x - \frac{8}{425}\sin 2x.$$

9. From $m^2 - m = 0$ we find $m_1 = 1$ and $m_2 = 0$. Then $y_c = c_1 e^x + c_2$ and we assume $y_p = Ax$. Substituting into the differential equation we obtain $-A = -3$. Then $A = 3$, $y_p = 3x$ and $y = c_1 e^x + c_2 + 3x$.

10. From $m^2 + 2m = 0$ we find $m_1 = -2$ and $m_2 = 0$. Then $y_c = c_1 e^{-2x} + c_2$ and we assume $y_p = Ax^2 + Bx + Cxe^{-2x}$. Substituting into the differential equation we obtain $2A + 2B = 5$, $4A = 2$, and $-2C = -1$. Then $A = \frac{1}{2}$, $B = 2$, $C = \frac{1}{2}$, $y_p = \frac{1}{2}x^2 + 2x + \frac{1}{2}xe^{-2x}$, and

$$y = c_1 e^{-2x} + c_2 + \frac{1}{2}x^2 + 2x + \frac{1}{2}xe^{-2x}.$$

11. From $m^2 - m + \frac{1}{4} = 0$ we find $m_1 = m_2 = \frac{1}{2}$. Then $y_c = c_1 e^{x/2} + c_2 xe^{x/2}$ and we assume $y_p = A + Bx^2 e^{x/2}$. Substituting into the differential equation we obtain $\frac{1}{4}A = 3$ and $2B = 1$. Then $A = 12$, $B = \frac{1}{2}$, $y_p = 12 + \frac{1}{2}x^2 e^{x/2}$, and

$$y = c_1 e^{x/2} + c_2 xe^{x/2} + 12 + \frac{1}{2}x^2 e^{x/2}.$$

12. From $m^2 - 16 = 0$ we find $m_1 = 4$ and $m_2 = -4$. Then $y_c = c_1 e^{4x} + c_2 e^{-4x}$ and we assume $y_p = Axe^{4x}$. Substituting into the differential equation we obtain $8A = 2$. Then $A = \frac{1}{4}$, $y_p = \frac{1}{4}xe^{4x}$ and

$$y = c_1 e^{4x} + c_2 e^{-4x} + \frac{1}{4}xe^{4x}.$$

13. From $m^2 + 4 = 0$ we find $m_1 = 2i$ and $m_2 = -2i$. Then $y_c = c_1 \cos 2x + c_2 \sin 2x$ and we assume $y_p = Ax \cos 2x + Bx \sin 2x$. Substituting into the differential equation we obtain $4B = 0$ and $-4A = 3$. Then $A = -\frac{3}{4}$, $B = 0$, $y_p = -\frac{3}{4}x \cos 2x$, and

$$y = c_1 \cos 2x + c_2 \sin 2x - \frac{3}{4}x \cos 2x.$$

14. From $m^2 - 4 = 0$ we find $m_1 = 2$ and $m_2 = -2$. Then $y_c = c_1 e^{2x} + c_2 e^{-2x}$ and we assume that $y_p = (Ax^2 + Bx + C)\cos 2x + (Dx^2 + Ex + F)\sin 2x$. Substituting into the differential equation we obtain

$$-8A = 0$$

$$-8B + 8D = 0$$

$$2A - 8C + 4E = 0$$

$$-8D = 1$$

$$-8A - 8E = 0$$

$$-4B + 2D - 8F = -3.$$

Then $A = 0$, $B = -\frac{1}{8}$, $C = 0$, $D = -\frac{1}{8}$, $E = 0$, $F = \frac{13}{32}$, so $y_p = -\frac{1}{8}x \cos 2x + \left(-\frac{1}{8}x^2 + \frac{13}{32}\right)\sin 2x$, and

$$y = c_1 e^{2x} + c_2 e^{-2x} - \frac{1}{8}x \cos 2x + \left(-\frac{1}{8}x^2 + \frac{13}{32}\right)\sin 2x.$$

15. From $m^2 + 1 = 0$ we find $m_1 = i$ and $m_2 = -i$. Then $y_c = c_1 \cos x + c_2 \sin x$ and we assume $y_p = (Ax^2 + Bx)\cos x + (Cx^2 + Dx)\sin x$. Substituting into the differential equation we obtain $4C = 0$, $2A + 2D = 0$, $-4A = 2$, and $-2B + 2C = 0$. Then $A = -\frac{1}{2}$, $B = 0$, $C = 0$, $D = \frac{1}{2}$, $y_p = -\frac{1}{2}x^2 \cos x + \frac{1}{2}x \sin x$, and

$$y = c_1 \cos x + c_2 \sin x - \frac{1}{2}x^2 \cos x + \frac{1}{2}x \sin x.$$

16. From $m^2 - 5m = 0$ we find $m_1 = 5$ and $m_2 = 0$. Then $y_c = c_1 e^{5x} + c_2$ and we assume $y_p = Ax^4 + Bx^3 + Cx^2 + Dx$. Substituting into the differential equation we obtain $-20A = 2$, $12A - 15B = -4$, $6B - 10C = -1$, and $2C - 5D = 6$. Then $A = -\frac{1}{10}$, $B = \frac{14}{75}$, $C = \frac{53}{250}$, $D = -\frac{697}{625}$, $y_p = -\frac{1}{10}x^4 + \frac{14}{75}x^3 + \frac{53}{250}x^2 - \frac{697}{625}x$, and

$$y = c_1 e^{5x} + c_2 - \frac{1}{10}x^4 + \frac{14}{75}x^3 + \frac{53}{250}x^2 - \frac{697}{625}x.$$

17. From $m^2 - 2m + 5 = 0$ we find $m_1 = 1 + 2i$ and $m_2 = 1 - 2i$. Then $y_c = e^x(c_1 \cos 2x + c_2 \sin 2x)$ and we assume $y_p = Axe^x \cos 2x + Bxe^x \sin 2x$. Substituting into the differential equation we obtain $4B = 1$ and $-4A = 0$. Then $A = 0$, $B = \frac{1}{4}$, $y_p = \frac{1}{4}xe^x \sin 2x$, and

$$y = e^x(c_1 \cos 2x + c_2 \sin 2x) + \frac{1}{4}xe^x \sin 2x.$$

18. From $m^2 - 2m + 2 = 0$ we find $m_1 = 1 + i$ and $m_2 = 1 - i$. Then $y_c = e^x(c_1 \cos x + c_2 \sin x)$ and we assume $y_p = Ae^{2x} \cos x + Be^{2x} \sin x$. Substituting into the differential equation we obtain $A + 2B = 1$ and $-2A + B = -3$. Then $A = \frac{7}{5}$, $B = -\frac{1}{5}$, $y_p = \frac{7}{5}e^{2x} \cos x - \frac{1}{5}e^{2x} \sin x$ and

$$y = e^x(c_1 \cos x + c_2 \sin x) + \frac{7}{5}e^{2x} \cos x - \frac{1}{5}e^{2x} \sin x.$$

19. From $m^2 + 2m + 1 = 0$ we find $m_1 = m_2 = -1$. Then $y_c = c_1e^{-x} + c_2xe^{-x}$ and we assume $y_p = A \cos x + B \sin x + C \cos 2x + D \sin 2x$. Substituting into the differential equation we obtain $2B = 0$, $-2A = 1$, $-3C + 4D = 3$, and $-4C - 3D = 0$. Then $A = -\frac{1}{2}$, $B = 0$, $C = -\frac{9}{25}$, $D = \frac{12}{25}$, $y_p = -\frac{1}{2} \cos x - \frac{9}{25} \cos 2x + \frac{12}{25} \sin 2x$, and

$$y = c_1e^{-x} + c_2xe^{-x} - \frac{1}{2} \cos x - \frac{9}{25} \cos 2x + \frac{12}{25} \sin 2x.$$

20. From $m^2 + 2m - 24 = 0$ we find $m_1 = -6$ and $m_2 = 4$. Then $y_c = c_1e^{-6x} + c_2e^{4x}$ and we assume $y_p = A + (Bx^2 + Cx)e^{4x}$. Substituting into the differential equation we obtain $-24A = 16$, $2B + 10C = -2$, and $20B = -1$. Then $A = -\frac{2}{3}$, $B = -\frac{1}{20}$, $C = -\frac{19}{100}$, $y_p = -\frac{2}{3} - \left(\frac{1}{20}x^2 + \frac{19}{100}x\right)e^{4x}$, and

$$y = c_1e^{-6x} + c_2e^{4x} - \frac{2}{3} - \left(\frac{1}{20}x^2 + \frac{19}{100}x\right)e^{4x}.$$

21. From $m^3 - 6m^2 = 0$ we find $m_1 = m_2 = 0$ and $m_3 = 6$. Then $y_c = c_1 + c_2x + c_3e^{6x}$ and we assume $y_p = Ax^2 + B \cos x + C \sin x$. Substituting into the differential equation we obtain $-12A = 3$, $6B - C = -1$, and $B + 6C = 0$. Then $A = -\frac{1}{4}$, $B = -\frac{6}{37}$, $C = \frac{1}{37}$, $y_p = -\frac{1}{4}x^2 - \frac{6}{37} \cos x + \frac{1}{37} \sin x$, and

$$y = c_1 + c_2x + c_3e^{6x} - \frac{1}{4}x^2 - \frac{6}{37} \cos x + \frac{1}{37} \sin x.$$

22. From $m^3 - 2m^2 - 4m + 8 = 0$ we find $m_1 = m_2 = 2$ and $m_3 = -2$. Then $y_c = c_1e^{2x} + c_2xe^{2x} + c_3e^{-2x}$ and we assume $y_p = (Ax^3 + Bx^2)e^{2x}$. Substituting into the differential equation we obtain $24A = 6$ and $6A + 8B = 0$. Then $A = \frac{1}{4}$, $B = -\frac{3}{16}$, $y_p = \left(\frac{1}{4}x^3 - \frac{3}{16}x^2\right)e^{2x}$, and

$$y = c_1e^{2x} + c_2xe^{2x} + c_3e^{-2x} + \left(\frac{1}{4}x^3 - \frac{3}{16}x^2\right)e^{2x}.$$

23. From $m^3 - 3m^2 + 3m - 1 = 0$ we find $m_1 = m_2 = m_3 = 1$. Then $y_c = c_1e^x + c_2xe^x + c_3x^2e^x$ and we assume $y_p = Ax + B + Cx^3e^x$. Substituting into the differential equation we obtain $-A = 1$,

Exercises 4.4 Undetermined Coefficients – Superposition Approach

$3A - B = 0$, and $6C = -4$. Then $A = -1$, $B = -3$, $C = -\frac{2}{3}$, $y_p = -x - 3 - \frac{2}{3}x^3 e^x$, and

$$y = c_1 e^x + c_2 x e^x + c_3 x^2 e^x - x - 3 - \frac{2}{3}x^3 e^x.$$

24. From $m^3 - m^2 - 4m + 4 = 0$ we find $m_1 = 1$, $m_2 = 2$, and $m_3 = -2$. Then $y_c = c_1 e^x + c_2 e^{2x} + c_3 e^{-2x}$ and we assume $y_p = A + Bxe^x + Cxe^{2x}$. Substituting into the differential equation we obtain $4A = 5$, $-3B = -1$, and $4C = 1$. Then $A = \frac{5}{4}$, $B = \frac{1}{3}$, $C = \frac{1}{4}$, $y_p = \frac{5}{4} + \frac{1}{3}xe^x + \frac{1}{4}xe^{2x}$, and

$$y = c_1 e^x + c_2 e^{2x} + c_3 e^{-2x} + \frac{5}{4} + \frac{1}{3}xe^x + \frac{1}{4}xe^{2x}.$$

25. From $m^4 + 2m^2 + 1 = 0$ we find $m_1 = m_3 = i$ and $m_2 = m_4 = -i$. Then $y_c = c_1 \cos x + c_2 \sin x + c_3 x \cos x + c_4 x \sin x$ and we assume $y_p = Ax^2 + Bx + C$. Substituting into the differential equation we obtain $A = 1$, $B = -2$, and $4A + C = 1$. Then $A = 1$, $B = -2$, $C = -3$, $y_p = x^2 - 2x - 3$, and

$$y = c_1 \cos x + c_2 \sin x + c_3 x \cos x + c_4 x \sin x + x^2 - 2x - 3.$$

26. From $m^4 - m^2 = 0$ we find $m_1 = m_2 = 0$, $m_3 = 1$, and $m_4 = -1$. Then $y_c = c_1 + c_2 x + c_3 e^x + c_4 e^{-x}$ and we assume $y_p = Ax^3 + Bx^2 + (Cx^2 + Dx)e^{-x}$. Substituting into the differential equation we obtain $-6A = 4$, $-2B = 0$, $10C - 2D = 0$, and $-4C = 2$. Then $A = -\frac{2}{3}$, $B = 0$, $C = -\frac{1}{2}$, $D = -\frac{5}{2}$, $y_p = -\frac{2}{3}x^3 - \left(\frac{1}{2}x^2 + \frac{5}{2}x\right)e^{-x}$, and

$$y = c_1 + c_2 x + c_3 e^x + c_4 e^{-x} - \frac{2}{3}x^3 - \left(\frac{1}{2}x^2 + \frac{5}{2}x\right)e^{-x}.$$

27. We have $y_c = c_1 \cos 2x + c_2 \sin 2x$ and we assume $y_p = A$. Substituting into the differential equation we find $A = -\frac{1}{2}$. Thus $y = c_1 \cos 2x + c_2 \sin 2x - \frac{1}{2}$. From the initial conditions we obtain $c_1 = 0$ and $c_2 = \sqrt{2}$, so $y = \sqrt{2} \sin 2x - \frac{1}{2}$.

28. We have $y_c = c_1 e^{-2x} + c_2 e^{x/2}$ and we assume $y_p = Ax^2 + Bx + C$. Substituting into the differential equation we find $A = -7$, $B = -19$, and $C = -37$. Thus $y = c_1 e^{-2x} + c_2 e^{x/2} - 7x^2 - 19x - 37$. From the initial conditions we obtain $c_1 = -\frac{1}{5}$ and $c_2 = \frac{186}{5}$, so

$$y = -\frac{1}{5}e^{-2x} + \frac{186}{5}e^{x/2} - 7x^2 - 19x - 37.$$

29. We have $y_c = c_1 e^{-x/5} + c_2$ and we assume $y_p = Ax^2 + Bx$. Substituting into the differential equation we find $A = -3$ and $B = 30$. Thus $y = c_1 e^{-x/5} + c_2 - 3x^2 + 30x$. From the initial conditions we obtain $c_1 = 200$ and $c_2 = -200$, so

$$y = 200e^{-x/5} - 200 - 3x^2 + 30x.$$

30. We have $y_c = c_1 e^{-2x} + c_2 x e^{-2x}$ and we assume $y_p = (Ax^3 + Bx^2)e^{-2x}$. Substituting into the differential equation we find $A = \frac{1}{6}$ and $B = \frac{3}{2}$. Thus $y = c_1 e^{-2x} + c_2 x e^{-2x} + \left(\frac{1}{6}x^3 + \frac{3}{2}x^2\right)e^{-2x}$. From the initial conditions we obtain $c_1 = 2$ and $c_2 = 9$, so

$$y = 2e^{-2x} + 9xe^{-2x} + \left(\frac{1}{6}x^3 + \frac{3}{2}x^2\right)e^{-2x}.$$

31. We have $y_c = e^{-2x}(c_1 \cos x + c_2 \sin x)$ and we assume $y_p = Ae^{-4x}$. Substituting into the differential equation we find $A = 7$. Thus $y = e^{-2x}(c_1 \cos x + c_2 \sin x) + 7e^{-4x}$. From the initial conditions we obtain $c_1 = -10$ and $c_2 = 9$, so

$$y = e^{-2x}(-10 \cos x + 9 \sin x) + 7e^{-4x}.$$

32. We have $y_c = c_1 \cosh x + c_2 \sinh x$ and we assume $y_p = Ax \cosh x + Bx \sinh x$. Substituting into the differential equation we find $A = 0$ and $B = \frac{1}{2}$. Thus

$$y = c_1 \cosh x + c_2 \sinh x + \frac{1}{2}x \sinh x.$$

From the initial conditions we obtain $c_1 = 2$ and $c_2 = 12$, so

$$y = 2 \cosh x + 12 \sinh x + \frac{1}{2}x \sinh x.$$

33. We have $x_c = c_1 \cos \omega t + c_2 \sin \omega t$ and we assume $x_p = At \cos \omega t + Bt \sin \omega t$. Substituting into the differential equation we find $A = -F_0/2\omega$ and $B = 0$. Thus $x = c_1 \cos \omega t + c_2 \sin \omega t - (F_0/2\omega)t \cos \omega t$. From the initial conditions we obtain $c_1 = 0$ and $c_2 = F_0/2\omega^2$, so

$$x = (F_0/2\omega^2) \sin \omega t - (F_0/2\omega)t \cos \omega t.$$

34. We have $x_c = c_1 \cos \omega t + c_2 \sin \omega t$ and we assume $x_p = A \cos \gamma t + B \sin \gamma t$, where $\gamma \neq \omega$. Substituting into the differential equation we find $A = F_0/(\omega^2 - \gamma^2)$ and $B = 0$. Thus

$$x = c_1 \cos \omega t + c_2 \sin \omega t + \frac{F_0}{\omega^2 - \gamma^2} \cos \gamma t.$$

From the initial conditions we obtain $c_1 = -F_0/(\omega^2 - \gamma^2)$ and $c_2 = 0$, so

$$x = -\frac{F_0}{\omega^2 - \gamma^2} \cos \omega t + \frac{F_0}{\omega^2 - \gamma^2} \cos \gamma t.$$

35. We have $y_c = c_1 + c_2 e^x + c_3 x e^x$ and we assume $y_p = Ax + Bx^2 e^x + Ce^{5x}$. Substituting into the differential equation we find $A = 2$, $B = -12$, and $C = \frac{1}{2}$. Thus

$$y = c_1 + c_2 e^x + c_3 x e^x + 2x - 12x^2 e^x + \frac{1}{2}e^{5x}.$$

From the initial conditions we obtain $c_1 = 11$, $c_2 = -11$, and $c_3 = 9$, so

$$y = 11 - 11e^x + 9xe^x + 2x - 12x^2 e^x + \frac{1}{2}e^{5x}.$$

36. We have $y_c = c_1 e^{-2x} + e^x(c_2 \cos \sqrt{3}\,x + c_3 \sin \sqrt{3}\,x)$ and we assume $y_p = Ax + B + Cxe^{-2x}$. Substituting into the differential equation we find $A = \frac{1}{4}$, $B = -\frac{5}{8}$, and $C = \frac{2}{3}$. Thus

$$y = c_1 e^{-2x} + e^x(c_2 \cos \sqrt{3}\,x + c_3 \sin \sqrt{3}\,x) + \frac{1}{4}x - \frac{5}{8} + \frac{2}{3}xe^{-2x}.$$

From the initial conditions we obtain $c_1 = -\frac{23}{12}$, $c_2 = -\frac{59}{24}$, and $c_3 = \frac{17}{72}\sqrt{3}$, so

$$y = -\frac{23}{12}e^{-2x} + e^x\left(-\frac{59}{24}\cos\sqrt{3}\,x + \frac{17}{72}\sqrt{3}\sin\sqrt{3}\,x\right) + \frac{1}{4}x - \frac{5}{8} + \frac{2}{3}xe^{-2x}.$$

37. We have $y_c = c_1\cos x + c_2\sin x$ and we assume $y_p = Ax^2 + Bx + C$. Substituting into the differential equation we find $A = 1$, $B = 0$, and $C = -1$. Thus $y = c_1\cos x + c_2\sin x + x^2 - 1$. From $y(0) = 5$ and $y(1) = 0$ we obtain

$$c_1 - 1 = 5$$

$$(\cos 1)c_1 + (\sin 1)c_2 = 0.$$

Solving this system we find $c_1 = 6$ and $c_2 = -6\cot 1$. The solution of the boundary-value problem is

$$y = 6\cos x - 6(\cot 1)\sin x + x^2 - 1.$$

38. We have $y_c = e^x(c_1\cos x + c_2\sin x)$ and we assume $y_p = Ax + B$. Substituting into the differential equation we find $A = 1$ and $B = 0$. Thus $y = e^x(c_1\cos x + c_2\sin x) + x$. From $y(0) = 0$ and $y(\pi) = \pi$ we obtain

$$c_1 = 0$$

$$\pi - e^\pi c_1 = \pi.$$

Solving this system we find $c_1 = 0$ and c_2 is any real number. The solution of the boundary-value problem is

$$y = c_2 e^x \sin x + x.$$

39. The general solution of the differential equation $y'' + 3y = 6x$ is $y = c_1\cos\sqrt{3}x + c_2\sin\sqrt{3}x + 2x$. The condition $y(0) = 0$ implies $c_1 = 0$ and so $y = c_2\sin\sqrt{3}x + 2x$. The condition $y(1) + y'(1) = 0$ implies $c_2\sin\sqrt{3} + 2 + c_2\sqrt{3}\cos\sqrt{3} + 2 = 0$ so $c_2 = -4/(\sin\sqrt{3} + \sqrt{3}\cos\sqrt{3})$. The solution is

$$y = \frac{-4\sin\sqrt{3}x}{\sin\sqrt{3} + \sqrt{3}\cos\sqrt{3}} + 2x.$$

40. Using the general solution $y = c_1\cos\sqrt{3}x + c_2\sin\sqrt{3}x + 2x$, the boundary conditions $y(0) + y'(0) = 0$, $y(1) = 0$ yield the system

$$c_1 + \sqrt{3}c_2 + 2 = 0$$

$$c_1\cos\sqrt{3} + c_2\sin\sqrt{3} + 2 = 0.$$

Solving gives

$$c_1 = \frac{2(-\sqrt{3} + \sin\sqrt{3})}{\sqrt{3}\cos\sqrt{3} - \sin\sqrt{3}} \quad \text{and} \quad c_2 = \frac{2(1 - \cos\sqrt{3})}{\sqrt{3}\cos\sqrt{3} - \sin\sqrt{3}}.$$

Thus,

$$y = \frac{2(-\sqrt{3} + \sin\sqrt{3}\,)\cos\sqrt{3}x}{\sqrt{3}\cos\sqrt{3} - \sin\sqrt{3}} + \frac{2(1 - \cos\sqrt{3}\,)\sin\sqrt{3}x}{\sqrt{3}\cos\sqrt{3} - \sin\sqrt{3}} + 2x.$$

41. We have $y_c = c_1\cos 2x + c_2\sin 2x$ and we assume $y_p = A\cos x + B\sin x$ on $[0, \pi/2]$. Substituting into the differential equation we find $A = 0$ and $B = \frac{1}{3}$. Thus $y = c_1\cos 2x + c_2\sin 2x + \frac{1}{3}\sin x$ on $[0, \pi/2]$. On $(\pi/2, \infty)$ we have $y = c_3\cos 2x + c_4\sin 2x$. From $y(0) = 1$ and $y'(0) = 2$ we obtain

$$c_1 = 1$$

$$\frac{1}{3} + 2c_2 = 2.$$

Solving this system we find $c_1 = 1$ and $c_2 = \frac{5}{6}$. Thus $y = \cos 2x + \frac{5}{6}\sin 2x + \frac{1}{3}\sin x$ on $[0, \pi/2]$. Now continuity of y at $x = \pi/2$ implies

$$\cos\pi + \frac{5}{6}\sin\pi + \frac{1}{3}\sin\frac{\pi}{2} = c_3\cos\pi + c_4\sin\pi$$

or $-1 + \frac{1}{3} = -c_3$. Hence $c_3 = \frac{2}{3}$. Continuity of y' at $x = \pi/2$ implies

$$-2\sin\pi + \frac{5}{3}\cos\pi + \frac{1}{3}\cos\frac{\pi}{2} = -2c_3\sin\pi + 2c_4\cos\pi$$

or $-\frac{5}{3} = -2c_4$. Then $c_4 = \frac{5}{6}$ and the solution of the initial-value problem is

$$y(x) = \begin{cases} \cos 2x + \frac{5}{6}\sin 2x + \frac{1}{3}\sin x, & 0 \le x \le \pi/2 \\ \frac{2}{3}\cos 2x + \frac{5}{6}\sin 2x, & x > \pi/2. \end{cases}$$

42. We have $y_c = e^x(c_1\cos 3x + c_2\sin 3x)$ and we assume $y_p = A$ on $[0, \pi]$. Substituting into the differential equation we find $A = 2$. Thus, $y = e^x(c_1\cos 3x + c_2\sin 3x) + 2$ on $[0, \pi]$. On (π, ∞) we have $y = e^x(c_3\cos 3x + c_4\sin 3x)$. From $y(0) = 0$ and $y'(0) = 0$ we obtain

$$c_1 = -2, \qquad c_1 + 3c_2 = 0.$$

Solving this system, we find $c_1 = -2$ and $c_2 = \frac{2}{3}$. Thus $y = e^x(-2\cos 3x + \frac{2}{3}\sin 3x) + 2$ on $[0, \pi]$. Now, continuity of y at $x = \pi$ implies

$$e^\pi(-2\cos 3\pi + \frac{2}{3}\sin 3\pi) + 2 = e^\pi(c_3\cos 3\pi + c_4\sin 3\pi)$$

or $2 + 2e^\pi = -c_3 e^\pi$ or $c_3 = -2e^{-\pi}(1 + e^\pi)$. Continuity of y' at π implies

$$\frac{20}{3}e^\pi\sin 3\pi = e^\pi[(c_3 + 3c_4)\cos 3\pi + (-3c_3 + c_4)\sin 3\pi]$$

or $-c_3 e^\pi - 3c_4 e^\pi = 0$. Since $c_3 = -2e^{-\pi}(1 + e^\pi)$ we have $c_4 = \frac{2}{3}e^{-\pi}(1 + e^\pi)$. The solution of the initial-value problem is

$$y(x) = \begin{cases} e^x(-2\cos 3x + \frac{2}{3}\sin 3x) + 2, & 0 \le x \le \pi \\ (1 + e^\pi)e^{x-\pi}(-2\cos 3x + \frac{2}{3}\sin 3x), & x > \pi. \end{cases}$$

Exercises 4.4 Undetermined Coefficients – Superposition Approach

43. (a) From $y_p = Ae^{kx}$ we find $y_p' = Ake^{kx}$ and $y_p'' = Ak^2e^{kx}$. Substituting into the differential equation we get

$$aAk^2e^{kx} + bAke^{kx} + cAe^{kx} = (ak^2 + bk + c)Ae^{kx} = e^{kx},$$

so $(ak^2 + bk + c)A = 1$. Since k is not a root of $am^2 + bm + c = 0$, $A = 1/(ak^2 + bk + c)$.

(b) From $y_p = Axe^{kx}$ we find $y_p' = Akxe^{kx} + Ae^{kx}$ and $y_p'' = Ak^2xe^{kx} + 2Ake^{kx}$. Substituting into the differential equation we get

$$aAk^2xe^{kx} + 2aAke^{kx} + bAkxe^{kx} + bAe^{kx} + cAxe^{kx}$$

$$= (ak^2 + bk + c)Axe^{kx} + (2ak + b)Ae^{kx}$$

$$= (0)Axe^{kx} + (2ak + b)Ae^{kx} = (2ak + b)Ae^{kx} = e^{kx}$$

where $ak^2 + bk + c = 0$ because k is a root of the auxiliary equation. Now, the roots of the auxiliary equation are $-b/2a \pm \sqrt{b^2 - 4ac}/2a$, and since k is a root of multiplicity one, $k \neq -b/2a$ and $2ak + b \neq 0$. Thus $(2ak + b)A = 1$ and $A = 1/(2ak + b)$.

(c) If k is a root of multiplicity two, then, as we saw in part (b), $k = -b/2a$ and $2ak + b = 0$. From $y_p = Ax^2e^{kx}$ we find $y_p' = Akx^2e^{kx} + 2Axe^{kx}$ and $y_p'' = Ak^2x^2e^{kx} + 4Akxe^{kx} = 2Ae^{kx}$. Substituting into the differential equation, we get

$$aAk^2x^2e^{kx} + 4aAkxe^{kx} + 2aAe^{kx} + bAkx^2e^{kx} + 2bAxe^{kx} + cAx^2e^{kx}$$

$$= (ak^2 + bk + c)Ax^2e^{kx} + 2(2ak + b)Axe^{kx} + 2aAe^{kx}$$

$$= (0)Ax^2e^{kx} + 2(0)Axe^{kx} + 2aAe^{kx} = 2aAe^{kx} = e^{kx}.$$

Since the differential equation is second order, $a \neq 0$ and $A = 1/(2a)$.

44. Using the double-angle formula for the cosine, we have

$$\sin x \cos 2x = \sin x(\cos^2 x - \sin^2 x) = \sin x(1 - 2\sin^2 x) = \sin x - 2\sin^3 x.$$

Since $\sin x$ is a solution of the related homogeneous differential equation we look for a particular solution of the form $y_p = Ax\sin x + Bx\cos x + C\sin^3 x$. Substituting into the differential equation we obtain

$$2A\cos x + (6C - 2B)\sin x - 8C\sin^3 x = \sin x - 2\sin^3 x.$$

Equating coefficients we find $A = 0$, $C = \frac{1}{4}$, and $B = \frac{1}{4}$. Thus, a particular solution is

$$y_p = \frac{1}{4}x\cos x + \frac{1}{4}\sin^3 x.$$

45. (a) $f(x) = e^x \sin x$. We see that $y_p \to \infty$ as $x \to \infty$ and $y_p \to 0$ as $x \to -\infty$.

(b) $f(x) = e^{-x}$. We see that $y_p \to \infty$ as $x \to \infty$ and $y_p \to \infty$ as $x \to -\infty$.

(c) $f(x) = \sin 2x$. We see that y_p is sinusoidal.

(d) $f(x) = 1$. We see that y_p is constant and simply translates y_c vertically.

46. The complementary function is $y_c = e^{2x}(c_1 \cos 2x + c_2 \sin 2x)$. We assume a particular solution of the form $y_p = (Ax^3 + Bx^2 + Cx)e^{2x} \cos 2x + (Dx^3 + Ex^2 + F)e^{2x} \sin 2x$. Substituting into the differential equation and using a CAS to simplify yields

$$[12Dx^2 + (6A + 8E)x + (2B + 4F)]e^{2x} \cos 2x$$

$$+ [-12Ax^2 + (-8B + 6D)x + (-4C + 2E)]e^{2x} \sin 2x$$

$$= (2x^2 - 3x)e^{2x} \cos 2x + (10x^2 - x - 1)e^{2x} \sin 2x.$$

This gives the system of equations

$$12D = 2, \qquad 6A + 8E = -3, \qquad 2B + 4F = 0,$$

$$-12A = 10, \qquad -8B + 6D = -1, \qquad -4C + 2E = -1,$$

from which we find $A = -\frac{5}{6}$, $B = \frac{1}{4}$, $C = \frac{3}{8}$, $D = \frac{1}{6}$, $E = \frac{1}{4}$, and $F = -\frac{1}{8}$. Thus, a particular solution of the differential equation is

$$y_p = \left(-\frac{5}{6}x^3 + \frac{1}{4}x^2 + \frac{3}{8}x\right)e^{2x} \cos 2x + \left(\frac{1}{6}x^3 + \frac{1}{4}x^2 - \frac{1}{8}x\right)e^{2x} \sin 2x.$$

47. The complementary function is $y_c = c_1 \cos x + c_2 \sin x + c_3 x \cos x + c_4 x \sin x$. We assume a particular solution of the form $y_p = Ax^2 \cos x + Bx^3 \sin x$. Substituting into the differential equation and using a CAS to simplify yields

$$(-8A + 24B) \cos x + 3Bx \sin x = 2 \cos x - 3x \sin x.$$

This implies $-8A + 24B = 2$ and $-24B = -3$. Thus $B = \frac{1}{8}$, $A = \frac{1}{8}$, and $y_p = \frac{1}{8}x^2 \cos x + \frac{1}{8}x^3 \sin x$.

Exercises 4.5

Undetermined Coefficients - Annihilator Approach

1. $(9D^2 - 4)y = (3D - 2)(3D + 2)y = \sin x$

2. $(D^2 - 5)y = (D - \sqrt{5})(D + \sqrt{5})y = x^2 - 2x$

3. $(D^2 - 4D - 12)y = (D - 6)(D + 2)y = x - 6$

4. $(2D^2 - 3D - 2)y = (2D + 1)(D - 2)y = 1$

5. $(D^3 + 10D^2 + 25D)y = D(D + 5)^2 y = e^x$

6. $(D^3 + 4D)y = D(D^2 + 4)y = e^x \cos 2x$

7. $(D^3 + 2D^2 - 13D + 10)y = (D-1)(D-2)(D+5)y = xe^{-x}$

8. $(D^3 + 4D^2 + 3D)y = D(D+1)(D+3)y = x^2 \cos x - 3x$

9. $(D^4 + 8D)y = D(D+2)(D^2 - 2D + 4)y = 4$

10. $(D^4 - 8D^2 + 16)y = (D-2)^2(D+2)^2 y = (x^3 - 2x)e^{4x}$

11. $D^4 y = D^4(10x^3 - 2x) = D^3(30x^2 - 2) = D^2(60x) = D(60) = 0$

12. $(2D-1)y = (2D-1)4e^{x/2} = 8De^{x/2} - 4e^{x/2} = 4e^{x/2} - 4e^{x/2} = 0$

13. $(D-2)(D+5)(e^{2x} + 3e^{-5x}) = (D-2)(2e^{2x} - 15e^{-5x} + 5e^{2x} + 15e^{-5x}) = (D-2)7e^{2x} = 14e^{2x} - 14e^{2x} = 0$

14. $(D^2 + 64)(2\cos 8x - 5\sin 8x) = D(-16\sin 8x - 40\cos 8x) + 64(2\cos 8x - 5\sin 8x)$

$$= -128\cos 8x + 320\sin 8x + 128\cos 8x - 320\sin 8x = 0$$

15. D^4 because of x^3

16. D^5 because of x^4

17. $D(D-2)$ because of 1 and e^{2x}

18. $D^2(D-6)^2$ because of x and xe^{6x}

19. $D^2 + 4$ because of $\cos 2x$

20. $D(D^2 + 1)$ because of 1 and $\sin x$

21. $D^3(D^2 + 16)$ because of x^2 and $\sin 4x$

22. $D^2(D^2 + 1)(D^2 + 25)$ because of x, $\sin x$, and $\cos 5x$

23. $(D+1)(D-1)^3$ because of e^{-x} and $x^2 e^x$

24. $D(D-1)(D-2)$ because of 1, e^x, and e^{2x}

25. $D(D^2 - 2D + 5)$ because of 1 and $e^x \cos 2x$

26. $(D^2 + 2D + 2)(D^2 - 4D + 5)$ because of $e^{-x}\sin x$ and $e^{2x}\cos x$

27. 1, x, x^2, x^3, x^4

28. $D^2 + 4D = D(D+4)$; 1, e^{-4x}

29. e^{6x}, $e^{-3x/2}$

30. $D^2 - 9D - 36 = (D-12)(D+3)$; e^{12x}, e^{-3x}

31. $\cos\sqrt{5}\,x$, $\sin\sqrt{5}\,x$

32. $D^2 - 6D + 10 = D^2 - 2(3)D + (3^2 + 1^2)$; $e^{3x}\cos x$, $e^{3x}\sin x$

33. $D^3 - 10D^2 + 25D = D(D-5)^2$; 1, e^{5x}, xe^{5x}

34. 1, x, e^{5x}, e^{7x}

35. Applying D to the differential equation we obtain

$$D(D^2 - 9)y = 0.$$

166

Then

$$y = \underbrace{c_1 e^{3x} + c_2 e^{-3x}}_{y_c} + c_3$$

and $y_p = A$. Substituting y_p into the differential equation yields $-9A = 54$ or $A = -6$. The general solution is

$$y = c_1 e^{3x} + c_2 e^{-3x} - 6.$$

36. Applying D to the differential equation we obtain

$$D(2D^2 - 7D + 5)y = 0.$$

Then

$$y = \underbrace{c_1 e^{5x/2} + c_2 e^x}_{y_c} + c_3$$

and $y_p = A$. Substituting y_p into the differential equation yields $5A = -29$ or $A = -29/5$. The general solution is

$$y = c_1 e^{5x/2} + c_2 e^x - \frac{29}{5}.$$

37. Applying D to the differential equation we obtain

$$D(D^2 + D)y = D^2(D + 1)y = 0.$$

Then

$$y = \underbrace{c_1 + c_2 e^{-x}}_{y_c} + c_3 x$$

and $y_p = Ax$. Substituting y_p into the differential equation yields $A = 3$. The general solution is

$$y = c_1 + c_2 e^{-3x} + 3x.$$

38. Applying D to the differential equation we obtain

$$D(D^3 + 2D^2 + D)y = D^2(D + 1)^2 y = 0.$$

Then

$$y = \underbrace{c_1 + c_2 e^{-x} + c_3 x e^{-x}}_{y_c} + c_4 x$$

and $y_p = Ax$. Substituting y_p into the differential equation yields $A = 10$. The general solution is

$$y = c_1 + c_2 e^{-x} + c_3 x e^{-x} + 10x.$$

39. Applying D^2 to the differential equation we obtain

$$D^2(D^2 + 4D + 4)y = D^2(D + 2)^2 y = 0.$$

Then

$$y = \underbrace{c_1 e^{-2x} + c_2 x e^{-2x}}_{y_c} + c_3 + c_4 x$$

and $y_p = Ax + B$. Substituting y_p into the differential equation yields $4Ax + (4A + 4B) = 2x + 6$. Equating coefficients gives

$$4A = 2$$

$$4A + 4B = 6.$$

Then $A = 1/2$, $B = 1$, and the general solution is

$$y = c_1 e^{-2x} + c_2 x e^{-2x} + \frac{1}{2}x + 1.$$

40. Applying D^2 to the differential equation we obtain

$$D^2(D^2 + 3D)y = D^3(D + 3)y = 0.$$

Then

$$y = \underbrace{c_1 + c_2 e^{-3x}}_{y_c} + c_3 x^2 + c_4 x$$

and $y_p = Ax^2 + Bx$. Substituting y_p into the differential equation yields $6Ax + (2A + 3B) = 4x - 5$. Equating coefficients gives

$$6A = 4$$

$$2A + 3B = -5.$$

Then $A = 2/3$, $B = -19/9$, and the general solution is

$$y = c_1 + c_2 e^{-3x} + \frac{2}{3}x^2 - \frac{19}{9}x.$$

41. Applying D^3 to the differential equation we obtain

$$D^3(D^3 + D^2)y = D^5(D + 1)y = 0.$$

Then

$$y = \underbrace{c_1 + c_2 x + c_3 e^{-x}}_{y_c} + c_4 x^4 + c_5 x^3 + c_6 x^2$$

and $y_p = Ax^4 + Bx^3 + Cx^2$. Substituting y_p into the differential equation yields

$$12Ax^2 + (24A + 6B)x + (6B + 2C) = 8x^2.$$

Equating coefficients gives

$$12A = 8$$

$$24A + 6B = 0$$

$$6B + 2C = 0.$$

Then $A = 2/3$, $B = -8/3$, $C = 8$, and the general solution is

$$y = c_1 + c_2 x + c_3 e^{-x} + \frac{2}{3}x^4 - \frac{8}{3}x^3 + 8x^2.$$

42. Applying D^4 to the differential equation we obtain

$$D^4(D^2 - 2D + 1)y = D^4(D - 1)^2 y = 0.$$

Then

$$y = \underbrace{c_1 e^x + c_2 x e^x}_{y_c} + c_3 x^3 + c_4 x^2 + c_5 x + c_6$$

and $y_p = Ax^3 + Bx^2 + Cx + E$. Substituting y_p into the differential equation yields

$$Ax^3 + (B - 6A)x^2 + (6A - 4B + C)x + (2B - 2C + E) = x^3 + 4x.$$

Equating coefficients gives

$$A = 1$$

$$B - 6A = 0$$

$$6A - 4B + C = 4$$

$$2B - 2C + E = 0.$$

Then $A = 1$, $B = 6$, $C = 22$, $E = 32$, and the general solution is

$$y = c_1 e^x + c_2 x e^x + x^3 + 6x^2 + 22x + 32.$$

43. Applying $D - 4$ to the differential equation we obtain

$$(D - 4)(D^2 - D - 12)y = (D - 4)^2(D + 3)y = 0.$$

Then

$$y = \underbrace{c_1 e^{4x} + c_2 e^{-3x}}_{y_c} + c_3 x e^{4x}$$

and $y_p = Axe^{4x}$. Substituting y_p into the differential equation yields $7Ae^{4x} = e^{4x}$. Equating coefficients gives $A = 1/7$. The general solution is

$$y = c_1 e^{4x} + c_2 e^{-3x} + \frac{1}{7}xe^{4x}.$$

44. Applying $D - 6$ to the differential equation we obtain

$$(D - 6)(D^2 + 2D + 2)y = 0.$$

Then

$$y = \underbrace{e^{-x}(c_1 \cos x + c_2 \sin x)}_{y_c} + c_3 e^{6x}$$

and $y_p = Ae^{6x}$. Substituting y_p into the differential equation yields $50Ae^{6x} = 5e^{6x}$. Equating coefficients gives $A = 1/10$. The general solution is

$$y = e^{-x}(c_1 \cos x + c_2 \sin x) + \frac{1}{10}e^{6x}.$$

45. Applying $D(D-1)$ to the differential equation we obtain

$$D(D-1)(D^2 - 2D - 3)y = D(D-1)(D+1)(D-3)y = 0.$$

Then

$$y = \underbrace{c_1 e^{3x} + c_2 e^{-x}}_{y_c} + c_3 e^x + c_4$$

and $y_p = Ae^x + B$. Substituting y_p into the differential equation yields $-4Ae^x - 3B = 4e^x - 9$. Equating coefficients gives $A = -1$ and $B = 3$. The general solution is

$$y = c_1 e^{3x} + c_2 e^{-x} - e^x + 3.$$

46. Applying $D^2(D+2)$ to the differential equation we obtain

$$D^2(D+2)(D^2 + 6D + 8)y = D^2(D+2)^2(D+4)y = 0.$$

Then

$$y = \underbrace{c_1 e^{-2x} + c_2 e^{-4x}}_{y_c} + c_3 x e^{-2x} + c_4 x + c_5$$

and $y_p = Axe^{-2x} + Bx + C$. Substituting y_p into the differential equation yields

$$2Ae^{-2x} + 8Bx + (6B + 8C) = 3e^{-2x} + 2x.$$

Equating coefficients gives

$$2A = 3$$

$$8B = 2$$

$$6B + 8C = 0.$$

Then $A = 3/2$, $B = 1/4$, $C = -3/16$, and the general solution is

$$y = c_1 e^{-2x} + c_2 e^{-4x} + \frac{3}{2}xe^{-2x} + \frac{1}{4}x - \frac{3}{16}.$$

47. Applying $D^2 + 1$ to the differential equation we obtain

$$(D^2 + 1)(D^2 + 25)y = 0.$$

Then

$$y = \underbrace{c_1 \cos 5x + c_2 \sin 5x}_{y_c} + c_3 \cos x + c_4 \sin x$$

and $y_p = A\cos x + B\sin x$. Substituting y_p into the differential equation yields

$$24A\cos x + 24B\sin x = 6\sin x.$$

Equating coefficients gives $A = 0$ and $B = 1/4$. The general solution is

$$y = c_1\cos 5x + c_2\sin 5x + \frac{1}{4}\sin x.$$

48. Applying $D(D^2 + 1)$ to the differential equation we obtain

$$D(D^2 + 1)(D^2 + 4)y = 0.$$

Then

$$y = \underbrace{c_1\cos 2x + c_2\sin 2x}_{y_c} + c_3\cos x + c_4\sin x + c_5$$

and $y_p = A\cos x + B\sin x + C$. Substituting y_p into the differential equation yields

$$3A\cos x + 3B\sin x + 4C = 4\cos x + 3\sin x - 8.$$

Equating coefficients gives $A = 4/3$, $B = 1$, and $C = -2$. The general solution is

$$y = c_1\cos 2x + c_2\sin 2x + \frac{4}{3}\cos x + \sin x - 2.$$

49. Applying $(D - 4)^2$ to the differential equation we obtain

$$(D - 4)^2(D^2 + 6D + 9)y = (D - 4)^2(D + 3)^2 y = 0.$$

Then

$$y = \underbrace{c_1 e^{-3x} + c_2 x e^{-3x}}_{y_c} + c_3 x e^{4x} + c_4 e^{4x}$$

and $y_p = Axe^{4x} + Be^{4x}$. Substituting y_p into the differential equation yields

$$49Axe^{4x} + (14A + 49B)e^{4x} = -xe^{4x}.$$

Equating coefficients gives

$$49A = -1$$

$$14A + 49B = 0.$$

Then $A = -1/49$, $B = 2/343$, and the general solution is

$$y = c_1 e^{-3x} + c_2 x e^{-3x} - \frac{1}{49}xe^{4x} + \frac{2}{343}e^{4x}.$$

50. Applying $D^2(D - 1)^2$ to the differential equation we obtain

$$D^2(D - 1)^2(D^2 + 3D - 10)y = D^2(D - 1)^2(D - 2)(D + 5)y = 0.$$

171

Then

$$y = \underbrace{c_1 e^{2x} + c_2 e^{-5x}}_{y_c} + c_3 x e^x + c_4 e^x + c_5 x + c_6$$

and $y_p = Axe^x + Be^x + Cx + E$. Substituting y_p into the differential equation yields

$$-6Axe^x + (5A - 6B)e^x - 10Cx + (3C - 10E) = xe^x + x.$$

Equating coefficients gives

$$-6A = 1$$

$$5A - 6B = 0$$

$$-10C = 1$$

$$3C - 10E = 0.$$

Then $A = -1/6$, $B = -5/36$, $C = -1/10$, $E = -3/100$, and the general solution is

$$y = c_1 e^{2x} + c_2 e^{-5x} - \frac{1}{6}xe^x - \frac{5}{36}e^x - \frac{1}{10}x - \frac{3}{100}.$$

51. Applying $D(D-1)^3$ to the differential equation we obtain

$$D(D-1)^3(D^2 - 1)y = D(D-1)^4(D+1)y = 0.$$

Then

$$y = \underbrace{c_1 e^x + c_2 e^{-x}}_{y_c} + c_3 x^3 e^x + c_4 x^2 e^x + c_5 x e^x + c_6$$

and $y_p = Ax^3 e^x + Bx^2 e^x + Cxe^x + E$. Substituting y_p into the differential equation yields

$$6Ax^2 e^x + (6A + 4B)xe^x + (2B + 2C)e^x - E = x^2 e^x + 5.$$

Equating coefficients gives

$$6A = 1$$

$$6A + 4B = 0$$

$$2B + 2C = 0$$

$$-E = 5.$$

Then $A = 1/6$, $B = -1/4$, $C = 1/4$, $E = -5$, and the general solution is

$$y = c_1 e^x + c_2 e^{-x} + \frac{1}{6}x^3 e^x - \frac{1}{4}x^2 e^x + \frac{1}{4}xe^x - 5.$$

52. Applying $(D+1)^3$ to the differential equation we obtain

$$(D+1)^3(D^2 + 2D + 1)y = (D+1)^5 y = 0.$$

Then

$$y = \underbrace{c_1 e^{-x} + c_2 x e^{-x}}_{y_c} + c_3 x^4 e^{-x} + c_4 x^3 e^{-x} + c_5 x^2 e^{-x}$$

and $y_p = A x^4 e^{-x} + B x^3 e^{-x} + C x^2 e^{-x}$. Substituting y_p into the differential equation yields

$$12 A x^2 e^{-x} + 6 B x e^{-x} + 2 C e^{-x} = x^2 e^{-x}.$$

Equating coefficients gives $A = \frac{1}{12}$, $B = 0$, and $C = 0$. The general solution is

$$y = c_1 e^{-x} + c_2 x e^{-x} + \frac{1}{12} x^4 e^{-x}.$$

53. Applying $D^2 - 2D + 2$ to the differential equation we obtain

$$(D^2 - 2D + 2)(D^2 - 2D + 5)y = 0.$$

Then

$$y = \underbrace{e^x (c_1 \cos 2x + c_2 \sin 2x)}_{y_c} + e^x (c_3 \cos x + c_4 \sin x)$$

and $y_p = A e^x \cos x + B e^x \sin x$. Substituting y_p into the differential equation yields

$$3 A e^x \cos x + 3 B e^x \sin x = e^x \sin x.$$

Equating coefficients gives $A = 0$ and $B = 1/3$. The general solution is

$$y = e^x (c_1 \cos 2x + c_2 \sin 2x) + \frac{1}{3} e^x \sin x.$$

54. Applying $D^2 - 2D + 10$ to the differential equation we obtain

$$(D^2 - 2D + 10)\left(D^2 + D + \frac{1}{4}\right)y = (D^2 - 2D + 10)\left(D + \frac{1}{2}\right)^2 y = 0.$$

Then

$$y = \underbrace{c_1 e^{-x/2} + c_2 x e^{-x/2}}_{y_c} + c_3 e^x \cos 3x + c_4 e^x \sin 3x$$

and $y_p = A e^x \cos 3x + B e^x \sin 3x$. Substituting y_p into the differential equation yields

$$(9B - 27A/4) e^x \cos 3x - (9A + 27B/4) e^x \sin 3x = -e^x \cos 3x + e^x \sin 3x.$$

Equating coefficients gives

$$-\frac{27}{4} A + 9B = -1$$

$$-9A - \frac{27}{4} B = 1.$$

Then $A = -4/225$, $B = -28/225$, and the general solution is

$$y = c_1 e^{-x/2} + c_2 x e^{-x/2} - \frac{4}{225} e^x \cos 3x - \frac{28}{225} e^x \sin 3x.$$

55. Applying $D^2 + 25$ to the differential equation we obtain

$$(D^2 + 25)(D^2 + 25) = (D^2 + 25)^2 = 0.$$

Then

$$y = \underbrace{c_1 \cos 5x + c_2 \sin 5x}_{y_c} + c_3 x \cos 5x + c_4 x \cos 5x$$

and $y_p = Ax \cos 5x + Bx \sin 5x$. Substituting y_p into the differential equation yields

$$10B \cos 5x - 10A \sin 5x = 20 \sin 5x.$$

Equating coefficients gives $A = -2$ and $B = 0$. The general solution is

$$y = c_1 \cos 5x + c_2 \sin 5x - 2x \cos 5x.$$

56. Applying $D^2 + 1$ to the differential equation we obtain

$$(D^2 + 1)(D^2 + 1) = (D^2 + 1)^2 = 0.$$

Then

$$y = \underbrace{c_1 \cos x + c_2 \sin x}_{y_c} + c_3 x \cos x + c_4 x \cos x$$

and $y_p = Ax \cos x + Bx \sin x$. Substituting y_p into the differential equation yields

$$2B \cos x - 2A \sin x = 4 \cos x - \sin x.$$

Equating coefficients gives $A = 1/2$ and $B = 2$. The general solution is

$$y = c_1 \cos x + c_2 \sin x + \frac{1}{2}x \cos x - 2x \sin x.$$

57. Applying $(D^2 + 1)^2$ to the differential equation we obtain

$$(D^2 + 1)^2(D^2 + D + 1) = 0.$$

Then

$$y = e^{-x/2}\underbrace{\left[c_1 \cos \frac{\sqrt{3}}{2}x + c_2 \sin \frac{\sqrt{3}}{2}x\right]}_{y_c} + c_3 \cos x + c_4 \sin x + c_5 x \cos x + c_6 x \sin x$$

and $y_p = A \cos x + B \sin x + Cx \cos x + Ex \sin x$. Substituting y_p into the differential equation yields

$$(B + C + 2E) \cos x + Ex \cos x + (-A - 2C + E) \sin x - Cx \sin x = x \sin x.$$

Equating coefficients gives

$$B + C + 2E = 0$$

$$E = 0$$

$$-A - 2C + E = 0$$

$$-C = 1.$$

174

Then $A = 2$, $B = 1$, $C = -1$, and $E = 0$, and the general solution is

$$y = e^{-x/2}\left[c_1 \cos \frac{\sqrt{3}}{2}x + c_2 \sin \frac{\sqrt{3}}{2}x\right] + 2\cos x + \sin x - x\cos x.$$

58. Writing $\cos^2 x = \frac{1}{2}(1 + \cos 2x)$ and applying $D(D^2 + 4)$ to the differential equation we obtain

$$D(D^2 + 4)(D^2 + 4) = D(D^2 + 4)^2 = 0.$$

Then

$$y = \underbrace{c_1 \cos 2x + c_2 \sin 2x}_{y_c} + c_3 x \cos 2x + c_4 x \sin 2x + c_5$$

and $y_p = Ax\cos 2x + Bx\sin 2x + C$. Substituting y_p into the differential equation yields

$$-4A\sin 2x + 4B\cos 2x + 4C = \frac{1}{2} + \frac{1}{2}\cos 2x.$$

Equating coefficients gives $A = 0$, $B = 1/8$, and $C = 1/8$. The general solution is

$$y = c_1 \cos 2x + c_2 \sin 2x + \frac{1}{8}x\sin 2x + \frac{1}{8}.$$

59. Applying D^3 to the differential equation we obtain

$$D^3(D^3 + 8D^2) = D^5(D + 8) = 0.$$

Then

$$y = \underbrace{c_1 + c_2 x + c_3 e^{-8x}}_{y_c} + c_4 x^2 + c_5 x^3 + c_6 x^4$$

and $y_p = Ax^2 + Bx^3 + Cx^4$. Substituting y_p into the differential equation yields

$$16A + 6B + (48B + 24C)x + 96Cx^2 = 2 + 9x - 6x^2.$$

Equating coefficients gives

$$16A + 6B = 2$$

$$48B + 24C = 9$$

$$96C = -6.$$

Then $A = 11/256$, $B = 7/32$, and $C = -1/16$, and the general solution is

$$y = c_1 + c_2 x + c_3 e^{-8x} + \frac{11}{256}x^2 + \frac{7}{32}x^3 - \frac{1}{16}x^4.$$

60. Applying $D(D-1)^2(D+1)$ to the differential equation we obtain

$$D(D-1)^2(D+1)(D^3 - D^2 + D - 1) = D(D-1)^3(D+1)(D^2+1) = 0.$$

Then

$$y = \underbrace{c_1 e^x + c_2 \cos x + c_3 \sin x}_{y_c} + c_4 + c_5 e^{-x} + c_6 x e^x + c_7 x^2 e^x$$

and $y_p = A + Be^{-x} + Cxe^x + Ex^2e^x$. Substituting y_p into the differential equation yields

$$4Exe^x + (2C + 4E)e^x - 4Be^{-x} - A = xe^x - e^{-x} + 7.$$

Equating coefficients gives

$$4E = 1$$

$$2C + 4E = 0$$

$$-4B = -1$$

$$-A = 7.$$

Then $A = -7$, $B = 1/4$, $C = -1/2$, and $E = 1/4$, and the general solution is

$$y = c_1e^x + c_2\cos x + c_3\sin x - 7 + \frac{1}{4}e^{-x} - \frac{1}{2}xe^x + \frac{1}{4}x^2e^x.$$

61. Applying $D^2(D - 1)$ to the differential equation we obtain

$$D^2(D - 1)(D^3 - 3D^2 + 3D - 1) = D^2(D - 1)^4 = 0.$$

Then

$$y = \underbrace{c_1e^x + c_2xe^x + c_3x^2e^x}_{y_c} + c_4 + c_5x + c_6x^3e^x$$

and $y_p = A + Bx + Cx^3e^x$. Substituting y_p into the differential equation yields

$$(-A + 3B) - Bx + 6Ce^x = 16 - x + e^x.$$

Equating coefficients gives

$$-A + 3B = 16$$

$$-B = -1$$

$$6C = 1.$$

Then $A = -13$, $B = 1$, and $C = 1/6$, and the general solution is

$$y = c_1e^x + c_2xe^x + c_3x^2e^x - 13 + x + \frac{1}{6}x^3e^x.$$

62. Writing $(e^x + e^{-x})^2 = 2 + e^{2x} + e^{-2x}$ and applying $D(D - 2)(D + 2)$ to the differential equation we obtain

$$D(D - 2)(D + 2)(2D^3 - 3D^2 - 3D + 2) = D(D - 2)^2(D + 2)(D + 1)(2D - 1) = 0.$$

Then

$$y = \underbrace{c_1e^{-x} + c_2e^{2x} + c_3e^{x/2}}_{y_c} + c_4 + c_5xe^{2x} + c_6e^{-2x}$$

176

and $y_p = A + Bxe^{2x} + Ce^{-2x}$. Substituting y_p into the differential equation yields

$$2A + 9Be^{2x} - 20Ce^{-2x} = 2 + e^{2x} + e^{-2x}.$$

Equating coefficients gives $A = 1$, $B = 1/9$, and $C = -1/20$. The general solution is

$$y = c_1 e^{-x} + c_2 e^{2x} + c_3 e^{x/2} + 1 + \frac{1}{9}xe^{2x} - \frac{1}{20}e^{-2x}.$$

63. Applying $D(D-1)$ to the differential equation we obtain

$$D(D-1)(D^4 - 2D^3 + D^2) = D^3(D-1)^3 = 0.$$

Then

$$y = \underbrace{c_1 + c_2 x + c_3 e^x + c_4 xe^x}_{y_c} + c_5 x^2 + c_6 x^2 e^x$$

and $y_p = Ax^2 + Bx^2 e^x$. Substituting y_p into the differential equation yields $2A + 2Be^x = 1 + e^x$. Equating coefficients gives $A = 1/2$ and $B = 1/2$. The general solution is

$$y = c_1 + c_2 x + c_3 e^x + c_4 xe^x + \frac{1}{2}x^2 + \frac{1}{2}x^2 e^x.$$

64. Applying $D^3(D-2)$ to the differential equation we obtain

$$D^3(D-2)(D^4 - 4D^2) = D^5(D-2)^2(D+2) = 0.$$

Then

$$y = \underbrace{c_1 + c_2 x + c_3 e^{2x} + c_4 e^{-2x}}_{y_c} + c_5 x^2 + c_6 x^3 + c_7 x^4 + c_8 xe^{2x}$$

and $y_p = Ax^2 + Bx^3 + Cx^4 + Exe^{2x}$. Substituting y_p into the differential equation yields

$$(-8A + 24C) - 24Bx - 48Cx^2 + 16Ee^{2x} = 5x^2 - e^{2x}.$$

Equating coefficients gives

$$-8A + 24C = 0$$

$$-24B = 0$$

$$-48C = 5$$

$$16E = -1.$$

Then $A = -5/16$, $B = 0$, $C = -5/48$, and $E = -1/16$, and the general solution is

$$y = c_1 + c_2 x + c_3 e^{2x} + c_4 e^{-2x} - \frac{5}{16}x^2 - \frac{5}{48}x^4 - \frac{1}{16}xe^{2x}.$$

65. The complementary function is $y_c = c_1 e^{8x} + c_2 e^{-8x}$. Using D to annihilate 16 we find $y_p = A$. Substituting y_p into the differential equation we obtain $-64A = 16$. Thus $A = -1/4$ and

$$y = c_1 e^{8x} + c_2 e^{-8x} - \frac{1}{4}$$

$$y' = 8c_1 e^{8x} - 8c_2 e^{-8x}.$$

The initial conditions imply

$$c_1 + c_2 = \frac{5}{4}$$

$$8c_1 - 8c_2 = 0.$$

Thus $c_1 = c_2 = 5/8$ and

$$y = \frac{5}{8} e^{8x} + \frac{5}{8} e^{-8x} - \frac{1}{4}.$$

66. The complementary function is $y_c = c_1 + c_2 e^{-x}$. Using D^2 to annihilate x we find $y_p = Ax + Bx^2$. Substituting y_p into the differential equation we obtain $(A + 2B) + 2Bx = x$. Thus $A = -1$ and $B = 1/2$, and

$$y = c_1 + c_2 e^{-x} - x + \frac{1}{2} x^2$$

$$y' = -c_2 e^{-x} - 1 + x.$$

The initial conditions imply

$$c_1 + c_2 = 1$$

$$-c_2 = 1.$$

Thus $c_1 = 2$ and $c_2 = -1$, and

$$y = 2 - e^{-x} - x + \frac{1}{2} x^2.$$

67. The complementary function is $y_c = c_1 + c_2 e^{5x}$. Using D^2 to annihilate $x - 2$ we find $y_p = Ax + Bx^2$. Substituting y_p into the differential equation we obtain $(-5A + 2B) - 10Bx = -2 + x$. Thus $A = 9/25$ and $B = -1/10$, and

$$y = c_1 + c_2 e^{5x} + \frac{9}{25} x - \frac{1}{10} x^2$$

$$y' = 5c_2 e^{5x} + \frac{9}{25} - \frac{1}{5} x.$$

The initial conditions imply

$$c_1 + c_2 = 0$$

$$c_2 = \frac{41}{125}.$$

Thus $c_1 = -41/125$ and $c_2 = 41/125$, and

$$y = -\frac{41}{125} + \frac{41}{125}e^{5x} + \frac{9}{25}x - \frac{1}{10}x^2.$$

68. The complementary function is $y_c = c_1 e^x + c_2 e^{-6x}$. Using $D - 2$ to annihilate $10e^{2x}$ we find $y_p = Ae^{2x}$. Substituting y_p into the differential equation we obtain $8Ae^{2x} = 10e^{2x}$. Thus $A = 5/4$ and

$$y = c_1 e^x + c_2 e^{-6x} + \frac{5}{4}e^{2x}$$

$$y' = c_1 e^x - 6c_2 e^{-6x} + \frac{5}{2}e^{2x}.$$

The initial conditions imply

$$c_1 + c_2 = -\frac{1}{4}$$

$$c_1 - 6c_2 = -\frac{3}{2}.$$

Thus $c_1 = -3/7$ and $c_2 = 5/28$, and

$$y = -\frac{3}{7}e^x + \frac{5}{28}e^{-6x} + \frac{5}{4}e^{2x}$$

69. The complementary function is $y_c = c_1 \cos x + c_2 \sin x$. Using $(D^2 + 1)(D^2 + 4)$ to annihilate $8 \cos 2x - 4 \sin x$ we find $y_p = Ax \cos x + Bx \sin x + C \cos 2x + E \sin 2x$. Substituting y_p into the differential equation we obtain $2B \cos x - 3C \cos 2x - 2A \sin x - 3E \sin 2x = 8 \cos 2x - 4 \sin x$. Thus $A = 2$, $B = 0$, $C = -8/3$, and $E = 0$, and

$$y = c_1 \cos x + c_2 \sin x + 2x \cos x - \frac{8}{3} \cos 2x$$

$$y' = -c_1 \sin x + c_2 \cos x + 2 \cos x - 2x \sin x + \frac{16}{3} \sin 2x.$$

The initial conditions imply

$$c_2 + \frac{8}{3} = -1$$

$$-c_1 - \pi = 0.$$

Thus $c_1 = -\pi$ and $c_2 = -11/3$, and

$$y = -\pi \cos x - \frac{11}{3} \sin x + 2x \cos x - \frac{8}{3} \cos 2x.$$

70. The complementary function is $y_c = c_1 + c_2 e^x + c_3 x e^x$. Using $D(D - 1)^2$ to annihilate $xe^x + 5$ we find $y_p = Ax + Bx^2 e^x + Cx^3 e^x$. Substituting y_p into the differential equation we obtain

179

Exercises 4.5   Undetermined Coefficients - Annihilator Approach

$A + (2B + 6C)e^x + 6Cxe^x = xe^x + 5$. Thus $A = 5$, $B = -1/2$, and $C = 1/6$, and

$$y = c_1 + c_2 e^x + c_3 xe^x + 5x - \frac{1}{2}x^2 e^x + \frac{1}{6}x^3 e^x$$

$$y' = c_2 e^x + c_3(xe^x + e^x) + 5 - xe^x + \frac{1}{6}x^3 e^x$$

$$y'' = c_2 e^x + c_3(xe^x + 2e^x) - e^x - xe^x + \frac{1}{2}x^2 e^x + \frac{1}{6}x^3 e^x.$$

The initial conditions imply

$$c_1 + c_2 = 2$$

$$c_2 + c_3 + 5 = 2$$

$$c_2 + 2c_3 - 1 = -1.$$

Thus $c_1 = 8$, $c_2 = -6$, and $c_3 = 3$, and

$$y = 8 - 6e^x + 3xe^x + 5x - \frac{1}{2}x^2 e^x + \frac{1}{6}x^3 e^x.$$

71. The complementary function is $y_c = e^{2x}(c_1 \cos 2x + c_2 \sin 2x)$. Using D^4 to annihilate x^3 we find $y_p = A + Bx + Cx^2 + Ex^3$. Substituting y_p into the differential equation we obtain $(8A - 4B + 2C) + (8B - 8C + 6E)x + (8C - 12E)x^2 + 8Ex^3 = x^3$. Thus $A = 0$, $B = 3/32$, $C = 3/16$, and $E = 1/8$, and

$$y = e^{2x}(c_1 \cos 2x + c_2 \sin 2x) + \frac{3}{32}x + \frac{3}{16}x^2 + \frac{1}{8}x^3$$

$$y' = e^{2x}[c_1(2\cos 2x - 2\sin 2x) + c_2(2\cos 2x + 2\sin 2x)] + \frac{3}{32} + \frac{3}{8}x + \frac{3}{8}x^2.$$

The initial conditions imply

$$c_1 = 2$$

$$2c_1 + 2c_2 + \frac{3}{32} = 4.$$

Thus $c_1 = 2$, $c_2 = -3/64$, and

$$y = e^{2x}\left(2\cos 2x - \frac{3}{64}\sin 2x\right) + \frac{3}{32}x + \frac{3}{16}x^2 + \frac{1}{8}x^3.$$

72. The complementary function is $y_c = c_1 + c_2 x + c_3 x^2 + c_4 e^x$. Using $D^2(D - 1)$ to annihilate $x + e^x$ we find $y_p = Ax^3 + Bx^4 + Cxe^x$. Substituting y_p into the differential equation we obtain

$(-6A + 24B) - 24Bx + Ce^x = x + e^x$. Thus $A = -1/6$, $B = -1/24$, and $C = 1$, and

$$y = c_1 + c_2 x + c_3 x^2 + c_4 e^x - \frac{1}{6} x^3 - \frac{1}{24} x^4 + x e^x$$

$$y' = c_2 + 2c_3 x + c_4 e^x - \frac{1}{2} x^2 - \frac{1}{6} x^3 + e^x + x e^x$$

$$y'' = 2c_3 + c_4 e^x - x - \frac{1}{2} x^2 + 2e^x + x e^x.$$

$$y''' = c_4 e^x - 1 - x + 3e^x + x e^x$$

The initial conditions imply

$$c_1 + c_4 = 0$$

$$c_2 + c_4 + 1 = 0$$

$$2c_3 + c_4 + 2 = 0$$

$$2 + c_4 = 0.$$

Thus $c_1 = 2$, $c_2 = 1$, $c_3 = 0$, and $c_4 = -2$, and

$$y = 2 + x - 2e^x - \frac{1}{6} x^3 - \frac{1}{24} x^4 + x e^x.$$

73. To see in this case that the factors of L do not commute consider the operators $(xD - 1)(D + 4)$ and $(D + 4)(xD - 1)$. Applying the operators to the function x we find

$$(xD - 1)(D + 4)x = (xD^2 + 4xD - D - 4)x$$

$$= xD^2 x + 4xDx - Dx - 4x$$

$$= x(0) + 4x(1) - 1 - 4x = -1$$

and

$$(D + 4)(xD - 1)x = (D + 4)(xDx - x)$$

$$= (D + 4)(x \cdot 1 - x) = 0.$$

Thus, the operators are not the same.

Exercises 4.6   Variation of Parameters

The particular solution, $y_p = u_1 y_1 + u_2 y_2$, in the following problems can take on a variety of forms, especially where trigonometric functions are involved. The validity of a particular form can best be checked by substituting it back into the differential equation.

1. The auxiliary equation is $m^2 + 1 = 0$, so $y_c = c_1 \cos x + c_2 \sin x$ and

$$W = \begin{vmatrix} \cos x & \sin x \\ -\sin x & \cos x \end{vmatrix} = 1.$$

Identifying $f(x) = \sec x$ we obtain

$$u_1' = -\frac{\sin x \sec x}{1} = -\tan x$$

$$u_2' = \frac{\cos x \sec x}{1} = 1.$$

Then $u_1 = \ln|\cos x|$, $u_2 = x$, and

$$y = c_1 \cos x + c_2 \sin x + \cos x \ln|\cos x| + x \sin x.$$

2. The auxiliary equation is $m^2 + 1 = 0$, so $y_c = c_1 \cos x + c_2 \sin x$ and

$$W = \begin{vmatrix} \cos x & \sin x \\ -\sin x & \cos x \end{vmatrix} = 1.$$

Identifying $f(x) = \tan x$ we obtain

$$u_1' = -\sin x \tan x = \frac{\cos^2 x - 1}{\cos x} = \cos x - \sec x$$

$$u_2' = \sin x.$$

Then $u_1 = \sin x - \ln|\sec x + \tan x|$, $u_2 = -\cos x$, and

$$y = c_1 \cos x + c_2 \sin x + \cos x \left(\sin x - \ln|\sec x + \tan x|\right) - \cos x \sin x$$

$$= c_1 \cos x + c_2 \sin x - \cos x \ln|\sec x + \tan x|.$$

3. The auxiliary equation is $m^2 + 1 = 0$, so $y_c = c_1 \cos x + c_2 \sin x$ and

$$W = \begin{vmatrix} \cos x & \sin x \\ -\sin x & \cos x \end{vmatrix} = 1.$$

Identifying $f(x) = \sin x$ we obtain

$$u_1' = -\sin^2 x$$

$$u_2' = \cos x \sin x.$$

Then

$$u_1 = \frac{1}{4}\sin 2x - \frac{1}{2}x = \frac{1}{2}\sin x \cos x - \frac{1}{2}x$$

$$u_2 = -\frac{1}{2}\cos^2 x.$$

and

$$y = c_1 \cos x + c_2 \sin x + \frac{1}{2}\sin x \cos^2 x - \frac{1}{2}x \cos x - \frac{1}{2}\cos^2 x \sin x$$

$$= c_1 \cos x + c_2 \sin x - \frac{1}{2}x \cos x.$$

4. The auxiliary equation is $m^2 + 1 = 0$, so $y_c = c_1 \cos x + c_2 \sin x$ and

$$W = \begin{vmatrix} \cos x & \sin x \\ -\sin x & \cos x \end{vmatrix} = 1.$$

Identifying $f(x) = \sec x \tan x$ we obtain

$$u_1' = -\sin x(\sec x \tan x) = -\tan^2 x = 1 - \sec^2 x$$

$$u_2' = \cos x(\sec x \tan x) = \tan x.$$

Then $u_1 = x - \tan x$, $u_2 = -\ln|\cos x|$, and

$$y = c_1 \cos x + c_2 \sin x + x \cos x - \sin x - \sin x \ln|\cos x|$$

$$= c_1 \cos x + c_3 \sin x + x \cos x - \sin x \ln|\cos x|.$$

5. The auxiliary equation is $m^2 + 1 = 0$, so $y_c = c_1 \cos x + c_2 \sin x$ and

$$W = \begin{vmatrix} \cos x & \sin x \\ -\sin x & \cos x \end{vmatrix} = 1.$$

Identifying $f(x) = \cos^2 x$ we obtain

$$u_1' = -\sin x \cos^2 x$$

$$u_2' = \cos^3 x = \cos x \left(1 - \sin^2 x\right).$$

183

Then $u_1 = \frac{1}{3}\cos^3 x$, $u_2 = \sin x - \frac{1}{3}\sin^3 x$, and

$$
\begin{aligned}
y &= c_1 \cos x + c_2 \sin x + \frac{1}{3}\cos^4 x + \sin^2 x - \frac{1}{3}\sin^4 x \\
&= c_1 \cos x + c_2 \sin x + \frac{1}{3}\left(\cos^2 x + \sin^2 x\right)\left(\cos^2 x - \sin^2 x\right) + \sin^2 x \\
&= c_1 \cos x + c_2 \sin x + \frac{1}{3}\cos^2 x + \frac{2}{3}\sin^2 x \\
&= c_1 \cos x + c_2 \sin x + \frac{1}{3} + \frac{1}{3}\sin^2 x.
\end{aligned}
$$

6. The auxiliary equation is $m^2 + 1 = 0$, so $y_c = c_1 \cos x + c_2 \sin x$ and

$$
W = \begin{vmatrix} \cos x & \sin x \\ -\sin x & \cos x \end{vmatrix} = 1.
$$

Identifying $f(x) = \sec^2 x$ we obtain

$$
u_1' = -\frac{\sin x}{\cos^2 x}
$$

$$
u_2' = \sec x.
$$

Then

$$
u_1 = -\frac{1}{\cos x} = -\sec x
$$

$$
u_2 = \ln|\sec x + \tan x|
$$

and

$$
\begin{aligned}
y &= c_1 \cos x + c_2 \sin x - \cos x \sec x + \sin x \ln|\sec x + \tan x| \\
&= c_1 \cos x + c_2 \sin x - 1 + \sin x \ln|\sec x + \tan x|.
\end{aligned}
$$

7. The auxiliary equation is $m^2 - 1 = 0$, so $y_c = c_1 e^x + c_2 e^{-x}$ and

$$
W = \begin{vmatrix} e^x & e^{-x} \\ e^x & -e^{-x} \end{vmatrix} = -2.
$$

Identifying $f(x) = \cosh x = \frac{1}{2}(e^{-x} + e^x)$ we obtain

$$
u_1' = \frac{1}{4}e^{-2x} + \frac{1}{4}
$$

$$
u_2' = -\frac{1}{4} - \frac{1}{4}e^{2x}.
$$

Then

$$
u_1 = -\frac{1}{8}e^{-2x} + \frac{1}{4}x
$$

$$
u_2 = -\frac{1}{8}e^{2x} - \frac{1}{4}x
$$

and

$$y = c_1 e^x + c_2 e^{-x} - \frac{1}{8} e^{-x} + \frac{1}{4} x e^x - \frac{1}{8} e^x - \frac{1}{4} x e^{-x}$$

$$= c_3 e^x + c_4 e^{-x} + \frac{1}{4} x(e^x - e^{-x})$$

$$= c_3 e^x + c_4 e^{-x} + \frac{1}{2} x \sinh x.$$

8. The auxiliary equation is $m^2 - 1 = 0$, so $y_c = c_1 e^x + c_2 e^{-x}$ and

$$W = \begin{vmatrix} e^x & e^{-x} \\ e^x & -e^{-x} \end{vmatrix} = -2.$$

Identifying $f(x) = \sinh 2x$ we obtain

$$u_1' = -\frac{1}{4} e^{-3x} + \frac{1}{4} e^x$$

$$u_2' = \frac{1}{4} e^{-x} - \frac{1}{4} e^{3x}.$$

Then

$$u_1 = \frac{1}{12} e^{-3x} + \frac{1}{4} e^x$$

$$u_2 = -\frac{1}{4} e^{-x} - \frac{1}{12} e^{3x}.$$

and

$$y = c_1 e^x + c_2 e^{-x} + \frac{1}{12} e^{-2x} + \frac{1}{4} e^{2x} - \frac{1}{4} e^{-2x} - \frac{1}{12} e^{2x}$$

$$= c_1 e^x + c_2 e^{-x} + \frac{1}{6} \left(e^{2x} - e^{-2x} \right)$$

$$= c_1 e^x + c_2 e^{-x} + \frac{1}{3} \sinh 2x.$$

9. The auxiliary equation is $m^2 - 4 = 0$, so $y_c = c_1 e^{2x} + c_2 e^{-2x}$ and

$$W = \begin{vmatrix} e^{2x} & e^{-2x} \\ 2e^{2x} & -2e^{-2x} \end{vmatrix} = -4.$$

Identifying $f(x) = e^{2x}/x$ we obtain $u_1' = 1/4x$ and $u_2' = -e^{4x}/4x$. Then

$$u_1 = \frac{1}{4} \ln|x|,$$

$$u_2 = -\frac{1}{4} \int_{x_0}^x \frac{e^{4t}}{t} \, dt$$

and

$$y = c_1 e^{2x} + c_2 e^{-2x} + \frac{1}{4} \left(e^{2x} \ln|x| - e^{-2x} \int_{x_0}^x \frac{e^{4t}}{t} \, dt \right), \qquad x_0 > 0.$$

185

10. The auxiliary equation is $m^2 - 9 = 0$, so $y_c = c_1 e^{3x} + c_2 e^{-3x}$ and

$$W = \begin{vmatrix} e^{3x} & e^{-3x} \\ 3e^{3x} & -3e^{-3x} \end{vmatrix} = -6.$$

Identifying $f(x) = 9x/e^{3x}$ we obtain $u_1' = \frac{3}{2}xe^{-6x}$ and $u_2' = -\frac{3}{2}x$. Then

$$u_1 = -\frac{1}{24}e^{-6x} - \frac{1}{4}xe^{-6x},$$

$$u_2 = -\frac{3}{4}x^2$$

and

$$y = c_1 e^{3x} + c_2 e^{-3x} - \frac{1}{24}e^{-3x} - \frac{1}{4}xe^{-3x} - \frac{3}{4}x^2 e^{-3x}$$

$$= c_1 e^{3x} + c_3 e^{-3x} - \frac{1}{4}xe^{-3x}(1 - 3x).$$

11. The auxiliary equation is $m^2 + 3m + 2 = (m+1)(m+2) = 0$, so $y_c = c_1 e^{-x} + c_2 e^{-2x}$ and

$$W = \begin{vmatrix} e^{-x} & e^{-2x} \\ -e^{-x} & -2e^{-2x} \end{vmatrix} = -e^{-3x}.$$

Identifying $f(x) = 1/(1 + e^x)$ we obtain

$$u_1' = \frac{e^x}{1 + e^x}$$

$$u_2' = -\frac{e^{2x}}{1 + e^x} = \frac{e^x}{1 + e^x} - e^x.$$

Then $u_1 = \ln(1 + e^x)$, $u_2 = \ln(1 + e^x) - e^x$, and

$$y = c_1 e^{-x} + c_2 e^{-2x} + e^{-x}\ln(1 + e^x) + e^{-2x}\ln(1 + e^x) - e^{-x}$$

$$= c_3 e^{-x} + c_2 e^{-2x} + (1 + e^{-x})e^{-x}\ln(1 + e^x).$$

12. The auxiliary equation is $m^2 - 2m + 1 = (m - 1)^2 = 0$, so $y_c = c_1 e^x + c_2 x e^x$ and

$$W = \begin{vmatrix} e^x & xe^x \\ e^x & xe^x + e^x \end{vmatrix} = e^{2x}.$$

Identifying $f(x) = e^x/\left(1 + x^2\right)$ we obtain

$$u_1' = -\frac{xe^x e^x}{e^{2x}\left(1 + x^2\right)} = -\frac{x}{1 + x^2}$$

$$u_2' = \frac{e^x e^x}{e^{2x}\left(1 + x^2\right)} = \frac{1}{1 + x^2}.$$

Then $u_1 = -\frac{1}{2}\ln\left(1 + x^2\right)$, $u_2 = \tan^{-1} x$, and

$$y = c_1 e^x + c_2 x e^x - \frac{1}{2} e^x \ln\left(1 + x^2\right) + x e^x \tan^{-1} x.$$

13. The auxiliary equation is $m^2 + 3m + 2 = (m+1)(m+2) = 0$, so $y_c = c_1 e^{-x} + c_2 e^{-2x}$ and

$$W = \begin{vmatrix} e^{-x} & e^{-2x} \\ -e^{-x} & -2e^{-2x} \end{vmatrix} = -e^{-3x}.$$

Identifying $f(x) = \sin e^x$ we obtain

$$u_1' = \frac{e^{-2x}\sin e^x}{e^{-3x}} = e^x \sin e^x$$

$$u_2' = \frac{e^{-x}\sin e^x}{-e^{-3x}} = -e^{2x}\sin e^x.$$

Then $u_1 = -\cos e^x$, $u_2 = e^x \cos e^x - \sin e^x$, and

$$y = c_1 e^{-x} + c_2 e^{-2x} - e^{-x}\cos e^x + e^{-x}\cos e^x - e^{-2x}\sin e^x$$

$$= c_1 e^{-x} + c_2 e^{-2x} - e^{-2x}\sin e^x.$$

14. The auxiliary equation is $m^2 - 2m + 1 = (m-1)^2 = 0$, so $y_c = c_1 e^t + c_2 t e^t$ and

$$W = \begin{vmatrix} e^t & te^t \\ e^t & te^t + e^t \end{vmatrix} = e^{2t}.$$

Identifying $f(t) = e^t \tan^{-1} t$ we obtain

$$u_1' = -\frac{te^t e^t \tan^{-1} t}{e^{2t}} = -t\tan^{-1} t$$

$$u_2' = \frac{e^t e^t \tan^{-1} t}{e^{2t}} = \tan^{-1} t.$$

Then

$$u_1 = -\frac{1 + t^2}{2}\tan^{-1} t + \frac{t}{2}$$

$$u_2 = t\tan^{-1} t - \frac{1}{2}\ln\left(1 + t^2\right)$$

and

$$y = c_1 e^t + c_2 t e^t + \left(-\frac{1 + t^2}{2}\tan^{-1} t + \frac{t}{2}\right) e^t + \left(t\tan^{-1} t - \frac{1}{2}\ln\left(1 + t^2\right)\right) te^t$$

$$= c_1 e^t + c_3 t e^t + \frac{1}{2}e^t \left[\left(t^2 - 1\right)\tan^{-1} t - \ln\left(1 + t^2\right)\right].$$

15. The auxiliary equation is $m^2 + 2m + 1 = (m+1)^2 = 0$, so $y_c = c_1 e^{-t} + c_2 t e^{-t}$ and

$$W = \begin{vmatrix} e^{-t} & te^{-t} \\ -e^{-t} & -te^{-t} + e^{-t} \end{vmatrix} = e^{-2t}.$$

Exercises 4.6 Variation of Parameters

Identifying $f(t) = e^{-t} \ln t$ we obtain

$$u_1' = -\frac{te^{-t}e^{-t}\ln t}{e^{-2t}} = -t\ln t$$

$$u_2' = \frac{e^{-t}e^{-t}\ln t}{e^{-2t}} = \ln t.$$

Then

$$u_1 = -\frac{1}{2}t^2\ln t + \frac{1}{4}t^2$$

$$u_2 = t\ln t - t$$

and

$$y = c_1 e^{-t} + c_2 t e^{-t} - \frac{1}{2}t^2 e^{-t}\ln t + \frac{1}{4}t^2 e^{-t} + t^2 e^{-t}\ln t - t^2 e^{-t}$$

$$= c_1 e^{-t} + c_2 t e^{-t} + \frac{1}{2}t^2 e^{-t}\ln t - \frac{3}{4}t^2 e^{-t}.$$

16. The auxiliary equation is $2m^2 + 2m + 1 = 0$, so $y_c = e^{-x/2}[c_1\cos(x/2) + c_2\sin(x/2)]$ and

$$W = \begin{vmatrix} e^{-x/2}\cos\dfrac{x}{2} & e^{-x/2}\sin\dfrac{x}{2} \\[2mm] -\dfrac{1}{2}e^{-x/2}\cos\dfrac{x}{2} - \dfrac{1}{2}e^{-x/2}\sin\dfrac{x}{2} & \dfrac{1}{2}e^{-x/2}\cos\dfrac{x}{2} - \dfrac{1}{2}e^{x/2}\sin\dfrac{x}{2} \end{vmatrix} = \frac{1}{2}e^{-x}.$$

Identifying $f(x) = 2\sqrt{x}$ we obtain

$$u_1' = -\frac{e^{-x/2}\sin(x/2)2\sqrt{x}}{e^{-x/2}} = -4e^{x/2}\sqrt{x}\sin\frac{x}{2}$$

$$u_2' = -\frac{e^{-x/2}\cos(x/2)2\sqrt{x}}{e^{-x/2}} = 4e^{x/2}\sqrt{x}\cos\frac{x}{2}.$$

Then

$$u_1 = -4\int_{x_0}^{x} e^{t/2}\sqrt{t}\sin\frac{t}{2}\,dt$$

$$u_2 = 4\int_{x_0}^{x} e^{t/2}\sqrt{t}\cos\frac{t}{2}\,dt$$

and

$$y = e^{-x/2}\left(c_1\cos\frac{x}{2} + c_2\sin\frac{x}{2}\right) - 4e^{-x/2}\cos\frac{x}{2}\int_{x_0}^{x} e^{t/2}\sqrt{t}\sin\frac{t}{2}\,dt + 4e^{-x/2}\sin\frac{x}{2}\int_{x_0}^{x} e^{t/2}\sqrt{t}\cos\frac{t}{2}\,dt.$$

17. The auxiliary equation is $3m^2 - 6m + 6 = 0$, so $y_c = e^x(c_1\cos x + c_2\sin x)$ and

$$W = \begin{vmatrix} e^x\cos x & e^x\sin x \\ e^x\cos x - e^x\sin x & e^x\cos x + e^x\sin x \end{vmatrix} = e^{2x}.$$

188

Identifying $f(x) = \frac{1}{3}e^x \sec x$ we obtain

$$u_1' = -\frac{(e^x \sin x)(e^x \sec x)/3}{e^{2x}} = -\frac{1}{3}\tan x$$

$$u_2' = \frac{(e^x \cos x)(e^x \sec x)/3}{e^{2x}} = \frac{1}{3}.$$

Then $u_1 = \frac{1}{3}\ln(\cos x)$, $u_2 = \frac{1}{3}x$, and

$$y = c_1 e^x \cos x + c_2 e^x \sin x + \frac{1}{3}\ln(\cos x)e^x \cos x + \frac{1}{3}xe^x \sin x.$$

18. The auxiliary equation is $4m^2 - 4m + 1 = (2m - 1)^2 = 0$, so $y_c = c_1 e^{x/2} + c_2 xe^{x/2}$ and

$$W = \begin{vmatrix} e^{x/2} & xe^{x/2} \\ \frac{1}{2}e^{x/2} & \frac{1}{2}xe^{x/2} + e^{x/2} \end{vmatrix} = e^x.$$

Identifying $f(x) = \frac{1}{4}e^{x/2}\sqrt{1 - x^2}$ we obtain

$$u_1' = -\frac{xe^{x/2}e^{x/2}\sqrt{1 - x^2}}{4e^x} = -\frac{1}{4}x\sqrt{1 - x^2}$$

$$u_2' = \frac{e^{x/2}e^{x/2}\sqrt{1 - x^2}}{4e^x} = \frac{1}{4}\sqrt{1 - x^2}.$$

To find u_1 and u_2 we use the substitution $v = 1 - x^2$ and the trig substitution $x = \sin\theta$, respectively:

$$u_1 = \frac{1}{12}\left(1 - x^2\right)^{3/2}$$

$$u_2 = \frac{x}{8}\sqrt{1 - x^2} + \frac{1}{8}\sin^{-1} x.$$

Thus

$$y = c_1 e^{x/2} + c_2 xe^{x/2} + \frac{1}{12}e^{x/2}\left(1 - x^2\right)^{3/2} + \frac{1}{8}x^2 e^{x/2}\sqrt{1 - x^2} + \frac{1}{8}xe^{x/2}\sin^{-1} x.$$

19. The auxiliary equation is $4m^2 - 1 = (2m - 1)(2m + 1) = 0$, so $y_c = c_1 e^{x/2} + c_2 e^{-x/2}$ and

$$W = \begin{vmatrix} e^{x/2} & e^{-x/2} \\ \frac{1}{2}e^{x/2} & -\frac{1}{2}e^{-x/2} \end{vmatrix} = -1.$$

Identifying $f(x) = xe^{x/2}/4$ we obtain $u_1' = x/4$ and $u_2' = -xe^x/4$. Then $u_1 = x^2/8$ and $u_2 = -xe^x/4 + e^x/4$. Thus

$$y = c_1 e^{x/2} + c_2 e^{-x/2} + \frac{1}{8}x^2 e^{x/2} - \frac{1}{4}xe^{x/2} + \frac{1}{4}e^{x/2}$$

$$= c_3 e^{x/2} + c_2 e^{-x/2} + \frac{1}{8}x^2 e^{x/2} - \frac{1}{4}xe^{x/2}$$

and

$$y' = \frac{1}{2}c_3 e^{x/2} - \frac{1}{2}c_2 e^{-x/2} + \frac{1}{16}x^2 e^{x/2} + \frac{1}{8}xe^{x/2} - \frac{1}{4}e^{x/2}.$$

Exercises 4.6 Variation of Parameters

The initial conditions imply

$$c_3 + c_2 = 1$$

$$\frac{1}{2}c_3 - \frac{1}{2}c_2 - \frac{1}{4} = 0.$$

Thus $c_3 = 3/4$ and $c_2 = 1/4$, and

$$y = \frac{3}{4}e^{x/2} + \frac{1}{4}e^{-x/2} + \frac{1}{8}x^2e^{x/2} - \frac{1}{4}xe^{x/2}.$$

20. The auxiliary equation is $2m^2 + m - 1 = (2m - 1)(m + 1) = 0$, so $y_c = c_1e^{x/2} + c_2e^{-x}$ and

$$W = \begin{vmatrix} e^{x/2} & e^{-x} \\ \frac{1}{2}e^{x/2} & -e^{-x} \end{vmatrix} = -\frac{3}{2}e^{-x/2}.$$

Identifying $f(x) = (x+1)/2$ we obtain

$$u_1' = \frac{1}{3}e^{-x/2}(x+1)$$

$$u_2' = -\frac{1}{3}e^x(x+1).$$

Then

$$u_1 = -e^{-x/2}\left(\frac{2}{3}x - 2\right)$$

$$u_2 = -\frac{1}{3}xe^x.$$

Thus

$$y = c_1e^{x/2} + c_2e^{-x} - x - 2$$

and

$$y' = \frac{1}{2}c_1e^{x/2} - c_2e^{-x} - 1.$$

The initial conditions imply

$$c_1 - c_2 - 2 = 1$$

$$\frac{1}{2}c_1 - c_2 - 1 = 0.$$

Thus $c_1 = 8/3$ and $c_2 = 1/3$, and

$$y = \frac{8}{3}e^{x/2} + \frac{1}{3}e^{-x} - x - 2.$$

21. The auxiliary equation is $m^2 + 2m - 8 = (m - 2)(m + 4) = 0$, so $y_c = c_1e^{2x} + c_2e^{-4x}$ and

$$W = \begin{vmatrix} e^{2x} & e^{-4x} \\ 2e^{2x} & -4e^{-4x} \end{vmatrix} = -6e^{-2x}.$$

Identifying $f(x) = 2e^{-2x} - e^{-x}$ we obtain

$$u_1' = \frac{1}{3}e^{-4x} - \frac{1}{6}e^{-3x}$$

$$u_2' = \frac{1}{6}e^{3x} - \frac{1}{3}e^{2x}.$$

Then

$$u_1 = -\frac{1}{12}e^{-4x} + \frac{1}{18}e^{-3x}$$

$$u_2 = \frac{1}{18}e^{3x} - \frac{1}{6}e^{2x}.$$

Thus

$$y = c_1e^{2x} + c_2e^{-4x} - \frac{1}{12}e^{-2x} + \frac{1}{18}e^{-x} + \frac{1}{18}e^{-x} - \frac{1}{6}e^{-2x}$$

$$= c_1e^{2x} + c_2e^{-4x} - \frac{1}{4}e^{-2x} + \frac{1}{9}e^{-x}$$

and

$$y' = 2c_1e^{2x} - 4c_2e^{-4x} + \frac{1}{2}e^{-2x} - \frac{1}{9}e^{-x}.$$

The initial conditions imply

$$c_1 + c_2 - \frac{5}{36} = 1$$

$$2c_1 - 4c_2 + \frac{7}{18} = 0.$$

Thus $c_1 = 25/36$ and $c_2 = 4/9$, and

$$y = \frac{25}{36}e^{2x} + \frac{4}{9}e^{-4x} - \frac{1}{4}e^{-2x} + \frac{1}{9}e^{-x}.$$

22. The auxiliary equation is $m^2 - 4m + 4 = (m-2)^2 = 0$, so $y_c = c_1e^{2x} + c_2xe^{2x}$ and

$$W = \begin{vmatrix} e^{2x} & xe^{2x} \\ 2e^{2x} & 2xe^{2x} + e^{2x} \end{vmatrix} = e^{4x}.$$

Identifying $f(x) = \left(12x^2 - 6x\right)e^{2x}$ we obtain

$$u_1' = 6x^2 - 12x^3$$

$$u_2' = 12x^2 - 6x.$$

Then

$$u_1 = 2x^3 - 3x^4$$

$$u_2 = 4x^3 - 3x^2.$$

Thus

$$y = c_1 e^{2x} + c_2 x e^{2x} + \left(2x^3 - 3x^4\right) e^{2x} + \left(4x^3 - 3x^2\right) x e^{2x}$$

$$= c_1 e^{2x} + c_2 x e^{2x} + e^{2x} \left(x^4 - x^3\right)$$

and

$$y' = 2c_1 e^{2x} + c_2 \left(2x e^{2x} + e^{2x}\right) + e^{2x} \left(4x^3 - 3x^2\right) + 2e^{2x} \left(x^4 - x^3\right).$$

The initial conditions imply

$$c_1 \qquad = 1$$

$$2c_1 + c_2 = 0.$$

Thus $c_1 = 1$ and $c_2 = -2$, and

$$y = e^{2x} - 2x e^{2x} + e^{2x} \left(x^4 - x^3\right) = e^{2x} \left(x^4 - x^3 - 2x + 1\right).$$

23. Write the equation in the form

$$y'' + \frac{1}{x} y' + \left(1 - \frac{1}{4x^2}\right) y = x^{-1/2}$$

and identify $f(x) = x^{-1/2}$. From $y_1 = x^{-1/2} \cos x$ and $y_2 = x^{-1/2} \sin x$ we compute

$$W(y_1, y_2) = \begin{vmatrix} x^{-1/2} \cos x & x^{-1/2} \sin x \\ -x^{-1/2} \sin x - \frac{1}{2} x^{-3/2} \cos x & x^{-1/2} \cos x - \frac{1}{2} x^{-3/2} \sin x \end{vmatrix} = \frac{1}{x}.$$

Now

$$u_1' = -\sin x \quad \text{so} \quad u_1 = \cos x,$$

and

$$u_2' = \cos x \quad \text{so} \quad u_2 = \sin x.$$

Thus a particular solution is

$$y_p = x^{-1/2} \cos^2 x + x^{-1/2} \sin^2 x,$$

and the general solution is

$$y = c_1 x^{-1/2} \cos x + c_2 x^{-1/2} \sin x + x^{-1/2} \cos^2 x + x^{-1/2} \sin^2 x$$

$$= c_1 x^{-1/2} \cos x + c_2 x^{-1/2} \sin x + x^{-1/2}.$$

24. Write the equation in the form

$$y'' + \frac{1}{x} y' + \frac{1}{x^2} y = \frac{\sec(\ln x)}{x^2}$$

and identify $f(x) = \sec(\ln x)/x^2$. From $y_1 = \cos(\ln x)$ and $y_2 = \sin(\ln x)$ we compute

$$W = \begin{vmatrix} \cos(\ln x) & \sin(\ln x) \\ -\dfrac{\sin(\ln x)}{x} & \dfrac{\cos(\ln x)}{x} \end{vmatrix} = \frac{1}{x}.$$

Now

$$u_1' = -\frac{\tan(\ln x)}{x} \quad \text{so} \quad u_1 = \ln|\cos(\ln x)|,$$

and

$$u_2' = \frac{1}{x} \quad \text{so} \quad u_2 = \ln x.$$

Thus, a particular solution is

$$y_p = \cos(\ln x)\ln|\cos(\ln x)| + (\ln x)\sin(\ln x),$$

and the general solution is

$$y = c_1\cos(\ln x) + c_2\sin(\ln x) + \cos(\ln x)\ln|\cos(\ln x)| + (\ln x)\sin(\ln x).$$

25. The auxiliary equation is $m^3 + m = m(m^2 + 1) = 0$, so $y_c = c_1 + c_2\cos x + c_3\sin x$ and

$$W = \begin{vmatrix} 1 & \cos x & \sin x \\ 0 & -\sin x & \cos x \\ 0 & -\cos x & -\sin x \end{vmatrix} = 1.$$

Identifying $f(x) = \tan x$ we obtain

$$u_1' = W_1 = \begin{vmatrix} 0 & \cos x & \sin x \\ 0 & -\sin x & \cos x \\ \tan x & -\cos x & -\sin x \end{vmatrix} = \tan x$$

$$u_2' = W_2 = \begin{vmatrix} 1 & 0 & \sin x \\ 0 & 0 & \cos x \\ 0 & \tan x & -\sin x \end{vmatrix} = -\sin x$$

$$u_3' = W_3 = \begin{vmatrix} 1 & \cos x & 0 \\ 0 & -\sin x & 0 \\ 0 & -\cos x & \tan x \end{vmatrix} = -\sin x\tan x = \frac{\cos^2 x - 1}{\cos x} = \cos x - \sec x.$$

Then

$$u_1 = -\ln|\cos x|$$

$$u_2 = \cos x$$

$$u_3 = \sin x - \ln|\sec x + \tan x|$$

and

$$y = c_1 + c_2\cos x + c_3\sin x - \ln|\cos x| + \cos^2 x$$

$$+ \sin^2 x - \sin x\ln|\sec x + \tan x|$$

$$= c_4 + c_2\cos x + c_3\sin x - \ln|\cos x| - \sin x\ln|\sec x + \tan x|$$

193

Exercises 4.6 Variation of Parameters

for $-\pi/2 < x < \pi/2$.

26. The auxiliary equation is $m^3 + 4m = m\left(m^2 + 4\right) = 0$, so $y_c = c_1 + c_2 \cos 2x + c_3 \sin 2x$ and

$$W = \begin{vmatrix} 1 & \cos 2x & \sin 2x \\ 0 & -2\sin 2x & 2\cos 2x \\ 0 & -4\cos 2x & -4\sin 2x \end{vmatrix} = 8.$$

Identifying $f(x) = \sec 2x$ we obtain

$$u_1' = \frac{1}{8}W_1 = \frac{1}{8}\begin{vmatrix} 0 & \cos 2x & \sin 2x \\ 0 & -2\sin 2x & 2\cos 2x \\ \sec 2x & -4\cos 2x & -4\sin 2x \end{vmatrix} = \frac{1}{4}\sec 2x$$

$$u_2' = \frac{1}{8}W_2 = \frac{1}{8}\begin{vmatrix} 1 & 0 & \sin 2x \\ 0 & 0 & 2\cos 2x \\ 0 & \sec 2x & -4\sin 2x \end{vmatrix} = -\frac{1}{4}$$

$$u_3' = \frac{1}{8}W_3 = \frac{1}{8}\begin{vmatrix} 1 & \cos 2x & 0 \\ 0 & -2\sin 2x & 0 \\ 0 & -4\cos 2x & \sec 2x \end{vmatrix} = -\frac{1}{4}\tan 2x.$$

Then

$$u_1 = \frac{1}{8}\ln|\sec 2x + \tan 2x|$$

$$u_2 = -\frac{1}{4}x$$

$$u_3 = \frac{1}{8}\ln|\cos 2x|$$

and

$$y = c_1 + c_2\cos 2x + c_3\sin 2x + \frac{1}{8}\ln|\sec 2x + \tan 2x| - \frac{1}{4}x\cos 2x + \frac{1}{8}\sin 2x\ln|\cos 2x|$$

for $-\pi/4 < x < \pi/4$.

27. The auxiliary equation is $3m^2 - 6m + 30 = 0$, which has roots $1 \pm 3i$, so $y_c = e^x(c_1\cos 3x + c_2\sin 3x)$. We consider first the differential equation $3y'' - 6y' + 30y = 15\sin x$, which can be solved using undetermined coefficients. Letting $y_{p_1} = A\cos x + B\sin x$ and substituting into the differential equation we get

$$(27A - 6B)\cos x + (6A + 27B)\sin x = 15\sin x.$$

Then

$$27A - 6B = 0 \quad \text{and} \quad 6A + 27B = 15,$$

194

so $A = \frac{2}{17}$ and $B = \frac{9}{17}$. Thus, $y_{p_1} = \frac{2}{17} \cos x + \frac{9}{17} \sin x$. Next, we consider the differential equation $3y'' - 6y' + 30y$, for which a particular solution y_{p_2} can be found using variation of parameters. The Wronskian is

$$W = \begin{vmatrix} e^x \cos 3x & e^x \sin 3x \\ e^x \cos 3x - 3e^x \sin 3x & 3e^x \cos 3x + e^x \sin 3x \end{vmatrix} = 3e^{2x}.$$

Identifying $f(x) = \frac{1}{3} e^x \tan x$ we obtain

$$u_1' = -\frac{1}{9} \sin 3x \tan 3x = -\frac{1}{9}\left(\frac{\sin^2 3x}{\cos 3x}\right) = -\frac{1}{9}\left(\frac{1 - \cos^2 3x}{\cos 3x}\right) = -\frac{1}{9}(\sec 3x - \cos 3x)$$

so

$$u_1 = -\frac{1}{27} \ln|\sec 3x + \tan 3x| + \frac{1}{27} \sin 3x.$$

Next

$$u_2' = \frac{1}{9} \sin 3x \quad \text{so} \quad u_2 = -\frac{1}{27} \cos 3x.$$

Thus

$$y_{p_2} = -\frac{1}{27} e^x \cos 3x(\ln|\sec 3x + \tan 3x| - \sin 3x) - \frac{1}{27} e^x \sin 3x \cos 3x$$

$$= -\frac{1}{27} e^x (\cos 3x) \ln|\sec 3x + \tan 3x|$$

and the general solution of the original differential equation is

$$y = e^x (c_1 \cos 3x + c_2 \sin 3x) + y_{p_1}(x) + y_{p_2}(x).$$

28. The auxiliary equation is $m^2 - 2m + 1 = (m-1)^2 = 0$, which has repeated root 1, so $y_c = c_1 e^x + c_2 x e^x$. We consider first the differential equation $y'' - 2y' + y = 4x^2 - 3$, which can be solved using undetermined coefficients. Letting $y_{p_1} = Ax^2 + Bx + C$ and substituting into the differential equation we get

$$Ax^2 + (-4A + B)x + (2A - 2B + C) = 4x^2 - 3.$$

Then

$$A = 4, \quad -4A + B = 0, \quad \text{and} \quad 2A - 2B + C = -3,$$

so $A = 4$, $B = 16$, and $C = 21$. Thus, $y_{p_1} = 4x^2 + 16x + 21$. Next we consider the differential equation $y'' - 2y' + y = x^{-1}e^x$, for which a particular solution y_{p_2} can be found using variation of parameters. The Wronskian is

$$W = \begin{vmatrix} e^x & xe^x \\ e^x & xe^x + e^x \end{vmatrix} = e^{2x}.$$

Identifying $f(x) = e^x/x$ we obtain $u_1' = -1$ and $u_2' = 1/x$. Then $u_1 = -x$ and $u_2 = \ln x$, so that

$$y_{p_2} = -xe^x + xe^x \ln x,$$

and the general solution of the original differential equation is

$$y = y_c + y_{p_1} + y_{p_2} = c_1 e^x + c_2 x e^x + 4x^2 + 16x + 21 - xe^x + xe^x \ln x$$

$$= c_1 e^x + c_3 x e^x + 4x^2 + 16x + 21 + xe^x \ln x$$

.

29. The interval of definition for Problem 1 is $(-\pi/2, \pi/2)$, for Problem 7 is $(-\infty, \infty)$, for Problem 9 is $(0, \infty)$, and for Problem 18 is $(-1, 1)$. In Problem 24 the general solution is

$$y = c_1 \cos(\ln x) + c_2 \sin(\ln x) + \cos(\ln x) \ln|\cos(\ln x)| + (\ln x) \sin(\ln x)$$

for $-\pi/2 < \ln x < \pi/2$ or $e^{-\pi/2} < x < e^{\pi/2}$. The bounds on $\ln x$ are due to the presence of $\sec(\ln x)$ in the differential equation.

30. We are given that $y_1 = x^2$ is a solution of $x^4 y'' + x^3 y' - 4x^2 y = 0$. To find a second solution we use reduction of order. Let $y = x^2 u(x)$. Then the product rule gives

$$y' = x^2 u' + 2xu \quad \text{and} \quad y'' = x^2 u'' + 4xu' + 2u,$$

so

$$x^4 y'' + x^3 y' - 4x^2 y = x^5 (xu'' + 5u') = 0.$$

Letting $w = u'$, this becomes $xw' + 5w = 0$. Separating variables and integrating we have

$$\frac{dw}{w} = -\frac{5}{x}\, dx \quad \text{and} \quad \ln|w| = -5 \ln x + c.$$

Thus, $w = x^{-5}$ and $u = -\frac{1}{4} x^{-4}$. A second solution is then $y_2 = x^2 x^{-4} = 1/x^2$, and the general solution of the homogeneous differential equation is $y_c = c_1 x^2 + c_2/x^2$. To find a particular solution, y_p, we use variation of parameters. The Wronskian is

$$W = \begin{vmatrix} x^2 & 1/x^2 \\ 2x & -2/x^3 \end{vmatrix} = -\frac{4}{x}.$$

Identifying $f(x) = 1/x^4$ we obtain $u_1' = \frac{1}{4} x^{-5}$ and $u_2' = -\frac{1}{4} x^{-1}$. Then $u_1 = -\frac{1}{16} x^{-4}$ and $u_2 = -\frac{1}{4} \ln x$, so

$$y_p = -\frac{1}{16} x^{-4} x^2 - \frac{1}{4} (\ln x) x^{-2} = -\frac{1}{16} x^{-2} - \frac{1}{4} x^{-2} \ln x.$$

The general solution is

$$y = c_1 x^2 + \frac{c_2}{x^2} - \frac{1}{16x^2} - \frac{1}{4x^2} \ln x.$$

31. Suppose $y_p(x) = u_1(x) y_1(x) + u_2(x) y_2(x)$, where u_1 and u_2 are defined by (5) of Section 4.6 in the text. Then, for x and x_0 in I,

$$y_p(x) = y_1(x) \int_{x_0}^{x} \frac{-y_2(t)f(t)}{W(t)}\,dt + y_2(x) \int_{x_0}^{x} \frac{y_1(t)f(t)}{W(t)}\,dt$$

$$= \int_{x_0}^{x} \frac{-y_1(x)y_2(t)f(t)}{W(t)}\,dt + \int_{x_0}^{x} \frac{y_1(t)y_2(x)f(t)}{W(t)}\,dt$$

$$= \int_{x_0}^{x} \left[\frac{y_1(t)y_2(x)f(t)}{W(t)} + \frac{-y_1(x)y_2(t)f(t)}{W(t)}\right]dt$$

$$= \int_{x_0}^{x} \frac{y_1(t)y_2(x)f(t) - y_1(x)y_2(t)f(t)}{W(t)}\,dt$$

$$= \int_{x_0}^{x} \frac{y_1(t)y_2(x) - y_1(x)y_2(t)}{W(t)}\,f(t)dt$$

$$= \int_{x_0}^{x} G(x,t)f(t)\,dt.$$

32. In the solution of Example 3 in the text we saw that $y_1 = e^x$, $y_2 = e^{-x}$, $f(x) = 1/x$, and $W(y_1, y_2) = -2$. From (13) the Green's function for the differential equation is

$$G(x,t) = \frac{e^t e^{-x} - e^x e^{-t}}{-2} = \frac{e^{x-t} - e^{-(x-t)}}{2} = \sinh(x-t).$$

The general solution of the differential equation on any interval $[x_0, x]$ not containing the origin is then

$$y = c_1 e^x + c_2 e^{-x} + \int_{x_0}^{x} \frac{\sinh(x-t)}{t}\,dt.$$

33. We already know that $y_p(x)$ is a particular solution of the differential equation. We simply need to show that it satisfies the initial conditions. Certainly

$$y(x_0) = \int_{x_0}^{x_0} G(x,t)f(t)dt = 0.$$

Using Leibniz's rule for differentiation under an integral sign we have

$$y_p'(x) = \frac{d}{dx}\int_{x_0}^{x} G(x,t)f(t)dt = \int_{x_0}^{x} \frac{d}{dx}G(x,t)f(t)dt + f(t)G(x,x)\cdot 1 - f(t)G(x_0,x)\cdot 0.$$

From (13) in the text, $G(x,x) = 0$ so

$$y_p'(x) = \frac{d}{dx}\int_{x_0}^{x} G(x,t)f(t)dt$$

and

$$y_p'(x_0) = \frac{d}{dx}\int_{x_0}^{x_0} G(x,t)f(t)dt = 0.$$

Exercises 4.6 Variation of Parameters

34. From the solution of Problem 32 we have that a particular solution of the differential equation is

$$y_p(x) = \int_0^x G(x,t) e^{2t} dt,$$

where $G(x,t) = \sinh(x-t)$. Then

$$y_p(x) = \int_0^x e^{2t} \sinh(x-t) dt = \int_0^x e^{2t} \frac{e^{x-t} - e^{-(x-t)}}{2} dt$$

$$= \frac{1}{2} \int_0^x \left[e^{x+t} - e^{-x+3t} \right] dt = \frac{1}{2} \left[e^{x+t} - \frac{1}{3} e^{-x+3t} \right] \Big|_0^x$$

$$= \frac{1}{2} e^{2x} - \frac{1}{6} e^{2x} - \frac{1}{2} e^x + \frac{1}{6} e^{-x} = \frac{1}{3} e^{2x} - \frac{1}{2} e^x + \frac{1}{6} e^{-x}.$$

Exercises 4.7

Cauchy-Euler Equation

1. The auxiliary equation is $m^2 - m - 2 = (m+1)(m-2) = 0$ so that $y = c_1 x^{-1} + c_2 x^2$.

2. The auxiliary equation is $4m^2 - 4m + 1 = (2m-1)^2 = 0$ so that $y = c_1 x^{1/2} + c_2 x^{1/2} \ln x$.

3. The auxiliary equation is $m^2 = 0$ so that $y = c_1 + c_2 \ln x$.

4. The auxiliary equation is $m^2 - 4m = m(m-4) = 0$ so that $y = c_1 + c_2 x^4$.

5. The auxiliary equation is $m^2 + 4 = 0$ so that $y = c_1 \cos(2 \ln x) + c_2 \sin(2 \ln x)$.

6. The auxiliary equation is $m^2 + 4m + 3 = (m+1)(m+3) = 0$ so that $y = c_1 x^{-1} + c_2 x^{-3}$.

7. The auxiliary equation is $m^2 - 4m - 2 = 0$ so that $y = c_1 x^{2-\sqrt{6}} + c_2 x^{2+\sqrt{6}}$.

8. The auxiliary equation is $m^2 + 2m - 4 = 0$ so that $y = c_1 x^{-1+\sqrt{5}} + c_2 x^{-1-\sqrt{5}}$.

9. The auxiliary equation is $25m^2 + 1 = 0$ so that $y = c_1 \cos\left(\frac{1}{5} \ln x\right) + c_2 \sin\left(\frac{1}{5} \ln x\right)$.

10. The auxiliary equation is $4m^2 - 1 = (2m-1)(2m+1) = 0$ so that $y = c_1 x^{1/2} + c_2 x^{-1/2}$.

11. The auxiliary equation is $m^2 + 4m + 4 = (m+2)^2 = 0$ so that $y = c_1 x^{-2} + c_2 x^{-2} \ln x$.

12. The auxiliary equation is $m^2 + 7m + 6 = (m+1)(m+6) = 0$ so that $y = c_1 x^{-1} + c_2 x^{-6}$.

13. The auxiliary equation is $3m^2 + 3m + 1 = 0$ so that

$$y = x^{-1/2} \left[c_1 \cos\left(\frac{\sqrt{3}}{6} \ln x\right) + c_2 \sin\left(\frac{\sqrt{3}}{6} \ln x\right) \right].$$

14. The auxiliary equation is $m^2 - 8m + 41 = 0$ so that $y = x^4 \left[c_1 \cos(5 \ln x) + c_2 \sin(5 \ln x) \right]$.

198

15. Assuming that $y = x^m$ and substituting into the differential equation we obtain

$$m(m-1)(m-2) - 6 = m^3 - 3m^2 + 2m - 6 = (m-3)(m^2+2) = 0.$$

Thus

$$y = c_1 x^3 + c_2 \cos\left(\sqrt{2}\ln x\right) + c_3 \sin\left(\sqrt{2}\ln x\right).$$

16. Assuming that $y = x^m$ and substituting into the differential equation we obtain

$$m(m-1)(m-2) + m - 1 = m^3 - 3m^2 + 3m - 1 = (m-1)^3 = 0.$$

Thus

$$y = c_1 x + c_2 x \ln x + c_3 x (\ln x)^2.$$

17. Assuming that $y = x^m$ and substituting into the differential equation we obtain

$$m(m-1)(m-2)(m-3) + 6m(m-1)(m-2) = m^4 - 7m^2 + 6m = m(m-1)(m-2)(m+3) = 0.$$

Thus

$$y = c_1 + c_2 x + c_3 x^2 + c_4 x^{-3}.$$

18. Assuming that $y = x^m$ and substituting into the differential equation we obtain

$$m(m-1)(m-2)(m-3) + 6m(m-1)(m-2) + 9m(m-1) + 3m + 1 = m^4 + 2m^2 + 1 = (m^2+1)^2 = 0.$$

Thus

$$y = c_1 \cos(\ln x) + c_2 \sin(\ln x) + c_3 (\ln x)\cos(\ln x) + c_4 (\ln x)\sin(\ln x).$$

19. The auxiliary equation is $m^2 - 5m = m(m-5) = 0$ so that $y_c = c_1 + c_2 x^5$ and

$$W(1, x^5) = \begin{vmatrix} 1 & x^5 \\ 0 & 5x^4 \end{vmatrix} = 5x^4.$$

Identifying $f(x) = x^3$ we obtain $u_1' = -\frac{1}{5}x^4$ and $u_2' = 1/5x$. Then $u_1 = -\frac{1}{25}x^5$, $u_2 = \frac{1}{5}\ln x$, and

$$y = c_1 + c_2 x^5 - \frac{1}{25}x^5 + \frac{1}{5}x^5 \ln x = c_1 + c_3 x^5 + \frac{1}{5}x^5 \ln x.$$

20. The auxiliary equation is $2m^2 + 3m + 1 = (2m+1)(m+1) = 0$ so that $y_c = c_1 x^{-1} + c_2 x^{-1/2}$ and

$$W(x^{-1}, x^{-1/2}) = \begin{vmatrix} x^{-1} & x^{-1/2} \\ -x^{-2} & -\frac{1}{2}x^{-3/2} \end{vmatrix} = \frac{1}{2}x^{-5/2}.$$

Identifying $f(x) = \frac{1}{2} - \frac{1}{2x}$ we obtain $u_1' = x - x^2$ and $u_2' = x^{3/2} - x^{1/2}$. Then $u_1 = \frac{1}{2}x^2 - \frac{1}{3}x^3$, $u_2 = \frac{2}{5}x^{5/2} - \frac{2}{3}x^{3/2}$, and

$$y = c_1 x^{-1} + c_2 x^{-1/2} + \frac{1}{2}x - \frac{1}{3}x^2 + \frac{2}{5}x^2 - \frac{2}{3}x = c_1 x^{-1} + c_2 x^{-1/2} - \frac{1}{6}x + \frac{1}{15}x^2.$$

Exercises 4.7   Cauchy-Euler Equation

21. The auxiliary equation is $m^2 - 2m + 1 = (m-1)^2 = 0$ so that $y_c = c_1 x + c_2 x \ln x$ and

$$W(x, x \ln x) = \begin{vmatrix} x & x \ln x \\ 1 & 1 + \ln x \end{vmatrix} = x.$$

Identifying $f(x) = 2/x$ we obtain $u_1' = -2 \ln x / x$ and $u_2' = 2/x$. Then $u_1 = -(\ln x)^2$, $u_2 = 2 \ln x$, and

$$y = c_1 x + c_2 x \ln x - x(\ln x)^2 + 2x(\ln x)^2$$

$$= c_1 x + c_2 x \ln x + x(\ln x)^2, \qquad x > 0.$$

22. The auxiliary equation is $m^2 - 3m + 2 = (m-1)(m-2) = 0$ so that $y_c = c_1 x + c_2 x^2$ and

$$W(x, x^2) = \begin{vmatrix} x & x^2 \\ 1 & 2x \end{vmatrix} = x^2.$$

Identifying $f(x) = x^2 e^x$ we obtain $u_1' = -x^2 e^x$ and $u_2' = xe^x$. Then $u_1 = -x^2 e^x + 2xe^x - 2e^x$, $u_2 = xe^x - e^x$, and

$$y = c_1 x + c_2 x^2 - x^3 e^x + 2x^2 e^x - 2xe^x + x^3 e^x - x^2 e^x$$

$$= c_1 x + c_2 x^2 + x^2 e^x - 2xe^x.$$

23. The auxiliary equation $m(m-1) + m - 1 = m^2 - 1 = 0$ has roots $m_1 = -1$, $m_2 = 1$, so $y_c = c_1 x^{-1} + c_2 x$. With $y_1 = x^{-1}$, $y_2 = x$, and the identification $f(x) = \ln x / x^2$, we get

$$W = 2x^{-1}, \qquad W_1 = -\ln x / x, \qquad \text{and} \qquad W_2 = \ln x / x^3.$$

Then $u_1' = W_1 / W = -(\ln x)/2$, $u_2' = W_2 / W = (\ln x)/2x^2$, and integration by parts gives

$$u_1 = \frac{1}{2}x - \frac{1}{2}x \ln x$$

$$u_2 = -\frac{1}{2}x^{-1} \ln x - \frac{1}{2}x^{-1},$$

so

$$y_p = u_1 y_1 + u_2 y_2 = \left(\frac{1}{2}x - \frac{1}{2}x \ln x\right)x^{-1} + \left(-\frac{1}{2}x^{-1} \ln x - \frac{1}{2}x^{-1}\right)x = -\ln x$$

and

$$y = y_c + y_p = c_1 x^{-1} + c_2 x - \ln x, \qquad x > 0.$$

24. The auxiliary equation $m(m-1) + m - 1 = m^2 - 1 = 0$ has roots $m_1 = -1$, $m_2 = 1$, so $y_c = c_1 x^{-1} + c_2 x$. With $y_1 = x^{-1}$, $y_2 = x$, and the identification $f(x) = 1/x^2(x+1)$, we get

$$W = 2x^{-1}, \qquad W_1 = -1/x(x+1), \qquad \text{and} \qquad W_2 = 1/x^3(x+1).$$

200

Then $u_1' = W_1/W = -1/2(x+1)$, $u_2' = W_2/W = 1/2x^2(x+1)$, and integration (by partial fractions for u_2') gives

$$u_1 = -\frac{1}{2}\ln(x+1)$$

$$u_2 = -\frac{1}{2}x^{-1} - \frac{1}{2}\ln x + \frac{1}{2}\ln(x+1),$$

so

$$y_p = u_1 y_1 + u_2 y_2 = \left[-\frac{1}{2}\ln(x+1)\right]x^{-1} + \left[-\frac{1}{2}x^{-1} - \frac{1}{2}\ln x + \frac{1}{2}\ln(x+1)\right]x$$

$$= -\frac{1}{2} - \frac{1}{2}x\ln x + \frac{1}{2}x\ln(x+1) - \frac{\ln(x+1)}{2x} = -\frac{1}{2} + \frac{1}{2}x\ln\left(1+\frac{1}{x}\right) - \frac{\ln(x+1)}{2x}$$

and

$$y = y_c + y_p = c_1 x^{-1} + c_2 x - \frac{1}{2} + \frac{1}{2}x\ln\left(1+\frac{1}{x}\right) - \frac{\ln(x+1)}{2x}, \qquad x > 0.$$

25. The auxiliary equation is $m^2 + 2m = m(m+2) = 0$, so that $y = c_1 + c_2 x^{-2}$ and $y' = -2c_2 x^{-3}$. The initial conditions imply

$$c_1 + c_2 = 0$$

$$-2c_2 = 4.$$

Thus, $c_1 = 2$, $c_2 = -2$, and $y = 2 - 2x^{-2}$. The graph is given to the right.

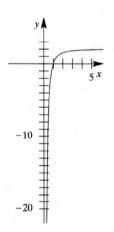

26. The auxiliary equation is $m^2 - 6m + 8 = (m-2)(m-4) = 0$, so that

$$y = c_1 x^2 + c_2 x^4 \quad \text{and} \quad y' = 2c_1 x + 4c_2 x^3.$$

The initial conditions imply

$$4c_1 + 16c_2 = 32$$

$$4c_1 + 32c_2 = 0.$$

Thus, $c_1 = 16$, $c_2 = -2$, and $y = 16x^2 - 2x^4$. The graph is given to the right.

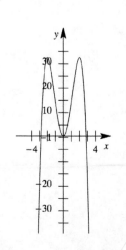

Exercises 4.7 Cauchy-Euler Equation

27. The auxiliary equation is $m^2 + 1 = 0$, so that

$$y = c_1 \cos(\ln x) + c_2 \sin(\ln x)$$

and

$$y' = -c_1 \frac{1}{x}\sin(\ln x) + c_2\frac{1}{x}\cos(\ln x).$$

The initial conditions imply $c_1 = 1$ and $c_2 = 2$. Thus $y = \cos(\ln x) + 2\sin(\ln x)$. The graph is given to the right.

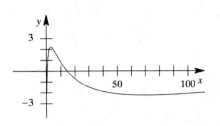

28. The auxiliary equation is $m^2 - 4m + 4 = (m-2)^2 = 0$, so that

$$y = c_1 x^2 + c_2 x^2 \ln x \quad \text{and} \quad y' = 2c_1 x + c_2(x + 2x\ln x).$$

The initial conditions imply $c_1 = 5$ and $c_2 + 10 = 3$. Thus $y = 5x^2 - 7x^2 \ln x$. The graph is given to the right.

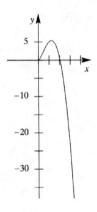

29. The auxiliary equation is $m^2 = 0$ so that $y_c = c_1 + c_2 \ln x$ and

$$W(1, \ln x) = \begin{vmatrix} 1 & \ln x \\ 0 & 1/x \end{vmatrix} = \frac{1}{x}.$$

Identifying $f(x) = 1$ we obtain $u_1' = -x\ln x$ and $u_2' = x$. Then $u_1 = \frac{1}{4}x^2 - \frac{1}{2}x^2\ln x$, $u_2 = \frac{1}{2}x^2$, and

$$y = c_1 + c_2 \ln x + \frac{1}{4}x^2 - \frac{1}{2}x^2\ln x + \frac{1}{2}x^2\ln x = c_1 + c_2 \ln x + \frac{1}{4}x^2.$$

The initial conditions imply $c_1 + \frac{1}{4} = 1$ and $c_2 + \frac{1}{2} = -\frac{1}{2}$. Thus, $c_1 = \frac{3}{4}$, $c_2 = -1$, and $y = \frac{3}{4} - \ln x + \frac{1}{4}x^2$. The graph is given to the right.

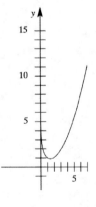

30. The auxiliary equation is $m^2 - 6m + 8 = (m-2)(m-4) = 0$, so that $y_c = c_1 x^2 + c_2 x^4$ and

$$W = \begin{vmatrix} x^2 & x^4 \\ 2x & 4x^3 \end{vmatrix} = 2x^5.$$

Identifying $f(x) = 8x^4$ we obtain $u_1' = -4x^3$ and $u_2' = 4x$. Then $u_1 = -x^4$, $u_2 = 2x^2$, and $y = c_1 x^2 + c_2 x^4 + x^6$. The initial conditions imply

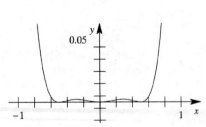

$$\frac{1}{4}c_1 + \frac{1}{16}c_2 = -\frac{1}{64}$$

$$c_1 + \frac{1}{2}c_2 = -\frac{3}{16}.$$

Thus $c_1 = \frac{1}{16}$, $c_2 = -\frac{1}{2}$, and $y = \frac{1}{16}x^2 - \frac{1}{2}x^4 + x^6$. The graph is given above.

31. Substituting $x = e^t$ into the differential equation we obtain

$$\frac{d^2y}{dt^2} + 8\frac{dy}{dt} - 20y = 0.$$

The auxiliary equation is $m^2 + 8m - 20 = (m + 10)(m - 2) = 0$ so that

$$y = c_1 e^{-10t} + c_2 e^{2t} = c_1 x^{-10} + c_2 x^2.$$

32. Substituting $x = e^t$ into the differential equation we obtain

$$\frac{d^2y}{dt^2} - 10\frac{dy}{dt} + 25y = 0.$$

The auxiliary equation is $m^2 - 10m + 25 = (m - 5)^2 = 0$ so that

$$y = c_1 e^{5t} + c_2 t e^{5t} = c_1 x^5 + c_2 x^5 \ln x.$$

33. Substituting $x = e^t$ into the differential equation we obtain

$$\frac{d^2y}{dt^2} + 9\frac{dy}{dt} + 8y = e^{2t}.$$

The auxiliary equation is $m^2 + 9m + 8 = (m + 1)(m + 8) = 0$ so that $y_c = c_1 e^{-t} + c_2 e^{-8t}$. Using undetermined coefficients we try $y_p = Ae^{2t}$. This leads to $30Ae^{2t} = e^{2t}$, so that $A = 1/30$ and

$$y = c_1 e^{-t} + c_2 e^{-8t} + \frac{1}{30}e^{2t} = c_1 x^{-1} + c_2 x^{-8} + \frac{1}{30}x^2.$$

34. Substituting $x = e^t$ into the differential equation we obtain

$$\frac{d^2y}{dt^2} - 5\frac{dy}{dt} + 6y = 2t.$$

The auxiliary equation is $m^2 - 5m + 6 = (m - 2)(m - 3) = 0$ so that $y_c = c_1 e^{2t} + c_2 e^{3t}$. Using undetermined coefficients we try $y_p = At + B$. This leads to $(-5A + 6B) + 6At = 2t$, so that $A = 1/3$, $B = 5/18$, and

$$y = c_1 e^{2t} + c_2 e^{3t} + \frac{1}{3}t + \frac{5}{18} = c_1 x^2 + c_2 x^3 + \frac{1}{3}\ln x + \frac{5}{18}.$$

35. Substituting $x = e^t$ into the differential equation we obtain

$$\frac{d^2y}{dt^2} - 4\frac{dy}{dt} + 13y = 4 + 3e^t.$$

203

The auxiliary equation is $m^2 - 4m + 13 = 0$ so that $y_c = e^{2t}(c_1 \cos 3t + c_2 \sin 3t)$. Using undetermined coefficients we try $y_p = A + Be^t$. This leads to $13A + 10Be^t = 4 + 3e^t$, so that $A = 4/13$, $B = 3/10$, and

$$y = e^{2t}(c_1 \cos 3t + c_2 \sin 3t) + \frac{4}{13} + \frac{3}{10}e^t$$

$$= x^2\left[c_1 \cos(3\ln x) + c_2 \sin(3\ln x)\right] + \frac{4}{13} + \frac{3}{10}x.$$

36. From

$$\frac{d^2y}{dx^2} = \frac{1}{x^2}\left(\frac{d^2y}{dt^2} - \frac{dy}{dt}\right)$$

it follows that

$$\frac{d^3y}{dx^3} = \frac{1}{x^2}\frac{d}{dx}\left(\frac{d^2y}{dt^2} - \frac{dy}{dt}\right) - \frac{2}{x^3}\left(\frac{d^2y}{dt^2} - \frac{dy}{dt}\right)$$

$$= \frac{1}{x^2}\frac{d}{dx}\left(\frac{d^2y}{dt^2}\right) - \frac{1}{x^2}\frac{d}{dx}\left(\frac{dy}{dt}\right) - \frac{2}{x^3}\frac{d^2y}{dt^2} + \frac{2}{x^3}\frac{dy}{dt}$$

$$= \frac{1}{x^2}\frac{d^3y}{dt^3}\left(\frac{1}{x}\right) - \frac{1}{x^2}\frac{d^2y}{dt^2}\left(\frac{1}{x}\right) - \frac{2}{x^3}\frac{d^2y}{dt^2} + \frac{2}{x^3}\frac{dy}{dt}$$

$$= \frac{1}{x^3}\left(\frac{d^3y}{dt^3} - 3\frac{d^2y}{dt^2} + 2\frac{dy}{dt}\right).$$

Substituting into the differential equation we obtain

$$\frac{d^3y}{dt^3} - 3\frac{d^2y}{dt^2} + 2\frac{dy}{dt} - 3\left(\frac{d^2y}{dt^2} - \frac{dy}{dt}\right) + 6\frac{dy}{dt} - 6y = 3 + 3t$$

or

$$\frac{d^3y}{dt^3} - 6\frac{d^2y}{dt^2} + 11\frac{dy}{dt} - 6y = 3 + 3t.$$

The auxiliary equation is $m^3 - 6m^2 + 11m - 6 = (m-1)(m-2)(m-3) = 0$ so that $y_c = c_1 e^t + c_2 e^{2t} + c_3 e^{3t}$. Using undetermined coefficients we try $y_p = A + Bt$. This leads to $(11B - 6A) - 6Bt = 3 + 3t$, so that $A = -17/12$, $B = -1/2$, and

$$y = c_1 e^t + c_2 e^{2t} + c_3 e^{3t} - \frac{17}{12} - \frac{1}{2}t = c_1 x + c_2 x^2 + c_3 x^3 - \frac{17}{12} - \frac{1}{2}\ln x.$$

In the next two problems we use the substitution $t = -x$ since the initial conditions are on the interval $(-\infty, 0)$. In this case

$$\frac{dy}{dt} = \frac{dy}{dx}\frac{dx}{dt} = -\frac{dy}{dx}$$

and

$$\frac{d^2y}{dt^2} = \frac{d}{dt}\left(\frac{dy}{dt}\right) = \frac{d}{dt}\left(-\frac{dy}{dx}\right) = -\frac{d}{dt}(y') = -\frac{dy'}{dx}\frac{dx}{dt} = -\frac{d^2y}{dx^2}\frac{dx}{dt} = \frac{d^2y}{dx^2}.$$

37. The differential equation and initial conditions become

$$4t^2 \frac{d^2y}{dt^2} + y = 0; \quad y(t)\Big|_{t=1} = 2, \quad y'(t)\Big|_{t=1} = -4.$$

The auxiliary equation is $4m^2 - 4m + 1 = (2m - 1)^2 = 0$, so that

$$y = c_1 t^{1/2} + c_2 t^{1/2} \ln t \quad \text{and} \quad y' = \frac{1}{2}c_1 t^{-1/2} + c_2 \left(t^{-1/2} + \frac{1}{2}t^{-1/2} \ln t\right).$$

The initial conditions imply $c_1 = 2$ and $1 + c_2 = -4$. Thus

$$y = 2t^{1/2} - 5t^{1/2} \ln t = 2(-x)^{1/2} - 5(-x)^{1/2} \ln(-x), \quad x < 0.$$

38. The differential equation and initial conditions become

$$t^2 \frac{d^2y}{dt^2} - 4t \frac{dy}{dt} + 6y = 0; \quad y(t)\Big|_{t=2} = 8, \quad y'(t)\Big|_{t=2} = 0.$$

The auxiliary equation is $m^2 - 5m + 6 = (m - 2)(m - 3) = 0$, so that

$$y = c_1 t^2 + c_2 t^3 \quad \text{and} \quad y' = 2c_1 t + 3c_2 t^2.$$

The initial conditions imply

$$4c_1 + 8c_2 = 8$$

$$4c_1 + 12c_2 = 0$$

from which we find $c_1 = 6$ and $c_2 = -2$. Thus

$$y = 6t^2 - 2t^3 = 6x^2 + 2x^3, \quad x < 0.$$

39. Letting $u = x + 2$ we obtain $dy/dx = dy/du$ and, using the Chain Rule,

$$\frac{d^2y}{dx^2} = \frac{d}{dx}\left(\frac{dy}{du}\right) = \frac{d^2y}{du^2}\frac{du}{dx} = \frac{d^2y}{du^2}(1) = \frac{d^2y}{du^2}.$$

Substituting into the differential equation we obtain

$$u^2 \frac{d^2y}{du^2} + u \frac{dy}{du} + y = 0.$$

The auxiliary equation is $m^2 + 1 = 0$ so that

$$y = c_1 \cos(\ln u) + c_2 \sin(\ln u) = c_1 \cos[\ln(x + 2)] + c_2 \sin[\ln(x + 2)].$$

40. If $1 - i$ is a root of the auxiliary equation then so is $1 + i$, and the auxiliary equation is

$$(m - 2)[m - (1 + i)][m - (1 - i)] = m^3 - 4m^2 + 6m - 4 = 0.$$

We need $m^3 - 4m^2 + 6m - 4$ to have the form $m(m-1)(m-2) + bm(m-1) + cm + d$. Expanding this last expression and equating coefficients we get $b = -1$, $c = 3$, and $d = -4$. Thus, the differential equation is

$$x^3 y''' - x^2 y'' + 3xy' - 4y = 0.$$

Exercises 4.7   Cauchy-Euler Equation

41. For $x^2y'' = 0$ the auxiliary equation is $m(m-1) = 0$ and the general solution is $y = c_1 + c_2x$. The initial conditions imply $c_1 = y_0$ and $c_2 = y_1$, so $y = y_0 + y_1x$. The initial conditions are satisfied for all real values of y_0 and y_1.

For $x^2y'' - 2xy' + 2y = 0$ the auxiliary equation is $m^2 - 3m + 2 = (m-1)(m-2) = 0$ and the general solution is $y = c_1x + c_2x^2$. The initial condition $y(0) = y_0$ implies $0 = y_0$ and the condition $y'(0) = y_1$ implies $c_1 = y_1$. Thus, the initial conditions are satisfied for $y_0 = 0$ and for all real values of y_1.

For $x^2y'' - 4xy' + 6y = 0$ the auxiliary equation is $m^2 - 5m + 6 = (m-2)(m-3) = 0$ and the general solution is $y = c_1x^2 + c_2x^3$. The initial conditions imply $y(0) = 0 = y_0$ and $y'(0) = 0$. Thus, the initial conditions are satisfied only for $y_0 = y_1 = 0$.

42. The function $y(x) = -\sqrt{x}\cos(\ln x)$ is defined for $x > 0$ and has x-intercepts where $\ln x = \pi/2 + k\pi$ for k an integer or where $x = e^{\pi/2 + k\pi}$. Solving $\pi/2 + k\pi = 0.5$ we get $k \approx -0.34$, so $e^{\pi/2 + k\pi} < 0.5$ for all negative integers and the graph has infinitely many x-intercepts in the interval $(0, 0.5)$.

43. The auxiliary equation is $2m(m-1)(m-2) - 10.98m(m-1) + 8.5m + 1.3 = 0$, so that $m_1 = -0.053299$, $m_2 = 1.81164$, $m_3 = 6.73166$, and

$$y = c_1x^{-0.053299} + c_2x^{1.81164} + c_3x^{6.73166}.$$

44. The auxiliary equation is $m(m-1)(m-2) + 4m(m-1) + 5m - 9 = 0$, so that $m_1 = 1.40819$ and the two complex roots are $-1.20409 \pm 2.22291i$. The general solution of the differential equation is

$$y = c_1x^{1.40819} + x^{-1.20409}[c_2\cos(2.22291\ln x) + c_3\sin(2.22291\ln x)].$$

45. The auxiliary equation is $m(m-1)(m-2)(m-3) + 6m(m-1)(m-2) + 3m(m-1) - 3m + 4 = 0$, so that $m_1 = m_2 = \sqrt{2}$ and $m_3 = m_4 = -\sqrt{2}$. The general solution of the differential equation is

$$y = c_1x^{\sqrt{2}} + c_2x^{\sqrt{2}}\ln x + c_3x^{-\sqrt{2}} + c_4x^{-\sqrt{2}}\ln x.$$

46. The auxiliary equation is $m(m-1)(m-2)(m-3) - 6m(m-1)(m-2) + 33m(m-1) - 105m + 169 = 0$, so that $m_1 = m_2 = 3 + 2i$ and $m_3 = m_4 = 3 - 2i$. The general solution of the differential equation is

$$y = x^3[c_1\cos(2\ln x) + c_2\sin(2\ln x)] + x^3\ln x[c_3\cos(2\ln x) + c_4\sin(2\ln x)].$$

47. The auxiliary equation

$$m(m-1)(m-2) - m(m-1) - 2m + 6 = m^3 - 4m^2 + m + 6 = 0$$

has roots $m_1 = -1$, $m_2 = 2$, and $m_3 = 3$, so $y_c = c_1x^{-1} + c_2x^2 + c_3x^3$. With $y_1 = x^{-1}$, $y_2 = x^2$, $y_3 = x^3$, and the identification $f(x) = 1/x$, we get from (11) of Section 4.6 in the text

$$W_1 = x^3, \qquad W_2 = -4, \qquad W_3 = 3/x, \qquad \text{and} \qquad W = 12x.$$

Then $u'_1 = W_1/W = x^2/12$, $u'_2 = W_2/W = -1/3x$, $u'_3 = 1/4x^2$, and integration gives

$$u_1 = \frac{x^3}{36}, \qquad u_2 = -\frac{1}{3}\ln x, \qquad \text{and} \qquad u_3 = -\frac{1}{4x},$$

so

$$y_p = u_1y_1 + u_2y_2 + u_3y_3 = \frac{x^3}{36}x^{-1} + x^2\left(-\frac{1}{3}\ln x\right) + x^3\left(-\frac{1}{4x}\right) = -\frac{2}{9}x^2 - \frac{1}{3}x^2\ln x,$$

and

$$y = y_c + y_p = c_1x^{-1} + c_2x^2 + c_3x^3 - \frac{2}{9}x^2 - \frac{1}{3}x^2\ln x, \qquad x > 0.$$

Exercises 4.8

Solving Systems of Linear DEs by Elimination

1. From $Dx = 2x - y$ and $Dy = x$ we obtain $y = 2x - Dx$, $Dy = 2Dx - D^2x$, and $(D^2 - 2D + 1)x = 0$. The solution is

$$x = c_1e^t + c_2te^t$$

$$y = (c_1 - c_2)e^t + c_2te^t.$$

2. From $Dx = 4x + 7y$ and $Dy = x - 2y$ we obtain $y = \frac{1}{7}Dx - \frac{4}{7}x$, $Dy = \frac{1}{7}D^2x - \frac{4}{7}Dx$, and $(D^2 - 2D - 15)x = 0$. The solution is

$$x = c_1e^{5t} + c_2e^{-3t}$$

$$y = \frac{1}{7}c_1e^{5t} - c_2e^{-3t}.$$

3. From $Dx = -y + t$ and $Dy = x - t$ we obtain $y = t - Dx$, $Dy = 1 - D^2x$, and $(D^2 + 1)x = 1 + t$. The solution is

$$x = c_1\cos t + c_2\sin t + 1 + t$$

$$y = c_1\sin t - c_2\cos t + t - 1.$$

4. From $Dx - 4y = 1$ and $x + Dy = 2$ we obtain $y = \frac{1}{4}Dx - \frac{1}{4}$, $Dy = \frac{1}{4}D^2x$, and $(D^2 + 1)x = 2$. The solution is

$$x = c_1\cos t + c_2\sin t + 2$$

$$y = \frac{1}{4}c_2\cos t - \frac{1}{4}c_1\sin t - \frac{1}{4}.$$

Exercises 4.8   Solving Systems of Linear DEs by Elimination

5. From $(D^2+5)x - 2y = 0$ and $-2x+(D^2+2)y = 0$ we obtain $y = \frac{1}{2}(D^2+5)x$, $D^2y = \frac{1}{2}(D^4+5D^2)x$, and $(D^2+1)(D^2+6)x = 0$. The solution is

$$x = c_1 \cos t + c_2 \sin t + c_3 \cos \sqrt{6}\, t + c_4 \sin \sqrt{6}\, t$$

$$y = 2c_1 \cos t + 2c_2 \sin t - \frac{1}{2}c_3 \cos \sqrt{6}\, t - \frac{1}{2}c_4 \sin \sqrt{6}\, t.$$

6. From $(D+1)x + (D-1)y = 2$ and $3x + (D+2)y = -1$ we obtain $x = -\frac{1}{3} - \frac{1}{3}(D+2)y$, $Dx = -\frac{1}{3}(D^2+2D)y$, and $(D^2+5)y = -7$. The solution is

$$y = c_1 \cos \sqrt{5}\, t + c_2 \sin \sqrt{5}\, t - \frac{7}{5}$$

$$x = \left(-\frac{2}{3}c_1 - \frac{\sqrt{5}}{3}c_2 \right) \cos \sqrt{5}\, t + \left(\frac{\sqrt{5}}{3}c_1 - \frac{2}{3}c_2 \right) \sin \sqrt{5}\, t + \frac{3}{5}.$$

7. From $D^2x = 4y + e^t$ and $D^2y = 4x - e^t$ we obtain $y = \frac{1}{4}D^2x - \frac{1}{4}e^t$, $D^2y = \frac{1}{4}D^4x - \frac{1}{4}e^t$, and $(D^2+4)(D-2)(D+2)x = -3e^t$. The solution is

$$x = c_1 \cos 2t + c_2 \sin 2t + c_3 e^{2t} + c_4 e^{-2t} + \frac{1}{5}e^t$$

$$y = -c_1 \cos 2t - c_2 \sin 2t + c_3 e^{2t} + c_4 e^{-2t} - \frac{1}{5}e^t.$$

8. From $(D^2+5)x + Dy = 0$ and $(D+1)x + (D-4)y = 0$ we obtain $(D-5)(D^2+4)x = 0$ and $(D-5)(D^2+4)y = 0$. The solution is

$$x = c_1 e^{5t} + c_2 \cos 2t + c_3 \sin 2t$$

$$y = c_4 e^{5t} + c_5 \cos 2t + c_6 \sin 2t.$$

Substituting into $(D+1)x + (D-4)y = 0$ gives

$$(6c_1 + c_4)e^{5t} + (c_2 + 2c_3 - 4c_5 + 2c_6) \cos 2t + (-2c_2 + c_3 - 2c_5 - 4c_6) \sin 2t = 0$$

so that $c_4 = -6c_1$, $c_5 = \frac{1}{2}c_3$, $c_6 = -\frac{1}{2}c_2$, and

$$y = -6c_1 e^{5t} + \frac{1}{2}c_3 \cos 2t - \frac{1}{2}c_2 \sin 2t.$$

9. From $Dx + D^2y = e^{3t}$ and $(D+1)x + (D-1)y = 4e^{3t}$ we obtain $D(D^2+1)x = 34e^{3t}$ and $D(D^2+1)y = -8e^{3t}$. The solution is

$$y = c_1 + c_2 \sin t + c_3 \cos t - \frac{4}{15}e^{3t}$$

$$x = c_4 + c_5 \sin t + c_6 \cos t + \frac{17}{15}e^{3t}.$$

Substituting into $(D+1)x + (D-1)y = 4e^{3t}$ gives

$$(c_4 - c_1) + (c_5 - c_6 - c_3 - c_2) \sin t + (c_6 + c_5 + c_2 - c_3) \cos t = 0$$

so that $c_4 = c_1$, $c_5 = c_3$, $c_6 = -c_2$, and

$$x = c_1 - c_2 \cos t + c_3 \sin t + \frac{17}{15}e^{3t}.$$

10. From $D^2 x - Dy = t$ and $(D+3)x + (D+3)y = 2$ we obtain $D(D+1)(D+3)x = 1 + 3t$ and $D(D+1)(D+3)y = -1 - 3t$. The solution is

$$x = c_1 + c_2 e^{-t} + c_3 e^{-3t} - t + \frac{1}{2}t^2$$

$$y = c_4 + c_5 e^{-t} + c_6 e^{-3t} + t - \frac{1}{2}t^2.$$

Substituting into $(D+3)x + (D+3)y = 2$ and $D^2 x - Dy = t$ gives

$$3(c_1 + c_4) + 2(c_2 + c_5)e^{-t} = 2$$

and

$$(c_2 + c_5)e^{-t} + 3(3c_3 + c_6)e^{-3t} = 0$$

so that $c_4 = -c_1$, $c_5 = -c_2$, $c_6 = -3c_3$, and

$$y = -c_1 - c_2 e^{-t} - 3c_3 e^{-3t} + t - \frac{1}{2}t^2.$$

11. From $(D^2 - 1)x - y = 0$ and $(D-1)x + Dy = 0$ we obtain $y = (D^2 - 1)x$, $Dy = (D^3 - D)x$, and $(D-1)(D^2 + D + 1)x = 0$. The solution is

$$x = c_1 e^t + e^{-t/2} \left[c_2 \cos \frac{\sqrt{3}}{2}t + c_3 \sin \frac{\sqrt{3}}{2}t \right]$$

$$y = \left(-\frac{3}{2}c_2 - \frac{\sqrt{3}}{2}c_3 \right) e^{-t/2} \cos \frac{\sqrt{3}}{2}t + \left(\frac{\sqrt{3}}{2}c_2 - \frac{3}{2}c_3 \right) e^{-t/2} \sin \frac{\sqrt{3}}{2}t.$$

12. From $(2D^2 - D - 1)x - (2D+1)y = 1$ and $(D-1)x + Dy = -1$ we obtain $(2D+1)(D-1)(D+1)x = -1$ and $(2D+1)(D+1)y = -2$. The solution is

$$x = c_1 e^{-t/2} + c_2 e^{-t} + c_3 e^t + 1$$

$$y = c_4 e^{-t/2} + c_5 e^{-t} - 2.$$

Substituting into $(D-1)x + Dy = -1$ gives

$$\left(-\frac{3}{2}c_1 - \frac{1}{2}c_4 \right) e^{-t/2} + (-2c_2 - c_5)e^{-t} = 0$$

so that $c_4 = -3c_1$, $c_5 = -2c_2$, and

$$y = -3c_1 e^{-t/2} - 2c_2 e^{-t} - 2.$$

13. From $(2D-5)x+Dy = e^t$ and $(D-1)x+Dy = 5e^t$ we obtain $Dy = (5-2D)x+e^t$ and $(4-D)x = 4e^t$. Then

$$x = c_1 e^{4t} + \frac{4}{3}e^t$$

and $Dy = -3c_1 e^{4t} + 5e^t$ so that

$$y = -\frac{3}{4}c_1 e^{4t} + c_2 + 5e^t.$$

14. From $Dx+Dy = e^t$ and $(-D^2+D+1)x+y = 0$ we obtain $y = (D^2-D-1)x$, $Dy = (D^3-D^2-D)x$, and $D^2(D-1)x = e^t$. The solution is

$$x = c_1 + c_2 t + c_3 e^t + te^t$$

$$y = -c_1 - c_2 - c_2 t - c_3 e^t - te^t + e^t.$$

15. Multiplying the first equation by $D+1$ and the second equation by D^2+1 and subtracting we obtain $(D^4 - D^2)x = 1$. Then

$$x = c_1 + c_2 t + c_3 e^t + c_4 e^{-t} - \frac{1}{2}t^2.$$

Multiplying the first equation by $D+1$ and subtracting we obtain $D^2(D+1)y = 1$. Then

$$y = c_5 + c_6 t + c_7 e^{-t} - \frac{1}{2}t^2.$$

Substituting into $(D-1)x + (D^2+1)y = 1$ gives

$$(-c_1 + c_2 + c_5 - 1) + (-2c_4 + 2c_7)e^{-t} + (-1 - c_2 + c_6)t = 1$$

so that $c_5 = c_1 - c_2 + 2$, $c_6 = c_2 + 1$, and $c_7 = c_4$. The solution of the system is

$$x = c_1 + c_2 t + c_3 e^t + c_4 e^{-t} - \frac{1}{2}t^2$$

$$y = (c_1 - c_2 + 2) + (c_2 + 1)t + c_4 e^{-t} - \frac{1}{2}t^2.$$

16. From $D^2 x - 2(D^2 + D)y = \sin t$ and $x + Dy = 0$ we obtain $x = -Dy$, $D^2 x = -D^3 y$, and $D(D^2 + 2D + 2)y = -\sin t$. The solution is

$$y = c_1 + c_2 e^{-t}\cos t + c_3 e^{-t}\sin t + \frac{1}{5}\cos t + \frac{2}{5}\sin t$$

$$x = (c_2 + c_3)e^{-t}\sin t + (c_2 - c_3)e^{-t}\cos t + \frac{1}{5}\sin t - \frac{2}{5}\cos t.$$

17. From $Dx = y$, $Dy = z$. and $Dz = x$ we obtain $x = D^2 y = D^3 x$ so that $(D-1)(D^2+D+1)x = 0$,

$$x = c_1 e^t + e^{-t/2}\left[c_2 \sin\frac{\sqrt{3}}{2}t + c_3 \cos\frac{\sqrt{3}}{2}t\right],$$

$$y = c_1 e^t + \left(-\frac{1}{2}c_2 - \frac{\sqrt{3}}{2}c_3\right) e^{-t/2} \sin\frac{\sqrt{3}}{2}t + \left(\frac{\sqrt{3}}{2}c_2 - \frac{1}{2}c_3\right) e^{-t/2} \cos\frac{\sqrt{3}}{2}t,$$

and

$$z = c_1 e^t + \left(-\frac{1}{2}c_2 + \frac{\sqrt{3}}{2}c_3\right) e^{-t/2} \sin\frac{\sqrt{3}}{2}t + \left(-\frac{\sqrt{3}}{2}c_2 - \frac{1}{2}c_3\right) e^{-t/2} \cos\frac{\sqrt{3}}{2}t.$$

18. From $Dx + z = e^t$, $(D-1)x + Dy + Dz = 0$, and $x + 2y + Dz = e^t$ we obtain $z = -Dx + e^t$, $Dz = -D^2x + e^t$, and the system $(-D^2 + D - 1)x + Dy = -e^t$ and $(-D^2 + 1)x + 2y = 0$. Then $y = \frac{1}{2}(D^2 - 1)x$, $Dy = \frac{1}{2}D(D^2 - 1)x$, and $(D-2)(D^2 + 1)x = -2e^t$ so that the solution is

$$x = c_1 e^{2t} + c_2 \cos t + c_3 \sin t + e^t$$

$$y = \frac{3}{2}c_1 e^{2t} - c_2 \cos t - c_3 \sin t$$

$$z = -2c_1 e^{2t} - c_3 \cos t + c_2 \sin t.$$

19. Write the system in the form

$$Dx - 6y = 0$$

$$x - Dy + z = 0$$

$$x + y - Dz = 0.$$

Multiplying the second equation by D and adding to the third equation we obtain $(D+1)x - (D^2 - 1)y = 0$. Eliminating y between this equation and $Dx - 6y = 0$ we find

$$(D^3 - D - 6D - 6)x = (D+1)(D+2)(D-3)x = 0.$$

Thus

$$x = c_1 e^{-t} + c_2 e^{-2t} + c_3 e^{3t},$$

and, successively substituting into the first and second equations, we get

$$y = -\frac{1}{6}c_1 e^{-t} - \frac{1}{3}c_2 e^{-2t} + \frac{1}{2}c_3 e^{3t}$$

$$z = -\frac{5}{6}c_1 e^{-t} - \frac{1}{3}c_2 e^{-2t} + \frac{1}{2}c_3 e^{3t}.$$

20. Write the system in the form

$$(D+1)x - z = 0$$

$$(D+1)y - z = 0$$

$$x - y + Dz = 0.$$

Multiplying the third equation by $D+1$ and adding to the second equation we obtain $(D+1)x + (D^2 + D - 1)z = 0$. Eliminating z between this equation and $(D+1)x - z = 0$

we find $D(D+1)^2 x = 0$. Thus

$$x = c_1 + c_2 e^{-t} + c_3 t e^{-t},$$

and, successively substituting into the first and third equations, we get

$$y = c_1 + (c_2 - c_3)e^{-t} + c_3 t e^{-t}$$

$$z = c_1 + c_3 e^{-t}.$$

21. From $(D+5)x + y = 0$ and $4x - (D+1)y = 0$ we obtain $y = -(D+5)x$ so that $Dy = -(D^2+5D)x$. Then $4x + (D^2 + 5D)x + (D+5)x = 0$ and $(D+3)^2 x = 0$. Thus

$$x = c_1 e^{-3t} + c_2 t e^{-3t}$$

$$y = -(2c_1 + c_2)e^{-3t} - 2c_2 t e^{-3t}.$$

Using $x(1) = 0$ and $y(1) = 1$ we obtain

$$c_1 e^{-3} + c_2 e^{-3} = 0$$

$$-(2c_1 + c_2)e^{-3} - 2c_2 e^{-3} = 1$$

or

$$c_1 + c_2 = 0$$

$$2c_1 + 3c_2 = -e^3.$$

Thus $c_1 = e^3$ and $c_2 = -e^3$. The solution of the initial value problem is

$$x = e^{-3t+3} - te^{-3t+3}$$

$$y = -e^{-3t+3} + 2te^{-3t+3}.$$

22. From $Dx - y = -1$ and $3x + (D-2)y = 0$ we obtain $x = -\frac{1}{3}(D-2)y$ so that $Dx = -\frac{1}{3}(D^2 - 2D)y$. Then $-\frac{1}{3}(D^2 - 2D)y = y - 1$ and $(D^2 - 2D + 3)y = 3$. Thus

$$y = e^t \left(c_1 \cos \sqrt{2}\, t + c_2 \sin \sqrt{2}\, t \right) + 1$$

and

$$x = \frac{1}{3} e^t \left[\left(c_1 - \sqrt{2}\, c_2 \right) \cos \sqrt{2}\, t + \left(\sqrt{2}\, c_1 + c_2 \right) \sin \sqrt{2}\, t \right] + \frac{2}{3}.$$

Using $x(0) = y(0) = 0$ we obtain

$$c_1 + 1 = 0$$

$$\frac{1}{3} \left(c_1 - \sqrt{2}\, c_2 \right) + \frac{2}{3} = 0.$$

Thus $c_1 = -1$ and $c_2 = \sqrt{2}/2$. The solution of the initial value problem is

$$x = e^t\left(-\frac{2}{3}\cos\sqrt{2}\,t - \frac{\sqrt{2}}{6}\sin\sqrt{2}\,t\right) + \frac{2}{3}$$

$$y = e^t\left(-\cos\sqrt{2}\,t + \frac{\sqrt{2}}{2}\sin\sqrt{2}\,t\right) + 1.$$

23. Equating Newton's law with the net forces in the x- and y-directions gives $m\,d^2x/dt^2 = 0$ and $m\,d^2y/dt^2 = -mg$, respectively. From $mD^2x = 0$ we obtain $x(t) = c_1t + c_2$, and from $mD^2y = -mg$ or $D^2y = -g$ we obtain $y(t) = -\frac{1}{2}gt^2 + c_3t + c_4$.

24. From Newton's second law in the x-direction we have

$$m\frac{d^2x}{dt^2} = -k\cos\theta = -k\frac{1}{v}\frac{dx}{dt} = -|c|\frac{dx}{dt}\,.$$

In the y-direction we have

$$m\frac{d^2y}{dt^2} = -mg - k\sin\theta = -mg - k\frac{1}{v}\frac{dy}{dt} = -mg - |c|\frac{dy}{dt}\,.$$

From $mD^2x + |c|Dx = 0$ we have $D(mD + |c|)x = 0$ so that $(mD + |c|)x = c_1$ or $(D + |c|/m)x = c_2$. This is a linear first-order differential equation. An integrating factor is $e^{\int |c|dt/m} = e^{|c|t/m}$ so that

$$\frac{d}{dt}[e^{|c|t/m}x] = c_2e^{|c|t/m}$$

and $e^{|c|t/m}x = (c_2m/|c|)e^{|c|t/m} + c_3$. The general solution of this equation is $x(t) = c_4 + c_3e^{-|c|t/m}$.

From $(mD^2 + |c|D)y = -mg$ we have $D(mD + |c|)y = -mg$ so that $(mD + |c|)y = -mgt + c_1$ or $(D + |c|/m)y = -gt + c_2$. This is a linear first-order differential equation with integrating factor $e^{\int |c|dt/m} = e^{|c|t/m}$. Thus

$$\frac{d}{dt}[e^{|c|t/m}y] = (-gt + c_2)e^{|c|t/m}$$

$$e^{|c|t/m}y = -\frac{mg}{|c|}te^{|c|t/m} + \frac{m^2g}{c^2}e^{|c|t/m} + c_3e^{|c|t/m} + c_4$$

and

$$y(t) = -\frac{mg}{|c|}t + \frac{m^2g}{c^2} + c_3 + c_4e^{-|c|t/m}.$$

25. Multiplying the first equation by $D + 1$ and the second equation by D we obtain

$$D(D + 1)x - 2D(D + 1)y = 2t + t^2$$

$$D(D + 1)x - 2D(D + 1)y = 0.$$

This leads to $2t + t^2 = 0$, so the system has no solution.

26. The **FindRoot** application of *Mathematica* gives a solution of $x_1(t) = x_2(t)$ as approximately $t = 13.73$ minutes. So tank B contains more salt than tank A for $t > 13.73$ minutes.

27. (a) Separating variables in the first equation, we have $dx_1/x_1 = -dt/50$, so $x_1 = c_1 e^{-t/50}$. From $x_1(0) = 15$ we get $c_1 = 15$. The second differential equation then becomes

$$\frac{dx_2}{dt} = \frac{15}{50}e^{-t/50} - \frac{2}{75}x_2 \qquad \text{or} \qquad \frac{dx_2}{dt} + \frac{2}{75}x_2 = \frac{3}{10}e^{-t/50}.$$

This differential equation is linear and has the integrating factor $e^{\int 2\,dt/75} = e^{2t/75}$. Then

$$\frac{d}{dt}[e^{2t/75}x_2] = \frac{3}{10}e^{-t/50+2t/75} = \frac{3}{10}e^{t/150}$$

so

$$e^{2t/75}x_2 = 45e^{t/150} + c_2$$

and

$$x_2 = 45e^{-t/50} + c_2 e^{-2t/75}.$$

From $x_2(0) = 10$ we get $c_2 = -35$. The third differential equation then becomes

$$\frac{dx_3}{dt} = \frac{90}{75}e^{-t/50} - \frac{70}{75}e^{-2t/75} - \frac{1}{25}x_3$$

or

$$\frac{dx_3}{dt} + \frac{1}{25}x_3 = \frac{6}{5}e^{-t/50} - \frac{14}{15}e^{-2t/75}.$$

This differential equation is linear and has the integrating factor $e^{\int dt/25} = e^{t/25}$. Then

$$\frac{d}{dt}[e^{t/25}x_3] = \frac{6}{5}e^{-t/50+t/25} - \frac{14}{15}e^{-2t/75+t/25} = \frac{6}{5}e^{t/50} - \frac{14}{15}e^{t/75},$$

so

$$e^{t/25}x_3 = 60e^{t/50} - 70e^{t/75} + c_3$$

and

$$x_3 = 60e^{-t/50} - 70e^{-2t/75} + c_3 e^{-t/25}.$$

From $x_3(0) = 5$ we get $c_3 = 15$. The solution of the initial-value problem is

$$x_1(t) = 15e^{-t/50}$$

$$x_2(t) = 45e^{-t/50} - 35e^{-2t/75}$$

$$x_3(t) = 60e^{-t/50} - 70e^{-2t/75} + 15e^{-t/25}.$$

(b)

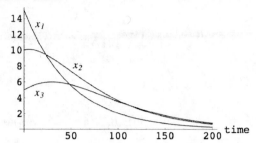

pounds salt

(c) Solving $x_1(t) = \frac{1}{2}$, $x_2(t) = \frac{1}{2}$, and $x_3(t) = \frac{1}{2}$, **FindRoot** gives, respectively, $t_1 = 170.06\,\text{min}$, $t_2 = 214.7\,\text{min}$, and $t_3 = 224.4\,\text{min}$. Thus, all three tanks will contain less than or equal to 0.5 pounds of salt after 224.4 minutes.

Exercises 4.9

Nonlinear Differential Equations

1. We have $y_1' = y_1'' = e^x$, so
$$(y_1'')^2 = (e^x)^2 = e^{2x} = y_1^2.$$

Also, $y_2' = -\sin x$ and $y_2'' = -\cos x$, so
$$(y_2'')^2 = (-\cos x)^2 = \cos^2 x = y_2^2.$$

However, if $y = c_1 y_1 + c_2 y_2$, we have $(y'')^2 = (c_1 e^x - c_2 \cos x)^2$ and $y^2 = (c_1 e^x + c_2 \cos x)^2$. Thus $(y'')^2 \neq y^2$.

2. We have $y_1' = y_1'' = 0$, so
$$y_1 y_1'' = 1 \cdot 0 = 0 = \frac{1}{2}(0)^2 = \frac{1}{2}(y_1')^2.$$

Also, $y_2' = 2x$ and $y_2'' = 2$, so
$$y_2 y_2'' = x^2(2) = 2x^2 = \frac{1}{2}(2x)^2 = \frac{1}{2}(y_2')^2.$$

However, if $y = c_1 y_1 + c_2 y_2$, we have $yy'' = (c_1 \cdot 1 + c_2 x^2)(c_1 \cdot 0 + 2c_2) = 2c_2(c_1 + c_2 x^2)$ and $\frac{1}{2}(y')^2 = \frac{1}{2}[c_1 \cdot 0 + c_2(2x)]^2 = 2c_2^2 x^2$. Thus $yy'' \neq \frac{1}{2}(y')^2$.

3. Let $u = y'$ so that $u' = y''$. The equation becomes $u' = -u^2 - 1$ which is separable. Thus
$$\frac{du}{u^2 + 1} = -dx \implies \tan^{-1} u = -x + c_1 \implies y' = \tan(c_1 - x) \implies y = \ln|\cos(c_1 - x)| + c_2.$$

4. Let $u = y'$ so that $u' = y''$. The equation becomes $u' = 1 + u^2$. Separating variables we obtain
$$\frac{du}{1 + u^2} = dx \implies \tan^{-1} u = x + c_1 \implies u = \tan(x + c_1) \implies y = -\ln|\cos(x + c_1)| + c_2.$$

5. Let $u = y'$ so that $u' = y''$. The equation becomes $x^2 u' + u^2 = 0$. Separating variables we obtain

$$\frac{du}{u^2} = -\frac{dx}{x^2} \implies -\frac{1}{u} = \frac{1}{x} + c_1 = \frac{c_1 x + 1}{x} \implies u = -\frac{1}{c_1}\left(\frac{x}{x + 1/c_1}\right) = \frac{1}{c_1}\left(\frac{1}{c_1 x + 1} - 1\right)$$

$$\implies y = \frac{1}{c_1^2}\ln|c_1 x + 1| - \frac{1}{c_1}x + c_2.$$

6. Let $u = y'$ so that $y'' = u\, du/dy$. The equation becomes $(y + 1)u\, du/dy = u^2$. Separating variables we obtain

$$\frac{du}{u} = \frac{dy}{y + 1} \implies \ln|u| = \ln|y + 1| + \ln c_1 \implies u = c_1(y + 1)$$

$$\implies \frac{dy}{dx} = c_1(y + 1) \implies \frac{dy}{y + 1} = c_1\, dx$$

$$\implies \ln|y + 1| = c_1 x + c_2 \implies y + 1 = c_3 e^{c_1 x}.$$

7. Let $u = y'$ so that $y'' = u\, du/dy$. The equation becomes $u\, du/dy + 2yu^3 = 0$. Separating variables we obtain

$$\frac{du}{u^2} + 2y\, dy = 0 \implies -\frac{1}{u} + y^2 = c_1 \implies u = \frac{1}{y^2 - c_1} \implies y' = \frac{1}{y^2 - c_1}$$

$$\implies \left(y^2 - c_1\right) dy = dx \implies \frac{1}{3}y^3 - c_1 y = x + c_2.$$

8. Let $u = y'$ so that $y'' = u\, du/dy$. The equation becomes $y^2 u\, du/dy = u$. Separating variables we obtain

$$du = \frac{dy}{y^2} \implies u = -\frac{1}{y} + c_1 \implies y' = \frac{c_1 y - 1}{y} \implies \frac{y}{c_1 y - 1}\, dy = dx$$

$$\implies \frac{1}{c_1}\left(1 + \frac{1}{c_1 y - 1}\right) dy = dx \text{ (for } c_1 \neq 0) \implies \frac{1}{c_1}y + \frac{1}{c_1^2}\ln|y - 1| = x + c_2.$$

If $c_1 = 0$, then $y\, dy = -dx$ and another solution is $\frac{1}{2}y^2 = -x + c_2$.

9. (a)

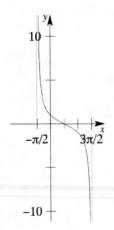

(b) Let $u = y'$ so that $y'' = u\,du/dy$. The equation becomes $u\,du/dy + yu = 0$. Separating variables we obtain

$$du = -y\,dy \implies u = -\frac{1}{2}y^2 + c_1 \implies y' = -\frac{1}{2}y^2 + c_1.$$

When $x = 0$, $y = 1$ and $y' = -1$ so $-1 = -1/2 + c_1$ and $c_1 = -1/2$. Then

$$\frac{dy}{dx} = -\frac{1}{2}y^2 - \frac{1}{2} \implies \frac{dy}{y^2 + 1} = -\frac{1}{2}\,dx \implies \tan^{-1} y = -\frac{1}{2}x + c_2$$

$$\implies y = \tan\left(-\frac{1}{2}x + c_2\right).$$

When $x = 0$, $y = 1$ so $1 = \tan c_2$ and $c_2 = \pi/4$. The solution of the initial-value problem is

$$y = \tan\left(\frac{\pi}{4} - \frac{1}{2}x\right).$$

The graph is shown in part (a).

(c) The interval of definition is $-\pi/2 < \pi/4 - x/2 < \pi/2$ or $-\pi/2 < x < 3\pi/2$.

10. Let $u = y'$ so that $u' = y''$. The equation becomes $(u')^2 + u^2 = 1$ which results in $u' = \pm\sqrt{1 - u^2}$. To solve $u' = \sqrt{1 - u^2}$ we separate variables:

$$\frac{du}{\sqrt{1 - u^2}} = dx \implies \sin^{-1} u = x + c_1 \implies u = \sin(x + c_1)$$

$$\implies y' = \sin(x + c_1).$$

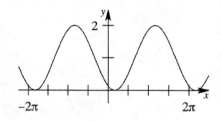

When $x = \pi/2$, $y' = \sqrt{3}/2$, so $\sqrt{3}/2 = \sin(\pi/2 + c_1)$ and $c_1 = -\pi/6$. Thus

$$y' = \sin\left(x - \frac{\pi}{6}\right) \implies y = -\cos\left(x - \frac{\pi}{6}\right) + c_2.$$

When $x = \pi/2$, $y = 1/2$, so $1/2 = -\cos(\pi/2 - \pi/6) + c_2 = -1/2 + c_2$ and $c_2 = 1$. The solution of the initial-value problem is $y = 1 - \cos(x - \pi/6)$.

To solve $u' = -\sqrt{1 - u^2}$ we separate variables:

$$\frac{du}{\sqrt{1 - u^2}} = -dx \implies \cos^{-1} u = x + c_1$$

$$\implies u = \cos(x + c_1) \implies y' = \cos(x + c_1).$$

When $x = \pi/2$, $y' = \sqrt{3}/2$, so $\sqrt{3}/2 = \cos(\pi/2 + c_1)$ and $c_1 = -\pi/3$. Thus

$$y' = \cos\left(x - \frac{\pi}{3}\right) \implies y = \sin\left(x - \frac{\pi}{3}\right) + c_2.$$

When $x = \pi/2$, $y = 1/2$, so $1/2 = \sin(\pi/2 - \pi/3) + c_2 = 1/2 + c_2$ and $c_2 = 0$. The solution of the initial-value problem is $y = \sin(x - \pi/3)$.

11. Let $u = y'$ so that $u' = y''$. The equation becomes $u' - (1/x)u = (1/x)u^3$, which is Bernoulli. Using $w = u^{-2}$ we obtain $dw/dx + (2/x)w = -2/x$. An integrating factor is x^2, so

$$\frac{d}{dx}[x^2 w] = -2x \implies x^2 w = -x^2 + c_1 \implies w = -1 + \frac{c_1}{x^2}$$

$$\implies u^{-2} = -1 + \frac{c_1}{x^2} \implies u = \frac{x}{\sqrt{c_1 - x^2}}$$

$$\implies \frac{dy}{dx} = \frac{x}{\sqrt{c_1 - x^2}} \implies y = -\sqrt{c_1 - x^2} + c_2$$

$$\implies c_1 - x^2 = (c_2 - y)^2 \implies x^2 + (c_2 - y)^2 = c_1.$$

12. Let $u = y'$ so that $u' = y''$. The equation becomes $u' - (1/x)u = u^2$, which is a Bernoulli differential equation. Using the substitution $w = u^{-1}$ we obtain $dw/dx + (1/x)w = -1$. An integrating factor is x, so

$$\frac{d}{dx}[xw] = -x \implies w = -\frac{1}{2}x + \frac{1}{x}c \implies \frac{1}{u} = \frac{c_1 - x^2}{2x} \implies u = \frac{2x}{c_1 - x^2} \implies y = -\ln\left|c_1 - x^2\right| + c_2.$$

In Problems 13-16 the thinner curve is obtained using a numerical solver, while the thicker curve is the graph of the Taylor polynomial.

13. We look for a solution of the form

$$y(x) = y(0) + y'(0)x + \frac{1}{2!}y''(0)x^2 + \frac{1}{3!}y'''(0)x^3 + \frac{1}{4!}y^{(4)}(0)x^4 + \frac{1}{5!}y^{(5)}(0)x^5.$$

From $y''(x) = x + y^2$ we compute

$$y'''(x) = 1 + 2yy'$$

$$y^{(4)}(x) = 2yy'' + 2(y')^2$$

$$y^{(5)}(x) = 2yy''' + 6y'y''.$$

Using $y(0) = 1$ and $y'(0) = 1$ we find

$$y''(0) = 1, \quad y'''(0) = 3, \quad y^{(4)}(0) = 4, \quad y^{(5)}(0) = 12.$$

An approximate solution is

$$y(x) = 1 + x + \frac{1}{2}x^2 + \frac{1}{2}x^3 + \frac{1}{6}x^4 + \frac{1}{10}x^5.$$

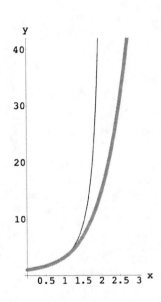

14. We look for a solution of the form

$$y(x) = y(0) + y'(0)x + \frac{1}{2!}y''(0)x^2 + \frac{1}{3!}y'''(0)x^3 + \frac{1}{4!}y^{(4)}(0)x^4 + \frac{1}{5!}y^{(5)}(0)x^5.$$

From $y''(x) = 1 - y^2$ we compute

$$y'''(x) = -2yy'$$

$$y^{(4)}(x) = -2yy'' - 2(y')^2$$

$$y^{(5)}(x) = -2yy''' - 6y'y''.$$

Using $y(0) = 2$ and $y'(0) = 3$ we find

$$y''(0) = -3, \quad y'''(0) = -12, \quad y^{(4)}(0) = -6, \quad y^{(5)}(0) = 102.$$

An approximate solution is

$$y(x) = 2 + 3x - \frac{3}{2}x^2 - 2x^3 - \frac{1}{4}x^4 + \frac{17}{20}x^5.$$

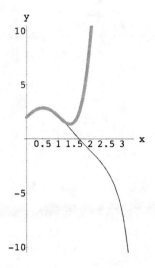

15. We look for a solution of the form

$$y(x) = y(0) + y'(0)x + \frac{1}{2!}y''(0)x^2 + \frac{1}{3!}y'''(0)x^3 + \frac{1}{4!}y^{(4)}(0)x^4 + \frac{1}{5!}y^{(5)}(0)x^5.$$

From $y''(x) = x^2 + y^2 - 2y'$ we compute

$$y'''(x) = 2x + 2yy' - 2y''$$

$$y^{(4)}(x) = 2 + 2(y')^2 + 2yy'' - 2y'''$$

$$y^{(5)}(x) = 6y'y'' + 2yy''' - 2y^{(4)}.$$

Using $y(0) = 1$ and $y'(0) = 1$ we find

$$y''(0) = -1, \quad y'''(0) = 4, \quad y^{(4)}(0) = -6, \quad y^{(5)}(0) = 14.$$

An approximate solution is

$$y(x) = 1 + x - \frac{1}{2}x^2 + \frac{2}{3}x^3 - \frac{1}{4}x^4 + \frac{7}{60}x^5.$$

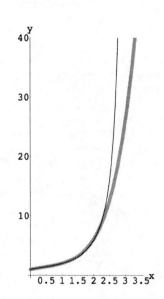

16. We look for a solution of the form

$$y(x) = y(0) + y'(0)x + \frac{1}{2!}y''(0)x^2 + \frac{1}{3!}y'''(0)x^3 + \frac{1}{4!}y^{(4)}(0)x^4$$

$$+ \frac{1}{5!}y^{(5)}(0)x^5 + \frac{1}{6!}y^{(6)}(0)x^6.$$

From $y''(x) = e^y$ we compute

$$y'''(x) = e^y y'$$

$$y^{(4)}(x) = e^y (y')^2 + e^y y''$$

$$y^{(5)}(x) = e^y (y')^3 + 3e^y y' y'' + e^y y'''$$

$$y^{(6)}(x) = e^y (y')^4 + 6e^y (y')^2 y'' + 3e^y (y'')^2 + 4e^y y' y''' + e^y y^{(4)}.$$

Using $y(0) = 0$ and $y'(0) = -1$ we find

$$y''(0) = 1, \quad y'''(0) = -1, \quad y^{(4)}(0) = 2, \quad y^{(5)}(0) = -5, \quad y^{(6)}(0) = 16.$$

An approximate solution is

$$y(x) = -x + \frac{1}{2}x^2 - \frac{1}{6}x^3 + \frac{1}{12}x^4 + \frac{1}{24}x^5 + \frac{1}{45}x^6.$$

17. We need to solve $[1 + (y')^2]^{3/2} = y''$. Let $u = y'$ so that $u' = y''$. The equation becomes $(1 + u^2)^{3/2} = u'$ or $(1 + u^2)^{3/2} = du/dx$. Separating variables and using the substitution $u = \tan\theta$ we have

$$\frac{du}{(1 + u^2)^{3/2}} = dx \implies \int \frac{\sec^2\theta}{\left(1 + \tan^2\theta\right)^{3/2}}\, d\theta = x \implies \int \frac{\sec^2\theta}{\sec^3\theta}\, d\theta = x$$

$$\implies \int \cos\theta\, d\theta = x \implies \sin\theta = x \implies \frac{u}{\sqrt{1 + u^2}} = x$$

$$\implies \frac{y'}{\sqrt{1 + (y')^2}} = x \implies (y')^2 = x^2 \left[1 + (y')^2\right] = \frac{x^2}{1 - x^2}$$

$$\implies y' = \frac{x}{\sqrt{1 - x^2}} \quad (\text{for } x > 0) \implies y = -\sqrt{1 - x^2}.$$

18. When $y = \sin x$, $y' = \cos x$, $y'' = -\sin x$, and

$$(y'')^2 - y^2 = \sin^2 x - \sin^2 x = 0.$$

When $y = e^{-x}$, $y' = -e^{-x}$, $y'' = e^{-x}$, and

$$(y'')^2 - y^2 = e^{-2x} - e^{-2x} = 0.$$

From $(y'')^2 - y^2 = 0$ we have $y'' = \pm y$, which can be treated as two linear equations. Since linear combinations of solutions of linear homogeneous differential equations are also solutions, we see that $y = c_1 e^x + c_2 e^{-x}$ and $y = c_3 \cos x + c_4 \sin x$ must satisfy the differential equation. However, linear combinations that involve both exponential and trigonometric functions will not be solutions since the differential equation is not linear and each type of function satisfies a different linear differential equation that is part of the original differential equation.

19. Letting $u = y''$, separating variables, and integrating we have

$$\frac{du}{dx} = \sqrt{1 + u^2}, \quad \frac{du}{\sqrt{1 + u^2}} = dx, \quad \text{and} \quad \sinh^{-1} u = x + c_1.$$

Then

$$u = y'' = \sinh(x + c_1), \quad y' = \cosh(x + c_1) + c_2, \quad \text{and} \quad y = \sinh(x + c_1) + c_2 x + c_3.$$

20. If the constant $-c_1^2$ is used instead of c_1^2, then, using partial fractions,

$$y = -\int \frac{dx}{x^2 - c_1^2} = -\frac{1}{2c_1} \int \left(\frac{1}{x - c_1} - \frac{1}{x + c_1} \right) dx = \frac{1}{2c_1} \ln \left| \frac{x + c_1}{x - c_1} \right| + c_2.$$

Alternatively, the inverse hyperbolic tangent can be used.

21. Let $u = dx/dt$ so that $d^2x/dt^2 = u \, du/dx$. The equation becomes $u \, du/dx = -k^2/x^2$. Separating variables we obtain

$$u \, du = -\frac{k^2}{x^2} \, dx \implies \frac{1}{2} u^2 = \frac{k^2}{x} + c \implies \frac{1}{2} v^2 = \frac{k^2}{x} + c.$$

When $t = 0$, $x = x_0$ and $v = 0$ so $0 = (k^2/x_0) + c$ and $c = -k^2/x_0$. Then

$$\frac{1}{2} v^2 = k^2 \left(\frac{1}{x} - \frac{1}{x_0} \right) \quad \text{and} \quad \frac{dx}{dt} = -k\sqrt{2} \sqrt{\frac{x_0 - x}{x x_0}}.$$

Separating variables we have

$$-\sqrt{\frac{x x_0}{x_0 - x}} \, dx = k\sqrt{2} \, dt \implies t = -\frac{1}{k} \sqrt{\frac{x_0}{2}} \int \sqrt{\frac{x}{x_0 - x}} \, dx.$$

Using *Mathematica* to integrate we obtain

$$t = -\frac{1}{k} \sqrt{\frac{x_0}{2}} \left[-\sqrt{x(x_0 - x)} - \frac{x_0}{2} \tan^{-1} \frac{(x_0 - 2x)}{2x} \sqrt{\frac{x}{x_0 - x}} \right]$$

$$= \frac{1}{k} \sqrt{\frac{x_0}{2}} \left[\sqrt{x(x_0 - x)} + \frac{x_0}{2} \tan^{-1} \frac{x_0 - 2x}{2\sqrt{x(x_0 - x)}} \right].$$

22.

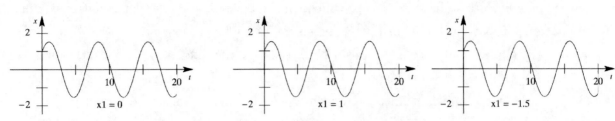

For $d^2x/dt^2 + \sin x = 0$ the motion appears to be periodic with amplitude 1 when $x_1 = 0$. The amplitude and period are larger for larger magnitudes of x_1.

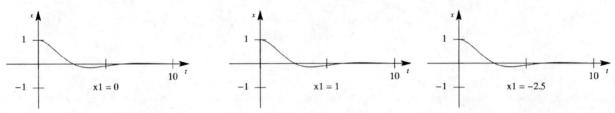

For $d^2x/dt^2 + dx/dt + \sin x = 0$ the motion appears to be periodic with decreasing amplitude. The dx/dt term could be said to have a damping effect.

Chapter 4 in Review

1. $y = 0$

2. Since $y_c = c_1 e^x + c_2 e^{-x}$, a particular solution for $y'' - y = 1 + e^x$ is $y_p = A + Bxe^x$.

3. It is not true unless the differential equation is homogeneous. For example, $y_1 = x$ is a solution of $y'' + y = x$, but $y_2 = 5x$ is not.

4. True

5. The set is linearly independent over $(-\infty, 0)$ and linearly dependent over $(0, \infty)$.

6. **(a)** Since $f_2(x) = 2\ln x = 2f_1(x)$, the set of functions is linearly dependent.

   (b) Since x^{n+1} is not a constant multiple of x^n, the set of functions is linearly independent.

   (c) Since $x + 1$ is not a constant multiple of x, the set of functions is linearly independent.

   (d) Since $f_1(x) = \cos x \cos(\pi/2) - \sin x \sin(\pi/2) = -\sin x = -f_2(x)$, the set of functions is linearly dependent.

   (e) Since $f_1(x) = 0 \cdot f_2(x)$, the set of functions is linearly dependent.

   (f) Since $2x$ is not a constant multiple of 2, the set of functions is linearly independent.

(g) Since $3(x^2) + 2(1 - x^2) - (2 + x^2) = 0$, the set of functions is linearly dependent.

(h) Since $xe^{x+1} + 0(4x - 5)e^x - exe^x = 0$, the set of functions is linearly dependent.

7. (a) The general solution is

$$y = c_1 e^{3x} + c_2 e^{-5x} + c_3 x e^{-5x} + c_4 e^x + c_5 x e^x + c_6 x^2 e^x.$$

(b) The general solution is

$$y = c_1 x^3 + c_2 x^{-5} + c_3 x^{-5} \ln x + c_4 x + c_5 x \ln x + c_6 x (\ln x)^2.$$

8. Variation of parameters will work for all choices of $g(x)$, although the integral involved may not always be able to be expressed in terms of elementary functions. The method of undetermined coefficients will work for the functions in (b), (c), and (e).

9. From $m^2 - 2m - 2 = 0$ we obtain $m = 1 \pm \sqrt{3}$ so that

$$y = c_1 e^{(1+\sqrt{3})x} + c_2 e^{(1-\sqrt{3})x}.$$

10. From $2m^2 + 2m + 3 = 0$ we obtain $m = -1/2 \pm (\sqrt{5}/2)i$ so that

$$y = e^{-x/2} \left(c_1 \cos \frac{\sqrt{5}}{2} x + c_2 \sin \frac{\sqrt{5}}{2} x \right).$$

11. From $m^3 + 10m^2 + 25m = 0$ we obtain $m = 0$, $m = -5$, and $m = -5$ so that

$$y = c_1 + c_2 e^{-5x} + c_3 x e^{-5x}.$$

12. From $2m^3 + 9m^2 + 12m + 5 = 0$ we obtain $m = -1$, $m = -1$, and $m = -5/2$ so that

$$y = c_1 e^{-5x/2} + c_2 e^{-x} + c_3 x e^{-x}.$$

13. From $3m^3 + 10m^2 + 15m + 4 = 0$ we obtain $m = -1/3$ and $m = -3/2 \pm (\sqrt{7}/2)i$ so that

$$y = c_1 e^{-x/3} + e^{-3x/2} \left(c_2 \cos \frac{\sqrt{7}}{2} x + c_3 \sin \frac{\sqrt{7}}{2} x \right).$$

14. From $2m^4 + 3m^3 + 2m^2 + 6m - 4 = 0$ we obtain $m = 1/2$, $m = -2$, and $m = \pm\sqrt{2}\,i$ so that

$$y = c_1 e^{x/2} + c_2 e^{-2x} + c_3 \cos \sqrt{2}\, x + c_4 \sin \sqrt{2}\, x.$$

15. Applying D^4 to the differential equation we obtain $D^4(D^2 - 3D + 5) = 0$. Then

$$y = \underbrace{e^{3x/2} \left(c_1 \cos \frac{\sqrt{11}}{2} x + c_2 \sin \frac{\sqrt{11}}{2} x \right)}_{y_c} + c_3 + c_4 x + c_5 x^2 + c_6 x^3$$

and $y_p = A + Bx + Cx^2 + Dx^3$. Substituting y_p into the differential equation yields

$$(5A - 3B + 2C) + (5B - 6C + 6D)x + (5C - 9D)x^2 + 5Dx^3 = -2x + 4x^3.$$

Equating coefficients gives $A = -222/625$, $B = 46/125$, $C = 36/25$, and $D = 4/5$. The general solution is

$$y = e^{3x/2}\left(c_1 \cos \frac{\sqrt{11}}{2}x + c_2 \sin \frac{\sqrt{11}}{2}x\right) - \frac{222}{625} + \frac{46}{125}x + \frac{36}{25}x^2 + \frac{4}{5}x^3.$$

16. Applying $(D-1)^3$ to the differential equation we obtain $(D-1)^3(D-2D+1) = (D-1)^5 = 0$. Then

$$y = \underbrace{c_1 e^x + c_2 x e^x}_{y_c} + c_3 x^2 e^x + c_4 x^3 e^x + c_5 x^4 e^x$$

and $y_p = Ax^2 e^x + Bx^3 e^x + Cx^4 e^x$. Substituting y_p into the differential equation yields

$$12Cx^2 e^x + 6Bxe^x + 2Ae^x = x^2 e^x.$$

Equating coefficients gives $A = 0$, $B = 0$, and $C = 1/12$. The general solution is

$$y = c_1 e^x + c_2 x e^x + \frac{1}{12}x^4 e^x.$$

17. Applying $D(D^2 + 1)$ to the differential equation we obtain

$$D(D^2 + 1)(D^3 - 5D^2 + 6D) = D^2(D^2 + 1)(D - 2)(D - 3) = 0.$$

Then

$$y = \underbrace{c_1 + c_2 e^{2x} + c_3 e^{3x}}_{y_c} + c_4 x + c_5 \cos x + c_6 \sin x$$

and $y_p = Ax + B \cos x + C \sin x$. Substituting y_p into the differential equation yields

$$6A + (5B + 5C) \cos x + (-5B + 5C) \sin x = 8 + 2 \sin x.$$

Equating coefficients gives $A = 4/3$, $B = -1/5$, and $C = 1/5$. The general solution is

$$y = c_1 + c_2 e^{2x} + c_3 e^{3x} + \frac{4}{3}x - \frac{1}{5}\cos x + \frac{1}{5}\sin x.$$

18. Applying D to the differential equation we obtain $D(D^3 - D^2) = D^3(D - 1) = 0$. Then

$$y = \underbrace{c_1 + c_2 x + c_3 e^x}_{y_c} + c_4 x^2$$

and $y_p = Ax^2$. Substituting y_p into the differential equation yields $-2A = 6$. Equating coefficients gives $A = -3$. The general solution is

$$y = c_1 + c_2 x + c_3 e^x - 3x^2.$$

19. The auxiliary equation is $m^2 - 2m + 2 = [m - (1+i)][m - (1-i)] = 0$, so $y_c = c_1 e^x \sin x + c_2 e^x \cos x$ and

$$W = \begin{vmatrix} e^x \sin x & e^x \cos x \\ e^x \cos x + e^x \sin x & -e^x \sin x + e^x \cos x \end{vmatrix} = -e^{2x}.$$

Identifying $f(x) = e^x \tan x$ we obtain

$$u_1' = -\frac{(e^x \cos x)(e^x \tan x)}{-e^{2x}} = \sin x$$

$$u_2' = \frac{(e^x \sin x)(e^x \tan x)}{-e^{2x}} = -\frac{\sin^2 x}{\cos x} = \cos x - \sec x.$$

Then $u_1 = -\cos x$, $u_2 = \sin x - \ln|\sec x + \tan x|$, and

$$y = c_1 e^x \sin x + c_2 e^x \cos x - e^x \sin x \cos x + e^x \sin x \cos x - e^x \cos x \ln|\sec x + \tan x|$$

$$= c_1 e^x \sin x + c_2 e^x \cos x - e^x \cos x \ln|\sec x + \tan x|.$$

20. The auxiliary equation is $m^2 - 1 = 0$, so $y_c = c_1 e^x + c_2 e^{-x}$ and

$$W = \begin{vmatrix} e^x & e^{-x} \\ e^x & -e^{-x} \end{vmatrix} = -2.$$

Identifying $f(x) = 2e^x/(e^x + e^{-x})$ we obtain

$$u_1' = \frac{1}{e^x + e^{-x}} = \frac{e^x}{1 + e^{2x}}$$

$$u_2' = -\frac{e^{2x}}{e^x + e^{-x}} = -\frac{e^{3x}}{1 + e^{2x}} = -e^x + \frac{e^x}{1 + e^{2x}}.$$

Then $u_1 = \tan^{-1} e^x$, $u_2 = -e^x + \tan^{-1} e^x$, and

$$y = c_1 e^x + c_2 e^{-x} + e^x \tan^{-1} e^x - 1 + e^{-x} \tan^{-1} e^x.$$

21. The auxiliary equation is $6m^2 - m - 1 = 0$ so that

$$y = c_1 x^{1/2} + c_2 x^{-1/3}.$$

22. The auxiliary equation is $2m^3 + 13m^2 + 24m + 9 = (m+3)^2(m+1/2) = 0$ so that

$$y = c_1 x^{-3} + c_2 x^{-3} \ln x + c_3 x^{-1/2}.$$

23. The auxiliary equation is $m^2 - 5m + 6 = (m-2)(m-3) = 0$ and a particular solution is $y_p = x^4 - x^2 \ln x$ so that

$$y = c_1 x^2 + c_2 x^3 + x^4 - x^2 \ln x.$$

24. The auxiliary equation is $m^2 - 2m + 1 = (m-1)^2 = 0$ and a particular solution is $y_p = \frac{1}{4} x^3$ so that

$$y = c_1 x + c_2 x \ln x + \frac{1}{4} x^3.$$

25. (a) The auxiliary equation is $m^2 + \omega^2 = 0$, so $y_c = c_1 \cos \omega x + c_2 \sin \omega x$. When $\omega \neq \alpha$, $y_p = A \cos \alpha x + B \sin \alpha x$ and

$$y = c_1 \cos \omega x + c_2 \sin \omega x + A \cos \alpha x + B \sin \alpha x.$$

When $\omega = \alpha$, $y_p = Ax \cos \omega x + Bx \sin \omega x$ and

$$y = c_1 \cos \omega x + c_2 \sin \omega x + Ax \cos \omega x + Bx \sin \omega x.$$

(b) The auxiliary equation is $m^2 - \omega^2 = 0$, so $y_c = c_1 e^{\omega x} + c_2 e^{-\omega x}$. When $\omega \neq \alpha$, $y_p = Ae^{\alpha x}$ and

$$y = c_1 e^{\omega x} + c_2 e^{-\omega x} + Ae^{\alpha x}.$$

When $\omega = \alpha$, $y_p = Axe^{\omega x}$ and

$$y = c_1 e^{\omega x} + c_2 e^{-\omega x} + Axe^{\omega x}.$$

26. (a) If $y = \sin x$ is a solution then so is $y = \cos x$ and $m^2 + 1$ is a factor of the auxiliary equation $m^4 + 2m^3 + 11m^2 + 2m + 10 = 0$. Dividing by $m^2 + 1$ we get $m^2 + 2m + 10$, which has roots $-1 \pm 3i$. The general solution of the differential equation is

$$y = c_1 \cos x + c_2 \sin x + e^{-x}(c_3 \cos 3x + c_4 \sin 3x).$$

(b) The auxiliary equation is $m(m+1) = m^2 + m = 0$, so the associated homogeneous differential equation is $y'' + y' = 0$. Letting $y = c_1 + c_2 e^{-x} + \frac{1}{2}x^2 - x$ and computing $y'' + y'$ we get x. Thus, the differential equation is $y'' + y' = x$.

27. (a) The auxiliary equation is $m^4 - 2m^2 + 1 = (m^2 - 1)^2 = 0$, so the general solution of the differential equation is

$$y = c_1 \sinh x + c_2 \cosh x + c_3 x \sinh x + c_4 x \cosh x.$$

(b) Since both $\sinh x$ and $x \sinh x$ are solutions of the associated homogeneous differential equation, a particular solution of $y^{(4)} - 2y'' + y = \sinh x$ has the form $y_p = Ax^2 \sinh x + Bx^2 \cosh x$.

28. Since $y_1' = 1$ and $y_1'' = 0$, $x^2 y_1'' - (x^2 + 2x)y_1' + (x + 2)y_1 = -x^2 - 2x + x^2 + 2x = 0$, and $y_1 = x$ is a solution of the associated homogeneous equation. Using the method of reduction of order, we let $y = ux$. Then $y' = xu' + u$ and $y'' = xu'' + 2u'$, so

$$x^2 y'' - (x^2 + 2x)y' + (x + 2)y = x^3 u'' + 2x^2 u' - x^3 u' - 2x^2 u' - x^2 u - 2xu + x^2 u + 2xu$$

$$= x^3 u'' - x^3 u' = x^3 (u'' - u').$$

To find a second solution of the homogeneous equation we note that $u = e^x$ is a solution of $u'' - u' = 0$. Thus, $y_c = c_1 x + c_2 x e^x$. To find a particular solution we set $x^3(u'' - u') = x^3$ so that $u'' - u' = 1$. This differential equation has a particular solution of the form Ax. Substituting, we find $A = -1$, so a particular solution of the original differential equation is $y_p = -x^2$ and the general solution is $y = c_1 x + c_2 x e^x - x^2$.

29. The auxiliary equation is $m^2 - 2m + 2 = 0$ so that $m = 1 \pm i$ and $y = e^x(c_1 \cos x + c_2 \sin x)$. Setting $y(\pi/2) = 0$ and $y(\pi) = -1$ we obtain $c_1 = e^{-\pi}$ and $c_2 = 0$. Thus, $y = e^{x - \pi} \cos x$.

30. The auxiliary equation is $m^2 + 2m + 1 = (m+1)^2 = 0$, so that $y = c_1 e^{-x} + c_2 x e^{-x}$. Setting $y(-1) = 0$ and $y'(0) = 0$ we get $c_1 e - c_2 e = 0$ and $-c_1 + c_2 = 0$. Thus $c_1 = c_2$ and $y = c_1(e^{-x} + x e^{-x})$ is a solution of the boundary-value problem for any real number c_1.

31. The auxiliary equation is $m^2 - 1 = (m-1)(m+1) = 0$ so that $m = \pm 1$ and $y = c_1 e^x + c_2 e^{-x}$. Assuming $y_p = Ax + B + C \sin x$ and substituting into the differential equation we find $A = -1$, $B = 0$, and $C = -\frac{1}{2}$. Thus $y_p = -x - \frac{1}{2}\sin x$ and

$$y = c_1 e^x + c_2 e^{-x} - x - \frac{1}{2}\sin x.$$

Setting $y(0) = 2$ and $y'(0) = 3$ we obtain

$$c_1 + c_2 = 2$$

$$c_1 - c_2 - \frac{3}{2} = 3.$$

Solving this system we find $c_1 = \frac{13}{4}$ and $c_2 = -\frac{5}{4}$. The solution of the initial-value problem is

$$y = \frac{13}{4} e^x - \frac{5}{4} e^{-x} - x - \frac{1}{2}\sin x.$$

32. The auxiliary equation is $m^2 + 1 = 0$, so $y_c = c_1 \cos x + c_2 \sin x$ and

$$W = \begin{vmatrix} \cos x & \sin x \\ -\sin x & \cos x \end{vmatrix} = 1.$$

Identifying $f(x) = \sec^3 x$ we obtain

$$u_1' = -\sin x \sec^3 x = -\frac{\sin x}{\cos^3 x}$$

$$u_2' = \cos x \sec^3 x = \sec^2 x.$$

Then

$$u_1 = -\frac{1}{2}\frac{1}{\cos^2 x} = -\frac{1}{2}\sec^2 x$$

$$u_2 = \tan x.$$

Thus

$$y = c_1 \cos x + c_2 \sin x - \frac{1}{2}\cos x \sec^2 x + \sin x \tan x$$

$$= c_1 \cos x + c_2 \sin x - \frac{1}{2}\sec x + \frac{1 - \cos^2 x}{\cos x}$$

$$= c_3 \cos x + c_2 \sin x + \frac{1}{2}\sec x.$$

and

$$y' = -c_3 \sin x + c_2 \cos x + \frac{1}{2} \sec x \tan x.$$

The initial conditions imply

$$c_3 + \frac{1}{2} = 1$$

$$c_2 = \frac{1}{2}.$$

Thus $c_3 = c_2 = 1/2$ and

$$y = \frac{1}{2} \cos x + \frac{1}{2} \sin x + \frac{1}{2} \sec x.$$

33. Let $u = y'$ so that $u' = y''$. The equation becomes $u\, du/dx = 4x$. Separating variables we obtain

$$u\, du = 4x\, dx \implies \frac{1}{2}u^2 = 2x^2 + c_1 \implies u^2 = 4x^2 + c_2.$$

When $x = 1$, $y' = u = 2$, so $4 = 4 + c_2$ and $c_2 = 0$. Then

$$u^2 = 4x^2 \implies \frac{dy}{dx} = 2x \quad \text{or} \quad \frac{dy}{dx} = -2x$$

$$\implies y = x^2 + c_3 \quad \text{or} \quad y = -x^2 + c_4.$$

When $x = 1$, $y = 5$, so $5 = 1 + c_3$ and $5 = -1 + c_4$. Thus $c_3 = 4$ and $c_4 = 6$. We have $y = x^2 + 4$ and $y = -x^2 + 6$. Note however that when $y = -x^2 + 6$, $y' = -2x$ and $y'(1) = -2 \neq 2$. Thus, the solution of the initial-value problem is $y = x^2 + 4$.

34. Let $u = y'$ so that $y'' = u\, du/dy$. The equation becomes $2u\, du/dy = 3y^2$. Separating variables we obtain

$$2u\, du = 3y^2\, dy \implies u^2 = y^3 + c_1.$$

When $x = 0$, $y = 1$ and $y' = u = 1$ so $1 = 1 + c_1$ and $c_1 = 0$. Then

$$u^2 = y^3 \implies \left(\frac{dy}{dx}\right)^2 = y^3 \implies \frac{dy}{dx} = y^{3/2} \implies y^{-3/2}\, dy = dx$$

$$\implies -2y^{-1/2} = x + c_2 \implies y = \frac{4}{(x + c_2)^2}.$$

When $x = 0$, $y = 1$, so $1 = 4/c_2^2$ and $c_2 = \pm 2$. Thus, $y = 4/(x + 2)^2$ and $y = 4/(x - 2)^2$. Note, however, that when $y = 4/(x + 2)^2$, $y' = -8/(x + 2)^3$ and $y'(0) = -1 \neq 1$. Thus, the solution of the initial-value problem is $y = 4/(x - 2)^2$.

35. (a) The auxiliary equation is $12m^4 + 64m^3 + 59m^2 - 23m - 12 = 0$ and has roots -4, $-\frac{3}{2}$, $-\frac{1}{3}$, and $\frac{1}{2}$. The general solution is

$$y = c_1 e^{-4x} + c_2 e^{-3x/2} + c_3 e^{-x/3} + c_4 e^{x/2}.$$

(b) The system of equations is

$$c_1 + c_2 + c_3 + c_4 = -1$$

$$-4c_1 - \frac{3}{2}c_2 - \frac{1}{3}c_3 + \frac{1}{2}c_4 = 2$$

$$16c_1 + \frac{9}{4}c_2 + \frac{1}{9}c_3 + \frac{1}{4}c_4 = 5$$

$$-64c_1 - \frac{27}{8}c_2 - \frac{1}{27}c_3 + \frac{1}{8}c_4 = 0.$$

Using a CAS we find $c_1 = -\frac{73}{495}$, $c_2 = \frac{109}{35}$, $c_3 = -\frac{3726}{385}$, and $c_4 = \frac{257}{45}$. The solution of the initial-value problem is

$$y = -\frac{73}{495}e^{-4x} + \frac{109}{35}e^{-3x/2} - \frac{3726}{385}e^{-x/3} + \frac{257}{45}e^{x/2}.$$

36. Consider $xy'' + y' = 0$ and look for a solution of the form $y = x^m$. Substituting into the differential equation we have

$$xy'' + y' = m(m-1)x^{m-1} + mx^{m-1} = m^2 x^{m-1}.$$

Thus, the general solution of $xy'' + y' = 0$ is $y_c = c_1 + c_2 \ln x$. To find a particular solution of $xy'' + y' = -\sqrt{x}$ we use variation of parameters. The Wronskian is

$$W = \begin{vmatrix} 1 & \ln x \\ 0 & 1/x \end{vmatrix} = \frac{1}{x}.$$

Identifying $f(x) = -x^{-1/2}$ we obtain

$$u_1' = \frac{x^{-1/2}\ln x}{1/x} = \sqrt{x}\ln x \quad \text{and} \quad u_2' = \frac{-x^{-1/2}}{1/x} = -\sqrt{x},$$

so that

$$u_1 = x^{3/2}\Big(\frac{2}{3}\ln x - \frac{4}{9}\Big) \quad \text{and} \quad u_2 = -\frac{2}{3}x^{3/2}.$$

Then

$$y_p = x^{3/2}\Big(\frac{2}{3}\ln x - \frac{4}{9}\Big) - \frac{2}{3}x^{3/2}\ln x = -\frac{4}{9}x^{3/2}$$

and the general solution of the differential equation is

$$y = c_1 + c_2 \ln x - \frac{4}{9}x^{3/2}.$$

The initial conditions are $y(1) = 0$ and $y'(1) = 0$. These imply that $c_1 = \frac{4}{9}$ and $c_2 = \frac{2}{3}$. The solution of the initial-value problem is

$$y = \frac{4}{9} + \frac{2}{3} \ln x - \frac{4}{9} x^{3/2}.$$

The graph is shown above.

37. From $(D - 2)x + (D - 2)y = 1$ and $Dx + (2D - 1)y = 3$ we obtain $(D - 1)(D - 2)y = -6$ and $Dx = 3 - (2D - 1)y$. Then

$$y = c_1 e^{2t} + c_2 e^t - 3 \quad \text{and} \quad x = -c_2 e^t - \frac{3}{2} c_1 e^{2t} + c_3.$$

Substituting into $(D - 2)x + (D - 2)y = 1$ gives $c_3 = \frac{5}{2}$ so that

$$x = -c_2 e^t - \frac{3}{2} c_1 e^{2t} + \frac{5}{2}.$$

38. From $(D - 2)x - y = t - 2$ and $-3x + (D - 4)y = -4t$ we obtain $(D - 1)(D - 5)x = 9 - 8t$. Then

$$x = c_1 e^t + c_2 e^{5t} - \frac{8}{5}t - \frac{3}{25}$$

and

$$y = (D - 2)x - t + 2 = -c_1 e^t + 3c_2 e^{5t} + \frac{16}{25} + \frac{11}{25}t.$$

39. From $(D - 2)x - y = -e^t$ and $-3x + (D - 4)y = -7e^t$ we obtain $(D - 1)(D - 5)x = -4e^t$ so that

$$x = c_1 e^t + c_2 e^{5t} + te^t.$$

Then

$$y = (D - 2)x + e^t = -c_1 e^t + 3c_2 e^{5t} - te^t + 2e^t.$$

40. From $(D+2)x + (D+1)y = \sin 2t$ and $5x + (D+3)y = \cos 2t$ we obtain $(D^2 + 5)y = 2\cos 2t - 7\sin 2t$. Then

$$y = c_1 \cos t + c_2 \sin t - \frac{2}{3} \cos 2t + \frac{7}{3} \sin 2t$$

and

$$x = -\frac{1}{5}(D + 3)y + \frac{1}{5} \cos 2t$$

$$= \left(\frac{1}{5} c_1 - \frac{3}{5} c_2 \right) \sin t + \left(-\frac{1}{5} c_2 - \frac{3}{5} c_1 \right) \cos t - \frac{5}{3} \sin 2t - \frac{1}{3} \cos 2t.$$

5 Modeling with Higher-Order Differential Equations

Exercises 5.1   Linear Models: Initial-Value Problems

1. From $\frac{1}{8}x'' + 16x = 0$ we obtain

$$x = c_1 \cos 8\sqrt{2}\,t + c_2 \sin 8\sqrt{2}\,t$$

so that the period of motion is $2\pi/8\sqrt{2} = \sqrt{2}\,\pi/8$ seconds.

2. From $20x'' + kx = 0$ we obtain

$$x = c_1 \cos \frac{1}{2}\sqrt{\frac{k}{5}}\,t + c_2 \sin \frac{1}{2}\sqrt{\frac{k}{5}}\,t$$

so that the frequency $2/\pi = \frac{1}{4}\sqrt{k/5}\,\pi$ and $k = 320$ N/m. If $80x'' + 320x = 0$ then

$$x = c_1 \cos 2t + c_2 \sin 2t$$

so that the frequency is $2/2\pi = 1/\pi$ cycles/s.

3. From $\frac{3}{4}x'' + 72x = 0$, $x(0) = -1/4$, and $x'(0) = 0$ we obtain $x = -\frac{1}{4}\cos 4\sqrt{6}\,t$.

4. From $\frac{3}{4}x'' + 72x = 0$, $x(0) = 0$, and $x'(0) = 2$ we obtain $x = \frac{\sqrt{6}}{12}\sin 4\sqrt{6}\,t$.

5. From $\frac{5}{8}x'' + 40x = 0$, $x(0) = 1/2$, and $x'(0) = 0$ we obtain $x = \frac{1}{2}\cos 8t$.

   (a) $x(\pi/12) = -1/4$, $x(\pi/8) = -1/2$, $x(\pi/6) = -1/4$, $x(\pi/4) = 1/2$, $x(9\pi/32) = \sqrt{2}/4$.

   (b) $x' = -4\sin 8t$ so that $x'(3\pi/16) = 4$ ft/s directed downward.

   (c) If $x = \frac{1}{2}\cos 8t = 0$ then $t = (2n+1)\pi/16$ for $n = 0, 1, 2, \ldots$.

6. From $50x'' + 200x = 0$, $x(0) = 0$, and $x'(0) = -10$ we obtain $x = -5\sin 2t$ and $x' = -10\cos 2t$.

7. From $20x'' + 20x = 0$, $x(0) = 0$, and $x'(0) = -10$ we obtain $x = -10\sin t$ and $x' = -10\cos t$.

   (a) The 20 kg mass has the larger amplitude.

   (b) 20 kg: $x'(\pi/4) = -5\sqrt{2}$ m/s, $x'(\pi/2) = 0$ m/s;   50 kg: $x'(\pi/4) = 0$ m/s, $x'(\pi/2) = 10$ m/s

   (c) If $-5\sin 2t = -10\sin t$ then $\sin t(\cos t - 1) = 0$ so that $t = n\pi$ for $n = 0, 1, 2, \ldots$, placing both masses at the equilibrium position. The 50 kg mass is moving upward; the 20 kg mass is moving upward when n is even and downward when n is odd.

8. From $x'' + 16x = 0$, $x(0) = -1$, and $x'(0) = -2$ we obtain

$$x = -\cos 4t - \frac{1}{2}\sin 4t = \frac{\sqrt{5}}{2}\sin(4t - 4.249).$$

The period is $\pi/2$ seconds and the amplitude is $\sqrt{5}/2$ feet. In 4π seconds it will make 8 complete cycles.

9. From $\frac{1}{4}x'' + x = 0$, $x(0) = 1/2$, and $x'(0) = 3/2$ we obtain

$$x = \frac{1}{2}\cos 2t + \frac{3}{4}\sin 2t = \frac{\sqrt{13}}{4}\sin(2t + 0.588).$$

10. From $1.6x'' + 40x = 0$, $x(0) = -1/3$, and $x'(0) = 5/4$ we obtain

$$x = -\frac{1}{3}\cos 5t + \frac{1}{4}\sin 5t = \frac{5}{12}\sin(5t - 0.927).$$

If $x = 5/24$ then $t = \frac{1}{5}\left(\frac{\pi}{6} + 0.927 + 2n\pi\right)$ and $t = \frac{1}{5}\left(\frac{5\pi}{6} + 0.927 + 2n\pi\right)$ for $n = 0, 1, 2, \ldots$.

11. From $2x'' + 200x = 0$, $x(0) = -2/3$, and $x'(0) = 5$ we obtain

(a) $x = -\frac{2}{3}\cos 10t + \frac{1}{2}\sin 10t = \frac{5}{6}\sin(10t - 0.927)$.

(b) The amplitude is $5/6$ ft and the period is $2\pi/10 = \pi/5$

(c) $3\pi = \pi k/5$ and $k = 15$ cycles.

(d) If $x = 0$ and the weight is moving downward for the second time, then $10t - 0.927 = 2\pi$ or $t = 0.721$ s.

(e) If $x' = \frac{25}{3}\cos(10t - 0.927) = 0$ then $10t - 0.927 = \pi/2 + n\pi$ or $t = (2n+1)\pi/20 + 0.0927$ for $n = 0, 1, 2, \ldots$.

(f) $x(3) = -0.597$ ft

(g) $x'(3) = -5.814$ ft/s

(h) $x''(3) = 59.702$ ft/s^2

(i) If $x = 0$ then $t = \frac{1}{10}(0.927 + n\pi)$ for $n = 0, 1, 2, \ldots$. The velocity at these times is $x' = \pm 8.33$ ft/s.

(j) If $x = 5/12$ then $t = \frac{1}{10}(\pi/6 + 0.927 + 2n\pi)$ and $t = \frac{1}{10}(5\pi/6 + 0.927 + 2n\pi)$ for $n = 0, 1, 2, \ldots$.

(k) If $x = 5/12$ and $x' < 0$ then $t = \frac{1}{10}(5\pi/6 + 0.927 + 2n\pi)$ for $n = 0, 1, 2, \ldots$.

12. From $x'' + 9x = 0$, $x(0) = -1$, and $x'(0) = -\sqrt{3}$ we obtain

$$x = -\cos 3t - \frac{\sqrt{3}}{3}\sin 3t = \frac{2}{\sqrt{3}}\sin\left(3t + \frac{4\pi}{3}\right)$$

and $x' = 2\sqrt{3}\cos(3t + 4\pi/3)$. If $x' = 3$ then $t = -7\pi/18 + 2n\pi/3$ and $t = -\pi/2 + 2n\pi/3$ for $n = 1, 2, 3, \ldots$.

13. From $k_1 = 40$ and $k_2 = 120$ we compute the effective spring constant $k = 4(40)(120)/160 = 120$. Now, $m = 20/32$ so $k/m = 120(32)/20 = 192$ and $x'' + 192x = 0$. Using $x(0) = 0$ and $x'(0) = 2$ we obtain $x(t) = \frac{\sqrt{3}}{12}\sin 8\sqrt{3}\,t$.

14. Let m be the mass and k_1 and k_2 the spring constants. Then $k = 4k_1k_2/(k_1 + k_2)$ is the effective spring constant of the system. Since the initial mass stretches one spring $\frac{1}{3}$ foot and another spring $\frac{1}{2}$ foot, using $F = ks$, we have $\frac{1}{3}k_1 = \frac{1}{2}k_2$ or $2k_1 = 3k_2$. The given period of the combined system is $2\pi/\omega = \pi/15$, so $\omega = 30$. Since a mass weighing 8 pounds is $\frac{1}{4}$ slug, we have from $w^2 = k/m$

$$30^2 = \frac{k}{1/4} = 4k \quad \text{or} \quad k = 225.$$

We now have the system of equations

$$\frac{4k_1k_2}{k_1 + k_2} = 225$$

$$2k_1 = 3k_2.$$

Solving the second equation for k_1 and substituting in the first equation, we obtain

$$\frac{4(3k_2/2)k_2}{3k_2/2 + k_2} = \frac{12k_2^2}{5k_2} = \frac{12k_2}{5} = 225.$$

Thus, $k_2 = 375/4$ and $k_1 = 1125/8$. Finally, the weight of the first mass is

$$32m = \frac{k_1}{3} = \frac{1125/8}{3} = \frac{375}{8} \approx 46.88 \text{ lb.}$$

15. For large values of t the differential equation is approximated by $x'' = 0$. The solution of this equation is the linear function $x = c_1t + c_2$. Thus, for large time, the restoring force will have decayed to the point where the spring is incapable of returning the mass, and the spring will simply keep on stretching.

16. As t becomes larger the spring constant increases; that is, the spring is stiffening. It would seem that the oscillations would become periodic and the spring would oscillate more rapidly. It is likely that the amplitudes of the oscillations would decrease as t increases.

17. (a) above   **(b)** heading upward

18. (a) below   **(b)** from rest

19. (a) below   **(b)** heading upward

20. (a) above   **(b)** heading downward

21. From $\frac{1}{8}x'' + x' + 2x = 0$, $x(0) = -1$, and $x'(0) = 8$ we obtain $x = 4te^{-4t} - e^{-4t}$ and $x' = 8e^{-4t} - 16te^{-4t}$. If $x = 0$ then $t = 1/4$ second. If $x' = 0$ then $t = 1/2$ second and the extreme displacement is $x = e^{-2}$ feet.

22. From $\frac{1}{4}x'' + \sqrt{2}\,x' + 2x = 0$, $x(0) = 0$, and $x'(0) = 5$ we obtain $x = 5te^{-2\sqrt{2}\,t}$ and

$x' = 5e^{-2\sqrt{2}\,t}\left(1 - 2\sqrt{2}\,t\right)$. If $x' = 0$ then $t = \sqrt{2}/4$ second and the extreme displacement is $x = 5\sqrt{2}\,e^{-1}/4$ feet.

23. (a) From $x'' + 10x' + 16x = 0$, $x(0) = 1$, and $x'(0) = 0$ we obtain $x = \frac{4}{3}e^{-2t} - \frac{1}{3}e^{-8t}$.

   (b) From $x'' + x' + 16x = 0$, $x(0) = 1$, and $x'(0) = -12$ then $x = -\frac{2}{3}e^{-2t} + \frac{5}{3}e^{-8t}$.

24. (a) $x = \frac{1}{3}e^{-8t}\left(4e^{6t} - 1\right)$ is not zero for $t \geq 0$; the extreme displacement is $x(0) = 1$ meter.

   (b) $x = \frac{1}{3}e^{-8t}\left(5 - 2e^{6t}\right) = 0$ when $t = \frac{1}{6}\ln\frac{5}{2} \approx 0.153$ second; if $x' = \frac{4}{3}e^{-8t}\left(e^{6t} - 10\right) = 0$ then $t = \frac{1}{6}\ln 10 \approx 0.384$ second and the extreme displacement is $x = -0.232$ meter.

25. (a) From $0.1x'' + 0.4x' + 2x = 0$, $x(0) = -1$, and $x'(0) = 0$ we obtain $x = e^{-2t}\left[-\cos 4t - \frac{1}{2}\sin 4t\right]$.

   (b) $x = \dfrac{\sqrt{5}}{2}e^{-2t}\sin(4t + 4.25)$

   (c) If $x = 0$ then $4t + 4.25 = 2\pi$, 3π, 4π, ... so that the first time heading upward is $t = 1.294$ seconds.

26. (a) From $\frac{1}{4}x'' + x' + 5x = 0$, $x(0) = 1/2$, and $x'(0) = 1$ we obtain $x = e^{-2t}\left(\frac{1}{2}\cos 4t + \frac{1}{2}\sin 4t\right)$.

   (b) $x = \dfrac{1}{\sqrt{2}}e^{-2t}\sin\left(4t + \dfrac{\pi}{4}\right)$.

   (c) If $x = 0$ then $4t + \pi/4 = \pi$, 2π, 3π, ... so that the times heading downward are $t = (7 + 8n)\pi/16$ for $n = 0, 1, 2, \ldots$.

   (d)

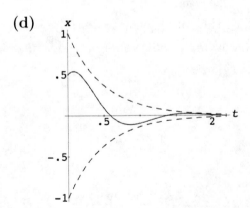

27. From $\frac{5}{16}x'' + \beta x' + 5x = 0$ we find that the roots of the auxiliary equation are $m = -\frac{8}{5}\beta \pm \frac{4}{5}\sqrt{4\beta^2 - 25}$.

   (a) If $4\beta^2 - 25 > 0$ then $\beta > 5/2$.

   (b) If $4\beta^2 - 25 = 0$ then $\beta = 5/2$.

   (c) If $4\beta^2 - 25 < 0$ then $0 < \beta < 5/2$.

28. From $0.75x'' + \beta x' + 6x = 0$ and $\beta > 3\sqrt{2}$ we find that the roots of the auxiliary equation are

$m = -\frac{2}{3}\beta \pm \frac{2}{3}\sqrt{\beta^2 - 18}$ and

$$x = e^{-2\beta t/3}\left[c_1 \cosh\frac{2}{3}\sqrt{\beta^2 - 18}\,t + c_2 \sinh\frac{2}{3}\sqrt{\beta^2 - 18}\,t\right].$$

If $x(0) = 0$ and $x'(0) = -2$ then $c_1 = 0$ and $c_2 = -3/\sqrt{\beta^2 - 18}$.

29. If $\frac{1}{2}x'' + \frac{1}{2}x' + 6x = 10\cos 3t$, $x(0) = 2$, and $x'(0) = 0$ then

$$x_c = e^{-t/2}\left(c_1 \cos\frac{\sqrt{47}}{2}t + c_2 \sin\frac{\sqrt{47}}{2}t\right)$$

and $x_p = \frac{10}{3}(\cos 3t + \sin 3t)$ so that the equation of motion is

$$x = e^{-t/2}\left(-\frac{4}{3}\cos\frac{\sqrt{47}}{2}t - \frac{64}{3\sqrt{47}}\sin\frac{\sqrt{47}}{2}t\right) + \frac{10}{3}(\cos 3t + \sin 3t).$$

30. (a) If $x'' + 2x' + 5x = 12\cos 2t + 3\sin 2t$, $x(0) = 1$, and $x'(0) = 5$ then $x_c = e^{-t}(c_1 \cos 2t + c_2 \sin 2t)$ and $x_p = 3\sin 2t$ so that the equation of motion is

$$x = e^{-t}\cos 2t + 3\sin 2t.$$

(b)

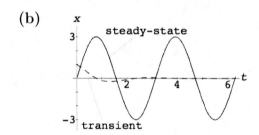

(c)

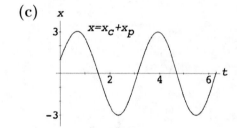

31. From $x'' + 8x' + 16x = 8\sin 4t$, $x(0) = 0$, and $x'(0) = 0$ we obtain $x_c = c_1 e^{-4t} + c_2 te^{-4t}$ and $x_p = -\frac{1}{4}\cos 4t$ so that the equation of motion is

$$x = \frac{1}{4}e^{-4t} + te^{-4t} - \frac{1}{4}\cos 4t.$$

32. From $x'' + 8x' + 16x = e^{-t}\sin 4t$, $x(0) = 0$, and $x'(0) = 0$ we obtain $x_c = c_1 e^{-4t} + c_2 te^{-4t}$ and $x_p = -\frac{24}{625}e^{-t}\cos 4t - \frac{7}{625}e^{-t}\sin 4t$ so that

$$x = \frac{1}{625}e^{-4t}(24 + 100t) - \frac{1}{625}e^{-t}(24\cos 4t + 7\sin 4t).$$

As $t \to \infty$ the displacement $x \to 0$.

33. From $2x'' + 32x = 68e^{-2t}\cos 4t$, $x(0) = 0$, and $x'(0) = 0$ we obtain $x_c = c_1 \cos 4t + c_2 \sin 4t$ and $x_p = \frac{1}{2}e^{-2t}\cos 4t - 2e^{-2t}\sin 4t$ so that

$$x = -\frac{1}{2}\cos 4t + \frac{9}{4}\sin 4t + \frac{1}{2}e^{-2t}\cos 4t - 2e^{-2t}\sin 4t.$$

34. Since $x = \frac{\sqrt{85}}{4}\sin(4t - 0.219) - \frac{\sqrt{17}}{2}e^{-2t}\sin(4t - 2.897)$, the amplitude approaches $\sqrt{85}/4$ as $t \to \infty$.

35. (a) By Hooke's law the external force is $F(t) = kh(t)$ so that $mx'' + \beta x' + kx = kh(t)$.

(b) From $\frac{1}{2}x'' + 2x' + 4x = 20\cos t$, $x(0) = 0$, and $x'(0) = 0$ we obtain $x_c = e^{-2t}(c_1\cos 2t + c_2\sin 2t)$ and $x_p = \frac{56}{13}\cos t + \frac{32}{13}\sin t$ so that

$$x = e^{-2t}\left(-\frac{56}{13}\cos 2t - \frac{72}{13}\sin 2t\right) + \frac{56}{13}\cos t + \frac{32}{13}\sin t.$$

36. (a) From $100x'' + 1600x = 1600\sin 8t$, $x(0) = 0$, and $x'(0) = 0$ we obtain $x_c = c_1\cos 4t + c_2\sin 4t$ and $x_p = -\frac{1}{3}\sin 8t$ so that by a trig identity

$$x = \frac{2}{3}\sin 4t - \frac{1}{3}\sin 8t = \frac{2}{3}\sin 4t - \frac{2}{3}\sin 4t\cos 4t.$$

(b) If $x = \frac{1}{3}\sin 4t(2 - 2\cos 4t) = 0$ then $t = n\pi/4$ for $n = 0, 1, 2, \ldots$.

(c) If $x' = \frac{8}{3}\cos 4t - \frac{8}{3}\cos 8t = \frac{8}{3}(1-\cos 4t)(1+2\cos 4t) = 0$ then $t = \pi/3+n\pi/2$ and $t = \pi/6+n\pi/2$ for $n = 0, 1, 2, \ldots$ at the extreme values. *Note*: There are many other values of t for which $x' = 0$.

(d) $x(\pi/6 + n\pi/2) = \sqrt{3}/2$ cm and $x(\pi/3 + n\pi/2) = -\sqrt{3}/2$ cm

(e)

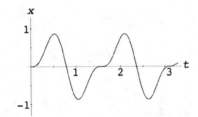

37. From $x'' + 4x = -5\sin 2t + 3\cos 2t$, $x(0) = -1$, and $x'(0) = 1$ we obtain $x_c = c_1\cos 2t + c_2\sin 2t$, $x_p = \frac{3}{4}t\sin 2t + \frac{5}{4}t\cos 2t$, and

$$x = -\cos 2t - \frac{1}{8}\sin 2t + \frac{3}{4}t\sin 2t + \frac{5}{4}t\cos 2t.$$

38. From $x'' + 9x = 5\sin 3t$, $x(0) = 2$, and $x'(0) = 0$ we obtain $x_c = c_1\cos 3t + c_2\sin 3t$, $x_p = -\frac{5}{6}t\cos 3t$, and

$$x = 2\cos 3t + \frac{5}{18}\sin 3t - \frac{5}{6}t\cos 3t.$$

39. (a) From $x'' + \omega^2 x = F_0\cos\gamma t$, $x(0) = 0$, and $x'(0) = 0$ we obtain $x_c = c_1\cos\omega t + c_2\sin\omega t$ and $x_p = (F_0\cos\gamma t)/\left(\omega^2 - \gamma^2\right)$ so that

$$x = -\frac{F_0}{\omega^2 - \gamma^2}\cos\omega t + \frac{F_0}{\omega^2 - \gamma^2}\cos\gamma t.$$

(b) $\displaystyle\lim_{\gamma\to\omega}\frac{F_0}{\omega^2 - \gamma^2}(\cos\gamma t - \cos\omega t) = \lim_{\gamma\to\omega}\frac{-F_0 t\sin\gamma t}{-2\gamma} = \frac{F_0}{2\omega}t\sin\omega t.$

40. From $x'' + \omega^2 x = F_0 \cos \omega t$, $x(0) = 0$, and $x'(0) = 0$ we obtain $x_c = c_1 \cos \omega t + c_2 \sin \omega t$ and $x_p = (F_0 t/2\omega) \sin \omega t$ so that $x = (F_0 t/2\omega) \sin \omega t$.

41. (a) From $\cos(u - v) = \cos u \cos v + \sin u \sin v$ and $\cos(u + v) = \cos u \cos v - \sin u \sin v$ we obtain $\sin u \sin v = \frac{1}{2}[\cos(u - v) - \cos(u + v)]$. Letting $u = \frac{1}{2}(\gamma - \omega)t$ and $v = \frac{1}{2}(\gamma + \omega)t$, the result follows.

(b) If $\epsilon = \frac{1}{2}(\gamma - \omega)$ then $\gamma \approx \omega$ so that $x = (F_0/2\epsilon\gamma) \sin \epsilon t \sin \gamma t$.

42. See the article "Distinguished Oscillations of a Forced Harmonic Oscillator" by T.G. Procter in *The College Mathematics Journal*, March, 1995. In this article the author illustrates that for $F_0 = 1$, $\lambda = 0.01$, $\gamma = 22/9$, and $\omega = 2$ the system exhibits beats oscillations on the interval $[0, 9\pi]$, but that this phenomenon is transient as $t \to \infty$.

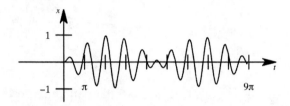

43. (a) The general solution of the homogeneous equation is

$$x_c(t) = c_1 e^{-\lambda t} \cos(\sqrt{\omega^2 - \lambda^2}\, t) + c_2 e^{-\lambda t} \sin(\sqrt{\omega^2 - \lambda^2}\, t)$$

$$= A e^{-\lambda t} \sin[\sqrt{\omega^2 - \lambda^2}\, t + \phi],$$

where $A = \sqrt{c_1^2 + c_2^2}$, $\sin \phi = c_1/A$, and $\cos \phi = c_2/A$. Now

$$x_p(t) = \frac{F_0(\omega^2 - \gamma^2)}{(\omega^2 - \gamma^2)^2 + 4\lambda^2\gamma^2} \sin \gamma t + \frac{F_0(-2\lambda\gamma)}{(\omega^2 - \gamma^2)^2 + 4\lambda^2\gamma^2} \cos \gamma t = A \sin(\gamma t + \theta),$$

where

$$\sin \theta = \frac{\dfrac{F_0(-2\lambda\gamma)}{(\omega^2 - \gamma^2)^2 + 4\lambda^2\gamma^2}}{\dfrac{F_0}{\sqrt{\omega^2 - \gamma^2 + 4\lambda^2\gamma^2}}} = \frac{-2\lambda\gamma}{\sqrt{(\omega^2 - \gamma^2)^2 + 4\lambda^2\gamma^2}}$$

and

$$\cos \theta = \frac{\dfrac{F_0(\omega^2 - \gamma^2)}{(\omega^2 - \gamma^2)^2 + 4\lambda^2\gamma^2}}{\dfrac{F_0}{\sqrt{(\omega^2 - \gamma^2)^2 + 4\lambda^2\gamma^2}}} = \frac{\omega^2 - \gamma^2}{\sqrt{(\omega^2 - \gamma^2)^2 + 4\lambda^2\gamma^2}}.$$

(b) If $g'(\gamma) = 0$ then $\gamma\left(\gamma^2 + 2\lambda^2 - \omega^2\right) = 0$ so that $\gamma = 0$ or $\gamma = \sqrt{\omega^2 - 2\lambda^2}$. The first derivative test shows that g has a maximum value at $\gamma = \sqrt{\omega^2 - 2\lambda^2}$. The maximum value of g is

$$g\left(\sqrt{\omega^2 - 2\lambda^2}\right) = F_0/2\lambda\sqrt{\omega^2 - \lambda^2}.$$

(c) We identify $\omega^2 = k/m = 4$, $\lambda = \beta/2$, and $\gamma_1 = \sqrt{\omega^2 - 2\lambda^2} = \sqrt{4 - \beta^2/2}$. As $\beta \to 0$, $\gamma_1 \to 2$ and the resonance curve grows without bound at $\gamma_1 = 2$. That is, the system approaches pure resonance.

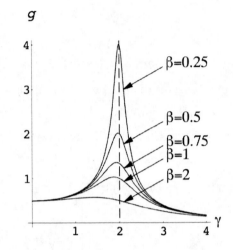

β	$\gamma1$	g
2.00	1.41	0.58
1.00	1.87	1.03
0.75	1.93	1.36
0.50	1.97	2.02
0.25	1.99	4.01

44. (a) For $n = 2$, $\sin^2 \gamma t = \frac{1}{2}(1 - \cos 2\gamma t)$. The system is in pure resonance when $2\gamma_1/2\pi = \omega/2\pi$, or when $\gamma_1 = \omega/2$.

(b) Note that

$$\sin^3 \gamma t = \sin \gamma t \sin^2 \gamma t = \frac{1}{2}[\sin \gamma t - \sin \gamma t \cos 2\gamma t].$$

Now

$$\sin(A + B) + \sin(A - B) = 2 \sin A \cos B$$

so

$$\sin \gamma t \cos 2\gamma t = \frac{1}{2}[\sin 3\gamma t - \sin \gamma t]$$

and

$$\sin^3 \gamma t = \frac{3}{4} \sin \gamma t - \frac{1}{4} \sin 3\gamma t.$$

Thus

$$x'' + \omega^2 x = \frac{3}{4} \sin \gamma t - \frac{1}{4} \sin 3\gamma t.$$

The frequency of free vibration is $\omega/2\pi$. Thus, when $\gamma_1/2\pi = \omega/2\pi$ or $\gamma_1 = \omega$, and when $3\gamma_2/2\pi = \omega/2\pi$ or $3\gamma_2 = \omega$ or $\gamma_3 = \omega/3$, the system will be in pure resonance.

(c)

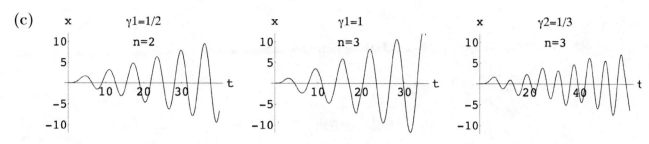

45. Solving $\frac{1}{20}q'' + 2q' + 100q = 0$ we obtain $q(t) = e^{-20t}(c_1 \cos 40t + c_2 \sin 40t)$. The initial conditions $q(0) = 5$ and $q'(0) = 0$ imply $c_1 = 5$ and $c_2 = 5/2$. Thus

$$q(t) = e^{-20t}\left(5 \cos 40t + \frac{5}{2}\sin 40t\right) = \sqrt{25 + 25/4}\, e^{-20t} \sin(40t + 1.1071)$$

and $q(0.01) \approx 4.5676$ coulombs. The charge is zero for the first time when $40t + 1.1071 = \pi$ or $t \approx 0.0509$ second.

46. Solving $\frac{1}{4}q'' + 20q' + 300q = 0$ we obtain $q(t) = c_1 e^{-20t} + c_2 e^{-60t}$. The initial conditions $q(0) = 4$ and $q'(0) = 0$ imply $c_1 = 6$ and $c_2 = -2$. Thus

$$q(t) = 6e^{-20t} - 2e^{-60t}.$$

Setting $q = 0$ we find $e^{40t} = 1/3$ which implies $t < 0$. Therefore the charge is not 0 for $t \geq 0$.

47. Solving $\frac{5}{3}q'' + 10q' + 30q = 300$ we obtain $q(t) = e^{-3t}(c_1 \cos 3t + c_2 \sin 3t) + 10$. The initial conditions $q(0) = q'(0) = 0$ imply $c_1 = c_2 = -10$. Thus

$$q(t) = 10 - 10e^{-3t}(\cos 3t + \sin 3t) \quad \text{and} \quad i(t) = 60e^{-3t} \sin 3t.$$

Solving $i(t) = 0$ we see that the maximum charge occurs when $t = \pi/3$ and $q(\pi/3) \approx 10.432$.

48. Solving $q'' + 100q' + 2500q = 30$ we obtain $q(t) = c_1 e^{-50t} + c_2 t e^{-50t} + 0.012$. The initial conditions $q(0) = 0$ and $q'(0) = 2$ imply $c_1 = -0.012$ and $c_2 = 1.4$. Thus, using $i(t) = q'(t)$ we get

$$q(t) = -0.012e^{-50t} + 1.4te^{-50t} + 0.012 \quad \text{and} \quad i(t) = 2e^{-50t} - 70te^{-50t}.$$

Solving $i(t) = 0$ we see that the maximum charge occurs when $t = 1/35$ second and $q(1/35) \approx 0.01871$ coulomb.

49. Solving $q'' + 2q' + 4q = 0$ we obtain $q_c = e^{-t}\left(\cos \sqrt{3}\,t + \sin \sqrt{3}\,t\right)$. The steady-state charge has the form $q_p = A \cos t + B \sin t$. Substituting into the differential equation we find

$$(3A + 2B)\cos t + (3B - 2A)\sin t = 50 \cos t.$$

Thus, $A = 150/13$ and $B = 100/13$. The steady-state charge is

$$q_p(t) = \frac{150}{13}\cos t + \frac{100}{13}\sin t$$

and the steady-state current is

$$i_p(t) = -\frac{150}{13}\sin t + \frac{100}{13}\cos t.$$

50. From

$$i_p(t) = \frac{E_0}{Z}\left(\frac{R}{Z}\sin\gamma t - \frac{X}{Z}\cos\gamma t\right)$$

and $Z = \sqrt{X^2 + R^2}$ we see that the amplitude of $i_p(t)$ is

$$A = \sqrt{\frac{E_0^2 R^2}{Z^4} + \frac{E_0^2 X^2}{Z^4}} = \frac{E_0}{Z^2}\sqrt{R^2 + X^2} = \frac{E_0}{Z}\,.$$

51. The differential equation is $\frac{1}{2}q'' + 20q' + 1000q = 100\sin 60t$. To use Example 10 in the text we identify $E_0 = 100$ and $\gamma = 60$. Then

$$X = L\gamma - \frac{1}{c\gamma} = \frac{1}{2}(60) - \frac{1}{0.001(60)} \approx 13.3333,$$

$$Z = \sqrt{X^2 + R^2} = \sqrt{X^2 + 400} \approx 24.0370,$$

and

$$\frac{E_0}{Z} = \frac{100}{Z} \approx 4.1603.$$

From Problem 50, then

$$i_p(t) \approx 4.1603\sin(60t + \phi)$$

where $\sin\phi = -X/Z$ and $\cos\phi = R/Z$. Thus $\tan\phi = -X/R \approx -0.6667$ and ϕ is a fourth quadrant angle. Now $\phi \approx -0.5880$ and

$$i_p(t) = 4.1603\sin(60t - 0.5880).$$

52. Solving $\frac{1}{2}q'' + 20q' + 1000q = 0$ we obtain $q_c(t) = e^{-20t}(c_1\cos 40t + c_2\sin 40t)$. The steady-state charge has the form $q_p(t) = A\sin 60t + B\cos 60t + C\sin 40t + D\cos 40t$. Substituting into the differential equation we find

$$(-1600A - 2400B)\sin 60t + (2400A - 1600B)\cos 60t$$

$$+ (400C - 1600D)\sin 40t + (1600C + 400D)\cos 40t$$

$$= 200\sin 60t + 400\cos 40t.$$

Equating coefficients we obtain $A = -1/26$, $B = -3/52$, $C = 4/17$, and $D = 1/17$. The steady-state charge is

$$q_p(t) = -\frac{1}{26}\sin 60t - \frac{3}{52}\cos 60t + \frac{4}{17}\sin 40t + \frac{1}{17}\cos 40t$$

and the steady-state current is

$$i_p(t) = -\frac{30}{13}\cos 60t + \frac{45}{13}\sin 60t + \frac{160}{17}\cos 40t - \frac{40}{17}\sin 40t.$$

53. Solving $\frac{1}{2}q'' + 10q' + 100q = 150$ we obtain $q(t) = e^{-10t}(c_1 \cos 10t + c_2 \sin 10t) + 3/2$. The initial conditions $q(0) = 1$ and $q'(0) = 0$ imply $c_1 = c_2 = -1/2$. Thus

$$q(t) = -\frac{1}{2}e^{-10t}(\cos 10t + \sin 10t) + \frac{3}{2}.$$

As $t \to \infty$, $q(t) \to 3/2$.

54. In Problem 50 it is shown that the amplitude of the steady-state current is E_0/Z, where $Z = \sqrt{X^2 + R^2}$ and $X = L\gamma - 1/C\gamma$. Since E_0 is constant the amplitude will be a maximum when Z is a minimum. Since R is constant, Z will be a minimum when $X = 0$. Solving $L\gamma - 1/C\gamma = 0$ for γ we obtain $\gamma = 1/\sqrt{LC}$. The maximum amplitude will be E_0/R.

55. By Problem 50 the amplitude of the steady-state current is E_0/Z, where $Z = \sqrt{X^2 + R^2}$ and $X = L\gamma - 1/C\gamma$. Since E_0 is constant the amplitude will be a maximum when Z is a minimum. Since R is constant, Z will be a minimum when $X = 0$. Solving $L\gamma - 1/C\gamma = 0$ for C we obtain $C = 1/L\gamma^2$.

56. Solving $0.1q'' + 10q = 100 \sin \gamma t$ we obtain

$$q(t) = c_1 \cos 10t + c_2 \sin 10t + q_p(t)$$

where $q_p(t) = A \sin \gamma t + B \cos \gamma t$. Substituting $q_p(t)$ into the differential equation we find

$$(100 - \gamma^2)A \sin \gamma t + (100 - \gamma^2)B \cos \gamma t = 100 \sin \gamma t.$$

Equating coefficients we obtain $A = 100/(100 - \gamma^2)$ and $B = 0$. Thus, $q_p(t) = \dfrac{100}{100 - \gamma^2} \sin \gamma t$. The initial conditions $q(0) = q'(0) = 0$ imply $c_1 = 0$ and $c_2 = -10\gamma/(100 - \gamma^2)$. The charge is

$$q(t) = \frac{10}{100 - \gamma^2}(10 \sin \gamma t - \gamma \sin 10t)$$

and the current is

$$i(t) = \frac{100\gamma}{100 - \gamma^2}(\cos \gamma t - \cos 10t).$$

57. In an LC-series circuit there is no resistor, so the differential equation is

$$L\frac{d^2q}{dt^2} + \frac{1}{C}q = E(t).$$

Then $q(t) = c_1 \cos\left(t/\sqrt{LC}\right) + c_2 \sin\left(t/\sqrt{LC}\right) + q_p(t)$ where $q_p(t) = A \sin \gamma t + B \cos \gamma t$. Substituting $q_p(t)$ into the differential equation we find

$$\left(\frac{1}{C} - L\gamma^2\right)A \sin \gamma t + \left(\frac{1}{C} - L\gamma^2\right)B \cos \gamma t = E_0 \cos \gamma t.$$

Equating coefficients we obtain $A = 0$ and $B = E_0C/(1 - LC\gamma^2)$. Thus, the charge is

$$q(t) = c_1 \cos \frac{1}{\sqrt{LC}}t + c_2 \sin \frac{1}{\sqrt{LC}}t + \frac{E_0C}{1 - LC\gamma^2} \cos \gamma t.$$

The initial conditions $q(0) = q_0$ and $q'(0) = i_0$ imply $c_1 = q_0 - E_0 C/(1 - LC\gamma^2)$ and $c_2 = i_0\sqrt{LC}$. The current is $i(t) = q'(t)$ or

$$i(t) = -\frac{c_1}{\sqrt{LC}}\sin\frac{1}{\sqrt{LC}}t + \frac{c_2}{\sqrt{LC}}\cos\frac{1}{\sqrt{LC}}t - \frac{E_0 C\gamma}{1 - LC\gamma^2}\sin\gamma t$$

$$= i_0\cos\frac{1}{\sqrt{LC}}t - \frac{1}{\sqrt{LC}}\left(q_0 - \frac{E_0 C}{1 - LC\gamma^2}\right)\sin\frac{1}{\sqrt{LC}}t - \frac{E_0 C\gamma}{1 - LC\gamma^2}\sin\gamma t.$$

58. When the circuit is in resonance the form of $q_p(t)$ is $q_p(t) = At\cos kt + Bt\sin kt$ where $k = 1/\sqrt{LC}$. Substituting $q_p(t)$ into the differential equation we find

$$q_p'' + k^2 q_p = -2kA\sin kt + 2kB\cos kt = \frac{E_0}{L}\cos kt.$$

Equating coefficients we obtain $A = 0$ and $B = E_0/2kL$. The charge is

$$q(t) = c_1\cos kt + c_2\sin kt + \frac{E_0}{2kL}t\sin kt.$$

The initial conditions $q(0) = q_0$ and $q'(0) = i_0$ imply $c_1 = q_0$ and $c_2 = i_0/k$. The current is

$$i(t) = -c_1 k\sin kt + c_2 k\cos kt + \frac{E_0}{2kL}(kt\cos kt + \sin kt)$$

$$= \left(\frac{E_0}{2kL} - q_0 k\right)\sin kt + i_0\cos kt + \frac{E_0}{2L}t\cos kt.$$

Exercises 5.2   Linear Models: Boundary-Value Problems

1. (a) The general solution is

$$y(x) = c_1 + c_2 x + c_3 x^2 + c_4 x^3 + \frac{w_0}{24EI}x^4.$$

The boundary conditions are $y(0) = 0$, $y'(0) = 0$, $y''(L) = 0$, $y'''(L) = 0$. The first two conditions give $c_1 = 0$ and $c_2 = 0$. The conditions at $x = L$ give the system

$$2c_3 + 6c_4 L + \frac{w_0}{2EI}L^2 = 0$$

$$6c_4 + \frac{w_0}{EI}L = 0.$$

Solving, we obtain $c_3 = w_0 L^2/4EI$ and $c_4 = -w_0 L/6EI$. The deflection is

$$y(x) = \frac{w_0}{24EI}(6L^2 x^2 - 4Lx^3 + x^4).$$

(b)

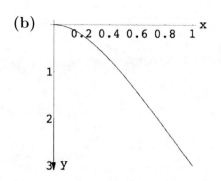

2. (a) The general solution is

$$y(x) = c_1 + c_2 x + c_3 x^2 + c_4 x^3 + \frac{w_0}{24EI} x^4.$$

The boundary conditions are $y(0) = 0$, $y''(0) = 0$, $y(L) = 0$, $y''(L) = 0$. The first two conditions give $c_1 = 0$ and $c_3 = 0$. The conditions at $x = L$ give the system

$$c_2 L + c_4 L^3 + \frac{w_0}{24EI} L^4 = 0$$

$$6c_4 L + \frac{w_0}{2EI} L^2 = 0.$$

Solving, we obtain $c_2 = w_0 L^3 / 24EI$ and $c_4 = -w_0 L / 12EI$. The deflection is

$$y(x) = \frac{w_0}{24EI} (L^3 x - 2Lx^3 + x^4).$$

(b)

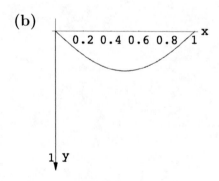

3. (a) The general solution is

$$y(x) = c_1 + c_2 x + c_3 x^2 + c_4 x^3 + \frac{w_0}{24EI} x^4.$$

The boundary conditions are $y(0) = 0$, $y'(0) = 0$, $y(L) = 0$, $y''(L) = 0$. The first two conditions give $c_1 = 0$ and $c_2 = 0$. The conditions at $x = L$ give the system

$$c_3 L^2 + c_4 L^3 + \frac{w_0}{24EI} L^4 = 0$$

$$2c_3 + 6c_4 L + \frac{w_0}{2EI} L^2 = 0.$$

Solving, we obtain $c_3 = w_0 L^2 / 16EI$ and $c_4 = -5w_0 L / 48EI$. The deflection is

$$y(x) = \frac{w_0}{48EI} (3L^2 x^2 - 5Lx^3 + 2x^4).$$

(b)

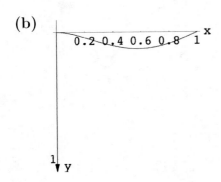

4. (a) The general solution is

$$y(x) = c_1 + c_2 x + c_3 x^2 + c_4 x^3 + \frac{w_0 L^4}{EI\pi^4} \sin \frac{\pi}{L} x.$$

The boundary conditions are $y(0) = 0$, $y'(0) = 0$, $y(L) = 0$, $y''(L) = 0$. The first two conditions give $c_1 = 0$ and $c_2 = -w_0 L^3/EI\pi^3$. The conditions at $x = L$ give the system

$$c_3 L^2 + c_4 L^3 + \frac{w_0}{EI\pi^3} L^4 = 0$$

$$2c_3 + 6c_4 L = 0.$$

Solving, we obtain $c_3 = 3w_0 L^2/2EI\pi^3$ and $c_4 = -w_0 L/2EI\pi^3$. The deflection is

$$y(x) = \frac{w_0 L}{2EI\pi^3} \left(-2L^2 x + 3Lx^2 - x^3 + \frac{2L^3}{\pi} \sin \frac{\pi}{L} x \right).$$

(b)

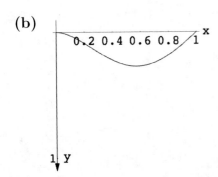

(c) Using a CAS we find the maximum deflection to be 0.270806 when $x = 0.572536$.

5. (a) The general solution is

$$y(x) = c_1 + c_2 x + c_3 x^2 + c_4 x^3 + \frac{w_0}{120EI} x^5.$$

The boundary conditions are $y(0) = 0$, $y''(0) = 0$, $y(L) = 0$, $y''(L) = 0$. The first two conditions give $c_1 = 0$ and $c_3 = 0$. The conditions at $x = L$ give the system

$$c_2 L + c_4 L^3 + \frac{w_0}{120EI} L^5 = 0$$

$$6c_4 L + \frac{w_0}{6EI} L^3 = 0.$$

Solving, we obtain $c_2 = 7w_0 L^4/360EI$ and $c_4 = -w_0 L^2/36EI$. The deflection is

$$y(x) = \frac{w_0}{360EI}(7L^4 x - 10L^2 x^3 + 3x^5).$$

(b)

(c) Using a CAS we find the maximum deflection to be 0.234799 when $x = 0.51933$.

6. (a) $y_{\max} = y(L) = w_0 L^4/8EI$

(b) Replacing both L and x by $L/2$ in $y(x)$ we obtain $w_0 L^4/128EI$, which is $1/16$ of the maximum deflection when the length of the beam is L.

(c) $y_{\max} = y(L/2) = 5w_0 L^4/384EI$

(d) The maximum deflection in Example 1 is $y(L/2) = (w_0/24EI)L^4/16 = w_0 L^4/384EI$, which is $1/5$ of the maximum displacement of the beam in part **(c)**.

7. The general solution of the differential equation is

$$y = c_1 \cosh \sqrt{\frac{P}{EI}}\, x + c_2 \sinh \sqrt{\frac{P}{EI}}\, x + \frac{w_0}{2P} x^2 + \frac{w_0 EI}{P^2}.$$

Setting $y(0) = 0$ we obtain $c_1 = -w_0 EI/P^2$, so that

$$y = -\frac{w_0 EI}{P^2} \cosh \sqrt{\frac{P}{EI}}\, x + c_2 \sinh \sqrt{\frac{P}{EI}}\, x + \frac{w_0}{2P} x^2 + \frac{w_0 EI}{P^2}.$$

Setting $y'(L) = 0$ we find

$$c_2 = \left(\sqrt{\frac{P}{EI}} \frac{w_0 EI}{P^2} \sinh \sqrt{\frac{P}{EI}}\, L - \frac{w_0 L}{P} \right) \Big/ \sqrt{\frac{P}{EI}} \cosh \sqrt{\frac{P}{EI}}\, L.$$

8. The general solution of the differential equation is

$$y = c_1 \cos \sqrt{\frac{P}{EI}}\, x + c_2 \sin \sqrt{\frac{P}{EI}}\, x + \frac{w_0}{2P} x^2 + \frac{w_0 EI}{P^2}.$$

Setting $y(0) = 0$ we obtain $c_1 = -w_0 EI/P^2$, so that

$$y = -\frac{w_0 EI}{P^2} \cos \sqrt{\frac{P}{EI}}\, x + c_2 \sin \sqrt{\frac{P}{EI}}\, x + \frac{w_0}{2P} x^2 + \frac{w_0 EI}{P^2}.$$

Setting $y'(L) = 0$ we find

$$c_2 = \left(-\sqrt{\frac{P}{EI}} \frac{w_0 EI}{P^2} \sin\sqrt{\frac{P}{EI}} L - \frac{w_0 L}{P} \right) \Big/ \sqrt{\frac{P}{EI}} \cos\sqrt{\frac{P}{EI}} L.$$

9. This is Example 2 in the text with $L = \pi$. The eigenvalues are $\lambda_n = n^2\pi^2/\pi^2 = n^2$, $n = 1, 2, 3, \ldots$ and the corresponding eigenfunctions are $y_n = \sin(n\pi x/\pi) = \sin nx$, $n = 1, 2, 3, \ldots$.

10. This is Example 2 in the text with $L = \pi/4$. The eigenvalues are $\lambda_n = n^2\pi^2/(\pi/4)^2 = 16n^2$, $n = 1$, 2, 3, $\ldots$ and the eigenfunctions are $y_n = \sin(n\pi x/(\pi/4)) = \sin 4nx$, $n = 1, 2, 3, \ldots$.

11. For $\lambda \leq 0$ the only solution of the boundary-value problem is $y = 0$. For $\lambda = \alpha^2 > 0$ we have

$$y = c_1 \cos \alpha x + c_2 \sin \alpha x.$$

Now

$$y'(x) = -c_1 \alpha \sin \alpha x + c_2 \alpha \cos \alpha x$$

and $y'(0) = 0$ implies $c_2 = 0$, so

$$y(L) = c_1 \cos \alpha L = 0$$

gives

$$\alpha L = \frac{(2n-1)\pi}{2} \quad \text{or} \quad \lambda = \alpha^2 = \frac{(2n-1)^2 \pi^2}{4L^2}, \quad n = 1, 2, 3, \ldots.$$

The eigenvalues $(2n-1)^2\pi^2/4L^2$ correspond to the eigenfunctions $\cos\dfrac{(2n-1)\pi}{2L}x$ for $n = 1, 2, 3, \ldots$.

12. For $\lambda \leq 0$ the only solution of the boundary-value problem is $y = 0$. For $\lambda = \alpha^2 > 0$ we have

$$y = c_1 \cos \alpha x + c_2 \sin \alpha x.$$

Since $y(0) = 0$ implies $c_1 = 0$, $y = c_2 \sin x\, dx$. Now

$$y'\left(\frac{\pi}{2}\right) = c_2 \alpha \cos \alpha \frac{\pi}{2} = 0$$

gives

$$\alpha \frac{\pi}{2} = \frac{(2n-1)\pi}{2} \quad \text{or} \quad \lambda = \alpha^2 = (2n-1)^2, \quad n = 1, 2, 3, \ldots.$$

The eigenvalues $\lambda_n = (2n-1)^2$ correspond to the eigenfunctions $y_n = \sin(2n-1)x$.

13. For $\lambda = -\alpha^2 < 0$ the only solution of the boundary-value problem is $y = 0$. For $\lambda = 0$ we have $y = c_1 x + c_2$. Now $y' = c_1$ and $y'(0) = 0$ implies $c_1 = 0$. Then $y = c_2$ and $y'(\pi) = 0$. Thus, $\lambda = 0$ is an eigenvalue with corresponding eigenfunction $y = 1$.

For $\lambda = \alpha^2 > 0$ we have

$$y = c_1 \cos \alpha x + c_2 \sin \alpha x.$$

Now

$$y'(x) = -c_1\alpha\sin\alpha x + c_2\alpha\cos\alpha x$$

and $y'(0) = 0$ implies $c_2 = 0$, so

$$y'(\pi) = -c_1\alpha\sin\alpha\pi = 0$$

gives

$$\alpha\pi = n\pi \quad \text{or} \quad \lambda = \alpha^2 = n^2, \ n = 1, 2, 3, \ldots .$$

The eigenvalues n^2 correspond to the eigenfunctions $\cos nx$ for $n = 0, 1, 2, \ldots .$

14. For $\lambda \leq 0$ the only solution of the boundary-value problem is $y = 0$. For $\lambda = \alpha^2 > 0$ we have

$$y = c_1\cos\alpha x + c_2\sin\alpha x.$$

Now $y(-\pi) = y(\pi) = 0$ implies

$$c_1\cos\alpha\pi - c_2\sin\alpha\pi = 0$$

$$\text{(1)}$$

$$c_1\cos\alpha\pi + c_2\sin\alpha\pi = 0.$$

This homogeneous system will have a nontrivial solution when

$$\begin{vmatrix} \cos\alpha\pi & -\sin\alpha\pi \\ \cos\alpha\pi & \sin\alpha\pi \end{vmatrix} = 2\sin\alpha\pi\cos\alpha\pi = \sin 2\alpha\pi = 0.$$

Then

$$2\alpha\pi = n\pi \quad \text{or} \quad \lambda = \alpha^2 = \frac{n^2}{4}; \quad n = 1, 2, 3, \ldots .$$

When $n = 2k - 1$ is odd, the eigenvalues are $(2k-1)^2/4$. Since $\cos(2k-1)\pi/2 = 0$ and $\sin(2k-1)\pi/2 \neq 0$, we see from either equation in (1) that $c_2 = 0$. Thus, the eigenfunctions corresponding to the eigenvalues $(2k-1)^2/4$ are $y = \cos(2k-1)x/2$ for $k = 1, 2, 3, \ldots .$ Similarly, when $n = 2k$ is even, the eigenvalues are k^2 with corresponding eigenfunctions $y = \sin kx$ for $k = 1, 2, 3, \ldots .$

15. The auxiliary equation has solutions

$$m = \frac{1}{2}\left(-2 \pm \sqrt{4 - 4(\lambda + 1)}\right) = -1 \pm \alpha.$$

For $\lambda = -\alpha^2 < 0$ we have

$$y = e^{-x}\left(c_1\cosh\alpha x + c_2\sinh\alpha x\right).$$

The boundary conditions imply

$$y(0) = c_1 = 0$$

$$y(5) = c_2 e^{-5}\sinh 5\alpha = 0$$

so $c_1 = c_2 = 0$ and the only solution of the boundary-value problem is $y = 0$.

For $\lambda = 0$ we have

$$y = c_1 e^{-x} + c_2 x e^{-x}$$

and the only solution of the boundary-value problem is $y = 0$.

For $\lambda = \alpha^2 > 0$ we have

$$y = e^{-x}\left(c_1 \cos \alpha x + c_2 \sin \alpha x\right).$$

Now $y(0) = 0$ implies $c_1 = 0$, so

$$y(5) = c_2 e^{-5} \sin 5\alpha = 0$$

gives

$$5\alpha = n\pi \quad \text{or} \quad \lambda = \alpha^2 = \frac{n^2 \pi^2}{25}, \ n = 1, 2, 3, \ldots .$$

The eigenvalues $\lambda_n = \dfrac{n^2 \pi^2}{25}$ correspond to the eigenfunctions $y_n = e^{-x} \sin \dfrac{n\pi}{5}x$ for $n = 1, 2, 3, \ldots .$

16. For $\lambda < -1$ the only solution of the boundary-value problem is $y = 0$. For $\lambda = -1$ we have $y = c_1 x + c_2$. Now $y' = c_1$ and $y'(0) = 0$ implies $c_1 = 0$. Then $y = c_2$ and $y'(1) = 0$. Thus, $\lambda = -1$ is an eigenvalue with corresponding eigenfunction $y = 1$.

For $\lambda > -1$ or $\lambda + 1 = \alpha^2 > 0$ we have

$$y = c_1 \cos \alpha x + c_2 \sin \alpha x.$$

Now

$$y' = -c_1 \alpha \sin \alpha x + c_2 \alpha \cos \alpha x$$

and $y'(0) = 0$ implies $c_2 = 0$, so

$$y'(1) = -c_1 \alpha \sin \alpha = 0$$

gives

$$\alpha = n\pi, \quad \lambda + 1 = \alpha^2 = n^2 \pi^2, \quad \text{or} \quad \lambda = n^2 \pi^2 - 1, \ n = 1, 2, 3, \ldots .$$

The eigenvalues $n^2 \pi^2 - 1$ correspond to the eigenfunctions $\cos n\pi x$ for $n = 0, 1, 2, \ldots .$

17. For $\lambda = \alpha^2 > 0$ a general solution of the given differential equation is

$$y = c_1 \cos(\alpha \ln x) + c_2 \sin(\alpha \ln x).$$

Since $\ln 1 = 0$, the boundary condition $y(1) = 0$ implies $c_1 = 0$. Therefore

$$y = c_2 \sin(\alpha \ln x).$$

Using $\ln e^{\pi} = \pi$ we find that $y\left(e^{\pi}\right) = 0$ implies

$$c_2 \sin \alpha \pi = 0$$

or $\alpha\pi = n\pi$, $n = 1, 2, 3, \ldots .$ The eigenvalues and eigenfunctions are, in turn,

$$\lambda = \alpha^2 = n^2, \quad n = 1, 2, 3, \ldots \quad \text{and} \quad y = \sin(n \ln x).$$

For $\lambda \leq 0$ the only solution of the boundary-value problem is $y = 0$.

18. For $\lambda = 0$ the general solution is $y = c_1 + c_2 \ln x$. Now $y' = c_2/x$, so $y'(e^{-1}) = c_2 e = 0$ implies $c_2 = 0$. Then $y = c_1$ and $y(1) = 0$ gives $c_1 = 0$. Thus $y(x) = 0$.

For $\lambda = -\alpha^2 < 0$, $y = c_1 x^{-\alpha} + c_2 x^{\alpha}$. The boundary conditions give $c_2 = c_1 e^{2\alpha}$ and $c_1 = 0$, so that $c_2 = 0$ and $y(x) = 0$.

For $\lambda = \alpha^2 > 0$, $y = c_1 \cos(\alpha \ln x) + c_2 \sin(\alpha \ln x)$. From $y(1) = 0$ we obtain $c_1 = 0$ and $y = c_2 \sin(\alpha \ln x)$. Now $y' = c_2(\alpha/x) \cos(\alpha \ln x)$, so $y'(e^{-1}) = c_2 e \alpha \cos \alpha = 0$ implies $\cos \alpha = 0$ or $\alpha = (2n-1)\pi/2$ and $\lambda = \alpha^2 = (2n-1)^2 \pi^2/4$ for $n = 1, 2, 3, \ldots$. The corresponding eigenfunctions are

$$y_n = \sin \left(\frac{2n-1}{2} \pi \ln x \right).$$

19. For $\lambda = \alpha^4$, $\alpha > 0$, the general solution of the boundary-value problem

$$y^{(4)} - \lambda y = 0, \quad y(0) = 0, \ y''(0) = 0, \ y(1) = 0, \ y''(1) = 0$$

is

$$y = c_1 \cos \alpha x + c_2 \sin \alpha x + c_3 \cosh \alpha x + c_4 \sinh \alpha x.$$

The boundary conditions $y(0) = 0$, $y''(0) = 0$ give $c_1 + c_3 = 0$ and $-c_1 \alpha^2 + c_3 \alpha^2 = 0$, from which we conclude $c_1 = c_3 = 0$. Thus, $y = c_2 \sin \alpha x + c_4 \sinh \alpha x$. The boundary conditions $y(1) = 0$, $y''(1) = 0$ then give

$$c_2 \sin \alpha + c_4 \sinh \alpha = 0$$

$$-c_2 \alpha^2 \sin \alpha + c_4 \alpha^2 \sinh \alpha = 0.$$

In order to have nonzero solutions of this system, we must have the determinant of the coefficients equal zero, that is,

$$\begin{vmatrix} \sin \alpha & \sinh \alpha \\ -\alpha^2 \sin \alpha & \alpha^2 \sinh \alpha \end{vmatrix} = 0 \quad \text{or} \quad 2\alpha^2 \sinh \alpha \sin \alpha = 0.$$

But since $\alpha > 0$, the only way that this is satisfied is to have $\sin \alpha = 0$ or $\alpha = n\pi$. The system is then satisfied by choosing $c_2 \neq 0$, $c_4 = 0$, and $\alpha = n\pi$. The eigenvalues and corresponding eigenfunctions are then

$$\lambda_n = \alpha^4 = (n\pi)^4, \ n = 1, 2, 3, \ldots \quad \text{and} \quad y = \sin n\pi x.$$

20. For $\lambda = \alpha^4$, $\alpha > 0$, the general solution of the differential equation is

$$y = c_1 \cos \alpha x + c_2 \sin \alpha x + c_3 \cosh \alpha x + c_4 \sinh \alpha x.$$

The boundary conditions $y'(0) = 0$, $y'''(0) = 0$ give $c_2 \alpha + c_4 \alpha = 0$ and $-c_2 \alpha^3 + c_4 \alpha^3 = 0$ from which we conclude $c_2 = c_4 = 0$. Thus, $y = c_1 \cos \alpha x + c_3 \cosh \alpha x$. The boundary conditions $y(\pi) = 0$,

$y''(\pi) = 0$ then give

$$c_2 \cos \alpha\pi + c_4 \cosh \alpha\pi = 0$$

$$-c_2\lambda^2 \cos \alpha\pi + c_4\lambda^2 \cosh \alpha\pi = 0.$$

The determinant of the coefficients is $2\alpha^2 \cosh \alpha \cos \alpha = 0$. But since $\alpha > 0$, the only way that this is satisfied is to have $\cos \alpha\pi = 0$ or $\alpha = (2n-1)/2$, $n = 1, 2, 3, \ldots$. The eigenvalues and corresponding eigenfunctions are

$$\lambda_n = \alpha^4 = \left(\frac{2n-1}{2}\right)^4, \ n = 1, 2, 3, \ldots \qquad \text{and} \qquad y = \cos\left(\frac{2n-1}{2}\right)x.$$

21. If restraints are put on the column at $x = L/4$, $x = L/2$, and $x = 3L/4$, then the critical load will be P_4.

22. **(a)** The general solution of the differential equation is

$$y = c_1 \cos\sqrt{\frac{P}{EI}}\,x + c_2 \sin\sqrt{\frac{P}{EI}}\,x + \delta.$$

Since the column is embedded at $x = 0$, the boundary conditions are $y(0) = y'(0) = 0$. If $\delta = 0$ this implies that $c_1 = c_2 = 0$ and $y(x) = 0$. That is, there is no deflection.

(b) If $\delta \neq 0$, the boundary conditions give, in turn, $c_1 = -\delta$ and $c_2 = 0$. Then

$$y = \delta\left(1 - \cos\sqrt{\frac{P}{EI}}\,x\right).$$

In order to satisfy the boundary condition $y(L) = \delta$ we must have

$$\delta = \delta\left(1 - \cos\sqrt{\frac{P}{EI}}\,L\right) \qquad \text{or} \qquad \cos\sqrt{\frac{P}{EI}}\,L = 0.$$

This gives $\sqrt{P/EI}\,L = n\pi/2$ for $n = 1, 2, 3, \ldots$. The smallest value of P_n, the Euler load, is then

$$\sqrt{\frac{P_1}{EI}}\,L = \frac{\pi}{2} \qquad \text{or} \qquad P_1 = \frac{1}{4}\left(\frac{\pi^2 EI}{L^2}\right).$$

23. If $\lambda = \alpha^2 = P/EI$, then the solution of the differential equation is

$$y = c_1 \cos \alpha x + c_2 \sin \alpha x + c_3 x + c_4.$$

The conditions $y(0) = 0$, $y''(0) = 0$ yield, in turn, $c_1 + c_4 = 0$ and $c_1 = 0$. With $c_1 = 0$ and $c_4 = 0$ the solution is $y = c_2 \sin \alpha x + c_3 x$. The conditions $y(L) = 0$, $y''(L) = 0$, then yield

$$c_2 \sin \alpha L + c_3 L = 0 \quad \text{and} \quad c_2 \sin \alpha L = 0.$$

Hence, nontrivial solutions of the problem exist only if $\sin \alpha L = 0$. From this point on, the analysis is the same as in Example 3 in the text.

24. **(a)** The boundary-value problem is

$$\frac{d^4 y}{dx^4} + \lambda \frac{d^2 y}{dx^2} = 0, \quad y(0) = 0, y''(0) = 0, \ y(L) = 0, y'(L) = 0,$$

where $\lambda = \alpha^2 = P/EI$. The solution of the differential equation is $y = c_1 \cos \alpha x + c_2 \sin \alpha x + c_3 x + c_4$ and the conditions $y(0) = 0$, $y''(0) = 0$ yield $c_1 = 0$ and $c_4 = 0$. Next, by applying $y(L) = 0$, $y'(L) = 0$ to $y = c_2 \sin \alpha x + c_3 x$ we get the system of equations

$$c_2 \sin \alpha L + c_3 L = 0$$

$$\alpha c_2 \cos \alpha L + c_3 = 0.$$

To obtain nontrivial solutions c_2, c_3, we must have the determinant of the coefficients equal to zero:

$$\begin{vmatrix} \sin \alpha L & L \\ \alpha \cos \alpha L & 1 \end{vmatrix} = 0 \quad \text{or} \quad \tan \beta = \beta,$$

where $\beta = \alpha L$. If β_n denotes the positive roots of the last equation, then the eigenvalues are found from $\beta_n = \alpha_n L = \sqrt{\lambda_n} L$ or $\lambda_n = (\beta_n / L)^2$. From $\lambda = P/EI$ we see that the critical loads are $P_n = \beta_n^2 EI/L^2$. With the aid of a CAS we find that the first positive root of $\tan \beta = \beta$ is (approximately) $\beta_1 = 4.4934$, and so the Euler load is (approximately) $P_1 = 20.1907 EI/L^2$. Finally, if we use $c_3 = -c_2 \alpha \cos \alpha L$, then the deflection curves are

$$y_n(x) = c_2 \sin \alpha_n x + c_3 x = c_2 \left[\sin \left(\frac{\beta_n}{L} x \right) - \left(\frac{\beta_n}{L} \cos \beta_n \right) x \right].$$

(b) With $L = 1$ and c_2 appropriately chosen, the general shape of the first buckling mode,

$$y_1(x) = c_2 \left[\sin \left(\frac{4.4934}{L} x \right) - \left(\frac{4.4934}{L} \cos(4.4934) \right) x \right],$$

is shown below.

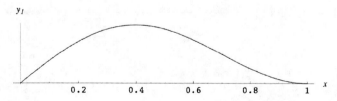

25. The general solution is

$$y = c_1 \cos \sqrt{\frac{\rho}{T}} \omega x + c_2 \sin \sqrt{\frac{\rho}{T}} \omega x.$$

From $y(0) = 0$ we obtain $c_1 = 0$. Setting $y(L) = 0$ we find $\sqrt{\rho/T}\,\omega L = n\pi$, $n = 1, 2, 3, \ldots$. Thus, critical speeds are $\omega_n = n\pi\sqrt{T}/L\sqrt{\rho}$, $n = 1, 2, 3, \ldots$. The corresponding deflection curves are

$$y(x) = c_2 \sin\frac{n\pi}{L}x, \quad n = 1, 2, 3, \ldots,$$

where $c_2 \neq 0$.

26. **(a)** When $T(x) = x^2$ the given differential equation is the Cauchy-Euler equation

$$x^2 y'' + 2xy' + \rho\omega^2 y = 0.$$

The solutions of the auxiliary equation

$$m(m-1) + 2m + \rho\omega^2 = m^2 + m + \rho\omega^2 = 0$$

are

$$m_1 = -\frac{1}{2} - \frac{1}{2}\sqrt{4\rho\omega^2 - 1}\,i, \quad m_2 = -\frac{1}{2} + \frac{1}{2}\sqrt{4\rho\omega^2 - 1}\,i$$

when $\rho\omega^2 > 0.25$. Thus

$$y = c_1 x^{-1/2}\cos(\lambda \ln x) + c_2 x^{-1/2}\sin(\lambda \ln x)$$

where $\lambda = \frac{1}{2}\sqrt{4\rho\omega^2 - 1}$. Applying $y(1) = 0$ gives $c_1 = 0$ and consequently

$$y = c_2 x^{-1/2}\sin(\lambda \ln x).$$

The condition $y(e) = 0$ requires $c_2 e^{-1/2}\sin\lambda = 0$. We obtain a nontrivial solution when $\lambda_n = n\pi$, $n = 1, 2, 3, \ldots$. But

$$\lambda_n = \frac{1}{2}\sqrt{4\rho\omega_n^2 - 1} = n\pi.$$

Solving for ω_n gives

$$\omega_n = \frac{1}{2}\sqrt{(4n^2\pi^2 + 1)/\rho}\,.$$

The corresponding solutions are

$$y_n(x) = c_2 x^{-1/2}\sin(n\pi \ln x).$$

(b)

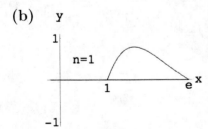

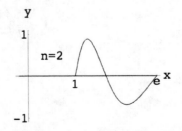

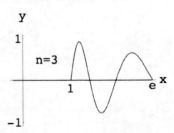

27. The auxiliary equation is $m^2 + m = m(m+1) = 0$ so that $u(r) = c_1 r^{-1} + c_2$. The boundary conditions $u(a) = u_0$ and $u(b) = u_1$ yield the system $c_1 a^{-1} + c_2 = u_0$, $c_1 b^{-1} + c_2 = u_1$. Solving gives

$$c_1 = \left(\frac{u_0 - u_1}{b - a}\right)ab \quad \text{and} \quad c_2 = \frac{u_1 b - u_0 a}{b - a}.$$

Thus

$$u(r) = \left(\frac{u_0 - u_1}{b - a}\right)\frac{ab}{r} + \frac{u_1 b - u_0 a}{b - a}.$$

28. The auxiliary equation is $m^2 = 0$ so that $u(r) = c_1 + c_2 \ln r$. The boundary conditions $u(a) = u_0$ and $u(b) = u_1$ yield the system $c_1 + c_2 \ln a = u_0$, $c_1 + c_2 \ln b = u_1$. Solving gives

$$c_1 = \frac{u_1 \ln a - u_0 \ln b}{\ln(a/b)} \quad \text{and} \quad c_2 = \frac{u_0 - u_1}{\ln(a/b)}.$$

Thus

$$u(r) = \frac{u_1 \ln a - u_0 \ln b}{\ln(a/b)} + \frac{u_0 - u_1}{\ln(a/b)}\ln r = \frac{u_0 \ln(r/b) - u_1 \ln(r/a)}{\ln(a/b)}.$$

29. The solution of the initial-value problem

$$x'' + \omega^2 x = 0, \quad x(0) = 0, \ x'(0) = v_0, \ \omega^2 = 10/m$$

is $x(t) = (v_0/\omega)\sin \omega t$. To satisfy the additional boundary condition $x(1) = 0$ we require that $\omega = n\pi$, $n = 1, 2, 3, \ldots$. The eigenvalues $\lambda = \omega^2 = n^2\pi^2$ and eigenfunctions of the problem are then $x(t) = (v_0/n\pi)\sin n\pi t$. Using $\omega^2 = 10/m$ we find that the *only* masses that can pass through the equilibrium position at $t = 1$ are $m_n = 10/n^2\pi^2$. Note for $n = 1$, the heaviest mass $m_1 = 10/\pi^2$ will *not* pass through the equilibrium position on the interval $0 < t < 1$ (the period of $x(t) = (v_0/\pi)\sin \pi t$ is $T = 2$, so on $0 \le t \le 1$ its graph passes through $x = 0$ only at $t = 0$ and $t = 1$). Whereas for $n > 1$, masses of lighter weight will pass through the equilibrium position $n - 1$ times prior to passing through at $t = 1$. For example, if $n = 2$, the period of $x(t) = (v_0/2\pi)\sin 2\pi t$ is $2\pi/2\pi = 1$, the mass will pass through $x = 0$ only *once* ($t = \frac{1}{2}$) prior to $t = 1$; if $n = 3$, the period of $x(t) = (v_0/3\pi)\sin 3\pi t$ is $\frac{2}{3}$, the mass will pass through $x = 0$ *twice* ($t = \frac{1}{3}$ and $t = \frac{2}{3}$) prior to $t = 1$; and so on.

30. The initial-value problem is

$$x'' + \frac{2}{m}x' + \frac{k}{m}x = 0, \quad x(0) = 0, \ x'(0) = v_0.$$

With $k = 10$, the auxiliary equation has roots $\gamma = -1/m \pm \sqrt{1 - 10m}/m$. Consider the three cases:

(*i*) $m = \frac{1}{10}$. The roots are $\gamma_1 = \gamma_2 = 10$ and the solution of the differential equation is $x(t) = c_1 e^{-10t} + c_2 t e^{-10t}$. The initial conditions imply $c_1 = 0$ and $c_2 = v_0$ and so $x(t) = v_0 t e^{-10t}$. The condition $x(1) = 0$ implies $v_0 e^{-10} = 0$ which is impossible because $v_0 \ne 0$.

(*ii*) $1 - 10m > 0$ or $0 < m < \frac{1}{10}$. The roots are

$$\gamma_1 = -\frac{1}{m} - \frac{1}{m}\sqrt{1 - 10m} \quad \text{and} \quad \gamma_2 = -\frac{1}{m} + \frac{1}{m}\sqrt{1 - 10m}$$

and the solution of the differential equation is $x(t) = c_1 e^{\gamma_1 t} + c_2 e^{\gamma_2 t}$. The initial conditions imply

$$c_1 + c_2 = 0$$

$$\gamma_1 c_1 + \gamma_2 c_2 = v_0$$

so $c_1 = v_0/(\gamma_1 - \gamma_2)$, $c_2 = -v_0/(\gamma_1 - \gamma_2)$, and

$$x(t) = \frac{v_0}{\gamma_1 - \gamma_2}(e^{\gamma_1 t} - e^{\gamma_2 t}).$$

Again, $x(1) = 0$ is impossible because $v_0 \neq 0$.

(*iii*) $1 - 10m < 0$ or $m > \frac{1}{10}$. The roots of the auxiliary equation are

$$\gamma_1 = -\frac{1}{m} - \frac{1}{m}\sqrt{10m - 1}\, i \qquad \text{and} \qquad \gamma_2 = -\frac{1}{m} + \frac{1}{m}\sqrt{10m - 1}\, i$$

and the solution of the differential equation is

$$x(t) = c_1 e^{-t/m}\cos\frac{1}{m}\sqrt{10m - 1}\, t + c_2 e^{-t/m}\sin\frac{1}{m}\sqrt{10m - 1}\, t.$$

The initial conditions imply $c_1 = 0$ and $c_2 = mv_0/\sqrt{10m - 1}$, so that

$$x(t) = \frac{mv_0}{\sqrt{10m - 1}}\, e^{-t/m}\sin\left(\frac{1}{m}\sqrt{10m - 1}\, t\right),$$

The condition $x(1) = 0$ implies

$$\frac{mv_0}{\sqrt{10m - 1}}e^{-1/m}\sin\frac{1}{m}\sqrt{10m - 1} = 0$$

$$\sin\frac{1}{m}\sqrt{10m - 1} = 0$$

$$\frac{1}{m}\sqrt{10m - 1} = n\pi$$

$$\frac{10m - 1}{m^2} = n^2\pi^2, \quad n = 1, 2, 3, \ldots$$

$$(n^2\pi^2)m^2 - 10m + 1 = 0$$

$$m = \frac{10\sqrt{100 - 4n^2\pi^2}}{2n^2\pi^2} = \frac{5 \pm \sqrt{25 - n^2\pi^2}}{n^2\pi^2}.$$

Since m is real, $25 - n^2\pi^2 \geq 0$. If $25 - n^2\pi^2 = 0$, then $n^2 = 25/\pi^2$, and n is not an integer. Thus, $25 - n^2\pi^2 = (5 - n\pi)(5 + n\pi) > 0$ and since $n > 0$, $5 + n\pi > 0$, so $5 - n\pi > 0$ also. Then $n < 5/\pi$, and so $n = 1$. Therefore, the mass m will pass through the equilibrium position when $t = 1$ for

$$m_1 = \frac{5 + \sqrt{25 - \pi^2}}{\pi^2} \qquad \text{and} \qquad m_2 = \frac{5 - \sqrt{25 - \pi^2}}{\pi^2}.$$

31. (a) The general solution of the differential equation is $y = c_1\cos 4x + c_2\sin 4x$. From $y_0 = y(0) = c_1$ we see that $y = y_0\cos 4x + c_2\sin 4x$. From $y_1 = y(\pi/2) = y_0$ we see that any solution must satisfy $y_0 = y_1$. We also see that when $y_0 = y_1$, $y = y_0\cos 4x + c_2\sin 4x$ is a solution of the boundary-value problem for any choice of c_2. Thus, the boundary-value problem does not have a unique solution for any choice of y_0 and y_1.

(b) Whenever $y_0 = y_1$ there are infinitely many solutions.

(c) When $y_0 \neq y_1$ there will be no solutions.

(d) The boundary-value problem will have the trivial solution when $y_0 = y_1 = 0$. This solution will not be unique.

32. (a) The general solution of the differential equation is $y = c_1 \cos 4x + c_2 \sin 4x$. From $1 = y(0) = c_1$ we see that $y = \cos 4x + c_2 \sin 4x$. From $1 = y(L) = \cos 4L + c_2 \sin 4L$ we see that $c_2 = (1 - \cos 4L)/\sin 4L$. Thus,

$$y = \cos 4x + \left(\frac{1 - \cos 4L}{\sin 4L} \right) \sin 4x$$

will be a unique solution when $\sin 4L \neq 0$; that is, when $L \neq k\pi/4$ where $k = 1,\, 2,\, 3,\, \ldots$.

(b) There will be infinitely many solutions when $\sin 4L = 0$ and $1 - \cos 4L = 0$; that is, when $L = k\pi/2$ where $k = 1,\, 2,\, 3,\, \ldots$.

(c) There will be no solution when $\sin 4L \neq 0$ and $1 - \cos 4L \neq 0$; that is, when $L = k\pi/4$ where $k = 1,\, 3,\, 5,\, \ldots$.

(d) There can be no trivial solution since it would fail to satisfy the boundary conditions.

33. (a) A solution curve has the same y-coordinate at both ends of the interval $[-\pi, \pi]$ and the tangent lines at the endpoints of the interval are parallel.

(b) For $\lambda = 0$ the solution of $y'' = 0$ is $y = c_1 x + c_2$. From the first boundary condition we have

$$y(-\pi) = -c_1 \pi + c_2 = y(\pi) = c_1 \pi + c_2$$

or $2c_1 \pi = 0$. Thus, $c_1 = 0$ and $y = c_2$. This constant solution is seen to satisfy the boundary-value problem.

For $\lambda = -\alpha^2 < 0$ we have $y = c_1 \cosh \alpha x + c_2 \sinh \alpha x$. In this case the first boundary condition gives

$$y(-\pi) = c_1 \cosh(-\alpha\pi) + c_2 \sinh(-\alpha\pi)$$
$$= c_1 \cosh \alpha\pi - c_2 \sinh \alpha\pi$$
$$= y(\pi) = c_1 \cosh \alpha\pi + c_2 \sinh \alpha\pi$$

or $2c_2 \sinh \alpha\pi = 0$. Thus $c_2 = 0$ and $y = c_1 \cosh \alpha x$. The second boundary condition implies in a similar fashion that $c_1 = 0$. Thus, for $\lambda < 0$, the only solution of the boundary-value problem is $y = 0$.

For $\lambda = \alpha^2 > 0$ we have $y = c_1 \cos \alpha x + c_2 \sin \alpha x$. The first boundary condition implies

$$y(-\pi) = c_1 \cos(-\alpha\pi) + c_2 \sin(-\alpha\pi)$$
$$= c_1 \cos \alpha\pi - c_2 \sin \alpha\pi$$
$$= y(\pi) = c_1 \cos \alpha\pi + c_2 \sin \alpha\pi$$

or $2c_2 \sin \alpha \pi = 0$. Similarly, the second boundary condition implies $2c_1 \alpha \sin \alpha \pi = 0$. If $c_1 = c_2 = 0$ the solution is $y = 0$. However, if $c_1 \neq 0$ or $c_2 \neq 0$, then $\sin \alpha \pi = 0$, which implies that α must be an integer, n. Therefore, for c_1 and c_2 not both 0, $y = c_1 \cos nx + c_2 \sin nx$ is a nontrivial solution of the boundary-value problem. Since $\cos(-nx) = \cos nx$ and $\sin(-nx) = -\sin nx$, we may assume without loss of generality that the eigenvalues are $\lambda_n = \alpha^2 = n^2$, for n a positive integer. The corresponding eigenfunctions are $y_n = \cos nx$ and $y_n = \sin nx$.

(c)

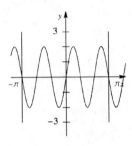

$$y = 2 \sin 3x$$

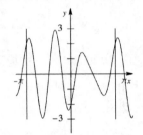

$$y = \sin 4x - 2 \cos 3x$$

34. For $\lambda = \alpha^2 > 0$ the general solution is $y = c_1 \cos \sqrt{\alpha}\, x + c_2 \sin \sqrt{\alpha}\, x$. Setting $y(0) = 0$ we find $c_1 = 0$, so that $y = c_2 \sin \sqrt{\alpha}\, x$. The boundary condition $y(1) + y'(1) = 0$ implies

$$c_2 \sin \sqrt{\alpha} + c_2 \sqrt{\alpha} \cos \sqrt{\alpha} = 0.$$

Taking $c_2 \neq 0$, this equation is equivalent to $\tan \sqrt{\alpha} = -\sqrt{\alpha}$. Thus, the eigenvalues are $\lambda_n = \alpha_n^2 = x_n^2$, $n = 1, 2, 3, \ldots$, where the x_n are the consecutive positive roots of $\tan \sqrt{\alpha} = -\sqrt{\alpha}$.

35. We see from the graph that $\tan x = -x$ has infinitely many roots. Since $\lambda_n = \alpha_n^2$, there are no new eigenvalues when $\alpha_n < 0$. For $\lambda = 0$, the differential equation $y'' = 0$ has general solution $y = c_1 x + c_2$. The boundary conditions imply $c_1 = c_2 = 0$, so $y = 0$.

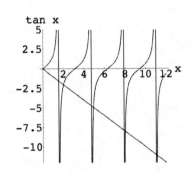

36. Using a CAS we find that the first four nonnegative roots of $\tan x = -x$ are approximately $2.02876, 4.91318, 7.97867$, and 11.0855. The corresponding eigenvalues are $4.11586, 24.1393$, 63.6591, and 122.889, with eigenfunctions $\sin(2.02876x), \sin(4.91318x), \sin(7.97867x)$, and $\sin(11.0855x)$.

37. In the case when $\lambda = -\alpha^2 < 0$, the solution of the differential equation is $y = c_1 \cosh \alpha x + c_2 \sinh \alpha x$. The condition $y(0) = 0$ gives $c_1 = 0$. The condition $y(1) - \frac{1}{2} y'(1) = 0$ applied to $y = c_2 \sinh \alpha x$ gives $c_2(\sinh \alpha - \frac{1}{2}\alpha \cosh \alpha) = 0$ or $\tanh \alpha = \frac{1}{2}\alpha$. As can be seen from the figure, the graphs of $y = \tanh x$ and $y = \frac{1}{2}x$ intersect at a single point with approximate x-coordinate $\alpha_1 = 1.915$. Thus, there is a single negative eigenvalue $\lambda_1 = -\alpha_1^2 \approx -3.667$ and the corresponding eigenfuntion is $y_1 = \sinh 1.915x$.

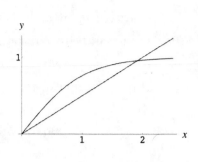

For $\lambda = 0$ the only solution of the boundary-value problem is $y = 0$.

For $\lambda = \alpha^2 > 0$ the solution of the differential equation is $y = c_1 \cos \alpha x + c_2 \sin \alpha x$. The condition $y(0) = 0$ gives $c_1 = 0$, so $y = c_2 \sin \alpha x$. The condition $y(1) - \frac{1}{2} y'(1) = 0$ gives $c_2(\sin \alpha - \frac{1}{2}\alpha \cos \alpha) = 0$, so the eigenvalues are $\lambda_n = \alpha_n^2$ when α_n, $n = 2, 3, 4, \ldots$, are the positive roots of $\tan \alpha = \frac{1}{2}\alpha$. Using a CAS we find that the first three values of α are $\alpha_2 = 4.27487$, $\alpha_3 = 7.59655$, and $\alpha_4 = 10.8127$. The first three eigenvalues are then $\lambda_2 = \alpha_2^2 = 18.2738$, $\lambda_3 = \alpha_3^2 = 57.7075$, and $\lambda_4 = \alpha_4^2 = 116.9139$ with corresponding eigenfunctions $y_2 = \sin 4.27487x$, $y_3 = \sin 7.59655x$, and $y_4 = \sin 10.8127x$.

38. For $\lambda = \alpha^4$, $\alpha > 0$, the solution of the differential equation is

$$y = c_1 \cos \alpha x + c_2 \sin \alpha x + c_3 \cosh \alpha x + c_4 \sinh \alpha x.$$

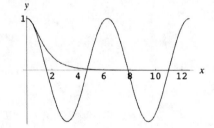

The boundary conditions $y(0) = 0$, $y'(0) = 0$, $y(1) = 0$, $y'(1) = 0$ give, in turn,

$$c_1 + c_3 = 0$$

$$\alpha c_2 + \alpha c_4 = 0,$$

$$c_1 \cos \alpha + c_2 \sin \alpha + c_3 \cosh \alpha + c_4 \sinh \alpha = 0$$

$$-c_1 \alpha \sin \alpha + c_2 \alpha \cos \alpha + c_3 \alpha \sinh \alpha + c_4 \alpha \cosh \alpha = 0.$$

The first two equations enable us to write

$$c_1(\cos \alpha - \cosh \alpha) + c_2(\sin \alpha - \sinh \alpha) = 0$$

$$c_1(-\sin \alpha - \sinh \alpha) + c_2(\cos \alpha - \cosh \alpha) = 0.$$

The determinant

$$\begin{vmatrix} \cos \alpha - \cosh \alpha & \sin \alpha - \sinh \alpha \\ -\sin \alpha - \sinh \alpha & \cos \alpha - \cosh \alpha \end{vmatrix} = 0$$

simplifies to $\cos \alpha \cosh \alpha = 1$. From the figure showing the graphs of $1/\cosh x$ and $\cos x$, we see that this equation has an infinite number of positive roots. With the aid of a CAS the first four roots are found to be $\alpha_1 = 4.73004$, $\alpha_2 = 7.8532$, $\alpha_3 = 10.9956$, and $\alpha_4 = 14.1372$, and the corresponding eigenvalues are $\lambda_1 = 500.5636$, $\lambda_2 = 3803.5281$, $\lambda_3 = 14{,}617.5885$, and $\lambda_4 = 39{,}944.1890$. Using the third equation in the system to eliminate c_2, we find that the eigenfunctions are

$$y_n = (-\sin \alpha_n + \sinh \alpha_n)(\cos \alpha_n x - \cosh \alpha_n x) + (\cos \alpha_n - \cosh \alpha_n)(\sin \alpha_n x - \sinh \alpha_n x).$$

Exercises 5.3   Nonlinear Models

1. The period corresponding to $x(0) = 1$, $x'(0) = 1$ is approximately 5.6. The period corresponding to $x(0) = 1/2$, $x'(0) = -1$ is approximately 6.2.

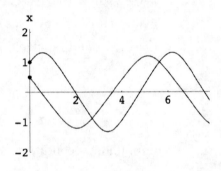

2. The solutions are not periodic.

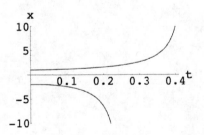

3. The period corresponding to $x(0) = 1$, $x'(0) = 1$ is approximately 5.8. The second initial-value problem does not have a periodic solution.

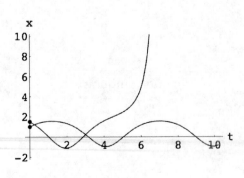

4. Both solutions have periods of approximately 6.3.

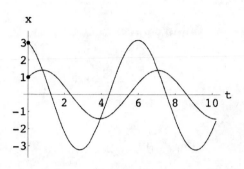

5. From the graph we see that $|x_1| \approx 1.2$.

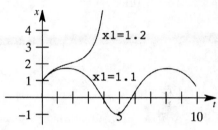

6. From the graphs we see that the interval is approximately $(-0.8, 1.1)$.

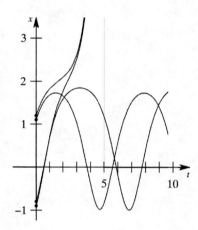

7. Since

$$xe^{0.01x} = x\left[1 + 0.01x + \frac{1}{2!}(0.01x)^2 + \cdots\right] \approx x$$

for small values of x, a linearization is $\dfrac{d^2x}{dt^2} + x = 0$.

8.

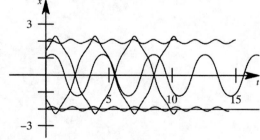

For $x(0) = 1$ and $x'(0) = 1$ the oscillations are symmetric about the line $x = 0$ with amplitude slightly greater than 1.

For $x(0) = -2$ and $x'(0) = 0.5$ the oscillations are symmetric about the line $x = -2$ with small amplitude.

For $x(0) = \sqrt{2}$ and $x'(0) = 1$ the oscillations are symmetric about the line $x = 0$ with amplitude a little greater than 2.

For $x(0) = 2$ and $x'(0) = 0.5$ the oscillations are symmetric about the line $x = 2$ with small amplitude.

For $x(0) = -2$ and $x'(0) = 0$ there is no oscillation; the solution is constant.

For $x(0) = -\sqrt{2}$ and $x'(0) = -1$ the oscillations are symmetric about the line $x = 0$ with amplitude a little greater than 2.

9. This is a damped hard spring, so x will approach 0 as t approaches ∞.

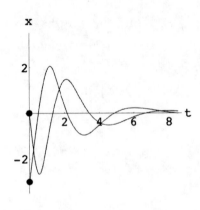

10. This is a damped soft spring, so we might expect no oscillatory solutions. However, if the initial conditions are sufficiently small the spring can oscillate.

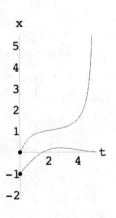

11.

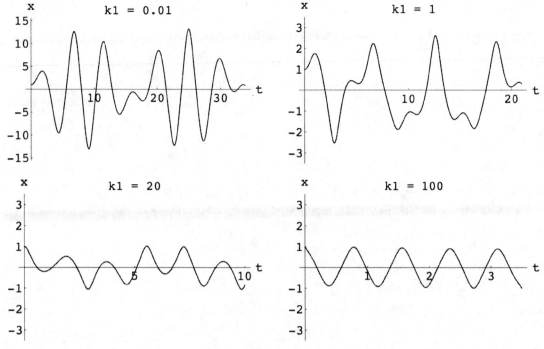

When k_1 is very small the effect of the nonlinearity is greatly diminished, and the system is close to pure resonance.

12. (a)

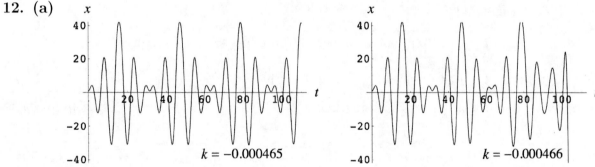

The system appears to be oscillatory for $-0.000465 \leq k_1 < 0$ and nonoscillatory for $k_1 \leq -0.000466$.

(b)

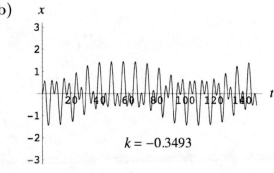

The system appears to be oscillatory for $-0.3493 \le k_1 < 0$ and nonoscillatory for $k_1 \le -0.3494$.

13. For $\lambda^2 - \omega^2 > 0$ we choose $\lambda = 2$ and $\omega = 1$ with $x(0) = 1$ and $x'(0) = 2$. For $\lambda^2 - \omega^2 < 0$ we choose $\lambda = 1/3$ and $\omega = 1$ with $x(0) = -2$ and $x'(0) = 4$. In both cases the motion corresponds to the overdamped and underdamped cases for spring/mass systems.

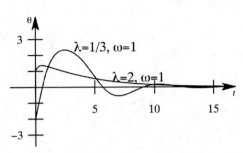

14. (a) Setting $dy/dt = v$, the differential equation in (13) becomes $dv/dt = -gR^2/y^2$. But, by the chain rule, $dv/dt = (dv/dy)(dy/dt) = v\,dv/dt$, so $v\,dv/dy = -gR^2/y^2$. Separating variables and integrating we obtain

$$v\,dv = -gR^2 \frac{dy}{y^2} \quad \text{and} \quad \frac{1}{2}v^2 = \frac{gR^2}{y} + c.$$

Setting $v = v_0$ and $y = R$ we find $c = -gR + \frac{1}{2}v_0^2$ and

$$v^2 = 2g\frac{R^2}{y} - 2gR + v_0^2.$$

(b) As $y \to \infty$ we assume that $v \to 0^+$. Then $v_0^2 = 2gR$ and $v_0 = \sqrt{2gR}$.

(c) Using $g = 32$ ft/s and $R = 4000(5280)$ ft we find

$$v_0 = \sqrt{2(32)(4000)(5280)} \approx 36765.2 \text{ ft/s} \approx 25067 \text{ mi/hr}.$$

(d) $v_0 = \sqrt{2(0.165)(32)(1080)} \approx 7760$ ft/s ≈ 5291 mi/hr

15. (a) Intuitively, one might expect that only half of a 10-pound chain could be lifted by a 5-pound vertical force.

(b) Since $x = 0$ when $t = 0$, and $v = dx/dt = \sqrt{160 - 64x/3}$, we have $v(0) = \sqrt{160} \approx 12.65$ ft/s.

(c) Since x should always be positive, we solve $x(t) = 0$, getting $t = 0$ and $t = \frac{3}{2}\sqrt{5/2} \approx 2.3717$. Since the graph of $x(t)$ is a parabola, the maximum value occurs at $t_m = \frac{3}{4}\sqrt{5/2}$. (This can also be obtained by solving $x'(t) = 0$.) At this time the height of the chain is $x(t_m) \approx 7.5$ ft. This is higher than predicted because of the momentum generated by the force. When the chain is 5 feet high it still has a positive velocity of about 7.3 ft/s, which keeps it going higher for a while.

(d) As discussed in the solution to part (c) of this problem, the chain has momentum generated by the force applied to it that will cause it to go higher than expected. It will then fall back to below the expected maximum height, again due to momentum. This, in turn, will cause it to next go higher than expected, and so on.

16. (a) Setting $dx/dt = v$, the differential equation becomes $(L - x)dv/dt - v^2 = Lg$. But, by the Chain Rule, $dv/dt = (dv/dx)(dx/dt) = v\, dv/dx$, so $(L - x)v\, dv/dx - v^2 = Lg$. Separating variables and integrating we obtain

$$\frac{v}{v^2 + Lg}\, dv = \frac{1}{L - x}\, dx \quad \text{and} \quad \frac{1}{2}\ln(v^2 + Lg) = -\ln(L - x) + \ln c,$$

so $\sqrt{v^2 + Lg} = c/(L - x)$. When $x = 0$, $v = 0$, and $c = L\sqrt{Lg}$. Solving for v and simplifying we get

$$\frac{dx}{dt} = v(x) = \frac{\sqrt{Lg(2Lx - x^2)}}{L - x}.$$

Again, separating variables and integrating we obtain

$$\frac{L - x}{\sqrt{Lg(2Lx - x^2)}}dx = dt \quad \text{and} \quad \frac{\sqrt{2Lx - x^2}}{\sqrt{Lg}} = t + c_1.$$

Since $x(0) = 0$, we have $c_1 = 0$ and $\sqrt{2Lx - x^2}/\sqrt{Lg} = t$. Solving for x we get

$$x(t) = L - \sqrt{L^2 - Lgt^2} \quad \text{and} \quad v(t) = \frac{dx}{dt} = \frac{\sqrt{Lg}\,t}{\sqrt{L - gt^2}}.$$

(b) The chain will be completely on the ground when $x(t) = L$ or $t = \sqrt{L/g}$.

(c) The predicted velocity of the upper end of the chain when it hits the ground is infinity.

17. (a) Let (x, y) be the coordinates of S_2 on the curve C. The slope at (x, y) is then

$$dy/dx = (v_1 t - y)/(0 - x) = (y - v_1 t)/x \quad \text{or} \quad xy' - y = -v_1 t.$$

(b) Differentiating with respect to x and using $r = v_1/v_2$ gives

$$xy'' + y' - y' = -v_1 \frac{dt}{dx}$$

$$xy'' = -v_1 \frac{dt}{ds}\frac{ds}{dx}$$

$$xy'' = -v_1 \frac{1}{v_2}\left(-\sqrt{1 + (y')^2}\right)$$

$$xy'' = r\sqrt{1 + (y')^2}.$$

Letting $u = y'$ and separating variables, we obtain

$$x \frac{du}{dx} = r\sqrt{1 + u^2}$$

$$\frac{du}{\sqrt{1 + u^2}} = \frac{r}{x} dx$$

$$\sinh^{-1} u = r \ln x + \ln c = \ln(cx^r)$$

$$u = \sinh(\ln cx^r)$$

$$\frac{dy}{dx} = \frac{1}{2}\left(cx^r - \frac{1}{cx^r}\right).$$

At $t = 0$, $dy/dx = 0$ and $x = a$, so $0 = ca^r - 1/ca^r$. Thus $c = 1/a^r$ and

$$\frac{dy}{dx} = \frac{1}{2}\left[\left(\frac{x}{a}\right)^r - \left(\frac{a}{x}\right)^r\right] = \frac{1}{2}\left[\left(\frac{x}{a}\right)^r - \left(\frac{x}{a}\right)^{-r}\right].$$

If $r > 1$ or $r < 1$, integrating gives

$$y = \frac{a}{2}\left[\frac{1}{1+r}\left(\frac{x}{a}\right)^{1+r} - \frac{1}{1-r}\left(\frac{x}{a}\right)^{1-r}\right] + c_1.$$

When $t = 0$, $y = 0$ and $x = a$, so $0 = (a/2)[1/(1+r) - 1/(1-r)] + c_1$. Thus $c_1 = ar/(1-r^2)$ and

$$y = \frac{a}{2}\left[\frac{1}{1+r}\left(\frac{x}{a}\right)^{1+r} - \frac{1}{1-r}\left(\frac{x}{a}\right)^{1-r}\right] + \frac{ar}{1-r^2}.$$

(c) To see if the paths ever intersect we first note that if $r > 1$, then $v_1 > v_2$ and $y \to \infty$ as $x \to 0^+$. In other words, S_2 always lags behind S_1. Next, if $r < 1$, then $v_1 < v_2$ and $y = ar/(1-r^2)$ when $x = 0$. In other words, when the submarine's speed is greater than the ship's, their paths will intersect at the point $(0, ar/(1-r^2))$.

Finally, if $r = 1$, then integration gives

$$y = \frac{1}{2}\left[\frac{x^2}{2a} - \frac{1}{a}\ln x\right] + c_2.$$

When $t = 0$, $y = 0$ and $x = a$, so $0 = (1/2)[a/2 - (1/a)\ln a] + c_2$. Thus $c_2 = -(1/2)[a/2 - (1/a)\ln a]$ and

$$y = \frac{1}{2}\left[\frac{x^2}{2a} - \frac{1}{a}\ln x\right] - \frac{1}{2}\left[\frac{a}{2} - \frac{1}{a}\ln a\right] = \frac{1}{2}\left[\frac{1}{2a}(x^2 - a^2) + \frac{1}{a}\ln\frac{a}{x}\right].$$

Since $y \to \infty$ as $x \to 0^+$, S_2 will never catch up with S_1.

18. (a) Let (r, θ) denote the polar coordinates of the destroyer S_1. When S_1 travels the 6 miles from $(9, 0)$ to $(3, 0)$ it stands to reason, since S_2 travels half as fast as S_1, that the polar coordinates of S_2 are $(3, \theta_2)$, where θ_2 is unknown. In other words, the distances of the ships from $(0, 0)$

are the same and $r(t) = 15t$ then gives the radial distance of both ships. This is necessary if S_1 is to intercept S_2.

(b) The differential of arc length in polar coordinates is $(ds)^2 = (r\,d\theta)^2 + (dr)^2$, so that

$$\left(\frac{ds}{dt}\right)^2 = r^2 \left(\frac{d\theta}{dt}\right)^2 + \left(\frac{dr}{dt}\right)^2.$$

Using $ds/dt = 30$ and $dr/dt = 15$ then gives

$$900 = 225t^2 \left(\frac{d\theta}{dt}\right)^2 + 225$$

$$675 = 225t^2 \left(\frac{d\theta}{dt}\right)^2$$

$$\frac{d\theta}{dt} = \frac{\sqrt{3}}{t}$$

$$\theta(t) = \sqrt{3}\ln t + c = \sqrt{3}\ln\frac{r}{15} + c.$$

When $r = 3$, $\theta = 0$, so $c = -\sqrt{3}\ln\frac{1}{5}$ and

$$\theta(t) = \sqrt{3}\left(\ln\frac{r}{15} - \ln\frac{1}{5}\right) = \sqrt{3}\ln\frac{r}{3}.$$

Thus $r = 3e^{\theta/\sqrt{3}}$, whose graph is a logarithmic spiral.

(c) The time for S_1 to go from $(9,0)$ to $(3,0) = \frac{1}{5}$ hour. Now S_1 must intercept the path of S_2 for some angle β, where $0 < \beta < 2\pi$. At the time of interception t_2 we have $15t_2 = 3e^{\beta/\sqrt{3}}$ or $t = \frac{1}{5}e^{\beta/\sqrt{3}}$. The total time is then

$$t = \frac{1}{5} + \frac{1}{5}e^{\beta/\sqrt{3}} < \frac{1}{5}(1 + e^{2\pi/\sqrt{3}}).$$

19. Since $(dx/dt)^2$ is always positive, it is necessary to use $|dx/dt|(dx/dt)$ in order to account for the fact that the motion is oscillatory and the velocity (or its square) should be negative when the spring is contracting.

20. (a) From the graph we see that the approximations appears to be quite good for $0 \le x \le 0.4$. Using an equation solver to solve $\sin x - x = 0.05$ and $\sin x - x = 0.005$, we find that the approximation is accurate to one decimal place for $\theta_1 = 0.67$ and to two decimal places for $\theta_1 = 0.31$.

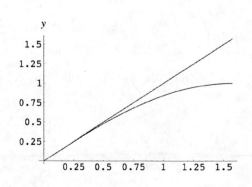

265

(b)

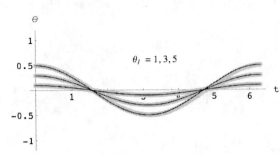

21. (a) Write the differential equation as

$$\frac{d^2\theta}{dt^2} + \omega^2 \sin\theta = 0,$$

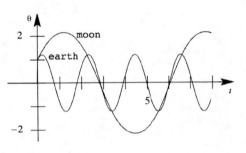

where $\omega^2 = g/l$. To test for differences between the earth and the moon we take $l = 3$, $\theta(0) = 1$, and $\theta'(0) = 2$. Using $g = 32$ on the earth and $g = 5.5$ on the moon we obtain the graphs shown in the figure. Comparing the apparent periods of the graphs, we see that the pendulum oscillates faster on the earth than on the moon.

(b) The amplitude is greater on the moon than on the earth.

(c) The linear model is

$$\frac{d^2\theta}{dt^2} + \omega^2\theta = 0,$$

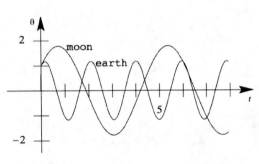

where $\omega^2 = g/l$. When $g = 32$, $l = 3$, $\theta(0) = 1$, and $\theta'(0) = 2$, the solution is

$$\theta(t) = \cos 3.266t + 0.612\sin 3.266t.$$

When $g = 5.5$ the solution is

$$\theta(t) = \cos 1.354t + 1.477\sin 1.354t.$$

As in the nonlinear case, the pendulum oscillates faster on the earth than on the moon and still has greater amplitude on the moon.

22. (a) The general solution of

$$\frac{d^2\theta}{dt^2} + \theta = 0$$

is $\theta(t) = c_1\cos t + c_2\sin t$. From $\theta(0) = \pi/12$ and $\theta'(0) = -1/3$ we find

$$\theta(t) = (\pi/12)\cos t - (1/3)\sin t.$$

Setting $\theta(t) = 0$ we have $\tan t = \pi/4$ which implies $t_1 = \tan^{-1}(\pi/4) \approx 0.66577$.

(b) We set $\theta(t) = \theta(0) + \theta'(0)t + \frac{1}{2}\theta''(0)t^2 + \frac{1}{6}\theta'''(0)t^3 + \cdots$ and use $\theta''(t) = -\sin\theta(t)$ together with $\theta(0) = \pi/12$ and $\theta'(0) = -1/3$. Then

$$\theta''(0) = -\sin(\pi/12) = -\sqrt{2}\left(\sqrt{3} - 1\right)/4$$

and

$$\theta'''(0) = -\cos\theta(0)\cdot\theta'(0) = -\cos(\pi/12)(-1/3) = \sqrt{2}\left(\sqrt{3}+1\right)/12.$$

Thus

$$\theta(t) = \frac{\pi}{12} - \frac{1}{3}t - \frac{\sqrt{2}\left(\sqrt{3}-1\right)}{8}t^2 + \frac{\sqrt{2}\left(\sqrt{3}+1\right)}{72}t^3 + \cdots.$$

(c) Setting $\pi/12 - t/3 = 0$ we obtain $t_1 = \pi/4 \approx 0.785398$.

(d) Setting

$$\frac{\pi}{12} - \frac{1}{3}t - \frac{\sqrt{2}\left(\sqrt{3}-1\right)}{8}t^2 = 0$$

and using the positive root we obtain $t_1 \approx 0.63088$.

(e) Setting

$$\frac{\pi}{12} - \frac{1}{3}t - \frac{\sqrt{2}\left(\sqrt{3}-1\right)}{8}t^2 + \frac{\sqrt{2}\left(\sqrt{3}+1\right)}{72}t^3 = 0$$

we find with the help of a CAS that $t_1 \approx 0.661973$ is the first positive root.

(f) From the output we see that $y(t)$ is an interpolating function on the interval $0 \le t \le 5$, whose graph is shown. The positive root of $y(t) = 0$ near $t = 1$ is $t_1 = 0.666404$.

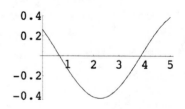

(g) To find the next two positive roots we change the interval used in **NDSolve** and **Plot** from $\{t,0,5\}$ to $\{t,0,10\}$. We see from the graph that the second and third positive roots are near 4 and 7, respectively. Replacing $\{t,1\}$ in **FindRoot** with $\{t,4\}$ and then $\{t,7\}$ we obtain $t_2 = 3.84411$ and $t_3 = 7.0218$.

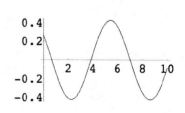

23. From the table below we see that the pendulum first passes the vertical position between 1.7 and 1.8 seconds. To refine our estimate of t_1 we estimate the solution of the differential equation on $[1.7, 1.8]$ using a step size of $h = 0.01$. From the resulting table we see that t_1 is between 1.76 and 1.77 seconds. Repeating the process with $h = 0.001$ we conclude that $t_1 \approx 1.767$. Then the period of the pendulum is approximately $4t_1 = 7.068$. The error when using $t_1 = 2\pi$ is $7.068 - 6.283 = 0.785$ and the percentage relative error is $(0.785/7.068)100 = 11.1$.

h=0.1		h=0.01	
t_n	θ_n	t_n	θ_n
0.00	0.78540	1.70	0.07706
0.10	0.78523	1.71	0.06572
0.20	0.78407	1.72	0.05428
0.30	0.78092	1.73	0.04275
0.40	0.77482	1.74	0.03111
0.50	0.76482	1.75	0.01938
0.60	0.75004	1.76	0.00755
0.70	0.72962	1.77	−0.00438
0.80	0.70275	1.78	−0.01641
0.90	0.66872	1.79	−0.02854
1.00	0.62687	1.80	−0.04076
1.10	0.57660		
1.20	0.51744	h=0.001	
1.30	0.44895	1.763	0.00398
1.40	0.37085	1.764	0.00279
1.50	0.28289	1.765	0.00160
1.60	0.18497	1.766	0.00040
1.70	0.07706	1.767	−0.00079
1.80	−0.04076	1.768	−0.00199
1.90	−0.16831	1.769	−0.00318
2.00	−0.30531	1.770	−0.00438

24. (*This is a Contributed Problem and the solution has been provided by the author of the problem.*)

(a) The auxiliary equation is $m^2 + g/\ell = 0$, so the general solution of the differential equation is

$$\theta(t) = c_1 \cos \sqrt{\frac{g}{\ell}}\, t + c_2 \sin \sqrt{\frac{g}{\ell}}\, t.$$

The initial condtion $\theta(0) = 0$ implies $c_1 = 0$ and $\theta'(0) = \omega_0$ implies $c_2 = \omega_0 \sqrt{\ell/g}$. Thus,

$$\theta(t) = \omega_0 \sqrt{\frac{\ell}{g}}\, \sin \sqrt{\frac{g}{\ell}}\, t.$$

(b) At $\theta_{\max}$, $\sin \sqrt{g/\ell}\, t = 1$, so

$$\theta_{\max} = \omega_0 \sqrt{\frac{\ell}{g}} = \frac{m_b}{m_w + m_b} \frac{v_b}{\ell} \sqrt{\frac{\ell}{g}} = \frac{m_b}{m_w + m_b} \frac{v_b}{\sqrt{\ell g}}$$

and

$$v_b = \frac{m_w + m_b}{m_b} \sqrt{\ell g}\, \theta_{\max}.$$

(c) We have $\cos \theta_{\max} = (\ell - h)/\ell = 1 - h/\ell$. Then

$$\cos \theta_{\max} \approx 1 - \frac{1}{2} \theta_{\max}^2 = 1 - \frac{h}{\ell}$$

and

$$\theta_{\max}^2 = \frac{2h}{\ell} \quad \text{or} \quad \theta_{\max} = \sqrt{\frac{2h}{\ell}}.$$

Thus

$$v_b = \frac{m_w + m_b}{m_b} \sqrt{\ell g} \sqrt{\frac{2h}{\ell}} = \frac{m_w + m_b}{m_b} \sqrt{2gh}.$$

(d) When $m_b = 5\,\text{g}$, $m_w = 1\,\text{kg}$, and $h = 6\,\text{cm}$, we have

$$v_b = \frac{1005}{5} \sqrt{2(980)(6)} \approx 21,797 \text{ cm/s}.$$

Chapter 5 in Review

1. 8 ft, since $k = 4$

2. $2\pi/5$, since $\frac{1}{4}x'' + 6.25x = 0$

3. $5/4$ m, since $x = -\cos 4t + \frac{3}{4}\sin 4t$

4. True

5. False; since an external force may exist

6. False; since the equation of motion in this case is $x(t) = e^{-\lambda t}(c_1 + c_2 t)$ and $x(t) = 0$ can have at most one real solution

7. overdamped

8. From $x(0) = (\sqrt{2}/2)\sin\phi = -1/2$ we see that $\sin\phi = -1/\sqrt{2}$, so ϕ is an angle in the third or fourth quadrant. Since $x'(t) = \sqrt{2}\cos(2t + \phi)$, $x'(0) = \sqrt{2}\cos\phi = 1$ and $\cos\phi > 0$. Thus ϕ is in the fourth quadrant and $\phi = -\pi/4$.

9. $y = 0$ because $\lambda = 8$ is not an eigenvalue

10. $y = \cos 6x$ because $\lambda = (6)^2 = 36$ is an eigenvalue

11. The period of a spring/mass system is given by $T = 2\pi/\omega$ where $\omega^2 = k/m = kg/W$, where k is the spring constant, W is the weight of the mass attached to the spring, and g is the acceleration due to gravity. Thus, the period of oscillation is $T = (2\pi/\sqrt{kg})\sqrt{W}$. If the weight of the original mass is W, then $(2\pi/\sqrt{kg})\sqrt{W} = 3$ and $(2\pi/\sqrt{kg})\sqrt{W - 8} = 2$. Dividing, we get $\sqrt{W}/\sqrt{W - 8} = 3/2$ or $W = \frac{9}{4}(W - 8)$. Solving for W we find that the weight of the original mass was 14.4 pounds.

12. (a) Solving $\frac{3}{8}x'' + 6x = 0$ subject to $x(0) = 1$ and $x'(0) = -4$ we obtain

$$x = \cos 4t - \sin 4t = \sqrt{2}\sin(4t + 3\pi/4).$$

(b) The amplitude is $\sqrt{2}$, period is $\pi/2$, and frequency is $2/\pi$.

Chapter 5 in Review

(c) If $x = 1$ then $t = n\pi/2$ and $t = -\pi/8 + n\pi/2$ for $n = 1, 2, 3, \ldots$.

(d) If $x = 0$ then $t = \pi/16 + n\pi/4$ for $n = 0, 1, 2, \ldots$. The motion is upward for n even and downward for n odd.

(e) $x'(3\pi/16) = 0$

(f) If $x' = 0$ then $4t + 3\pi/4 = \pi/2 + n\pi$ or $t = 3\pi/16 + n\pi$.

13. We assume that he spring is initially compressed by 4 inches and that the positive direction on the x-axis is in the direction of elongation of the spring. Then, from $\frac{1}{4}x'' + \frac{3}{2}x' + 2x = 0$, $x(0) = -1/3$, and $x'(0) = 0$ we obtain $x = -\frac{2}{3}e^{-2t} + \frac{1}{3}e^{-4t}$.

14. From $x'' + \beta x' + 64x = 0$ we see that oscillatory motion results if $\beta^2 - 256 < 0$ or $0 \le \beta < 16$.

15. From $mx'' + 4x' + 2x = 0$ we see that nonoscillatory motion results if $16 - 8m \ge 0$ or $0 < m \le 2$.

16. From $\frac{1}{4}x'' + x' + x = 0$, $x(0) = 4$, and $x'(0) = 2$ we obtain $x = 4e^{-2t} + 10te^{-2t}$. If $x'(t) = 0$, then $t = 1/10$, so that the maximum displacement is $x = 5e^{-0.2} \approx 4.094$.

17. Writing $\frac{1}{8}x'' + \frac{8}{3}x = \cos\gamma t + \sin\gamma t$ in the form $x'' + \frac{64}{3}x = 8\cos\gamma t + 8\sin\gamma t$ we identify $\omega^2 = \frac{64}{3}$. The system is in a state of pure resonance when $\gamma = \omega = \sqrt{64/3} = 8/\sqrt{3}$.

18. Clearly $x_p = A/\omega^2$ suffices.

19. From $\frac{1}{8}x'' + x' + 3x = e^{-t}$, $x(0) = 2$, and $x'(0) = 0$ we obtain $x_c = e^{-4t}\left(c_1\cos 2\sqrt{2}t + c_2\sin 2\sqrt{2}t\right)$, $x_p = \frac{8}{17}e^{-t}$, and

$$x = e^{-4t}\left(\frac{26}{17}\cos 2\sqrt{2}t + \frac{28\sqrt{2}}{17}\sin 2\sqrt{2}t\right) + \frac{8}{17}e^{-t}.$$

20. (a) Let k be the effective spring constant and x_1 and x_2 the elongation of springs k_1 and k_2. The restoring forces satisfy $k_1x_1 = k_2x_2$ so $x_2 = (k_1/k_2)x_1$. From $k(x_1 + x_2) = k_1x_1$ we have

$$k\left(x_1 + \frac{k_1}{k_2}x_2\right) = k_1x_1$$

$$k\left(\frac{k_2 + k_1}{k_2}\right) = k_1$$

$$k = \frac{k_1k_2}{k_1 + k_2}$$

$$\frac{1}{k} = \frac{1}{k_1} + \frac{1}{k_2}.$$

(b) From $k_1 = 2W$ and $k_2 = 4W$ we find $1/k = 1/2W + 1/4W = 3/4W$. Then $k = 4W/3 = 4mg/3$. The differential equation $mx'' + kx = 0$ then becomes $x'' + (4g/3)x = 0$. The solution is

$$x(t) = c_1\cos 2\sqrt{\frac{g}{3}}t + c_2\sin 2\sqrt{\frac{g}{3}}t.$$

The initial conditions $x(0) = 1$ and $x'(0) = 2/3$ imply $c_1 = 1$ and $c_2 = 1/\sqrt{3g}$.

(c) To compute the maximum speed of the mass we compute

$$x'(t) = 2\sqrt{\frac{g}{3}}\sin 2\sqrt{\frac{g}{3}}\,t + \frac{2}{3}\cos 2\sqrt{\frac{g}{3}}\,t \quad \text{and} \quad |x'(t)| = \sqrt{4\frac{g}{3} + \frac{4}{9}} = \frac{2}{3}\sqrt{3g + 1}.$$

21. From $q'' + 10^4 q = 100\sin 50t$, $q(0) = 0$, and $q'(0) = 0$ we obtain $q_c = c_1\cos 100t + c_2\sin 100t$, $q_p = \frac{1}{75}\sin 50t$, and

(a) $q = -\frac{1}{150}\sin 100t + \frac{1}{75}\sin 50t$,

(b) $i = -\frac{2}{3}\cos 100t + \frac{2}{3}\cos 50t$, and

(c) $q = 0$ when $\sin 50t(1 - \cos 50t) = 0$ or $t = n\pi/50$ for $n = 0, 1, 2, \ldots$.

22. (a) By Kirchhoff's second law,

$$L\frac{d^2q}{dt^2} + R\frac{dq}{dt} + \frac{1}{C}q = E(t).$$

Using $q'(t) = i(t)$ we can write the differential equation in the form

$$L\frac{di}{dt} + Ri + \frac{1}{C}q = E(t).$$

Then differentiating we obtain

$$L\frac{d^2i}{dt^2} + R\frac{di}{dt} + \frac{1}{C}i = E'(t).$$

(b) From $Li'(t) + Ri(t) + (1/C)q(t) = E(t)$ we find

$$Li'(0) + Ri(0) + (1/C)q(0) = E(0)$$

or

$$Li'(0) + Ri_0 + (1/C)q_0 = E(0).$$

Solving for $i'(0)$ we get

$$i'(0) = \frac{1}{L}\left[E(0) - \frac{1}{C}q_0 - Ri_0\right].$$

23. For $\lambda = \alpha^2 > 0$ the general solution is $y = c_1\cos\alpha x + c_2\sin\alpha x$. Now

$$y(0) = c_1 \quad \text{and} \quad y(2\pi) = c_1\cos 2\pi\alpha + c_2\sin 2\pi\alpha,$$

so the condition $y(0) = y(2\pi)$ implies

$$c_1 = c_1\cos 2\pi\alpha + c_2\sin 2\pi\alpha$$

which is true when $\alpha = \sqrt{\lambda} = n$ or $\lambda = n^2$ for $n = 1, 2, 3, \ldots$. Since

$$y' = -\alpha c_1\sin\alpha x + \alpha c_2\cos\alpha x = -nc_1\sin nx + nc_2\cos nx,$$

we see that $y'(0) = nc_2 = y'(2\pi)$ for $n = 1, 2, 3, \ldots$. Thus, the eigenvalues are n^2 for $n = 1, 2, 3, \ldots$, with corresponding eigenfunctions $\cos nx$ and $\sin nx$. When $\lambda = 0$, the general solution is $y = c_1 x + c_2$ and the corresponding eigenfunction is $y = 1$.

For $\lambda = -\alpha^2 < 0$ the general solution is $y = c_1 \cosh \alpha x + c_2 \sinh \alpha x$. In this case $y(0) = c_1$ and $y(2\pi) = c_1 \cosh 2\pi\alpha + c_2 \sinh 2\pi\alpha$, so $y(0) = y(2\pi)$ can only be valid for $\alpha = 0$. Thus, there are no eigenvalues corresponding to $\lambda < 0$.

24. (a) The differential equation is $d^2r/dt^2 - \omega^2 r = -g \sin \omega t$. The auxiliary equation is $m^2 - \omega^2 = 0$, so $r_c = c_1 e^{\omega t} + c_2 e^{-\omega t}$. A particular solution has the form $r_p = A \sin \omega t + B \cos \omega t$. Substituting into the differential equation we find $-2A\omega^2 \sin \omega t - 2B\omega^2 \cos \omega t = -g \sin \omega t$. Thus, $B = 0$, $A = g/2\omega^2$, and $r_p = (g/2\omega^2) \sin \omega t$. The general solution of the differential equation is $r(t) = c_1 e^{\omega t} + c_2 e^{-\omega t} + (g/2\omega^2) \sin \omega t$. The initial conditions imply $c_1 + c_2 = r_0$ and $g/2\omega - \omega c_1 + \omega c_2 = v_0$. Solving for c_1 and c_2 we get

$$c_1 = (2\omega^2 r_0 + 2\omega v_0 - g)/4\omega^2 \quad \text{and} \quad c_2 = (2\omega^2 r_0 - 2\omega v_0 + g)/4\omega^2,$$

so that

$$r(t) = \frac{2\omega^2 r_0 + 2\omega v_0 - g}{4\omega^2} e^{\omega t} + \frac{2\omega^2 r_0 - 2\omega v_0 + g}{4\omega^2} e^{-\omega t} + \frac{g}{2\omega^2} \sin \omega t.$$

(b) The bead will exhibit simple harmonic motion when the exponential terms are missing. Solving $c_1 = 0$, $c_2 = 0$ for r_0 and v_0 we find $r_0 = 0$ and $v_0 = g/2\omega$.

To find the minimum length of rod that will accommodate simple harmonic motion we determine the amplitude of $r(t)$ and double it. Thus $L = g/\omega^2$.

(c) As t increases, $e^{\omega t}$ approaches infinity and $e^{-\omega t}$ approaches 0. Since $\sin \omega t$ is bounded, the distance, $r(t)$, of the bead from the pivot point increases without bound and the distance of the bead from P will eventually exceed $L/2$.

(d)

(e) For each v_0 we want to find the smallest value of t for which $r(t) = \pm 20$. Whether we look for $r(t) = -20$ or $r(t) = 20$ is determined by looking at the graphs in part (d). The total times that the bead stays on the rod is shown in the table below.

v_0	0	10	15	16.1	17
r	−20	−20	−20	20	20
t	1.55007	2.35494	3.43088	6.11627	4.22339

When $v_0 = 16$ the bead never leaves the rod.

25. Unlike the derivation given in (1) of Section 5.1 in the text, the weight mg of the mass m does not appear in the net force since the spring is not stretched by the weight of the mass when it is in the equilibrium position (i.e. there is no $mg - ks$ term in the net force). The only force acting on the mass when it is in motion is the restoring force of the spring. By Newton's second law,

$$m\frac{d^2x}{dt^2} = -kx \qquad \text{or} \qquad \frac{d^2x}{dt^2} + \frac{k}{m}x = 0.$$

26. The force of kinetic friction opposing the motion of the mass in μN, where μ is the coefficient of sliding friction and N is the normal component of the weight. Since friction is a force opposite to the direction of motion and since N is pointed directly downward (it is simply the weight of the mass), Newton's second law gives, for motion to the right $(x' > 0)$,

$$m\frac{d^2x}{dt^2} = -kx - \mu mg,$$

and for motion to the left $(x' < 0)$,

$$m\frac{d^2x}{dt^2} = -kx + \mu mg.$$

Traditionally, these two equations are written as one expression

$$m\frac{d^2x}{dt^2} + f_x \, \text{sgn}(x') + kx = 0,$$

where $f_k = \mu mg$ and

$$\text{sgn}(x') = \begin{cases} 1, & x' > 0 \\ -1, & x' < 0. \end{cases}$$

6 Series Solutions of Linear Equations

1. $\displaystyle\lim_{n\to\infty}\left|\frac{2^{n+1}x^{n+1}/(n+1)}{2^n x^n/n}\right| = \lim_{n\to\infty}\frac{2n}{n+1}|x| = 2|x|$

The series is absolutely convergent for $2|x| < 1$ or $|x| < \frac{1}{2}$. The radius of convergence is $R = \frac{1}{2}$. At $x = -\frac{1}{2}$, the series $\sum_{n=1}^{\infty}(-1)^n/n$ converges by the alternating series test. At $x = \frac{1}{2}$, the series $\sum_{n=1}^{\infty}1/n$ is the harmonic series which diverges. Thus, the given series converges on $[-\frac{1}{2}, \frac{1}{2})$.

2. $\displaystyle\lim_{n\to\infty}\left|\frac{100^{n+1}(x+7)^{n+1}/(n+1)!}{100^n(x+7)^n/n!}\right| = \lim_{n\to\infty}\frac{100}{n+1}|x+7| = 0$

The radius of convergence is $R = \infty$. The series is absolutely convergent on $(-\infty, \infty)$.

3. By the ratio test,

$$\lim_{k\to\infty}\left|\frac{(x-5)^{k+1}/10^{k+1}}{(x-5)^k/10^k}\right| = \lim_{k\to\infty}\frac{1}{10}|x-5| = \frac{1}{10}|x-5|.$$

The series is absolutely convergent for $\frac{1}{10}|x-5| < 1$, $|x-5| < 10$, or on $(-5, 15)$. The radius of convergence is $R = 10$. At $x = -5$, the series $\sum_{k=1}^{\infty}(-1)^k(-10)^k/10^k = \sum_{k=1}^{\infty}1$ diverges by the nth term test. At $x = 15$, the series $\sum_{k=1}^{\infty}(-1)^k 10^k/10^k = \sum_{k=1}^{\infty}(-1)^k$ diverges by the nth term test. Thus, the series converges on $(-5, 15)$.

4. $\displaystyle\lim_{k\to\infty}\left|\frac{(k+1)!(x-1)^{k+1}}{k!(x-1)^k}\right| = \lim_{k\to\infty}(k+1)|x-1| = \begin{cases} \infty, & x \neq 1 \\ 0, & x = 1 \end{cases}$

The radius of convergence is $R = 0$ and the series converges only for $x = 1$.

5. $\sin x \cos x = \left(x - \dfrac{x^3}{6} + \dfrac{x^5}{120} - \dfrac{x^7}{5040} + \cdots\right)\left(1 - \dfrac{x^2}{2} + \dfrac{x^4}{24} - \dfrac{x^6}{720} + \cdots\right) = x - \dfrac{2x^3}{3} + \dfrac{2x^5}{15} - \dfrac{4x^7}{315} + \cdots$

6. $e^{-x}\cos x = \left(1 - x + \dfrac{x^2}{2} - \dfrac{x^3}{6} + \dfrac{x^4}{24} - \cdots\right)\left(1 - \dfrac{x^2}{2} + \dfrac{x^4}{24} - \cdots\right) = 1 - x + \dfrac{x^3}{3} - \dfrac{x^4}{6} + \cdots$

7. $\dfrac{1}{\cos x} = \dfrac{1}{1 - \dfrac{x^2}{2} + \dfrac{x^4}{4!} - \dfrac{x^6}{6!} + \cdots} = 1 + \dfrac{x^2}{2} + \dfrac{5x^4}{4!} + \dfrac{61x^6}{6!} + \cdots$

Since $\cos(\pi/2) = \cos(-\pi/2) = 0$, the series converges on $(-\pi/2, \pi/2)$.

8. $\dfrac{1-x}{2+x} = \dfrac{1}{2} - \dfrac{3}{4}x + \dfrac{3}{8}x^2 - \dfrac{3}{16}x^3 + \cdots$

Since the function is undefined at $x = -2$, the series converges on $(-2, 2)$.

9. Let $k = n + 2$ so that $n = k - 2$ and

$$\sum_{n=1}^{\infty} nc_n x^{n+2} = \sum_{k=3}^{\infty} (k-2)c_{k-2}x^k.$$

10. Let $k = n - 3$ so that $n = k + 3$ and

$$\sum_{n=3}^{\infty} (2n-1)c_n x^{n-3} = \sum_{k=0}^{\infty} (2k+5)c_{k+3}x^k.$$

11. $\displaystyle \sum_{n=1}^{\infty} 2nc_n x^{n-1} + \sum_{n=0}^{\infty} 6c_n x^{n+1} = 2 \cdot 1 \cdot c_1 x^0 + \underbrace{\sum_{n=2}^{\infty} 2nc_n x^{n-1}}_{k=n-1} + \underbrace{\sum_{n=0}^{\infty} 6c_n x^{n+1}}_{k=n+1}$

$$= 2c_1 + \sum_{k=1}^{\infty} 2(k+1)c_{k+1}x^k + \sum_{k=1}^{\infty} 6c_{k-1}x^k$$

$$= 2c_1 + \sum_{k=1}^{\infty} [2(k+1)c_{k+1} + 6c_{k-1}]x^k$$

12. $\displaystyle \sum_{n=2}^{\infty} n(n-1)c_n x^n + 2\sum_{n=2}^{\infty} n(n-1)c_n x^{n-2} + 3\sum_{n=1}^{\infty} nc_n x^n$

$$= 2 \cdot 2 \cdot 1 c_2 x^0 + 2 \cdot 3 \cdot 2 c_3 x^1 + 3 \cdot 1 \cdot c_1 x^1 + \underbrace{\sum_{n=2}^{\infty} n(n-1)c_n x^n}_{k=n} + 2\underbrace{\sum_{n=4}^{\infty} n(n-1)c_n x^{n-2}}_{k=n-2} + 3\underbrace{\sum_{n=2}^{\infty} nc_n x^n}_{k=n}$$

$$= 4c_2 + (3c_1 + 12c_3)x + \sum_{k=2}^{\infty} k(k-1)c_k x^k + 2\sum_{k=2}^{\infty} (k+2)(k+1)c_{k+2}x^k + 3\sum_{k=2}^{\infty} kc_k x^k$$

$$= 4c_2 + (3c_1 + 12c_3)x + \sum_{k=2}^{\infty} [(k(k-1) + 3k)c_k + 2(k+2)(k+1)c_{k+2}]x^k$$

$$= 4c_2 + (3c_1 + 12c_3)x + \sum_{k=2}^{\infty} [k(k+2)c_k + 2(k+1)(k+2)c_{k+2}]x^k$$

13. $\displaystyle y' = \sum_{n=1}^{\infty} (-1)^{n+1}x^{n-1}, \qquad y'' = \sum_{n=2}^{\infty} (-1)^{n+1}(n-1)x^{n-2}$

$$(x+1)y'' + y' = (x+1)\sum_{n=2}^{\infty}(-1)^{n+1}(n-1)x^{n-2} + \sum_{n=1}^{\infty}(-1)^{n+1}x^{n-1}$$

$$= \sum_{n=2}^{\infty}(-1)^{n+1}(n-1)x^{n-1} + \sum_{n=2}^{\infty}(-1)^{n+1}(n-1)x^{n-2} + \sum_{n=1}^{\infty}(-1)^{n+1}x^{n-1}$$

$$= -x^0 + x^0 + \underbrace{\sum_{n=2}^{\infty}(-1)^{n+1}(n-1)x^{n-1}}_{k=n-1} + \underbrace{\sum_{n=3}^{\infty}(-1)^{n+1}(n-1)x^{n-2}}_{k=n-2} + \underbrace{\sum_{n=2}^{\infty}(-1)^{n+1}x^{n-1}}_{k=n-1}$$

$$= \sum_{k=1}^{\infty}(-1)^{k+2}kx^k + \sum_{k=1}^{\infty}(-1)^{k+3}(k+1)x^k + \sum_{k=1}^{\infty}(-1)^{k+2}x^k$$

$$= \sum_{k=1}^{\infty}\left[(-1)^{k+2}k - (-1)^{k+2}k - (-1)^{k+2} + (-1)^{k+2}\right]x^k = 0$$

14. $y' = \displaystyle\sum_{n=1}^{\infty}\frac{(-1)^n 2n}{2^{2n}(n!)^2}x^{2n-1}, \qquad y'' = \sum_{n=1}^{\infty}\frac{(-1)^n 2n(2n-1)}{2^{2n}(n!)^2}x^{2n-2}$

$$xy'' + y' + xy = \underbrace{\sum_{n=1}^{\infty}\frac{(-1)^n 2n(2n-1)}{2^{2n}(n!)^2}x^{2n-1}}_{k=n} + \underbrace{\sum_{n=1}^{\infty}\frac{(-1)^n 2n}{2^{2n}(n!)^2}x^{2n-1}}_{k=n} + \underbrace{\sum_{n=0}^{\infty}\frac{(-1)^n}{2^{2n}(n!)^2}x^{2n+1}}_{k=n+1}$$

$$= \sum_{k=1}^{\infty}\left[\frac{(-1)^k 2k(2k-1)}{2^{2k}(k!)^2} + \frac{(-1)^k 2k}{2^{2k}(k!)^2} + \frac{(-1)^{k-1}}{2^{2k-2}[(k-1)!]^2}\right]x^{2k-1}$$

$$= \sum_{k=1}^{\infty}\left[\frac{(-1)^k(2k)^2}{2^{2k}(k!)^2} - \frac{(-1)^k}{2^{2k-2}[(k-1)!]^2}\right]x^{2k-1}$$

$$= \sum_{k=1}^{\infty}(-1)^k\left[\frac{(2k)^2 - 2^2 k^2}{2^{2k}(k!)^2}\right]x^{2k-1} = 0$$

15. The singular points of $(x^2 - 25)y'' + 2xy' + y = 0$ are -5 and 5. The distance from 0 to either of these points is 5. The distance from 1 to the closest of these points is 4.

16. The singular points of $(x^2 - 2x + 10)y'' + xy' - 4y = 0$ are $1 + 3i$ and $1 - 3i$. The distance from 0 to either of these points is $\sqrt{10}$. The distance from 1 to either of these points is 3.

17. Substituting $y = \sum_{n=0}^{\infty} c_n x^n$ into the differential equation we have

$$y'' - xy = \underbrace{\sum_{n=2}^{\infty}n(n-1)c_n x^{n-2}}_{k=n-2} - \underbrace{\sum_{n=0}^{\infty}c_n x^{n+1}}_{k=n+1} = \sum_{k=0}^{\infty}(k+2)(k+1)c_{k+2}x^k - \sum_{k=1}^{\infty}c_{k-1}x^k$$

$$= 2c_2 + \sum_{k=1}^{\infty}[(k+2)(k+1)c_{k+2} - c_{k-1}]x^k = 0.$$

Thus

$$c_2 = 0$$

$$(k+2)(k+1)c_{k+2} - c_{k-1} = 0$$

and

$$c_{k+2} = \frac{1}{(k+2)(k+1)} c_{k-1}, \quad k = 1, 2, 3, \ldots.$$

Choosing $c_0 = 1$ and $c_1 = 0$ we find

$$c_3 = \frac{1}{6}$$

$$c_4 = c_5 = 0$$

$$c_6 = \frac{1}{180}$$

and so on. For $c_0 = 0$ and $c_1 = 1$ we obtain

$$c_3 = 0$$

$$c_4 = \frac{1}{12}$$

$$c_5 = c_6 = 0$$

$$c_7 = \frac{1}{504}$$

and so on. Thus, two solutions are

$$y_1 = 1 + \frac{1}{6}x^3 + \frac{1}{180}x^6 + \cdots \qquad \text{and} \qquad y_2 = x + \frac{1}{12}x^4 + \frac{1}{504}x^7 + \cdots.$$

18. Substituting $y = \sum_{n=0}^{\infty} c_n x^n$ into the differential equation we have

$$y'' + x^2 y = \underbrace{\sum_{n=2}^{\infty} n(n-1)c_n x^{n-2}}_{k=n-2} + \underbrace{\sum_{n=0}^{\infty} c_n x^{n+2}}_{k=n+2} = \sum_{k=0}^{\infty}(k+2)(k+1)c_{k+2}x^k + \sum_{k=2}^{\infty} c_{k-2}x^k$$

$$= 2c_2 + 6c_3 x + \sum_{k=2}^{\infty}[(k+2)(k+1)c_{k+2} + c_{k-2}]x^k = 0.$$

Thus

$$c_2 = c_3 = 0$$

$$(k+2)(k+1)c_{k+2} + c_{k-2} = 0$$

and

$$c_{k+2} = -\frac{1}{(k+2)(k+1)} c_{k-2}, \quad k = 2, 3, 4, \ldots.$$

Choosing $c_0 = 1$ and $c_1 = 0$ we find

$$c_4 = -\frac{1}{12}$$

$$c_5 = c_6 = c_7 = 0$$

$$c_8 = \frac{1}{672}$$

and so on. For $c_0 = 0$ and $c_1 = 1$ we obtain

$$c_4 = 0$$

$$c_5 = -\frac{1}{20}$$

$$c_6 = c_7 = c_8 = 0$$

$$c_9 = \frac{1}{1440}$$

and so on. Thus, two solutions are

$$y_1 = 1 - \frac{1}{12}x^4 + \frac{1}{672}x^8 - \cdots \qquad \text{and} \qquad y_2 = x - \frac{1}{20}x^5 + \frac{1}{1440}x^9 - \cdots .$$

19. Substituting $y = \sum_{n=0}^{\infty} c_n x^n$ into the differential equation we have

$$y'' - 2xy' + y = \underbrace{\sum_{n=2}^{\infty} n(n-1)c_n x^{n-2}}_{k=n-2} - 2\underbrace{\sum_{n=1}^{\infty} nc_n x^n}_{k=n} + \underbrace{\sum_{n=0}^{\infty} c_n x^n}_{k=n}$$

$$= \sum_{k=0}^{\infty}(k+2)(k+1)c_{k+2}x^k - 2\sum_{k=1}^{\infty} kc_k x^k + \sum_{k=0}^{\infty} c_k x^k$$

$$= 2c_2 + c_0 + \sum_{k=1}^{\infty}[(k+2)(k+1)c_{k+2} - (2k-1)c_k]x^k = 0.$$

Thus

$$2c_2 + c_0 = 0$$

$$(k+2)(k+1)c_{k+2} - (2k-1)c_k = 0$$

and

$$c_2 = -\frac{1}{2}c_0$$

$$c_{k+2} = \frac{2k-1}{(k+2)(k+1)}c_k, \quad k = 1, 2, 3, \ldots .$$

Choosing $c_0 = 1$ and $c_1 = 0$ we find

$$c_2 = -\frac{1}{2}$$

$$c_3 = c_5 = c_7 = \cdots = 0$$

$$c_4 = -\frac{1}{8}$$

$$c_6 = -\frac{7}{240}$$

and so on. For $c_0 = 0$ and $c_1 = 1$ we obtain

$$c_2 = c_4 = c_6 = \cdots = 0$$

$$c_3 = \frac{1}{6}$$

$$c_5 = \frac{1}{24}$$

$$c_7 = \frac{1}{112}$$

and so on. Thus, two solutions are

$$y_1 = 1 - \frac{1}{2}x^2 - \frac{1}{8}x^4 - \frac{7}{240}x^6 - \cdots \qquad \text{and} \qquad y_2 = x + \frac{1}{6}x^3 + \frac{1}{24}x^5 + \frac{1}{112}x^7 + \cdots.$$

20. Substituting $y = \sum_{n=0}^{\infty} c_n x^n$ into the differential equation we have

$$y'' - xy' + 2y = \underbrace{\sum_{n=2}^{\infty} n(n-1)c_n x^{n-2}}_{k=n-2} - \underbrace{\sum_{n=1}^{\infty} nc_n x^n}_{k=n} + 2\underbrace{\sum_{n=0}^{\infty} c_n x^n}_{k=n}$$

$$= \sum_{k=0}^{\infty} (k+2)(k+1)c_{k+2}x^k - \sum_{k=1}^{\infty} kc_k x^k + 2\sum_{k=0}^{\infty} c_k x^k$$

$$= 2c_2 + 2c_0 + \sum_{k=1}^{\infty} [(k+2)(k+1)c_{k+2} - (k-2)c_k]x^k = 0.$$

Thus

$$2c_2 + 2c_0 = 0$$

$$(k+2)(k+1)c_{k+2} - (k-2)c_k = 0$$

and

$$c_2 = -c_0$$

$$c_{k+2} = \frac{k-2}{(k+2)(k+1)}c_k, \quad k = 1, 2, 3, \ldots.$$

Exercises 6.1   Solutions About Ordinary Points

Choosing $c_0 = 1$ and $c_1 = 0$ we find

$$c_2 = -1$$

$$c_3 = c_5 = c_7 = \cdots = 0$$

$$c_4 = 0$$

$$c_6 = c_8 = c_{10} = \cdots = 0.$$

For $c_0 = 0$ and $c_1 = 1$ we obtain

$$c_2 = c_4 = c_6 = \cdots = 0$$

$$c_3 = -\frac{1}{6}$$

$$c_5 = -\frac{1}{120}$$

and so on. Thus, two solutions are

$$y_1 = 1 - x^2 \quad \text{and} \quad y_2 = x - \frac{1}{6}x^3 - \frac{1}{120}x^5 - \cdots .$$

21. Substituting $y = \sum_{n=0}^{\infty} c_n x^n$ into the differential equation we have

$$y'' + x^2 y' + xy = \underbrace{\sum_{n=2}^{\infty} n(n-1)c_n x^{n-2}}_{k=n-2} + \underbrace{\sum_{n=1}^{\infty} nc_n x^{n+1}}_{k=n+1} + \underbrace{\sum_{n=0}^{\infty} c_n x^{n+1}}_{k=n+1}$$

$$= \sum_{k=0}^{\infty} (k+2)(k+1)c_{k+2} x^k + \sum_{k=2}^{\infty} (k-1)c_{k-1} x^k + \sum_{k=1}^{\infty} c_{k-1} x^k$$

$$= 2c_2 + (6c_3 + c_0)x + \sum_{k=2}^{\infty} [(k+2)(k+1)c_{k+2} + kc_{k-1}]x^k = 0.$$

Thus

$$c_2 = 0$$

$$6c_3 + c_0 = 0$$

$$(k+2)(k+1)c_{k+2} + kc_{k-1} = 0$$

and

$$c_2 = 0$$

$$c_3 = -\frac{1}{6}c_0$$

$$c_{k+2} = -\frac{k}{(k+2)(k+1)}c_{k-1}, \quad k = 2, 3, 4, \ldots .$$

Choosing $c_0 = 1$ and $c_1 = 0$ we find

$$c_3 = -\frac{1}{6}$$

$$c_4 = c_5 = 0$$

$$c_6 = \frac{1}{45}$$

and so on. For $c_0 = 0$ and $c_1 = 1$ we obtain

$$c_3 = 0$$

$$c_4 = -\frac{1}{6}$$

$$c_5 = c_6 = 0$$

$$c_7 = \frac{5}{252}$$

and so on. Thus, two solutions are

$$y_1 = 1 - \frac{1}{6}x^3 + \frac{1}{45}x^6 - \cdots \quad \text{and} \quad y_2 = x - \frac{1}{6}x^4 + \frac{5}{252}x^7 - \cdots .$$

22. Substituting $y = \sum_{n=0}^{\infty} c_n x^n$ into the differential equation we have

$$y'' + 2xy' + 2y = \underbrace{\sum_{n=2}^{\infty} n(n-1)c_n x^{n-2}}_{k=n-2} + 2\underbrace{\sum_{n=1}^{\infty} nc_n x^n}_{k=n} + 2\underbrace{\sum_{n=0}^{\infty} c_n x^n}_{k=n}$$

$$= \sum_{k=0}^{\infty}(k+2)(k+1)c_{k+2}x^k + 2\sum_{k=1}^{\infty} kc_k x^k + 2\sum_{k=0}^{\infty} c_k x^k$$

$$= 2c_2 + 2c_0 + \sum_{k=1}^{\infty}[(k+2)(k+1)c_{k+2} + 2(k+1)c_k]x^k = 0.$$

Thus

$$2c_2 + 2c_0 = 0$$

$$(k+2)(k+1)c_{k+2} + 2(k+1)c_k = 0$$

and

$$c_2 = -c_0$$

$$c_{k+2} = -\frac{2}{k+2}c_k, \quad k = 1, 2, 3, \ldots .$$

Choosing $c_0 = 1$ and $c_1 = 0$ we find

$$c_2 = -1$$

$$c_3 = c_5 = c_7 = \cdots = 0$$

$$c_4 = \frac{1}{2}$$

$$c_6 = -\frac{1}{6}$$

and so on. For $c_0 = 0$ and $c_1 = 1$ we obtain

$$c_2 = c_4 = c_6 = \cdots = 0$$

$$c_3 = -\frac{2}{3}$$

$$c_5 = \frac{4}{15}$$

$$c_7 = -\frac{8}{105}$$

and so on. Thus, two solutions are

$$y_1 = 1 - x^2 + \frac{1}{2}x^4 - \frac{1}{6}x^6 + \cdots \quad \text{and} \quad y_2 = x - \frac{2}{3}x^3 + \frac{4}{15}x^5 - \frac{8}{105}x^7 + \cdots .$$

23. Substituting $y = \sum_{n=0}^{\infty} c_n x^n$ into the differential equation we have

$$(x - 1)y'' + y' = \underbrace{\sum_{n=2}^{\infty} n(n-1)c_n x^{n-1}}_{k=n-1} - \underbrace{\sum_{n=2}^{\infty} n(n-1)c_n x^{n-2}}_{k=n-2} + \underbrace{\sum_{n=1}^{\infty} nc_n x^{n-1}}_{k=n-1}$$

$$= \sum_{k=1}^{\infty} (k+1)kc_{k+1}x^k - \sum_{k=0}^{\infty} (k+2)(k+1)c_{k+2}x^k + \sum_{k=0}^{\infty} (k+1)c_{k+1}x^k$$

$$= -2c_2 + c_1 + \sum_{k=1}^{\infty} [(k+1)kc_{k+1} - (k+2)(k+1)c_{k+2} + (k+1)c_{k+1}]x^k = 0.$$

Thus

$$-2c_2 + c_1 = 0$$

$$(k+1)^2 c_{k+1} - (k+2)(k+1)c_{k+2} = 0$$

and

$$c_2 = \frac{1}{2}c_1$$

$$c_{k+2} = \frac{k+1}{k+2}c_{k+1}, \quad k = 1, 2, 3, \ldots .$$

Choosing $c_0 = 1$ and $c_1 = 0$ we find $c_2 = c_3 = c_4 = \cdots = 0$. For $c_0 = 0$ and $c_1 = 1$ we obtain

$$c_2 = \frac{1}{2}, \qquad c_3 = \frac{1}{3}, \qquad c_4 = \frac{1}{4},$$

and so on. Thus, two solutions are

$$y_1 = 1 \qquad \text{and} \qquad y_2 = x + \frac{1}{2}x^2 + \frac{1}{3}x^3 + \frac{1}{4}x^4 + \cdots.$$

24. Substituting $y = \sum_{n=0}^{\infty} c_n x^n$ into the differential equation we have

$$(x+2)y'' + xy' - y = \underbrace{\sum_{n=2}^{\infty} n(n-1)c_n x^{n-1}}_{k=n-1} + \underbrace{\sum_{n=2}^{\infty} 2n(n-1)c_n x^{n-2}}_{k=n-2} + \underbrace{\sum_{n=1}^{\infty} nc_n x^n}_{k=n} - \underbrace{\sum_{n=0}^{\infty} c_n x^n}_{k=n}$$

$$= \sum_{k=1}^{\infty} (k+1)kc_{k+1}x^k + \sum_{k=0}^{\infty} 2(k+2)(k+1)c_{k+2}x^k + \sum_{k=1}^{\infty} kc_k x^k - \sum_{k=0}^{\infty} c_k x^k$$

$$= 4c_2 - c_0 + \sum_{k=1}^{\infty} [(k+1)kc_{k+1} + 2(k+2)(k+1)c_{k+2} + (k-1)c_k]x^k = 0.$$

Thus

$$4c_2 - c_0 = 0$$

$$(k+1)kc_{k+1} + 2(k+2)(k+1)c_{k+2} + (k-1)c_k = 0, \quad k = 1, 2, 3, \ldots$$

and

$$c_2 = \frac{1}{4}c_0$$

$$c_{k+2} = -\frac{(k+1)kc_{k+1} + (k-1)c_k}{2(k+2)(k+1)}, \quad k = 1, 2, 3, \ldots.$$

Choosing $c_0 = 1$ and $c_1 = 0$ we find

$$c_1 = 0, \qquad c_2 = \frac{1}{4}, \qquad c_3 = -\frac{1}{24}, \qquad c_4 = 0, \qquad c_5 = \frac{1}{480}$$

and so on. For $c_0 = 0$ and $c_1 = 1$ we obtain

$$c_2 = 0$$

$$c_3 = 0$$

$$c_4 = c_5 = c_6 = \cdots = 0.$$

Thus, two solutions are

$$y_1 = c_0 \left[1 + \frac{1}{4}x^2 - \frac{1}{24}x^3 + \frac{1}{480}x^5 + \cdots \right] \qquad \text{and} \qquad y_2 = c_1 x.$$

25. Substituting $y = \sum_{n=0}^{\infty} c_n x^n$ into the differential equation we have

$$y'' - (x+1)y' - y = \underbrace{\sum_{n=2}^{\infty} n(n-1)c_n x^{n-2}}_{k=n-2} - \underbrace{\sum_{n=1}^{\infty} nc_n x^n}_{k=n} - \underbrace{\sum_{n=1}^{\infty} nc_n x^{n-1}}_{k=n-1} - \underbrace{\sum_{n=0}^{\infty} c_n x^n}_{k=n}$$

$$= \sum_{k=0}^{\infty} (k+2)(k+1)c_{k+2} x^k - \sum_{k=1}^{\infty} kc_k x^k - \sum_{k=0}^{\infty} (k+1)c_{k+1} x^k - \sum_{k=0}^{\infty} c_k x^k$$

$$= 2c_2 - c_1 - c_0 + \sum_{k=1}^{\infty} [(k+2)(k+1)c_{k+2} - (k+1)c_{k+1} - (k+1)c_k]x^k = 0.$$

Thus

$$2c_2 - c_1 - c_0 = 0$$

$$(k+2)(k+1)c_{k+2} - (k+1)(c_{k+1} + c_k) = 0$$

and

$$c_2 = \frac{c_1 + c_0}{2}$$

$$c_{k+2} = \frac{c_{k+1} + c_k}{k+2}, \quad k = 1, 2, 3, \ldots.$$

Choosing $c_0 = 1$ and $c_1 = 0$ we find

$$c_2 = \frac{1}{2}, \qquad c_3 = \frac{1}{6}, \qquad c_4 = \frac{1}{6},$$

and so on. For $c_0 = 0$ and $c_1 = 1$ we obtain

$$c_2 = \frac{1}{2}, \qquad c_3 = \frac{1}{2}, \qquad c_4 = \frac{1}{4},$$

and so on. Thus, two solutions are

$$y_1 = 1 + \frac{1}{2}x^2 + \frac{1}{6}x^3 + \frac{1}{6}x^4 + \cdots \qquad \text{and} \qquad y_2 = x + \frac{1}{2}x^2 + \frac{1}{2}x^3 + \frac{1}{4}x^4 + \cdots.$$

26. Substituting $y = \sum_{n=0}^{\infty} c_n x^n$ into the differential equation we have

$$\left(x^2 + 1\right) y'' - 6y = \underbrace{\sum_{n=2}^{\infty} n(n-1)c_n x^n}_{k=n} + \underbrace{\sum_{n=2}^{\infty} n(n-1)c_n x^{n-2}}_{k=n-2} - 6\underbrace{\sum_{n=0}^{\infty} c_n x^n}_{k=n}$$

$$= \sum_{k=2}^{\infty} k(k-1)c_k x^k + \sum_{k=0}^{\infty} (k+2)(k+1)c_{k+2} x^k - 6\sum_{k=0}^{\infty} c_k x^k$$

$$= 2c_2 - 6c_0 + (6c_3 - 6c_1)x + \sum_{k=2}^{\infty} \left[\left(k^2 - k - 6\right)c_k + (k+2)(k+1)c_{k+2}\right]x^k = 0.$$

Thus

$$2c_2 - 6c_0 = 0$$

$$6c_3 - 6c_1 = 0$$

$$(k-3)(k+2)c_k + (k+2)(k+1)c_{k+2} = 0$$

and

$$c_2 = 3c_0$$

$$c_3 = c_1$$

$$c_{k+2} = -\frac{k-3}{k+1}c_k, \quad k = 2, 3, 4, \ldots .$$

Choosing $c_0 = 1$ and $c_1 = 0$ we find

$$c_2 = 3$$

$$c_3 = c_5 = c_7 = \cdots = 0$$

$$c_4 = 1$$

$$c_6 = -\frac{1}{5}$$

and so on. For $c_0 = 0$ and $c_1 = 1$ we obtain

$$c_2 = c_4 = c_6 = \cdots = 0$$

$$c_3 = 1$$

$$c_5 = c_7 = c_9 = \cdots = 0.$$

Thus, two solutions are

$$y_1 = 1 + 3x^2 + x^4 - \frac{1}{5}x^6 + \cdots \qquad \text{and} \qquad y_2 = x + x^3.$$

27. Substituting $y = \sum_{n=0}^{\infty} c_n x^n$ into the differential equation we have

$$\left(x^2 + 2\right)y'' + 3xy' - y = \underbrace{\sum_{n=2}^{\infty} n(n-1)c_n x^n}_{k=n} + 2\underbrace{\sum_{n=2}^{\infty} n(n-1)c_n x^{n-2}}_{k=n-2} + 3\underbrace{\sum_{n=1}^{\infty} nc_n x^n}_{k=n} - \underbrace{\sum_{n=0}^{\infty} c_n x^n}_{k=n}$$

$$= \sum_{k=2}^{\infty} k(k-1)c_k x^k + 2\sum_{k=0}^{\infty} (k+2)(k+1)c_{k+2} x^k + 3\sum_{k=1}^{\infty} kc_k x^k - \sum_{k=0}^{\infty} c_k x^k$$

$$= (4c_2 - c_0) + (12c_3 + 2c_1)x + \sum_{k=2}^{\infty} \left[2(k+2)(k+1)c_{k+2} + \left(k^2 + 2k - 1\right)c_k\right] x^k = 0.$$

285

Thus

$$4c_2 - c_0 = 0$$

$$12c_3 + 2c_1 = 0$$

$$2(k+2)(k+1)c_{k+2} + \left(k^2 + 2k - 1\right)c_k = 0$$

and

$$c_2 = \frac{1}{4}c_0$$

$$c_3 = -\frac{1}{6}c_1$$

$$c_{k+2} = -\frac{k^2 + 2k - 1}{2(k+2)(k+1)}c_k, \quad k = 2, 3, 4, \dots.$$

Choosing $c_0 = 1$ and $c_1 = 0$ we find

$$c_2 = \frac{1}{4}$$

$$c_3 = c_5 = c_7 = \cdots = 0$$

$$c_4 = -\frac{7}{96}$$

and so on. For $c_0 = 0$ and $c_1 = 1$ we obtain

$$c_2 = c_4 = c_6 = \cdots = 0$$

$$c_3 = -\frac{1}{6}$$

$$c_5 = \frac{7}{120}$$

and so on. Thus, two solutions are

$$y_1 = 1 + \frac{1}{4}x^2 - \frac{7}{96}x^4 + \cdots \qquad \text{and} \qquad y_2 = x - \frac{1}{6}x^3 + \frac{7}{120}x^5 - \cdots.$$

28. Substituting $y = \sum_{n=0}^{\infty} c_n x^n$ into the differential equation we have

$$\left(x^2 - 1\right)y'' + xy' - y = \underbrace{\sum_{n=2}^{\infty} n(n-1)c_n x^n}_{k=n} - \underbrace{\sum_{n=2}^{\infty} n(n-1)c_n x^{n-2}}_{k=n-2} + \underbrace{\sum_{n=1}^{\infty} nc_n x^n}_{k=n} - \underbrace{\sum_{n=0}^{\infty} c_n x^n}_{k=n}$$

$$= \sum_{k=2}^{\infty} k(k-1)c_k x^k - \sum_{k=0}^{\infty}(k+2)(k+1)c_{k+2}x^k + \sum_{k=1}^{\infty} kc_k x^k - \sum_{k=0}^{\infty} c_k x^k$$

$$= (-2c_2 - c_0) - 6c_3 x + \sum_{k=2}^{\infty}\left[-(k+2)(k+1)c_{k+2} + \left(k^2 - 1\right)c_k\right]x^k = 0.$$

286

Thus

$$-2c_2 - c_0 = 0$$

$$-6c_3 = 0$$

$$-(k+2)(k+1)c_{k+2} + (k-1)(k+1)c_k = 0$$

and

$$c_2 = -\frac{1}{2}c_0$$

$$c_3 = 0$$

$$c_{k+2} = \frac{k-1}{k+2}\,c_k, \quad k = 2, 3, 4, \ldots .$$

Choosing $c_0 = 1$ and $c_1 = 0$ we find

$$c_2 = -\frac{1}{2}$$

$$c_3 = c_5 = c_7 = \cdots = 0$$

$$c_4 = -\frac{1}{8}$$

and so on. For $c_0 = 0$ and $c_1 = 1$ we obtain

$$c_2 = c_4 = c_6 = \cdots = 0$$

$$c_3 = c_5 = c_7 = \cdots = 0.$$

Thus, two solutions are

$$y_1 = 1 - \frac{1}{2}x^2 - \frac{1}{8}x^4 - \cdots \quad \text{and} \quad y_2 = x.$$

29. Substituting $y = \sum_{n=0}^{\infty} c_n x^n$ into the differential equation we have

$$(x-1)y'' - xy' + y = \underbrace{\sum_{n=2}^{\infty} n(n-1)c_n x^{n-1}}_{k=n-1} - \underbrace{\sum_{n=2}^{\infty} n(n-1)c_n x^{n-2}}_{k=n-2} - \underbrace{\sum_{n=1}^{\infty} nc_n x^n}_{k=n} + \underbrace{\sum_{n=0}^{\infty} c_n x^n}_{k=n}$$

$$= \sum_{k=1}^{\infty}(k+1)kc_{k+1}x^k - \sum_{k=0}^{\infty}(k+2)(k+1)c_{k+2}x^k - \sum_{k=1}^{\infty} kc_k x^k + \sum_{k=0}^{\infty} c_k x^k$$

$$= -2c_2 + c_0 + \sum_{k=1}^{\infty}[-(k+2)(k+1)c_{k+2} + (k+1)kc_{k+1} - (k-1)c_k]x^k = 0.$$

Thus

$$-2c_2 + c_0 = 0$$

$$-(k+2)(k+1)c_{k+2} + (k+1)kc_{k+1} - (k-1)c_k = 0$$

and

$$c_2 = \frac{1}{2}c_0$$

$$c_{k+2} = \frac{kc_{k+1}}{k+2} - \frac{(k-1)c_k}{(k+2)(k+1)}, \quad k = 1, 2, 3, \ldots.$$

Choosing $c_0 = 1$ and $c_1 = 0$ we find

$$c_2 = \frac{1}{2}, \qquad c_3 = \frac{1}{6}, \qquad c_4 = \frac{1}{24},$$

and so on. For $c_0 = 0$ and $c_1 = 1$ we obtain $c_2 = c_3 = c_4 = \cdots = 0$. Thus,

$$y = C_1\left(1 + \frac{1}{2}x^2 + \frac{1}{6}x^3 + \cdots\right) + C_2 x$$

and

$$y' = C_1\left(x + \frac{1}{2}x^2 + \cdots\right) + C_2.$$

The initial conditions imply $C_1 = -2$ and $C_2 = 6$, so

$$y = -2\left(1 + \frac{1}{2}x^2 + \frac{1}{6}x^3 + \cdots\right) + 6x = 8x - 2e^x.$$

30. Substituting $y = \sum_{n=0}^{\infty} c_n x^n$ into the differential equation we have

$$(x+1)y'' - (2-x)y' + y$$

$$= \underbrace{\sum_{n=2}^{\infty} n(n-1)c_n x^{n-1}}_{k=n-1} + \underbrace{\sum_{n=2}^{\infty} n(n-1)c_n x^{n-2}}_{k=n-2} - \underbrace{2\sum_{n=1}^{\infty} nc_n x^{n-1}}_{k=n-1} + \underbrace{\sum_{n=1}^{\infty} nc_n x^n}_{k=n} + \underbrace{\sum_{n=0}^{\infty} c_n x^n}_{k=n}$$

$$= \sum_{k=1}^{\infty}(k+1)kc_{k+1}x^k + \sum_{k=0}^{\infty}(k+2)(k+1)c_{k+2}x^k - 2\sum_{k=0}^{\infty}(k+1)c_{k+1}x^k + \sum_{k=1}^{\infty} kc_k x^k + \sum_{k=0}^{\infty} c_k x^k$$

$$= 2c_2 - 2c_1 + c_0 + \sum_{k=1}^{\infty}[(k+2)(k+1)c_{k+2} - (k+1)c_{k+1} + (k+1)c_k]x^k = 0.$$

Thus

$$2c_2 - 2c_1 + c_0 = 0$$

$$(k+2)(k+1)c_{k+2} - (k+1)c_{k+1} + (k+1)c_k = 0$$

and

$$c_2 = c_1 - \frac{1}{2}c_0$$

$$c_{k+2} = \frac{1}{k+2}c_{k+1} - \frac{1}{k+2}c_k, \quad k = 1, 2, 3, \ldots.$$

Choosing $c_0 = 1$ and $c_1 = 0$ we find

$$c_2 = -\frac{1}{2}, \qquad c_3 = -\frac{1}{6}, \qquad c_4 = \frac{1}{12},$$

and so on. For $c_0 = 0$ and $c_1 = 1$ we obtain

$$c_2 = 1, \qquad c_3 = 0, \qquad c_4 = -\frac{1}{4},$$

and so on. Thus,

$$y = C_1 \left(1 - \frac{1}{2}x^2 - \frac{1}{6}x^3 + \frac{1}{12}x^4 + \cdots\right) + C_2 \left(x + x^2 - \frac{1}{4}x^4 + \cdots\right)$$

and

$$y' = C_1 \left(-x - \frac{1}{2}x^2 + \frac{1}{3}x^3 + \cdots\right) + C_2 \left(1 + 2x - x^3 + \cdots\right).$$

The initial conditions imply $C_1 = 2$ and $C_2 = -1$, so

$$y = 2\left(1 - \frac{1}{2}x^2 - \frac{1}{6}x^3 + \frac{1}{12}x^4 + \cdots\right) - \left(x + x^2 - \frac{1}{4}x^4 + \cdots\right)$$

$$= 2 - x - 2x^2 - \frac{1}{3}x^3 + \frac{5}{12}x^4 + \cdots.$$

31. Substituting $y = \sum_{n=0}^{\infty} c_n x^n$ into the differential equation we have

$$y'' - 2xy' + 8y = \underbrace{\sum_{n=2}^{\infty} n(n-1)c_n x^{n-2}}_{k=n-2} - 2\underbrace{\sum_{n=1}^{\infty} nc_n x^n}_{k=n} + 8\underbrace{\sum_{n=0}^{\infty} c_n x^n}_{k=n}$$

$$= \sum_{k=0}^{\infty}(k+2)(k+1)c_{k+2}x^k - 2\sum_{k=1}^{\infty} kc_k x^k + 8\sum_{k=0}^{\infty} c_k x^k$$

$$= 2c_2 + 8c_0 + \sum_{k=1}^{\infty}[(k+2)(k+1)c_{k+2} + (8-2k)c_k]x^k = 0.$$

Thus

$$2c_2 + 8c_0 = 0$$

$$(k+2)(k+1)c_{k+2} + (8-2k)c_k = 0$$

and

$$c_2 = -4c_0$$

$$c_{k+2} = \frac{2(k-4)}{(k+2)(k+1)}c_k, \qquad k = 1, 2, 3, \ldots.$$

Choosing $c_0 = 1$ and $c_1 = 0$ we find

$$c_2 = -4$$

$$c_3 = c_5 = c_7 = \cdots = 0$$

$$c_4 = \frac{4}{3}$$

$$c_6 = c_8 = c_{10} = \cdots = 0.$$

For $c_0 = 0$ and $c_1 = 1$ we obtain

$$c_2 = c_4 = c_6 = \cdots = 0$$

$$c_3 = -1$$

$$c_5 = \frac{1}{10}$$

and so on. Thus,

$$y = C_1 \left(1 - 4x^2 + \frac{4}{3}x^4 \right) + C_2 \left(x - x^3 + \frac{1}{10}x^5 + \cdots \right)$$

and

$$y' = C_1 \left(-8x + \frac{16}{3}x^3 \right) + C_2 \left(1 - 3x^2 + \frac{1}{2}x^4 + \cdots \right).$$

The initial conditions imply $C_1 = 3$ and $C_2 = 0$, so

$$y = 3 \left(1 - 4x^2 + \frac{4}{3}x^4 \right) = 3 - 12x^2 + 4x^4.$$

32. Substituting $y = \sum_{n=0}^{\infty} c_n x^n$ into the differential equation we have

$$(x^2 + 1)y'' + 2xy' = \underbrace{\sum_{n=2}^{\infty} n(n-1)c_n x^n}_{k=n} + \underbrace{\sum_{n=2}^{\infty} n(n-1)c_n x^{n-2}}_{k=n-2} + \underbrace{\sum_{n=1}^{\infty} 2nc_n x^n}_{k=n}$$

$$= \sum_{k=2}^{\infty} k(k-1)c_k x^k + \sum_{k=0}^{\infty} (k+2)(k+1)c_{k+2} x^k + \sum_{k=1}^{\infty} 2kc_k x^k$$

$$= 2c_2 + (6c_3 + 2c_1)x + \sum_{k=2}^{\infty} [k(k+1)c_k + (k+2)(k+1)c_{k+2}]x^k = 0.$$

Thus

$$2c_2 = 0$$

$$6c_3 + 2c_1 = 0$$

$$k(k+1)c_k + (k+2)(k+1)c_{k+2} = 0$$

and

$$c_2 = 0$$

$$c_3 = -\frac{1}{3}c_1$$

$$c_{k+2} = -\frac{k}{k+2}c_k, \quad k = 2, 3, 4, \ldots .$$

Choosing $c_0 = 1$ and $c_1 = 0$ we find $c_3 = c_4 = c_5 = \cdots = 0$. For $c_0 = 0$ and $c_1 = 1$ we obtain

$$c_3 = -\frac{1}{3}$$

$$c_4 = c_6 = c_8 = \cdots = 0$$

$$c_5 = -\frac{1}{5}$$

$$c_7 = \frac{1}{7}$$

and so on. Thus

$$y = C_0 + C_1 \left(x - \frac{1}{3}x^3 + \frac{1}{5}x^5 - \frac{1}{7}x^7 + \cdots \right)$$

and

$$y' = c_1 \left(1 - x^2 + x^4 - x^6 + \cdots \right).$$

The initial conditions imply $c_0 = 0$ and $c_1 = 1$, so

$$y = x - \frac{1}{3}x^3 + \frac{1}{5}x^5 - \frac{1}{7}x^7 + \cdots .$$

33. Substituting $y = \sum_{n=0}^{\infty} c_n x^n$ into the differential equation we have

$$y'' + (\sin x)y = \sum_{n=2}^{\infty} n(n-1)c_n x^{n-2} + \left(x - \frac{1}{6}x^3 + \frac{1}{120}x^5 - \cdots \right)\left(c_0 + c_1 x + c_2 x^2 + \cdots \right)$$

$$= \left[2c_2 + 6c_3 x + 12c_4 x^2 + 20c_5 x^3 + \cdots \right] + \left[c_0 x + c_1 x^2 + \left(c_2 - \frac{1}{6}c_0 \right) x^3 + \cdots \right]$$

$$= 2c_2 + (6c_3 + c_0)x + (12c_4 + c_1)x^2 + \left(20c_5 + c_2 - \frac{1}{6}c_0 \right) x^3 + \cdots = 0.$$

Thus

$$2c_2 = 0$$

$$6c_3 + c_0 = 0$$

$$12c_4 + c_1 = 0$$

$$20c_5 + c_2 - \frac{1}{6}c_0 = 0$$

Exercises 6.1   Solutions About Ordinary Points

and
$$c_2 = 0$$
$$c_3 = -\frac{1}{6}c_0$$
$$c_4 = -\frac{1}{12}c_1$$
$$c_5 = -\frac{1}{20}c_2 + \frac{1}{120}c_0.$$

Choosing $c_0 = 1$ and $c_1 = 0$ we find
$$c_2 = 0, \qquad c_3 = -\frac{1}{6}, \qquad c_4 = 0, \qquad c_5 = \frac{1}{120}$$

and so on. For $c_0 = 0$ and $c_1 = 1$ we obtain
$$c_2 = 0, \qquad c_3 = 0, \qquad c_4 = -\frac{1}{12}, \qquad c_5 = 0$$

and so on. Thus, two solutions are
$$y_1 = 1 - \frac{1}{6}x^3 + \frac{1}{120}x^5 + \cdots \qquad \text{and} \qquad y_2 = x - \frac{1}{12}x^4 + \cdots.$$

34. Substituting $y = \sum_{n=0}^{\infty} c_n x^n$ into the differential equation we have

$$y'' + e^x y' - y = \sum_{n=2}^{\infty} n(n-1)c_n x^{n-2}$$

$$+ \left(1 + x + \frac{1}{2}x^2 + \frac{1}{6}x^3 + \cdots\right)\left(c_1 + 2c_2 x + 3c_3 x^2 + 4c_4 x^3 + \cdots\right) - \sum_{n=0}^{\infty} c_n x^n$$

$$= \left[2c_2 + 6c_3 x + 12c_4 x^2 + 20c_5 x^3 + \cdots\right]$$

$$+ \left[c_1 + (2c_2 + c_1)x + \left(3c_3 + 2c_2 + \frac{1}{2}c_1\right)x^2 + \cdots\right] - \left[c_0 + c_1 x + c_2 x^2 + \cdots\right]$$

$$= (2c_2 + c_1 - c_0) + (6c_3 + 2c_2)x + \left(12c_4 + 3c_3 + c_2 + \frac{1}{2}c_1\right)x^2 + \cdots = 0.$$

Thus
$$2c_2 + c_1 - c_0 = 0$$
$$6c_3 + 2c_2 = 0$$
$$12c_4 + 3c_3 + c_2 + \frac{1}{2}c_1 = 0$$

and

$$c_2 = \frac{1}{2}c_0 - \frac{1}{2}c_1$$

$$c_3 = -\frac{1}{3}c_2$$

$$c_4 = -\frac{1}{4}c_3 + \frac{1}{12}c_2 - \frac{1}{24}c_1.$$

Choosing $c_0 = 1$ and $c_1 = 0$ we find

$$c_2 = \frac{1}{2}, \qquad c_3 = -\frac{1}{6}, \qquad c_4 = 0$$

and so on. For $c_0 = 0$ and $c_1 = 1$ we obtain

$$c_2 = -\frac{1}{2}, \qquad c_3 = \frac{1}{6}, \qquad c_4 = -\frac{1}{24}$$

and so on. Thus, two solutions are

$$y_1 = 1 + \frac{1}{2}x^2 - \frac{1}{6}x^3 + \cdots \qquad \text{and} \qquad y_2 = x - \frac{1}{2}x^2 + \frac{1}{6}x^3 - \frac{1}{24}x^4 + \cdots .$$

35. The singular points of $(\cos x)y'' + y' + 5y = 0$ are odd integer multiples of $\pi/2$. The distance from 0 to either $\pm\pi/2$ is $\pi/2$. The singular point closest to 1 is $\pi/2$. The distance from 1 to the closest singular point is then $\pi/2 - 1$.

36. Substituting $y = \sum_{n=0}^{\infty} c_n x^n$ into the first differential equation leads to

$$y'' - xy = \underbrace{\sum_{n=2}^{\infty} n(n-1)c_n x^{n-2}}_{k=n-2} - \underbrace{\sum_{n=0}^{\infty} c_n x^{n+1}}_{k=n+1} = \sum_{k=0}^{\infty}(k+2)(k+1)c_{k+2}x^k - \sum_{k=1}^{\infty} c_{k-1}x^k$$

$$= 2c_2 + \sum_{k=1}^{\infty}[(k+2)(k+1)c_{k+2} - c_{k-1}]x^k = 1.$$

Thus

$$2c_2 = 1$$

$$(k+2)(k+1)c_{k+2} - c_{k-1} = 0$$

and

$$c_2 = \frac{1}{2}$$

$$c_{k+2} = \frac{c_{k-1}}{(k+2)(k+1)}, \qquad k = 1, 2, 3, \ldots .$$

Let c_0 and c_1 be arbitrary and iterate to find

$$c_2 = \frac{1}{2}$$

$$c_3 = \frac{1}{6}c_0$$

$$c_4 = \frac{1}{12}c_1$$

$$c_5 = \frac{1}{20}c_2 = \frac{1}{40}$$

and so on. The solution is

$$y = c_0 + c_1 x + \frac{1}{2}x^2 + \frac{1}{6}c_0 x^3 + \frac{1}{12}c_1 x^4 + \frac{1}{40}c_5 + \cdots$$

$$= c_0\left(1 + \frac{1}{6}x^3 + \cdots\right) + c_1\left(x + \frac{1}{12}x^4 + \cdots\right) + \frac{1}{2}x^2 + \frac{1}{40}x^5 + \cdots .$$

Substituting $y = \sum_{n=0}^{\infty} c_n x^n$ into the second differential equation leads to

$$y'' - 4xy' - 4y = \underbrace{\sum_{n=2}^{\infty} n(n-1)c_n x^{n-2}}_{k=n-2} - \underbrace{\sum_{n=1}^{\infty} 4nc_n x^n}_{k=n} - \underbrace{\sum_{n=0}^{\infty} 4c_n x^n}_{k=n}$$

$$= \sum_{k=0}^{\infty} (k+2)(k+1)c_{k+2}x^k - \sum_{k=1}^{\infty} 4kc_k x^k - \sum_{k=0}^{\infty} 4c_k x^k$$

$$= 2c_2 - 4c_0 + \sum_{k=1}^{\infty} [(k+2)(k+1)c_{k+2} - 4(k+1)c_k]x^k$$

$$= e^x = 1 + \sum_{k=1}^{\infty} \frac{1}{k!}x^k.$$

Thus

$$2c_2 - 4c_0 = 1$$

$$(k+2)(k+1)c_{k+2} - 4(k+1)c_k = \frac{1}{k!}$$

and

$$c_2 = \frac{1}{2} + 2c_0$$

$$c_{k+2} = \frac{1}{(k+2)!} + \frac{4}{k+2}c_k, \qquad k = 1, 2, 3, \ldots .$$

Let c_0 and c_1 be arbitrary and iterate to find

$$c_2 = \frac{1}{2} + 2c_0$$

$$c_3 = \frac{1}{3!} + \frac{4}{3}c_1 = \frac{1}{3!} + \frac{4}{3}c_1$$

$$c_4 = \frac{1}{4!} + \frac{4}{4}c_2 = \frac{1}{4!} + \frac{1}{2} + 2c_0 = \frac{13}{4!} + 2c_0$$

$$c_5 = \frac{1}{5!} + \frac{4}{5}c_3 = \frac{1}{5!} + \frac{4}{5\cdot3!} + \frac{16}{15}c_1 = \frac{17}{5!} + \frac{16}{15}c_1$$

$$c_6 = \frac{1}{6!} + \frac{4}{6}c_4 = \frac{1}{6!} + \frac{4\cdot13}{6\cdot4!} + \frac{8}{6}c_0 = \frac{261}{6!} + \frac{4}{3}c_0$$

$$c_7 = \frac{1}{7!} + \frac{4}{7}c_5 = \frac{1}{7!} + \frac{4\cdot17}{7\cdot5!} + \frac{64}{105}c_1 = \frac{409}{7!} + \frac{64}{105}c_1$$

and so on. The solution is

$$y = c_0 + c_1 x + \left(\frac{1}{2} + 2c_0\right)x^2 + \left(\frac{1}{3!} + \frac{4}{3}c_1\right)x^3 + \left(\frac{13}{4!} + 2c_0\right)x^4 + \left(\frac{17}{5!} + \frac{16}{15}c_1\right)x^5$$

$$+ \left(\frac{261}{6!} + \frac{4}{3}c_0\right)x^6 + \left(\frac{409}{7!} + \frac{64}{105}c_1\right)x^7 + \cdots$$

$$= c_0\left[1 + 2x^2 + 2x^4 + \frac{4}{3}x^6 + \cdots\right] + c_1\left[x + \frac{4}{3}x^3 + \frac{16}{15}x^5 + \frac{64}{105}x^7 + \cdots\right]$$

$$+ \frac{1}{2}x^2 + \frac{1}{3!}x^3 + \frac{13}{4!}x^4 + \frac{17}{5!}x^5 + \frac{261}{6!}x^6 + \frac{409}{7!}x^7 + \cdots.$$

37. We identify $P(x) = 0$ and $Q(x) = \sin x/x$. The Taylor series representation for $\sin x/x$ is $1 - x^2/3! + x^4/5! - \cdots$, for $|x| < \infty$. Thus, $Q(x)$ is analytic at $x = 0$ and $x = 0$ is an ordinary point of the differential equation.

38. If $x > 0$ and $y > 0$, then $y'' = -xy < 0$ and the graph of a solution curve is concave down. Thus, whatever portion of a solution curve lies in the first quadrant is concave down. When $x > 0$ and $y < 0$, $y'' = -xy > 0$, so whatever portion of a solution curve lies in the fourth quadrant is concave up.

39. (a) Substituting $y = \sum_{n=0}^{\infty} c_n x^n$ into the differential equation we have

$$y'' + xy' + y = \underbrace{\sum_{n=2}^{\infty} n(n-1)c_n x^{n-2}}_{k=n-2} + \underbrace{\sum_{n=1}^{\infty} nc_n x^n}_{k=n} + \underbrace{\sum_{n=0}^{\infty} c_n x^n}_{k=n}$$

$$= \sum_{k=0}^{\infty} (k+2)(k+1)c_{k+2} x^k + \sum_{k=1}^{\infty} kc_k x^k + \sum_{k=0}^{\infty} c_k x^k$$

$$= (2c_2 + c_0) + \sum_{k=1}^{\infty} [(k+2)(k+1)c_{k+2} + (k+1)c_k]x^k = 0.$$

Thus

$$2c_2 + c_0 = 0$$

$$(k+2)(k+1)c_{k+2} + (k+1)c_k = 0$$

and

$$c_2 = -\frac{1}{2}c_0$$

$$c_{k+2} = -\frac{1}{k+2}c_k, \quad k = 1, 2, 3, \ldots .$$

Choosing $c_0 = 1$ and $c_1 = 0$ we find

$$c_2 = -\frac{1}{2}$$

$$c_3 = c_5 = c_7 = \cdots = 0$$

$$c_4 = -\frac{1}{4}\left(-\frac{1}{2}\right) = \frac{1}{2^2 \cdot 2}$$

$$c_6 = -\frac{1}{6}\left(\frac{1}{2^2 \cdot 2}\right) = -\frac{1}{2^3 \cdot 3!}$$

and so on. For $c_0 = 0$ and $c_1 = 1$ we obtain

$$c_2 = c_4 = c_6 = \cdots = 0$$

$$c_3 = -\frac{1}{3} = -\frac{2}{3!}$$

$$c_5 = -\frac{1}{5}\left(-\frac{1}{3}\right) = \frac{1}{5 \cdot 3} = \frac{4 \cdot 2}{5!}$$

$$c_7 = -\frac{1}{7}\left(\frac{4 \cdot 2}{5!}\right) = -\frac{6 \cdot 4 \cdot 2}{7!}$$

and so on. Thus, two solutions are

$$y_1 = \sum_{k=0}^{\infty} \frac{(-1)^k}{2^k \cdot k!} x^{2k} \qquad \text{and} \qquad y_2 = \sum_{k=0}^{\infty} \frac{(-1)^k 2^k k!}{(2k+1)!} x^{2k+1}.$$

(b) For y_1, $S_3 = S_2$ and $S_5 = S_4$, so we plot S_2, S_4, S_6, S_8, and S_{10}.

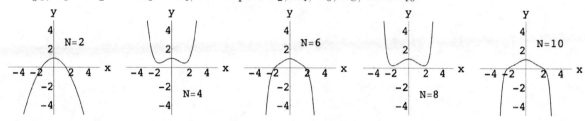

For y_2, $S_3 = S_4$ and $S_5 = S_6$, so we plot S_2, S_4, S_6, S_8, and S_{10}.

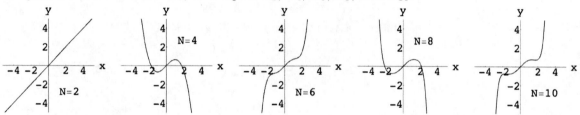

(c)

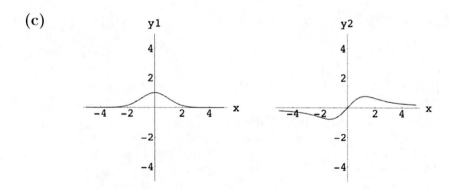

The graphs of y_1 and y_2 obtained from a numerical solver are shown. We see that the partial sum representations indicate the even and odd natures of the solution, but don't really give a very accurate representation of the true solution. Increasing N to about 20 gives a much more accurate representation on $[-4, 4]$.

(d) From $e^x = \sum_{k=0}^{\infty} x^k/k!$ we see that $e^{-x^2/2} = \sum_{k=0}^{\infty}(-x^2/2)^k/k! = \sum_{k=0}^{\infty}(-1)^k x^{2k}/2^k k!$. From (5) of Section 4.2 we have

$$y_2 = y_1 \int \frac{e^{-\int x\, dx}}{y_1^2}\, dx = e^{-x^2/2} \int \frac{e^{-x^2/2}}{(e^{-x^2/2})^2}\, dx = e^{-x^2/2} \int \frac{e^{-x^2/2}}{e^{-x^2}}\, dx = e^{-x^2/2} \int e^{x^2/2} dx$$

$$= \sum_{k=0}^{\infty} \frac{(-1)^k}{2^k k!} x^{2k} \int \sum_{k=0}^{\infty} \frac{1}{2^k k!} x^{2k}\, dx = \left(\sum_{k=0}^{\infty} \frac{(-1)^k}{2^k k!} x^{2k} \right) \left(\sum_{k=0}^{\infty} \int \frac{1}{2^k k!} x^{2k}\, dx \right)$$

$$= \left(\sum_{k=0}^{\infty} \frac{(-1)^k}{2^k k!} x^{2k} \right) \left(\sum_{k=0}^{\infty} \frac{1}{(2k+1)2^k k!} x^{2k+1} \right)$$

$$= \left(1 - \frac{1}{2}x^2 + \frac{1}{2^2 \cdot 2}x^4 - \frac{1}{2^3 \cdot 3!}x^6 + \cdots \right)\left(x + \frac{1}{3 \cdot 2}x^3 + \frac{1}{5 \cdot 2^2 \cdot 2}x^5 + \frac{1}{7 \cdot 2^3 \cdot 3!}x^7 + \cdots \right)$$

$$= x - \frac{2}{3!}x^3 + \frac{4 \cdot 2}{5!}x^5 - \frac{6 \cdot 4 \cdot 2}{7!}x^7 + \cdots = \sum_{k=0}^{\infty} \frac{(-1)^k 2^k k!}{(2k+1)!} x^{2k+1}.$$

40. (a) We have

$$y'' + (\cos x)y = 2c_2 + 6c_3 x + 12c_4 x^2 + 20c_5 x^3 + 30c_6 x^4 + 42c_7 x^5 + \cdots$$

$$+ \left(1 - \frac{x^2}{2!} + \frac{x^4}{4!} - \frac{x^6}{6!} + \cdots \right)(c_0 + c_1 x + c_2 x^2 + c_3 x^3 + c_4 x^4 + c_5 x^5 + \cdots)$$

$$= (2c_2 + c_0) + (6c_3 + c_1)x + \left(12c_4 + c_2 - \frac{1}{2}c_0 \right)x^2 + \left(20c_5 + c_3 - \frac{1}{2}c_1 \right)x^3$$

$$+ \left(30c_6 + c_4 + \frac{1}{24}c_0 - \frac{1}{2}c_2 \right)x^4 + \left(42c_7 + c_5 + \frac{1}{24}c_1 - \frac{1}{2}c_3 \right)x^5 + \cdots.$$

Then

$$30c_6 + c_4 + \frac{1}{24}c_0 - \frac{1}{2}c_2 = 0 \quad \text{and} \quad 42c_7 + c_5 + \frac{1}{24}c_1 - \frac{1}{2}c_3 = 0,$$

which gives $c_6 = -c_0/80$ and $c_7 = -19c_1/5040$. Thus

$$y_1(x) = 1 - \frac{1}{2}x^2 + \frac{1}{12}x^4 - \frac{1}{80}x^6 + \cdots$$

and

$$y_2(x) = x - \frac{1}{6}x^3 + \frac{1}{30}x^5 - \frac{19}{5040}x^7 + \cdots.$$

(b) From part (a) the general solution of the differential equation is $y = c_1 y_1 + c_2 y_2$. Then $y(0) = c_1 + c_2 \cdot 0 = c_1$ and $y'(0) = c_1 \cdot 0 + c_2 = c_2$, so the solution of the initial-value problem is

$$y = y_1 + y_2 = 1 + x - \frac{1}{2}x^2 - \frac{1}{6}x^3 + \frac{1}{12}x^4 + \frac{1}{30}x^5 - \frac{1}{80}x^6 - \frac{19}{5040}x^7 + \cdots.$$

(c)

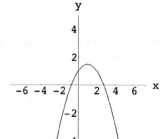
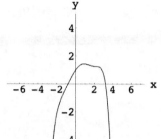
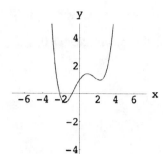

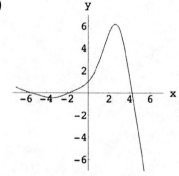
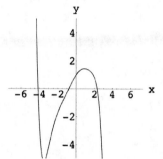

(d)

Exercises 6.2

Solutions About Singular Points

1. Irregular singular point: $x = 0$

2. Regular singular points: $x = 0, -3$

3. Irregular singular point: $x = 3$; regular singular point: $x = -3$

4. Irregular singular point: $x = 1$; regular singular point: $x = 0$

5. Regular singular points: $x = 0, \pm 2i$

6. Irregular singular point: $x = 5$; regular singular point: $x = 0$

Exercises 6.2 Solutions About Singular Points

7. Regular singular points: $x = -3, 2$

8. Regular singular points: $x = 0, \pm i$

9. Irregular singular point: $x = 0$; regular singular points: $x = 2, \pm 5$

10. Irregular singular point: $x = -1$; regular singular points: $x = 0, 3$

11. Writing the differential equation in the form

$$y'' + \frac{5}{x-1} y' + \frac{x}{x+1} y = 0$$

we see that $x_0 = 1$ and $x_0 = -1$ are regular singular points. For $x_0 = 1$ the differential equation can be put in the form

$$(x-1)^2 y'' + 5(x-1) y' + \frac{x(x-1)^2}{x+1} y = 0.$$

In this case $p(x) = 5$ and $q(x) = x(x-1)^2/(x+1)$. For $x_0 = -1$ the differential equation can be put in the form

$$(x+1)^2 y'' + 5(x+1) \frac{x+1}{x-1} y' + x(x+1) y = 0.$$

In this case $p(x) = 5(x+1)/(x-1)$ and $q(x) = x(x+1)$.

12. Writing the differential equation in the form

$$y'' + \frac{x+3}{x} y' + 7xy = 0$$

we see that $x_0 = 0$ is a regular singular point. Multiplying by x^2, the differential equation can be put in the form

$$x^2 y'' + x(x+3) y' + 7x^3 y = 0.$$

We identify $p(x) = x + 3$ and $q(x) = 7x^3$.

13. We identify $P(x) = 5/3x + 1$ and $Q(x) = -1/3x^2$, so that $p(x) = xP(x) = \frac{5}{3} + x$ and $q(x) = x^2 Q(x) = -\frac{1}{3}$. Then $a_0 = \frac{5}{3}$, $b_0 = -\frac{1}{3}$, and the indicial equation is

$$r(r-1) + \frac{5}{3} r - \frac{1}{3} = r^2 + \frac{2}{3} r - \frac{1}{3} = \frac{1}{3}(3r^2 + 2r - 1) = \frac{1}{3}(3r - 1)(r + 1) = 0.$$

The indicial roots are $\frac{1}{3}$ and -1. Since these do not differ by an integer we expect to find two series solutions using the method of Frobenius.

14. We identify $P(x) = 1/x$ and $Q(x) = 10/x$, so that $p(x) = xP(x) = 1$ and $q(x) = x^2 Q(x) = 10x$. Then $a_0 = 1$, $b_0 = 0$, and the indicial equation is

$$r(r-1) + r = r^2 = 0.$$

The indicial roots are 0 and 0. Since these are equal, we expect the method of Frobenius to yield a single series solution.

15. Substituting $y = \sum_{n=0}^{\infty} c_n x^{n+r}$ into the differential equation and collecting terms, we obtain

$$2xy'' - y' + 2y = \left(2r^2 - 3r\right) c_0 x^{r-1} + \sum_{k=1}^{\infty} [2(k+r-1)(k+r)c_k - (k+r)c_k + 2c_{k-1}]x^{k+r-1} = 0,$$

which implies

$$2r^2 - 3r = r(2r - 3) = 0$$

and

$$(k+r)(2k+2r-3)c_k + 2c_{k-1} = 0.$$

The indicial roots are $r = 0$ and $r = 3/2$. For $r = 0$ the recurrence relation is

$$c_k = -\frac{2c_{k-1}}{k(2k-3)}, \quad k = 1, 2, 3, \ldots,$$

and

$$c_1 = 2c_0, \qquad c_2 = -2c_0, \qquad c_3 = \frac{4}{9}c_0,$$

and so on. For $r = 3/2$ the recurrence relation is

$$c_k = -\frac{2c_{k-1}}{(2k+3)k}, \quad k = 1, 2, 3, \ldots,$$

and

$$c_1 = -\frac{2}{5}c_0, \qquad c_2 = \frac{2}{35}c_0, \qquad c_3 = -\frac{4}{945}c_0,$$

and so on. The general solution on $(0, \infty)$ is

$$y = C_1 \left(1 + 2x - 2x^2 + \frac{4}{9}x^3 + \cdots\right) + C_2 x^{3/2} \left(1 - \frac{2}{5}x + \frac{2}{35}x^2 - \frac{4}{945}x^3 + \cdots\right).$$

16. Substituting $y = \sum_{n=0}^{\infty} c_n x^{n+r}$ into the differential equation and collecting terms, we obtain

$$2xy'' + 5y' + xy = \left(2r^2 + 3r\right) c_0 x^{r-1} + \left(2r^2 + 7r + 5\right) c_1 x^r$$

$$+ \sum_{k=2}^{\infty} [2(k+r)(k+r-1)c_k + 5(k+r)c_k + c_{k-2}]x^{k+r-1}$$

$$= 0,$$

which implies

$$2r^2 + 3r = r(2r + 3) = 0,$$

$$\left(2r^2 + 7r + 5\right) c_1 = 0,$$

and

$$(k+r)(2k+2r+3)c_k + c_{k-2} = 0.$$

The indicial roots are $r = -3/2$ and $r = 0$, so $c_1 = 0$. For $r = -3/2$ the recurrence relation is

$$c_k = -\frac{c_{k-2}}{(2k-3)k}, \quad k = 2, 3, 4, \ldots,$$

and

$$c_2 = -\frac{1}{2}c_0, \qquad c_3 = 0, \qquad c_4 = \frac{1}{40}c_0,$$

and so on. For $r = 0$ the recurrence relation is

$$c_k = -\frac{c_{k-2}}{k(2k+3)}, \quad k = 2, 3, 4, \ldots,$$

and

$$c_2 = -\frac{1}{14}c_0, \qquad c_3 = 0, \qquad c_4 = \frac{1}{616}c_0,$$

and so on. The general solution on $(0, \infty)$ is

$$y = C_1 x^{-3/2} \left(1 - \frac{1}{2}x^2 + \frac{1}{40}x^4 + \cdots \right) + C_2 \left(1 - \frac{1}{14}x^2 + \frac{1}{616}x^4 + \cdots \right).$$

17. Substituting $y = \sum_{n=0}^{\infty} c_n x^{n+r}$ into the differential equation and collecting terms, we obtain

$$4xy'' + \frac{1}{2}y' + y = \left(4r^2 - \frac{7}{2}r \right) c_0 x^{r-1} + \sum_{k=1}^{\infty} \left[4(k+r)(k+r-1)c_k + \frac{1}{2}(k+r)c_k + c_{k-1} \right] x^{k+r-1}$$

$$= 0,$$

which implies

$$4r^2 - \frac{7}{2}r = r\left(4r - \frac{7}{2} \right) = 0$$

and

$$\frac{1}{2}(k+r)(8k+8r-7)c_k + c_{k-1} = 0.$$

The indicial roots are $r = 0$ and $r = 7/8$. For $r = 0$ the recurrence relation is

$$c_k = -\frac{2c_{k-1}}{k(8k-7)}, \quad k = 1, 2, 3, \ldots,$$

and

$$c_1 = -2c_0, \qquad c_2 = \frac{2}{9}c_0, \qquad c_3 = -\frac{4}{459}c_0,$$

and so on. For $r = 7/8$ the recurrence relation is

$$c_k = -\frac{2c_{k-1}}{(8k+7)k}, \quad k = 1, 2, 3, \ldots,$$

and

$$c_1 = -\frac{2}{15}c_0, \qquad c_2 = \frac{2}{345}c_0, \qquad c_3 = -\frac{4}{32,085}c_0,$$

302

and so on. The general solution on $(0, \infty)$ is

$$y = C_1 \left(1 - 2x + \frac{2}{9}x^2 - \frac{4}{459}x^3 + \cdots \right) + C_2 x^{7/8} \left(1 - \frac{2}{15}x + \frac{2}{345}x^2 - \frac{4}{32{,}085}x^3 + \cdots \right).$$

18. Substituting $y = \sum_{n=0}^{\infty} c_n x^{n+r}$ into the differential equation and collecting terms, we obtain

$$2x^2 y'' - xy' + \left(x^2 + 1 \right) y = \left(2r^2 - 3r + 1 \right) c_0 x^r + \left(2r^2 + r \right) c_1 x^{r+1}$$

$$+ \sum_{k=2}^{\infty} [2(k+r)(k+r-1)c_k - (k+r)c_k + c_k + c_{k-2}] x^{k+r}$$

$$= 0,$$

which implies

$$2r^2 - 3r + 1 = (2r - 1)(r - 1) = 0,$$

$$\left(2r^2 + r \right) c_1 = 0,$$

and

$$[(k+r)(2k+2r-3) + 1]c_k + c_{k-2} = 0.$$

The indicial roots are $r = 1/2$ and $r = 1$, so $c_1 = 0$. For $r = 1/2$ the recurrence relation is

$$c_k = -\frac{c_{k-2}}{k(2k-1)}, \quad k = 2, 3, 4, \ldots,$$

and

$$c_2 = -\frac{1}{6}c_0, \qquad c_3 = 0, \qquad c_4 = \frac{1}{168}c_0,$$

and so on. For $r = 1$ the recurrence relation is

$$c_k = -\frac{c_{k-2}}{k(2k+1)}, \quad k = 2, 3, 4, \ldots,$$

and

$$c_2 = -\frac{1}{10}c_0, \qquad c_3 = 0, \qquad c_4 = \frac{1}{360}c_0,$$

and so on. The general solution on $(0, \infty)$ is

$$y = C_1 x^{1/2} \left(1 - \frac{1}{6}x^2 + \frac{1}{168}x^4 + \cdots \right) + C_2 x \left(1 - \frac{1}{10}x^2 + \frac{1}{360}x^4 + \cdots \right).$$

19. Substituting $y = \sum_{n=0}^{\infty} c_n x^{n+r}$ into the differential equation and collecting terms, we obtain

$$3xy'' + (2 - x)y' - y = \left(3r^2 - r \right) c_0 x^{r-1}$$

$$+ \sum_{k=1}^{\infty} [3(k+r-1)(k+r)c_k + 2(k+r)c_k - (k+r)c_{k-1}] x^{k+r-1}$$

$$= 0,$$

which implies

$$3r^2 - r = r(3r - 1) = 0$$

and

$$(k + r)(3k + 3r - 1)c_k - (k + r)c_{k-1} = 0.$$

The indicial roots are $r = 0$ and $r = 1/3$. For $r = 0$ the recurrence relation is

$$c_k = \frac{c_{k-1}}{3k - 1}, \quad k = 1, 2, 3, \ldots,$$

and

$$c_1 = \frac{1}{2}c_0, \qquad c_2 = \frac{1}{10}c_0, \qquad c_3 = \frac{1}{80}c_0,$$

and so on. For $r = 1/3$ the recurrence relation is

$$c_k = \frac{c_{k-1}}{3k}, \quad k = 1, 2, 3, \ldots,$$

and

$$c_1 = \frac{1}{3}c_0, \qquad c_2 = \frac{1}{18}c_0, \qquad c_3 = \frac{1}{162}c_0,$$

and so on. The general solution on $(0, \infty)$ is

$$y = C_1 \left(1 + \frac{1}{2}x + \frac{1}{10}x^2 + \frac{1}{80}x^3 + \cdots \right) + C_2 x^{1/3} \left(1 + \frac{1}{3}x + \frac{1}{18}x^2 + \frac{1}{162}x^3 + \cdots \right).$$

20. Substituting $y = \sum_{n=0}^{\infty} c_n x^{n+r}$ into the differential equation and collecting terms, we obtain

$$x^2 y'' - \left(x - \frac{2}{9} \right) y = \left(r^2 - r + \frac{2}{9} \right) c_0 x^r + \sum_{k=1}^{\infty} \left[(k + r)(k + r - 1)c_k + \frac{2}{9}c_k - c_{k-1} \right] x^{k+r}$$

$$= 0,$$

which implies

$$r^2 - r + \frac{2}{9} = \left(r - \frac{2}{3} \right) \left(r - \frac{1}{3} \right) = 0$$

and

$$\left[(k + r)(k + r - 1) + \frac{2}{9} \right] c_k - c_{k-1} = 0.$$

The indicial roots are $r = 2/3$ and $r = 1/3$. For $r = 2/3$ the recurrence relation is

$$c_k = \frac{3c_{k-1}}{3k^2 + k}, \quad k = 1, 2, 3, \ldots,$$

and

$$c_1 = \frac{3}{4}c_0, \qquad c_2 = \frac{9}{56}c_0, \qquad c_3 = \frac{9}{560}c_0,$$

and so on. For $r = 1/3$ the recurrence relation is

$$c_k = \frac{3c_{k-1}}{3k^2 - k}, \quad k = 1, 2, 3, \ldots,$$

and

$$c_1 = \frac{3}{2}c_0, \qquad c_2 = \frac{9}{20}c_0, \qquad c_3 = \frac{9}{160}c_0,$$

and so on. The general solution on $(0, \infty)$ is

$$y = C_1 x^{2/3}\left(1 + \frac{3}{4}x + \frac{9}{56}x^2 + \frac{9}{560}x^3 + \cdots\right) + C_2 x^{1/3}\left(1 + \frac{3}{2}x + \frac{9}{20}x^2 + \frac{9}{160}x^3 + \cdots\right).$$

21. Substituting $y = \sum_{n=0}^{\infty} c_n x^{n+r}$ into the differential equation and collecting terms, we obtain

$$2xy'' - (3 + 2x)y' + y = \left(2r^2 - 5r\right)c_0 x^{r-1} + \sum_{k=1}^{\infty}[2(k+r)(k+r-1)c_k$$

$$- 3(k+r)c_k - 2(k+r-1)c_{k-1} + c_{k-1}]x^{k+r-1}$$

$$= 0,$$

which implies

$$2r^2 - 5r = r(2r - 5) = 0$$

and

$$(k+r)(2k + 2r - 5)c_k - (2k + 2r - 3)c_{k-1} = 0.$$

The indicial roots are $r = 0$ and $r = 5/2$. For $r = 0$ the recurrence relation is

$$c_k = \frac{(2k-3)c_{k-1}}{k(2k-5)}, \qquad k = 1, 2, 3, \ldots,$$

and

$$c_1 = \frac{1}{3}c_0, \qquad c_2 = -\frac{1}{6}c_0, \qquad c_3 = -\frac{1}{6}c_0,$$

and so on. For $r = 5/2$ the recurrence relation is

$$c_k = \frac{2(k+1)c_{k-1}}{k(2k+5)}, \qquad k = 1, 2, 3, \ldots,$$

and

$$c_1 = \frac{4}{7}c_0, \qquad c_2 = \frac{4}{21}c_0, \qquad c_3 = \frac{32}{693}c_0,$$

and so on. The general solution on $(0, \infty)$ is

$$y = C_1\left(1 + \frac{1}{3}x - \frac{1}{6}x^2 - \frac{1}{6}x^3 + \cdots\right) + C_2 x^{5/2}\left(1 + \frac{4}{7}x + \frac{4}{21}x^2 + \frac{32}{693}x^3 + \cdots\right).$$

22. Substituting $y = \sum_{n=0}^{\infty} c_n x^{n+r}$ into the differential equation and collecting terms, we obtain

$$x^2 y'' + xy' + \left(x^2 - \frac{4}{9}\right)y = \left(r^2 - \frac{4}{9}\right)c_0 x^r + \left(r^2 + 2r + \frac{5}{9}\right)c_1 x^{r+1}$$

$$+ \sum_{k=2}^{\infty}\left[(k+r)(k+r-1)c_k + (k+r)c_k - \frac{4}{9}c_k + c_{k-2}\right]x^{k+r}$$

$$= 0,$$

which implies

$$r^2 - \frac{4}{9} = \left(r + \frac{2}{3}\right)\left(r - \frac{2}{3}\right) = 0,$$

$$\left(r^2 + 2r + \frac{5}{9}\right)c_1 = 0,$$

and

$$\left[(k+r)^2 - \frac{4}{9}\right]c_k + c_{k-2} = 0.$$

The indicial roots are $r = -2/3$ and $r = 2/3$, so $c_1 = 0$. For $r = -2/3$ the recurrence relation is

$$c_k = -\frac{9c_{k-2}}{3k(3k-4)}, \quad k = 2, 3, 4, \ldots,$$

and

$$c_2 = -\frac{3}{4}c_0, \qquad c_3 = 0, \qquad c_4 = \frac{9}{128}c_0,$$

and so on. For $r = 2/3$ the recurrence relation is

$$c_k = -\frac{9c_{k-2}}{3k(3k+4)}, \quad k = 2, 3, 4, \ldots,$$

and

$$c_2 = -\frac{3}{20}c_0, \qquad c_3 = 0, \qquad c_4 = \frac{9}{1,280}c_0,$$

and so on. The general solution on $(0, \infty)$ is

$$y = C_1 x^{-2/3}\left(1 - \frac{3}{4}x^2 + \frac{9}{128}x^4 + \cdots\right) + C_2 x^{2/3}\left(1 - \frac{3}{20}x^2 + \frac{9}{1,280}x^4 + \cdots\right).$$

23. Substituting $y = \sum_{n=0}^{\infty} c_n x^{n+r}$ into the differential equation and collecting terms, we obtain

$$9x^2 y'' + 9x^2 y' + 2y = \left(9r^2 - 9r + 2\right)c_0 x^r$$

$$+ \sum_{k=1}^{\infty}[9(k+r)(k+r-1)c_k + 2c_k + 9(k+r-1)c_{k-1}]x^{k+r}$$

$$= 0,$$

which implies

$$9r^2 - 9r + 2 = (3r-1)(3r-2) = 0$$

and

$$[9(k+r)(k+r-1) + 2]c_k + 9(k+r-1)c_{k-1} = 0.$$

The indicial roots are $r = 1/3$ and $r = 2/3$. For $r = 1/3$ the recurrence relation is

$$c_k = -\frac{(3k-2)c_{k-1}}{k(3k-1)}, \quad k = 1, 2, 3, \ldots,$$

and

$$c_1 = -\frac{1}{2}c_0, \qquad c_2 = \frac{1}{5}c_0, \qquad c_3 = -\frac{7}{120}c_0,$$

and so on. For $r = 2/3$ the recurrence relation is

$$c_k = -\frac{(3k-1)c_{k-1}}{k(3k+1)}, \qquad k = 1, 2, 3, \dots,$$

and

$$c_1 = -\frac{1}{2}c_0, \qquad c_2 = \frac{5}{28}c_0, \qquad c_3 = -\frac{1}{21}c_0,$$

and so on. The general solution on $(0, \infty)$ is

$$y = C_1 x^{1/3}\left(1 - \frac{1}{2}x + \frac{1}{5}x^2 - \frac{7}{120}x^3 + \cdots\right) + C_2 x^{2/3}\left(1 - \frac{1}{2}x + \frac{5}{28}x^2 - \frac{1}{21}x^3 + \cdots\right).$$

24. Substituting $y = \sum_{n=0}^{\infty} c_n x^{n+r}$ into the differential equation and collecting terms, we obtain

$$2x^2 y'' + 3xy' + (2x-1)y = \left(2r^2 + r - 1\right)c_0 x^r$$

$$+ \sum_{k=1}^{\infty}[2(k+r)(k+r-1)c_k + 3(k+r)c_k - c_k + 2c_{k-1}]x^{k+r}$$

$$= 0,$$

which implies

$$2r^2 + r - 1 = (2r-1)(r+1) = 0$$

and

$$[(k+r)(2k+2r+1) - 1]c_k + 2c_{k-1} = 0.$$

The indicial roots are $r = -1$ and $r = 1/2$. For $r = -1$ the recurrence relation is

$$c_k = -\frac{2c_{k-1}}{k(2k-3)}, \qquad k = 1, 2, 3, \dots,$$

and

$$c_1 = 2c_0, \qquad c_2 = -2c_0, \qquad c_3 = \frac{4}{9}c_0,$$

and so on. For $r = 1/2$ the recurrence relation is

$$c_k = -\frac{2c_{k-1}}{k(2k+3)}, \qquad k = 1, 2, 3, \dots,$$

and

$$c_1 = -\frac{2}{5}c_0, \qquad c_2 = \frac{2}{35}c_0, \qquad c_3 = -\frac{4}{945}c_0,$$

and so on. The general solution on $(0, \infty)$ is

$$y = C_1 x^{-1}\left(1 + 2x - 2x^2 + \frac{4}{9}x^3 + \cdots\right) + C_2 x^{1/2}\left(1 - \frac{2}{5}x + \frac{2}{35}x^2 - \frac{4}{945}x^3 + \cdots\right).$$

Exercises 6.2   Solutions About Singular Points

25. Substituting $y = \sum_{n=0}^{\infty} c_n x^{n+r}$ into the differential equation and collecting terms, we obtain

$$xy'' + 2y' - xy = \left(r^2 + r\right)c_0 x^{r-1} + \left(r^2 + 3r + 2\right)c_1 x^r$$

$$+ \sum_{k=2}^{\infty}[(k+r)(k+r-1)c_k + 2(k+r)c_k - c_{k-2}]x^{k+r-1}$$

$$= 0,$$

which implies

$$r^2 + r = r(r+1) = 0,$$
$$\left(r^2 + 3r + 2\right)c_1 = 0,$$

and

$$(k+r)(k+r+1)c_k - c_{k-2} = 0.$$

The indicial roots are $r_1 = 0$ and $r_2 = -1$, so $c_1 = 0$. For $r_1 = 0$ the recurrence relation is

$$c_k = \frac{c_{k-2}}{k(k+1)}, \quad k = 2, 3, 4, \ldots,$$

and

$$c_2 = \frac{1}{3!}c_0$$

$$c_3 = c_5 = c_7 = \cdots = 0$$

$$c_4 = \frac{1}{5!}c_0$$

$$c_{2n} = \frac{1}{(2n+1)!}c_0.$$

For $r_2 = -1$ the recurrence relation is

$$c_k = \frac{c_{k-2}}{k(k-1)}, \quad k = 2, 3, 4, \ldots,$$

and

$$c_2 = \frac{1}{2!}c_0$$

$$c_3 = c_5 = c_7 = \cdots = 0$$

$$c_4 = \frac{1}{4!}c_0$$

$$c_{2n} = \frac{1}{(2n)!}c_0.$$

The general solution on $(0, \infty)$ is

$$y = C_1 \sum_{n=0}^{\infty} \frac{1}{(2n+1)!} x^{2n} + C_2 x^{-1} \sum_{n=0}^{\infty} \frac{1}{(2n)!} x^{2n}$$

$$= \frac{1}{x} \left[C_1 \sum_{n=0}^{\infty} \frac{1}{(2n+1)!} x^{2n+1} + C_2 \sum_{n=0}^{\infty} \frac{1}{(2n)!} x^{2n} \right]$$

$$= \frac{1}{x} [C_1 \sinh x + C_2 \cosh x].$$

26. Substituting $y = \sum_{n=0}^{\infty} c_n x^{n+r}$ into the differential equation and collecting terms, we obtain

$$x^2 y'' + xy' + \left(x^2 - \frac{1}{4} \right) y = \left(r^2 - \frac{1}{4} \right) c_0 x^r + \left(r^2 + 2r + \frac{3}{4} \right) c_1 x^{r+1}$$

$$+ \sum_{k=2}^{\infty} \left[(k+r)(k+r-1)c_k + (k+r)c_k - \frac{1}{4} c_k + c_{k-2} \right] x^{k+r}$$

$$= 0,$$

which implies

$$r^2 - \frac{1}{4} = \left(r - \frac{1}{2} \right) \left(r + \frac{1}{2} \right) = 0,$$

$$\left(r^2 + 2r + \frac{3}{4} \right) c_1 = 0,$$

and

$$\left[(k+r)^2 - \frac{1}{4} \right] c_k + c_{k-2} = 0.$$

The indicial roots are $r_1 = 1/2$ and $r_2 = -1/2$, so $c_1 = 0$. For $r_1 = 1/2$ the recurrence relation is

$$c_k = -\frac{c_{k-2}}{k(k+1)}, \quad k = 2, 3, 4, \ldots,$$

and

$$c_2 = -\frac{1}{3!} c_0$$

$$c_3 = c_5 = c_7 = \cdots = 0$$

$$c_4 = \frac{1}{5!} c_0$$

$$c_{2n} = \frac{(-1)^n}{(2n+1)!} c_0.$$

For $r_2 = -1/2$ the recurrence relation is

$$c_k = -\frac{c_{k-2}}{k(k-1)}, \quad k = 2, 3, 4, \ldots,$$

and

$$c_2 = -\frac{1}{2!}c_0$$

$$c_3 = c_5 = c_7 = \cdots = 0$$

$$c_4 = \frac{1}{4!}c_0$$

$$c_{2n} = \frac{(-1)^n}{(2n)!}c_0.$$

The general solution on $(0, \infty)$ is

$$y = C_1 x^{1/2} \sum_{n=0}^{\infty} \frac{(-1)^n}{(2n+1)!} x^{2n} + C_2 x^{-1/2} \sum_{n=0}^{\infty} \frac{(-1)^n}{(2n)!} x^{2n}$$

$$= C_1 x^{-1/2} \sum_{n=0}^{\infty} \frac{(-1)^n}{(2n+1)!} x^{2n+1} + C_2 x^{-1/2} \sum_{n=0}^{\infty} \frac{(-1)^n}{(2n)!} x^{2n}$$

$$= x^{-1/2}[C_1 \sin x + C_2 \cos x].$$

27. Substituting $y = \sum_{n=0}^{\infty} c_n x^{n+r}$ into the differential equation and collecting terms, we obtain

$$xy'' - xy' + y = \left(r^2 - r\right) c_0 x^{r-1} + \sum_{k=0}^{\infty} [(k+r+1)(k+r)c_{k+1} - (k+r)c_k + c_k]x^{k+r} = 0$$

which implies

$$r^2 - r = r(r - 1) = 0$$

and

$$(k+r+1)(k+r)c_{k+1} - (k+r-1)c_k = 0.$$

The indicial roots are $r_1 = 1$ and $r_2 = 0$. For $r_1 = 1$ the recurrence relation is

$$c_{k+1} = \frac{kc_k}{(k+2)(k+1)}, \quad k = 0, 1, 2, \ldots,$$

and one solution is $y_1 = c_0 x$. A second solution is

$$y_2 = x \int \frac{e^{-\int -1\,dx}}{x^2}\,dx = x \int \frac{e^x}{x^2}\,dx = x \int \frac{1}{x^2}\left(1 + x + \frac{1}{2}x^2 + \frac{1}{3!}x^3 + \cdots\right)dx$$

$$= x \int \left(\frac{1}{x^2} + \frac{1}{x} + \frac{1}{2} + \frac{1}{3!}x + \frac{1}{4!}x^2 + \cdots\right)dx = x\left[-\frac{1}{x} + \ln x + \frac{1}{2}x + \frac{1}{12}x^2 + \frac{1}{72}x^3 + \cdots\right]$$

$$= x \ln x - 1 + \frac{1}{2}x^2 + \frac{1}{12}x^3 + \frac{1}{72}x^4 + \cdots.$$

The general solution on $(0, \infty)$ is

$$y = C_1 x + C_2 y_2(x).$$

28. Substituting $y = \sum_{n=0}^{\infty} c_n x^{n+r}$ into the differential equation and collecting terms, we obtain

$$y'' + \frac{3}{x}y' - 2y = \left(r^2 + 2r\right)c_0 x^{r-2} + \left(r^2 + 4r + 3\right)c_1 x^{r-1}$$

$$+ \sum_{k=2}^{\infty}[(k+r)(k+r-1)c_k + 3(k+r)c_k - 2c_{k-2}]x^{k+r-2}$$

$$= 0,$$

which implies

$$r^2 + 2r = r(r+2) = 0$$

$$\left(r^2 + 4r + 3\right)c_1 = 0$$

$$(k+r)(k+r+2)c_k - 2c_{k-2} = 0.$$

The indicial roots are $r_1 = 0$ and $r_2 = -2$, so $c_1 = 0$. For $r_1 = 0$ the recurrence relation is

$$c_k = \frac{2c_{k-2}}{k(k+2)}, \quad k = 2, 3, 4, \ldots,$$

and

$$c_2 = \frac{1}{4}c_0$$

$$c_3 = c_5 = c_7 = \cdots = 0$$

$$c_4 = \frac{1}{48}c_0$$

$$c_6 = \frac{1}{1,152}c_0.$$

The result is

$$y_1 = c_0\left(1 + \frac{1}{4}x^2 + \frac{1}{48}x^4 + \frac{1}{1,152}x^6 + \cdots\right).$$

A second solution is

$$y_2 = y_1 \int \frac{e^{-\int(3/x)dx}}{y_1^2}\, dx = y_1 \int \frac{dx}{x^3\left(1 + \frac{1}{4}x^2 + \frac{1}{48}x^4 + \cdots\right)^2}$$

$$= y_1 \int \frac{dx}{x^3\left(1 + \frac{1}{2}x^2 + \frac{5}{48}x^4 + \frac{7}{576}x^6 + \cdots\right)} = y_1 \int \frac{1}{x^3}\left(1 - \frac{1}{2}x^2 + \frac{7}{48}x^4 + \frac{19}{576}x^6 + \cdots\right)dx$$

$$= y_1 \int \left(\frac{1}{x^3} - \frac{1}{2x} + \frac{7}{48}x - \frac{19}{576}x^3 + \cdots\right)dx = y_1\left[-\frac{1}{2x^2} - \frac{1}{2}\ln x + \frac{7}{96}x^2 - \frac{19}{2,304}x^4 + \cdots\right]$$

$$= -\frac{1}{2}y_1 \ln x + y\left[-\frac{1}{2x^2} + \frac{7}{96}x^2 - \frac{19}{2,304}x^4 + \cdots\right].$$

Exercises 6.2 Solutions About Singular Points

The general solution on $(0, \infty)$ is

$$y = C_1 y_1(x) + C_2 y_2(x).$$

29. Substituting $y = \sum_{n=0}^{\infty} c_n x^{n+r}$ into the differential equation and collecting terms, we obtain

$$xy'' + (1-x)y' - y = r^2 c_0 x^{r-1} + \sum_{k=1}^{\infty} [(k+r)(k+r-1)c_k + (k+r)c_k - (k+r)c_{k-1}]x^{k+r-1} = 0,$$

which implies $r^2 = 0$ and

$$(k+r)^2 c_k - (k+r)c_{k-1} = 0.$$

The indicial roots are $r_1 = r_2 = 0$ and the recurrence relation is

$$c_k = \frac{c_{k-1}}{k}, \quad k = 1, 2, 3, \ldots.$$

One solution is

$$y_1 = c_0 \left(1 + x + \frac{1}{2}x^2 + \frac{1}{3!}x^3 + \cdots\right) = c_0 e^x.$$

A second solution is

$$y_2 = y_1 \int \frac{e^{-\int(1/x - 1)dx}}{e^{2x}}\,dx = e^x \int \frac{e^x/x}{e^{2x}}\,dx = e^x \int \frac{1}{x}e^{-x}dx$$

$$= e^x \int \frac{1}{x}\left(1 - x + \frac{1}{2}x^2 - \frac{1}{3!}x^3 + \cdots\right)dx = e^x \int \left(\frac{1}{x} - 1 + \frac{1}{2}x - \frac{1}{3!}x^2 + \cdots\right)dx$$

$$= e^x \left[\ln x - x + \frac{1}{2\cdot 2}x^2 - \frac{1}{3\cdot 3!}x^3 + \cdots\right] = e^x \ln x - e^x \sum_{n=1}^{\infty} \frac{(-1)^{n+1}}{n\cdot n!}x^n.$$

The general solution on $(0, \infty)$ is

$$y = C_1 e^x + C_2 e^x \left(\ln x - \sum_{n=1}^{\infty} \frac{(-1)^{n+1}}{n\cdot n!}x^n\right).$$

30. Substituting $y = \sum_{n=0}^{\infty} c_n x^{n+r}$ into the differential equation and collecting terms, we obtain

$$xy'' + y' + y = r^2 c_0 x^{r-1} + \sum_{k=1}^{\infty} [(k+r)(k+r-1)c_k + (k+r)c_k + c_{k-1}]x^{k+r-1} = 0$$

which implies $r^2 = 0$ and

$$(k+r)^2 c_k + c_{k-1} = 0.$$

The indicial roots are $r_1 = r_2 = 0$ and the recurrence relation is

$$c_k = -\frac{c_{k-1}}{k^2}, \quad k = 1, 2, 3, \ldots.$$

One solution is

$$y_1 = c_0 \left(1 - x + \frac{1}{2^2}x^2 - \frac{1}{(3!)^2}x^3 + \frac{1}{(4!)^2}x^4 - \cdots\right) = c_0 \sum_{n=0}^{\infty} \frac{(-1)^n}{(n!)^2}x^n.$$

A second solution is

$$y_2 = y_1 \int \frac{e^{-\int (1/x)dx}}{y_1^2}\, dx = y_1 \int \frac{dx}{x\left(1 - x + \frac{1}{4}x^2 - \frac{1}{36}x^3 + \cdots\right)^2}$$

$$= y_1 \int \frac{dx}{x\left(1 - 2x + \frac{3}{2}x^2 - \frac{5}{9}x^3 + \frac{35}{288}x^4 - \cdots\right)}$$

$$= y_1 \int \frac{1}{x}\left(1 + 2x + \frac{5}{2}x^2 + \frac{23}{9}x^3 + \frac{677}{288}x^4 + \cdots\right) dx$$

$$= y_1 \int \left(\frac{1}{x} + 2 + \frac{5}{2}x + \frac{23}{9}x^2 + \frac{677}{288}x^3 + \cdots\right) dx$$

$$= y_1 \left[\ln x + 2x + \frac{5}{4}x^2 + \frac{23}{27}x^3 + \frac{677}{1{,}152}x^4 + \cdots\right]$$

$$= y_1 \ln x + y_1 \left(2x + \frac{5}{4}x^2 + \frac{23}{27}x^3 + \frac{677}{1{,}152}x^4 + \cdots\right).$$

The general solution on $(0, \infty)$ is

$$y = C_1 y_1(x) + C_2 y_2(x).$$

31. Substituting $y = \sum_{n=0}^{\infty} c_n x^{n+r}$ into the differential equation and collecting terms, we obtain

$$xy'' + (x - 6)y' - 3y = (r^2 - 7r)c_0 x^{r-1} + \sum_{k=1}^{\infty}[(k+r)(k+r-1)c_k + (k+r-1)c_{k-1}$$

$$- 6(k+r)c_k - 3c_{k-1}]x^{k+r-1} = 0,$$

which implies

$$r^2 - 7r = r(r - 7) = 0$$

and

$$(k+r)(k+r-7)c_k + (k+r-4)c_{k-1} = 0.$$

The indicial roots are $r_1 = 7$ and $r_2 = 0$. For $r_1 = 7$ the recurrence relation is

$$(k+7)kc_k + (k+3)c_{k-1} = 0, \quad k = 1, 2, 3, \dots,$$

or

$$c_k = -\frac{k+3}{k(k+7)}c_{k-1}, \quad k = 1, 2, 3, \dots.$$

Taking $c_0 \neq 0$ we obtain

$$c_1 = -\frac{1}{2}c_0$$

$$c_2 = \frac{5}{18}c_0$$

$$c_3 = -\frac{1}{6}c_0,$$

and so on. Thus, the indicial root $r_1 = 7$ yields a single solution. Now, for $r_2 = 0$ the recurrence relation is

$$k(k-7)c_k + (k-4)c_{k-1} = 0, \quad k = 1, 2, 3, \ldots.$$

Then

$$-6c_1 - 3c_0 = 0$$

$$-10c_2 - 2c_1 = 0$$

$$-12c_3 - c_2 = 0$$

$$-12c_4 + 0c_3 = 0 \implies c_4 = 0$$

$$-10c_5 + c_4 = 0 \implies c_5 = 0$$

$$-6c_6 + 2c_5 = 0 \implies c_6 = 0$$

$$0c_7 + 3c_6 = 0 \implies c_7 \text{ is arbitrary}$$

and

$$c_k = -\frac{k-4}{k(k-7)}\,c_{k-1}, \quad k = 8, 9, 10, \ldots.$$

Taking $c_0 \neq 0$ and $c_7 = 0$ we obtain

$$c_1 = -\frac{1}{2}c_0$$

$$c_2 = \frac{1}{10}c_0$$

$$c_3 = -\frac{1}{120}c_0$$

$$c_4 = c_5 = c_6 = \cdots = 0.$$

Taking $c_0 = 0$ and $c_7 \neq 0$ we obtain

$$c_1 = c_2 = c_3 = c_4 = c_5 = c_6 = 0$$

$$c_8 = -\frac{1}{2}c_7$$

$$c_9 = \frac{5}{36}c_7$$

$$c_{10} = -\frac{1}{36}c_7,$$

and so on. In this case we obtain the two solutions

$$y_1 = 1 - \frac{1}{2}x + \frac{1}{10}x^2 - \frac{1}{120}x^3 \quad \text{and} \quad y_2 = x^7 - \frac{1}{2}x^8 + \frac{5}{36}x^9 - \frac{1}{36}x^{10} + \cdots .$$

32. Substituting $y = \sum_{n=0}^{\infty} c_n x^{n+r}$ into the differential equation and collecting terms, we obtain

$$x(x-1)y'' + 3y' - 2y$$

$$= \left(4r - r^2\right)c_0 x^{r-1} + \sum_{k=1}^{\infty}[(k+r-1)(k+r-12)c_{k-1} - (k+r)(k+r-1)c_k$$

$$+ 3(k+r)c_k - 2c_{k-1}]x^{k+r-1}$$

$$= 0,$$

which implies

$$4r - r^2 = r(4 - r) = 0$$

and

$$-(k+r)(k+r-4)c_k + [(k+r-1)(k+r-2) - 2]c_{k-1} = 0.$$

The indicial roots are $r_1 = 4$ and $r_2 = 0$. For $r_1 = 4$ the recurrence relation is

$$-(k+4)kc_k + [(k+3)(k+2) - 2]c_{k-1} = 0$$

or

$$c_k = \frac{k+1}{k}c_{k-1}, \quad k = 1, 2, 3, \dots .$$

Taking $c_0 \neq 0$ we obtain

$$c_1 = 2c_0$$

$$c_2 = 3c_0$$

$$c_3 = 4c_0,$$

315

and so on. Thus, the indicial root $r_1 = 4$ yields a single solution. For $r_2 = 0$ the recurrence relation is

$$-k(k-4)c_k + k(k-3)c_{k-1} = 0, \quad k = 1, 2, 3, \ldots,$$

or

$$-(k-4)c_k + (k-3)c_{k-1} = 0, \quad k = 1, 2, 3, \ldots.$$

Then

$$3c_1 - 2c_0 = 0$$

$$2c_2 - c_1 = 0$$

$$c_3 + 0c_2 = 0 \quad \Rightarrow \quad c_3 = 0$$

$$0c_4 + c_3 = 0 \quad \Rightarrow \quad c_4 \text{ is arbitrary}$$

and

$$c_k = \frac{(k-3)c_{k-1}}{k-4}, \quad k = 5, 6, 7, \ldots.$$

Taking $c_0 \neq 0$ and $c_4 = 0$ we obtain

$$c_1 = \frac{2}{3}c_0$$

$$c_2 = \frac{1}{3}c_0$$

$$c_3 = c_4 = c_5 = \cdots = 0.$$

Taking $c_0 = 0$ and $c_4 \neq 0$ we obtain

$$c_1 = c_2 = c_3 = 0$$

$$c_5 = 2c_4$$

$$c_6 = 3c_4$$

$$c_7 = 4c_4,$$

and so on. In this case we obtain the two solutions

$$y_1 = 1 + \frac{2}{3}x + \frac{1}{3}x^2 \quad \text{and} \quad y_2 = x^4 + 2x^5 + 3x^6 + 4x^7 + \cdots.$$

33. (a) From $t = 1/x$ we have $dt/dx = -1/x^2 = -t^2$. Then

$$\frac{dy}{dx} = \frac{dy}{dt}\frac{dt}{dx} = -t^2\frac{dy}{dt}$$

and

$$\frac{d^2y}{dx^2} = \frac{d}{dx}\left(\frac{dy}{dx}\right) = \frac{d}{dx}\left(-t^2\frac{dy}{dt}\right) = -t^2\frac{d^2y}{dt^2}\frac{dt}{dx} - \frac{dy}{dt}\left(2t\frac{dt}{dx}\right) = t^4\frac{d^2y}{dt^2} + 2t^3\frac{dy}{dt}.$$

Now

$$x^4 \frac{d^2y}{dx^2} + \lambda y = \frac{1}{t^4}\left(t^4\frac{d^2y}{dt^2} + 2t^3\frac{dy}{dt}\right) + \lambda y = \frac{d^2y}{dt^2} + \frac{2}{t}\frac{dy}{dt} + \lambda y = 0$$

becomes

$$t\frac{d^2y}{dt^2} + 2\frac{dy}{dt} + \lambda ty = 0.$$

(b) Substituting $y = \sum_{n=0}^{\infty} c_n t^{n+r}$ into the differential equation and collecting terms, we obtain

$$t\frac{d^2y}{dt^2} + 2\frac{dy}{dt} + \lambda ty = (r^2 + r)c_0 t^{r-1} + (r^2 + 3r + 2)c_1 t^r$$

$$+ \sum_{k=2}^{\infty}[(k+r)(k+r-1)c_k + 2(k+r)c_k + \lambda c_{k-2}]t^{k+r-1}$$

$$= 0,$$

which implies

$$r^2 + r = r(r+1) = 0,$$

$$\left(r^2 + 3r + 2\right)c_1 = 0,$$

and

$$(k+r)(k+r+1)c_k + \lambda c_{k-2} = 0.$$

The indicial roots are $r_1 = 0$ and $r_2 = -1$, so $c_1 = 0$. For $r_1 = 0$ the recurrence relation is

$$c_k = -\frac{\lambda c_{k-2}}{k(k+1)}, \quad k = 2, 3, 4, \ldots,$$

and

$$c_2 = -\frac{\lambda}{3!}c_0$$

$$c_3 = c_5 = c_7 = \cdots = 0$$

$$c_4 = \frac{\lambda^2}{5!}c_0$$

$$\vdots$$

$$c_{2n} = (-1)^n\frac{\lambda^n}{(2n+1)!}c_0.$$

For $r_2 = -1$ the recurrence relation is

$$c_k = -\frac{\lambda c_{k-2}}{k(k-1)}, \quad k = 2, 3, 4, \ldots,$$

and

$$c_2 = -\frac{\lambda}{2!}c_0$$

$$c_3 = c_5 = c_7 = \cdots = 0$$

$$c_4 = \frac{\lambda^2}{4!}c_0$$

$$\vdots$$

$$c_{2n} = (-1)^n \frac{\lambda^n}{(2n)!}c_0.$$

The general solution on $(0, \infty)$ is

$$y(t) = c_1 \sum_{n=0}^{\infty} \frac{(-1)^n}{(2n+1)!}(\sqrt{\lambda}\,t)^{2n} + c_2 t^{-1} \sum_{n=0}^{\infty} \frac{(-1)^n}{(2n)!}(\sqrt{\lambda}\,t)^{2n}$$

$$= \frac{1}{t}\left[C_1 \sum_{n=0}^{\infty} \frac{(-1)^n}{(2n+1)!}(\sqrt{\lambda}\,t)^{2n+1} + C_2 \sum_{n=0}^{\infty} \frac{(-1)^n}{(2n)!}(\sqrt{\lambda}\,t)^{2n} \right]$$

$$= \frac{1}{t}[C_1 \sin\sqrt{\lambda}\,t + C_2 \cos\sqrt{\lambda}\,t].$$

(c) Using $t = 1/x$, the solution of the original equation is

$$y(x) = C_1 x \sin\frac{\sqrt{\lambda}}{x} + C_2 x \cos\frac{\sqrt{\lambda}}{x}.$$

34. (a) From the boundary conditions $y(a) = 0$, $y(b) = 0$ we find

$$C_1 \sin\frac{\sqrt{\lambda}}{a} + C_2 \cos\frac{\sqrt{\lambda}}{a} = 0$$

$$C_1 \sin\frac{\sqrt{\lambda}}{b} + C_2 \cos\frac{\sqrt{\lambda}}{b} = 0.$$

Since this is a homogeneous system of linear equations, it will have nontrivial solutions for C_1 and C_2 if

$$\begin{vmatrix} \sin\dfrac{\sqrt{\lambda}}{a} & \cos\dfrac{\sqrt{\lambda}}{a} \\ \sin\dfrac{\sqrt{\lambda}}{b} & \cos\dfrac{\sqrt{\lambda}}{b} \end{vmatrix} = \sin\frac{\sqrt{\lambda}}{a}\cos\frac{\sqrt{\lambda}}{b} - \cos\frac{\sqrt{\lambda}}{a}\sin\frac{\sqrt{\lambda}}{b}$$

$$= \sin\left(\frac{\sqrt{\lambda}}{a} - \frac{\sqrt{\lambda}}{b}\right) = \sin\left(\sqrt{\lambda}\,\frac{b-a}{ab}\right) = 0.$$

318

This will be the case if

$$\sqrt{\lambda}\left(\frac{b-a}{ab}\right) = n\pi \qquad \text{or} \qquad \sqrt{\lambda} = \frac{n\pi ab}{b-a} = \frac{n\pi ab}{L}, \quad n = 1, 2, \ldots,$$

or, if

$$\lambda_n = \frac{n^2\pi^2 a^2 b^2}{L^2} = \frac{P_n b^4}{EI}.$$

The critical loads are then $P_n = n^2\pi^2(a/b)^2 EI_0/L^2$. Using $C_2 = -C_1\sin(\sqrt{\lambda}/a)/\cos(\sqrt{\lambda}/a)$ we have

$$y = C_1 x\left[\sin\frac{\sqrt{\lambda}}{x} - \frac{\sin(\sqrt{\lambda}/a)}{\cos(\sqrt{\lambda}/a)}\cos\frac{\sqrt{\lambda}}{x}\right]$$

$$= C_3 x\left[\sin\frac{\sqrt{\lambda}}{x}\cos\frac{\sqrt{\lambda}}{a} - \cos\frac{\sqrt{\lambda}}{x}\sin\frac{\sqrt{\lambda}}{a}\right]$$

$$= C_3 x \sin\sqrt{\lambda}\left(\frac{1}{x} - \frac{1}{a}\right),$$

and

$$y_n(x) = C_3 x\sin\frac{n\pi ab}{L}\left(\frac{1}{x} - \frac{1}{a}\right) = C_3 x\sin\frac{n\pi ab}{La}\left(\frac{a}{x} - 1\right) = C_4 x\sin\frac{n\pi ab}{L}\left(1 - \frac{a}{x}\right).$$

(b) When $n = 1$, $b = 11$, and $a = 1$, we have, for $C_4 = 1$,

$$y_1(x) = x\sin 1.1\pi\left(1 - \frac{1}{x}\right).$$

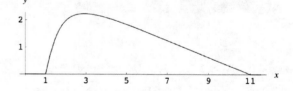

35. Express the differential equation in standard form:

$$y''' + P(x)y'' + Q(x)y' + R(x)y = 0.$$

Suppose x_0 is a singular point of the differential equation. Then we say that x_0 is a regular singular point if $(x - x_0)P(x)$, $(x - x_0)^2 Q(x)$, and $(x - x_0)^3 R(x)$ are analytic at $x = x_0$.

36. Substituting $y = \sum_{n=0}^{\infty} c_n x^{n+r}$ into the first differential equation and collecting terms, we obtain

$$x^3 y'' + y = c_0 x^r + \sum_{k=1}^{\infty}[c_k + (k+r-1)(k+r-2)c_{k-1}]x^{k+r} = 0.$$

It follows that $c_0 = 0$ and

$$c_k = -(k+r-1)(k+r-2)c_{k-1}.$$

The only solution we obtain is $y(x) = 0$.

Substituting $y = \sum_{n=0}^{\infty} c_n x^{n+r}$ into the second differential equation and collecting terms, we obtain

$$x^2 y'' + (3x-1)y' + y = -rc_0 + \sum_{k=0}^{\infty}[(k+r+1)^2 c_k - (k+r+1)c_{k+1}]x^{k+r} = 0,$$

which implies

$$-rc_0 = 0$$

$$(k + r + 1)^2 c_k - (k + r + 1)c_{k+1} = 0.$$

If $c_0 = 0$, then the solution of the differential equation is $y = 0$. Thus, we take $r = 0$, from which we obtain

$$c_{k+1} = (k + 1)c_k, \quad k = 0, 1, 2, \ldots.$$

Letting $c_0 = 1$ we get $c_1 = 2$, $c_2 = 3!$, $c_3 = 4!$, and so on. The solution of the differential equation is then $y = \sum_{n=0}^{\infty}(n + 1)!x^n$, which converges only at $x = 0$.

37. We write the differential equation in the form $x^2 y'' + (b/a)xy' + (c/a)y = 0$ and identify $a_0 = b/a$ and $b_0 = c/a$ as in (12) in the text. Then the indicial equation is

$$r(r - 1) + \frac{b}{a}r + \frac{c}{a} = 0 \quad \text{or} \quad ar^2 + (b - a)r + c = 0,$$

which is also the auxiliary equation of $ax^2 y'' + bxy' + cy = 0$.

Exercises 6.3   Special Functions

1. Since $\nu^2 = 1/9$ the general solution is $y = c_1 J_{1/3}(x) + c_2 J_{-1/3}(x)$.

2. Since $\nu^2 = 1$ the general solution is $y = c_1 J_1(x) + c_2 Y_1(x)$.

3. Since $\nu^2 = 25/4$ the general solution is $y = c_1 J_{5/2}(x) + c_2 J_{-5/2}(x)$.

4. Since $\nu^2 = 1/16$ the general solution is $y = c_1 J_{1/4}(x) + c_2 J_{-1/4}(x)$.

5. Since $\nu^2 = 0$ the general solution is $y = c_1 J_0(x) + c_2 Y_0(x)$.

6. Since $\nu^2 = 4$ the general solution is $y = c_1 J_2(x) + c_2 Y_2(x)$.

7. We identify $\alpha = 3$ and $\nu = 2$. Then the general solution is $y = c_1 J_2(3x) + c_2 Y_2(3x)$.

8. We identify $\alpha = 6$ and $\nu = \frac{1}{2}$. Then the general solution is $y = c_1 J_{1/2}(6x) + c_2 J_{-1/2}(6x)$.

9. We identify $\alpha = 5$ and $\nu = \frac{2}{3}$. Then the general solution is $y = c_1 J_{2/3}(5x) + c_2 J_{-2/3}(5x)$.

10. We identify $\alpha = \sqrt{2}$ and $\nu = 8$. Then the general solution is $y = c_1 J_8(\sqrt{2}x) + c_2 Y_8(\sqrt{2}x)$.

11. If $y = x^{-1/2}v(x)$ then

$$y' = x^{-1/2}v'(x) - \frac{1}{2}x^{-3/2}v(x),$$

$$y'' = x^{-1/2}v''(x) - x^{-3/2}v'(x) + \frac{3}{4}x^{-5/2}v(x),$$

and

$$x^2 y'' + 2xy' + \alpha^2 x^2 y = x^{3/2} v''(x) + x^{1/2} v'(x) + \left(\alpha^2 x^{3/2} - \frac{1}{4} x^{-1/2} \right) v(x) = 0.$$

Multiplying by $x^{1/2}$ we obtain

$$x^2 v''(x) + x v'(x) + \left(\alpha^2 x^2 - \frac{1}{4} \right) v(x) = 0,$$

whose solution is $v = c_1 J_{1/2}(\alpha x) + c_2 J_{-1/2}(\alpha x)$. Then $y = c_1 x^{-1/2} J_{1/2}(\alpha x) + c_2 x^{-1/2} J_{-1/2}(\alpha x)$.

12. If $y = \sqrt{x}\, v(x)$ then

$$y' = x^{1/2} v'(x) + \frac{1}{2} x^{-1/2} v(x)$$

$$y'' = x^{1/2} v''(x) + x^{-1/2} v'(x) - \frac{1}{4} x^{-3/2} v(x)$$

and

$$x^2 y'' + \left(\alpha^2 x^2 - \nu^2 + \frac{1}{4} \right) y = x^{5/2} v''(x) + x^{3/2} v'(x) - \frac{1}{4} x^{1/2} v(x) + \left(\alpha^2 x^2 - \nu^2 + \frac{1}{4} \right) x^{1/2} v(x)$$

$$= x^{5/2} v''(x) + x^{3/2} v'(x) + (\alpha^2 x^{5/2} - \nu^2 x^{1/2}) v(x) = 0.$$

Multiplying by $x^{-1/2}$ we obtain

$$x^2 v''(x) + x v'(x) + (\alpha^2 x^2 - \nu^2) v(x) = 0,$$

whose solution is $v(x) = c_1 J_\nu(\alpha x) + c_2 Y_\nu(\alpha x)$. Then $y = c_1 \sqrt{x}\, J_\nu(\alpha x) + c_2 \sqrt{x}\, Y_\nu(\alpha x)$.

13. Write the differential equation in the form $y'' + (2/x)y' + (4/x)y = 0$. This is the form of (18) in the text with $a = -\frac{1}{2}$, $c = \frac{1}{2}$, $b = 4$, and $p = 1$, so, by (19) in the text, the general solution is

$$y = x^{-1/2}[c_1 J_1(4x^{1/2}) + c_2 Y_1(4x^{1/2})].$$

14. Write the differential equation in the form $y'' + (3/x)y' + y = 0$. This is the form of (18) in the text with $a = -1$, $c = 1$, $b = 1$, and $p = 1$, so, by (19) in the text, the general solution is

$$y = x^{-1}[c_1 J_1(x) + c_2 Y_1(x)].$$

15. Write the differential equation in the form $y'' - (1/x)y' + y = 0$. This is the form of (18) in the text with $a = 1$, $c = 1$, $b = 1$, and $p = 1$, so, by (19) in the text, the general solution is

$$y = x[c_1 J_1(x) + c_2 Y_1(x)].$$

16. Write the differential equation in the form $y'' - (5/x)y' + y = 0$. This is the form of (18) in the text with $a = 3$, $c = 1$, $b = 1$, and $p = 2$, so, by (19) in the text, the general solution is

$$y = x^3[c_1 J_3(x) + c_2 Y_3(x)].$$

321

17. Write the differential equation in the form $y'' + (1 - 2/x^2)y = 0$. This is the form of (18) in the text with $a = \frac{1}{2}$, $c = 1$, $b = 1$, and $p = \frac{3}{2}$, so, by (19) in the text, the general solution is

$$y = x^{1/2}[c_1 J_{3/2}(x) + c_2 Y_{3/2}(x)] = x^{1/2}[C_1 J_{3/2}(x) + C_2 J_{-3/2}(x)].$$

18. Write the differential equation in the form $y'' + (4 + 1/4x^2)y = 0$. This is the form of (18) in the text with $a = \frac{1}{2}$, $c = 1$, $b = 2$, and $p = 0$, so, by (19) in the text, the general solution is

$$y = x^{1/2}[c_1 J_0(2x) + c_2 Y_0(2x)].$$

19. Write the differential equation in the form $y'' + (3/x)y' + x^2 y = 0$. This is the form of (18) in the text with $a = -1$, $c = 2$, $b = \frac{1}{2}$, and $p = \frac{1}{2}$, so, by (19) in the text, the general solution is

$$y = x^{-1}\left[c_1 J_{1/2}\left(\frac{1}{2}x^2\right) + c_2 Y_{1/2}\left(\frac{1}{2}x^2\right)\right]$$

or

$$y = x^{-1}\left[C_1 J_{1/2}\left(\frac{1}{2}x^2\right) + C_2 J_{-1/2}\left(\frac{1}{2}x^2\right)\right].$$

20. Write the differential equation in the form $y'' + (1/x)y' + (\frac{1}{9}x^4 - 4/x^2)y = 0$. This is the form of (18) in the text with $a = 0$, $c = 3$, $b = \frac{1}{9}$, and $p = \frac{2}{3}$, so, by (19) in the text, the general solution is

$$y = c_1 J_{2/3}\left(\frac{1}{9}x^3\right) + c_2 Y_{2/3}\left(\frac{1}{9}x^3\right)$$

or

$$y = C_1 J_{2/3}\left(\frac{1}{9}x^3\right) + C_2 J_{-2/3}\left(\frac{1}{9}x^3\right).$$

21. Using the fact that $i^2 = -1$, along with the definition of $J_\nu(x)$ in (7) in the text, we have

$$I_\nu(x) = i^{-\nu} J_\nu(ix) = i^{-\nu} \sum_{n=0}^{\infty} \frac{(-1)^n}{n!\Gamma(1+\nu+n)}\left(\frac{ix}{2}\right)^{2n+\nu}$$

$$= \sum_{n=0}^{\infty} \frac{(-1)^n}{n!\Gamma(1+\nu+n)} i^{2n+\nu-\nu}\left(\frac{x}{2}\right)^{2n+\nu}$$

$$= \sum_{n=0}^{\infty} \frac{(-1)^n}{n!\Gamma(1+\nu+n)}(i^2)^n\left(\frac{x}{2}\right)^{2n+\nu}$$

$$= \sum_{n=0}^{\infty} \frac{(-1)^{2n}}{n!\Gamma(1+\nu+n)}\left(\frac{x}{2}\right)^{2n+\nu}$$

$$= \sum_{n=0}^{\infty} \frac{1}{n!\Gamma(1+\nu+n)}\left(\frac{x}{2}\right)^{2n+\nu},$$

which is a real function.

22. (a) The differential equation has the form of (18) in the text with

$$1 - 2a = 0 \implies a = \frac{1}{2}$$

$$2c - 2 = 2 \implies c = 2$$

$$b^2 c^2 = -\beta^2 c^2 = -1 \implies \beta = \frac{1}{2} \quad \text{and} \quad b = \frac{1}{2}i$$

$$a^2 - p^2 c^2 = 0 \implies p = \frac{1}{4}.$$

Then, by (19) in the text,

$$y = x^{1/2} \left[c_1 J_{1/4} \left(\frac{1}{2} i x^2 \right) + c_2 J_{-1/4} \left(\frac{1}{2} i x^2 \right) \right].$$

In terms of real functions the general solution can be written

$$y = x^{1/2} \left[C_1 I_{1/4} \left(\frac{1}{2} x^2 \right) + C_2 K_{1/4} \left(\frac{1}{2} x^2 \right) \right].$$

(b) Write the differential equation in the form $y'' + (1/x)y' - 7x^2 y = 0$. This is the form of (18) in the text with

$$1 - 2a = 1 \implies a = 0$$

$$2c - 2 = 2 \implies c = 2$$

$$b^2 c^2 = -\beta^2 c^2 = -7 \implies \beta = \frac{1}{2}\sqrt{7} \quad \text{and} \quad b = \frac{1}{2}\sqrt{7}\, i$$

$$a^2 - p^2 c^2 = 0 \implies p = 0.$$

Then, by (19) in the text,

$$y = c_1 J_0 \left(\frac{1}{2}\sqrt{7}\, i x^2 \right) + c_2 Y_0 \left(\frac{1}{2}\sqrt{7}\, i x^2 \right).$$

In terms of real functions the general solution can be written

$$y = C_1 I_0 \left(\frac{1}{2}\sqrt{7} x^2 \right) + C_2 K_0 \left(\frac{1}{2}\sqrt{7} x^2 \right).$$

23. The differential equation has the form of (18) in the text with

$$1 - 2a = 0 \implies a = \frac{1}{2}$$

$$2c - 2 = 0 \implies c = 1$$

$$b^2 c^2 = 1 \implies b = 1$$

$$a^2 - p^2 c^2 = 0 \implies p = \frac{1}{2}.$$

Then, by (19) in the text,

$$y = x^{1/2}[c_1 J_{1/2}(x) + c_2 J_{-1/2}(x)] = x^{1/2}\left[c_1\sqrt{\frac{2}{\pi x}}\sin x + c_2\sqrt{\frac{2}{\pi x}}\cos x\right] = C_1\sin x + C_2\cos x.$$

24. Write the differential equation in the form $y'' + (4/x)y' + (1 + 2/x^2)y = 0$. This is the form of (18) in the text with

$$1 - 2a = 4 \implies a = -\frac{3}{2}$$

$$2c - 2 = 0 \implies c = 1$$

$$b^2 c^2 = 1 \implies b = 1$$

$$a^2 - p^2 c^2 = 2 \implies p = \frac{1}{2}.$$

Then, by (19), (23), and (24) in the text,

$$y = x^{-3/2}[c_1 J_{1/2}(x) + c_2 J_{-1/2}(x)] = x^{-3/2}\left[c_1\sqrt{\frac{2}{\pi x}}\sin x + c_2\sqrt{\frac{2}{\pi x}}\cos x\right]$$

$$= C_1\frac{1}{x^2}\sin x + C_2\frac{1}{x^2}\cos x.$$

25. Write the differential equation in the form $y'' + (2/x)y' + (\frac{1}{16}x^2 - 3/4x^2)y = 0$. This is the form of (18) in the text with

$$1 - 2a = 2 \implies a = -\frac{1}{2}$$

$$2c - 2 = 2 \implies c = 2$$

$$b^2 c^2 = \frac{1}{16} \implies b = \frac{1}{8}$$

$$a^2 - p^2 c^2 = -\frac{3}{4} \implies p = \frac{1}{2}.$$

Then, by (19) in the text,

$$y = x^{-1/2}\left[c_1 J_{1/2}\left(\frac{1}{8}x^2\right) + c_2 J_{-1/2}\left(\frac{1}{8}x^2\right)\right]$$

$$= x^{-1/2}\left[c_1\sqrt{\frac{16}{\pi x^2}}\sin\left(\frac{1}{8}x^2\right) + c_2\sqrt{\frac{16}{\pi x^2}}\cos\left(\frac{1}{8}x^2\right)\right]$$

$$= C_1 x^{-3/2}\sin\left(\frac{1}{8}x^2\right) + C_2 x^{-3/2}\cos\left(\frac{1}{8}x^2\right).$$

26. Write the differential equation in the form $y'' - (1/x)y' + (4 + 3/4x^2)y = 0$. This is the form of (18) in the text with

$$1 - 2a = -1 \implies a = 1$$

$$2c - 2 = 0 \implies c = 1$$

$$b^2 c^2 = 4 \implies b = 2$$

$$a^2 - p^2 c^2 = \frac{3}{4} \implies p = \frac{1}{2}.$$

Then, by (19) in the text,

$$y = x[c_1 J_{1/2}(2x) + c_2 J_{-1/2}(2x)] = x\left[c_1 \sqrt{\frac{2}{\pi 2x}} \sin 2x + c_2 \sqrt{\frac{2}{\pi 2x}} \cos 2x\right]$$

$$= C_1 x^{1/2} \sin 2x + C_2 x^{1/2} \cos 2x.$$

27. (a) The recurrence relation follows from

$$-\nu J_\nu(x) + x J_{\nu-1}(x) = -\sum_{n=0}^{\infty} \frac{(-1)^n \nu}{n! \Gamma(1+\nu+n)} \left(\frac{x}{2}\right)^{2n+\nu} + x \sum_{n=0}^{\infty} \frac{(-1)^n}{n! \Gamma(\nu+n)} \left(\frac{x}{2}\right)^{2n+\nu-1}$$

$$= -\sum_{n=0}^{\infty} \frac{(-1)^n \nu}{n! \Gamma(1+\nu+n)} \left(\frac{x}{2}\right)^{2n+\nu} + \sum_{n=0}^{\infty} \frac{(-1)^n (\nu+n)}{n! \Gamma(1+\nu+n)} \cdot 2 \left(\frac{x}{2}\right) \left(\frac{x}{2}\right)^{2n+\nu-1}$$

$$= \sum_{n=0}^{\infty} \frac{(-1)^n (2n+\nu)}{n! \Gamma(1+\nu+n)} \left(\frac{x}{2}\right)^{2n+\nu} = x J_\nu'(x).$$

(b) The formula in part (a) is a linear first-order differential equation in $J_\nu(x)$. An integrating factor for this equation is x^ν, so

$$\frac{d}{dx}[x^\nu J_\nu(x)] = x^\nu J_{\nu-1}(x).$$

28. Subtracting the formula in part (a) of Problem 27 from the formula in Example 5 we obtain

$$0 = 2\nu J_\nu(x) - x J_{\nu+1}(x) - x J_{\nu-1}(x) \quad \text{or} \quad 2\nu J_\nu(x) = x J_{\nu+1}(x) + x J_{\nu-1}(x).$$

29. Letting $\nu = 1$ in (21) in the text we have

$$x J_0(x) = \frac{d}{dx}[x J_1(x)] \quad \text{so} \quad \int_0^x r J_0(r)\, dr = r J_1(r) \Big|_{r=0}^{r=x} = x J_1(x).$$

30. From (20) we obtain $J_0'(x) = -J_1(x)$, and from (21) we obtain $J_0'(x) = J_{-1}(x)$. Thus $J_0'(x) = J_{-1}(x) = -J_1(x)$.

31. Since $\Gamma(\frac{1}{2}) = \sqrt{\pi}$ and

$$\Gamma\left(1 - \frac{1}{2} + n\right) = \frac{(2n-1)!}{(n-1)! 2^{2n-1}} \sqrt{\pi} \quad n = 1, 2, 3, \ldots,$$

we obtain

$$J_{-1/2}(x) = \sum_{n=0}^{\infty} \frac{(-1)^n}{n!\,\Gamma(1-\frac{1}{2}+n)} \left(\frac{x}{2}\right)^{2n-1/2} = \frac{1}{\Gamma(\frac{1}{2})}\left(\frac{x}{2}\right)^{-1/2} + \sum_{n=1}^{\infty} \frac{(-1)^n (n-1)!\,2^{2n-1} x^{2n-1/2}}{n!\,(2n-1)!\,2^{2n-1/2}\sqrt{\pi}}$$

$$= \frac{1}{\sqrt{\pi}}\sqrt{\frac{2}{x}} + \sum_{n=1}^{\infty} \frac{(-1)^n 2^{1/2} x^{-1/2}}{2n(2n-1)!\,\sqrt{\pi}}\,x^{2n} = \sqrt{\frac{2}{\pi x}} + \sqrt{\frac{2}{\pi x}}\sum_{n=1}^{\infty} \frac{(-1)^n}{(2n)!}\,x^{2n} = \sqrt{\frac{2}{\pi x}}\cos x.$$

32. (a) By Problem 28, with $\nu = 1/2$, we obtain $J_{1/2}(x) = x J_{3/2}(x) + x J_{-1/2}(x)$ so that

$$J_{3/2}(x) = \sqrt{\frac{2}{\pi x}}\left(\frac{\sin x}{x} - \cos x\right);$$

with $\nu = -1/2$ we obtain $-J_{-1/2}(x) = x J_{1/2}(x) + x J_{-3/2}(x)$ so that

$$J_{-3/2}(x) = -\sqrt{\frac{2}{\pi x}}\left(\frac{\cos x}{x} + \sin x\right);$$

and with $\nu = 3/2$ we obtain $3J_{3/2}(x) = x J_{5/2}(x) + x J_{1/2}(x)$ so that

$$J_{5/2}(x) = \sqrt{\frac{2}{\pi x}}\left(\frac{3\sin x}{x^2} - \frac{3\cos x}{x} - \sin x\right).$$

(b)

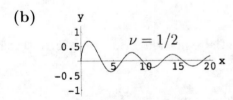
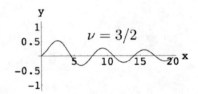
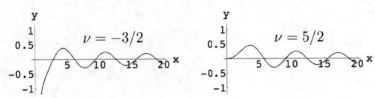
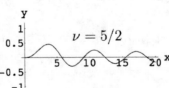

33. Letting

$$s = \frac{2}{\alpha}\sqrt{\frac{k}{m}}\,e^{-\alpha t/2},$$

we have

$$\frac{dx}{dt} = \frac{dx}{ds}\frac{ds}{dt} = \frac{dx}{dt}\left[\frac{2}{\alpha}\sqrt{\frac{k}{m}}\left(-\frac{\alpha}{2}\right)e^{-\alpha t/2}\right] = \frac{dx}{ds}\left(-\sqrt{\frac{k}{m}}\,e^{-\alpha t/2}\right)$$

and

$$\frac{d^2x}{dt^2} = \frac{d}{dt}\left(\frac{dx}{dt}\right) = \frac{dx}{ds}\left(\frac{\alpha}{2}\sqrt{\frac{k}{m}}\,e^{-\alpha t/2}\right) + \frac{d}{dt}\left(\frac{dx}{ds}\right)\left(-\sqrt{\frac{k}{m}}\,e^{-\alpha t/2}\right)$$

$$= \frac{dx}{ds}\left(\frac{\alpha}{2}\sqrt{\frac{k}{m}}\,e^{-\alpha t/2}\right) + \frac{d^2x}{ds^2}\frac{ds}{dt}\left(-\sqrt{\frac{k}{m}}\,e^{-\alpha t/2}\right)$$

$$= \frac{dx}{ds}\left(\frac{\alpha}{2}\sqrt{\frac{k}{m}}\,e^{-\alpha t/2}\right) + \frac{d^2x}{ds^2}\left(\frac{k}{m}\,e^{-\alpha t}\right).$$

Then

$$m\frac{d^2x}{dt^2} + ke^{-\alpha t}x = ke^{-\alpha t}\frac{d^2x}{ds^2} + \frac{m\alpha}{2}\sqrt{\frac{k}{m}}\,e^{-\alpha t/2}\frac{dx}{ds} + ke^{-\alpha t}x = 0.$$

Multiplying by $2^2/\alpha^2 m$ we have

$$\frac{2^2}{\alpha^2}\frac{k}{m}e^{-\alpha t}\frac{d^2x}{ds^2} + \frac{2}{\alpha}\sqrt{\frac{k}{m}}\,e^{-\alpha t/2}\frac{dx}{ds} + \frac{2^2}{\alpha^2}\frac{k}{m}e^{-\alpha t}x = 0$$

or, since $s = (2/\alpha)\sqrt{k/m}\,e^{-\alpha t/2}$,

$$s^2\frac{d^2x}{ds^2} + s\frac{dx}{ds} + s^2x = 0.$$

34. Differentiating $y = x^{1/2}w\left(\frac{2}{3}\alpha x^{3/2}\right)$ with respect to $\frac{2}{3}\alpha x^{3/2}$ we obtain

$$y' = x^{1/2}w'\left(\frac{2}{3}\alpha x^{3/2}\right)\alpha x^{1/2} + \frac{1}{2}x^{-1/2}w\left(\frac{2}{3}\alpha x^{3/2}\right)$$

and

$$y'' = \alpha xw''\left(\frac{2}{3}\alpha x^{3/2}\right)\alpha x^{1/2} + \alpha w'\left(\frac{2}{3}\alpha x^{3/2}\right)$$

$$+ \frac{1}{2}\alpha w'\left(\frac{2}{3}\alpha x^{3/2}\right) - \frac{1}{4}x^{-3/2}w\left(\frac{2}{3}\alpha x^{3/2}\right).$$

Then, after combining terms and simplifying, we have

$$y'' + \alpha^2 xy = \alpha\left[\alpha x^{3/2}w'' + \frac{3}{2}w' + \left(\alpha x^{3/2} - \frac{1}{4\alpha x^{3/2}}\right)w\right] = 0.$$

Letting $t = \frac{2}{3}\alpha x^{3/2}$ or $\alpha x^{3/2} = \frac{3}{2}t$ this differential equation becomes

$$\frac{3}{2}\frac{\alpha}{t}\left[t^2w''(t) + tw'(t) + \left(t^2 - \frac{1}{9}\right)w(t)\right] = 0, \qquad t > 0.$$

35. (a) By Problem 34, a solution of Airy's equation is $y = x^{1/2}w(\frac{2}{3}\alpha x^{3/2})$, where

$$w(t) = c_1 J_{1/3}(t) + c_2 J_{-1/3}(t)$$

is a solution of Bessel's equation of order $\frac{1}{3}$. Thus, the general solution of Airy's equation for $x > 0$ is

$$y = x^{1/2}w\left(\frac{2}{3}\alpha x^{3/2}\right) = c_1 x^{1/2}J_{1/3}\left(\frac{2}{3}\alpha x^{3/2}\right) + c_2 x^{1/2}J_{-1/3}\left(\frac{2}{3}\alpha x^{3/2}\right).$$

(b) Airy's equation, $y'' + \alpha^2 xy = 0$, has the form of (18) in the text with

$$1 - 2a = 0 \implies a = \frac{1}{2}$$

$$2c - 2 = 1 \implies c = \frac{3}{2}$$

$$b^2 c^2 = \alpha^2 \implies b = \frac{2}{3}\alpha$$

$$a^2 - p^2 c^2 = 0 \implies p = \frac{1}{3}.$$

Then, by (19) in the text,

$$y = x^{1/2}\left[c_1 J_{1/3}\left(\frac{2}{3}\alpha x^{3/2}\right) + c_2 J_{-1/3}\left(\frac{2}{3}\alpha x^{3/2}\right)\right].$$

36. The general solution of the differential equation is

$$y(x) = c_1 J_0(\alpha x) + c_2 Y_0(\alpha x).$$

In order to satisfy the conditions that $\lim_{x \to 0^+} y(x)$ and $\lim_{x \to 0^+} y'(x)$ are finite we are forced to define $c_2 = 0$. Thus, $y(x) = c_1 J_0(\alpha x)$. The second boundary condition, $y(2) = 0$, implies $c_1 = 0$ or $J_0(2\alpha) = 0$. In order to have a nontrivial solution we require that $J_0(2\alpha) = 0$. From Table 6.1, the first three positive zeros of J_0 are found to be

$$2\alpha_1 = 2.4048, \quad 2\alpha_2 = 5.5201, \quad 2\alpha_3 = 8.6537$$

and so $\alpha_1 = 1.2024$, $\alpha_2 = 2.7601$, $\alpha_3 = 4.3269$. The eigenfunctions corresponding to the eigenvalues $\lambda_1 = \alpha_1^2$, $\lambda_2 = \alpha_2^2$, $\lambda_3 = \alpha_3^2$ are $J_0(1.2024x)$, $J_0(2.7601x)$, and $J_0(4.3269x)$.

37. (a) The differential equation $y'' + (\lambda/x)y = 0$ has the form of (18) in the text with

$$1 - 2a = 0 \implies a = \frac{1}{2}$$

$$2c - 2 = -1 \implies c = \frac{1}{2}$$

$$b^2 c^2 = \lambda \implies b = 2\sqrt{\lambda}$$

$$a^2 - p^2 c^2 = 0 \implies p = 1.$$

Then, by (19) in the text,

$$y = x^{1/2}[c_1 J_1(2\sqrt{\lambda x}) + c_2 Y_1(2\sqrt{\lambda x})].$$

(b) We first note that $y = J_1(t)$ is a solution of Bessel's equation, $t^2 y'' + ty' + (t^2 - 1)y = 0$, with $\nu = 1$. That is,

$$t^2 J_1''(t) + t J_1'(t) + (t^2 - 1)J_1(t) = 0,$$

or, letting $t = 2\sqrt{x}$,

$$4x J_1''(2\sqrt{x}) + 2\sqrt{x} J_1'(2\sqrt{x}) + (4x - 1) J_1(2\sqrt{x}) = 0.$$

Now, if $y = \sqrt{x} J_1(2\sqrt{x})$, we have

$$y' = \sqrt{x} J_1'(2\sqrt{x}) \frac{1}{\sqrt{x}} + \frac{1}{2\sqrt{x}} J_1(2\sqrt{x}) = J_1'(2\sqrt{x}) + \frac{1}{2} x^{-1/2} J_1(2\sqrt{x})$$

and

$$y'' = x^{-1/2} J_1''(2\sqrt{x}) + \frac{1}{2x} J_1'(2\sqrt{x}) - \frac{1}{4} x^{-3/2} J_1(2\sqrt{x}).$$

Then

$$xy'' + y = \sqrt{x} J_1'' 2\sqrt{x} + \frac{1}{2} J_1'(2\sqrt{x}) - \frac{1}{4} x^{-1/2} J_1(2\sqrt{x}) + \sqrt{x} J(2\sqrt{x})$$

$$= \frac{1}{4\sqrt{x}} [4x J_1''(2\sqrt{x}) + 2\sqrt{x} J_1'(2\sqrt{x}) - J_1(2\sqrt{x}) + 4x J(2\sqrt{x})]$$

$$= 0,$$

and $y = \sqrt{x} J_1(2\sqrt{x})$ is a solution of Airy's differential equation.

38. We see from the graphs below that the graphs of the modified Bessel functions are not oscillatory, while those of the Bessel functions, shown in Figures 6.3.1 and 6.3.2 in the text, are oscillatory.

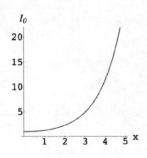
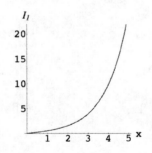
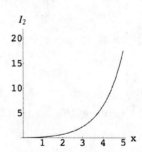
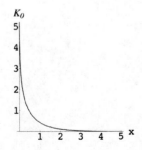
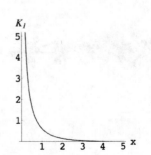
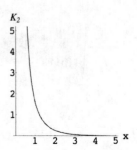

39. (a) We identify $m = 4$, $k = 1$, and $\alpha = 0.1$. Then

$$x(t) = c_1 J_0(10 e^{-0.05t}) + c_2 Y_0(10 e^{-0.05t})$$

and

$$x'(t) = -0.5 c_1 J_0'(10 e^{-0.05t}) - 0.5 c_2 Y_0'(10 e^{-0.05t}).$$

Now $x(0) = 1$ and $x'(0) = -1/2$ imply

$$c_1 J_0(10) + c_2 Y_0(10) = 1$$

$$c_1 J_0'(10) + c_2 Y_0'(10) = 1.$$

Using Cramer's rule we obtain

$$c_1 = \frac{Y_0'(10) - Y_0(10)}{J_0(10)Y_0'(10) - J_0'(10)Y_0(10)}$$

and

$$c_2 = \frac{J_0(10) - J_0'(10)}{J_0(10)Y_0'(10) - J_0'(10)Y_0(10)}.$$

Using $Y_0' = -Y_1$ and $J_0' = -J_1$ and Table 6.2 we find $c_1 = -4.7860$ and $c_2 = -3.1803$. Thus

$$x(t) = -4.7860 J_0(10e^{-0.05t}) - 3.1803 Y_0(10e^{-0.05t}).$$

(b)

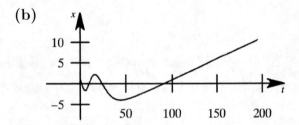

40. (a) Identifying $\alpha = \frac{1}{2}$, the general solution of $x'' + \frac{1}{4}tx = 0$ is

$$x(t) = c_1 x^{1/2} J_{1/3}\left(\frac{1}{3}x^{3/2}\right) + c_2 x^{1/2} J_{-1/3}\left(\frac{1}{3}x^{3/2}\right).$$

Solving the system $x(0.1) = 1$, $x'(0.1) = -\frac{1}{2}$ we find $c_1 = -0.809264$ and $c_2 = 0.782397$.

(b)

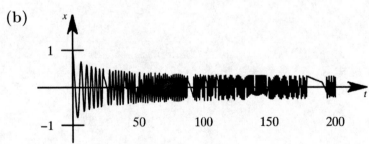

41. (a) Letting $t = L - x$, the boundary-value problem becomes

$$\frac{d^2\theta}{dt^2} + \alpha^2 t\theta = 0, \qquad \theta'(0) = 0, \quad \theta(L) = 0,$$

where $\alpha^2 = \delta g/EI$. This is Airy's differential equation, so by Problem 35 its solution is

$$y = c_1 t^{1/2} J_{1/3}\left(\frac{2}{3}\alpha t^{3/2}\right) + c_2 t^{1/2} J_{-1/3}\left(\frac{2}{3}\alpha t^{3/2}\right) = c_1\theta_1(t) + c_2\theta_2(t).$$

(b) Looking at the series forms of θ_1 and θ_2 we see that $\theta_1'(0) \neq 0$, while $\theta_2'(0) = 0$. Thus, the boundary condition $\theta'(0) = 0$ implies $c_1 = 0$, and so

$$\theta(t) = c_2\sqrt{t}\, J_{-1/3}\left(\frac{2}{3}\alpha t^{3/2}\right).$$

From $\theta(L) = 0$ we have

$$c_2\sqrt{L}\, J_{-1/3}\left(\frac{2}{3}\alpha L^{3/2}\right) = 0,$$

so either $c_2 = 0$, in which case $\theta(t) = 0$, or $J_{-1/3}(\frac{2}{3}\alpha L^{3/2}) = 0$. The column will just start to bend when L is the length corresponding to the smallest positive zero of $J_{-1/3}$.

(c) Using *Mathematica*, the first positive root of $J_{-1/3}(x)$ is $x_1 \approx 1.86635$. Thus $\frac{2}{3}\alpha L^{3/2} = 1.86635$ implies

$$L = \left(\frac{3(1.86635)}{2\alpha}\right)^{2/3} = \left[\frac{9EI}{4\delta g}(1.86635)^2\right]^{1/3}$$

$$= \left[\frac{9(2.6 \times 10^7)\pi(0.05)^4/4}{4(0.28)\pi(0.05)^2}(1.86635)^2\right]^{1/3} \approx 76.9 \text{ in.}$$

42. (a) Writing the differential equation in the form $xy'' + (PL/M)y = 0$, we identify $\lambda = PL/M$. From Problem 37 the solution of this differential equation is

$$y = c_1\sqrt{x}\, J_1\left(2\sqrt{PLx/M}\right) + c_2\sqrt{x}\, Y_1\left(2\sqrt{PLx/M}\right).$$

Now $J_1(0) = 0$, so $y(0) = 0$ implies $c_2 = 0$ and

$$y = c_1\sqrt{x}\, J_1\left(2\sqrt{PLx/M}\right).$$

(b) From $y(L) = 0$ we have $y = J_1(2L\sqrt{PM}) = 0$. The first positive zero of J_1 is 3.8317 so, solving $2L\sqrt{P_1/M} = 3.8317$, we find $P_1 = 3.6705M/L^2$. Therefore,

$$y_1(x) = c_1\sqrt{x}\, J_1\left(2\sqrt{\frac{3.6705x}{L}}\right) = c_1\sqrt{x}\, J_1\left(\frac{3.8317}{\sqrt{L}}\sqrt{x}\right).$$

(c) For $c_1 = 1$ and $L = 1$ the graph of $y_1 = \sqrt{x}\, J_1(3.8317\sqrt{x})$ is shown.

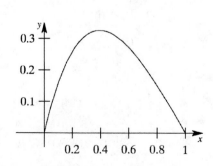

43. (a) Since $l' = v$, we integrate to obtain $l(t) = vt + c$. Now $l(0) = l_0$ implies $c = l_0$, so $l(t) = vt + l_0$.

Exercises 6.3 Special Functions

Using $\sin\theta \approx \theta$ in $l\, d^2\theta/dt^2 + 2l'\, d\theta/dt + g\sin\theta = 0$ gives

$$(l_0 + vt)\frac{d^2\theta}{dt^2} + 2v\frac{d\theta}{dt} + g\theta = 0.$$

(b) Dividing by v, the differential equation in part (a) becomes

$$\frac{l_0 + vt}{v}\frac{d^2\theta}{dt^2} + 2\frac{d\theta}{dt} + \frac{g}{v}\theta = 0.$$

Letting $x = (l_0 + vt)/v = t + l_0/v$ we have $dx/dt = 1$, so

$$\frac{d\theta}{dt} = \frac{d\theta}{dx}\frac{dx}{dt} = \frac{d\theta}{dx}$$

and

$$\frac{d^2\theta}{dt^2} = \frac{d(d\theta/dt)}{dt} = \frac{d(d\theta/dx)}{dx}\frac{dx}{dt} = \frac{d^2\theta}{dx^2}.$$

Thus, the differential equation becomes

$$x\frac{d^2\theta}{dx^2} + 2\frac{d\theta}{dx} + \frac{g}{v}\theta = 0 \qquad \text{or} \qquad \frac{d^2\theta}{dx^2} + \frac{2}{x}\frac{d\theta}{dx} + \frac{g}{vx}\theta = 0.$$

(c) The differential equation in part (b) has the form of (18) in the text with

$$1 - 2a = 2 \implies a = -\frac{1}{2}$$

$$2c - 2 = -1 \implies c = \frac{1}{2}$$

$$b^2 c^2 = \frac{g}{v} \implies b = 2\sqrt{\frac{g}{v}}$$

$$a^2 - p^2 c^2 = 0 \implies p = 1.$$

Then, by (19) in the text,

$$\theta(x) = x^{-1/2}\left[c_1 J_1\left(2\sqrt{\frac{g}{v}}\,x^{1/2}\right) + c_2 Y_1\left(2\sqrt{\frac{g}{v}}\,x^{1/2}\right)\right]$$

or

$$\theta(t) = \sqrt{\frac{v}{l_0 + vt}}\left[c_1 J_1\left(\frac{2}{v}\sqrt{g(l_0 + vt)}\right) + c_2 Y_1\left(\frac{2}{v}\sqrt{g(l_0 + vt)}\right)\right].$$

(d) To simplify calculations, let

$$u = \frac{2}{v}\sqrt{g(l_0 + vt)} = 2\sqrt{\frac{g}{v}}\,x^{1/2},$$

and at $t = 0$ let $u_0 = 2\sqrt{gl_0}/v$. The general solution for $\theta(t)$ can then be written

$$\theta = C_1 u^{-1} J_1(u) + C_2 u^{-1} Y_1(u). \tag{1}$$

Before applying the initial conditions, note that

$$\frac{d\theta}{dt} = \frac{d\theta}{du}\frac{du}{dt}$$

so when $d\theta/dt = 0$ at $t = 0$ we have $d\theta/du = 0$ at $u = u_0$. Also,

$$\frac{d\theta}{du} = C_1 \frac{d}{du}[u^{-1}J_1(u)] + C_2 \frac{d}{du}[u^{-1}Y_1(u)]$$

which, in view of (20) in the text, is the same as

$$\frac{d\theta}{du} = -C_1 u^{-1} J_2(u) - C_2 u^{-1} Y_2(u). \tag{2}$$

Now at $t = 0$, or $u = u_0$, (1) and (2) give the system

$$C_1 u_0^{-1} J_1(u_0) + C_2 u_0^{-1} Y_1(u_0) = \theta_0$$

$$C_1 u_0^{-1} J_2(u_0) + C_2 u_0^{-1} Y_2(u_0) = 0$$

whose solution is easily obtained using Cramer's rule:

$$C_1 = \frac{u_0 \theta_0 Y_2(u_0)}{J_1(u_0)Y_2(u_0) - J_2(u_0)Y_1(u_0)}, \qquad C_2 = \frac{-u_0 \theta_0 J_2(u_0)}{J_1(u_0)Y_2(u_0) - J_2(u_0)Y_1(u_0)}.$$

In view of the given identity these results simplify to

$$C_1 = -\frac{\pi}{2} u_0^2 \theta_0 Y_2(u_0) \qquad \text{and} \qquad C_2 = \frac{\pi}{2} u_0^2 \theta_0 J_2(u_0).$$

The solution is then

$$\theta = \frac{\pi}{2} u_0^2 \theta_0 \left[-Y_2(u_0)\frac{J_1(u)}{u} + J_2(u_0)\frac{Y_1(u)}{u} \right].$$

Returning to $u = (2/v)\sqrt{g(l_0 + vt)}$ and $u_0 = (2/v)\sqrt{gl_0}$, we have

$$\theta(t) = \frac{\pi\sqrt{gl_0}\,\theta_0}{v}\left[-Y_2\left(\frac{2}{v}\sqrt{gl_0}\right)\frac{J_1\left(\frac{2}{v}\sqrt{g(l_0+vt)}\right)}{\sqrt{l_0+vt}} + J_2\left(\frac{2}{v}\sqrt{gl_0}\right)\frac{Y_1\left(\frac{2}{v}\sqrt{g(l_0+vt)}\right)}{\sqrt{l_0+vt}} \right].$$

(e) When $l_0 = 1$ ft, $\theta_0 = \frac{1}{10}$ radian, and $v = \frac{1}{60}$ ft/s, the above function is

$$\theta(t) = -1.69045\,\frac{J_1(480\sqrt{2}(1+t/60))}{\sqrt{1+t/60}} - 2.79381\,\frac{Y_1(480\sqrt{2}(1+t/60))}{\sqrt{1+t/60}}.$$

The plots of $\theta(t)$ on $[0, 10]$, $[0, 30]$, and $[0, 60]$ are

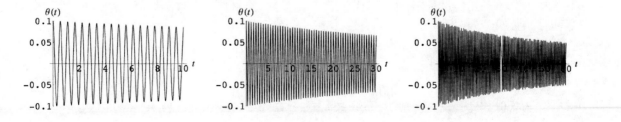

(f) The graphs indicate that $\theta(t)$ decreases as l increases.
The graph of $\theta(t)$ on $[0, 300]$ is shown.

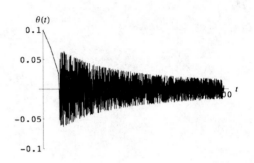

44. (a) From (26) in the text, we have

$$P_6(x) = c_0 \left(1 - \frac{6 \cdot 7}{2!} x^2 + \frac{4 \cdot 6 \cdot 7 \cdot 9}{4!} x^4 = \frac{2 \cdot 4 \cdot 6 \cdot 7 \cdot 9 \cdot 11}{6!} x^6 \right),$$

where

$$c_0 = (-1)^3 \frac{1 \cdot 3 \cdot 5}{2 \cdot 4 \cdot 6} = -\frac{5}{16}.$$

Thus,

$$P_6(x) = -\frac{5}{16} \left(1 - 21x^2 + 63x^4 - \frac{231}{5} x^6 \right) = \frac{1}{16} (231x^6 - 315x^4 + 105x^2 - 5).$$

Also, from (26) in the text we have

$$P_7(x) = c_1 \left(x - \frac{6 \cdot 9}{3!} x^3 + \frac{4 \cdot 6 \cdot 9 \cdot 11}{5!} x^5 - \frac{2 \cdot 4 \cdot 6 \cdot 9 \cdot 11 \cdot 13}{7!} x^7 \right)$$

where

$$c_1 = (-1)^3 \frac{1 \cdot 3 \cdot 5 \cdot 7}{2 \cdot 4 \cdot 6} = -\frac{35}{16}.$$

Thus

$$P_7(x) = -\frac{35}{16} \left(x - 9x^3 + \frac{99}{5} x^5 - \frac{429}{35} x^7 \right) = \frac{1}{16} (429x^7 - 693x^5 + 315x^3 - 35x).$$

(b) $P_6(x)$ satisfies $\left(1 - x^2 \right) y'' - 2xy' + 42y = 0$ and $P_7(x)$ satisfies $\left(1 - x^2 \right) y'' - 2xy' + 56y = 0$.

45. The recurrence relation can be written

$$P_{k+1}(x) = \frac{2k+1}{k+1} x P_k(x) - \frac{k}{k+1} P_{k-1}(x), \qquad k = 2, 3, 4, \ldots .$$

$k = 1$: $\quad P_2(x) = \frac{3}{2} x^2 - \frac{1}{2}$

$k = 2$: $\quad P_3(x) = \frac{5}{3} x \left(\frac{3}{2} x^2 - \frac{1}{2} \right) - \frac{2}{3} x = \frac{5}{2} x^3 - \frac{3}{2} x$

$k = 3$: $\quad P_4(x) = \frac{7}{4} x \left(\frac{5}{2} x^3 - \frac{3}{2} x \right) - \frac{3}{4} \left(\frac{3}{2} x^2 - \frac{1}{2} \right) = \frac{35}{8} x^4 - \frac{30}{8} x^2 + \frac{3}{8}$

$k = 4$: $\quad P_5(x) = \frac{9}{5} x \left(\frac{35}{8} x^4 - \frac{30}{8} x^2 + \frac{3}{8} \right) - \frac{4}{5} \left(\frac{5}{2} x^3 - \frac{3}{2} x \right) = \frac{63}{8} x^5 - \frac{35}{4} x^3 + \frac{15}{8} x$

$$k = 5: \quad P_6(x) = \frac{11}{6}x\left(\frac{63}{8}x^5 - \frac{35}{4}x^3 + \frac{15}{8}x\right) - \frac{5}{6}\left(\frac{35}{8}x^4 - \frac{30}{8}x^2 + \frac{3}{8}\right) = \frac{231}{16}x^6 - \frac{315}{16}x^4 + \frac{105}{16}x^2 - \frac{5}{16}$$

$$k = 6: \quad P_7(x) = \frac{13}{7}x\left(\frac{231}{16}x^6 - \frac{315}{16}x^4 + \frac{105}{16}x^2 - \frac{5}{16}\right) - \frac{6}{7}\left(\frac{63}{8}x^5 - \frac{35}{4}x^3 + \frac{15}{8}x\right)$$

$$= \frac{429}{16}x^7 - \frac{693}{16}x^5 + \frac{315}{16}x^3 - \frac{35}{16}x$$

46. If $x = \cos\theta$ then

$$\frac{dy}{d\theta} = -\sin\theta\frac{dy}{dx},$$

$$\frac{d^2y}{d\theta^2} = \sin^2\theta\frac{d^2y}{dx^2} - \cos\theta\frac{dy}{dx},$$

and

$$\sin\theta\frac{d^2y}{d\theta^2} + \cos\theta\frac{dy}{d\theta} + n(n+1)(\sin\theta)y = \sin\theta\left[\left(1 - \cos^2\theta\right)\frac{d^2y}{dx^2} - 2\cos\theta\frac{dy}{dx} + n(n+1)y\right] = 0.$$

That is,

$$\left(1 - x^2\right)\frac{d^2y}{dx^2} - 2x\frac{dy}{dx} + n(n+1)y = 0.$$

47. The only solutions bounded on $[-1, 1]$ are $y = cP_n(x)$, c a constant and $n = 0, 1, 2, \ldots$. By (iv) of the properties of the Legendre polynomials, $y(0) = 0$ or $P_n(0) = 0$ implies n must be odd. Thus the first three positive eigenvalues correspond to $n = 1, 3$, and 5 or $\lambda_1 = 1 \cdot 2$, $\lambda_2 = 3 \cdot 4 = 12$, and $\lambda_3 = 5 \cdot 6 = 30$. We can take the eigenfunctions to be $y_1 = P_1(x)$, $y_2 = P_3(x)$, and $y_3 = P_5(x)$.

48. Using a CAS we find

$$P_1(x) = \frac{1}{2}\frac{d}{dx}\left(x^2 - 1\right)^1 = x$$

$$P_2(x) = \frac{1}{2^2 2!}\frac{d^2}{dx^2}\left(x^2 - 1\right)^2 = \frac{1}{2}(3x^2 - 1)$$

$$P_3(x) = \frac{1}{2^3 3!}\frac{d^3}{dx^3}\left(x^2 - 1\right)^3 = \frac{1}{2}(5x^3 - 3x)$$

$$P_4(x) = \frac{1}{2^4 4!}\frac{d^4}{dx^4}\left(x^2 - 1\right)^4 = \frac{1}{8}(35x^4 - 30x^2 + 3)$$

$$P_5(x) = \frac{1}{2^5 5!}\frac{d^5}{dx^5}\left(x^2 - 1\right)^5 = \frac{1}{8}(63x^5 - 70x^3 + 15x)$$

$$P_6(x) = \frac{1}{2^6 6!}\frac{d^6}{dx^6}\left(x^2 - 1\right)^6 = \frac{1}{16}(231x^6 - 315x^4 + 105x^2 - 5)$$

$$P_7(x) = \frac{1}{2^7 7!}\frac{d^7}{dx^7}\left(x^2 - 1\right)^7 = \frac{1}{16}(429x^7 - 693x^5 + 315x^3 - 35x)$$

Exercises 6.3 Special Functions

49.

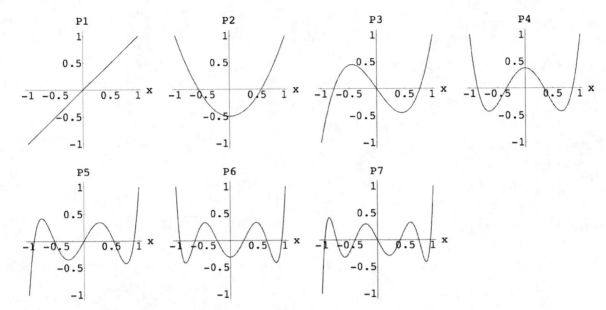

50. Zeros of Legendre polynomials for $n \geq 1$ are

$P_1(x):\ 0$

$P_2(x):\ \pm 0.57735$

$P_3(x):\ 0,\ \pm 0.77460$

$P_4(x):\ \pm 0.33998,\ \pm 0.86115$

$P_5(x):\ 0,\ \pm 0.53847,\ \pm 0.90618$

$P_6(x):\ \pm 0.23862,\ \pm 0.66121,\ \pm 0.93247$

$P_7(x):\ 0,\ \pm 0.40585,\ \pm 0.74153\ ,\pm 0.94911$

$P_{10}(x):\ \pm 0.14887,\ \pm 0.43340,\ \pm 0.67941,\ \pm 0.86506,\ \pm 0.097391$

The zeros of any Legendre polynomial are in the interval $(-1, 1)$ and are symmetric with respect to 0.

Chapter 6 in Review

1. False; $J_1(x)$ and $J_{-1}(x)$ are not linearly independent when ν is a positive integer. (In this case $\nu = 1$). The general solution of $x^2 y'' + xy' + (x^2 - 1)y = 0$ is $y = c_1 J_1(x) + c_2 Y_1(x)$.

2. False; $y = x$ is a solution that is analytic at $x = 0$.

3. $x = -1$ is the nearest singular point to the ordinary point $x = 0$. Theorem 6.1.1 guarantees the existence of two power series solutions $y = \sum_{n=1}^{\infty} c_n x^n$ of the differential equation that converge at least for $-1 < x < 1$. Since $-\frac{1}{2} \leq x \leq \frac{1}{2}$ is properly contained in $-1 < x < 1$, both power series must converge for all points contained in $-\frac{1}{2} \leq x \leq \frac{1}{2}$.

4. The easiest way to solve the system

$$2c_2 + 2c_1 + c_0 = 0$$

$$6c_3 + 4c_2 + c_1 = 0$$

$$12c_4 + 6c_3 - \frac{1}{3}c_1 + c_2 = 0$$

$$20c_5 + 8c_4 - \frac{2}{3}c_2 + c_3 = 0$$

is to choose, in turn, $c_0 \neq 0$, $c_1 = 0$ and $c_0 = 0$, $c_1 \neq 0$. Assuming that $c_0 \neq 0$, $c_1 = 0$, we have

$$c_2 = -\frac{1}{2}c_0$$

$$c_3 = -\frac{2}{3}c_2 = \frac{1}{3}c_0$$

$$c_4 = -\frac{1}{2}c_3 - \frac{1}{12}c_2 = -\frac{1}{8}c_0$$

$$c_5 = -\frac{2}{5}c_4 + \frac{1}{30}c_2 - \frac{1}{20}c_3 = \frac{1}{60}c_0;$$

whereas the assumption that $c_0 = 0$, $c_1 \neq 0$ implies

$$c_2 = -c_1$$

$$c_3 = -\frac{2}{3}c_2 - \frac{1}{6}c_1 = \frac{1}{2}c_1$$

$$c_4 = -\frac{1}{2}c_3 + \frac{1}{36}c_1 - \frac{1}{12}c_2 = -\frac{5}{36}c_1$$

$$c_5 = -\frac{2}{5}c_4 + \frac{1}{30}c_2 - \frac{1}{20}c_3 = -\frac{1}{360}c_1.$$

five terms of two power series solutions are then

$$y_1(x) = c_0 \left[1 - \frac{1}{2}x^2 + \frac{1}{3}x^3 - \frac{1}{8}x^4 + \frac{1}{60}x^5 + \cdots \right]$$

and

$$y_2(x) = c_1 \left[x - x^2 + \frac{1}{2}x^3 - \frac{5}{36}x^4 - \frac{1}{360}x^5 + \cdots \right].$$

5. The interval of convergence is centered at 4. Since the series converges at -2, it converges at least on the interval $[-2, 10)$. Since it diverges at 13, it converges at most on the interval $[-5, 13)$. Thus, at -7 it does not converge, at 0 and 7 it does converge, and at 10 and 11 it might converge.

6. We have

$$f(x) = \frac{\sin x}{\cos x} = \frac{x - \dfrac{x^3}{6} + \dfrac{x^5}{120} - \cdots}{1 - \dfrac{x^2}{2} + \dfrac{x^4}{24} - \cdots} = x + \frac{x^3}{3} + \frac{2x^5}{15} + \cdots .$$

7. The differential equation $(x^3 - x^2)y'' + y' + y = 0$ has a regular singular point at $x = 1$ and an irregular singular point at $x = 0$.

8. The differential equation $(x - 1)(x + 3)y'' + y = 0$ has regular singular points at $x = 1$ and $x = -3$.

9. Substituting $y = \sum_{n=0}^{\infty} c_n x^{n+r}$ into the differential equation we obtain

$$2xy'' + y' + y = \left(2r^2 - r\right)c_0 x^{r-1} + \sum_{k=1}^{\infty}[2(k+r)(k+r-1)c_k + (k+r)c_k + c_{k-1}]x^{k+r-1} = 0$$

which implies

$$2r^2 - r = r(2r - 1) = 0$$

and

$$(k+r)(2k + 2r - 1)c_k + c_{k-1} = 0.$$

The indicial roots are $r = 0$ and $r = 1/2$. For $r = 0$ the recurrence relation is

$$c_k = -\frac{c_{k-1}}{k(2k-1)}, \quad k = 1, 2, 3, \ldots,$$

so

$$c_1 = -c_0, \qquad c_2 = \frac{1}{6}c_0, \qquad c_3 = -\frac{1}{90}c_0.$$

For $r = 1/2$ the recurrence relation is

$$c_k = -\frac{c_{k-1}}{k(2k+1)}, \quad k = 1, 2, 3, \ldots,$$

so

$$c_1 = -\frac{1}{3}c_0, \qquad c_2 = \frac{1}{30}c_0, \qquad c_3 = -\frac{1}{630}c_0.$$

Two linearly independent solutions are

$$y_1 = 1 - x + \frac{1}{6}x^2 - \frac{1}{90}x^3 + \cdots$$

and

$$y_2 = x^{1/2}\left(1 - \frac{1}{3}x + \frac{1}{30}x^2 - \frac{1}{630}x^3 + \cdots\right).$$

10. Substituting $y = \sum_{n=0}^{\infty} c_n x^n$ into the differential equation we have

$$y'' - xy' - y = \underbrace{\sum_{n=2}^{\infty} n(n-1)c_n x^{n-2}}_{k=n-2} - \underbrace{\sum_{n=1}^{\infty} nc_n x^n}_{k=n} - \underbrace{\sum_{n=0}^{\infty} c_n x^n}_{k=n}$$

$$= \sum_{k=0}^{\infty} (k+2)(k+1)c_{k+2}x^k - \sum_{k=1}^{\infty} kc_k x^k - \sum_{k=0}^{\infty} c_k x^k$$

$$= 2c_2 - c_0 + \sum_{k=1}^{\infty} [(k+2)(k+1)c_{k+2} - (k+1)c_k]x^k = 0.$$

Thus

$$2c_2 - c_0 = 0$$

$$(k+2)(k+1)c_{k+2} - (k+1)c_k = 0$$

and

$$c_2 = \frac{1}{2}c_0$$

$$c_{k+2} = \frac{1}{k+2}c_k, \quad k = 1, 2, 3, \ldots.$$

Choosing $c_0 = 1$ and $c_1 = 0$ we find

$$c_2 = \frac{1}{2}$$

$$c_3 = c_5 = c_7 = \cdots = 0$$

$$c_4 = \frac{1}{8}$$

$$c_6 = \frac{1}{48}$$

and so on. For $c_0 = 0$ and $c_1 = 1$ we obtain

$$c_2 = c_4 = c_6 = \cdots = 0$$

$$c_3 = \frac{1}{3}$$

$$c_5 = \frac{1}{15}$$

$$c_7 = \frac{1}{105}$$

and so on. Thus, two solutions are

$$y_1 = 1 + \frac{1}{2}x^2 + \frac{1}{8}x^4 + \frac{1}{48}x^6 + \cdots$$

and

$$y_2 = x + \frac{1}{3}x^3 + \frac{1}{15}x^5 + \frac{1}{105}x^7 + \cdots.$$

11. Substituting $y = \sum_{n=0}^{\infty} c_n x^n$ into the differential equation we obtain

$$(x-1)y'' + 3y = (-2c_2 + 3c_0) + \sum_{k=1}^{\infty} [(k+1)kc_{k+1} - (k+2)(k+1)c_{k+2} + 3c_k]x^k = 0$$

which implies $c_2 = 3c_0/2$ and

$$c_{k+2} = \frac{(k+1)kc_{k+1} + 3c_k}{(k+2)(k+1)}, \quad k = 1, 2, 3, \ldots.$$

Choosing $c_0 = 1$ and $c_1 = 0$ we find

$$c_2 = \frac{3}{2}, \qquad c_3 = \frac{1}{2}, \qquad c_4 = \frac{5}{8}$$

and so on. For $c_0 = 0$ and $c_1 = 1$ we obtain

$$c_2 = 0, \qquad c_3 = \frac{1}{2}, \qquad c_4 = \frac{1}{4}$$

and so on. Thus, two solutions are

$$y_1 = 1 + \frac{3}{2}x^2 + \frac{1}{2}x^3 + \frac{5}{8}x^4 + \cdots$$

and

$$y_2 = x + \frac{1}{2}x^3 + \frac{1}{4}x^4 + \cdots.$$

12. Substituting $y = \sum_{n=0}^{\infty} c_n x^n$ into the differential equation we obtain

$$y'' - x^2 y' + xy = 2c_2 + (6c_3 + c_0)x + \sum_{k=1}^{\infty} [(k+3)(k+2)c_{k+3} - (k-1)c_k]x^{k+1} = 0$$

which implies $c_2 = 0$, $c_3 = -c_0/6$, and

$$c_{k+3} = \frac{k-1}{(k+3)(k+2)}c_k, \quad k = 1, 2, 3, \ldots.$$

Choosing $c_0 = 1$ and $c_1 = 0$ we find

$$c_3 = -\frac{1}{6}$$

$$c_4 = c_7 = c_{10} = \cdots = 0$$

$$c_5 = c_8 = c_{11} = \cdots = 0$$

$$c_6 = -\frac{1}{90}$$

and so on. For $c_0 = 0$ and $c_1 = 1$ we obtain

$$c_3 = c_6 = c_9 = \cdots = 0$$

$$c_4 = c_7 = c_{10} = \cdots = 0$$

$$c_5 = c_8 = c_{11} = \cdots = 0$$

and so on. Thus, two solutions are

$$y_1 = 1 - \frac{1}{6}x^3 - \frac{1}{90}x^6 - \cdots \quad \text{and} \quad y_2 = x.$$

13. Substituting $y = \sum_{n=0}^{\infty} c_n x^{n+r}$ into the differential equation, we obtain

$$xy'' - (x+2)y' + 2y = (r^2 - 3r)c_0 x^{r-1} + \sum_{k=1}^{\infty} [(k+r)(k+r-3)c_k$$
$$- (k+r-3)c_{k-1}]x^{k+r-1} = 0,$$

which implies

$$r^2 - 3r = r(r-3) = 0$$

and

$$(k+r)(k+r-3)c_k - (k+r-3)c_{k-1} = 0.$$

The indicial roots are $r_1 = 3$ and $r_2 = 0$. For $r_2 = 0$ the recurrence relation is

$$k(k-3)c_k - (k-3)c_{k-1} = 0, \qquad k = 1, 2, 3, \ldots.$$

Then

$$c_1 - c_0 = 0$$

$$2c_2 - c_1 = 0$$

$$0c_3 - 0c_2 = 0 \implies c_3 \text{ is arbitrary}$$

and

$$c_k = \frac{1}{k}c_{k-1}, \qquad k = 4, 5, 6, \ldots.$$

Taking $c_0 \neq 0$ and $c_3 = 0$ we obtain

$$c_1 = c_0$$

$$c_2 = \frac{1}{2}c_0$$

$$c_3 = c_4 = c_5 = \cdots = 0.$$

Taking $c_0 = 0$ and $c_3 \neq 0$ we obtain

$$c_0 = c_1 = c_2 = 0$$

$$c_4 = \frac{1}{4}c_3 = \frac{6}{4!}c_3$$

$$c_5 = \frac{1}{5 \cdot 4}c_3 = \frac{6}{5!}c_3$$

$$c_6 = \frac{1}{6 \cdot 5 \cdot 4}c_3 = \frac{6}{6!}c_3,$$

and so on. In this case we obtain the two solutions

$$y_1 = 1 + x + \frac{1}{2}x^2$$

and

$$y_2 = x^3 + \frac{6}{4!}x^4 + \frac{6}{5!}x^5 + \frac{6}{6!}x^6 + \cdots = 6e^x - 6\left(1 + x + \frac{1}{2}x^2\right).$$

14. Substituting $y = \sum_{n=0}^{\infty} c_n x^n$ into the differential equation we have

$$(\cos x)y'' + y = \left(1 - \frac{1}{2}x^2 + \frac{1}{24}x^4 - \frac{1}{720}x^6 + \cdots\right)(2c_2 + 6c_3 x + 12c_4 x^2 + 20c_5 x^3 + 30c_6 x^4 + \cdots)$$

$$+ \sum_{n=0}^{\infty} c_n x^n$$

$$= \left[2c_2 + 6c_3 x + (12c_4 - c_2)x^2 + (20c_5 - 3c_3)x^3 + \left(30c_6 - 6c_4 + \frac{1}{12}c_2\right)x^4 + \cdots\right]$$

$$+ [c_0 + c_1 x + c_2 x^2 + c_3 x^3 + c_4 x^4 + \cdots]$$

$$= (c_0 + 2c_2) + (c_1 + 6c_3)x + 12c_4 x^2 + (20c_5 - 2c_3)x^3 + \left(30c_6 - 5c_4 + \frac{1}{12}c_2\right)x^4 + \cdots$$

$$= 0.$$

Thus

$$c_0 + 2c_2 = 0$$

$$c_1 + 6c_3 = 0$$

$$12c_4 = 0$$

$$20c_5 - 2c_3 = 0$$

$$30c_6 - 5c_4 + \frac{1}{12}c_2 = 0$$

and

$$c_2 = -\frac{1}{2}c_0$$

$$c_3 = -\frac{1}{6}c_1$$

$$c_4 = 0$$

$$c_5 = \frac{1}{10}c_3$$

$$c_6 = \frac{1}{6}c_4 - \frac{1}{360}c_2.$$

Choosing $c_0 = 1$ and $c_1 = 0$ we find

$$c_2 = -\frac{1}{2}, \quad c_3 = 0, \quad c_4 = 0, \quad c_5 = 0, \quad c_6 = \frac{1}{720}$$

and so on. For $c_0 = 0$ and $c_1 = 1$ we find

$$c_2 = 0, \quad c_3 = -\frac{1}{6}, \quad c_4 = 0, \quad c_5 = -\frac{1}{60}, \quad c_6 = 0$$

and so on. Thus, two solutions are

$$y_1 = 1 - \frac{1}{2}x^2 + \frac{1}{720}x^6 + \cdots \quad \text{and} \quad y_2 = x - \frac{1}{6}x^3 - \frac{1}{60}x^5 + \cdots.$$

15.

$$y'' + xy' + 2y = \underbrace{\sum_{n=2}^{\infty} n(n-1)c_n x^{n-2}}_{k=n-2} + \underbrace{\sum_{n=1}^{\infty} nc_n x^n}_{k=n} + 2\underbrace{\sum_{n=0}^{\infty} c_n x^n}_{k=n}$$

$$= \sum_{k=0}^{\infty}(k+2)(k+1)c_{k+2}x^k + \sum_{k=1}^{\infty} kc_k x^k + 2\sum_{k=0}^{\infty} c_k x^k$$

$$= 2c_2 + 2c_0 + \sum_{k=1}^{\infty}[(k+2)(k+1)c_{k+2} + (k+2)c_k]x^k = 0.$$

Thus

$$2c_2 + 2c_0 = 0$$

$$(k+2)(k+1)c_{k+2} + (k+2)c_k = 0$$

and

$$c_2 = -c_0$$

$$c_{k+2} = -\frac{1}{k+1}c_k, \quad k = 1, 2, 3, \ldots.$$

Choosing $c_0 = 1$ and $c_1 = 0$ we find

$$c_2 = -1$$

$$c_3 = c_5 = c_7 = \cdots = 0$$

$$c_4 = \frac{1}{3}$$

$$c_6 = -\frac{1}{15}$$

and so on. For $c_0 = 0$ and $c_1 = 1$ we obtain

$$c_2 = c_4 = c_6 = \cdots = 0$$

$$c_3 = -\frac{1}{2}$$

$$c_5 = \frac{1}{8}$$

$$c_7 = -\frac{1}{48}$$

and so on. Thus, the general solution is

$$y = C_0 \left(1 - x^2 + \frac{1}{3}x^4 - \frac{1}{15}x^6 + \cdots \right) + C_1 \left(x - \frac{1}{2}x^3 + \frac{1}{8}x^5 - \frac{1}{48}x^7 + \cdots \right)$$

and

$$y' = C_0 \left(-2x + \frac{4}{3}x^3 - \frac{2}{5}x^5 + \cdots \right) + C_1 \left(1 - \frac{3}{2}x^2 + \frac{5}{8}x^4 - \frac{7}{48}x^6 + \cdots \right).$$

Setting $y(0) = 3$ and $y'(0) = -2$ we find $c_0 = 3$ and $c_1 = -2$. Therefore, the solution of the initial-value problem is

$$y = 3 - 2x - 3x^2 + x^3 + x^4 - \frac{1}{4}x^5 - \frac{1}{5}x^6 + \frac{1}{24}x^7 + \cdots.$$

16. Substituting $y = \sum_{n=0}^{\infty} c_n x^n$ into the differential equation we have

$$(x+2)y'' + 3y = \underbrace{\sum_{n=2}^{\infty} n(n-1)c_n x^{n-1}}_{k=n-1} + 2\underbrace{\sum_{n=2}^{\infty} n(n-1)c_n x^{n-2}}_{k=n-2} + 3\underbrace{\sum_{n=0}^{\infty} c_n x^n}_{k=n}$$

$$= \sum_{k=1}^{\infty}(k+1)kc_{k+1}x^k + 2\sum_{k=0}^{\infty}(k+2)(k+1)c_{k+2}x^k + 3\sum_{k=0}^{\infty} c_k x^k$$

$$= 4c_2 + 3c_0 + \sum_{k=1}^{\infty}[(k+1)kc_{k+1} + 2(k+2)(k+1)c_{k+2} + 3c_k]x^k = 0.$$

Thus

$$4c_2 + 3c_0 = 0$$

$$(k+1)kc_{k+1} + 2(k+2)(k+1)c_{k+2} + 3c_k = 0$$

and

$$c_2 = -\frac{3}{4}c_0$$

$$c_{k+2} = -\frac{k}{2(k+2)}c_{k+1} - \frac{3}{2(k+2)(k+1)}c_k, \quad k = 1, 2, 3, \ldots.$$

Choosing $c_0 = 1$ and $c_1 = 0$ we find

$$c_2 = -\frac{3}{4}$$

$$c_3 = \frac{1}{8}$$

$$c_4 = \frac{1}{16}$$

$$c_5 = -\frac{9}{320}$$

and so on. For $c_0 = 0$ and $c_1 = 1$ we obtain

$$c_2 = 0$$

$$c_3 = -\frac{1}{4}$$

$$c_4 = \frac{1}{16}$$

$$c_5 = 0$$

and so on. Thus, the general solution is

$$y = C_0\left(1 - \frac{3}{4}x^2 + \frac{1}{8}x^3 + \frac{1}{16}x^4 - \frac{9}{320}x^5 + \cdots\right) + C_1\left(x - \frac{1}{4}x^3 + \frac{1}{16}x^4 + \cdots\right)$$

and

$$y' = C_0\left(-\frac{3}{2}x + \frac{3}{8}x^2 + \frac{1}{4}x^3 - \frac{9}{64}x^4 + \cdots\right) + C_1\left(1 - \frac{3}{4}x^2 + \frac{1}{4}x^3 + \cdots\right).$$

Setting $y(0) = 0$ and $y'(0) = 1$ we find $c_0 = 0$ and $c_1 = 1$. Therefore, the solution of the initial-value problem is

$$y = x - \frac{1}{4}x^3 + \frac{1}{16}x^4 + \cdots.$$

17. The singular point of $(1 - 2\sin x)y'' + xy = 0$ closest to $x = 0$ is $\pi/6$. Hence a lower bound is $\pi/6$.

18. While we can find two solutions of the form

$$y_1 = c_0[1 + \cdots] \quad \text{and} \quad y_2 = c_1[x + \cdots],$$

the initial conditions at $x = 1$ give solutions for c_0 and c_1 in terms of infinite series. Letting $t = x - 1$ the initial-value problem becomes

$$\frac{d^2y}{dt^2} + (t+1)\frac{dy}{dt} + y = 0, \qquad y(0) = -6, \ y'(0) = 3.$$

Substituting $y = \sum_{n=0}^{\infty} c_n t^n$ into the differential equation, we have

$$\frac{d^2y}{dt^2} + (t+1)\frac{dy}{dt} + y = \underbrace{\sum_{n=2}^{\infty} n(n-1)c_n t^{n-2}}_{k=n-2} + \underbrace{\sum_{n=1}^{\infty} nc_n t^n}_{k=n} + \underbrace{\sum_{n=1}^{\infty} nc_n t^{n-1}}_{k=n-1} + \underbrace{\sum_{n=0}^{\infty} c_n t^n}_{k=n}$$

$$= \sum_{k=0}^{\infty}(k+2)(k+1)c_{k+2}t^k + \sum_{k=1}^{\infty} kc_k t^k + \sum_{k=0}^{\infty}(k+1)c_{k+1}t^k + \sum_{k=0}^{\infty} c_k t^k$$

$$= 2c_2 + c_1 + c_0 + \sum_{k=1}^{\infty}[(k+2)(k+1)c_{k+2} + (k+1)c_{k+1} + (k+1)c_k]t^k = 0.$$

Thus

$$2c_2 + c_1 + c_0 = 0$$

$$(k+2)(k+1)c_{k+2} + (k+1)c_{k+1} + (k+1)c_k = 0$$

and
$$c_2 = -\frac{c_1 + c_0}{2}$$

$$c_{k+2} = -\frac{c_{k+1} + c_k}{k+2}, \quad k = 1, 2, 3, \ldots.$$

Choosing $c_0 = 1$ and $c_1 = 0$ we find

$$c_2 = -\frac{1}{2}, \quad c_3 = \frac{1}{6}, \quad c_4 = \frac{1}{12},$$

and so on. For $c_0 = 0$ and $c_1 = 1$ we find

$$c_2 = -\frac{1}{2}, \quad c_3 = -\frac{1}{6}, \quad c_4 = \frac{1}{6},$$

and so on. Thus, the general solution is

$$y = c_0 \left[1 - \frac{1}{2}t^2 + \frac{1}{6}t^3 + \frac{1}{12}t^4 + \cdots \right] + c_1 \left[t - \frac{1}{2}t^2 - \frac{1}{6}t^3 + \frac{1}{6}t^4 + \cdots \right].$$

The initial conditions then imply $c_0 = -6$ and $c_1 = 3$. Thus the solution of the initial-value problem is

$$y = -6 \left[1 - \frac{1}{2}(x-1)^2 + \frac{1}{6}(x-1)^3 + \frac{1}{12}(x-1)^4 + \cdots \right]$$

$$+ 3 \left[(x-1) - \frac{1}{2}(x-1)^2 - \frac{1}{6}(x-1)^3 + \frac{1}{6}(x-1)^4 + \cdots \right].$$

19. Writing the differential equation in the form

$$y'' + \left(\frac{1 - \cos x}{x} \right) y' + xy = 0,$$

and noting that

$$\frac{1 - \cos x}{x} = \frac{x}{2} - \frac{x^3}{24} + \frac{x^5}{720} - \cdots$$

is analytic at $x = 0$, we conclude that $x = 0$ is an ordinary point of the differential equation.

20. Writing the differential equation in the form

$$y'' + \left(\frac{x}{e^x - 1 - x} \right) y = 0$$

and noting that

$$\frac{x}{e^x - 1 - x} = \frac{2}{x} - \frac{2}{3} + \frac{x}{18} + \frac{x^2}{270} - \cdots$$

we see that $x = 0$ is a singular point of the differential equation. Since

$$x^2 \left(\frac{x}{e^x - 1 - x} \right) = 2x - \frac{2x^2}{3} + \frac{x^3}{18} + \frac{x^4}{270} - \cdots,$$

we conclude that $x = 0$ is a regular singular point.

21. Substituting $y = \sum_{n=0}^{\infty} c_n x^n$ into the differential equation we have

$$y'' + x^2 y' + 2xy = \underbrace{\sum_{n=2}^{\infty} n(n-1)c_n x^{n-2}}_{k=n-2} + \underbrace{\sum_{n=1}^{\infty} nc_n x^{n+1}}_{k=n+1} + 2\underbrace{\sum_{n=0}^{\infty} c_n x^{n+1}}_{k=n+1}$$

$$= \sum_{k=0}^{\infty} (k+2)(k+1)c_{k+2} x^k + \sum_{k=2}^{\infty} (k-1)c_{k-1} x^k + 2\sum_{k=1}^{\infty} c_{k-1} x^k$$

$$= 2c_2 + (6c_3 + 2c_0)x + \sum_{k=2}^{\infty} [(k+2)(k+1)c_{k+2} + (k+1)c_{k-1}]x^k = 5 - 2x + 10x^3.$$

Thus, equating coefficients of like powers of x gives

$$2c_2 = 5$$

$$6c_3 + 2c_0 = -2$$

$$12c_4 + 3c_1 = 0$$

$$20c_5 + 4c_2 = 10$$

$$(k+2)(k+1)c_{k+2} + (k+1)c_{k-1} = 0, \quad k = 4, 5, 6, \ldots,$$

and

$$c_2 = \frac{5}{2}$$

$$c_3 = -\frac{1}{3}c_0 - \frac{1}{3}$$

$$c_4 = -\frac{1}{4}c_1$$

$$c_5 = \frac{1}{2} - \frac{1}{5}c_2 = \frac{1}{2} - \frac{1}{5}\left(\frac{5}{2}\right) = 0$$

$$c_{k+2} = -\frac{1}{k+2}c_{k-1}.$$

Using the recurrence relation, we find

$$c_6 = -\frac{1}{6}c_3 = \frac{1}{3 \cdot 6}(c_0 + 1) = \frac{1}{3^2 \cdot 2!}c_0 + \frac{1}{3^2 \cdot 2!}$$

$$c_7 = -\frac{1}{7}c_4 = \frac{1}{4 \cdot 7}c_1$$

$$c_8 = c_{11} = c_{14} = \cdots = 0$$

$$c_9 = -\frac{1}{9}c_6 = -\frac{1}{3^3 \cdot 3!}c_0 - \frac{1}{3^3 \cdot 3!}$$

$$c_{10} = -\frac{1}{10}c_7 = -\frac{1}{4 \cdot 7 \cdot 10}c_1$$

$$c_{12} = -\frac{1}{12}c_9 = \frac{1}{3^4 \cdot 4!}c_0 + \frac{1}{3^4 \cdot 4!}$$

$$c_{13} = -\frac{1}{13}c_0 = \frac{1}{4 \cdot 7 \cdot 10 \cdot 13}c_1$$

and so on. Thus

$$y = c_0 \left[1 - \frac{1}{3}x^3 + \frac{1}{3^2 \cdot 2!}x^6 - \frac{1}{3^3 \cdot 3!}x^9 + \frac{1}{3^4 \cdot 4!}x^{12} - \cdots \right]$$

$$+ c_1 \left[x - \frac{1}{4}x^4 + \frac{1}{4 \cdot 7}x^7 - \frac{1}{4 \cdot 7 \cdot 10}x^{10} + \frac{1}{4 \cdot 7 \cdot 10 \cdot 13}x^{13} - \cdots \right]$$

$$+ \left[\frac{5}{2}x^2 - \frac{1}{3}x^3 + \frac{1}{3^2 \cdot 2!}x^6 - \frac{1}{3^3 \cdot 3!}x^9 + \frac{1}{3^4 \cdot 4!}x^{12} - \cdots \right].$$

22. (a) From $y = -\frac{1}{u}\frac{du}{dx}$ we obtain

$$\frac{dy}{dx} = -\frac{1}{u}\frac{d^2u}{dx^2} + \frac{1}{u^2}\left(\frac{du}{dx}\right)^2.$$

Then $dy/dx = x^2 + y^2$ becomes

$$-\frac{1}{u}\frac{d^2u}{dx^2} + \frac{1}{u^2}\left(\frac{du}{dx}\right)^2 = x^2 + \frac{1}{u^2}\left(\frac{du}{dx}\right)^2,$$

so $\quad \dfrac{d^2u}{dx^2} + x^2u = 0.$

(b) The differential equation $u'' + x^2u = 0$ has the form of (18) in Section 6.3 in the text with

$$1 - 2a = 0 \implies a = \frac{1}{2}$$

$$2c - 2 = 2 \implies c = 2$$

$$b^2c^2 = 1 \implies b = \frac{1}{2}$$

$$a^2 - p^2c^2 = 0 \implies p = \frac{1}{4}.$$

Then, by (19) of Section 6.3 in the text,

$$u = x^{1/2}\left[c_1 J_{1/4}\left(\frac{1}{2}x^2\right) + c_2 J_{-1/4}\left(\frac{1}{2}x^2\right) \right].$$

(c) We have

$$y = -\frac{1}{u}\frac{du}{dx} = -\frac{1}{x^{1/2}w(t)}\frac{d}{dx}x^{1/2}w(t)$$

$$= -\frac{1}{x^{1/2}w}\left[x^{1/2}\frac{dw}{dt}\frac{dt}{dx} + \frac{1}{2}x^{-1/2}w\right]$$

$$= -\frac{1}{x^{1/2}w}\left[x^{3/2}\frac{dw}{dt} + \frac{1}{2x^{1/2}}w\right]$$

$$= -\frac{1}{2xw}\left[2x^2\frac{dw}{dt} + w\right] = -\frac{1}{2xw}\left[4t\frac{dw}{dt} + w\right].$$

Now

$$4t\frac{dw}{dt} + w = 4t\frac{d}{dt}[c_1 J_{1/4}(t) + c_2 J_{-1/4}(t)] + c_1 J_{1/4}(t) + c_2 J_{-1/4}(t)$$

$$= 4t\left[c_1\left(J_{-3/4}(t) - \frac{1}{4t}J_{1/4}(t)\right) + c_2\left(-\frac{1}{4t}J_{-1/4}(t) - J_{3/4}(t)\right)\right]$$

$$+ c_1 J_{1/4}(t) + c_2 J_{-1/4}(t)$$

$$= 4c_1 t J_{-3/4}(t) - 4c_2 t J_{3/4}(t)$$

$$= 2c_1 x^2 J_{-3/4}\left(\frac{1}{2}x^2\right) - 2c_2 x^2 J_{3/4}\left(\frac{1}{2}x^2\right),$$

so

$$y = -\frac{2c_1 x^2 J_{-3/4}(\frac{1}{2}x^2) - 2c_2 x^2 J_{3/4}(\frac{1}{2}x^2)}{2x[c_1 J_{1/4}(\frac{1}{2}x^2) + c_2 J_{-1/4}(\frac{1}{2}x^2)]}$$

$$= x\frac{-c_1 J_{-3/4}(\frac{1}{2}x^2) + c_2 J_{3/4}(\frac{1}{2}x^2)}{c_1 J_{1/4}(\frac{1}{2}x^2) + c_2 J_{-1/4}(\frac{1}{2}x^2)}.$$

Letting $c = c_1/c_2$ we have

$$y = x\frac{J_{3/4}(\frac{1}{2}x^2) - cJ_{-3/4}(\frac{1}{2}x^2)}{cJ_{1/4}(\frac{1}{2}x^2) + J_{-1/4}(\frac{1}{2}x^2)}.$$

23. (a) Equations (10) and (24) of Section 6.3 in the text imply

$$Y_{1/2}(x) = \frac{\cos\frac{\pi}{2}J_{1/2}(x) - J_{-1/2}(x)}{\sin\frac{\pi}{2}} = -J_{-1/2}(x) = -\sqrt{\frac{2}{\pi x}}\cos x.$$

Chapter 6 in Review

(b) From (15) of Section 6.3 in the text

$$I_{1/2}(x) = i^{-1/2} J_{1/2}(ix) \qquad \text{and} \qquad I_{-1/2}(x) = i^{1/2} J_{-1/2}(ix)$$

so

$$I_{1/2}(x) = \sqrt{\frac{2}{\pi x}} \sum_{n=0}^{\infty} \frac{1}{(2n+1)!} x^{2n+1} = \sqrt{\frac{2}{\pi x}} \sinh x$$

and

$$I_{-1/2}(x) = \sqrt{\frac{2}{\pi x}} \sum_{n=0}^{\infty} \frac{1}{(2n)!} x^{2n} = \sqrt{\frac{2}{\pi x}} \cosh x.$$

(c) Equation (16) of Section 6.3 in the text and part (b) imply

$$K_{1/2}(x) = \frac{\pi}{2} \frac{I_{-1/2}(x) - I_{1/2}(x)}{\sin \frac{\pi}{2}} = \frac{\pi}{2} \left[\sqrt{\frac{2}{\pi x}} \cosh x - \sqrt{\frac{2}{\pi x}} \sinh x \right]$$

$$= \sqrt{\frac{\pi}{2x}} \left[\frac{e^x + e^{-x}}{2} - \frac{e^x - e^{-x}}{2} \right] = \sqrt{\frac{\pi}{2x}} \, e^{-x}.$$

24. (a) Using formula (5) of Section 4.2 in the text, we find that a second solution of $(1-x^2)y'' - 2xy' = 0$ is

$$y_2(x) = 1 \cdot \int \frac{e^{\int 2x\,dx/(1-x^2)}}{1^2} \, dx = \int e^{-\ln(1-x^2)} \, dx$$

$$= \int \frac{dx}{1-x^2} = \frac{1}{2} \ln \left(\frac{1+x}{1-x} \right),$$

where partial fractions was used to obtain the last integral.

(b) Using formula (5) of Section 4.2 in the text, we find that a second solution of $(1-x^2)y'' - 2xy' + 2y = 0$ is

$$y_2(x) = x \cdot \int \frac{e^{\int 2x\,dx/(1-x^2)}}{x^2} \, dx = x \int \frac{e^{-\ln(1-x^2)}}{x^2} \, dx$$

$$= x \int \frac{dx}{x^2(1-x^2)} \, dx = x \left[\frac{1}{2} \ln \left(\frac{1+x}{1-x} \right) - \frac{1}{x} \right]$$

$$= \frac{x}{2} \ln \left(\frac{1+x}{1-x} \right) - 1,$$

where partial fractions was used to obtain the last integral.

(c)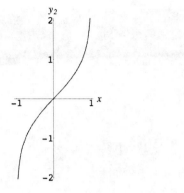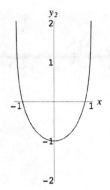

$$y_2(x) = \frac{1}{2}\ln\left(\frac{1+x}{1-x}\right) \qquad y_2 = \frac{x}{2}\ln\left(\frac{1+x}{1-x}\right) - 1$$

25. (a) By the binomial theorem we have

$$\left[1 + \left(t^2 - 2xt\right)\right]^{-1/2} = 1 - \frac{1}{2}\left(t^2 - 2xt\right) + \frac{(-1/2)(-3/2)}{2!}\left(t^2 - 2xt\right)^2$$

$$+ \frac{(-1/2)(-3/2)(-5/2)}{3!}\left(t^2 - 2xt\right)^3 + \cdots$$

$$= 1 - \frac{1}{2}(t^2 - 2xt) + \frac{3}{8}(t^2 - 2xt)^2 - \frac{5}{16}(t^2 - 2xt)^3 + \cdots$$

$$= 1 + xt + \frac{1}{2}(3x^2 - 1)t^2 + \frac{1}{2}(5x^3 - 3x)t^3 + \cdots$$

$$= \sum_{n=0}^{\infty} P_n(x)t^n.$$

(b) Letting $x = 1$ in $(1 - 2xt + t^2)^{-1/2}$, we have

$$(1 - 2t + t^2)^{-1/2} = (1 - t)^{-1} = \frac{1}{1 - t} = 1 + t + t^2 + t^3 + \cdots \qquad (|t| < 1)$$

$$= \sum_{n=0}^{\infty} t^n.$$

From part (a) we have

$$\sum_{n=0}^{\infty} P_n(1)t^n = (1 - 2t + t^2)^{-1/2} = \sum_{n=0}^{\infty} t^n.$$

Equating the coefficients of corresponding terms in the two series, we see that $P_n(1) = 1$. Similarly, letting $x = -1$ we have

$$(1 + 2t + t^2)^{-1/2} = (1 + t)^{-1} = \frac{1}{1 + t} = 1 - t + t^2 - 3t^3 + \cdots \qquad (|t| < 1)$$

$$= \sum_{n=0}^{\infty} (-1)^n t^n = \sum_{n=0}^{\infty} P_n(-1)t^n,$$

so that $P_n(-1) = (-1)^n$.

7 The Laplace Transform

Definition of the Laplace Transform

1. $\mathscr{L}\{f(t)\} = \int_0^1 -e^{-st} dt + \int_1^\infty e^{-st} dt = \frac{1}{s} e^{-st} \Big|_0^1 - \frac{1}{s} e^{-st} \Big|_1^\infty$

$= \frac{1}{s} e^{-s} - \frac{1}{s} - \left(0 - \frac{1}{s} e^{-s}\right) = \frac{2}{s} e^{-s} - \frac{1}{s}, \quad s > 0$

2. $\mathscr{L}\{f(t)\} = \int_0^2 4e^{-st} dt = -\frac{4}{s} e^{-st} \Big|_0^2 = -\frac{4}{s}(e^{-2s} - 1), \quad s > 0$

3. $\mathscr{L}\{f(t)\} = \int_0^1 te^{-st} dt + \int_1^\infty e^{-st} dt = \left(-\frac{1}{s} te^{-st} - \frac{1}{s^2} e^{-st}\right) \Big|_0^1 - \frac{1}{s} e^{-st} \Big|_1^\infty$

$= \left(-\frac{1}{s} e^{-s} - \frac{1}{s^2} e^{-s}\right) - \left(0 - \frac{1}{s^2}\right) - \frac{1}{s}(0 - e^{-s}) = \frac{1}{s^2}(1 - e^{-s}), \quad s > 0$

4. $\mathscr{L}\{f(t)\} = \int_0^1 (2t + 1)e^{-st} dt = \left(-\frac{2}{s} te^{-st} - \frac{2}{s^2} e^{-st} - \frac{1}{s} e^{-st}\right) \Big|_0^1$

$= \left(-\frac{2}{s} e^{-s} - \frac{2}{s^2} e^{-s} - \frac{1}{s} e^{-s}\right) - \left(0 - \frac{2}{s^2} - \frac{1}{s}\right) = \frac{1}{s}(1 - 3e^{-s}) + \frac{2}{s^2}(1 - e^{-s}), \quad s > 0$

5. $\mathscr{L}\{f(t)\} = \int_0^\pi (\sin t)e^{-st} dt = \left(-\frac{s}{s^2 + 1} e^{-st} \sin t - \frac{1}{s^2 + 1} e^{-st} \cos t\right) \Big|_0^\pi$

$= \left(0 + \frac{1}{s^2 + 1} e^{-\pi s}\right) - \left(0 - \frac{1}{s^2 + 1}\right) = \frac{1}{s^2 + 1}(e^{-\pi s} + 1), \quad s > 0$

6. $\mathscr{L}\{f(t)\} = \int_{\pi/2}^\infty (\cos t)e^{-st} dt = \left(-\frac{s}{s^2 + 1} e^{-st} \cos t + \frac{1}{s^2 + 1} e^{-st} \sin t\right) \Big|_{\pi/2}^\infty$

$= 0 - \left(0 + \frac{1}{s^2 + 1} e^{-\pi s/2}\right) = -\frac{1}{s^2 + 1} e^{-\pi s/2}, \quad s > 0$

7. $f(t) = \begin{cases} 0, & 0 < t < 1 \\ t, & t > 1 \end{cases}$

$\mathscr{L}\{f(t)\} = \int_1^\infty te^{-st} dt = \left(-\frac{1}{s} te^{-st} - \frac{1}{s^2} e^{-st}\right) \Big|_1^\infty = \frac{1}{s} e^{-s} + \frac{1}{s^2} e^{-s}, \quad s > 0$

8. $f(t) = \begin{cases} 0, & 0 < t < 1 \\ 2t - 2, & t > 1 \end{cases}$

$$\mathcal{L}\{f(t)\} = 2\int_1^\infty (t-1)e^{-st}\,dt = 2\left(-\frac{1}{s}(t-1)e^{-st} - \frac{1}{s^2}e^{-st}\right)\bigg|_1^\infty = \frac{2}{s^2}e^{-s}, \quad s > 0$$

9. The function is $f(t) = \begin{cases} 1-t, & 0 < t < 1 \\ 0, & t > 1 \end{cases}$ so

$$\mathcal{L}\{f(t)\} = \int_0^1 (1-t)e^{-st}\,dt + \int_1^\infty 0e^{-st}\,dt = \int_0^1 (1-t)e^{-st}\,dt = \left(-\frac{1}{s}(1-t)e^{-st} + \frac{1}{s^2}e^{-st}\right)\bigg|_0^1$$

$$= \frac{1}{s^2}e^{-s} + \frac{1}{s} - \frac{1}{s^2}, \quad s > 0$$

10. $f(t) = \begin{cases} 0, & 0 < t < a \\ c, & a < t < b; \\ 0, & t > b \end{cases}$ $\mathcal{L}\{f(t)\} = \int_a^b ce^{-st}\,dt = -\frac{c}{s}e^{-st}\bigg|_a^b = \frac{c}{s}(e^{-sa} - e^{-sb}), \quad s > 0$

11. $\mathcal{L}\{f(t)\} = \int_0^\infty e^{t+7}e^{-st}\,dt = e^7\int_0^\infty e^{(1-s)t}\,dt = \frac{e^7}{1-s}e^{(1-s)t}\bigg|_0^\infty = 0 - \frac{e^7}{1-s} = \frac{e^7}{s-1}, \quad s > 1$

12. $\mathcal{L}\{f(t)\} = \int_0^\infty e^{-2t-5}e^{-st}\,dt = e^{-5}\int_0^\infty e^{-(s+2)t}\,dt = -\frac{e^{-5}}{s+2}e^{-(s+2)t}\bigg|_0^\infty = \frac{e^{-5}}{s+2}, \quad s > -2$

13. $\mathcal{L}\{f(t)\} = \int_0^\infty te^{4t}e^{-st}\,dt = \int_0^\infty te^{(4-s)t}\,dt = \left(\frac{1}{4-s}te^{(4-s)t} - \frac{1}{(4-s)^2}e^{(4-s)t}\right)\bigg|_0^\infty$

$$= \frac{1}{(4-s)^2}, \quad s > 4$$

14. $\mathcal{L}\{f(t)\} = \int_0^\infty t^2 e^{-2t}e^{-st}\,dt = \int_0^\infty t^2 e^{-(s+2)t}\,dt$

$$= \left(-\frac{1}{s+2}t^2 e^{-(s+2)t} - \frac{2}{(s+2)^2}te^{-(s+2)t} - \frac{2}{(s+2)^3}e^{-(s+2)t}\right)\bigg|_0^\infty = \frac{2}{(s+2)^3}, \quad s > -2$$

15. $\mathcal{L}\{f(t)\} = \int_0^\infty e^{-t}(\sin t)e^{-st}\,dt = \int_0^\infty (\sin t)e^{-(s+1)t}\,dt$

$$= \left(\frac{-(s+1)}{(s+1)^2+1}e^{-(s+1)t}\sin t - \frac{1}{(s+1)^2+1}e^{-(s+1)t}\cos t\right)\bigg|_0^\infty$$

$$= \frac{1}{(s+1)^2+1} = \frac{1}{s^2+2s+2}, \quad s > -1$$

16. $\mathcal{L}\{f(t)\} = \int_0^\infty e^t(\cos t)e^{-st}\,dt = \int_0^\infty (\cos t)e^{(1-s)t}\,dt$

$$= \left(\frac{1-s}{(1-s)^2+1}e^{(1-s)t}\cos t + \frac{1}{(1-s)^2+1}e^{(1-s)t}\sin t\right)\bigg|_0^\infty$$

$$= -\frac{1-s}{(1-s)^2+1} = \frac{s-1}{s^2-2s+2}, \quad s > 1$$

353

Exercises 7.1   Definition of the Laplace Transform

17. $\mathcal{L}\{f(t)\} = \int_0^\infty t(\cos t)e^{-st}dt$

$$= \left[\left(-\frac{st}{s^2+1} - \frac{s^2-1}{(s^2+1)^2}\right)(\cos t)e^{-st} + \left(\frac{t}{s^2+1} + \frac{2s}{(s^2+1)^2}\right)(\sin t)e^{-st}\right]_0^\infty$$

$$= \frac{s^2-1}{(s^2+1)^2}, \quad s > 0$$

18. $\mathcal{L}\{f(t)\} = \int_0^\infty t(\sin t)e^{-st}dt$

$$= \left[\left(-\frac{t}{s^2+1} - \frac{2s}{(s^2+1)^2}\right)(\cos t)e^{-st} - \left(\frac{st}{s^2+1} + \frac{s^2-1}{(s^2+1)^2}\right)(\sin t)e^{-st}\right]_0^\infty$$

$$= \frac{2s}{(s^2+1)^2}, \quad s > 0$$

19. $\mathcal{L}\{2t^4\} = 2\dfrac{4!}{s^5}$

20. $\mathcal{L}\{t^5\} = \dfrac{5!}{s^6}$

21. $\mathcal{L}\{4t - 10\} = \dfrac{4}{s^2} - \dfrac{10}{s}$

22. $\mathcal{L}\{7t + 3\} = \dfrac{7}{s^2} + \dfrac{3}{s}$

23. $\mathcal{L}\{t^2 + 6t - 3\} = \dfrac{2}{s^3} + \dfrac{6}{s^2} - \dfrac{3}{s}$

24. $\mathcal{L}\{-4t^2 + 16t + 9\} = -4\dfrac{2}{s^3} + \dfrac{16}{s^2} + \dfrac{9}{s}$

25. $\mathcal{L}\{t^3 + 3t^2 + 3t + 1\} = \dfrac{3!}{s^4} + 3\dfrac{2}{s^3} + \dfrac{3}{s^2} + \dfrac{1}{s}$

26. $\mathcal{L}\{8t^3 - 12t^2 + 6t - 1\} = 8\dfrac{3!}{s^4} - 12\dfrac{2}{s^3} + \dfrac{6}{s^2} - \dfrac{1}{s}$

27. $\mathcal{L}\{1 + e^{4t}\} = \dfrac{1}{s} + \dfrac{1}{s-4}$

28. $\mathcal{L}\{t^2 - e^{-9t} + 5\} = \dfrac{2}{s^3} - \dfrac{1}{s+9} + \dfrac{5}{s}$

29. $\mathcal{L}\{1 + 2e^{2t} + e^{4t}\} = \dfrac{1}{s} + \dfrac{2}{s-2} + \dfrac{1}{s-4}$

30. $\mathcal{L}\{e^{2t} - 2 + e^{-2t}\} = \dfrac{1}{s-2} - \dfrac{2}{s} + \dfrac{1}{s+2}$

31. $\mathcal{L}\{4t^2 - 5\sin 3t\} = 4\dfrac{2}{s^3} - 5\dfrac{3}{s^2+9}$

32. $\mathcal{L}\{\cos 5t + \sin 2t\} = \dfrac{s}{s^2+25} + \dfrac{2}{s^2+4}$

33. $\mathcal{L}\{\sinh kt\} = \dfrac{1}{2}\mathcal{L}\{e^{kt} - e^{-kt}\} = \dfrac{1}{2}\left[\dfrac{1}{s-k} - \dfrac{1}{s+k}\right] = \dfrac{k}{s^2-k^2}$

34. $\mathcal{L}\{\cosh kt\} = \dfrac{1}{2}\mathcal{L}\{e^{kt} + e^{kt}\} = \dfrac{s}{s^2-k^2}$

35. $\mathcal{L}\{e^t \sinh t\} = \mathcal{L}\left\{e^t\dfrac{e^t - e^{-t}}{2}\right\} = \mathcal{L}\left\{\dfrac{1}{2}e^{2t} - \dfrac{1}{2}\right\} = \dfrac{1}{2(s-2)} - \dfrac{1}{2s}$

36. $\mathcal{L}\{e^{-t}\cosh t\} = \mathcal{L}\left\{e^{-t}\dfrac{e^t + e^{-t}}{2}\right\} = \mathcal{L}\left\{\dfrac{1}{2} + \dfrac{1}{2}e^{-2t}\right\} = \dfrac{1}{2s} + \dfrac{1}{2(s+2)}$

37. $\mathscr{L}\{\sin 2t \cos 2t\} = \mathscr{L}\left\{\dfrac{1}{2}\sin 4t\right\} = \dfrac{2}{s^2 + 16}$

38. $\mathscr{L}\{\cos^2 t\} = \mathscr{L}\left\{\dfrac{1}{2} + \dfrac{1}{2}\cos 2t\right\} = \dfrac{1}{2s} + \dfrac{1}{2}\dfrac{s}{s^2 + 4}$

39. From the addition formula for the sine function, $\sin(4t + 5) = (\sin 4t)(\cos 5) + (\cos 4t)(\sin 5)$ so

$$\mathscr{L}\{\sin(4t + 5)\} = (\cos 5)\,\mathscr{L}\{\sin 4t\} + (\sin 5)\,\mathscr{L}\{\cos 4t\}$$

$$= (\cos 5)\frac{4}{s^2 + 16} + (\sin 5)\frac{s}{s^2 + 16}$$

$$= \frac{4\cos 5 + (\sin 5)s}{s^2 + 16}.$$

40. From the addition formula for the cosine function,

$$\cos\left(t - \frac{\pi}{6}\right) = \cos t \cos\frac{\pi}{6} + \sin t \sin\frac{\pi}{6} = \frac{\sqrt{3}}{2}\cos t + \frac{1}{2}\sin t$$

so

$$\mathscr{L}\left\{\cos\left(t - \frac{\pi}{6}\right)\right\} = \frac{\sqrt{3}}{2}\mathscr{L}\{\cos t\} + \frac{1}{2}\mathscr{L}\{\sin t\}$$

$$= \frac{\sqrt{3}}{2}\frac{s}{s^2 + 1} + \frac{1}{2}\frac{1}{s^2 + 1} = \frac{1}{2}\frac{\sqrt{3}\,s + 1}{s^2 + 1}.$$

41. (a) Using integration by parts for $\alpha > 0$,

$$\Gamma(\alpha + 1) = \int_0^\infty t^\alpha e^{-t}\,dt = -t^\alpha e^{-t}\Big|_0^\infty + \alpha \int_0^\infty t^{\alpha-1} e^{-t}\,dt = \alpha\Gamma(\alpha).$$

(b) Let $u = st$ so that $du = s\,dt$. Then

$$\mathscr{L}\{t^\alpha\} = \int_0^\infty e^{-st} t^\alpha dt = \int_0^\infty e^{-u}\left(\frac{u}{s}\right)^\alpha \frac{1}{s}\,du = \frac{1}{s^{\alpha+1}}\Gamma(\alpha + 1), \quad \alpha > -1.$$

42. (a) $\mathscr{L}\{t^{-1/2}\} = \dfrac{\Gamma(1/2)}{s^{1/2}} = \sqrt{\dfrac{\pi}{s}}$

(b) $\mathscr{L}\{t^{1/2}\} = \dfrac{\Gamma(3/2)}{s^{3/2}} = \dfrac{\sqrt{\pi}}{2s^{3/2}}$

(c) $\mathscr{L}\{t^{3/2}\} = \dfrac{\Gamma(5/2)}{s^{5/2}} = \dfrac{3\sqrt{\pi}}{4s^{5/2}}$

43. Let $F(t) = t^{1/3}$. Then $F(t)$ is of exponential order, but $f(t) = F'(t) = \frac{1}{3}t^{-2/3}$ is unbounded near $t = 0$ and hence is not of exponential order. Let

$$f(t) = 2te^{t^2}\cos e^{t^2} = \frac{d}{dt}\sin e^{t^2}.$$

Exercises 7.1 Definition of the Laplace Transform

This function is not of exponential order, but we can show that its Laplace transform exists. Using integration by parts we have

$$\mathscr{L}\{2te^{t^2}\cos e^{t^2}\} = \int_0^\infty e^{-st}\left(\frac{d}{dt}\sin e^{t^2}\right) dt = \lim_{a\to\infty}\left[e^{-st}\sin e^{t^2}\Big|_0^a + s\int_0^a e^{-st}\sin e^{t^2}\, dt\right]$$

$$= -\sin 1 + s\int_0^\infty e^{-st}\sin e^{t^2}\, dt = s\mathscr{L}\{\sin e^{t^2}\} - \sin 1.$$

Since $\sin e^{t^2}$ is continuous and of exponential order, $\mathscr{L}\{\sin e^{t^2}\}$ exists, and therefore $\mathscr{L}\{2te^{t^2}\cos e^{t^2}\}$ exists.

44. The relation will be valid when s is greater than the maximum of c_1 and c_2.

45. Since e^t is an increasing function and $t^2 > \ln M + ct$ for $M > 0$ we have $e^{t^2} > e^{\ln M + ct} = Me^{ct}$ for t sufficiently large and for any c. Thus, e^{t^2} is not of exponential order.

46. Assuming that (c) of Theorem 7.1.1 is applicable with a complex exponent, we have

$$\mathscr{L}\{e^{(a+ib)t}\} = \frac{1}{s-(a+ib)} = \frac{1}{(s-a)-ib}\frac{(s-a)+ib}{(s-a)+ib} = \frac{s-a+ib}{(s-a)^2+b^2}.$$

By Euler's formula, $e^{i\theta} = \cos\theta + i\sin\theta$, so

$$\mathscr{L}\{e^{(a+ib)t}\} = \mathscr{L}\{e^{at}e^{ibt}\} = \mathscr{L}\{e^{at}(\cos bt + i\sin bt)\}$$

$$= \mathscr{L}\{e^{at}\cos bt\} + i\mathscr{L}\{e^{at}\sin bt\}$$

$$= \frac{s-a}{(s-a)^2+b^2} + i\frac{b}{(s-a)^2+b^2}.$$

Equating real and imaginary parts we get

$$\mathscr{L}\{e^{at}\cos bt\} = \frac{s-a}{(s-a)^2+b^2} \quad \text{and} \quad \mathscr{L}\{e^{at}\sin bt\} = \frac{b}{(s-a)^2+b^2}.$$

47. We want $f(\alpha x + \beta y) = \alpha f(x) + \beta f(y)$ or

$$m(\alpha x + \beta y) + b = \alpha(mx + b) + \beta(my + b) = m(\alpha x + \beta y) + (\alpha + \beta)b$$

for all real numbers α and β. Taking $\alpha = \beta = 1$ we see that $b = 2b$, so $b = 0$. Thus, $f(x) = mx + b$ will be a linear transformation when $b = 0$.

48. Assume that $\mathscr{L}\{t^{n-1}\} = (n-1)!/s^n$. Then, using the definition of the Laplace transform and integration by parts, we have

$$\mathscr{L}\{t^n\} = \int_0^\infty e^{-st}t^n\, dt = -\frac{1}{s}e^{-st}t^n\Big|_0^\infty + \frac{n}{s}\int_0^\infty e^{-st}t^{n-1}\, dt$$

$$= 0 + \frac{n}{s}\mathscr{L}\{t^{n-1}\} = \frac{n}{s}\frac{(n-1)!}{s^n} = \frac{n!}{s^{n+1}}.$$

Exercises 7.2

Inverse Transforms and Transforms of Derivatives

1. $\mathscr{L}^{-1}\left\{\dfrac{1}{s^3}\right\} = \dfrac{1}{2}\mathscr{L}^{-1}\left\{\dfrac{2}{s^3}\right\} = \dfrac{1}{2}t^2$

2. $\mathscr{L}^{-1}\left\{\dfrac{1}{s^4}\right\} = \dfrac{1}{6}\mathscr{L}^{-1}\left\{\dfrac{3!}{s^4}\right\} = \dfrac{1}{6}t^3$

3. $\mathscr{L}^{-1}\left\{\dfrac{1}{s^2} - \dfrac{48}{s^5}\right\} = \mathscr{L}^{-1}\left\{\dfrac{1}{s^2} - \dfrac{48}{24}\cdot\dfrac{4!}{s^5}\right\} = t - 2t^4$

4. $\mathscr{L}^{-1}\left\{\left(\dfrac{2}{s} - \dfrac{1}{s^3}\right)^2\right\} = \mathscr{L}^{-1}\left\{4\cdot\dfrac{1}{s^2} - \dfrac{4}{6}\cdot\dfrac{3!}{s^4} + \dfrac{1}{120}\cdot\dfrac{5!}{s^6}\right\} = 4t - \dfrac{2}{3}t^3 + \dfrac{1}{120}t^5$

5. $\mathscr{L}^{-1}\left\{\dfrac{(s+1)^3}{s^4}\right\} = \mathscr{L}^{-1}\left\{\dfrac{1}{s} + 3\cdot\dfrac{1}{s^2} + \dfrac{3}{2}\cdot\dfrac{2}{s^3} + \dfrac{1}{6}\cdot\dfrac{3!}{s^4}\right\} = 1 + 3t + \dfrac{3}{2}t^2 + \dfrac{1}{6}t^3$

6. $\mathscr{L}^{-1}\left\{\dfrac{(s+2)^2}{s^3}\right\} = \mathscr{L}^{-1}\left\{\dfrac{1}{s} + 4\cdot\dfrac{1}{s^2} + 2\cdot\dfrac{2}{s^3}\right\} = 1 + 4t + 2t^2$

7. $\mathscr{L}^{-1}\left\{\dfrac{1}{s^2} - \dfrac{1}{s} + \dfrac{1}{s-2}\right\} = t - 1 + e^{2t}$

8. $\mathscr{L}^{-1}\left\{\dfrac{4}{s} + \dfrac{6}{s^5} - \dfrac{1}{s+8}\right\} = \mathscr{L}^{-1}\left\{4\cdot\dfrac{1}{s} + \dfrac{1}{4}\cdot\dfrac{4!}{s^5} - \dfrac{1}{s+8}\right\} = 4 + \dfrac{1}{4}t^4 - e^{-8t}$

9. $\mathscr{L}^{-1}\left\{\dfrac{1}{4s+1}\right\} = \dfrac{1}{4}\mathscr{L}^{-1}\left\{\dfrac{1}{s+1/4}\right\} = \dfrac{1}{4}e^{-t/4}$

10. $\mathscr{L}^{-1}\left\{\dfrac{1}{5s-2}\right\} = \mathscr{L}^{-1}\left\{\dfrac{1}{5}\cdot\dfrac{1}{s-2/5}\right\} = \dfrac{1}{5}e^{2t/5}$

11. $\mathscr{L}^{-1}\left\{\dfrac{5}{s^2+49}\right\} = \mathscr{L}^{-1}\left\{\dfrac{5}{7}\cdot\dfrac{7}{s^2+49}\right\} = \dfrac{5}{7}\sin 7t$

12. $\mathscr{L}^{-1}\left\{\dfrac{10s}{s^2+16}\right\} = 10\cos 4t$

13. $\mathscr{L}^{-1}\left\{\dfrac{4s}{4s^2+1}\right\} = \mathscr{L}^{-1}\left\{\dfrac{s}{s^2+1/4}\right\} = \cos\dfrac{1}{2}t$

14. $\mathscr{L}^{-1}\left\{\dfrac{1}{4s^2+1}\right\} = \mathscr{L}^{-1}\left\{\dfrac{1}{2}\cdot\dfrac{1/2}{s^2+1/4}\right\} = \dfrac{1}{2}\sin\dfrac{1}{2}t$

Exercises 7.2   Inverse Transforms and Transforms of Derivatives

15. $\mathcal{L}^{-1}\left\{\dfrac{2s-6}{s^2+9}\right\} = \mathcal{L}^{-1}\left\{2\cdot\dfrac{s}{s^2+9} - 2\cdot\dfrac{3}{s^2+9}\right\} = 2\cos 3t - 2\sin 3t$

16. $\mathcal{L}^{-1}\left\{\dfrac{s+1}{s^2+2}\right\} = \mathcal{L}^{-1}\left\{\dfrac{s}{s^2+2} + \dfrac{1}{\sqrt{2}}\dfrac{\sqrt{2}}{s^2+2}\right\} = \cos\sqrt{2}\,t + \dfrac{\sqrt{2}}{2}\sin\sqrt{2}\,t$

17. $\mathcal{L}^{-1}\left\{\dfrac{1}{s^2+3s}\right\} = \mathcal{L}^{-1}\left\{\dfrac{1}{3}\cdot\dfrac{1}{s} - \dfrac{1}{3}\cdot\dfrac{1}{s+3}\right\} = \dfrac{1}{3} - \dfrac{1}{3}e^{-3t}$

18. $\mathcal{L}^{-1}\left\{\dfrac{s+1}{s^2-4s}\right\} = \mathcal{L}^{-1}\left\{-\dfrac{1}{4}\cdot\dfrac{1}{s} + \dfrac{5}{4}\cdot\dfrac{1}{s-4}\right\} = -\dfrac{1}{4} + \dfrac{5}{4}e^{4t}$

19. $\mathcal{L}^{-1}\left\{\dfrac{s}{s^2+2s-3}\right\} = \mathcal{L}^{-1}\left\{\dfrac{1}{4}\cdot\dfrac{1}{s-1} + \dfrac{3}{4}\cdot\dfrac{1}{s+3}\right\} = \dfrac{1}{4}e^{t} + \dfrac{3}{4}e^{-3t}$

20. $\mathcal{L}^{-1}\left\{\dfrac{1}{s^2+s-20}\right\} = \mathcal{L}^{-1}\left\{\dfrac{1}{9}\cdot\dfrac{1}{s-4} - \dfrac{1}{9}\cdot\dfrac{1}{s+5}\right\} = \dfrac{1}{9}e^{4t} - \dfrac{1}{9}e^{-5t}$

21. $\mathcal{L}^{-1}\left\{\dfrac{0.9s}{(s-0.1)(s+0.2)}\right\} = \mathcal{L}^{-1}\left\{(0.3)\cdot\dfrac{1}{s-0.1} + (0.6)\cdot\dfrac{1}{s+0.2}\right\} = 0.3e^{0.1t} + 0.6e^{-0.2t}$

22. $\mathcal{L}^{-1}\left\{\dfrac{s-3}{(s-\sqrt{3})(s+\sqrt{3})}\right\} = \mathcal{L}^{-1}\left\{\dfrac{s}{s^2-3} - \sqrt{3}\cdot\dfrac{\sqrt{3}}{s^2-3}\right\} = \cosh\sqrt{3}\,t - \sqrt{3}\sinh\sqrt{3}\,t$

23. $\mathcal{L}^{-1}\left\{\dfrac{s}{(s-2)(s-3)(s-6)}\right\} = \mathcal{L}^{-1}\left\{\dfrac{1}{2}\cdot\dfrac{1}{s-2} - \dfrac{1}{s-3} + \dfrac{1}{2}\cdot\dfrac{1}{s-6}\right\} = \dfrac{1}{2}e^{2t} - e^{3t} + \dfrac{1}{2}e^{6t}$

24. $\mathcal{L}^{-1}\left\{\dfrac{s^2+1}{s(s-1)(s+1)(s-2)}\right\} = \mathcal{L}^{-1}\left\{\dfrac{1}{2}\cdot\dfrac{1}{s} - \dfrac{1}{s-1} - \dfrac{1}{3}\cdot\dfrac{1}{s+1} + \dfrac{5}{6}\cdot\dfrac{1}{s-2}\right\}$

$$= \dfrac{1}{2} - e^{t} - \dfrac{1}{3}e^{-t} + \dfrac{5}{6}e^{2t}$$

25. $\mathcal{L}^{-1}\left\{\dfrac{1}{s^3+5s}\right\} = \mathcal{L}^{-1}\left\{\dfrac{1}{s(s^2+5)}\right\} = \mathcal{L}^{-1}\left\{\dfrac{1}{5}\cdot\dfrac{1}{s} - \dfrac{1}{5}\dfrac{s}{s^2+5}\right\} = \dfrac{1}{5} - \dfrac{1}{5}\cos\sqrt{5}\,t$

26. $\mathcal{L}^{-1}\left\{\dfrac{s}{(s^2+4)(s+2)}\right\} = \mathcal{L}^{-1}\left\{\dfrac{1}{4}\cdot\dfrac{s}{s^2+4} + \dfrac{1}{4}\cdot\dfrac{2}{s^2+4} - \dfrac{1}{4}\cdot\dfrac{1}{s+2}\right\} = \dfrac{1}{4}\cos 2t + \dfrac{1}{4}\sin 2t - \dfrac{1}{4}e^{-2t}$

27. $\mathcal{L}^{-1}\left\{\dfrac{2s-4}{(s^2+s)(s^2+1)}\right\} = \mathcal{L}^{-1}\left\{\dfrac{2s-4}{s(s+1)(s^2+1)}\right\} = \mathcal{L}^{-1}\left\{-\dfrac{4}{s} + \dfrac{3}{s+1} + \dfrac{s}{s^2+1} + \dfrac{3}{s^2+1}\right\}$

$$= -4 + 3e^{-t} + \cos t + 3\sin t$$

28. $\mathcal{L}^{-1}\left\{\dfrac{1}{s^4-9}\right\} = \mathcal{L}^{-1}\left\{\dfrac{1}{6\sqrt{3}}\cdot\dfrac{\sqrt{3}}{s^2-3} - \dfrac{1}{6\sqrt{3}}\cdot\dfrac{\sqrt{3}}{s^2+3}\right\} = \dfrac{1}{6\sqrt{3}}\sinh\sqrt{3}\,t - \dfrac{1}{6\sqrt{3}}\sin\sqrt{3}\,t$

29. $\mathscr{L}^{-1}\left\{\dfrac{1}{(s^2+1)(s^2+4)}\right\} = \mathscr{L}^{-1}\left\{\dfrac{1}{3}\cdot\dfrac{1}{s^2+1} - \dfrac{1}{3}\cdot\dfrac{1}{s^2+4}\right\}$

$\qquad\qquad\qquad\qquad = \mathscr{L}^{-1}\left\{\dfrac{1}{3}\cdot\dfrac{1}{s^2+1} - \dfrac{1}{6}\cdot\dfrac{2}{s^2+4}\right\}$

$\qquad\qquad\qquad\qquad = \dfrac{1}{3}\sin t - \dfrac{1}{6}\sin 2t$

30. $\mathscr{L}^{-1}\left\{\dfrac{6s+3}{(s^2+1)(s^2+4)}\right\} = \mathscr{L}^{-1}\left\{2\cdot\dfrac{s}{s^2+1} + \dfrac{1}{s^2+1} - 2\cdot\dfrac{s}{s^2+4} - \dfrac{1}{2}\cdot\dfrac{2}{s^2+4}\right\}$

$\qquad\qquad\qquad\qquad\qquad = 2\cos t + \sin t - 2\cos 2t - \dfrac{1}{2}\sin 2t$

31. The Laplace transform of the initial-value problem is

$$s\,\mathscr{L}\{y\} - y(0) - \mathscr{L}\{y\} = \dfrac{1}{s}.$$

Solving for $\mathscr{L}\{y\}$ we obtain

$$\mathscr{L}\{y\} = -\dfrac{1}{s} + \dfrac{1}{s-1}.$$

Thus

$$y = -1 + e^t.$$

32. The Laplace transform of the initial-value problem is

$$2s\,\mathscr{L}\{y\} - 2y(0) + \mathscr{L}\{y\} = 0.$$

Solving for $\mathscr{L}\{y\}$ we obtain

$$\mathscr{L}\{y\} = \dfrac{6}{2s+1} = \dfrac{3}{s+1/2}.$$

Thus

$$y = 3e^{-t/2}.$$

33. The Laplace transform of the initial-value problem is

$$s\,\mathscr{L}\{y\} - y(0) + 6\mathscr{L}\{y\} = \dfrac{1}{s-4}.$$

Solving for $\mathscr{L}\{y\}$ we obtain

$$\mathscr{L}\{y\} = \dfrac{1}{(s-4)(s+6)} + \dfrac{2}{s+6} = \dfrac{1}{10}\cdot\dfrac{1}{s-4} + \dfrac{19}{10}\cdot\dfrac{1}{s+6}.$$

Thus

$$y = \dfrac{1}{10}e^{4t} + \dfrac{19}{10}e^{-6t}.$$

34. The Laplace transform of the initial-value problem is

$$s\,\mathscr{L}\{y\} - \mathscr{L}\{y\} = \dfrac{2s}{s^2+25}.$$

Exercises 7.2 Inverse Transforms and Transforms of Derivatives

Solving for $\mathcal{L}\{y\}$ we obtain

$$\mathcal{L}\{y\} = \frac{2s}{(s-1)(s^2+25)} = \frac{1}{13} \cdot \frac{1}{s-1} - \frac{1}{13} \frac{s}{s^2+25} + \frac{5}{13} \cdot \frac{5}{s^2+25}.$$

Thus

$$y = \frac{1}{13}e^t - \frac{1}{13}\cos 5t + \frac{5}{13}\sin 5t.$$

35. The Laplace transform of the initial-value problem is

$$s^2 \mathcal{L}\{y\} - sy(0) - y'(0) + 5\left[s\,\mathcal{L}\{y\} - y(0)\right] + 4\mathcal{L}\{y\} = 0.$$

Solving for $\mathcal{L}\{y\}$ we obtain

$$\mathcal{L}\{y\} = \frac{s+5}{s^2+5s+4} = \frac{4}{3}\frac{1}{s+1} - \frac{1}{3}\frac{1}{s+4}.$$

Thus

$$y = \frac{4}{3}e^{-t} - \frac{1}{3}e^{-4t}.$$

36. The Laplace transform of the initial-value problem is

$$s^2 \mathcal{L}\{y\} - sy(0) - y'(0) - 4\left[s\,\mathcal{L}\{y\} - y(0)\right] = \frac{6}{s-3} - \frac{3}{s+1}.$$

Solving for $\mathcal{L}\{y\}$ we obtain

$$\mathcal{L}\{y\} = \frac{6}{(s-3)(s^2-4s)} - \frac{3}{(s+1)(s^2-4s)} + \frac{s-5}{s^2-4s}$$

$$= \frac{5}{2} \cdot \frac{1}{s} - \frac{2}{s-3} - \frac{3}{5} \cdot \frac{1}{s+1} + \frac{11}{10} \cdot \frac{1}{s-4}.$$

Thus

$$y = \frac{5}{2} - 2e^{3t} - \frac{3}{5}e^{-t} + \frac{11}{10}e^{4t}.$$

37. The Laplace transform of the initial-value problem is

$$s^2 \mathcal{L}\{y\} - sy(0) + \mathcal{L}\{y\} = \frac{2}{s^2+2}.$$

Solving for $\mathcal{L}\{y\}$ we obtain

$$\mathcal{L}\{y\} = \frac{2}{(s^2+1)(s^2+2)} + \frac{10s}{s^2+1} = \frac{10s}{s^2+1} + \frac{2}{s^2+1} - \frac{2}{s^2+2}.$$

Thus

$$y = 10\cos t + 2\sin t - \sqrt{2}\sin\sqrt{2}\,t.$$

38. The Laplace transform of the initial-value problem is

$$s^2 \mathcal{L}\{y\} + 9\mathcal{L}\{y\} = \frac{1}{s-1}.$$

Solving for $\mathscr{L}\{y\}$ we obtain

$$\mathscr{L}\{y\} = \frac{1}{(s-1)(s^2+9)} = \frac{1}{10} \cdot \frac{1}{s-1} - \frac{1}{10} \cdot \frac{1}{s^2+9} - \frac{1}{10} \cdot \frac{s}{s^2+9}.$$

Thus

$$y = \frac{1}{10}e^t - \frac{1}{30}\sin 3t - \frac{1}{10}\cos 3t.$$

39. The Laplace transform of the initial-value problem is

$$2\left[s^3 \mathscr{L}\{y\} - s^2 y(0) - sy'(0) - y''(0)\right] + 3[s^2 \mathscr{L}\{y\} - sy(0) - y'(0)] - 3[s \mathscr{L}\{y\} - y(0)] - 2\mathscr{L}\{y\} = \frac{1}{s+1}.$$

Solving for $\mathscr{L}\{y\}$ we obtain

$$\mathscr{L}\{y\} = \frac{2s+3}{(s+1)(s-1)(2s+1)(s+2)} = \frac{1}{2}\frac{1}{s+1} + \frac{5}{18}\frac{1}{s-1} - \frac{8}{9}\frac{1}{s+1/2} + \frac{1}{9}\frac{1}{s+2}.$$

Thus

$$y = \frac{1}{2}e^{-t} + \frac{5}{18}e^t - \frac{8}{9}e^{-t/2} + \frac{1}{9}e^{-2t}.$$

40. The Laplace transform of the initial-value problem is

$$s^3 \mathscr{L}\{y\} - s^2(0) - sy'(0) - y''(0) + 2[s^2 \mathscr{L}\{y\} - sy(0) - y'(0)] - [s \mathscr{L}\{y\} - y(0)] - 2\mathscr{L}\{y\} = \frac{3}{s^2+9}.$$

Solving for $\mathscr{L}\{y\}$ we obtain

$$\mathscr{L}\{y\} = \frac{s^2+12}{(s-1)(s+1)(s+2)(s^2+9)}$$

$$= \frac{13}{60}\frac{1}{s-1} - \frac{13}{20}\frac{1}{s+1} + \frac{16}{39}\frac{1}{s+2} + \frac{3}{130}\frac{s}{s^2+9} - \frac{1}{65}\frac{3}{s^2+9}.$$

Thus

$$y = \frac{13}{60}e^t - \frac{13}{20}e^{-t} + \frac{16}{39}e^{-2t} + \frac{3}{130}\cos 3t - \frac{1}{65}\sin 3t.$$

41. The Laplace transform of the initial-value problem is

$$s \mathscr{L}\{y\} + \mathscr{L}\{y\} = \frac{s+3}{s^2+6s+13}.$$

Solving for $\mathscr{L}\{y\}$ we obtain

$$\mathscr{L}\{y\} = \frac{s+3}{(s+1)(s^2+6s+13)} = \frac{1}{4} \cdot \frac{1}{s+1} - \frac{1}{4} \cdot \frac{s+1}{s^2+6s+13}$$

$$= \frac{1}{4} \cdot \frac{1}{s+1} - \frac{1}{4}\left(\frac{s+3}{(s+3)^2+4} - \frac{2}{(s+3)^2+4}\right).$$

Thus

$$y = \frac{1}{4}e^{-t} - \frac{1}{4}e^{-3t}\cos 2t + \frac{1}{4}e^{-3t}\sin 2t.$$

Exercises 7.2 Inverse Transforms and Transforms of Derivatives

42. The Laplace transform of the initial-value problem is

$$s^2 \mathscr{L}\{y\} - s \cdot 1 - 3 - 2[s\,\mathscr{L}\{y\} - 1] + 5\,\mathscr{L}\{y\} = (s^2 - 2s + 5)\,\mathscr{L}\{y\} - s - 1 = 0.$$

Solving for $\mathscr{L}\{y\}$ we obtain

$$\mathscr{L}\{y\} = \frac{s+1}{s^2 - 2s + 5} = \frac{s-1+2}{(s-1)^2 + 2^2} = \frac{s-1}{(s-1)^2 + 2^2} + \frac{2}{(s-1)^2 + 2^2}.$$

Thus

$$y = e^t \cos 2t + e^t \sin 2t.$$

43. (a) Differentiating $f(t) = te^{at}$ we get $f'(t) = ate^{at} + e^{at}$ so $\mathscr{L}\{ate^{at} + e^{at}\} = s\mathscr{L}\{te^{at}\}$, where we have used $f(0) = 0$. Writing the equation as

$$a\,\mathscr{L}\{te^{at}\} + \mathscr{L}\{e^{at}\} = s\,\mathscr{L}\{te^{at}\}$$

and solving for $\mathscr{L}\{te^{at}\}$ we get

$$\mathscr{L}\{te^{at}\} = \frac{1}{s-a}\,\mathscr{L}\{e^{at}\} = \frac{1}{(s-a)^2}.$$

(b) Starting with $f(t) = t\sin kt$ we have

$$f'(t) = kt\cos kt + \sin kt$$

$$f''(t) = -k^2 t\sin kt + 2k\cos kt.$$

Then

$$\mathscr{L}\{-k^2 t\sin t + 2k\cos kt\} = s^2\,\mathscr{L}\{t\sin kt\}$$

where we have used $f(0) = 0$ and $f'(0) = 0$. Writing the above equation as

$$-k^2\,\mathscr{L}\{t\sin kt\} + 2k\,\mathscr{L}\{\cos kt\} = s^2\,\mathscr{L}\{t\sin kt\}$$

and solving for $\mathscr{L}\{t\sin kt\}$ gives

$$\mathscr{L}\{t\sin kt\} = \frac{2k}{s^2 + k^2}\,\mathscr{L}\{\cos kt\} = \frac{2k}{s^2 + k^2}\frac{s}{s^2 + k^2} = \frac{2ks}{(s^2 + k^2)^2}.$$

44. Let $f_1(t) = 1$ and $f_2(t) = \begin{cases} 1, & t \geq 0,\ t \neq 1 \\ 0, & t = 1 \end{cases}$. Then $\mathscr{L}\{f_1(t)\} = \mathscr{L}\{f_2(t)\} = 1/s$, but $f_1(t) \neq f_2(t)$.

45. For $y'' - 4y' = 6e^{3t} - 3e^{-t}$ the transfer function is $W(s) = 1/(s^2 - 4s)$. The zero-input response is

$$y_0(t) = \mathscr{L}^{-1}\left\{\frac{s-5}{s^2 - 4s}\right\} = \mathscr{L}^{-1}\left\{\frac{5}{4}\cdot\frac{1}{s} - \frac{1}{4}\cdot\frac{1}{s-4}\right\} = \frac{5}{4} - \frac{1}{4}e^{4t},$$

362

and the zero-state response is

$$y_1(t) = \mathcal{L}^{-1}\left\{ \frac{6}{(s-3)(s^2-4s)} - \frac{3}{(s+1)(s^2-4s)} \right\}$$

$$= \mathcal{L}^{-1}\left\{ \frac{27}{20}\cdot\frac{1}{s-4} - \frac{2}{s-3} + \frac{5}{4}\cdot\frac{1}{s} - \frac{3}{5}\cdot\frac{1}{s+1} \right\}$$

$$= \frac{27}{20}e^{4t} - 2e^{3t} + \frac{5}{4} - \frac{3}{5}e^{-t}.$$

46. From Theorem 7.2.2, if f and f' are continuous and of exponential order, $\mathcal{L}\{f'(t)\} = sF(s) - f(0)$. From Theorem 7.1.3, $\lim_{s\to\infty}\mathcal{L}\{f'(t)\} = 0$ so

$$\lim_{s\to\infty}[sF(s) - f(0)] = 0 \quad \text{and} \quad \lim_{s\to\infty}F(s) = f(0).$$

For $f(t) = \cos kt$,

$$\lim_{s\to\infty} sF(s) = \lim_{s\to\infty} s\frac{s}{s^2+k^2} = 1 = f(0).$$

Exercises 7.3
Operational Properties I

1. $\mathcal{L}\{te^{10t}\} = \dfrac{1}{(s-10)^2}$

2. $\mathcal{L}\{te^{-6t}\} = \dfrac{1}{(s+6)^2}$

3. $\mathcal{L}\{t^3 e^{-2t}\} = \dfrac{3!}{(s+2)^4}$

4. $\mathcal{L}\{t^{10}e^{-7t}\} = \dfrac{10!}{(s+7)^{11}}$

5. $\mathcal{L}\{t(e^t + e^{2t})^2\} = \mathcal{L}\{te^{2t} + 2te^{3t} + te^{4t}\} = \dfrac{1}{(s-2)^2} + \dfrac{2}{(s-3)^2} + \dfrac{1}{(s-4)^2}$

6. $\mathcal{L}\{e^{2t}(t-1)^2\} = \mathcal{L}\{t^2 e^{2t} - 2te^{2t} + e^{2t}\} = \dfrac{2}{(s-2)^3} - \dfrac{2}{(s-2)^2} + \dfrac{1}{s-2}$

7. $\mathcal{L}\{e^t \sin 3t\} = \dfrac{3}{(s-1)^2 + 9}$

8. $\mathcal{L}\{e^{-2t}\cos 4t\} = \dfrac{s+2}{(s+2)^2 + 16}$

Exercises 7.3 Operational Properties I

9. $\mathscr{L}\{(1 - e^t + 3e^{-4t})\cos 5t\} = \mathscr{L}\{\cos 5t - e^t \cos 5t + 3e^{-4t}\cos 5t\}$

$$= \frac{s}{s^2 + 25} - \frac{s-1}{(s-1)^2 + 25} + \frac{3(s+4)}{(s+4)^2 + 25}$$

10. $\mathscr{L}\left\{e^{3t}\left(9 - 4t + 10\sin\frac{t}{2}\right)\right\} = \mathscr{L}\left\{9e^{3t} - 4te^{3t} + 10e^{3t}\sin\frac{t}{2}\right\} = \frac{9}{s-3} - \frac{4}{(s-3)^2} + \frac{5}{(s-3)^2 + 1/4}$

11. $\mathscr{L}^{-1}\left\{\dfrac{1}{(s+2)^3}\right\} = \mathscr{L}^{-1}\left\{\dfrac{1}{2}\dfrac{2}{(s+2)^3}\right\} = \dfrac{1}{2}t^2 e^{-2t}$

12. $\mathscr{L}^{-1}\left\{\dfrac{1}{(s-1)^4}\right\} = \dfrac{1}{6}\mathscr{L}^{-1}\left\{\dfrac{3!}{(s-1)^4}\right\} = \dfrac{1}{6}t^3 e^t$

13. $\mathscr{L}^{-1}\left\{\dfrac{1}{s^2 - 6s + 10}\right\} = \mathscr{L}^{-1}\left\{\dfrac{1}{(s-3)^2 + 1^2}\right\} = e^{3t}\sin t$

14. $\mathscr{L}^{-1}\left\{\dfrac{1}{s^2 + 2s + 5}\right\} = \mathscr{L}^{-1}\left\{\dfrac{1}{2}\dfrac{2}{(s+1)^2 + 2^2}\right\} = \dfrac{1}{2}e^{-t}\sin 2t$

15. $\mathscr{L}^{-1}\left\{\dfrac{s}{s^2 + 4s + 5}\right\} = \mathscr{L}^{-1}\left\{\dfrac{s+2}{(s+2)^2 + 1^2} - 2\dfrac{1}{(s+2)^2 + 1^2}\right\} = e^{-2t}\cos t - 2e^{-2t}\sin t$

16. $\mathscr{L}^{-1}\left\{\dfrac{2s+5}{s^2 + 6s + 34}\right\} = \mathscr{L}^{-1}\left\{2\dfrac{(s+3)}{(s+3)^2 + 5^2} - \dfrac{1}{5}\dfrac{5}{(s+3)^2 + 5^2}\right\} = 2e^{-3t}\cos 5t - \dfrac{1}{5}e^{-3t}\sin 5t$

17. $\mathscr{L}^{-1}\left\{\dfrac{s}{(s+1)^2}\right\} = \mathscr{L}^{-1}\left\{\dfrac{s+1-1}{(s+1)^2}\right\} = \mathscr{L}^{-1}\left\{\dfrac{1}{s+1} - \dfrac{1}{(s+1)^2}\right\} = e^{-t} - te^{-t}$

18. $\mathscr{L}^{-1}\left\{\dfrac{5s}{(s-2)^2}\right\} = \mathscr{L}^{-1}\left\{\dfrac{5(s-2) + 10}{(s-2)^2}\right\} = \mathscr{L}^{-1}\left\{\dfrac{5}{s-2} + \dfrac{10}{(s-2)^2}\right\} = 5e^{2t} + 10te^{2t}$

19. $\mathscr{L}^{-1}\left\{\dfrac{2s-1}{s^2(s+1)^3}\right\} = \mathscr{L}^{-1}\left\{\dfrac{5}{s} - \dfrac{1}{s^2} - \dfrac{5}{s+1} - \dfrac{4}{(s+1)^2} - \dfrac{3}{2}\dfrac{2}{(s+1)^3}\right\} = 5 - t - 5e^{-t} - 4te^{-t} - \dfrac{3}{2}t^2 e^{-t}$

20. $\mathscr{L}^{-1}\left\{\dfrac{(s+1)^2}{(s+2)^4}\right\} = \mathscr{L}^{-1}\left\{\dfrac{1}{(s+2)^2} - \dfrac{2}{(s+2)^3} + \dfrac{1}{6}\dfrac{3!}{(s+2)^4}\right\} = te^{-2t} - t^2 e^{-2t} + \dfrac{1}{6}t^3 e^{-2t}$

21. The Laplace transform of the differential equation is

$$s\mathscr{L}\{y\} - y(0) + 4\mathscr{L}\{y\} = \frac{1}{s+4}.$$

Solving for $\mathscr{L}\{y\}$ we obtain

$$\mathscr{L}\{y\} = \frac{1}{(s+4)^2} + \frac{2}{s+4}.$$

Thus

$$y = te^{-4t} + 2e^{-4t}.$$

22. The Laplace transform of the differential equation is

$$s\,\mathscr{L}\{y\} - \mathscr{L}\{y\} = \frac{1}{s} + \frac{1}{(s-1)^2}.$$

Solving for $\mathscr{L}\{y\}$ we obtain

$$\mathscr{L}\{y\} = \frac{1}{s(s-1)} + \frac{1}{(s-1)^3} = -\frac{1}{s} + \frac{1}{s-1} + \frac{1}{(s-1)^3}.$$

Thus

$$y = -1 + e^t + \frac{1}{2}t^2 e^t.$$

23. The Laplace transform of the differential equation is

$$s^2\,\mathscr{L}\{y\} - sy(0) - y'(0) + 2[s\,\mathscr{L}\{y\} - y(0)] + \mathscr{L}\{y\} = 0.$$

Solving for $\mathscr{L}\{y\}$ we obtain

$$\mathscr{L}\{y\} = \frac{s+3}{(s+1)^2} = \frac{1}{s+1} + \frac{2}{(s+1)^2}.$$

Thus

$$y = e^{-t} + 2te^{-t}.$$

24. The Laplace transform of the differential equation is

$$s^2\,\mathscr{L}\{y\} - sy(0) - y'(0) - 4\,[s\,\mathscr{L}\{y\} - y(0)] + 4\,\mathscr{L}\{y\} = \frac{6}{(s-2)^4}.$$

Solving for $\mathscr{L}\{y\}$ we obtain $\mathscr{L}\{y\} = \dfrac{1}{20}\dfrac{5!}{(s-2)^6}$. Thus, $y = \dfrac{1}{20}t^5 e^{2t}$.

25. The Laplace transform of the differential equation is

$$s^2\,\mathscr{L}\{y\} - sy(0) - y'(0) - 6\,[s\,\mathscr{L}\{y\} - y(0)] + 9\,\mathscr{L}\{y\} = \frac{1}{s^2}.$$

Solving for $\mathscr{L}\{y\}$ we obtain

$$\mathscr{L}\{y\} = \frac{1+s^2}{s^2(s-3)^2} = \frac{2}{27}\frac{1}{s} + \frac{1}{9}\frac{1}{s^2} - \frac{2}{27}\frac{1}{s-3} + \frac{10}{9}\frac{1}{(s-3)^2}.$$

Thus

$$y = \frac{2}{27} + \frac{1}{9}t - \frac{2}{27}e^{3t} + \frac{10}{9}te^{3t}.$$

26. The Laplace transform of the differential equation is

$$s^2\,\mathscr{L}\{y\} - sy(0) - y'(0) - 4\,[s\,\mathscr{L}\{y\} - y(0)] + 4\,\mathscr{L}\{y\} = \frac{6}{s^4}.$$

Solving for $\mathscr{L}\{y\}$ we obtain

$$\mathscr{L}\{y\} = \frac{s^5 - 4s^4 + 6}{s^4(s-2)^2} = \frac{3}{4}\frac{1}{s} + \frac{9}{8}\frac{1}{s^2} + \frac{3}{4}\frac{2}{s^3} + \frac{1}{4}\frac{3!}{s^4} + \frac{1}{4}\frac{1}{s-2} - \frac{13}{8}\frac{1}{(s-2)^2}.$$

Thus

$$y = \frac{3}{4} + \frac{9}{8}t + \frac{3}{4}t^2 + \frac{1}{4}t^3 + \frac{1}{4}e^{2t} - \frac{13}{8}te^{2t}.$$

27. The Laplace transform of the differential equation is

$$s^2 \mathscr{L}\{y\} - sy(0) - y'(0) - 6\left[s\mathscr{L}\{y\} - y(0)\right] + 13\,\mathscr{L}\{y\} = 0.$$

Solving for $\mathscr{L}\{y\}$ we obtain

$$\mathscr{L}\{y\} = -\frac{3}{s^2 - 6s + 13} = -\frac{3}{2}\frac{2}{(s-3)^2 + 2^2}.$$

Thus

$$y = -\frac{3}{2}e^{3t}\sin 2t.$$

28. The Laplace transform of the differential equation is

$$2[s^2 \mathscr{L}\{y\} - sy(0)] + 20[s\mathscr{L}\{y\} - y(0)] + 51\,\mathscr{L}\{y\} = 0.$$

Solving for $\mathscr{L}\{y\}$ we obtain

$$\mathscr{L}\{y\} = \frac{4s + 40}{2s^2 + 20s + 51} = \frac{2s + 20}{(s+5)^2 + 1/2} = \frac{2(s+5)}{(s+5)^2 + 1/2} + \frac{10}{(s+5)^2 + 1/2}.$$

Thus

$$y = 2e^{-5t}\cos(t/\sqrt{2}) + 10\sqrt{2}\,e^{-5t}\sin(t/\sqrt{2}).$$

29. The Laplace transform of the differential equation is

$$s^2 \mathscr{L}\{y\} - sy(0) - y'(0) - [s\mathscr{L}\{y\} - y(0)] = \frac{s-1}{(s-1)^2 + 1}.$$

Solving for $\mathscr{L}\{y\}$ we obtain

$$\mathscr{L}\{y\} = \frac{1}{s(s^2 - 2s + 2)} = \frac{1}{2}\frac{1}{s} - \frac{1}{2}\frac{s-1}{(s-1)^2 + 1} + \frac{1}{2}\frac{1}{(s-1)^2 + 1}.$$

Thus

$$y = \frac{1}{2} - \frac{1}{2}e^t\cos t + \frac{1}{2}e^t\sin t.$$

30. The Laplace transform of the differential equation is

$$s^2 \mathscr{L}\{y\} - sy(0) - y'(0) - 2\left[s\mathscr{L}\{y\} - y(0)\right] + 5\,\mathscr{L}\{y\} = \frac{1}{s} + \frac{1}{s^2}.$$

Solving for $\mathscr{L}\{y\}$ we obtain

$$\mathscr{L}\{y\} = \frac{4s^2 + s + 1}{s^2(s^2 - 2s + 5)} = \frac{7}{25}\frac{1}{s} + \frac{1}{5}\frac{1}{s^2} + \frac{-7s/25 + 109/25}{s^2 - 2s + 5}$$

$$= \frac{7}{25}\frac{1}{s} + \frac{1}{5}\frac{1}{s^2} - \frac{7}{25}\frac{s-1}{(s-1)^2 + 2^2} + \frac{51}{25}\frac{2}{(s-1)^2 + 2^2}.$$

Thus

$$y = \frac{7}{25} + \frac{1}{5}t - \frac{7}{25}e^t \cos 2t + \frac{51}{25}e^t \sin 2t.$$

31. Taking the Laplace transform of both sides of the differential equation and letting $c = y(0)$ we obtain

$$\mathscr{L}\{y''\} + \mathscr{L}\{2y'\} + \mathscr{L}\{y\} = 0$$

$$s^2\mathscr{L}\{y\} - sy(0) - y'(0) + 2s\,\mathscr{L}\{y\} - 2y(0) + \mathscr{L}\{y\} = 0$$

$$s^2\mathscr{L}\{y\} - cs - 2 + 2s\,\mathscr{L}\{y\} - 2c + \mathscr{L}\{y\} = 0$$

$$\left(s^2 + 2s + 1\right)\mathscr{L}\{y\} = cs + 2c + 2$$

$$\mathscr{L}\{y\} = \frac{cs}{(s+1)^2} + \frac{2c+2}{(s+1)^2}$$

$$= c\frac{s+1-1}{(s+1)^2} + \frac{2c+2}{(s+1)^2}$$

$$= \frac{c}{s+1} + \frac{c+2}{(s+1)^2}.$$

Therefore,

$$y(t) = c\mathscr{L}^{-1}\left\{\frac{1}{s+1}\right\} + (c+2)\,\mathscr{L}^{-1}\left\{\frac{1}{(s+1)^2}\right\} = ce^{-t} + (c+2)te^{-t}.$$

To find c we let $y(1) = 2$. Then $2 = ce^{-1} + (c+2)e^{-1} = 2(c+1)e^{-1}$ and $c = e - 1$. Thus

$$y(t) = (e-1)e^{-t} + (e+1)te^{-t}.$$

32. Taking the Laplace transform of both sides of the differential equation and letting $c = y'(0)$ we obtain

$$\mathscr{L}\{y''\} + \mathscr{L}\{8y'\} + \mathscr{L}\{20y\} = 0$$

$$s^2\mathscr{L}\{y\} - y'(0) + 8s\,\mathscr{L}\{y\} + 20\,\mathscr{L}\{y\} = 0$$

$$s^2\mathscr{L}\{y\} - c + 8s\,\mathscr{L}\{y\} + 20\,\mathscr{L}\{y\} = 0$$

$$(s^2 + 8s + 20)\,\mathscr{L}\{y\} = c$$

$$\mathscr{L}\{y\} = \frac{c}{s^2 + 8s + 20} = \frac{c}{(s+4)^2 + 4}.$$

Therefore,

$$y(t) = \mathscr{L}^{-1}\left\{\frac{c}{(s+4)^2 + 4}\right\} = \frac{c}{2}e^{-4t}\sin 2t = c_1 e^{-4t} \sin 2t.$$

Exercises 7.3 Operational Properties I

To find c we let $y'(\pi) = 0$. Then $0 = y'(\pi) = ce^{-4\pi}$ and $c = 0$. Thus, $y(t) = 0$. (Since the differential equation is homogeneous and both boundary conditions are 0, we can see immediately that $y(t) = 0$ is a solution. We have shown that it is the only solution.)

33. Recall from Section 5.1 that $mx'' = -kx - \beta x'$. Now $m = W/g = 4/32 = \frac{1}{8}$ slug, and $4 = 2k$ so that $k = 2$ lb/ft. Thus, the differential equation is $x'' + 7x' + 16x = 0$. The initial conditions are $x(0) = -3/2$ and $x'(0) = 0$. The Laplace transform of the differential equation is

$$s^2\mathscr{L}\{x\} + \frac{3}{2}s + 7s\mathscr{L}\{x\} + \frac{21}{2} + 16\mathscr{L}\{x\} = 0.$$

Solving for $\mathscr{L}\{x\}$ we obtain

$$\mathscr{L}\{x\} = \frac{-3s/2 - 21/2}{s^2 + 7s + 16} = -\frac{3}{2}\frac{s + 7/2}{(s + 7/2)^2 + (\sqrt{15}/2)^2} - \frac{7\sqrt{15}}{10}\frac{\sqrt{15}/2}{(s + 7/2)^2 + (\sqrt{15}/2)^2}.$$

Thus

$$x = -\frac{3}{2}e^{-7t/2}\cos\frac{\sqrt{15}}{2}t - \frac{7\sqrt{15}}{10}e^{-7t/2}\sin\frac{\sqrt{15}}{2}t.$$

34. The differential equation is

$$\frac{d^2q}{dt^2} + 20\frac{dq}{dt} + 200q = 150, \quad q(0) = q'(0) = 0.$$

The Laplace transform of this equation is

$$s^2\mathscr{L}\{q\} + 20s\mathscr{L}\{q\} + 200\mathscr{L}\{q\} = \frac{150}{s}.$$

Solving for $\mathscr{L}\{q\}$ we obtain

$$\mathscr{L}\{q\} = \frac{150}{s(s^2 + 20s + 200)} = \frac{3}{4}\frac{1}{s} - \frac{3}{4}\frac{s + 10}{(s + 10)^2 + 10^2} - \frac{3}{4}\frac{10}{(s + 10)^2 + 10^2}.$$

Thus

$$q(t) = \frac{3}{4} - \frac{3}{4}e^{-10t}\cos 10t - \frac{3}{4}e^{-10t}\sin 10t$$

and

$$i(t) = q'(t) = 15e^{-10t}\sin 10t.$$

35. The differential equation is

$$\frac{d^2q}{dt^2} + 2\lambda\frac{dq}{dt} + \omega^2 q = \frac{E_0}{L}, \quad q(0) = q'(0) = 0.$$

The Laplace transform of this equation is

$$s^2\mathscr{L}\{q\} + 2\lambda s\mathscr{L}\{q\} + \omega^2\mathscr{L}\{q\} = \frac{E_0}{L}\frac{1}{s}$$

or

$$\left(s^2 + 2\lambda s + \omega^2\right)\mathscr{L}\{q\} = \frac{E_0}{L}\frac{1}{s}.$$

Solving for $\mathscr{L}\{q\}$ and using partial fractions we obtain

$$\mathscr{L}\{q\} = \frac{E_0}{L}\left(\frac{1/\omega^2}{s} - \frac{(1/\omega^2)s + 2\lambda/\omega^2}{s^2 + 2\lambda s + \omega^2}\right) = \frac{E_0}{L\omega^2}\left(\frac{1}{s} - \frac{s + 2\lambda}{s^2 + 2\lambda s + \omega^2}\right).$$

For $\lambda > \omega$ we write $s^2 + 2\lambda s + \omega^2 = (s + \lambda)^2 - (\lambda^2 - \omega^2)$, so (recalling that $\omega^2 = 1/LC$)

$$\mathscr{L}\{q\} = E_0 C\left(\frac{1}{s} - \frac{s + \lambda}{(s + \lambda)^2 - (\lambda^2 - \omega^2)} - \frac{\lambda}{(s + \lambda)^2 - (\lambda^2 - \omega^2)}\right).$$

Thus for $\lambda > \omega$,

$$q(t) = E_0 C\left[1 - e^{-\lambda t}\left(\cosh\sqrt{\lambda^2 - \omega^2}\,t - \frac{\lambda}{\sqrt{\lambda^2 - \omega^2}}\sinh\sqrt{\lambda^2 - \omega^2}\,t\right)\right].$$

For $\lambda < \omega$ we write $s^2 + 2\lambda s + \omega^2 = (s + \lambda)^2 + (\omega^2 - \lambda^2)$, so

$$\mathscr{L}\{q\} = E_0 C\left(\frac{1}{s} - \frac{s + \lambda}{(s + \lambda)^2 + (\omega^2 - \lambda^2)} - \frac{\lambda}{(s + \lambda)^2 + (\omega^2 - \lambda^2)}\right).$$

Thus for $\lambda < \omega$,

$$q(t) = E_0 C\left[1 - e^{-\lambda t}\left(\cos\sqrt{\omega^2 - \lambda^2}\,t - \frac{\lambda}{\sqrt{\omega^2 - \lambda^2}}\sin\sqrt{\omega^2 - \lambda^2}\,t\right)\right].$$

For $\lambda = \omega$, $s^2 + 2\lambda + \omega^2 = (s + \lambda)^2$ and

$$\mathscr{L}\{q\} = \frac{E_0}{L}\frac{1}{s(s + \lambda)^2} = \frac{E_0}{L}\left(\frac{1/\lambda^2}{s} - \frac{1/\lambda^2}{s + \lambda} - \frac{1/\lambda}{(s + \lambda)^2}\right) = \frac{E_0}{L\lambda^2}\left(\frac{1}{s} - \frac{1}{s + \lambda} - \frac{\lambda}{(s + \lambda)^2}\right).$$

Thus for $\lambda = \omega$,

$$q(t) = E_0 C\left(1 - e^{-\lambda t} - \lambda t e^{-\lambda t}\right).$$

36. The differential equation is

$$R\frac{dq}{dt} + \frac{1}{C}q = E_0 e^{-kt}, \quad q(0) = 0.$$

The Laplace transform of this equation is

$$Rs\,\mathscr{L}\{q\} + \frac{1}{C}\mathscr{L}\{q\} = E_0\frac{1}{s + k}.$$

Solving for $\mathscr{L}\{q\}$ we obtain

$$\mathscr{L}\{q\} = \frac{E_0 C}{(s + k)(RCs + 1)} = \frac{E_0/R}{(s + k)(s + 1/RC)}.$$

When $1/RC \neq k$ we have by partial fractions

$$\mathscr{L}\{q\} = \frac{E_0}{R}\left(\frac{1/(1/RC - k)}{s + k} - \frac{1/(1/RC - k)}{s + 1/RC}\right) = \frac{E_0}{R}\frac{1}{1/RC - k}\left(\frac{1}{s + k} - \frac{1}{s + 1/RC}\right).$$

Thus

$$q(t) = \frac{E_0 C}{1 - kRC}\left(e^{-kt} - e^{-t/RC}\right).$$

Exercises 7.3 Operational Properties I

When $1/RC = k$ we have

$$\mathcal{L}\{q\} = \frac{E_0}{R} \frac{1}{(s+k)^2}.$$

Thus

$$q(t) = \frac{E_0}{R} t e^{-kt} = \frac{E_0}{R} t e^{-t/RC}.$$

37. $\mathcal{L}\{(t-1)\mathcal{U}(t-1)\} = \dfrac{e^{-s}}{s^2}$

38. $\mathcal{L}\{e^{2-t}\mathcal{U}(t-2)\} = \mathcal{L}\left\{e^{-(t-2)}\mathcal{U}(t-2)\right\} = \dfrac{e^{-2s}}{s+1}$

39. $\mathcal{L}\{t\mathcal{U}(t-2)\} = \mathcal{L}\left\{(t-2)\mathcal{U}(t-2) + 2\mathcal{U}(t-2)\right\} = \dfrac{e^{-2s}}{s^2} + \dfrac{2e^{-2s}}{s}$

Alternatively, (16) of this section in the text could be used:

$$\mathcal{L}\{t\,\mathcal{U}(t-2)\} = e^{-2s}\mathcal{L}\{t+2\} = e^{-2s}\left(\frac{1}{s^2} + \frac{2}{s}\right).$$

40. $\mathcal{L}\{(3t+1)\mathcal{U}(t-1)\} = 3\mathcal{L}\{(t-1)\mathcal{U}(t-1)\} + 4\mathcal{L}\{\mathcal{U}(t-1)\} = \dfrac{3e^{-s}}{s^2} + \dfrac{4e^{-s}}{s}$

Alternatively, (16) of this section in the text could be used:

$$\mathcal{L}\{(3t+1)\mathcal{U}(t-1)\} = e^{-s}\mathcal{L}\{3t+4\} = e^{-s}\left(\frac{3}{s^2} + \frac{4}{s}\right).$$

41. $\mathcal{L}\{\cos 2t\,\mathcal{U}(t-\pi)\} = \mathcal{L}\left\{\cos 2(t-\pi)\,\mathcal{U}(t-\pi)\right\} = \dfrac{se^{-\pi s}}{s^2+4}$

Alternatively, (16) of this section in the text could be used:

$$\mathcal{L}\{\cos 2t\,\mathcal{U}(t-\pi)\} = e^{-\pi s}\mathcal{L}\{\cos 2(t+\pi)\} = e^{-\pi s}\mathcal{L}\{\cos 2t\} = e^{-\pi s}\frac{s}{s^2+4}.$$

42. $\mathcal{L}\left\{\sin t\,\mathcal{U}\left(t-\dfrac{\pi}{2}\right)\right\} = \mathcal{L}\left\{\cos\left(t-\dfrac{\pi}{2}\right)\mathcal{U}\left(t-\dfrac{\pi}{2}\right)\right\} = \dfrac{se^{-\pi s/2}}{s^2+1}$

Alternatively, (16) of this section in the text could be used:

$$\mathcal{L}\left\{\sin t\,\mathcal{U}\left(t-\frac{\pi}{2}\right)\right\} = e^{-\pi s/2}\mathcal{L}\left\{\sin\left(t+\frac{\pi}{2}\right)\right\} = e^{-\pi s/2}\mathcal{L}\{\cos t\} = e^{-\pi s/2}\frac{s}{s^2+1}.$$

43. $\mathcal{L}^{-1}\left\{\dfrac{e^{-2s}}{s^3}\right\} = \mathcal{L}^{-1}\left\{\dfrac{1}{2} \cdot \dfrac{2}{s^3} e^{-2s}\right\} = \dfrac{1}{2}(t-2)^2\,\mathcal{U}(t-2)$

44. $\mathcal{L}^{-1}\left\{\dfrac{(1+e^{-2s})^2}{s+2}\right\} = \mathcal{L}^{-1}\left\{\dfrac{1}{s+2} + \dfrac{2e^{-2s}}{s+2} + \dfrac{e^{-4s}}{s+2}\right\} = e^{-2t} + 2e^{-2(t-2)}\mathcal{U}(t-2) + e^{-2(t-4)}\mathcal{U}(t-4)$

45. $\mathcal{L}^{-1}\left\{\dfrac{e^{-\pi s}}{s^2+1}\right\} = \sin(t-\pi)\mathcal{U}(t-\pi) = -\sin t\,\mathcal{U}(t-\pi)$

370

46. $\mathcal{L}^{-1}\left\{\dfrac{se^{-\pi s/2}}{s^2+4}\right\} = \cos 2\left(t-\dfrac{\pi}{2}\right)\mathcal{U}\left(t-\dfrac{\pi}{2}\right) = -\cos 2t\,\mathcal{U}\left(t-\dfrac{\pi}{2}\right)$

47. $\mathcal{L}^{-1}\left\{\dfrac{e^{-s}}{s(s+1)}\right\} = \mathcal{L}^{-1}\left\{\dfrac{e^{-s}}{s}-\dfrac{e^{-s}}{s+1}\right\} = \mathcal{U}(t-1) - e^{-(t-1)}\mathcal{U}(t-1)$

48. $\mathcal{L}^{-1}\left\{\dfrac{e^{-2s}}{s^2(s-1)}\right\} = \mathcal{L}^{-1}\left\{-\dfrac{e^{-2s}}{s}-\dfrac{e^{-2s}}{s^2}+\dfrac{e^{-2s}}{s-1}\right\} = -\mathcal{U}(t-2) - (t-2)\mathcal{U}(t-2) + e^{t-2}\mathcal{U}(t-2)$

49. (c)   **50. (e)**   **51. (f)**   **52. (b)**   **53. (a)**   **54. (d)**

55. $\mathcal{L}\{2-4\,\mathcal{U}(t-3)\} = \dfrac{2}{s} - \dfrac{4}{s}e^{-3s}$

56. $\mathcal{L}\{1-\mathcal{U}(t-4)+\mathcal{U}(t-5)\} = \dfrac{1}{s} - \dfrac{e^{-4s}}{s} + \dfrac{e^{-5s}}{s}$

57. $\mathcal{L}\{t^2\,\mathcal{U}(t-1)\} = \mathcal{L}\{[(t-1)^2+2t-1]\,\mathcal{U}(t-1)\} = \mathcal{L}\{[(t-1)^2+2(t-1)+1]\,\mathcal{U}(t-1)\}$

$\qquad = \left(\dfrac{2}{s^3}+\dfrac{2}{s^2}+\dfrac{1}{s}\right)e^{-s}$

Alternatively, by (16) of this section in the text,

$$\mathcal{L}\{t^2\,\mathcal{U}(t-1)\} = e^{-s}\mathcal{L}\{t^2+2t+1\} = e^{-s}\left(\dfrac{2}{s^3}+\dfrac{2}{s^2}+\dfrac{1}{s}\right).$$

58. $\mathcal{L}\left\{\sin t\,\mathcal{U}\left(t-\dfrac{3\pi}{2}\right)\right\} = \mathcal{L}\left\{-\cos\left(t-\dfrac{3\pi}{2}\right)\mathcal{U}\left(t-\dfrac{3\pi}{2}\right)\right\} = -\dfrac{se^{-3\pi s/2}}{s^2+1}$

59. $\mathcal{L}\{t-t\,\mathcal{U}(t-2)\} = \mathcal{L}\{t-(t-2)\mathcal{U}(t-2)-2\mathcal{U}(t-2)\} = \dfrac{1}{s^2} - \dfrac{e^{-2s}}{s^2} - \dfrac{2e^{-2s}}{s}$

60. $\mathcal{L}\{\sin t - \sin t\,\mathcal{U}(t-2\pi)\} = \mathcal{L}\{\sin t - \sin(t-2\pi)\mathcal{U}(t-2\pi)\} = \dfrac{1}{s^2+1} - \dfrac{e^{-2\pi s}}{s^2+1}$

61. $\mathcal{L}\{f(t)\} = \mathcal{L}\{\mathcal{U}(t-a)-\mathcal{U}(t-b)\} = \dfrac{e^{-as}}{s} - \dfrac{e^{-bs}}{s}$

62. $\mathcal{L}\{f(t)\} = \mathcal{L}\{\mathcal{U}(t-1)+\mathcal{U}(t-2)+\mathcal{U}(t-3)+\cdots\} = \dfrac{e^{-s}}{s} + \dfrac{e^{-2s}}{s} + \dfrac{e^{-3s}}{s} + \cdots = \dfrac{1}{s}\dfrac{e^{-s}}{1-e^{-s}}$

63. The Laplace transform of the differential equation is

$$s\mathcal{L}\{y\} - y(0) + \mathcal{L}\{y\} = \dfrac{5}{s}e^{-s}.$$

Solving for $\mathcal{L}\{y\}$ we obtain

$$\mathcal{L}\{y\} = \dfrac{5e^{-s}}{s(s+1)} = 5e^{-s}\left[\dfrac{1}{s}-\dfrac{1}{s+1}\right].$$

371

Thus

$$y = 5\,\mathcal{U}(t-1) - 5e^{-(t-1)}\,\mathcal{U}(t-1).$$

64. The Laplace transform of the differential equation is

$$s\,\mathscr{L}\{y\} - y(0) + \mathscr{L}\{y\} = \frac{1}{s} - \frac{2}{s}e^{-s}.$$

Solving for $\mathscr{L}\{y\}$ we obtain

$$\mathscr{L}\{y\} = \frac{1}{s(s+1)} - \frac{2e^{-s}}{s(s+1)} = \frac{1}{s} - \frac{1}{s+1} - 2e^{-s}\left[\frac{1}{s} - \frac{1}{s+1}\right].$$

Thus

$$y = 1 - e^{-t} - 2\left[1 - e^{-(t-1)}\right]\mathcal{U}(t-1).$$

65. The Laplace transform of the differential equation is

$$s\,\mathscr{L}\{y\} - y(0) + 2\,\mathscr{L}\{y\} = \frac{1}{s^2} - e^{-s}\frac{s+1}{s^2}.$$

Solving for $\mathscr{L}\{y\}$ we obtain

$$\mathscr{L}\{y\} = \frac{1}{s^2(s+2)} - e^{-s}\frac{s+1}{s^2(s+2)} = -\frac{1}{4}\frac{1}{s} + \frac{1}{2}\frac{1}{s^2} + \frac{1}{4}\frac{1}{s+2} - e^{-s}\left[\frac{1}{4}\frac{1}{s} + \frac{1}{2}\frac{1}{s^2} - \frac{1}{4}\frac{1}{s+2}\right].$$

Thus

$$y = -\frac{1}{4} + \frac{1}{2}t + \frac{1}{4}e^{-2t} - \left[\frac{1}{4} + \frac{1}{2}(t-1) - \frac{1}{4}e^{-2(t-1)}\right]\mathcal{U}(t-1).$$

66. The Laplace transform of the differential equation is

$$s^2\,\mathscr{L}\{y\} - sy(0) - y'(0) + 4\,\mathscr{L}\{y\} = \frac{1}{s} - \frac{e^{-s}}{s}.$$

Solving for $\mathscr{L}\{y\}$ we obtain

$$\mathscr{L}\{y\} = \frac{1-s}{s(s^2+4)} - e^{-s}\frac{1}{s(s^2+4)} = \frac{1}{4}\frac{1}{s} - \frac{1}{4}\frac{s}{s^2+4} - \frac{1}{2}\frac{2}{s^2+4} - e^{-s}\left[\frac{1}{4}\frac{1}{s} - \frac{1}{4}\frac{s}{s^2+4}\right].$$

Thus

$$y = \frac{1}{4} - \frac{1}{4}\cos 2t - \frac{1}{2}\sin 2t - \left[\frac{1}{4} - \frac{1}{4}\cos 2(t-1)\right]\mathcal{U}(t-1).$$

67. The Laplace transform of the differential equation is

$$s^2\,\mathscr{L}\{y\} - sy(0) - y'(0) + 4\,\mathscr{L}\{y\} = e^{-2\pi s}\frac{1}{s^2+1}.$$

Solving for $\mathscr{L}\{y\}$ we obtain

$$\mathscr{L}\{y\} = \frac{s}{s^2+4} + e^{-2\pi s}\left[\frac{1}{3}\frac{1}{s^2+1} - \frac{1}{6}\frac{2}{s^2+4}\right].$$

Thus

$$y = \cos 2t + \left[\frac{1}{3}\sin(t-2\pi) - \frac{1}{6}\sin 2(t-2\pi)\right]\mathcal{U}(t-2\pi).$$

68. The Laplace transform of the differential equation is

$$s^2 \mathcal{L}\{y\} - sy(0) - y'(0) - 5\left[s\mathcal{L}\{y\} - y(0)\right] + 6\mathcal{L}\{y\} = \frac{e^{-s}}{s}.$$

Solving for $\mathcal{L}\{y\}$ we obtain

$$\mathcal{L}\{y\} = e^{-s}\frac{1}{s(s-2)(s-3)} + \frac{1}{(s-2)(s-3)}$$

$$= e^{-s}\left[\frac{1}{6}\frac{1}{s} - \frac{1}{2}\frac{1}{s-2} + \frac{1}{3}\frac{1}{s-3}\right] - \frac{1}{s-2} + \frac{1}{s-3}.$$

Thus

$$y = \left[\frac{1}{6} - \frac{1}{2}e^{2(t-1)} + \frac{1}{3}e^{3(t-1)}\right]\mathcal{U}(t-1) - e^{2t} + e^{3t}.$$

69. The Laplace transform of the differential equation is

$$s^2 \mathcal{L}\{y\} - sy(0) - y'(0) + \mathcal{L}\{y\} = \frac{e^{-\pi s}}{s} - \frac{e^{-2\pi s}}{s}.$$

Solving for $\mathcal{L}\{y\}$ we obtain

$$\mathcal{L}\{y\} = e^{-\pi s}\left[\frac{1}{s} - \frac{s}{s^2+1}\right] - e^{-2\pi s}\left[\frac{1}{s} - \frac{s}{s^2+1}\right] + \frac{1}{s^2+1}.$$

Thus

$$y = \left[1 - \cos(t-\pi)\right]\mathcal{U}(t-\pi) - \left[1 - \cos(t-2\pi)\right]\mathcal{U}(t-2\pi) + \sin t.$$

70. The Laplace transform of the differential equation is

$$s^2 \mathcal{L}\{y\} - sy(0) - y'(0) + 4[s\mathcal{L}\{y\} - y(0)] + 3\mathcal{L}\{y\} = \frac{1}{s} - \frac{e^{-2s}}{s} - \frac{e^{-4s}}{s} + \frac{e^{-6s}}{s}.$$

Solving for $\mathcal{L}\{y\}$ we obtain

$$\mathcal{L}\{y\} = \frac{1}{3}\frac{1}{s} - \frac{1}{2}\frac{1}{s+1} + \frac{1}{6}\frac{1}{s+3} - e^{-2s}\left[\frac{1}{3}\frac{1}{s} - \frac{1}{2}\frac{1}{s+1} + \frac{1}{6}\frac{1}{s+3}\right]$$

$$- e^{-4s}\left[\frac{1}{3}\frac{1}{s} - \frac{1}{2}\frac{1}{s+1} + \frac{1}{6}\frac{1}{s+3}\right] + e^{-6s}\left[\frac{1}{3}\frac{1}{s} - \frac{1}{2}\frac{1}{s+1} + \frac{1}{6}\frac{1}{s+3}\right].$$

Thus

$$y = \frac{1}{3} - \frac{1}{2}e^{-t} + \frac{1}{6}e^{-3t} - \left[\frac{1}{3} - \frac{1}{2}e^{-(t-2)} + \frac{1}{6}e^{-3(t-2)}\right]\mathcal{U}(t-2)$$

$$- \left[\frac{1}{3} - \frac{1}{2}e^{-(t-4)} + \frac{1}{6}e^{-3(t-4)}\right]\mathcal{U}(t-4) + \left[\frac{1}{3} - \frac{1}{2}e^{-(t-6)} + \frac{1}{6}e^{-3(t-6)}\right]\mathcal{U}(t-6).$$

71. Recall from Section 5.1 that $mx'' = -kx + f(t)$. Now $m = W/g = 32/32 = 1$ slug, and $32 = 2k$ so that $k = 16$ lb/ft. Thus, the differential equation is $x'' + 16x = f(t)$. The initial conditions are $x(0) = 0$, $x'(0) = 0$. Also, since

$$f(t) = \begin{cases} 20t, & 0 \le t < 5 \\ 0, & t \ge 5 \end{cases}$$

and $20t = 20(t - 5) + 100$ we can write

$$f(t) = 20t - 20t\,\mathscr{U}(t - 5) = 20t - 20(t - 5)\,\mathscr{U}(t - 5) - 100\,\mathscr{U}(t - 5).$$

The Laplace transform of the differential equation is

$$s^2\mathscr{L}\{x\} + 16\,\mathscr{L}\{x\} = \frac{20}{s^2} - \frac{20}{s^2}e^{-5s} - \frac{100}{s}e^{-5s}.$$

Solving for $\mathscr{L}\{x\}$ we obtain

$$\mathscr{L}\{x\} = \frac{20}{s^2(s^2 + 16)} - \frac{20}{s^2(s^2 + 16)}e^{-5s} - \frac{100}{s(s^2 + 16)}e^{-5s}$$

$$= \left(\frac{5}{4} \cdot \frac{1}{s^2} - \frac{5}{16} \cdot \frac{4}{s^2 + 16}\right)(1 - e^{-5s}) - \left(\frac{25}{4} \cdot \frac{1}{s} - \frac{25}{4} \cdot \frac{s}{s^2 + 16}\right)e^{-5s}.$$

Thus

$$x(t) = \frac{5}{4}t - \frac{5}{16}\sin 4t - \left[\frac{5}{4}(t - 5) - \frac{5}{16}\sin 4(t - 5)\right]\mathscr{U}(t - 5) - \left[\frac{25}{4} - \frac{25}{4}\cos 4(t - 5)\right]\mathscr{U}(t - 5)$$

$$= \frac{5}{4}t - \frac{5}{16}\sin 4t - \frac{5}{4}t\,\mathscr{U}(t - 5) + \frac{5}{16}\sin 4(t - 5)\,\mathscr{U}(t - 5) + \frac{25}{4}\cos 4(t - 5)\,\mathscr{U}(t - 5).$$

72. Recall from Section 5.1 that $mx'' = -kx + f(t)$. Now $m = W/g = 32/32 = 1$ slug, and $32 = 2k$ so that $k = 16$ lb/ft. Thus, the differential equation is $x'' + 16x = f(t)$. The initial conditions are $x(0) = 0$, $x'(0) = 0$. Also, since

$$f(t) = \begin{cases} \sin t, & 0 \le t < 2\pi \\ 0, & t \ge 2\pi \end{cases}$$

and $\sin t = \sin(t - 2\pi)$ we can write

$$f(t) = \sin t - \sin(t - 2\pi)\mathscr{U}(t - 2\pi).$$

The Laplace transform of the differential equation is

$$s^2\mathscr{L}\{x\} + 16\,\mathscr{L}\{x\} = \frac{1}{s^2 + 1} - \frac{1}{s^2 + 1}e^{-2\pi s}.$$

Solving for $\mathscr{L}\{x\}$ we obtain

$$\mathscr{L}\{x\} = \frac{1}{(s^2 + 16)(s^2 + 1)} - \frac{1}{(s^2 + 16)(s^2 + 1)}e^{-2\pi s}$$

$$= \frac{-1/15}{s^2 + 16} + \frac{1/15}{s^2 + 1} - \left[\frac{-1/15}{s^2 + 16} + \frac{1/15}{s^2 + 1}\right]e^{-2\pi s}.$$

Thus

$$x(t) = -\frac{1}{60}\sin 4t + \frac{1}{15}\sin t + \frac{1}{60}\sin 4(t - 2\pi)\mathscr{U}(t - 2\pi) - \frac{1}{15}\sin(t - 2\pi)\mathscr{U}(t - 2\pi)$$

$$= \begin{cases} -\frac{1}{60}\sin 4t + \frac{1}{15}\sin t, & 0 \le t < 2\pi \\ 0, & t \ge 2\pi. \end{cases}$$

73. The differential equation is

$$2.5\frac{dq}{dt} + 12.5q = 5\,\mathcal{U}(t-3).$$

The Laplace transform of this equation is

$$s\mathcal{L}\{q\} + 5\mathcal{L}\{q\} = \frac{2}{s}e^{-3s}.$$

Solving for $\mathcal{L}\{q\}$ we obtain

$$\mathcal{L}\{q\} = \frac{2}{s(s+5)}e^{-3s} = \left(\frac{2}{5}\cdot\frac{1}{s} - \frac{2}{5}\cdot\frac{1}{s+5}\right)e^{-3s}.$$

Thus

$$q(t) = \frac{2}{5}\,\mathcal{U}(t-3) - \frac{2}{5}e^{-5(t-3)}\,\mathcal{U}(t-3).$$

74. The differential equation is

$$10\frac{dq}{dt} + 10q = 30e^t - 30e^t\,\mathcal{U}(t-1.5).$$

The Laplace transform of this equation is

$$s\mathcal{L}\{q\} - q_0 + \mathcal{L}\{q\} = \frac{3}{s-1} - \frac{3e^{1.5}}{s-1.5}e^{-1.5s}.$$

Solving for $\mathcal{L}\{q\}$ we obtain

$$\mathcal{L}\{q\} = \left(q_0 - \frac{3}{2}\right)\cdot\frac{1}{s+1} + \frac{3}{2}\cdot\frac{1}{s-1} - 3e^{1.5}\left(\frac{-2/5}{s+1} + \frac{2/5}{s-1.5}\right)e^{-1.5s}.$$

Thus

$$q(t) = \left(q_0 - \frac{3}{2}\right)e^{-t} + \frac{3}{2}e^t + \frac{6}{5}e^{1.5}\left(e^{-(t-1.5)} - e^{1.5(t-1.5)}\right)\mathcal{U}(t-1.5).$$

75. (a) The differential equation is

$$\frac{di}{dt} + 10i = \sin t + \cos\left(t - \frac{3\pi}{2}\right)\mathcal{U}\left(t - \frac{3\pi}{2}\right), \quad i(0) = 0.$$

The Laplace transform of this equation is

$$s\mathcal{L}\{i\} + 10\mathcal{L}\{i\} = \frac{1}{s^2+1} + \frac{se^{-3\pi s/2}}{s^2+1}.$$

Solving for $\mathcal{L}\{i\}$ we obtain

$$\mathcal{L}\{i\} = \frac{1}{(s^2+1)(s+10)} + \frac{s}{(s^2+1)(s+10)}e^{-3\pi s/2}$$

$$= \frac{1}{101}\left(\frac{1}{s+10} - \frac{s}{s^2+1} + \frac{10}{s^2+1}\right) + \frac{1}{101}\left(\frac{-10}{s+10} + \frac{10s}{s^2+1} + \frac{1}{s^2+1}\right)e^{-3\pi s/2}.$$

Thus

$$i(t) = \frac{1}{101}\left(e^{-10t} - \cos t + 10\sin t\right)$$

$$+ \frac{1}{101}\left[-10e^{-10(t-3\pi/2)} + 10\cos\left(t - \frac{3\pi}{2}\right) + \sin\left(t - \frac{3\pi}{2}\right)\right]\mathscr{U}\left(t - \frac{3\pi}{2}\right).$$

(b)

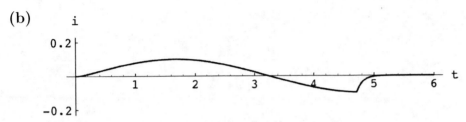

The maximum value of $i(t)$ is approximately 0.1 at $t = 1.7$, the minimum is approximately -0.1 at 4.7. [Using *Mathematica* we see that the maximum value is $i(t)$ is 0.0995037 at $t = 1.670465$, and the mininum value is $i(3\pi/2) \approx -0.0990099$ at $t = 3\pi/2$.]

76. (a) The differential equation is

$$50\frac{dq}{dt} + \frac{1}{0.01}q = E_0[\mathscr{U}(t-1) - \mathscr{U}(t-3)], \quad q(0) = 0$$

or

$$50\frac{dq}{dt} + 100q = E_0[\mathscr{U}(t-1) - \mathscr{U}(t-3)], \quad q(0) = 0.$$

The Laplace transform of this equation is

$$50s\,\mathscr{L}\{q\} + 100\,\mathscr{L}\{q\} = E_0\left(\frac{1}{s}e^{-s} - \frac{1}{s}e^{-3s}\right).$$

Solving for $\mathscr{L}\{q\}$ we obtain

$$\mathscr{L}\{q\} = \frac{E_0}{50}\left[\frac{e^{-s}}{s(s+2)} - \frac{e^{-3s}}{s(s+2)}\right] = \frac{E_0}{50}\left[\frac{1}{2}\left(\frac{1}{s} - \frac{1}{s+2}\right)e^{-s} - \frac{1}{2}\left(\frac{1}{s} - \frac{1}{s+2}\right)e^{-3s}\right].$$

Thus

$$q(t) = \frac{E_0}{100}\left[\left(1 - e^{-2(t-1)}\right)\mathscr{U}(t-1) - \left(1 - e^{-2(t-3)}\right)\mathscr{U}(t-3)\right].$$

(b)

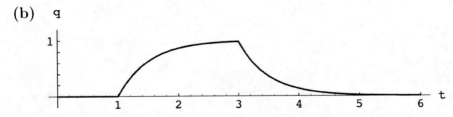

Assuming $E_0 = 100$, the maximum value of $q(t)$ is approximately 1 at $t = 3$. [Using *Mathematica* we see that the maximum value of $q(t)$ is 0.981684 at $t = 3$.]

77. The differential equation is

$$EI\frac{d^4y}{dx^4} = w_0[1 - \mathcal{U}(x - L/2)].$$

Taking the Laplace transform of both sides and using $y(0) = y'(0) = 0$ we obtain

$$s^4\mathcal{L}\{y\} - sy''(0) - y'''(0) = \frac{w_0}{EI}\frac{1}{s}\left(1 - e^{-Ls/2}\right).$$

Letting $y''(0) = c_1$ and $y'''(0) = c_2$ we have

$$\mathcal{L}\{y\} = \frac{c_1}{s^3} + \frac{c_2}{s^4} + \frac{w_0}{EI}\frac{1}{s^5}\left(1 - e^{-Ls/2}\right)$$

so that

$$y(x) = \frac{1}{2}c_1x^2 + \frac{1}{6}c_2x^3 + \frac{1}{24}\frac{w_0}{EI}\left[x^4 - \left(x - \frac{L}{2}\right)^4\mathcal{U}\left(x - \frac{L}{2}\right)\right].$$

To find c_1 and c_2 we compute

$$y''(x) = c_1 + c_2x + \frac{1}{2}\frac{w_0}{EI}\left[x^2 - \left(x - \frac{L}{2}\right)^2\mathcal{U}\left(x - \frac{L}{2}\right)\right]$$

and

$$y'''(x) = c_2 + \frac{w_0}{EI}\left[x - \left(x - \frac{L}{2}\right)\mathcal{U}\left(x - \frac{L}{2}\right)\right].$$

Then $y''(L) = y'''(L) = 0$ yields the system

$$c_1 + c_2L + \frac{1}{2}\frac{w_0}{EI}\left[L^2 - \left(\frac{L}{2}\right)^2\right] = c_1 + c_2L + \frac{3}{8}\frac{w_0L^2}{EI} = 0$$

$$c_2 + \frac{w_0}{EI}\left(\frac{L}{2}\right) = c_2 + \frac{1}{2}\frac{w_0L}{EI} = 0.$$

Solving for c_1 and c_2 we obtain $c_1 = \frac{1}{8}w_0L^2/EI$ and $c_2 = -\frac{1}{2}w_0L/EI$. Thus

$$y(x) = \frac{w_0}{EI}\left[\frac{1}{16}L^2x^2 - \frac{1}{12}Lx^3 + \frac{1}{24}x^4 - \frac{1}{24}\left(x - \frac{L}{2}\right)^4\mathcal{U}\left(x - \frac{L}{2}\right)\right].$$

78. The differential equation is

$$EI\frac{d^4y}{dx^4} = w_0[\mathcal{U}(x - L/3) - \mathcal{U}(x - 2L/3)].$$

Taking the Laplace transform of both sides and using $y(0) = y'(0) = 0$ we obtain

$$s^4\mathcal{L}\{y\} - sy''(0) - y'''(0) = \frac{w_0}{EI}\frac{1}{s}\left(e^{-Ls/3} - e^{-2Ls/3}\right).$$

Letting $y''(0) = c_1$ and $y'''(0) = c_2$ we have

$$\mathcal{L}\{y\} = \frac{c_1}{s^3} + \frac{c_2}{s^4} + \frac{w_0}{EI}\frac{1}{s^5}\left(e^{-Ls/3} - e^{-2Ls/3}\right)$$

so that

$$y(x) = \frac{1}{2}c_1 x^2 + \frac{1}{6}c_2 x^3 + \frac{1}{24}\frac{w_0}{EI}\left[\left(x - \frac{L}{3}\right)^4 \mathcal{U}\left(x - \frac{L}{3}\right) - \left(x - \frac{2L}{3}\right)^4 \mathcal{U}\left(x - \frac{2L}{3}\right)\right].$$

To find c_1 and c_2 we compute

$$y''(x) = c_1 + c_2 x + \frac{1}{2}\frac{w_0}{EI}\left[\left(x - \frac{L}{3}\right)^2 \mathcal{U}\left(x - \frac{L}{3}\right) - \left(x - \frac{2L}{3}\right)^2 \mathcal{U}\left(x - \frac{2L}{3}\right)\right]$$

and

$$y'''(x) = c_2 + \frac{w_0}{EI}\left[\left(x - \frac{L}{3}\right)\mathcal{U}\left(x - \frac{L}{3}\right) - \left(x - \frac{2L}{3}\right)\mathcal{U}\left(x - \frac{2L}{3}\right)\right].$$

Then $y''(L) = y'''(L) = 0$ yields the system

$$c_1 + c_2 L + \frac{1}{2}\frac{w_0}{EI}\left[\left(\frac{2L}{3}\right)^2 - \left(\frac{L}{3}\right)^2\right] = c_1 + c_2 L + \frac{1}{6}\frac{w_0 L^2}{EI} = 0$$

$$c_2 + \frac{w_0}{EI}\left[\frac{2L}{3} - \frac{L}{3}\right] = c_2 + \frac{1}{3}\frac{w_0 L}{EI} = 0.$$

Solving for c_1 and c_2 we obtain $c_1 = \frac{1}{6}w_0 L^2/EI$ and $c_2 = -\frac{1}{3}w_0 L/EI$. Thus

$$y(x) = \frac{w_0}{EI}\left(\frac{1}{12}L^2 x^2 - \frac{1}{18}L x^3 + \frac{1}{24}\left[\left(x - \frac{L}{3}\right)^4 \mathcal{U}\left(x - \frac{L}{3}\right) - \left(x - \frac{2L}{3}\right)^4 \mathcal{U}\left(x - \frac{2L}{3}\right)\right]\right).$$

79. The differential equation is

$$EI\frac{d^4 y}{dx^4} = \frac{2w_0}{L}\left[\frac{L}{2} - x + \left(x - \frac{L}{2}\right)\mathcal{U}\left(x - \frac{L}{2}\right)\right].$$

Taking the Laplace transform of both sides and using $y(0) = y'(0) = 0$ we obtain

$$s^4 \mathcal{L}\{y\} - sy''(0) - y'''(0) = \frac{2w_0}{EIL}\left[\frac{L}{2s} - \frac{1}{s^2} + \frac{1}{s^2}e^{-Ls/2}\right].$$

Letting $y''(0) = c_1$ and $y'''(0) = c_2$ we have

$$\mathcal{L}\{y\} = \frac{c_1}{s^3} + \frac{c_2}{s^4} + \frac{2w_0}{EIL}\left[\frac{L}{2s^5} - \frac{1}{s^6} + \frac{1}{s^6}e^{-Ls/2}\right]$$

so that

$$y(x) = \frac{1}{2}c_1 x^2 + \frac{1}{6}c_2 x^3 + \frac{2w_0}{EIL}\left[\frac{L}{48}x^4 - \frac{1}{120}x^5 + \frac{1}{120}\left(x - \frac{L}{2}\right)^5 \mathcal{U}\left(x - \frac{L}{2}\right)\right]$$

$$= \frac{1}{2}c_1 x^2 + \frac{1}{6}c_2 x^3 + \frac{w_0}{60EIL}\left[\frac{5L}{2}x^4 - x^5 + \left(x - \frac{L}{2}\right)^5 \mathcal{U}\left(x - \frac{L}{2}\right)\right].$$

To find c_1 and c_2 we compute

$$y''(x) = c_1 + c_2 x + \frac{w_0}{60EIL}\left[30L x^2 - 20x^3 + 20\left(x - \frac{L}{2}\right)^3 \mathcal{U}\left(x - \frac{L}{2}\right)\right]$$

and

$$y'''(x) = c_2 + \frac{w_0}{60EIL}\left[60Lx - 60x^2 + 60\left(x - \frac{L}{2}\right)^2 \mathcal{U}\left(x - \frac{L}{2}\right)\right].$$

Then $y''(L) = y'''(L) = 0$ yields the system

$$c_1 + c_2 L + \frac{w_0}{60EIL}\left[30L^3 - 20L^3 + \frac{5}{2}L^3\right] = c_1 + c_2 L + \frac{5w_0 L^2}{24EI} = 0$$

$$c_2 + \frac{w_0}{60EIL}[60L^2 - 60L^2 + 15L^2] = c_2 + \frac{w_0 L}{4EI} = 0.$$

Solving for c_1 and c_2 we obtain $c_1 = w_0 L^2/24EI$ and $c_2 = -w_0 L/4EI$. Thus

$$y(x) = \frac{w_0 L^2}{48EI}x^2 - \frac{w_0 L}{24EI}x^3 + \frac{w_0}{60EIL}\left[\frac{5L}{2}x^4 - x^5 + \left(x - \frac{L}{2}\right)^5 \mathcal{U}\left(x - \frac{L}{2}\right)\right].$$

80. The differential equation is

$$EI\frac{d^4 y}{dx^4} = w_0[1 - \mathcal{U}(x - L/2)].$$

Taking the Laplace transform of both sides and using $y(0) = y'(0) = 0$ we obtain

$$s^4 \mathcal{L}\{y\} - sy''(0) - y'''(0) = \frac{w_0}{EI}\frac{1}{s}\left(1 - e^{-Ls/2}\right).$$

Letting $y''(0) = c_1$ and $y'''(0) = c_2$ we have

$$\mathcal{L}\{y\} = \frac{c_1}{s^3} + \frac{c_2}{s^4} + \frac{w_0}{EI}\frac{1}{s^5}\left(1 - e^{-Ls/2}\right)$$

so that

$$y(x) = \frac{1}{2}c_1 x^2 + \frac{1}{6}c_2 x^3 + \frac{1}{24}\frac{w_0}{EI}\left[x^4 - \left(x - \frac{L}{2}\right)^4 \mathcal{U}\left(x - \frac{L}{2}\right)\right].$$

To find c_1 and c_2 we compute

$$y''(x) = c_1 + c_2 x + \frac{1}{2}\frac{w_0}{EI}\left[x^2 - \left(x - \frac{L}{2}\right)^2 \mathcal{U}\left(x - \frac{L}{2}\right)\right].$$

Then $y(L) = y''(L) = 0$ yields the system

$$\frac{1}{2}c_1 L^2 + \frac{1}{6}c_2 L^3 + \frac{1}{24}\frac{w_0}{EI}\left[L^4 - \left(\frac{L}{2}\right)^4\right] = \frac{1}{2}c_1 L^2 + \frac{1}{6}c_2 L^3 + \frac{5w_0}{128EI}L^4 = 0$$

$$c_1 + c_2 L + \frac{1}{2}\frac{w_0}{EI}\left[L^2 - \left(\frac{L}{2}\right)^2\right] = c_1 + c_2 L + \frac{3w_0}{8EI}L^2 = 0.$$

Solving for c_1 and c_2 we obtain $c_1 = \frac{9}{128} w_0 L^2/EI$ and $c_2 = -\frac{57}{128} w_0 L/EI$. Thus

$$y(x) = \frac{w_0}{EI}\left[\frac{9}{256}L^2 x^2 - \frac{19}{256}Lx^3 + \frac{1}{24}x^4 - \frac{1}{24}\left(x - \frac{L}{2}\right)^4 \mathcal{U}\left(x - \frac{L}{2}\right)\right].$$

Exercises 7.3 Operational Properties I

81. (a) The temperature T of the cake inside the oven is modeled by

$$\frac{dT}{dt} = k(T - T_m)$$

where T_m is the ambient temperature of the oven. For $0 \le t \le 4$, we have

$$T_m = 70 + \frac{300 - 70}{4 - 0} t = 70 + 57.5t.$$

Hence for $t \ge 0$,

$$T_m = \begin{cases} 70 + 57.5t, & 0 \le t < 4 \\ 300, & t \ge 4. \end{cases}$$

In terms of the unit step function,

$$T_m = (70 + 57.5t)[1 - \mathcal{U}(t - 4)] + 300\,\mathcal{U}(t - 4) = 70 + 57.5t + (230 - 57.5t)\,\mathcal{U}(t - 4).$$

The initial-value problem is then

$$\frac{dT}{dt} = k[T - 70 - 57.5t - (230 - 57.5t)\,\mathcal{U}(t - 4)], \qquad T(0) = 70.$$

(b) Let $t(s) = \mathcal{L}\{T(t)\}$. Transforming the equation, using $230 - 57.5t = -57.5(t - 4)$ and Theorem 7.3.2, gives

$$st(s) - 70 = k\left(t(s) - \frac{70}{s} - \frac{57.5}{s^2} + \frac{57.5}{s^2} e^{-4s} \right)$$

or

$$t(s) = \frac{70}{s - k} - \frac{70k}{s(s - k)} - \frac{57.5k}{s^2(s - k)} + \frac{57.5k}{s^2(s - k)} e^{-4s}.$$

After using partial functions, the inverse transform is then

$$T(t) = 70 + 57.5\left(\frac{1}{k} + t - \frac{1}{k} e^{kt} \right) - 57.5\left(\frac{1}{k} + t - 4 - \frac{1}{k} e^{k(t-4)} \right) \mathcal{U}(t - 4).$$

Of course, the obvious question is: What is k? If the cake is supposed to bake for, say, 20 minutes, then $T(20) = 300$. That is,

$$300 = 70 + 57.5\left(\frac{1}{k} + 20 - \frac{1}{k} e^{20k} \right) - 57.5\left(\frac{1}{k} + 16 - \frac{1}{k} e^{16k} \right).$$

But this equation has no physically meaningful solution. This should be no surprise since the model predicts the asymptotic behavior $T(t) \to 300$ as t increases. Using $T(20) = 299$ instead, we find, with the help of a CAS, that $k \approx -0.3$.

82. We use the fact that Theorem 7.3.2 can be written as

$$\mathcal{L}\{f(t - a)\,\mathcal{U}(t - a)\} = e^{-as}\,\mathcal{L}\{f(t)\}.$$

(a) Indentifying $a = 1$ we have

$$\mathcal{L}\{(2t + 1)\,\mathcal{U}(t - 1)\} = \mathcal{L}\{[2(t - 1) + 3]\,\mathcal{U}(t - 1)\} = e^{-s}\,\mathcal{L}\{2t + 3\} = e^{-s}\left(\frac{2}{s^2} + \frac{3}{s} \right).$$

Using (16) in the text we have

$$\mathscr{L}\{(2t+1)\,\mathscr{U}(t-1)\} = e^{-s}\,\mathscr{L}\{2(t+1)+1\} = e^{-s}\,\mathscr{L}\{2t+3\} = e^{-s}\left(\frac{2}{s^2}+\frac{3}{s}\right).$$

(b) Indentifying $a = 5$ we have

$$\mathscr{L}\{e^t\,\mathscr{U}(t-5)\} = \mathscr{L}\,\{e^{t-5+5}\,\mathscr{U}(t-5)\} = e^5\,\mathscr{L}\{e^{t-5}\,\mathscr{U}(t-5)\} = e^5 e^{-5s}\,\mathscr{L}\{e^t\} = \frac{e^{-5(s-1)}}{s-1}.$$

Using (16) in the text we have

$$\mathscr{L}\{e^t\,\mathscr{U}(t-5)\} = e^{-5s}\,\mathscr{L}\{e^{t+5}\} = e^{-5s}e^5\,\mathscr{L}\{e^t\} = \frac{e^{-5(s-1)}}{s-1}.$$

(c) Indentifying $a = \pi$ we have

$$\mathscr{L}\{\cos t\,\mathscr{U}(t-\pi)\} = -\,\mathscr{L}\{\cos(t-\pi)\,\mathscr{U}(t-\pi)\} = -e^{-\pi s}\,\mathscr{L}\{\cos t\} = -\frac{se^{-\pi s}}{s^2+1}.$$

Using (16) in the text we have

$$\mathscr{L}\{\cos t\,\mathscr{U}(t-\pi)\} = e^{-\pi s}\,\mathscr{L}\{\cos(t+\pi)\} = -e^{-\pi s}\,\mathscr{L}\{\cos t\} = -\frac{se^{-\pi s}}{s^2+1}.$$

(d) Indentifying $a = 2$ we have

$$\mathscr{L}\{(t^2-3t)\,\mathscr{U}(t-2)\} = \mathscr{L}\,\{[(t-2)^2 + 4t - 4 - 3t]\,\mathscr{U}(t-2)\}$$

$$= \mathscr{L}\,\{[(t-2)^2 + (t-2) - 2]\,\mathscr{U}(t-2)\}$$

$$= e^{-2s}\,\mathscr{L}\{t^2 + t - 2\} = e^{-2s}\left(\frac{2}{s^3}+\frac{1}{s^2}-\frac{2}{s}\right).$$

Using (16) in the text we have

$$\mathscr{L}\{(t^2-3t)\,\mathscr{U}(t-2)\} = e^{-2s}\,\mathscr{L}\{(t+2)^2 - 3(t+2)\}$$

$$= e^{-2s}\,\mathscr{L}\{t^2 + t - 2\} = e^{-2s}\left(\frac{2}{s^3}+\frac{1}{s^2}-\frac{2}{s}\right).$$

83. (a) From Theorem 7.3.1 we have $\mathscr{L}\{te^{kti}\} = 1/(s-ki)^2$. Then, using Euler's formula,

$$\mathscr{L}\{te^{kti}\} = \mathscr{L}\,\{t\cos kt + it\sin kt\} = \mathscr{L}\,\{t\cos kt\} + i\,\mathscr{L}\{t\sin kt\}$$

$$= \frac{1}{(s-ki)^2} = \frac{(s+ki)^2}{(s^2+k^2)^2} = \frac{s^2-k^2}{(s^2+k^2)^2} + i\,\frac{2ks}{(s^2+k^2)^2}.$$

Equating real and imaginary parts we have

$$\mathscr{L}\{t\cos kt\} = \frac{s^2-k^2}{(s^2+k^2)^2} \quad \text{and} \quad \mathscr{L}\{t\sin kt\} = \frac{2ks}{(s^2+k^2)^2}.$$

(b) The Laplace transform of the differential equation is

$$s^2 \mathcal{L}\{x\} + \omega^2 \mathcal{L}\{x\} = \frac{s}{s^2 + \omega^2}.$$

Solving for $\mathcal{L}\{x\}$ we obtain $\mathcal{L}\{x\} = s/(s^2 + \omega^2)^2$. Thus $x = (1/2\omega)t \sin \omega t$.

Exercises 7.4   Operational Properties II

1. $\mathcal{L}\{te^{-10t}\} = -\dfrac{d}{ds}\left(\dfrac{1}{s + 10}\right) = \dfrac{1}{(s + 10)^2}$

2. $\mathcal{L}\{t^3 e^t\} = (-1)^3 \dfrac{d^3}{ds^3}\left(\dfrac{1}{s - 1}\right) = \dfrac{6}{(s - 1)^4}$

3. $\mathcal{L}\{t \cos 2t\} = -\dfrac{d}{ds}\left(\dfrac{s}{s^2 + 4}\right) = \dfrac{s^2 - 4}{\left(s^2 + 4\right)^2}$

4. $\mathcal{L}\{t \sinh 3t\} = -\dfrac{d}{ds}\left(\dfrac{3}{s^2 - 9}\right) = \dfrac{6s}{\left(s^2 - 9\right)^2}$

5. $\mathcal{L}\{t^2 \sinh t\} = \dfrac{d^2}{ds^2}\left(\dfrac{1}{s^2 - 1}\right) = \dfrac{6s^2 + 2}{\left(s^2 - 1\right)^3}$

6. $\mathcal{L}\{t^2 \cos t\} = \dfrac{d^2}{ds^2}\left(\dfrac{s}{s^2 + 1}\right) = \dfrac{d}{ds}\left(\dfrac{1 - s^2}{(s^2 + 1)^2}\right) = \dfrac{2s\left(s^2 - 3\right)}{\left(s^2 + 1\right)^3}$

7. $\mathcal{L}\left\{te^{2t} \sin 6t\right\} = -\dfrac{d}{ds}\left(\dfrac{6}{(s - 2)^2 + 36}\right) = \dfrac{12(s - 2)}{\left[(s - 2)^2 + 36\right]^2}$

8. $\mathcal{L}\left\{te^{-3t} \cos 3t\right\} = -\dfrac{d}{ds}\left(\dfrac{s + 3}{(s + 3)^2 + 9}\right) = \dfrac{(s + 3)^2 - 9}{\left[(s + 3)^2 + 9\right]^2}$

9. The Laplace transform of the differential equation is

$$s \mathcal{L}\{y\} + \mathcal{L}\{y\} = \frac{2s}{(s^2 + 1)^2}.$$

Solving for $\mathcal{L}\{y\}$ we obtain

$$\mathcal{L}\{y\} = \frac{2s}{(s + 1)(s^2 + 1)^2} = -\frac{1}{2}\frac{1}{s + 1} - \frac{1}{2}\frac{1}{s^2 + 1} + \frac{1}{2}\frac{s}{s^2 + 1} + \frac{1}{(s^2 + 1)^2} + \frac{s}{(s^2 + 1)^2}.$$

Thus

$$y(t) = -\frac{1}{2}e^{-t} - \frac{1}{2}\sin t + \frac{1}{2}\cos t + \frac{1}{2}(\sin t - t\cos t) + \frac{1}{2}t\sin t$$

$$= -\frac{1}{2}e^{-t} + \frac{1}{2}\cos t - \frac{1}{2}t\cos t + \frac{1}{2}t\sin t.$$

10. The Laplace transform of the differential equation is

$$s\mathscr{L}\{y\} - \mathscr{L}\{y\} = \frac{2(s-1)}{((s-1)^2 + 1)^2}.$$

Solving for $\mathscr{L}\{y\}$ we obtain

$$\mathscr{L}\{y\} = \frac{2}{((s-1)^2 + 1)^2}.$$

Thus

$$y = e^t \sin t - te^t \cos t.$$

11. The Laplace transform of the differential equation is

$$s^2 \mathscr{L}\{y\} - sy(0) - y'(0) + 9\mathscr{L}\{y\} = \frac{s}{s^2 + 9}.$$

Letting $y(0) = 2$ and $y'(0) = 5$ and solving for $\mathscr{L}\{y\}$ we obtain

$$\mathscr{L}\{y\} = \frac{2s^3 + 5s^2 + 19s + 45}{(s^2 + 9)^2} = \frac{2s}{s^2 + 9} + \frac{5}{s^2 + 9} + \frac{s}{(s^2 + 9)^2}.$$

Thus

$$y = 2\cos 3t + \frac{5}{3}\sin 3t + \frac{1}{6}t\sin 3t.$$

12. The Laplace transform of the differential equation is

$$s^2 \mathscr{L}\{y\} - sy(0) - y'(0) + \mathscr{L}\{y\} = \frac{1}{s^2 + 1}.$$

Solving for $\mathscr{L}\{y\}$ we obtain

$$\mathscr{L}\{y\} = \frac{s^3 - s^2 + s}{(s^2 + 1)^2} = \frac{s}{s^2 + 1} - \frac{1}{s^2 + 1} + \frac{1}{(s^2 + 1)^2}.$$

Thus

$$y = \cos t - \sin t + \left(\frac{1}{2}\sin t - \frac{1}{2}t\cos t\right) = \cos t - \frac{1}{2}\sin t - \frac{1}{2}t\cos t.$$

13. The Laplace transform of the differential equation is

$$s^2 \mathscr{L}\{y\} - sy(0) - y'(0) + 16\mathscr{L}\{y\} = \mathscr{L}\left\{\cos 4t - \cos 4t\,\mathscr{U}(t - \pi)\right\}$$

or by (16) of Section 7.3,

$$(s^2 + 16)\,\mathscr{L}\{y\} = 1 + \frac{s}{s^2 + 16} - e^{-\pi s}\,\mathscr{L}\{\cos 4(t + \pi)\}$$

$$= 1 + \frac{s}{s^2 + 16} - e^{-\pi s}\,\mathscr{L}\{\cos 4t\}$$

$$= 1 + \frac{s}{s^2 + 16} - \frac{s}{s^2 + 16}e^{-\pi s}.$$

Thus

$$\mathscr{L}\{y\} = \frac{1}{s^2 + 16} + \frac{s}{(s^2 + 16)^2} - \frac{s}{(s^2 + 16)^2} e^{-\pi s}$$

and

$$y = \frac{1}{4}\sin 4t + \frac{1}{8}t \sin 4t - \frac{1}{8}(t - \pi)\sin 4(t - \pi)\,\mathcal{U}(t - \pi).$$

14. The Laplace transform of the differential equation is

$$s^2\,\mathscr{L}\{y\} - sy(0) - y'(0) + \mathscr{L}\{y\} = \mathscr{L}\left\{1 - \mathcal{U}\left(t - \frac{\pi}{2}\right) + \sin t\,\mathcal{U}\left(t - \frac{\pi}{2}\right)\right\}$$

or

$$(s^2 + 1)\,\mathscr{L}\{y\} = s + \frac{1}{s} - \frac{1}{s}e^{-\pi s/2} + e^{-\pi s/2}\,\mathscr{L}\left\{\sin\left(t + \frac{\pi}{2}\right)\right\}$$

$$= s + \frac{1}{s} - \frac{1}{s}e^{-\pi s/2} + e^{-\pi s/2}\,\mathscr{L}\{\cos t\}$$

$$= s + \frac{1}{s} - \frac{1}{s}e^{-\pi s/2} + \frac{s}{s^2 + 1}e^{-\pi s/2}.$$

Thus

$$\mathscr{L}\{y\} = \frac{s}{s^2 + 1} + \frac{1}{s(s^2 + 1)} - \frac{1}{s(s^2 + 1)}e^{-\pi s/2} + \frac{s}{(s^2 + 1)^2}e^{-\pi s/2}$$

$$= \frac{s}{s^2 + 1} + \frac{1}{s} - \frac{s}{s^2 + 1} - \left(\frac{1}{s} - \frac{s}{s^2 + 1}\right)e^{-\pi s/2} + \frac{s}{(s^2 + 1)^2}e^{-\pi s/2}$$

$$= \frac{1}{s} - \left(\frac{1}{s} - \frac{s}{s^2 + 1}\right)e^{-\pi s/2} + \frac{s}{(s^2 + 1)^2}e^{-\pi s/2}$$

and

$$y = 1 - \left[1 - \cos\left(t - \frac{\pi}{2}\right)\right]\mathcal{U}\left(t - \frac{\pi}{2}\right) + \frac{1}{2}\left(t - \frac{\pi}{2}\right)\sin\left(t - \frac{\pi}{2}\right)\mathcal{U}\left(t - \frac{\pi}{2}\right)$$

$$= 1 - (1 - \sin t)\,\mathcal{U}\left(t - \frac{\pi}{2}\right) - \frac{1}{2}\left(t - \frac{\pi}{2}\right)\cos t\,\mathcal{U}\left(t - \frac{\pi}{2}\right).$$

15.

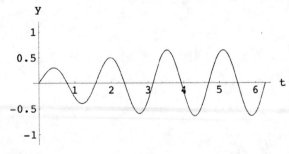

16.

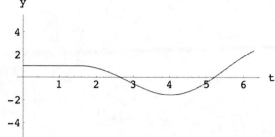

17. From (7) of Section 7.2 in the text along with Theorem 7.4.1,

$$\mathscr{L}\{ty''\} = -\frac{d}{ds}\,\mathscr{L}\{y''\} = -\frac{d}{ds}[s^2 Y(s) - sy(0) - y'(0)] = -s^2\frac{dY}{ds} - 2sY + y(0),$$

so that the transform of the given second-order differential equation is the linear first-order differential equation in $Y(s)$:

$$s^2 Y' + 3sY = -\frac{4}{s^3} \qquad \text{or} \qquad Y' + \frac{3}{s}Y = -\frac{4}{s^5}.$$

The solution of the latter equation is $Y(s) = 4/s^4 + c/s^3$, so

$$y(t) = \mathscr{L}^{-1}\{Y(s)\} = \frac{2}{3}t^3 + \frac{c}{2}t^2.$$

18. From Theorem 7.4.1 in the text

$$\mathscr{L}\{ty'\} = -\frac{d}{ds}\,\mathscr{L}\{y'\} = -\frac{d}{ds}[sY(s) - y(0)] = -s\frac{dY}{ds} - Y$$

so that the transform of the given second-order differential equation is the linear first-order differential equation in $Y(s)$:

$$Y' + \left(\frac{3}{s} - 2s\right)Y = -\frac{10}{s}.$$

Using the integrating factor $s^3 e^{-s^2}$, the last equation yields

$$Y(s) = \frac{5}{s^3} + \frac{c}{s^3}\,e^{s^2}.$$

But if $Y(s)$ is the Laplace transform of a piecewise-continuous function of exponential order, we must have, in view of Theorem 7.1.3, $\lim_{s\to\infty} Y(s) = 0$. In order to obtain this condition we require $c = 0$. Hence

$$y(t) = \mathscr{L}^{-1}\left\{\frac{5}{s^3}\right\} = \frac{5}{2}t^2.$$

19. $\mathscr{L}\left\{1 * t^3\right\} = \dfrac{1}{s}\dfrac{3!}{s^4} = \dfrac{6}{s^5}$

20. $\mathscr{L}\left\{t^2 * te^t\right\} = \dfrac{2}{s^3(s-1)^2}$

21. $\mathscr{L}\left\{e^{-t} * e^t \cos t\right\} = \dfrac{s-1}{(s+1)\left[(s-1)^2 + 1\right]}$

22. $\mathscr{L}\left\{e^{2t} * \sin t\right\} = \dfrac{1}{(s-2)(s^2+1)}$

23. $\mathscr{L}\left\{\displaystyle\int_0^t e^{\tau}\,d\tau\right\} = \dfrac{1}{s}\mathscr{L}\{e^t\} = \dfrac{1}{s(s-1)}$

24. $\mathscr{L}\left\{\displaystyle\int_0^t \cos\tau\,d\tau\right\} = \dfrac{1}{s}\mathscr{L}\{\cos t\} = \dfrac{s}{s(s^2+1)} = \dfrac{1}{s^2+1}$

25. $\mathscr{L}\left\{\displaystyle\int_0^t e^{-\tau}\cos\tau\,d\tau\right\} = \dfrac{1}{s}\,\mathscr{L}\{e^{-t}\cos t\} = \dfrac{1}{s}\dfrac{s+1}{(s+1)^2+1} = \dfrac{s+1}{s\,(s^2+2s+2)}$

26. $\mathscr{L}\left\{\displaystyle\int_0^t \tau\sin\tau\,d\tau\right\} = \dfrac{1}{s}\,\mathscr{L}\{t\sin t\} = \dfrac{1}{s}\left(-\dfrac{d}{ds}\dfrac{1}{s^2+1}\right) = -\dfrac{1}{s}\dfrac{-2s}{(s^2+1)^2} = \dfrac{2}{(s^2+1)^2}$

27. $\mathscr{L}\left\{\displaystyle\int_0^t \tau e^{t-\tau}\,d\tau\right\} = \mathscr{L}\{t\}\,\mathscr{L}\{e^t\} = \dfrac{1}{s^2(s-1)}$

28. $\mathscr{L}\left\{\displaystyle\int_0^t \sin\tau\cos(t-\tau)\,d\tau\right\} = \mathscr{L}\{\sin t\}\,\mathscr{L}\{\cos t\} = \dfrac{s}{(s^2+1)^2}$

29. $\mathscr{L}\left\{t\displaystyle\int_0^t \sin\tau\,d\tau\right\} = -\dfrac{d}{ds}\mathscr{L}\left\{\displaystyle\int_0^t \sin\tau\,d\tau\right\} = -\dfrac{d}{ds}\left(\dfrac{1}{s}\dfrac{1}{s^2+1}\right) = \dfrac{3s^2+1}{s^2\,(s^2+1)^2}$

30. $\mathscr{L}\left\{t\displaystyle\int_0^t \tau e^{-\tau}\,d\tau\right\} = -\dfrac{d}{ds}\mathscr{L}\left\{\displaystyle\int_0^t \tau e^{-\tau}\,d\tau\right\} = -\dfrac{d}{ds}\left(\dfrac{1}{s}\dfrac{1}{(s+1)^2}\right) = \dfrac{3s+1}{s^2(s+1)^3}$

31. $\mathscr{L}^{-1}\left\{\dfrac{1}{s(s-1)}\right\} = \mathscr{L}^{-1}\left\{\dfrac{1/(s-1)}{s}\right\} = \displaystyle\int_0^t e^{\tau}\,d\tau = e^t - 1$

32. $\mathscr{L}^{-1}\left\{\dfrac{1}{s^2(s-1)}\right\} = \mathscr{L}^{-1}\left\{\dfrac{1/s(s-1)}{s}\right\} = \displaystyle\int_0^t (e^{\tau}-1)d\tau = e^t - t - 1$

33. $\mathscr{L}^{-1}\left\{\dfrac{1}{s^3(s-1)}\right\} = \mathscr{L}^{-1}\left\{\dfrac{1/s^2(s-1)}{s}\right\} = \displaystyle\int_0^t (e^{\tau}-\tau-1)d\tau = e^t - \dfrac{1}{2}t^2 - t - 1$

34. Using $\mathscr{L}^{-1}\left\{\dfrac{1}{(s-a)^2}\right\} = te^{at}$, (8) in the text gives

$$\mathscr{L}^{-1}\left\{\dfrac{1}{s(s-a)^2}\right\} = \int_0^t \tau e^{a\tau}\,d\tau = \dfrac{1}{a^2}(ate^{at} - e^{at} + 1).$$

35. (a) The result in (4) in the text is $\mathscr{L}^{-1}\{F(s)G(s)\} = f * g$, so identify

$$F(s) = \dfrac{2k^3}{(s^2+k^2)^2} \qquad \text{and} \qquad G(s) = \dfrac{4s}{s^2+k^2}.$$

Then

$$f(t) = \sin kt - kt \cos kt \qquad \text{and} \qquad g(t) = 4 \cos kt$$

so

$$\mathscr{L}^{-1}\left\{ \frac{8k^3 s}{(s^2 + k^2)^3} \right\} = \mathscr{L}^{-1}\left\{ F(s)G(s) \right\} = f * g = 4 \int_0^t f(\tau)g(t - \tau)\,dt$$

$$= 4 \int_0^t (\sin k\tau - k\tau \cos k\tau) \cos k(t - \tau)\,d\tau.$$

Using a CAS to evaluate the integral we get

$$\mathscr{L}^{-1}\left\{ \frac{8k^3 s}{(s^2 + k^2)^3} \right\} = t \sin kt - kt^2 \cos kt.$$

(b) Observe from part (a) that

$$\mathscr{L}\{t(\sin kt - kt \cos kt)\} = \frac{8k^3 s}{(s^2 + k^2)^3},$$

and from Theorem 7.4.1 that $\mathscr{L}\{tf(t)\} = -F'(s)$. We saw in (5) in the text that

$$\mathscr{L}\{\sin kt - kt \cos kt\} = 2k^3/(s^2 + k^2)^2,$$

so

$$\mathscr{L}\{t(\sin kt - kt \cos kt)\} = -\frac{d}{ds}\frac{2k^3}{(s^2 + k^2)^2} = \frac{8k^3 s}{(s^2 + k^2)^3}.$$

36. The Laplace transform of the differential equation is

$$s^2 \mathscr{L}\{y\} + \mathscr{L}\{y\} = \frac{1}{(s^2 + 1)} + \frac{2s}{(s^2 + 1)^2}.$$

Thus

$$\mathscr{L}\{y\} = \frac{1}{(s^2 + 1)^2} + \frac{2s}{(s^2 + 1)^3}$$

and, using Problem 35 with $k = 1$,

$$y = \frac{1}{2}(\sin t - t \cos t) + \frac{1}{4}(t \sin t - t^2 \cos t).$$

37. The Laplace transform of the given equation is

$$\mathscr{L}\{f\} + \mathscr{L}\{t\}\,\mathscr{L}\{f\} = \mathscr{L}\{t\}.$$

Solving for $\mathscr{L}\{f\}$ we obtain $\mathscr{L}\{f\} = \dfrac{1}{s^2 + 1}$. Thus, $f(t) = \sin t$.

38. The Laplace transform of the given equation is

$$\mathscr{L}\{f\} = \mathscr{L}\{2t\} - 4\mathscr{L}\{\sin t\}\,\mathscr{L}\{f\}.$$

Exercises 7.4 Operational Properties II

Solving for $\mathcal{L}\{f\}$ we obtain

$$\mathcal{L}\{f\} = \frac{2s^2 + 2}{s^2(s^2 + 5)} = \frac{2}{5}\frac{1}{s^2} + \frac{8}{5\sqrt{5}}\frac{\sqrt{5}}{s^2 + 5}.$$

Thus

$$f(t) = \frac{2}{5}t + \frac{8}{5\sqrt{5}}\sin\sqrt{5}\,t.$$

39. The Laplace transform of the given equation is

$$\mathcal{L}\{f\} = \mathcal{L}\{te^t\} + \mathcal{L}\{t\}\mathcal{L}\{f\}.$$

Solving for $\mathcal{L}\{f\}$ we obtain

$$\mathcal{L}\{f\} = \frac{s^2}{(s-1)^3(s+1)} = \frac{1}{8}\frac{1}{s-1} + \frac{3}{4}\frac{1}{(s-1)^2} + \frac{1}{4}\frac{2}{(s-1)^3} - \frac{1}{8}\frac{1}{s+1}.$$

Thus

$$f(t) = \frac{1}{8}e^t + \frac{3}{4}te^t + \frac{1}{4}t^2e^t - \frac{1}{8}e^{-t}$$

40. The Laplace transform of the given equation is

$$\mathcal{L}\{f\} + 2\mathcal{L}\{\cos t\}\mathcal{L}\{f\} = 4\mathcal{L}\{e^{-t}\} + \mathcal{L}\{\sin t\}.$$

Solving for $\mathcal{L}\{f\}$ we obtain

$$\mathcal{L}\{f\} = \frac{4s^2 + s + 5}{(s+1)^3} = \frac{4}{s+1} - \frac{7}{(s+1)^2} + 4\frac{2}{(s+1)^3}.$$

Thus

$$f(t) = 4e^{-t} - 7te^{-t} + 4t^2e^{-t}.$$

41. The Laplace transform of the given equation is

$$\mathcal{L}\{f\} + \mathcal{L}\{1\}\mathcal{L}\{f\} = \mathcal{L}\{1\}.$$

Solving for $\mathcal{L}\{f\}$ we obtain $\mathcal{L}\{f\} = \dfrac{1}{s+1}$. Thus, $f(t) = e^{-t}$.

42. The Laplace transform of the given equation is

$$\mathcal{L}\{f\} = \mathcal{L}\{\cos t\} + \mathcal{L}\{e^{-t}\}\mathcal{L}\{f\}.$$

Solving for $\mathcal{L}\{f\}$ we obtain

$$\mathcal{L}\{f\} = \frac{s}{s^2 + 1} + \frac{1}{s^2 + 1}.$$

Thus

$$f(t) = \cos t + \sin t.$$

43. The Laplace transform of the given equation is

$$\mathscr{L}\{f\} = \mathscr{L}\{1\} + \mathscr{L}\{t\} - \mathscr{L}\left\{\frac{8}{3}\int_0^t (t-\tau)^3 f(\tau)\,d\tau\right\}$$

$$= \frac{1}{s} + \frac{1}{s^2} + \frac{8}{3}\mathscr{L}\{t^3\}\,\mathscr{L}\{f\} = \frac{1}{s} + \frac{1}{s^2} + \frac{16}{s^4}\mathscr{L}\{f\}.$$

Solving for $\mathscr{L}\{f\}$ we obtain

$$\mathscr{L}\{f\} = \frac{s^2(s+1)}{s^4-16} = \frac{1}{8}\frac{1}{s+2} + \frac{3}{8}\frac{1}{s-2} + \frac{1}{4}\frac{2}{s^2+4} + \frac{1}{2}\frac{s}{s^2+4}.$$

Thus

$$f(t) = \frac{1}{8}e^{-2t} + \frac{3}{8}e^{2t} + \frac{1}{4}\sin 2t + \frac{1}{2}\cos 2t.$$

44. The Laplace transform of the given equation is

$$\mathscr{L}\{t\} - 2\mathscr{L}\{f\} = \mathscr{L}\left\{e^t - e^{-t}\right\}\mathscr{L}\{f\}.$$

Solving for $\mathscr{L}\{f\}$ we obtain

$$\mathscr{L}\{f\} = \frac{s^2-1}{2s^4} = \frac{1}{2}\frac{1}{s^2} - \frac{1}{12}\frac{3!}{s^4}.$$

Thus

$$f(t) = \frac{1}{2}t - \frac{1}{12}t^3.$$

45. The Laplace transform of the given equation is

$$s\mathscr{L}\{y\} - y(0) = \mathscr{L}\{1\} - \mathscr{L}\{\sin t\} - \mathscr{L}\{1\}\mathscr{L}\{y\}.$$

Solving for $\mathscr{L}\{f\}$ we obtain

$$\mathscr{L}\{y\} = \frac{s^2-s+1}{(s^2+1)^2} = \frac{1}{s^2+1} - \frac{1}{2}\frac{2s}{(s^2+1)^2}.$$

Thus

$$y = \sin t - \frac{1}{2}t\sin t.$$

46. The Laplace transform of the given equation is

$$s\mathscr{L}\{y\} - y(0) + 6\mathscr{L}\{y\} + 9\mathscr{L}\{1\}\mathscr{L}\{y\} = \mathscr{L}\{1\}.$$

Solving for $\mathscr{L}\{f\}$ we obtain $\mathscr{L}\{y\} = \dfrac{1}{(s+3)^2}$. Thus, $y = te^{-3t}$.

47. The differential equation is

$$0.1\frac{di}{dt} + 3i + \frac{1}{0.05}\int_0^t i(\tau)d\tau = 100[\mathscr{U}(t-1) - \mathscr{U}(t-2)]$$

or

$$\frac{di}{dt} + 30i + 200\int_0^t i(\tau)d\tau = 1000[\mathscr{U}(t-1) - \mathscr{U}(t-2)],$$

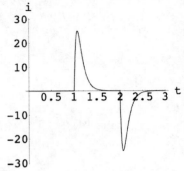

where $i(0) = 0$. The Laplace transform of the differential equation is

$$s\mathscr{L}\{i\} - y(0) + 30\,\mathscr{L}\{i\} + \frac{200}{s}\mathscr{L}\{i\} = \frac{1000}{s}(e^{-s} - e^{-2s}).$$

Solving for $\mathscr{L}\{i\}$ we obtain

$$\mathscr{L}\{i\} = \frac{1000e^{-s} - 1000e^{-2s}}{s^2 + 30s + 200} = \left(\frac{100}{s+10} - \frac{100}{s+20}\right)(e^{-s} - e^{-2s}).$$

Thus

$$i(t) = 100(e^{-10(t-1)} - e^{-20(t-1)})\,\mathscr{U}(t-1) - 100(e^{-10(t-2)} - e^{-20(t-2)})\,\mathscr{U}(t-2).$$

48. The differential equation is

$$0.005\frac{di}{dt} + i + \frac{1}{0.02}\int_0^t i(\tau)d\tau = 100[t - (t-1)\,\mathscr{U}(t-1)]$$

or

$$\frac{di}{dt} + 200i + 10{,}000\int_0^t i(\tau)d\tau = 20{,}000[t - (t-1)\,\mathscr{U}(t-1)],$$

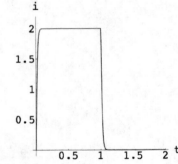

where $i(0) = 0$. The Laplace transform of the differential equation is

$$s\mathscr{L}\{i\} + 200\,\mathscr{L}\{i\} + \frac{10{,}000}{s}\mathscr{L}\{i\} = 20{,}000\left(\frac{1}{s^2} - \frac{1}{s^2}e^{-s}\right).$$

Solving for $\mathscr{L}\{i\}$ we obtain

$$\mathscr{L}\{i\} = \frac{20{,}000}{s(s+100)^2}(1 - e^{-s}) = \left[\frac{2}{s} - \frac{2}{s+100} - \frac{200}{(s+100)^2}\right](1 - e^{-s}).$$

Thus

$$i(t) = 2 - 2e^{-100t} - 200te^{-100t} - 2\,\mathscr{U}(t-1) + 2e^{-100(t-1)}\,\mathscr{U}(t-1) + 200(t-1)e^{-100(t-1)}\,\mathscr{U}(t-1).$$

49. $\mathscr{L}\{f(t)\} = \dfrac{1}{1 - e^{-2as}}\left[\displaystyle\int_0^a e^{-st}dt - \int_a^{2a} e^{-st}dt\right] = \dfrac{(1 - e^{-as})^2}{s(1 - e^{-2as})} = \dfrac{1 - e^{-as}}{s(1 + e^{-as})}$

50. $\mathscr{L}\{f(t)\} = \dfrac{1}{1 - e^{-2as}}\displaystyle\int_0^a e^{-st}dt = \dfrac{1}{s(1 + e^{-as})}$

51. Using integration by parts,

$$\mathcal{L}\{f(t)\} = \frac{1}{1 - e^{-bs}} \int_0^b \frac{a}{b} t e^{-st} dt = \frac{a}{s} \left(\frac{1}{bs} - \frac{1}{e^{bs} - 1} \right).$$

52. $\mathcal{L}\{f(t)\} = \dfrac{1}{1 - e^{-2s}} \left[\displaystyle\int_0^1 t e^{-st} dt + \int_1^2 (2 - t) e^{-st} dt \right] = \dfrac{1 - e^{-s}}{s^2 (1 - e^{-2s})}$

53. $\mathcal{L}\{f(t)\} = \dfrac{1}{1 - e^{-\pi s}} \displaystyle\int_0^\pi e^{-st} \sin t \, dt = \dfrac{1}{s^2 + 1} \cdot \dfrac{e^{\pi s/2} + e^{-\pi s/2}}{e^{\pi s/2} - e^{-\pi s/2}} = \dfrac{1}{s^2 + 1} \coth \dfrac{\pi s}{2}$

54. $\mathcal{L}\{f(t)\} = \dfrac{1}{1 - e^{-2\pi s}} \displaystyle\int_0^\pi e^{-st} \sin t \, dt = \dfrac{1}{s^2 + 1} \cdot \dfrac{1}{1 - e^{-\pi s}}$

55. The differential equation is $L\, di/dt + Ri = E(t)$, where $i(0) = 0$. The Laplace transform of the equation is

$$Ls \mathcal{L}\{i\} + R \mathcal{L}\{i\} = \mathcal{L}\{E(t)\}.$$

From Problem 49 we have $\mathcal{L}\{E(t)\} = (1 - e^{-s})/s(1 + e^{-s})$. Thus

$$(Ls + R) \mathcal{L}\{i\} = \frac{1 - e^{-s}}{s(1 + e^{-s})}$$

and

$$\mathcal{L}\{i\} = \frac{1}{L} \frac{1 - e^{-s}}{s(s + R/L)(1 + e^{-s})} = \frac{1}{L} \frac{1 - e^{-s}}{s(s + R/L)} \frac{1}{1 + e^{-s}}$$

$$= \frac{1}{R} \left(\frac{1}{s} - \frac{1}{s + R/L} \right) (1 - e^{-s})(1 - e^{-s} + e^{-2s} - e^{-3s} + e^{-4s} - \cdots)$$

$$= \frac{1}{R} \left(\frac{1}{s} - \frac{1}{s + R/L} \right) (1 - 2e^{-s} + 2e^{-2s} - 2e^{-3s} + 2e^{-4s} - \cdots).$$

Therefore,

$$i(t) = \frac{1}{R} \left(1 - e^{-Rt/L} \right) - \frac{2}{R} \left(1 - e^{-R(t-1)/L} \right) \mathcal{U}(t - 1)$$

$$+ \frac{2}{R} \left(1 - e^{-R(t-2)/L} \right) \mathcal{U}(t - 2) - \frac{2}{R} \left(1 - e^{-R(t-3)/L} \right) \mathcal{U}(t - 3) + \cdots$$

$$= \frac{1}{R} \left(1 - e^{-Rt/L} \right) + \frac{2}{R} \sum_{n=1}^{\infty} (-1)^n \left(1 - e^{-R(t-n)/L} \right) \mathcal{U}(t - n).$$

The graph of $i(t)$ with $L = 1$ and $R = 1$ is shown below.

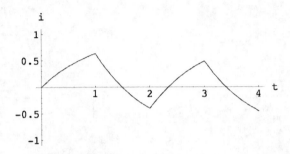

56. The differential equation is $L\,di/dt + Ri = E(t)$, where $i(0) = 0$. The Laplace transform of the equation is

$$Ls\,\mathscr{L}\{i\} + R\,\mathscr{L}\{i\} = \mathscr{L}\{E(t)\}.$$

From Problem 51 we have

$$\mathscr{L}\{E(t)\} = \frac{1}{s}\left(\frac{1}{s} - \frac{1}{e^s - 1}\right) = \frac{1}{s^2} - \frac{1}{s}\frac{1}{e^s - 1}.$$

Thus

$$(Ls + R)\,\mathscr{L}\{i\} = \frac{1}{s^2} - \frac{1}{s}\frac{1}{e^s - 1}$$

and

$$\mathscr{L}\{i\} = \frac{1}{L}\frac{1}{s^2(s + R/L)} - \frac{1}{L}\frac{1}{s(s + R/L)}\frac{1}{e^s - 1}$$

$$= \frac{1}{R}\left(\frac{1}{s^2} - \frac{L}{R}\frac{1}{s} + \frac{L}{R}\frac{1}{s + R/L}\right) - \frac{1}{R}\left(\frac{1}{s} - \frac{1}{s + R/L}\right)(e^{-s} + e^{-2s} + e^{-3s} + \cdots).$$

Therefore

$$i(t) = \frac{1}{R}\left(t - \frac{L}{R} + \frac{L}{R}e^{-Rt/L}\right) - \frac{1}{R}\left(1 - e^{-R(t-1)/L}\right)\mathscr{U}(t - 1)$$

$$- \frac{1}{R}\left(1 - e^{-R(t-2)/L}\right)\mathscr{U}(t - 2) - \frac{1}{R}\left(1 - e^{-R(t-3)/L}\right)\mathscr{U}(t - 3) - \cdots$$

$$= \frac{1}{R}\left(t - \frac{L}{R} + \frac{L}{R}e^{-Rt/L}\right) - \frac{1}{R}\sum_{n=1}^{\infty}\left(1 - e^{-R(t-n)/L}\right)\mathscr{U}(t - n).$$

The graph of $i(t)$ with $L = 1$ and $R = 1$ is shown below.

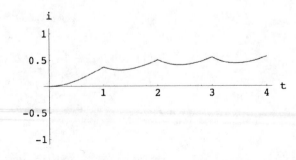

57. The differential equation is $x'' + 2x' + 10x = 20f(t)$, where $f(t)$ is the meander function in Problem 49 with $a = \pi$. Using the initial conditions $x(0) = x'(0) = 0$ and taking the Laplace transform we obtain

$$(s^2 + 2s + 10)\,\mathcal{L}\{x(t)\} = \frac{20}{s}(1 - e^{-\pi s})\frac{1}{1 + e^{-\pi s}}$$

$$= \frac{20}{s}(1 - e^{-\pi s})(1 - e^{-\pi s} + e^{-2\pi s} - e^{-3\pi s} + \cdots)$$

$$= \frac{20}{s}(1 - 2e^{-\pi s} + 2e^{-2\pi s} - 2e^{-3\pi s} + \cdots)$$

$$= \frac{20}{s} + \frac{40}{s}\sum_{n=1}^{\infty}(-1)^n e^{-n\pi s}.$$

Then

$$\mathcal{L}\{x(t)\} = \frac{20}{s(s^2 + 2s + 10)} + \frac{40}{s(s^2 + 2s + 10)}\sum_{n=1}^{\infty}(-1)^n e^{-n\pi s}$$

$$= \frac{2}{s} - \frac{2s + 4}{s^2 + 2s + 10} + \sum_{n=1}^{\infty}(-1)^n\left[\frac{4}{s} - \frac{4s + 8}{s^2 + 2s + 10}\right]e^{-n\pi s}$$

$$= \frac{2}{s} - \frac{2(s + 1) + 2}{(s + 1)^2 + 9} + 4\sum_{n=1}^{\infty}(-1)^n\left[\frac{1}{s} - \frac{(s + 1) + 1}{(s + 1)^2 + 9}\right]e^{-n\pi s}$$

and

$$x(t) = 2\left(1 - e^{-t}\cos 3t - \frac{1}{3}e^{-t}\sin 3t\right) + 4\sum_{n=1}^{\infty}(-1)^n\left[1 - e^{-(t-n\pi)}\cos 3(t - n\pi)\right.$$

$$\left. - \frac{1}{3}e^{-(t-n\pi)}\sin 3(t - n\pi)\right]\mathcal{U}(t - n\pi).$$

The graph of $x(t)$ on the interval $[0, 2\pi)$ is shown below.

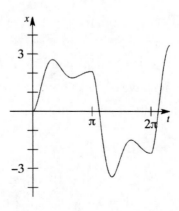

58. The differential equation is $x'' + 2x' + x = 5f(t)$, where $f(t)$ is the square wave function with $a = \pi$.

Using the initial conditions $x(0) = x'(0) = 0$ and taking the Laplace transform, we obtain

$$(s^2 + 2s + 1)\,\mathscr{L}\{x(t)\} = \frac{5}{s}\frac{1}{1 + e^{-\pi s}} = \frac{5}{s}(1 - e^{-\pi s} + e^{-2\pi s} - e^{-3\pi s} + e^{-4\pi s} - \cdots)$$

$$= \frac{5}{s}\sum_{n=0}^{\infty}(-1)^n e^{-n\pi s}.$$

Then

$$\mathscr{L}\{x(t)\} = \frac{5}{s(s+1)^2}\sum_{n=0}^{\infty}(-1)^n e^{-n\pi s} = 5\sum_{n=0}^{\infty}(-1)^n\left(\frac{1}{s} - \frac{1}{s+1} - \frac{1}{(s+1)^2}\right)e^{-n\pi s}$$

and

$$x(t) = 5\sum_{n=0}^{\infty}(-1)^n(1 - e^{-(t-n\pi)} - (t - n\pi)e^{-(t-n\pi)})\,\mathscr{U}(t - n\pi).$$

The graph of $x(t)$ on the interval $[0, 4\pi)$ is shown below.

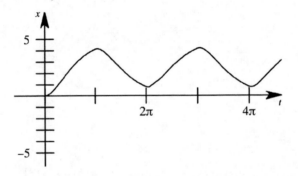

59. $f(t) = -\dfrac{1}{t}\mathscr{L}^{-1}\left\{\dfrac{d}{ds}[\ln(s - 3) - \ln(s + 1)]\right\} = -\dfrac{1}{t}\mathscr{L}^{-1}\left\{\dfrac{1}{s - 3} - \dfrac{1}{s + 1}\right\} = -\dfrac{1}{t}\left(e^{3t} - e^{-t}\right)$

60. The transform of Bessel's equation is

$$-\frac{d}{ds}[s^2 Y(s) - sy(0) - y'(0)] + sY(s) - y(0) - \frac{d}{ds}Y(s) = 0$$

or, after simplifying and using the initial condition, $(s^2 + 1)Y' + sY = 0$. This equation is both separable and linear. Solving gives $Y(s) = c/\sqrt{s^2 + 1}$. Now $Y(s) = \mathscr{L}\{J_0(t)\}$, where J_0 has a derivative that is continuous and of exponential order, implies by Problem 46 of Exercises 7.2 that

$$1 = J_0(0) = \lim_{s \to \infty} sY(s) = c\lim_{s \to \infty}\frac{s}{\sqrt{s^2 + k^2}} = c$$

so $c = 1$ and

$$Y(s) = \frac{1}{\sqrt{s^2 + 1}} \qquad \text{or} \qquad \mathscr{L}\{J_0(t)\} = \frac{1}{\sqrt{s^2 + 1}}.$$

61. (a) Using Theorem 7.4.1, the Laplace transform of the differential equation is

$$-\frac{d}{ds}[s^2Y - sy(0) - y'(0)] + sY - y(0) + \frac{d}{ds}[sY - y(0)] + nY$$

$$= -\frac{d}{ds}[s^2Y] + sY + \frac{d}{ds}[sY] + nY$$

$$= -s^2\left(\frac{dY}{ds}\right) - 2sY + sY + s\left(\frac{dY}{ds}\right) + Y + nY$$

$$= (s - s^2)\left(\frac{dY}{ds}\right) + (1 + n - s)Y = 0.$$

Separating variables, we find

$$\frac{dY}{Y} = \frac{1 + n - s}{s^2 - s}\, ds = \left(\frac{n}{s - 1} - \frac{1 + n}{s}\right) ds$$

$$\ln Y = n\ln(s - 1) - (1 + n)\ln s + c$$

$$Y = c_1 \frac{(s - 1)^n}{s^{1+n}}.$$

Since the differential equation is homogeneous, any constant multiple of a solution will still be a solution, so for convenience we take $c_1 = 1$. The following polynomials are solutions of Laguerre's differential equation:

$$n = 0: \quad L_0(t) = \mathcal{L}^{-1}\left\{\frac{1}{s}\right\} = 1$$

$$n = 1: \quad L_1(t) = \mathcal{L}^{-1}\left\{\frac{s - 1}{s^2}\right\} = \mathcal{L}^{-1}\left\{\frac{1}{s} - \frac{1}{s^2}\right\} = 1 - t$$

$$n = 2: \quad L_2(t) = \mathcal{L}^{-1}\left\{\frac{(s - 1)^2}{s^3}\right\} = \mathcal{L}^{-1}\left\{\frac{1}{s} - \frac{2}{s^2} + \frac{1}{s^3}\right\} = 1 - 2t + \frac{1}{2}t^2$$

$$n = 3: \quad L_3(t) = \mathcal{L}^{-1}\left\{\frac{(s - 1)^3}{s^4}\right\} = \mathcal{L}^{-1}\left\{\frac{1}{s} - \frac{3}{s^2} + \frac{3}{s^3} - \frac{1}{s^4}\right\} = 1 - 3t + \frac{3}{2}t^2 - \frac{1}{6}t^3$$

$$n = 4: \quad L_4(t) = \mathcal{L}^{-1}\left\{\frac{(s - 1)^4}{s^5}\right\} = \mathcal{L}^{-1}\left\{\frac{1}{s} - \frac{4}{s^2} + \frac{6}{s^3} - \frac{4}{s^4} + \frac{1}{s^5}\right\}$$

$$= 1 - 4t + 3t^2 - \frac{2}{3}t^3 + \frac{1}{24}t^4.$$

(b) Letting $f(t) = t^n e^{-t}$ we note that $f^{(k)}(0) = 0$ for $k = 0, 1, 2, \ldots, n - 1$ and $f^{(n)}(0) = n!$.

Now, by the first translation theorem,

$$\mathscr{L}\left\{\frac{e^t}{n!}\frac{d^n}{dt^n}t^n e^{-t}\right\} = \frac{1}{n!}\mathscr{L}\{e^t f^{(n)}(t)\} = \frac{1}{n!}\mathscr{L}\{f^{(n)}(t)\}\,|_{s\to s-1}$$

$$= \frac{1}{n!}\left[s^n\,\mathscr{L}\{t^n e^{-t}\} - s^{n-1}f(0) - s^{n-2}f'(0) - \cdots - f^{(n-1)}(0)\right]_{s\to s-1}$$

$$= \frac{1}{n!}\left[s^n\,\mathscr{L}\{t^n e^{-t}\}\right]_{s\to s-1}$$

$$= \frac{1}{n!}\left[s^n\,\frac{n!}{(s+1)^{n+1}}\right]_{s\to s-1} = \frac{(s-1)^n}{s^{n+1}} = Y,$$

where $Y = \mathscr{L}\{L_n(t)\}$. Thus

$$L_n(t) = \frac{e^t}{n!}\frac{d^n}{dt^n}(t^n e^{-t}), \quad n = 0,\,1,\,2,\,\ldots.$$

62. The output for the first three lines of the program are

$$9y[t] + 6y'[t] + y''[t] == t\,\sin[t]$$

$$1 - 2s + 9Y + s^2 Y + 6(-2 + sY) == \frac{2s}{(1+s^2)^2}$$

$$Y \to -\left(\frac{-11 - 4s - 22s^2 - 4s^3 - 11s^4 - 2s^5}{(1+s^2)^2(9 + 6s + s^2)}\right)$$

The fourth line is the same as the third line with $Y \to$ removed. The final line of output shows a solution involving complex coefficients of e^{it} and e^{-it}. To get the solution in more standard form write the last line as two lines:

euler={E^(It)–>Cos[t] + I Sin[t], E^(-It)–>Cos[t] - I Sin[t]}
InverseLaplaceTransform[Y, s, t]/.euler//Expand

We see that the solution is

$$y(t) = \left(\frac{487}{250} + \frac{247}{50}t\right)e^{-3t} + \frac{1}{250}(13\cos t - 15t\cos t - 9\sin t + 20t\sin t).$$

63. The solution is

$$y(t) = \frac{1}{6}e^t - \frac{1}{6}e^{-t/2}\cos\sqrt{15}\,t - \frac{\sqrt{3/5}}{6}e^{-t/2}\sin\sqrt{15}\,t.$$

64. The solution is

$$q(t) = 1 - \cos t + (6 - 6\cos t)\,\mathscr{U}(t - 3\pi) - (4 + 4\cos t)\,\mathscr{U}(t - \pi).$$

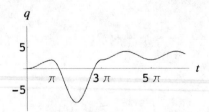

1. The Laplace transform of the differential equation yields

$$\mathscr{L}\{y\} = \frac{1}{s-3}e^{-2s}$$

so that

$$y = e^{3(t-2)}\,\mathscr{U}(t-2).$$

2. The Laplace transform of the differential equation yields

$$\mathscr{L}\{y\} = \frac{2}{s+1} + \frac{e^{-s}}{s+1}$$

so that

$$y = 2e^{-t} + e^{-(t-1)}\mathscr{U}(t-1).$$

3. The Laplace transform of the differential equation yields

$$\mathscr{L}\{y\} = \frac{1}{s^2+1}\left(1 + e^{-2\pi s}\right)$$

so that

$$y = \sin t + \sin t\,\mathscr{U}(t-2\pi).$$

4. The Laplace transform of the differential equation yields

$$\mathscr{L}\{y\} = \frac{1}{4}\frac{4}{s^2+16}e^{-2\pi s}$$

so that

$$y = \frac{1}{4}\sin 4(t-2\pi)\,\mathscr{U}(t-2\pi) = \frac{1}{4}\sin 4t\,\mathscr{U}(t-2\pi).$$

5. The Laplace transform of the differential equation yields

$$\mathscr{L}\{y\} = \frac{1}{s^2+1}\left(e^{-\pi s/2} + e^{-3\pi s/2}\right)$$

so that

$$y = \sin\left(t - \frac{\pi}{2}\right)\mathscr{U}\left(t - \frac{\pi}{2}\right) + \sin\left(t - \frac{3\pi}{2}\right)\mathscr{U}\left(t - \frac{3\pi}{2}\right)$$

$$= -\cos t\,\mathscr{U}\left(t - \frac{\pi}{2}\right) + \cos t\,\mathscr{U}\left(t - \frac{3\pi}{2}\right).$$

6. The Laplace transform of the differential equation yields

$$\mathscr{L}\{y\} = \frac{s}{s^2+1} + \frac{1}{s^2+1}\left(e^{-2\pi s} + e^{-4\pi s}\right)$$

so that

$$y = \cos t + \sin t[\mathcal{U}(t - 2\pi) + \mathcal{U}(t - 4\pi)].$$

7. The Laplace transform of the differential equation yields

$$\mathscr{L}\{y\} = \frac{1}{s^2 + 2s}(1 + e^{-s}) = \left[\frac{1}{2}\frac{1}{s} - \frac{1}{2}\frac{1}{s+2}\right](1 + e^{-s})$$

so that

$$y = \frac{1}{2} - \frac{1}{2}e^{-2t} + \left[\frac{1}{2} - \frac{1}{2}e^{-2(t-1)}\right]\mathcal{U}(t - 1).$$

8. The Laplace transform of the differential equation yields

$$\mathscr{L}\{y\} = \frac{s+1}{s^2(s-2)} + \frac{1}{s(s-2)}e^{-2s} = \frac{3}{4}\frac{1}{s-2} - \frac{3}{4}\frac{1}{s} - \frac{1}{2}\frac{1}{s^2} + \left[\frac{1}{2}\frac{1}{s-2} - \frac{1}{2}\frac{1}{s}\right]e^{-2s}$$

so that

$$y = \frac{3}{4}e^{2t} - \frac{3}{4} - \frac{1}{2}t + \left[\frac{1}{2}e^{2(t-2)} - \frac{1}{2}\right]\mathcal{U}(t - 2).$$

9. The Laplace transform of the differential equation yields

$$\mathscr{L}\{y\} = \frac{1}{(s+2)^2 + 1}e^{-2\pi s}$$

so that

$$y = e^{-2(t-2\pi)}\sin t\, \mathcal{U}(t - 2\pi).$$

10. The Laplace transform of the differential equation yields

$$\mathscr{L}\{y\} = \frac{1}{(s+1)^2}e^{-s}$$

so that

$$y = (t - 1)e^{-(t-1)}\mathcal{U}(t - 1).$$

11. The Laplace transform of the differential equation yields

$$\mathscr{L}\{y\} = \frac{4+s}{s^2 + 4s + 13} + \frac{e^{-\pi s} + e^{-3\pi s}}{s^2 + 4s + 13}$$

$$= \frac{2}{3}\frac{3}{(s+2)^2 + 3^2} + \frac{s+2}{(s+2)^2 + 3^2} + \frac{1}{3}\frac{3}{(s+2)^2 + 3^2}\left(e^{-\pi s} + e^{-3\pi s}\right)$$

so that

$$y = \frac{2}{3}e^{-2t}\sin 3t + e^{-2t}\cos 3t + \frac{1}{3}e^{-2(t-\pi)}\sin 3(t - \pi)\mathcal{U}(t - \pi)$$

$$+ \frac{1}{3}e^{-2(t-3\pi)}\sin 3(t - 3\pi)\mathcal{U}(t - 3\pi).$$

12. The Laplace transform of the differential equation yields

$$\mathscr{L}\{y\} = \frac{1}{(s-1)^2(s-6)} + \frac{e^{-2s} + e^{-4s}}{(s-1)(s-6)}$$

$$= -\frac{1}{25}\frac{1}{s-1} - \frac{1}{5}\frac{1}{(s-1)^2} + \frac{1}{25}\frac{1}{s-6} + \left[-\frac{1}{5}\frac{1}{s-1} + \frac{1}{5}\frac{1}{s-6} \right]\left(e^{-2s} + e^{-4s} \right)$$

so that

$$y = -\frac{1}{25}e^t - \frac{1}{5}te^t + \frac{1}{25}e^{6t} + \left[-\frac{1}{5}e^{t-2} + \frac{1}{5}e^{6(t-2)} \right]\mathscr{U}(t-2)$$

$$+ \left[-\frac{1}{5}e^{t-4} + \frac{1}{5}e^{6(t-4)} \right]\mathscr{U}(t-4).$$

13. The Laplace transform of the differential equation yields

$$\mathscr{L}\{y\} = \frac{1}{2}\frac{2}{s^3}y''(0) + \frac{1}{6}\frac{3!}{s^4}y'''(0) + \frac{1}{6}\frac{P_0}{EI}\frac{3!}{s^4}e^{-Ls/2}$$

so that

$$y = \frac{1}{2}y''(0)x^2 + \frac{1}{6}y'''(0)x^3 + \frac{1}{6}\frac{P_0}{EI}\left(x - \frac{L}{2} \right)^3\mathscr{U}\left(x - \frac{L}{2} \right).$$

Using $y''(L) = 0$ and $y'''(L) = 0$ we obtain

$$y = \frac{1}{4}\frac{P_0 L}{EI}x^2 - \frac{1}{6}\frac{P_0}{EI}x^3 + \frac{1}{6}\frac{P_0}{EI}\left(x - \frac{L}{2} \right)^3\mathscr{U}\left(x - \frac{L}{2} \right)$$

$$= \begin{cases} \dfrac{P_0}{EI}\left(\dfrac{L}{4}x^2 - \dfrac{1}{6}x^3 \right), & 0 \le x < \dfrac{L}{2} \\[3mm] \dfrac{P_0 L^2}{4EI}\left(\dfrac{1}{2}x - \dfrac{L}{12} \right), & \dfrac{L}{2} \le x \le L. \end{cases}$$

14. From Problem 13 we know that

$$y = \frac{1}{2}y''(0)x^2 + \frac{1}{6}y'''(0)x^3 + \frac{1}{6}\frac{P_0}{EI}\left(x - \frac{L}{2} \right)^3\mathscr{U}\left(x - \frac{L}{2} \right).$$

Using $y(L) = 0$ and $y'(L) = 0$ we obtain

$$y = \frac{1}{16}\frac{P_0 L}{EI}x^2 - \frac{1}{12}\frac{P_0}{EI}x^3 + \frac{1}{6}\frac{P_0}{EI}\left(x - \frac{L}{2} \right)^3\mathscr{U}\left(x - \frac{L}{2} \right)$$

$$= \begin{cases} \dfrac{P_0}{EI}\left(\dfrac{L}{16}x^2 - \dfrac{1}{12}x^3 \right), & 0 \le x < \dfrac{L}{2} \\[3mm] \dfrac{P_0}{EI}\left(\dfrac{L}{16}x^2 - \dfrac{1}{12}x^3 \right) + \dfrac{1}{6}\dfrac{P_0}{EI}\left(x - \dfrac{L}{2} \right)^3, & \dfrac{L}{2} \le x \le L. \end{cases}$$

15. You should disagree. Although formal manipulations of the Laplace transform lead to $y(t) = \frac{1}{3}e^{-t}\sin 3t$ in both cases, this function does not satisfy the initial condition $y'(0) = 0$ of the second initial-value problem.

1. Taking the Laplace transform of the system gives

$$s\mathcal{L}\{x\} = -\mathcal{L}\{x\} + \mathcal{L}\{y\}$$

$$s\mathcal{L}\{y\} - 1 = 2\mathcal{L}\{x\}$$

so that

$$\mathcal{L}\{x\} = \frac{1}{(s-1)(s+2)} = \frac{1}{3}\frac{1}{s-1} - \frac{1}{3}\frac{1}{s+2}$$

and

$$\mathcal{L}\{y\} = \frac{1}{s} + \frac{2}{s(s-1)(s+2)} = \frac{2}{3}\frac{1}{s-1} + \frac{1}{3}\frac{1}{s+2}.$$

Then

$$x = \frac{1}{3}e^t - \frac{1}{3}e^{-2t} \quad \text{and} \quad y = \frac{2}{3}e^t + \frac{1}{3}e^{-2t}.$$

2. Taking the Laplace transform of the system gives

$$s\mathcal{L}\{x\} - 1 = 2\mathcal{L}\{y\} + \frac{1}{s-1}$$

$$s\mathcal{L}\{y\} - 1 = 8\mathcal{L}\{x\} - \frac{1}{s^2}$$

so that

$$\mathcal{L}\{y\} = \frac{s^3 + 7s^2 - s + 1}{s(s-1)(s^2-16)} = \frac{1}{16}\frac{1}{s} - \frac{8}{15}\frac{1}{s-1} + \frac{173}{96}\frac{1}{s-4} - \frac{53}{160}\frac{1}{s+4}$$

and

$$y = \frac{1}{16} - \frac{8}{15}e^t + \frac{173}{96}e^{4t} - \frac{53}{160}e^{-4t}.$$

Then

$$x = \frac{1}{8}y' + \frac{1}{8}t = \frac{1}{8}t - \frac{1}{15}e^t + \frac{173}{192}e^{4t} + \frac{53}{320}e^{-4t}.$$

3. Taking the Laplace transform of the system gives

$$s\mathcal{L}\{x\} + 1 = \mathcal{L}\{x\} - 2\mathcal{L}\{y\}$$

$$s\mathcal{L}\{y\} - 2 = 5\mathcal{L}\{x\} - \mathcal{L}\{y\}$$

so that

$$\mathcal{L}\{x\} = \frac{-s-5}{s^2+9} = -\frac{s}{s^2+9} - \frac{5}{3}\frac{3}{s^2+9}$$

and

$$x = -\cos 3t - \frac{5}{3}\sin 3t.$$

Then

$$y = \frac{1}{2}x - \frac{1}{2}x' = 2\cos 3t - \frac{7}{3}\sin 3t.$$

4. Taking the Laplace transform of the system gives

$$(s+3)\,\mathscr{L}\{x\} + s\mathscr{L}\{y\} = \frac{1}{s}$$

$$(s-1)\,\mathscr{L}\{x\} + (s-1)\,\mathscr{L}\{y\} = \frac{1}{s-1}$$

so that

$$\mathscr{L}\{y\} = \frac{5s-1}{3s(s-1)^2} = -\frac{1}{3}\frac{1}{s} + \frac{1}{3}\frac{1}{s-1} + \frac{4}{3}\frac{1}{(s-1)^2}$$

and

$$\mathscr{L}\{x\} = \frac{1-2s}{3s(s-1)^2} = \frac{1}{3}\frac{1}{s} - \frac{1}{3}\frac{1}{s-1} - \frac{1}{3}\frac{1}{(s-1)^2}.$$

Then

$$x = \frac{1}{3} - \frac{1}{3}e^t - \frac{1}{3}te^t \qquad \text{and} \qquad y = -\frac{1}{3} + \frac{1}{3}e^t + \frac{4}{3}te^t.$$

5. Taking the Laplace transform of the system gives

$$(2s-2)\,\mathscr{L}\{x\} + s\mathscr{L}\{y\} = \frac{1}{s}$$

$$(s-3)\,\mathscr{L}\{x\} + (s-3)\,\mathscr{L}\{y\} = \frac{2}{s}$$

so that

$$\mathscr{L}\{x\} = \frac{-s-3}{s(s-2)(s-3)} = -\frac{1}{2}\frac{1}{s} + \frac{5}{2}\frac{1}{s-2} - \frac{2}{s-3}$$

and

$$\mathscr{L}\{y\} = \frac{3s-1}{s(s-2)(s-3)} = -\frac{1}{6}\frac{1}{s} - \frac{5}{2}\frac{1}{s-2} + \frac{8}{3}\frac{1}{s-3}.$$

Then

$$x = -\frac{1}{2} + \frac{5}{2}e^{2t} - 2e^{3t} \qquad \text{and} \qquad y = -\frac{1}{6} - \frac{5}{2}e^{2t} + \frac{8}{3}e^{3t}.$$

6. Taking the Laplace transform of the system gives

$$(s+1)\,\mathscr{L}\{x\} - (s-1)\mathscr{L}\{y\} = -1$$

$$s\mathscr{L}\{x\} + (s+2)\,\mathscr{L}\{y\} = 1$$

so that

$$\mathscr{L}\{y\} = \frac{s+1/2}{s^2+s+1} = \frac{s+1/2}{(s+1/2)^2 + (\sqrt{3}/2)^2}$$

and

$$\mathscr{L}\{x\} = \frac{-3/2}{s^2 + s + 1} = -\sqrt{3}\,\frac{\sqrt{3}/2}{(s + 1/2)^2 + (\sqrt{3}/2)^2}.$$

Then

$$y = e^{-t/2} \cos \frac{\sqrt{3}}{2}t \qquad \text{and} \qquad x = -\sqrt{3}\,e^{-t/2} \sin \frac{\sqrt{3}}{2}t.$$

7. Taking the Laplace transform of the system gives

$$(s^2 + 1)\,\mathscr{L}\{x\} - \mathscr{L}\{y\} = -2$$

$$-\mathscr{L}\{x\} + (s^2 + 1)\,\mathscr{L}\{y\} = 1$$

so that

$$\mathscr{L}\{x\} = \frac{-2s^2 - 1}{s^4 + 2s^2} = -\frac{1}{2}\frac{1}{s^2} - \frac{3}{2}\frac{1}{s^2 + 2}$$

and

$$x = -\frac{1}{2}t - \frac{3}{2\sqrt{2}} \sin \sqrt{2}\,t.$$

Then

$$y = x'' + x = -\frac{1}{2}t + \frac{3}{2\sqrt{2}} \sin \sqrt{2}\,t.$$

8. Taking the Laplace transform of the system gives

$$(s + 1)\,\mathscr{L}\{x\} + \mathscr{L}\{y\} = 1$$

$$4\mathscr{L}\{x\} - (s + 1)\,\mathscr{L}\{y\} = 1$$

so that

$$\mathscr{L}\{x\} = \frac{s + 2}{s^2 + 2s + 5} = \frac{s + 1}{(s + 1)^2 + 2^2} + \frac{1}{2}\frac{2}{(s + 1)^2 + 2^2}$$

and

$$\mathscr{L}\{y\} = \frac{-s + 3}{s^2 + 2s + 5} = -\frac{s + 1}{(s + 1)^2 + 2^2} + 2\frac{2}{(s + 1)^2 + 2^2}.$$

Then

$$x = e^{-t} \cos 2t + \frac{1}{2}e^{-t} \sin 2t \qquad \text{and} \qquad y = -e^{-t} \cos 2t + 2e^{-t} \sin 2t.$$

9. Adding the equations and then subtracting them gives

$$\frac{d^2x}{dt^2} = \frac{1}{2}t^2 + 2t$$

$$\frac{d^2y}{dt^2} = \frac{1}{2}t^2 - 2t.$$

Taking the Laplace transform of the system gives

$$\mathscr{L}\{x\} = 8\frac{1}{s} + \frac{1}{24}\frac{4!}{s^5} + \frac{1}{3}\frac{3!}{s^4}$$

and

$$\mathscr{L}\{y\} = \frac{1}{24}\frac{4!}{s^5} - \frac{1}{3}\frac{3!}{s^4}$$

so that

$$x = 8 + \frac{1}{24}t^4 + \frac{1}{3}t^3 \qquad \text{and} \qquad y = \frac{1}{24}t^4 - \frac{1}{3}t^3.$$

10. Taking the Laplace transform of the system gives

$$(s-4)\,\mathscr{L}\{x\} + s^3\mathscr{L}\{y\} = \frac{6}{s^2+1}$$

$$(s+2)\,\mathscr{L}\{x\} - 2s^3\mathscr{L}\{y\} = 0$$

so that

$$\mathscr{L}\{x\} = \frac{4}{(s-2)(s^2+1)} = \frac{4}{5}\frac{1}{s-2} - \frac{4}{5}\frac{s}{s^2+1} - \frac{8}{5}\frac{1}{s^2+1}$$

and

$$\mathscr{L}\{y\} = \frac{2s+4}{s^3(s-2)(s^2+1)} = \frac{1}{s} - \frac{2}{s^2} - 2\frac{2}{s^3} + \frac{1}{5}\frac{1}{s-2} - \frac{6}{5}\frac{s}{s^2+1} + \frac{8}{5}\frac{1}{s^2+1}.$$

Then

$$x = \frac{4}{5}e^{2t} - \frac{4}{5}\cos t - \frac{8}{5}\sin t$$

and

$$y = 1 - 2t - 2t^2 + \frac{1}{5}e^{2t} - \frac{6}{5}\cos t + \frac{8}{5}\sin t.$$

11. Taking the Laplace transform of the system gives

$$s^2\mathscr{L}\{x\} + 3(s+1)\mathscr{L}\{y\} = 2$$

$$s^2\mathscr{L}\{x\} + 3\mathscr{L}\{y\} = \frac{1}{(s+1)^2}$$

so that

$$\mathscr{L}\{x\} = -\frac{2s+1}{s^3(s+1)} = \frac{1}{s} + \frac{1}{s^2} + \frac{1}{2}\frac{2}{s^3} - \frac{1}{s+1}.$$

Then

$$x = 1 + t + \frac{1}{2}t^2 - e^{-t}$$

and

$$y = \frac{1}{3}te^{-t} - \frac{1}{3}x'' = \frac{1}{3}te^{-t} + \frac{1}{3}e^{-t} - \frac{1}{3}.$$

12. Taking the Laplace transform of the system gives

$$(s-4)\,\mathscr{L}\{x\} + 2\mathscr{L}\{y\} = \frac{2e^{-s}}{s}$$

$$-3\,\mathscr{L}\{x\} + (s+1)\,\mathscr{L}\{y\} = \frac{1}{2} + \frac{e^{-s}}{s}$$

so that

$$\mathscr{L}\{x\} = \frac{-1/2}{(s-1)(s-2)} + e^{-s}\frac{1}{(s-1)(s-2)}$$

$$= \frac{1}{2}\frac{1}{s-1} - \frac{1}{2}\frac{1}{s-2} + e^{-s}\left[-\frac{1}{s-1} + \frac{1}{s-2}\right]$$

and

$$\mathscr{L}\{y\} = \frac{e^{-s}}{s} + \frac{s/4-1}{(s-1)(s-2)} + e^{-s}\frac{-s/2+2}{(s-1)(s-2)}$$

$$= \frac{3}{4}\frac{1}{s-1} - \frac{1}{2}\frac{1}{s-2} + e^{-s}\left[\frac{1}{s} - \frac{3}{2}\frac{1}{s-1} + \frac{1}{s-2}\right].$$

Then

$$x = \frac{1}{2}e^t - \frac{1}{2}e^{2t} + \left[-e^{t-1} + e^{2(t-1)}\right]\mathscr{U}\,(t-1)$$

and

$$y = \frac{3}{4}e^t - \frac{1}{2}e^{2t} + \left[1 - \frac{3}{2}e^{t-1} + e^{2(t-1)}\right]\mathscr{U}\,(t-1).$$

13. The system is

$$x_1'' = -3x_1 + 2(x_2 - x_1)$$

$$x_2'' = -2(x_2 - x_1)$$

$$x_1(0) = 0$$

$$x_1'(0) = 1$$

$$x_2(0) = 1$$

$$x_2'(0) = 0.$$

Taking the Laplace transform of the system gives

$$(s^2 + 5)\,\mathscr{L}\{x_1\} - 2\mathscr{L}\{x_2\} = 1$$

$$-2\,\mathscr{L}\{x_1\} + (s^2 + 2)\,\mathscr{L}\{x_2\} = s$$

so that

$$\mathscr{L}\{x_1\} = \frac{s^2 + 2s + 2}{s^4 + 7s^2 + 6} = \frac{2}{5}\frac{s}{s^2+1} + \frac{1}{5}\frac{1}{s^2+1} - \frac{2}{5}\frac{s}{s^2+6} + \frac{4}{5\sqrt{6}}\frac{\sqrt{6}}{s^2+6}$$

and

$$\mathscr{L}\{x_2\} = \frac{s^3 + 5s + 2}{(s^2+1)(s^2+6)} = \frac{4}{5}\frac{s}{s^2+1} + \frac{2}{5}\frac{1}{s^2+1} + \frac{1}{5}\frac{s}{s^2+6} - \frac{2}{5\sqrt{6}}\frac{\sqrt{6}}{s^2+6}.$$

Then

$$x_1 = \frac{2}{5}\cos t + \frac{1}{5}\sin t - \frac{2}{5}\cos\sqrt{6}\,t + \frac{4}{5\sqrt{6}}\sin\sqrt{6}\,t$$

and

$$x_2 = \frac{4}{5}\cos t + \frac{2}{5}\sin t + \frac{1}{5}\cos\sqrt{6}\,t - \frac{2}{5\sqrt{6}}\sin\sqrt{6}\,t.$$

14. In this system x_1 and x_2 represent displacements of masses m_1 and m_2 from their equilibrium positions. Since the net forces acting on m_1 and m_2 are

$$-k_1 x_1 + k_2(x_2 - x_1) \qquad \text{and} \qquad -k_2(x_2 - x_1) - k_3 x_2,$$

respectively, Newton's second law of motion gives

$$m_1 x_1'' = -k_1 x_1 + k_2(x_2 - x_1)$$

$$m_2 x_2'' = -k_2(x_2 - x_1) - k_3 x_2.$$

Using $k_1 = k_2 = k_3 = 1$, $m_1 = m_2 = 1$, $x_1(0) = 0$, $x_1(0) = -1$, $x_2(0) = 0$, and $x_2'(0) = 1$, and taking the Laplace transform of the system, we obtain

$$(2 + s^2)\mathscr{L}\{x_1\} - \mathscr{L}\{x_2\} = -1$$

$$\mathscr{L}\{x_1\} - (2 + s^2)\mathscr{L}\{x_2\} = -1$$

so that

$$\mathscr{L}\{x_1\} = -\frac{1}{s^2 + 3} \qquad \text{and} \qquad \mathscr{L}\{x_2\} = \frac{1}{s^2 + 3}.$$

Then

$$x_1 = -\frac{1}{\sqrt{3}}\sin\sqrt{3}\,t \qquad \text{and} \qquad x_2 = \frac{1}{\sqrt{3}}\sin\sqrt{3}\,t.$$

15. **(a)** By Kirchhoff's first law we have $i_1 = i_2 + i_3$. By Kirchhoff's second law, on each loop we have $E(t) = Ri_1 + L_1 i_2'$ and $E(t) = Ri_1 + L_2 i_3'$ or $L_1 i_2' + Ri_2 + Ri_3 = E(t)$ and $L_2 i_3' + Ri_2 + Ri_3 = E(t)$.

(b) Taking the Laplace transform of the system

$$0.01 i_2' + 5i_2 + 5i_3 = 100$$

$$0.0125 i_3' + 5i_2 + 5i_3 = 100$$

gives

$$(s + 500)\mathscr{L}\{i_2\} + 500\mathscr{L}\{i_3\} = \frac{10{,}000}{s}$$

$$400\mathscr{L}\{i_2\} + (s + 400)\mathscr{L}\{i_3\} = \frac{8{,}000}{s}$$

so that

$$\mathscr{L}\{i_3\} = \frac{8{,}000}{s^2 + 900s} = \frac{80}{9}\frac{1}{s} - \frac{80}{9}\frac{1}{s + 900}.$$

Then

$$i_3 = \frac{80}{9} - \frac{80}{9}e^{-900t} \qquad \text{and} \qquad i_2 = 20 - 0.0025 i_3' - i_3 = \frac{100}{9} - \frac{100}{9}e^{-900t}.$$

(c) $i_1 = i_2 + i_3 = 20 - 20e^{-900t}$

16. (a) Taking the Laplace transform of the system

$$i_2' + i_3' + 10i_2 = 120 - 120\,\mathcal{U}(t - 2)$$

$$-10i_2' + 5i_3' + 5i_3 = 0$$

gives

$$(s + 10)\,\mathcal{L}\{i_2\} + s\mathcal{L}\{i_3\} = \frac{120}{s}\left(1 - e^{-2s}\right)$$

$$-10s\mathcal{L}\{i_2\} + 5(s + 1)\,\mathcal{L}\{i_3\} = 0$$

so that

$$\mathcal{L}\{i_2\} = \frac{120(s + 1)}{(3s^2 + 11s + 10)s}\left(1 - e^{-2s}\right) = \left[\frac{48}{s + 5/3} - \frac{60}{s + 2} + \frac{12}{s}\right]\left(1 - e^{-2s}\right)$$

and

$$\mathcal{L}\{i_3\} = \frac{240}{3s^2 + 11s + 10}\left(1 - e^{-2s}\right) = \left[\frac{240}{s + 5/3} - \frac{240}{s + 2}\right]\left(1 - e^{-2s}\right).$$

Then

$$i_2 = 12 + 48e^{-5t/3} - 60e^{-2t} - \left[12 + 48e^{-5(t-2)/3} - 60e^{-2(t-2)}\right]\mathcal{U}(t - 2)$$

and

$$i_3 = 240e^{-5t/3} - 240e^{-2t} - \left[240e^{-5(t-2)/3} - 240e^{-2(t-2)}\right]\mathcal{U}(t - 2).$$

(b) $i_1 = i_2 + i_3 = 12 + 288e^{-5t/3} - 300e^{-2t} - \left[12 + 288e^{-5(t-2)/3} - 300e^{-2(t-2)}\right]\mathcal{U}(t - 2)$

17. Taking the Laplace transform of the system

$$i_2' + 11i_2 + 6i_3 = 50\sin t$$

$$i_3' + 6i_2 + 6i_3 = 50\sin t$$

gives

$$(s + 11)\,\mathcal{L}\{i_2\} + 6\mathcal{L}\{i_3\} = \frac{50}{s^2 + 1}$$

$$6\mathcal{L}\{i_2\} + (s + 6)\,\mathcal{L}\{i_3\} = \frac{50}{s^2 + 1}$$

so that

$$\mathcal{L}\{i_2\} = \frac{50s}{(s + 2)(s + 15)(s^2 + 1)} = -\frac{20}{13}\frac{1}{s + 2} + \frac{375}{1469}\frac{1}{s + 15} + \frac{145}{113}\frac{s}{s^2 + 1} + \frac{85}{113}\frac{1}{s^2 + 1}.$$

Then

$$i_2 = -\frac{20}{13}e^{-2t} + \frac{375}{1469}e^{-15t} + \frac{145}{113}\cos t + \frac{85}{113}\sin t$$

and

$$i_3 = \frac{25}{3}\sin t - \frac{1}{6}i_2' - \frac{11}{6}i_2 = \frac{30}{13}e^{-2t} + \frac{250}{1469}e^{-15t} - \frac{280}{113}\cos t + \frac{810}{113}\sin t.$$

18. Taking the Laplace transform of the system

$$0.5i_1' + 50i_2 = 60$$

$$0.005i_2' + i_2 - i_1 = 0$$

gives

$$s\,\mathscr{L}\{i_1\} + 100\,\mathscr{L}\{i_2\} = \frac{120}{s}$$

$$-200\,\mathscr{L}\{i_1\} + (s+200)\,\mathscr{L}\{i_2\} = 0$$

so that

$$\mathscr{L}\{i_2\} = \frac{24{,}000}{s(s^2 + 200s + 20{,}000)} = \frac{6}{5}\frac{1}{s} - \frac{6}{5}\frac{s+100}{(s+100)^2 + 100^2} - \frac{6}{5}\frac{100}{(s+100)^2 + 100^2}.$$

Then

$$i_2 = \frac{6}{5} - \frac{6}{5}e^{-100t}\cos 100t - \frac{6}{5}e^{-100t}\sin 100t$$

and

$$i_1 = 0.005i_2' + i_2 = \frac{6}{5} - \frac{6}{5}e^{-100t}\cos 100t.$$

19. Taking the Laplace transform of the system

$$2i_1' + 50i_2 = 60$$

$$0.005i_2' + i_2 - i_1 = 0$$

gives

$$2s\,\mathscr{L}\{i_1\} + 50\,\mathscr{L}\{i_2\} = \frac{60}{s}$$

$$-200\,\mathscr{L}\{i_1\} + (s+200)\,\mathscr{L}\{i_2\} = 0$$

so that

$$\mathscr{L}\{i_2\} = \frac{6{,}000}{s(s^2 + 200s + 5{,}000)}$$

$$= \frac{6}{5}\frac{1}{s} - \frac{6}{5}\frac{s+100}{(s+100)^2 - (50\sqrt{2})^2} - \frac{6\sqrt{2}}{5}\frac{50\sqrt{2}}{(s+100)^2 - (50\sqrt{2})^2}.$$

Then

$$i_2 = \frac{6}{5} - \frac{6}{5}e^{-100t}\cosh 50\sqrt{2}\,t - \frac{6\sqrt{2}}{5}e^{-100t}\sinh 50\sqrt{2}\,t$$

and

$$i_1 = 0.005i_2' + i_2 = \frac{6}{5} - \frac{6}{5}e^{-100t}\cosh 50\sqrt{2}\,t - \frac{9\sqrt{2}}{10}e^{-100t}\sinh 50\sqrt{2}\,t.$$

Exercises 7.6 Systems of Linear Differential Equations

20. (a) Using Kirchhoff's first law we write $i_1 = i_2 + i_3$. Since $i_2 = dq/dt$ we have $i_1 - i_3 = dq/dt$. Using Kirchhoff's second law and summing the voltage drops across the shorter loop gives

$$E(t) = iR_1 + \frac{1}{C}q, \tag{1}$$

so that

$$i_1 = \frac{1}{R_1}E(t) - \frac{1}{R_1 C}q.$$

Then

$$\frac{dq}{dt} = i_1 - i_3 = \frac{1}{R_1}E(t) - \frac{1}{R_1 C}q - i_3$$

and

$$R_1\frac{dq}{dt} + \frac{1}{C}q + R_1 i_3 = E(t).$$

Summing the voltage drops across the longer loop gives

$$E(t) = i_1 R_1 + L\frac{di_3}{dt} + R_2 i_3.$$

Combining this with (1) we obtain

$$i_1 R_1 + L\frac{di_3}{dt} + R_2 i_3 = i_1 R_1 + \frac{1}{C}q$$

or

$$L\frac{di_3}{dt} + R_2 i_3 - \frac{1}{C}q = 0.$$

(b) Using $L = R_1 = R_2 = C = 1$, $E(t) = 50e^{-t}\,\mathcal{U}(t-1) = 50e^{-1}e^{-(t-1)}\,\mathcal{U}(t-1)$, $q(0) = i_3(0) = 0$, and taking the Laplace transform of the system we obtain

$$(s+1)\,\mathcal{L}\{q\} + \mathcal{L}\{i_3\} = \frac{50e^{-1}}{s+1}e^{-s}$$

$$(s+1)\,\mathcal{L}\{i_3\} - \mathcal{L}\{q\} = 0,$$

so that

$$\mathcal{L}\{q\} = \frac{50e^{-1}e^{-s}}{(s+1)^2 + 1}$$

and

$$q(t) = 50e^{-1}e^{-(t-1)}\sin(t-1)\mathcal{U}(t-1) = 50e^{-t}\sin(t-1)\mathcal{U}(t-1).$$

21. (a) Taking the Laplace transform of the system

$$4\theta_1'' + \theta_2'' + 8\theta_1 = 0$$

$$\theta_1'' + \theta_2'' + 2\theta_2 = 0$$

408

gives

$$4\left(s^2+2\right)\mathscr{L}\{\theta_1\}+s^2\mathscr{L}\{\theta_2\}=3s$$

$$s^2\mathscr{L}\{\theta_1\}+\left(s^2+2\right)\mathscr{L}\{\theta_2\}=0$$

so that

$$\left(3s^2+4\right)\left(s^2+4\right)\mathscr{L}\{\theta_2\}=-3s^3$$

or

$$\mathscr{L}\{\theta_2\}=\frac{1}{2}\frac{s}{s^2+4/3}-\frac{3}{2}\frac{s}{s^2+4}.$$

Then

$$\theta_2=\frac{1}{2}\cos\frac{2}{\sqrt{3}}t-\frac{3}{2}\cos 2t \qquad \text{and} \qquad \theta_1''=-\theta_2''-2\theta_2$$

so that

$$\theta_1=\frac{1}{4}\cos\frac{2}{\sqrt{3}}t+\frac{3}{4}\cos 2t.$$

(b)

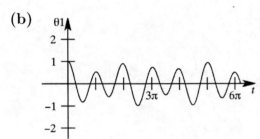 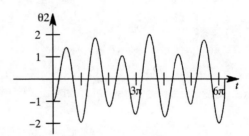

Mass m_2 has extreme displacements of greater magnitude. Mass m_1 first passes through its equilibrium position at about $t=0.87$, and mass m_2 first passes through its equilibrium position at about $t=0.66$. The motion of the pendulums is not periodic since $\cos(2t/\sqrt{3})$ has period $\sqrt{3}\,\pi$, $\cos 2t$ has period π, and the ratio of these periods is $\sqrt{3}$, which is not a rational number.

(c) The Lissajous curve is plotted for $0\le t\le 30$.

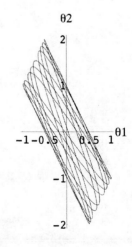

(d)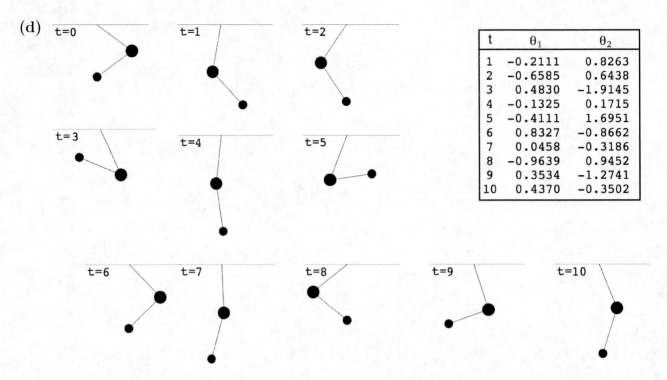

t	θ_1	θ_2
1	-0.2111	0.8263
2	-0.6585	0.6438
3	0.4830	-1.9145
4	-0.1325	0.1715
5	-0.4111	1.6951
6	0.8327	-0.8662
7	0.0458	-0.3186
8	-0.9639	0.9452
9	0.3534	-1.2741
10	0.4370	-0.3502

(e) Using a CAS to solve $\theta_1(t) = \theta_2(t)$ we see that $\theta_1 = \theta_2$ (so that the double pendulum is straight out) when t is about 0.75 seconds.

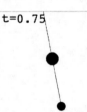

(f) To make a movie of the pendulum it is necessary to locate the mass in the plane as a function of time. Suppose that the upper arm is attached to the origin and that the equilibrium position lies along the negative y-axis. Then mass m_1 is at $(x, (t), y_1(t))$ and mass m_2 is at $(x_2(t), y_2(t))$, where

$$x_1(t) = 16 \sin \theta_1(t) \qquad \text{and} \qquad y_1(t) = -16 \cos \theta_1(t)$$

and

$$x_2(t) = x_1(t) + 16 \sin \theta_2(t) \qquad \text{and} \qquad y_2(t) = y_1(t) - 16 \cos \theta_2(t).$$

A reasonable movie can be constructed by letting t range from 0 to 10 in increments of 0.1 seconds.

1. $\mathscr{L}\{f(t)\} = \int_0^1 te^{-st}dt + \int_1^\infty (2-t)e^{-st}dt = \dfrac{1}{s^2} - \dfrac{2}{s^2}e^{-s}$

2. $\mathscr{L}\{f(t)\} = \int_2^4 e^{-st}dt = \dfrac{1}{s}\left(e^{-2s} - e^{-4s}\right)$

3. False; consider $f(t) = t^{-1/2}$.

4. False, since $f(t) = (e^t)^{10} = e^{10t}$.

5. True, since $\lim_{s\to\infty} F(s) = 1 \neq 0$. (See Theorem 7.1.3 in the text.)

6. False; consider $f(t) = 1$ and $g(t) = 1$.

7. $\mathscr{L}\left\{e^{-7t}\right\} = \dfrac{1}{s+7}$

8. $\mathscr{L}\left\{te^{-7t}\right\} = \dfrac{1}{(s+7)^2}$

9. $\mathscr{L}\{\sin 2t\} = \dfrac{2}{s^2+4}$

10. $\mathscr{L}\left\{e^{-3t}\sin 2t\right\} = \dfrac{2}{(s+3)^2+4}$

11. $\mathscr{L}\{t\sin 2t\} = -\dfrac{d}{ds}\left[\dfrac{2}{s^2+4}\right] = \dfrac{4s}{(s^2+4)^2}$

12. $\mathscr{L}\{\sin 2t\,\mathscr{U}(t-\pi)\} = \mathscr{L}\{\sin 2(t-\pi)\mathscr{U}(t-\pi)\} = \dfrac{2}{s^2+4}e^{-\pi s}$

13. $\mathscr{L}^{-1}\left\{\dfrac{20}{s^6}\right\} = \mathscr{L}^{-1}\left\{\dfrac{1}{6}\dfrac{5!}{s^6}\right\} = \dfrac{1}{6}t^5$

14. $\mathscr{L}^{-1}\left\{\dfrac{1}{3s-1}\right\} = \mathscr{L}^{-1}\left\{\dfrac{1}{3}\dfrac{1}{s-1/3}\right\} = \dfrac{1}{3}e^{t/3}$

15. $\mathscr{L}^{-1}\left\{\dfrac{1}{(s-5)^3}\right\} = \dfrac{1}{2}\mathscr{L}^{-1}\left\{\dfrac{2}{(s-5)^3}\right\} = \dfrac{1}{2}t^2e^{5t}$

16. $\mathscr{L}^{-1}\left\{\dfrac{1}{s^2-5}\right\} = \mathscr{L}^{-1}\left\{-\dfrac{1}{2\sqrt{5}}\dfrac{1}{s+\sqrt{5}} + \dfrac{1}{2\sqrt{5}}\dfrac{1}{s-\sqrt{5}}\right\} = -\dfrac{1}{2\sqrt{5}}e^{-\sqrt{5}t} + \dfrac{1}{2\sqrt{5}}e^{\sqrt{5}t}$

Chapter 7 in Review

17. $\mathscr{L}^{-1}\left\{\dfrac{s}{s^2-10s+29}\right\} = \mathscr{L}^{-1}\left\{\dfrac{s-5}{(s-5)^2+2^2} + \dfrac{5}{2}\dfrac{2}{(s-5)^2+2^2}\right\} = e^{5t}\cos 2t + \dfrac{5}{2}e^{5t}\sin 2t$

18. $\mathscr{L}^{-1}\left\{\dfrac{1}{s^2}e^{-5s}\right\} = (t-5)\,\mathscr{U}(t-5)$

19. $\mathscr{L}^{-1}\left\{\dfrac{s+\pi}{s^2+\pi^2}\,e^{-s}\right\} = \mathscr{L}^{-1}\left\{\dfrac{s}{s^2+\pi^2}\,e^{-s} + \dfrac{\pi}{s^2+\pi^2}\,e^{-s}\right\}$

$$= \cos\pi(t-1)\,\mathscr{U}(t-1) + \sin\pi(t-1)\,\mathscr{U}(t-1)$$

20. $\mathscr{L}^{-1}\left\{\dfrac{1}{L^2s^2+n^2\pi^2}\right\} = \dfrac{1}{L^2}\dfrac{L}{n\pi}\mathscr{L}^{-1}\left\{\dfrac{n\pi/L}{s^2+(n^2\pi^2)/L^2}\right\} = \dfrac{1}{Ln\pi}\sin\dfrac{n\pi}{L}t$

21. $\mathscr{L}\left\{e^{-5t}\right\}$ exists for $s > -5$.

22. $\mathscr{L}\left\{te^{8t}f(t)\right\} = -\dfrac{d}{ds}F(s-8)$.

23. $\mathscr{L}\{e^{at}f(t-k)\,\mathscr{U}(t-k)\} = e^{-ks}\,\mathscr{L}\{e^{a(t+k)}f(t)\} = e^{-ks}e^{ak}\,\mathscr{L}\{e^{at}f(t)\} = e^{-k(s-a)}F(s-a)$

24. $\mathscr{L}\left\{\displaystyle\int_0^t e^{a\tau}f(\tau)\,d\tau\right\} = \dfrac{1}{s}\,\mathscr{L}\{e^{at}f(t)\} = \dfrac{F(s-a)}{s}$, whereas

$$\mathscr{L}\left\{e^{at}\int_0^t f(\tau)\,d\tau\right\} = \mathscr{L}\left\{\int_0^t f(\tau)\,d\tau\right\}\Bigg|_{s\to s-a} = \dfrac{F(s)}{s}\Bigg|_{s\to s-a} = \dfrac{F(s-a)}{s-a}\,.$$

25. $f(t)\,\mathscr{U}(t-t_0)$

26. $f(t) - f(t)\,\mathscr{U}(t-t_0)$

27. $f(t-t_0)\,\mathscr{U}(t-t_0)$

28. $f(t) - f(t)\,\mathscr{U}(t-t_0) + f(t)\,\mathscr{U}(t-t_1)$

29. $f(t) = t - [(t-1)+1]\,\mathscr{U}(t-1) + \mathscr{U}(t-1) - \mathscr{U}(t-4) = t - (t-1)\,\mathscr{U}(t-1) - \mathscr{U}(t-4)$

$$\mathscr{L}\{f(t)\} = \dfrac{1}{s^2} - \dfrac{1}{s^2}e^{-s} - \dfrac{1}{s}e^{-4s}$$

$$\mathscr{L}\{e^t f(t)\} = \dfrac{1}{(s-1)^2} - \dfrac{1}{(s-1)^2}e^{-(s-1)} - \dfrac{1}{s-1}e^{-4(s-1)}$$

30. $f(t) = \sin t\,\mathscr{U}(t-\pi) - \sin t\,\mathscr{U}(t-3\pi) = -\sin(t-\pi)\,\mathscr{U}(t-\pi) + \sin(t-3\pi)\,\mathscr{U}(t-3\pi)$

$$\mathscr{L}\{f(t)\} = -\dfrac{1}{s^2+1}e^{-\pi s} + \dfrac{1}{s^2+1}e^{-3\pi s}$$

$$\mathscr{L}\{e^t f(t)\} = -\dfrac{1}{(s-1)^2+1}e^{-\pi(s-1)} + \dfrac{1}{(s-1)^2+1}e^{-3\pi(s-1)}$$

31. $f(t) = 2 - 2\mathscr{U}(t-2) + [(t-2)+2]\,\mathscr{U}(t-2) = 2 + (t-2)\,\mathscr{U}(t-2)$

$$\mathcal{L}\{f(t)\} = \frac{2}{s} + \frac{1}{s^2}e^{-2s}$$

$$\mathcal{L}\{e^t f(t)\} = \frac{2}{s-1} + \frac{1}{(s-1)^2}e^{-2(s-1)}$$

32. $f(t) = t - t\,\mathcal{U}(t-1) + (2-t)\mathcal{U}(t-1) - (2-t)\mathcal{U}(t-2) = t - 2(t-1)\mathcal{U}(t-1) + (t-2)\mathcal{U}(t-2)$

$$\mathcal{L}\{f(t)\} = \frac{1}{s^2} - \frac{2}{s^2}e^{-s} + \frac{1}{s^2}e^{-2s}$$

$$\mathcal{L}\{e^t f(t)\} = \frac{1}{(s-1)^2} - \frac{2}{(s-1)^2}e^{-(s-1)} + \frac{1}{(s-1)^2}e^{-2(s-1)}$$

33. Taking the Laplace transform of the differential equation we obtain

$$\mathcal{L}\{y\} = \frac{5}{(s-1)^2} + \frac{1}{2}\frac{2}{(s-1)^3}$$

so that

$$y = 5te^t + \frac{1}{2}t^2 e^t.$$

34. Taking the Laplace transform of the differential equation we obtain

$$\mathcal{L}\{y\} = \frac{1}{(s-1)^2(s^2 - 8s + 20)}$$

$$= \frac{6}{169}\frac{1}{s-1} + \frac{1}{13}\frac{1}{(s-1)^2} - \frac{6}{169}\frac{s-4}{(s-4)^2 + 2^2} + \frac{5}{338}\frac{2}{(s-4)^2 + 2^2}$$

so that

$$y = \frac{6}{169}e^t + \frac{1}{13}te^t - \frac{6}{169}e^{4t}\cos 2t + \frac{5}{338}e^{4t}\sin 2t.$$

35. Taking the Laplace transform of the given differential equation we obtain

$$\mathcal{L}\{y\} = \frac{s^3 + 6s^2 + 1}{s^2(s+1)(s+5)} - \frac{1}{s^2(s+1)(s+5)}e^{-2s} - \frac{2}{s(s+1)(s+5)}e^{-2s}$$

$$= -\frac{6}{25}\cdot\frac{1}{s} + \frac{1}{5}\cdot\frac{1}{s^2} + \frac{3}{2}\cdot\frac{1}{s+1} - \frac{13}{50}\cdot\frac{1}{s+5}$$

$$- \left(-\frac{6}{25}\cdot\frac{1}{s} + \frac{1}{5}\cdot\frac{1}{s^2} + \frac{1}{4}\cdot\frac{1}{s+1} - \frac{1}{100}\cdot\frac{1}{s+5}\right)e^{-2s}$$

$$- \left(\frac{2}{5}\cdot\frac{1}{s} - \frac{1}{2}\cdot\frac{1}{s+1} + \frac{1}{10}\cdot\frac{1}{s+5}\right)e^{-2s}$$

so that

$$y = -\frac{6}{25} + \frac{1}{5}t + \frac{3}{2}e^{-t} - \frac{13}{50}e^{-5t} - \frac{4}{25}\mathcal{U}(t-2) - \frac{1}{5}(t-2)\mathcal{U}(t-2)$$

$$+ \frac{1}{4}e^{-(t-2)}\mathcal{U}(t-2) - \frac{9}{100}e^{-5(t-2)}\mathcal{U}(t-2).$$

36. Taking the Laplace transform of the differential equation we obtain

$$\mathcal{L}\{y\} = \frac{s^3 + 2}{s^3(s-5)} - \frac{2 + 2s + s^2}{s^3(s-5)} e^{-s}$$

$$= -\frac{2}{125}\frac{1}{s} - \frac{2}{25}\frac{1}{s^2} - \frac{1}{5}\frac{2}{s^3} + \frac{127}{125}\frac{1}{s-5} - \left[-\frac{37}{125}\frac{1}{s} - \frac{12}{25}\frac{1}{s^2} - \frac{1}{5}\frac{2}{s^3} + \frac{37}{125}\frac{1}{s-5} \right] e^{-s}$$

so that

$$y = -\frac{2}{125} - \frac{2}{25}t - \frac{1}{5}t^2 + \frac{127}{125}e^{5t} - \left[-\frac{37}{125} - \frac{12}{25}(t-1) - \frac{1}{5}(t-1)^2 + \frac{37}{125}e^{5(t-1)} \right]\mathcal{U}(t-1).$$

37. Taking the Laplace transform of the integral equation we obtain

$$\mathcal{L}\{y\} = \frac{1}{s} + \frac{1}{s^2} + \frac{1}{2}\frac{2}{s^3}$$

so that

$$y(t) = 1 + t + \frac{1}{2}t^2.$$

38. Taking the Laplace transform of the integral equation we obtain

$$(\mathcal{L}\{f\})^2 = 6 \cdot \frac{6}{s^4} \quad \text{or} \quad \mathcal{L}\{f\} = \pm 6 \cdot \frac{1}{s^2}$$

so that $f(t) = \pm 6t$.

39. Taking the Laplace transform of the system gives

$$s\mathcal{L}\{x\} + \mathcal{L}\{y\} = \frac{1}{s^2} + 1$$

$$4\mathcal{L}\{x\} + s\mathcal{L}\{y\} = 2$$

so that

$$\mathcal{L}\{x\} = \frac{s^2 - 2s + 1}{s(s-2)(s+2)} = -\frac{1}{4}\frac{1}{s} + \frac{1}{8}\frac{1}{s-2} + \frac{9}{8}\frac{1}{s+2}.$$

Then

$$x = -\frac{1}{4} + \frac{1}{8}e^{2t} + \frac{9}{8}e^{-2t} \quad \text{and} \quad y = -x' + t = \frac{9}{4}e^{-2t} - \frac{1}{4}e^{2t} + t.$$

40. Taking the Laplace transform of the system gives

$$s^2\mathcal{L}\{x\} + s^2\mathcal{L}\{y\} = \frac{1}{s-2}$$

$$2s\mathcal{L}\{x\} + s^2\mathcal{L}\{y\} = -\frac{1}{s-2}$$

so that

$$\mathcal{L}\{x\} = \frac{2}{s(s-2)^2} = \frac{1}{2}\frac{1}{s} - \frac{1}{2}\frac{1}{s-2} + \frac{1}{(s-2)^2}$$

and

$$\mathscr{L}\{y\} = \frac{-s-2}{s^2(s-2)^2} = -\frac{3}{4}\frac{1}{s} - \frac{1}{2}\frac{1}{s^2} + \frac{3}{4}\frac{1}{s-2} - \frac{1}{(s-2)^2}.$$

Then

$$x = \frac{1}{2} - \frac{1}{2}e^{2t} + te^{2t} \quad \text{and} \quad y = -\frac{3}{4} - \frac{1}{2}t + \frac{3}{4}e^{2t} - te^{2t}.$$

41. The integral equation is

$$10i + 2\int_0^t i(\tau)\,d\tau = 2t^2 + 2t.$$

Taking the Laplace transform we obtain

$$\mathscr{L}\{i\} = \left(\frac{4}{s^3} + \frac{2}{s^2}\right)\frac{s}{10s+2} = \frac{s+2}{s^2(5s+2)} = -\frac{9}{s} + \frac{2}{s^2} + \frac{45}{5s+1} = -\frac{9}{s} + \frac{2}{s^2} + \frac{9}{s+1/5}.$$

Thus

$$i(t) = -9 + 2t + 9e^{-t/5}.$$

42. The differential equation is

$$\frac{1}{2}\frac{d^2q}{dt^2} + 10\frac{dq}{dt} + 100q = 10 - 10\,\mathscr{U}(t-5).$$

Taking the Laplace transform we obtain

$$\mathscr{L}\{q\} = \frac{20}{s(s^2 + 20s + 200)}\left(1 - e^{-5s}\right)$$

$$= \left[\frac{1}{10}\frac{1}{s} - \frac{1}{10}\frac{s+10}{(s+10)^2 + 10^2} - \frac{1}{10}\frac{10}{(s+10)^2 + 10^2}\right]\left(1 - e^{-5s}\right)$$

so that

$$q(t) = \frac{1}{10} - \frac{1}{10}e^{-10t}\cos 10t - \frac{1}{10}e^{-10t}\sin 10t$$

$$- \left[\frac{1}{10} - \frac{1}{10}e^{-10(t-5)}\cos 10(t-5) - \frac{1}{10}e^{-10(t-5)}\sin 10(t-5)\right]\mathscr{U}(t-5).$$

43. Taking the Laplace transform of the given differential equation we obtain

$$\mathscr{L}\{y\} = \frac{2w_0}{EIL}\left(\frac{L}{48}\cdot\frac{4!}{s^5} - \frac{1}{120}\cdot\frac{5!}{s^6} + \frac{1}{120}\cdot\frac{5!}{s^6}e^{-sL/2}\right) + \frac{c_1}{2}\cdot\frac{2!}{s^3} + \frac{c_2}{6}\cdot\frac{3!}{s^4}$$

so that

$$y = \frac{2w_0}{EIL}\left[\frac{L}{48}x^4 - \frac{1}{120}x^5 + \frac{1}{120}\left(x - \frac{L}{2}\right)^5\mathscr{U}\left(x - \frac{L}{2}\right) + \frac{c_1}{2}x^2 + \frac{c_2}{6}x^3\right]$$

where $y''(0) = c_1$ and $y'''(0) = c_2$. Using $y''(L) = 0$ and $y'''(L) = 0$ we find

$$c_1 = w_0L^2/24EI, \qquad c_2 = -w_0L/4EI.$$

Hence

$$y = \frac{w_0}{12EIL}\left[-\frac{1}{5}x^5 + \frac{L}{2}x^4 - \frac{L^2}{2}x^3 + \frac{L^3}{4}x^2 + \frac{1}{5}\left(x - \frac{L}{2}\right)^5\mathscr{U}\left(x - \frac{L}{2}\right)\right].$$

Chapter 7 in Review

44. **(a)** In this case the boundary conditions are $y(0) = y''(0) = 0$ and $y(\pi) = y''(\pi) = 0$. If we let $c_1 = y'(0)$ and $c_2 = y'''(0)$ then

$$s^4 \mathscr{L}\{y\} - s^3 y(0) - s^2 y'(0) - sy(0) - y'''(0) + 4\mathscr{L}\{y\} = \mathscr{L}\{w_0/EI\}$$

and

$$\mathscr{L}\{y\} = \frac{c_1}{2} \cdot \frac{2s^2}{s^4 + 4} + \frac{c_2}{4} \cdot \frac{4}{s^4 + 4} + \frac{w_0}{8EI}\left(\frac{2}{s} - \frac{s-1}{(s-1)^2 + 1} - \frac{s+1}{(s+1)^2 + 1}\right).$$

From the table of transforms we get

$$y = \frac{c_1}{2}(\sin x \cosh x + \cos x \sinh x) + \frac{c_2}{4}(\sin x \cosh x - \cos x \sinh x) + \frac{w_0}{4EI}(1 - \cos x \cosh x)$$

Using $y(\pi) = 0$ and $y''(\pi) = 0$ we find

$$c_1 = \frac{w_0}{4EI}(1 + \cosh\pi)\operatorname{csch}\pi, \qquad c_2 = -\frac{w_0}{2EI}(1 + \cosh\pi)\operatorname{csch}\pi.$$

Hence

$$y = \frac{w_0}{8EI}(1 + \cosh\pi)\operatorname{csch}\pi(\sin x \cosh x + \cos x \sinh x)$$

$$- \frac{w_0}{8EI}(1 + \cosh\pi)\operatorname{csch}\pi(\sin x \cosh x - \cos x \sinh x) + \frac{w_0}{4EI}(1 - \cos x \cosh x).$$

(b) In this case the boundary conditions are $y(0) = y'(0) = 0$ and $y(\pi) = y'(\pi) = 0$. If we let $c_1 = y''(0)$ and $c_2 = y'''(0)$ then

$$s^4 \mathscr{L}\{y\} - s^3 y(0) - s^2 y'(0) - sy(0) - y'''(0) + 4\mathscr{L}\{y\} = \mathscr{L}\{\delta(t - \pi/2)\}$$

and

$$\mathscr{L}\{y\} = \frac{c_1}{2} \cdot \frac{2s}{s^4 + 4} + \frac{c_2}{4} \cdot \frac{4}{s^4 + 4} + \frac{w_0}{4EI} \cdot \frac{4}{s^4 + 4} e^{-s\pi/2}.$$

From the table of transforms we get

$$y = \frac{c_1}{2}\sin x \sinh x + \frac{c_2}{4}(\sin x \cosh x - \cos x \sinh x)$$

$$+ \frac{w_0}{4EI}\left[\sin\left(x - \frac{\pi}{2}\right)\cosh\left(x - \frac{\pi}{2}\right) - \cos\left(x - \frac{\pi}{2}\right)\sinh\left(x - \frac{\pi}{2}\right)\right]\mathscr{U}\left(x - \frac{\pi}{2}\right)$$

Using $y(\pi) = 0$ and $y'(\pi) = 0$ we find

$$c_1 = \frac{w_0}{EI}\frac{\sinh\frac{\pi}{2}}{\sinh\pi}, \qquad c_2 = -\frac{w_0}{EI}\frac{\cosh\frac{\pi}{2}}{\sinh\pi}.$$

Hence

$$y = \frac{w_0}{2EI}\frac{\sinh\frac{\pi}{2}}{\sinh\pi}\sin x \sinh x - \frac{w_0}{4EI}\frac{\cosh\frac{\pi}{2}}{\sinh\pi}(\sin x \cosh x - \cos x \sinh x)$$

$$+ \frac{w_0}{4EI}\left[\sin\left(x - \frac{\pi}{2}\right)\cosh\left(x - \frac{\pi}{2}\right) - \cos\left(x - \frac{\pi}{2}\right)\sinh\left(x - \frac{\pi}{2}\right)\right]\mathscr{U}\left(x - \frac{\pi}{2}\right).$$

45. (a) With $\omega^2 = g/l$ and $K = k/m$ the system of differential equations is

$$\theta_1'' + \omega^2\theta_1 = -K(\theta_1 - \theta_2)$$

$$\theta_2'' + \omega^2\theta_2 = K(\theta_1 - \theta_2).$$

Denoting the Laplace transform of $\theta(t)$ by $\Theta(s)$ we have that the Laplace transform of the system is

$$(s^2 + \omega^2)\Theta_1(s) = -K\Theta_1(s) + K\Theta_2(s) + s\theta_0$$

$$(s^2 + \omega^2)\Theta_2(s) = K\Theta_1(s) - K\Theta_2(s) + s\psi_0.$$

If we add the two equations, we get

$$\Theta_1(s) + \Theta_2(s) = (\theta_0 + \psi_0)\frac{s}{s^2 + \omega^2}$$

which implies

$$\theta_1(t) + \theta_2(t) = (\theta_0 + \psi_0)\cos\omega t.$$

This enables us to solve for first, say, $\theta_1(t)$ and then find $\theta_2(t)$ from

$$\theta_2(t) = -\theta_1(t) + (\theta_0 + \psi_0)\cos\omega t.$$

Now solving

$$(s^2 + \omega^2 + K)\Theta_1(s) - K\Theta_2(s) = s\theta_0$$

$$-k\Theta_1(s) + (s^2 + \omega^2 + K)\Theta_2(s) = s\psi_0$$

gives

$$[(s^2 + \omega^2 + K)^2 - K^2]\Theta_1(s) = s(s^2 + \omega^2 + K)\theta_0 + Ks\psi_0.$$

Factoring the difference of two squares and using partial fractions we get

$$\Theta_1(s) = \frac{s(s^2 + \omega^2 + K)\theta_0 + Ks\psi_0}{(s^2 + \omega^2)(s^2 + \omega^2 + 2K)} = \frac{\theta_0 + \psi_0}{2}\frac{s}{s^2 + \omega^2} + \frac{\theta_0 - \psi_0}{2}\frac{s}{s^2 + \omega^2 + 2K},$$

so

$$\theta_1(t) = \frac{\theta_0 + \psi_0}{2}\cos\omega t + \frac{\theta_0 - \psi_0}{2}\cos\sqrt{\omega^2 + 2K}\,t.$$

Then from $\theta_2(t) = -\theta_1(t) + (\theta_0 + \psi_0)\cos\omega t$ we get

$$\theta_2(t) = \frac{\theta_0 + \psi_0}{2}\cos\omega t - \frac{\theta_0 - \psi_0}{2}\cos\sqrt{\omega^2 + 2K}\,t.$$

(b) With the initial conditions $\theta_1(0) = \theta_0$, $\theta_1'(0) = 0$, $\theta_2(0) = \theta_0$, $\theta_2'(0) = 0$ we have

$$\theta_1(t) = \theta_0\cos\omega t, \qquad \theta_2(t) = \theta_0\cos\omega t.$$

Physically this means that both pendulums swing in the same direction as if they were free since the spring exerts no influence on the motion ($\theta_1(t)$ and $\theta_2(t)$ are free of K).

With the initial conditions $\theta_1(0) = \theta_0$, $\theta_1'(0) = 0$, $\theta_2(0) = -\theta_0$, $\theta_2'(0) = 0$ we have

$$\theta_1(t) = \theta_0 \cos \sqrt{\omega^2 + 2K}\, t, \qquad \theta_2(t) = -\theta_0 \cos \sqrt{\omega^2 + 2K}\, t.$$

Physically this means that both pendulums swing in the opposite directions, stretching and compressing the spring. The amplitude of both displacements is $|\theta_0|$. Moreover, $\theta_1(t) = \theta_0$ and $\theta_2(t) = -\theta_0$ at precisely the same times. At these times the spring is stretched to its maximum.

8 Systems of Linear First-Order Differential Equations

Preliminary Theory—Linear Systems

1. Let $\mathbf{X} = \begin{pmatrix} x \\ y \end{pmatrix}$. Then $\mathbf{X}' = \begin{pmatrix} 3 & -5 \\ 4 & 8 \end{pmatrix} \mathbf{X}$.

2. Let $\mathbf{X} = \begin{pmatrix} x \\ y \end{pmatrix}$. Then $\mathbf{X}' = \begin{pmatrix} 4 & -7 \\ 5 & 0 \end{pmatrix} \mathbf{X}$.

3. Let $\mathbf{X} = \begin{pmatrix} x \\ y \\ z \end{pmatrix}$. Then $\mathbf{X}' = \begin{pmatrix} -3 & 4 & -9 \\ 6 & -1 & 0 \\ 10 & 4 & 3 \end{pmatrix} \mathbf{X}$.

4. Let $\mathbf{X} = \begin{pmatrix} x \\ y \\ z \end{pmatrix}$. Then $\mathbf{X}' = \begin{pmatrix} 1 & -1 & 0 \\ 1 & 0 & 2 \\ -1 & 0 & 1 \end{pmatrix} \mathbf{X}$.

5. Let $\mathbf{X} = \begin{pmatrix} x \\ y \\ z \end{pmatrix}$. Then $\mathbf{X}' = \begin{pmatrix} 1 & -1 & 1 \\ 2 & 1 & -1 \\ 1 & 1 & 1 \end{pmatrix} \mathbf{X} + \begin{pmatrix} 0 \\ -3t^2 \\ t^2 \end{pmatrix} + \begin{pmatrix} t \\ 0 \\ -t \end{pmatrix} + \begin{pmatrix} -1 \\ 0 \\ 2 \end{pmatrix}$.

6. Let $\mathbf{X} = \begin{pmatrix} x \\ y \\ z \end{pmatrix}$. Then $\mathbf{X}' = \begin{pmatrix} -3 & 4 & 0 \\ 5 & 9 & 0 \\ 0 & 1 & 6 \end{pmatrix} \mathbf{X} + \begin{pmatrix} e^{-t}\sin 2t \\ 4e^{-t}\cos 2t \\ -e^{-t} \end{pmatrix}$.

7. $\dfrac{dx}{dt} = 4x + 2y + e^t; \quad \dfrac{dy}{dt} = -x + 3y - e^t$

8. $\dfrac{dx}{dt} = 7x + 5y - 9z - 8e^{-2t}; \quad \dfrac{dy}{dt} = 4x + y + z + 2e^{5t}; \quad \dfrac{dz}{dt} = -2y + 3z + e^{5t} - 3e^{-2t}$

9. $\dfrac{dx}{dt} = x - y + 2z + e^{-t} - 3t; \quad \dfrac{dy}{dt} = 3x - 4y + z + 2e^{-t} + t; \quad \dfrac{dz}{dt} = -2x + 5y + 6z + 2e^{-t} - t$

10. $\dfrac{dx}{dt} = 3x - 7y + 4\sin t + (t-4)e^{4t}; \quad \dfrac{dy}{dt} = x + y + 8\sin t + (2t+1)e^{4t}$

11. Since

$$\mathbf{X}' = \begin{pmatrix} -5 \\ -10 \end{pmatrix} e^{-5t} \quad \text{and} \quad \begin{pmatrix} 3 & -4 \\ 4 & -7 \end{pmatrix} \mathbf{X} = \begin{pmatrix} -5 \\ -10 \end{pmatrix} e^{-5t}$$

we see that

$$\mathbf{X}' = \begin{pmatrix} 3 & -4 \\ 4 & -7 \end{pmatrix} \mathbf{X}.$$

12. Since

$$\mathbf{X}' = \begin{pmatrix} 5\cos t - 5\sin t \\ 2\cos t - 4\sin t \end{pmatrix} e^{t} \quad \text{and} \quad \begin{pmatrix} -2 & 5 \\ -2 & 4 \end{pmatrix} \mathbf{X} = \begin{pmatrix} 5\cos t - 5\sin t \\ 2\cos t - 4\sin t \end{pmatrix} e^{t}$$

we see that

$$\mathbf{X}' = \begin{pmatrix} -2 & 5 \\ -2 & 4 \end{pmatrix} \mathbf{X}.$$

13. Since

$$\mathbf{X}' = \begin{pmatrix} 3/2 \\ -3 \end{pmatrix} e^{-3t/2} \quad \text{and} \quad \begin{pmatrix} -1 & 1/4 \\ 1 & -1 \end{pmatrix} \mathbf{X} = \begin{pmatrix} 3/2 \\ -3 \end{pmatrix} e^{-3t/2}$$

we see that

$$\mathbf{X}' = \begin{pmatrix} -1 & 1/4 \\ 1 & -1 \end{pmatrix} \mathbf{X}.$$

14. Since

$$\mathbf{X}' = \begin{pmatrix} 5 \\ -1 \end{pmatrix} e^{t} + \begin{pmatrix} 4 \\ -4 \end{pmatrix} te^{t} \quad \text{and} \quad \begin{pmatrix} 2 & 1 \\ -1 & 0 \end{pmatrix} \mathbf{X} = \begin{pmatrix} 5 \\ -1 \end{pmatrix} e^{t} + \begin{pmatrix} 4 \\ -4 \end{pmatrix} te^{t}$$

we see that

$$\mathbf{X}' = \begin{pmatrix} 2 & 1 \\ -1 & 0 \end{pmatrix} \mathbf{X}.$$

15. Since

$$\mathbf{X}' = \begin{pmatrix} 0 \\ 0 \\ 0 \end{pmatrix} \quad \text{and} \quad \begin{pmatrix} 1 & 2 & 1 \\ 6 & -1 & 0 \\ -1 & -2 & -1 \end{pmatrix} \mathbf{X} = \begin{pmatrix} 0 \\ 0 \\ 0 \end{pmatrix}$$

we see that

$$\mathbf{X}' = \begin{pmatrix} 1 & 2 & 1 \\ 6 & -1 & 0 \\ -1 & -2 & -1 \end{pmatrix} \mathbf{X}.$$

16. Since

$$\mathbf{X}' = \begin{pmatrix} \cos t \\ \frac{1}{2}\sin t - \frac{1}{2}\cos t \\ -\cos t - \sin t \end{pmatrix} \quad \text{and} \quad \begin{pmatrix} 1 & 0 & 1 \\ 1 & 1 & 0 \\ -2 & 0 & -1 \end{pmatrix} \mathbf{X} = \begin{pmatrix} \cos t \\ \frac{1}{2}\sin t - \frac{1}{2}\cos t \\ -\cos t - \sin t \end{pmatrix}$$

we see that

$$\mathbf{X}' = \begin{pmatrix} 1 & 0 & 1 \\ 1 & 1 & 0 \\ -2 & 0 & -1 \end{pmatrix} \mathbf{X}.$$

17. Yes, since $W(\mathbf{X}_1, \mathbf{X}_2) = -2e^{-8t} \neq 0$ the set $\mathbf{X}_1$, $\mathbf{X}_2$ is linearly independent on $-\infty < t < \infty$.

18. Yes, since $W(\mathbf{X}_1, \mathbf{X}_2) = 8e^{2t} \neq 0$ the set $\mathbf{X}_1$, $\mathbf{X}_2$ is linearly independent on $-\infty < t < \infty$.

19. No, since $W(\mathbf{X}_1, \mathbf{X}_2, \mathbf{X}_3) = 0$ the set $\mathbf{X}_1$, $\mathbf{X}_2$, $\mathbf{X}_3$ is linearly dependent on $-\infty < t < \infty$.

20. Yes, since $W(\mathbf{X}_1, \mathbf{X}_2, \mathbf{X}_3) = -84e^{-t} \neq 0$ the set $\mathbf{X}_1$, $\mathbf{X}_2$, $\mathbf{X}_3$ is linearly independent on $-\infty < t < \infty$.

21. Since

$$\mathbf{X}'_p = \begin{pmatrix} 2 \\ -1 \end{pmatrix} \quad \text{and} \quad \begin{pmatrix} 1 & 4 \\ 3 & 2 \end{pmatrix} \mathbf{X}_p + \begin{pmatrix} 2 \\ -4 \end{pmatrix} t + \begin{pmatrix} -7 \\ -18 \end{pmatrix} = \begin{pmatrix} 2 \\ -1 \end{pmatrix}$$

we see that

$$\mathbf{X}'_p = \begin{pmatrix} 1 & 4 \\ 3 & 2 \end{pmatrix} \mathbf{X}_p + \begin{pmatrix} 2 \\ -4 \end{pmatrix} t + \begin{pmatrix} -7 \\ -18 \end{pmatrix}.$$

22. Since

$$\mathbf{X}'_p = \begin{pmatrix} 0 \\ 0 \end{pmatrix}. \quad \text{and} \quad \begin{pmatrix} 2 & 1 \\ 1 & -1 \end{pmatrix} \mathbf{X}_p + \begin{pmatrix} -5 \\ 2 \end{pmatrix} = \begin{pmatrix} 0 \\ 0 \end{pmatrix}$$

we see that

$$\mathbf{X}'_p = \begin{pmatrix} 2 & 1 \\ 1 & -1 \end{pmatrix} \mathbf{X}_p + \begin{pmatrix} -5 \\ 2 \end{pmatrix}.$$

23. Since

$$\mathbf{X}'_p = \begin{pmatrix} 2 \\ 0 \end{pmatrix} e^t + \begin{pmatrix} 1 \\ -1 \end{pmatrix} t e^t \quad \text{and} \quad \begin{pmatrix} 2 & 1 \\ 3 & 4 \end{pmatrix} \mathbf{X}_p - \begin{pmatrix} 1 \\ 7 \end{pmatrix} e^t = \begin{pmatrix} 2 \\ 0 \end{pmatrix} e^t + \begin{pmatrix} 1 \\ -1 \end{pmatrix} t e^t$$

we see that

$$\mathbf{X}'_p = \begin{pmatrix} 2 & 1 \\ 3 & 4 \end{pmatrix} \mathbf{X}_p - \begin{pmatrix} 1 \\ 7 \end{pmatrix} e^t.$$

24. Since

$$\mathbf{X}'_p = \begin{pmatrix} 3\cos 3t \\ 0 \\ -3\sin 3t \end{pmatrix} \quad \text{and} \quad \begin{pmatrix} 1 & 2 & 3 \\ -4 & 2 & 0 \\ -6 & 1 & 0 \end{pmatrix} \mathbf{X}_p + \begin{pmatrix} -1 \\ 4 \\ 3 \end{pmatrix} \sin 3t = \begin{pmatrix} 3\cos 3t \\ 0 \\ -3\sin 3t \end{pmatrix}$$

we see that

$$\mathbf{X}'_p = \begin{pmatrix} 1 & 2 & 3 \\ -4 & 2 & 0 \\ -6 & 1 & 0 \end{pmatrix} \mathbf{X}_p + \begin{pmatrix} -1 \\ 4 \\ 3 \end{pmatrix} \sin 3t.$$

25. Let

$$\mathbf{X}_1 = \begin{pmatrix} 6 \\ -1 \\ -5 \end{pmatrix} e^{-t}, \quad \mathbf{X}_2 = \begin{pmatrix} -3 \\ 1 \\ 1 \end{pmatrix} e^{-2t}, \quad \mathbf{X}_3 = \begin{pmatrix} 2 \\ 1 \\ 1 \end{pmatrix} e^{3t}, \quad \text{and} \quad \mathbf{A} = \begin{pmatrix} 0 & 6 & 0 \\ 1 & 0 & 1 \\ 1 & 1 & 0 \end{pmatrix}.$$

Then

$$\mathbf{X}_1' = \begin{pmatrix} -6 \\ 1 \\ 5 \end{pmatrix} e^{-t} = \mathbf{A}\mathbf{X}_1,$$

$$\mathbf{X}_2' = \begin{pmatrix} 6 \\ -2 \\ -2 \end{pmatrix} e^{-2t} = \mathbf{A}\mathbf{X}_2,$$

$$\mathbf{X}_3' = \begin{pmatrix} 6 \\ 3 \\ 3 \end{pmatrix} e^{3t} = \mathbf{A}\mathbf{X}_3,$$

and $W(\mathbf{X}_1, \mathbf{X}_2, \mathbf{X}_3) = 20 \neq 0$ so that $\mathbf{X}_1$, $\mathbf{X}_2$, and $\mathbf{X}_3$ form a fundamental set for $\mathbf{X}' = \mathbf{A}\mathbf{X}$ on $-\infty < t < \infty$.

26. Let

$$\mathbf{X}_1 = \begin{pmatrix} 1 \\ -1 - \sqrt{2} \end{pmatrix} e^{\sqrt{2}t},$$

$$\mathbf{X}_2 = \begin{pmatrix} 1 \\ -1 + \sqrt{2} \end{pmatrix} e^{-\sqrt{2}t},$$

$$\mathbf{X}_p = \begin{pmatrix} 1 \\ 0 \end{pmatrix} t^2 + \begin{pmatrix} -2 \\ 4 \end{pmatrix} t + \begin{pmatrix} 1 \\ 0 \end{pmatrix},$$

and

$$\mathbf{A} = \begin{pmatrix} -1 & -1 \\ -1 & 1 \end{pmatrix}.$$

Then

$$\mathbf{X}_1' = \begin{pmatrix} \sqrt{2} \\ -2 - \sqrt{2} \end{pmatrix} e^{\sqrt{2}t} = \mathbf{A}\mathbf{X}_1,$$

$$\mathbf{X}_2' = \begin{pmatrix} -\sqrt{2} \\ -2 + \sqrt{2} \end{pmatrix} e^{-\sqrt{2}t} = \mathbf{A}\mathbf{X}_2,$$

$$\mathbf{X}_p' = \begin{pmatrix} 2 \\ 0 \end{pmatrix} t + \begin{pmatrix} -2 \\ 4 \end{pmatrix} = \mathbf{A}\mathbf{X}_p + \begin{pmatrix} 1 \\ 1 \end{pmatrix} t^2 + \begin{pmatrix} 4 \\ -6 \end{pmatrix} t + \begin{pmatrix} -1 \\ 5 \end{pmatrix},$$

and $W(\mathbf{X}_1, \mathbf{X}_2) = 2\sqrt{2} \neq 0$ so that $\mathbf{X}_p$ is a particular solution and $\mathbf{X}_1$ and $\mathbf{X}_2$ form a fundamental set on $-\infty < t < \infty$.

Homogeneous Linear Systems

1. The system is

$$\mathbf{X}' = \begin{pmatrix} 1 & 2 \\ 4 & 3 \end{pmatrix} \mathbf{X}$$

and $\det(\mathbf{A} - \lambda\mathbf{I}) = (\lambda - 5)(\lambda + 1) = 0$. For $\lambda_1 = 5$ we obtain

$$\begin{pmatrix} -4 & 2 & | & 0 \\ 4 & -2 & | & 0 \end{pmatrix} \Longrightarrow \begin{pmatrix} 1 & -1/2 & | & 0 \\ 0 & 0 & | & 0 \end{pmatrix} \quad \text{so that} \quad \mathbf{K}_1 = \begin{pmatrix} 1 \\ 2 \end{pmatrix}.$$

For $\lambda_2 = -1$ we obtain

$$\begin{pmatrix} 2 & 2 & | & 0 \\ 4 & 4 & | & 0 \end{pmatrix} \Longrightarrow \begin{pmatrix} 1 & 1 & | & 0 \\ 0 & 0 & | & 0 \end{pmatrix} \quad \text{so that} \quad \mathbf{K}_2 = \begin{pmatrix} -1 \\ 1 \end{pmatrix}.$$

Then

$$\mathbf{X} = c_1 \begin{pmatrix} 1 \\ 2 \end{pmatrix} e^{5t} + c_2 \begin{pmatrix} -1 \\ 1 \end{pmatrix} e^{-t}.$$

2. The system is

$$\mathbf{X}' = \begin{pmatrix} 2 & 2 \\ 1 & 3 \end{pmatrix} \mathbf{X}$$

and $\det(\mathbf{A} - \lambda\mathbf{I}) = (\lambda - 1)(\lambda - 4) = 0$. For $\lambda_1 = 1$ we obtain

$$\begin{pmatrix} 1 & 2 & | & 0 \\ 1 & 2 & | & 0 \end{pmatrix} \Longrightarrow \begin{pmatrix} 1 & 2 & | & 0 \\ 0 & 0 & | & 0 \end{pmatrix} \quad \text{so that} \quad \mathbf{K}_1 = \begin{pmatrix} -2 \\ 1 \end{pmatrix}.$$

For $\lambda_2 = 4$ we obtain

$$\begin{pmatrix} -2 & 2 & | & 0 \\ 1 & -1 & | & 0 \end{pmatrix} \Longrightarrow \begin{pmatrix} -1 & 1 & | & 0 \\ 0 & 0 & | & 0 \end{pmatrix} \quad \text{so that} \quad \mathbf{K}_2 = \begin{pmatrix} 1 \\ 1 \end{pmatrix}.$$

Then

$$\mathbf{X} = c_1 \begin{pmatrix} -2 \\ 1 \end{pmatrix} e^t + c_2 \begin{pmatrix} 1 \\ 1 \end{pmatrix} e^{4t}.$$

3. The system is

$$\mathbf{X}' = \begin{pmatrix} -4 & 2 \\ -5/2 & 2 \end{pmatrix} \mathbf{X}$$

and $\det(\mathbf{A} - \lambda\mathbf{I}) = (\lambda - 1)(\lambda + 3) = 0$. For $\lambda_1 = 1$ we obtain

$$\begin{pmatrix} -5 & 2 & | & 0 \\ -5/2 & 1 & | & 0 \end{pmatrix} \Longrightarrow \begin{pmatrix} -5 & 2 & | & 0 \\ 0 & 0 & | & 0 \end{pmatrix} \quad \text{so that} \quad \mathbf{K}_1 = \begin{pmatrix} 2 \\ 5 \end{pmatrix}.$$

For $\lambda_2 = -3$ we obtain

$$\begin{pmatrix} -1 & 2 & | & 0 \\ -5/2 & 5 & | & 0 \end{pmatrix} \Longrightarrow \begin{pmatrix} -1 & 2 & | & 0 \\ 0 & 0 & | & 0 \end{pmatrix} \quad \text{so that} \quad \mathbf{K}_2 = \begin{pmatrix} 2 \\ 1 \end{pmatrix}.$$

Then

$$\mathbf{X} = c_1 \begin{pmatrix} 2 \\ 5 \end{pmatrix} e^t + c_2 \begin{pmatrix} 2 \\ 1 \end{pmatrix} e^{-3t}.$$

4. The system is

$$\mathbf{X}' = \begin{pmatrix} -5/2 & 2 \\ 3/4 & -2 \end{pmatrix} \mathbf{X}$$

and $\det(\mathbf{A} - \lambda\mathbf{I}) = \frac{1}{2}(\lambda + 1)(2\lambda + 7) = 0$. For $\lambda_1 = -7/2$ we obtain

$$\begin{pmatrix} 1 & 2 & | & 0 \\ 3/4 & 3/2 & | & 0 \end{pmatrix} \Longrightarrow \begin{pmatrix} 1 & 2 & | & 0 \\ 0 & 0 & | & 0 \end{pmatrix} \quad \text{so that} \quad \mathbf{K}_1 = \begin{pmatrix} -2 \\ 1 \end{pmatrix}.$$

For $\lambda_2 = -1$ we obtain

$$\begin{pmatrix} -3/2 & 2 & | & 0 \\ 3/4 & -1 & | & 0 \end{pmatrix} \Longrightarrow \begin{pmatrix} -3 & 4 & | & 0 \\ 0 & 0 & | & 0 \end{pmatrix} \quad \text{so that} \quad \mathbf{K}_2 = \begin{pmatrix} 4 \\ 3 \end{pmatrix}.$$

Then

$$\mathbf{X} = c_1 \begin{pmatrix} -2 \\ 1 \end{pmatrix} e^{-7t/2} + c_2 \begin{pmatrix} 4 \\ 3 \end{pmatrix} e^{-t}.$$

5. The system is

$$\mathbf{X}' = \begin{pmatrix} 10 & -5 \\ 8 & -12 \end{pmatrix} \mathbf{X}$$

and $\det(\mathbf{A} - \lambda\mathbf{I}) = (\lambda - 8)(\lambda + 10) = 0$. For $\lambda_1 = 8$ we obtain

$$\begin{pmatrix} 2 & -5 & | & 0 \\ 8 & -20 & | & 0 \end{pmatrix} \Longrightarrow \begin{pmatrix} 1 & -5/2 & | & 0 \\ 0 & 0 & | & 0 \end{pmatrix} \quad \text{so that} \quad \mathbf{K}_1 = \begin{pmatrix} 5 \\ 2 \end{pmatrix}.$$

For $\lambda_2 = -10$ we obtain

$$\begin{pmatrix} 20 & -5 & | & 0 \\ 8 & -2 & | & 0 \end{pmatrix} \Longrightarrow \begin{pmatrix} 1 & -1/4 & | & 0 \\ 0 & 0 & | & 0 \end{pmatrix} \quad \text{so that} \quad \mathbf{K}_2 = \begin{pmatrix} 1 \\ 4 \end{pmatrix}.$$

Then

$$\mathbf{X} = c_1 \begin{pmatrix} 5 \\ 2 \end{pmatrix} e^{8t} + c_2 \begin{pmatrix} 1 \\ 4 \end{pmatrix} e^{-10t}.$$

6. The system is

$$\mathbf{X}' = \begin{pmatrix} -6 & 2 \\ -3 & 1 \end{pmatrix} \mathbf{X}$$

and $\det(\mathbf{A} - \lambda\mathbf{I}) = \lambda(\lambda + 5) = 0$. For $\lambda_1 = 0$ we obtain

$$\begin{pmatrix} -6 & 2 & | & 0 \\ -3 & 1 & | & 0 \end{pmatrix} \Longrightarrow \begin{pmatrix} 1 & -1/3 & | & 0 \\ 0 & 0 & | & 0 \end{pmatrix} \quad \text{so that} \quad \mathbf{K}_1 = \begin{pmatrix} 1 \\ 3 \end{pmatrix}.$$

For $\lambda_2 = -5$ we obtain

$$\begin{pmatrix} -1 & 2 & | & 0 \\ -3 & 6 & | & 0 \end{pmatrix} \implies \begin{pmatrix} 1 & -2 & | & 0 \\ 0 & 0 & | & 0 \end{pmatrix} \quad \text{so that} \quad \mathbf{K}_2 = \begin{pmatrix} 2 \\ 1 \end{pmatrix}.$$

Then

$$\mathbf{X} = c_1 \begin{pmatrix} 1 \\ 3 \end{pmatrix} + c_2 \begin{pmatrix} 2 \\ 1 \end{pmatrix} e^{-5t}.$$

7. The system is

$$\mathbf{X}' = \begin{pmatrix} 1 & 1 & -1 \\ 0 & 2 & 0 \\ 0 & 1 & -1 \end{pmatrix} \mathbf{X}$$

and $\det(\mathbf{A} - \lambda\mathbf{I}) = (\lambda - 1)(2 - \lambda)(\lambda + 1) = 0$. For $\lambda_1 = 1$, $\lambda_2 = 2$, and $\lambda_3 = -1$ we obtain

$$\mathbf{K}_1 = \begin{pmatrix} 1 \\ 0 \\ 0 \end{pmatrix}, \quad \mathbf{K}_2 = \begin{pmatrix} 2 \\ 3 \\ 1 \end{pmatrix}, \quad \text{and} \quad \mathbf{K}_3 = \begin{pmatrix} 1 \\ 0 \\ 2 \end{pmatrix},$$

so that

$$\mathbf{X} = c_1 \begin{pmatrix} 1 \\ 0 \\ 0 \end{pmatrix} e^t + c_2 \begin{pmatrix} 2 \\ 3 \\ 1 \end{pmatrix} e^{2t} + c_3 \begin{pmatrix} 1 \\ 0 \\ 2 \end{pmatrix} e^{-t}.$$

8. The system is

$$\mathbf{X}' = \begin{pmatrix} 2 & -7 & 0 \\ 5 & 10 & 4 \\ 0 & 5 & 2 \end{pmatrix} \mathbf{X}$$

and $\det(\mathbf{A} - \lambda\mathbf{I}) = (2 - \lambda)(\lambda - 5)(\lambda - 7) = 0$. For $\lambda_1 = 2$, $\lambda_2 = 5$, and $\lambda_3 = 7$ we obtain

$$\mathbf{K}_1 = \begin{pmatrix} 4 \\ 0 \\ -5 \end{pmatrix}, \quad \mathbf{K}_2 = \begin{pmatrix} -7 \\ 3 \\ 5 \end{pmatrix}, \quad \text{and} \quad \mathbf{K}_3 = \begin{pmatrix} -7 \\ 5 \\ 5 \end{pmatrix},$$

so that

$$\mathbf{X} = c_1 \begin{pmatrix} 4 \\ 0 \\ -5 \end{pmatrix} e^{2t} + c_2 \begin{pmatrix} -7 \\ 3 \\ 5 \end{pmatrix} e^{5t} + c_3 \begin{pmatrix} -7 \\ 5 \\ 5 \end{pmatrix} e^{7t}.$$

9. We have $\det(\mathbf{A} - \lambda\mathbf{I}) = -(\lambda + 1)(\lambda - 3)(\lambda + 2) = 0$. For $\lambda_1 = -1$, $\lambda_2 = 3$, and $\lambda_3 = -2$ we obtain

$$\mathbf{K}_1 = \begin{pmatrix} -1 \\ 0 \\ 1 \end{pmatrix}, \quad \mathbf{K}_2 = \begin{pmatrix} 1 \\ 4 \\ 3 \end{pmatrix}, \quad \text{and} \quad \mathbf{K}_3 = \begin{pmatrix} 1 \\ -1 \\ 3 \end{pmatrix},$$

so that

$$\mathbf{X} = c_1 \begin{pmatrix} -1 \\ 0 \\ 1 \end{pmatrix} e^{-t} + c_2 \begin{pmatrix} 1 \\ 4 \\ 3 \end{pmatrix} e^{3t} + c_3 \begin{pmatrix} 1 \\ -1 \\ 3 \end{pmatrix} e^{-2t}.$$

10. We have $\det(\mathbf{A} - \lambda\mathbf{I}) = -\lambda(\lambda - 1)(\lambda - 2) = 0$. For $\lambda_1 = 0$, $\lambda_2 = 1$, and $\lambda_3 = 2$ we obtain

$$\mathbf{K}_1 = \begin{pmatrix} 1 \\ 0 \\ -1 \end{pmatrix}, \quad \mathbf{K}_2 = \begin{pmatrix} 0 \\ 1 \\ 0 \end{pmatrix}, \quad \text{and} \quad \mathbf{K}_3 = \begin{pmatrix} 1 \\ 0 \\ 1 \end{pmatrix},$$

so that

$$\mathbf{X} = c_1 \begin{pmatrix} 1 \\ 0 \\ -1 \end{pmatrix} + c_2 \begin{pmatrix} 0 \\ 1 \\ 0 \end{pmatrix} e^{t} + c_3 \begin{pmatrix} 1 \\ 0 \\ 1 \end{pmatrix} e^{2t}.$$

11. We have $\det(\mathbf{A} - \lambda\mathbf{I}) = -(\lambda + 1)(\lambda + 1/2)(\lambda + 3/2) = 0$. For $\lambda_1 = -1$, $\lambda_2 = -1/2$, and $\lambda_3 = -3/2$ we obtain

$$\mathbf{K}_1 = \begin{pmatrix} 4 \\ 0 \\ -1 \end{pmatrix}, \quad \mathbf{K}_2 = \begin{pmatrix} -12 \\ 6 \\ 5 \end{pmatrix}, \quad \text{and} \quad \mathbf{K}_3 = \begin{pmatrix} 4 \\ 2 \\ -1 \end{pmatrix},$$

so that

$$\mathbf{X} = c_1 \begin{pmatrix} 4 \\ 0 \\ -1 \end{pmatrix} e^{-t} + c_2 \begin{pmatrix} -12 \\ 6 \\ 5 \end{pmatrix} e^{-t/2} + c_3 \begin{pmatrix} 4 \\ 2 \\ -1 \end{pmatrix} e^{-3t/2}.$$

12. We have $\det(\mathbf{A} - \lambda\mathbf{I}) = (\lambda - 3)(\lambda + 5)(6 - \lambda) = 0$. For $\lambda_1 = 3$, $\lambda_2 = -5$, and $\lambda_3 = 6$ we obtain

$$\mathbf{K}_1 = \begin{pmatrix} 1 \\ 1 \\ 0 \end{pmatrix}, \quad \mathbf{K}_2 = \begin{pmatrix} 1 \\ -1 \\ 0 \end{pmatrix}, \quad \text{and} \quad \mathbf{K}_3 = \begin{pmatrix} 2 \\ -2 \\ 11 \end{pmatrix},$$

so that

$$\mathbf{X} = c_1 \begin{pmatrix} 1 \\ 1 \\ 0 \end{pmatrix} e^{3t} + c_2 \begin{pmatrix} 1 \\ -1 \\ 0 \end{pmatrix} e^{-5t} + c_3 \begin{pmatrix} 2 \\ -2 \\ 11 \end{pmatrix} e^{6t}.$$

13. We have $\det(\mathbf{A} - \lambda\mathbf{I}) = (\lambda + 1/2)(\lambda - 1/2) = 0$. For $\lambda_1 = -1/2$ and $\lambda_2 = 1/2$ we obtain

$$\mathbf{K}_1 = \begin{pmatrix} 0 \\ 1 \end{pmatrix} \quad \text{and} \quad \mathbf{K}_2 = \begin{pmatrix} 1 \\ 1 \end{pmatrix},$$

so that

$$\mathbf{X} = c_1 \begin{pmatrix} 0 \\ 1 \end{pmatrix} e^{-t/2} + c_2 \begin{pmatrix} 1 \\ 1 \end{pmatrix} e^{t/2}.$$

If

$$\mathbf{X}(0) = \begin{pmatrix} 3 \\ 5 \end{pmatrix}$$

then $c_1 = 2$ and $c_2 = 3$.

14. We have $\det(\mathbf{A} - \lambda\mathbf{I}) = (2 - \lambda)(\lambda - 3)(\lambda + 1) = 0$. For $\lambda_1 = 2$, $\lambda_2 = 3$, and $\lambda_3 = -1$ we obtain

$$\mathbf{K}_1 = \begin{pmatrix} 5 \\ -3 \\ 2 \end{pmatrix}, \quad \mathbf{K}_2 = \begin{pmatrix} 2 \\ 0 \\ 1 \end{pmatrix}, \quad \text{and} \quad \mathbf{K}_3 = \begin{pmatrix} -2 \\ 0 \\ 1 \end{pmatrix},$$

so that

$$\mathbf{X} = c_1 \begin{pmatrix} 5 \\ -3 \\ 2 \end{pmatrix} e^{2t} + c_2 \begin{pmatrix} 2 \\ 0 \\ 1 \end{pmatrix} e^{3t} + c_3 \begin{pmatrix} -2 \\ 0 \\ 1 \end{pmatrix} e^{-t}.$$

If

$$\mathbf{X}(0) = \begin{pmatrix} 1 \\ 3 \\ 0 \end{pmatrix}$$

then $c_1 = -1$, $c_2 = 5/2$, and $c_3 = -1/2$.

15. $\mathbf{X} = c_1 \begin{pmatrix} 0.382175 \\ 0.851161 \\ 0.359815 \end{pmatrix} e^{8.58979t} + c_2 \begin{pmatrix} 0.405188 \\ -0.676043 \\ 0.615458 \end{pmatrix} e^{2.25684t} + c_3 \begin{pmatrix} -0.923562 \\ -0.132174 \\ 0.35995 \end{pmatrix} e^{-0.0466321t}$

16. $\mathbf{X} = c_1 \begin{pmatrix} 0.0312209 \\ 0.949058 \\ 0.239535 \\ 0.195825 \\ 0.0508861 \end{pmatrix} e^{5.05452t} + c_2 \begin{pmatrix} -0.280232 \\ -0.836611 \\ -0.275304 \\ 0.176045 \\ 0.338775 \end{pmatrix} e^{4.09561t} + c_3 \begin{pmatrix} 0.262219 \\ -0.162664 \\ -0.826218 \\ -0.346439 \\ 0.31957 \end{pmatrix} e^{-2.92362t}$

$+ c_4 \begin{pmatrix} 0.313235 \\ 0.64181 \\ 0.31754 \\ 0.173787 \\ -0.599108 \end{pmatrix} e^{2.02882t} + c_5 \begin{pmatrix} -0.301294 \\ 0.466599 \\ 0.222136 \\ 0.0534311 \\ -0.799567 \end{pmatrix} e^{-0.155338t}$

17. (a)

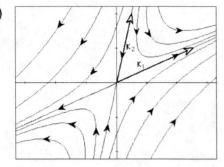

(b) Letting $c_1 = 1$ and $c_2 = 0$ we get $x = 5e^{8t}$, $y = 2e^{8t}$. Eliminating the parameter we find $y = \frac{2}{5}x$, $x > 0$. When $c_1 = -1$ and $c_2 = 0$ we find $y = \frac{2}{5}x$, $x < 0$. Letting $c_1 = 0$ and $c_2 = 1$ we get $x = e^{-10t}$, $y = 4e^{-10t}$. Eliminating the parameter we find $y = 4x$, $x > 0$. Letting $c_1 = 0$ and $c_2 = -1$ we find $y = 4x$, $x < 0$.

(c) The eigenvectors $\mathbf{K}_1 = (5, 2)$ and $\mathbf{K}_2 = (1, 4)$ are shown in the figure in part (a).

18. In Problem 2, letting $c_1 = 1$ and $c_2 = 0$ we get $x = -2e^t$, $y = e^t$. Eliminating the parameter we find $y = -\frac{1}{2}x$, $x < 0$. When $c_1 = -1$ and $c_2 = 0$ we find $y = -\frac{1}{2}x$, $x > 0$. Letting $c_1 = 0$ and $c_2 = 1$ we get $x = e^{4t}$, $y = e^{4t}$. Eliminating the parameter we find $y = x$, $x > 0$. When $c_1 = 0$ and $c_2 = -1$ we find $y = x$, $x < 0$.

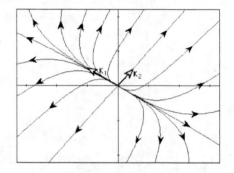

In Problem 4, letting $c_1 = 1$ and $c_2 = 0$ we get $x = -2e^{-7t/2}$, $y = e^{-7t/2}$. Eliminating the parameter we find $y = -\frac{1}{2}x$, $x < 0$. When $c_1 = -1$ and $c_2 = 0$ we find $y = -\frac{1}{2}x$, $x > 0$. Letting $c_1 = 0$ and $c_2 = 1$ we get $x = 4e^{-t}$, $y = 3e^{-t}$. Eliminating the parameter we find $y = \frac{3}{4}x$, $x > 0$. When $c_1 = 0$ and $c_2 = -1$ we find $y = \frac{3}{4}x$, $x < 0$.

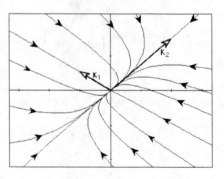

19. We have $\det(\mathbf{A} - \lambda\mathbf{I}) = \lambda^2 = 0$. For $\lambda_1 = 0$ we obtain

$$\mathbf{K} = \begin{pmatrix} 1 \\ 3 \end{pmatrix}.$$

A solution of $(\mathbf{A} - \lambda_1\mathbf{I})\mathbf{P} = \mathbf{K}$ is

$$\mathbf{P} = \begin{pmatrix} 1 \\ 2 \end{pmatrix}$$

so that

$$\mathbf{X} = c_1 \begin{pmatrix} 1 \\ 3 \end{pmatrix} + c_2 \left[\begin{pmatrix} 1 \\ 3 \end{pmatrix} t + \begin{pmatrix} 1 \\ 2 \end{pmatrix} \right].$$

20. We have $\det(\mathbf{A} - \lambda\mathbf{I}) = (\lambda + 1)^2 = 0$. For $\lambda_1 = -1$ we obtain

$$\mathbf{K} = \begin{pmatrix} 1 \\ 1 \end{pmatrix}.$$

A solution of $(\mathbf{A} - \lambda_1\mathbf{I})\mathbf{P} = \mathbf{K}$ is

$$\mathbf{P} = \begin{pmatrix} 0 \\ 1/5 \end{pmatrix}$$

so that

$$\mathbf{X} = c_1 \begin{pmatrix} 1 \\ 1 \end{pmatrix} e^{-t} + c_2 \left[\begin{pmatrix} 1 \\ 1 \end{pmatrix} te^{-t} + \begin{pmatrix} 0 \\ 1/5 \end{pmatrix} e^{-t} \right].$$

21. We have $\det(\mathbf{A} - \lambda\mathbf{I}) = (\lambda - 2)^2 = 0$. For $\lambda_1 = 2$ we obtain

$$\mathbf{K} = \begin{pmatrix} 1 \\ 1 \end{pmatrix}.$$

A solution of $(\mathbf{A} - \lambda_1\mathbf{I})\mathbf{P} = \mathbf{K}$ is

$$\mathbf{P} = \begin{pmatrix} -1/3 \\ 0 \end{pmatrix}$$

so that

$$\mathbf{X} = c_1 \begin{pmatrix} 1 \\ 1 \end{pmatrix} e^{2t} + c_2 \left[\begin{pmatrix} 1 \\ 1 \end{pmatrix} te^{2t} + \begin{pmatrix} -1/3 \\ 0 \end{pmatrix} e^{2t} \right].$$

22. We have $\det(\mathbf{A} - \lambda\mathbf{I}) = (\lambda - 6)^2 = 0$. For $\lambda_1 = 6$ we obtain

$$\mathbf{K} = \begin{pmatrix} 3 \\ 2 \end{pmatrix}.$$

A solution of $(\mathbf{A} - \lambda_1\mathbf{I})\mathbf{P} = \mathbf{K}$ is

$$\mathbf{P} = \begin{pmatrix} 1/2 \\ 0 \end{pmatrix}$$

so that

$$\mathbf{X} = c_1 \begin{pmatrix} 3 \\ 2 \end{pmatrix} e^{6t} + c_2 \left[\begin{pmatrix} 3 \\ 2 \end{pmatrix} te^{6t} + \begin{pmatrix} 1/2 \\ 0 \end{pmatrix} e^{6t} \right].$$

23. We have $\det(\mathbf{A} - \lambda\mathbf{I}) = (1 - \lambda)(\lambda - 2)^2 = 0$. For $\lambda_1 = 1$ we obtain

$$\mathbf{K}_1 = \begin{pmatrix} 1 \\ 1 \\ 1 \end{pmatrix}.$$

For $\lambda_2 = 2$ we obtain

$$\mathbf{K}_2 = \begin{pmatrix} 1 \\ 0 \\ 1 \end{pmatrix} \quad \text{and} \quad \mathbf{K}_3 = \begin{pmatrix} 1 \\ 1 \\ 0 \end{pmatrix}.$$

Then

$$\mathbf{X} = c_1 \begin{pmatrix} 1 \\ 1 \\ 1 \end{pmatrix} e^t + c_2 \begin{pmatrix} 1 \\ 0 \\ 1 \end{pmatrix} e^{2t} + c_3 \begin{pmatrix} 1 \\ 1 \\ 0 \end{pmatrix} e^{2t}.$$

24. We have $\det(\mathbf{A} - \lambda\mathbf{I}) = (\lambda - 8)(\lambda + 1)^2 = 0$. For $\lambda_1 = 8$ we obtain

$$\mathbf{K}_1 = \begin{pmatrix} 2 \\ 1 \\ 2 \end{pmatrix}.$$

For $\lambda_2 = -1$ we obtain

$$\mathbf{K}_2 = \begin{pmatrix} 0 \\ -2 \\ 1 \end{pmatrix} \quad \text{and} \quad \mathbf{K}_3 = \begin{pmatrix} 1 \\ -2 \\ 0 \end{pmatrix}.$$

Then

$$\mathbf{X} = c_1 \begin{pmatrix} 2 \\ 1 \\ 2 \end{pmatrix} e^{8t} + c_2 \begin{pmatrix} 0 \\ -2 \\ 1 \end{pmatrix} e^{-t} + c_3 \begin{pmatrix} 1 \\ -2 \\ 0 \end{pmatrix} e^{-t}.$$

25. We have $\det(\mathbf{A} - \lambda\mathbf{I}) = -\lambda(5 - \lambda)^2 = 0$. For $\lambda_1 = 0$ we obtain

$$\mathbf{K}_1 = \begin{pmatrix} -4 \\ -5 \\ 2 \end{pmatrix}.$$

For $\lambda_2 = 5$ we obtain

$$\mathbf{K} = \begin{pmatrix} -2 \\ 0 \\ 1 \end{pmatrix}.$$

A solution of $(\mathbf{A} - \lambda_2\mathbf{I})\mathbf{P} = \mathbf{K}$ is

$$\mathbf{P} = \begin{pmatrix} 5/2 \\ 1/2 \\ 0 \end{pmatrix}$$

so that

$$\mathbf{X} = c_1 \begin{pmatrix} -4 \\ -5 \\ 2 \end{pmatrix} + c_2 \begin{pmatrix} -2 \\ 0 \\ 1 \end{pmatrix} e^{5t} + c_3 \left[\begin{pmatrix} -2 \\ 0 \\ 1 \end{pmatrix} te^{5t} + \begin{pmatrix} 5/2 \\ 1/2 \\ 0 \end{pmatrix} e^{5t} \right].$$

26. We have $\det(\mathbf{A} - \lambda\mathbf{I}) = (1 - \lambda)(\lambda - 2)^2 = 0$. For $\lambda_1 = 1$ we obtain

$$\mathbf{K}_1 = \begin{pmatrix} 1 \\ 0 \\ 0 \end{pmatrix}.$$

For $\lambda_2 = 2$ we obtain

$$\mathbf{K} = \begin{pmatrix} 0 \\ -1 \\ 1 \end{pmatrix}.$$

A solution of $(\mathbf{A} - \lambda_2\mathbf{I})\mathbf{P} = \mathbf{K}$ is

$$\mathbf{P} = \begin{pmatrix} 0 \\ -1 \\ 0 \end{pmatrix}$$

so that

$$\mathbf{X} = c_1 \begin{pmatrix} 1 \\ 0 \\ 0 \end{pmatrix} e^t + c_2 \begin{pmatrix} 0 \\ -1 \\ 1 \end{pmatrix} e^{2t} + c_3 \left[\begin{pmatrix} 0 \\ -1 \\ 1 \end{pmatrix} te^{2t} + \begin{pmatrix} 0 \\ -1 \\ 0 \end{pmatrix} e^{2t} \right].$$

27. We have $\det(\mathbf{A} - \lambda\mathbf{I}) = -(\lambda - 1)^3 = 0$. For $\lambda_1 = 1$ we obtain

$$\mathbf{K} = \begin{pmatrix} 0 \\ 1 \\ 1 \end{pmatrix}.$$

Solutions of $(\mathbf{A} - \lambda_1\mathbf{I})\mathbf{P} = \mathbf{K}$ and $(\mathbf{A} - \lambda_1\mathbf{I})\mathbf{Q} = \mathbf{P}$ are

$$\mathbf{P} = \begin{pmatrix} 0 \\ 1 \\ 0 \end{pmatrix} \quad \text{and} \quad \mathbf{Q} = \begin{pmatrix} 1/2 \\ 0 \\ 0 \end{pmatrix}$$

so that

$$\mathbf{X} = c_1 \begin{pmatrix} 0 \\ 1 \\ 1 \end{pmatrix} e^t + c_2 \left[\begin{pmatrix} 0 \\ 1 \\ 1 \end{pmatrix} te^t + \begin{pmatrix} 0 \\ 1 \\ 0 \end{pmatrix} e^t \right] + c_3 \left[\begin{pmatrix} 0 \\ 1 \\ 1 \end{pmatrix} \frac{t^2}{2}e^t + \begin{pmatrix} 0 \\ 1 \\ 0 \end{pmatrix} te^t + \begin{pmatrix} 1/2 \\ 0 \\ 0 \end{pmatrix} e^t \right].$$

28. We have $\det(\mathbf{A} - \lambda\mathbf{I}) = (\lambda - 4)^3 = 0$. For $\lambda_1 = 4$ we obtain

$$\mathbf{K} = \begin{pmatrix} 1 \\ 0 \\ 0 \end{pmatrix}.$$

Solutions of $(\mathbf{A} - \lambda_1\mathbf{I})\mathbf{P} = \mathbf{K}$ and $(\mathbf{A} - \lambda_1\mathbf{I})\mathbf{Q} = \mathbf{P}$ are

$$\mathbf{P} = \begin{pmatrix} 0 \\ 1 \\ 0 \end{pmatrix} \quad \text{and} \quad \mathbf{Q} = \begin{pmatrix} 0 \\ 0 \\ 1 \end{pmatrix}$$

so that

$$\mathbf{X} = c_1 \begin{pmatrix} 1 \\ 0 \\ 0 \end{pmatrix} e^{4t} + c_2 \left[\begin{pmatrix} 1 \\ 0 \\ 0 \end{pmatrix} te^{4t} + \begin{pmatrix} 0 \\ 1 \\ 0 \end{pmatrix} e^{4t} \right] + c_3 \left[\begin{pmatrix} 1 \\ 0 \\ 0 \end{pmatrix} \frac{t^2}{2}e^{4t} + \begin{pmatrix} 0 \\ 1 \\ 0 \end{pmatrix} te^{4t} + \begin{pmatrix} 0 \\ 0 \\ 1 \end{pmatrix} e^{4t} \right].$$

Exercises 8.2 Homogeneous Linear Systems

29. We have $\det(\mathbf{A} - \lambda\mathbf{I}) = (\lambda - 4)^2 = 0$. For $\lambda_1 = 4$ we obtain

$$\mathbf{K} = \begin{pmatrix} 2 \\ 1 \end{pmatrix}.$$

A solution of $(\mathbf{A} - \lambda_1\mathbf{I})\mathbf{P} = \mathbf{K}$ is

$$\mathbf{P} = \begin{pmatrix} 1 \\ 1 \end{pmatrix}$$

so that

$$\mathbf{X} = c_1 \begin{pmatrix} 2 \\ 1 \end{pmatrix} e^{4t} + c_2 \left[\begin{pmatrix} 2 \\ 1 \end{pmatrix} t e^{4t} + \begin{pmatrix} 1 \\ 1 \end{pmatrix} e^{4t} \right].$$

If

$$\mathbf{X}(0) = \begin{pmatrix} -1 \\ 6 \end{pmatrix}$$

then $c_1 = -7$ and $c_2 = 13$.

30. We have $\det(\mathbf{A} - \lambda\mathbf{I}) = -(\lambda + 1)(\lambda - 1)^2 = 0$. For $\lambda_1 = -1$ we obtain

$$\mathbf{K}_1 = \begin{pmatrix} -1 \\ 0 \\ 1 \end{pmatrix}.$$

For $\lambda_2 = 1$ we obtain

$$\mathbf{K}_2 = \begin{pmatrix} 1 \\ 0 \\ 1 \end{pmatrix} \quad \text{and} \quad \mathbf{K}_3 = \begin{pmatrix} 0 \\ 1 \\ 0 \end{pmatrix}$$

so that

$$\mathbf{X} = c_1 \begin{pmatrix} -1 \\ 0 \\ 1 \end{pmatrix} e^{-t} + c_2 \begin{pmatrix} 1 \\ 0 \\ 1 \end{pmatrix} e^t + c_3 \begin{pmatrix} 0 \\ 1 \\ 0 \end{pmatrix} e^t.$$

If

$$\mathbf{X}(0) = \begin{pmatrix} 1 \\ 2 \\ 5 \end{pmatrix}$$

then $c_1 = 2$, $c_2 = 3$, and $c_3 = 2$.

31. In this case $\det(\mathbf{A} - \lambda\mathbf{I}) = (2 - \lambda)^5$, and $\lambda_1 = 2$ is an eigenvalue of multiplicity 5. Linearly independent eigenvectors are

$$\mathbf{K}_1 = \begin{pmatrix} 1 \\ 0 \\ 0 \\ 0 \\ 0 \end{pmatrix}, \quad \mathbf{K}_2 = \begin{pmatrix} 0 \\ 0 \\ 1 \\ 0 \\ 0 \end{pmatrix}, \quad \text{and} \quad \mathbf{K}_3 = \begin{pmatrix} 0 \\ 0 \\ 0 \\ 1 \\ 0 \end{pmatrix}.$$

32. In Problem 20 letting $c_1 = 1$ and $c_2 = 0$ we get $x = e^t$, $y = e^t$. Eliminating the parameter we find $y = x$, $x > 0$. When $c_1 = -1$ and $c_2 = 0$ we find $y = x$, $x < 0$.

In Problem 21 letting $c_1 = 1$ and $c_2 = 0$ we get $x = e^{2t}$, $y = e^{2t}$. Eliminating the parameter we find $y = x$, $x > 0$. When $c_1 = -1$ and $c_2 = 0$ we find $y = x$, $x < 0$.

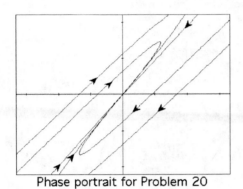

Phase portrait for Problem 20

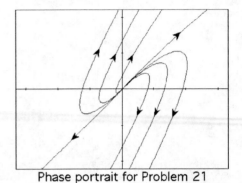

Phase portrait for Problem 21

In Problems 33-46 the form of the answer will vary according to the choice of eigenvector. For example, in Problem 33, if $\mathbf{K}_1$ is chosen to be $\begin{pmatrix} 1 \\ 2 - i \end{pmatrix}$ the solution has the form

$$\mathbf{X} = c_1 \begin{pmatrix} \cos t \\ 2\cos t + \sin t \end{pmatrix} e^{4t} + c_2 \begin{pmatrix} \sin t \\ 2\sin t - \cos t \end{pmatrix} e^{4t}.$$

33. We have $\det(\mathbf{A} - \lambda\mathbf{I}) = \lambda^2 - 8\lambda + 17 = 0$. For $\lambda_1 = 4 + i$ we obtain

$$\mathbf{K}_1 = \begin{pmatrix} 2 + i \\ 5 \end{pmatrix}$$

so that

$$\mathbf{X}_1 = \begin{pmatrix} 2 + i \\ 5 \end{pmatrix} e^{(4+i)t} = \begin{pmatrix} 2\cos t - \sin t \\ 5\cos t \end{pmatrix} e^{4t} + i \begin{pmatrix} \cos t + 2\sin t \\ 5\sin t \end{pmatrix} e^{4t}.$$

Then

$$\mathbf{X} = c_1 \begin{pmatrix} 2\cos t - \sin t \\ 5\cos t \end{pmatrix} e^{4t} + c_2 \begin{pmatrix} \cos t + 2\sin t \\ 5\sin t \end{pmatrix} e^{4t}.$$

34. We have $\det(\mathbf{A} - \lambda\mathbf{I}) = \lambda^2 + 1 = 0$. For $\lambda_1 = i$ we obtain

$$\mathbf{K}_1 = \begin{pmatrix} -1 - i \\ 2 \end{pmatrix}$$

so that

$$\mathbf{X}_1 = \begin{pmatrix} -1 - i \\ 2 \end{pmatrix} e^{it} = \begin{pmatrix} \sin t - \cos t \\ 2\cos t \end{pmatrix} + i \begin{pmatrix} -\cos t - \sin t \\ 2\sin t \end{pmatrix}.$$

Then

$$\mathbf{X} = c_1 \begin{pmatrix} \sin t - \cos t \\ 2\cos t \end{pmatrix} + c_2 \begin{pmatrix} -\cos t - \sin t \\ 2\sin t \end{pmatrix}.$$

35. We have $\det(\mathbf{A} - \lambda\mathbf{I}) = \lambda^2 - 8\lambda + 17 = 0$. For $\lambda_1 = 4 + i$ we obtain

$$\mathbf{K}_1 = \begin{pmatrix} -1 - i \\ 2 \end{pmatrix}$$

so that

$$\mathbf{X}_1 = \begin{pmatrix} -1 - i \\ 2 \end{pmatrix} e^{(4+i)t} = \begin{pmatrix} \sin t - \cos t \\ 2\cos t \end{pmatrix} e^{4t} + i \begin{pmatrix} -\sin t - \cos t \\ 2\sin t \end{pmatrix} e^{4t}.$$

Then

$$\mathbf{X} = c_1 \begin{pmatrix} \sin t - \cos t \\ 2\cos t \end{pmatrix} e^{4t} + c_2 \begin{pmatrix} -\sin t - \cos t \\ 2\sin t \end{pmatrix} e^{4t}.$$

36. We have $\det(\mathbf{A} - \lambda\mathbf{I}) = \lambda^2 - 10\lambda + 34 = 0$. For $\lambda_1 = 5 + 3i$ we obtain

$$\mathbf{K}_1 = \begin{pmatrix} 1 - 3i \\ 2 \end{pmatrix}$$

so that

$$\mathbf{X}_1 = \begin{pmatrix} 1 - 3i \\ 2 \end{pmatrix} e^{(5+3i)t} = \begin{pmatrix} \cos 3t + 3\sin 3t \\ 2\cos 3t \end{pmatrix} e^{5t} + i \begin{pmatrix} \sin 3t - 3\cos 3t \\ 2\sin 3t \end{pmatrix} e^{5t}.$$

Then

$$\mathbf{X} = c_1 \begin{pmatrix} \cos 3t + 3\sin 3t \\ 2\cos 3t \end{pmatrix} e^{5t} + c_2 \begin{pmatrix} \sin 3t - 3\cos 3t \\ 2\sin 3t \end{pmatrix} e^{5t}.$$

37. We have $\det(\mathbf{A} - \lambda\mathbf{I}) = \lambda^2 + 9 = 0$. For $\lambda_1 = 3i$ we obtain

$$\mathbf{K}_1 = \begin{pmatrix} 4 + 3i \\ 5 \end{pmatrix}$$

so that

$$\mathbf{X}_1 = \begin{pmatrix} 4 + 3i \\ 5 \end{pmatrix} e^{3it} = \begin{pmatrix} 4\cos 3t - 3\sin 3t \\ 5\cos 3t \end{pmatrix} + i \begin{pmatrix} 4\sin 3t + 3\cos 3t \\ 5\sin 3t \end{pmatrix}.$$

Then

$$\mathbf{X} = c_1 \begin{pmatrix} 4\cos 3t - 3\sin 3t \\ 5\cos 3t \end{pmatrix} + c_2 \begin{pmatrix} 4\sin 3t + 3\cos 3t \\ 5\sin 3t \end{pmatrix}.$$

38. We have $\det(\mathbf{A} - \lambda\mathbf{I}) = \lambda^2 + 2\lambda + 5 = 0$. For $\lambda_1 = -1 + 2i$ we obtain

$$\mathbf{K}_1 = \begin{pmatrix} 2 + 2i \\ 1 \end{pmatrix}$$

434

so that

$$\mathbf{X}_1 = \begin{pmatrix} 2 + 2i \\ 1 \end{pmatrix} e^{(-1+2i)t}$$

$$= \begin{pmatrix} 2\cos 2t - 2\sin 2t \\ \cos 2t \end{pmatrix} e^{-t} + i \begin{pmatrix} 2\cos 2t + 2\sin 2t \\ \sin 2t \end{pmatrix} e^{-t}.$$

Then

$$\mathbf{X} = c_1 \begin{pmatrix} 2\cos 2t - 2\sin 2t \\ \cos 2t \end{pmatrix} e^{-t} + c_2 \begin{pmatrix} 2\cos 2t + 2\sin 2t \\ \sin 2t \end{pmatrix} e^{-t}.$$

39. We have $\det(\mathbf{A} - \lambda\mathbf{I}) = -\lambda\left(\lambda^2 + 1\right) = 0$. For $\lambda_1 = 0$ we obtain

$$\mathbf{K}_1 = \begin{pmatrix} 1 \\ 0 \\ 0 \end{pmatrix}.$$

For $\lambda_2 = i$ we obtain

$$\mathbf{K}_2 = \begin{pmatrix} -i \\ i \\ 1 \end{pmatrix}$$

so that

$$\mathbf{X}_2 = \begin{pmatrix} -i \\ i \\ 1 \end{pmatrix} e^{it} = \begin{pmatrix} \sin t \\ -\sin t \\ \cos t \end{pmatrix} + i \begin{pmatrix} -\cos t \\ \cos t \\ \sin t \end{pmatrix}.$$

Then

$$\mathbf{X} = c_1 \begin{pmatrix} 1 \\ 0 \\ 0 \end{pmatrix} + c_2 \begin{pmatrix} \sin t \\ -\sin t \\ \cos t \end{pmatrix} + c_3 \begin{pmatrix} -\cos t \\ \cos t \\ \sin t \end{pmatrix}.$$

40. We have $\det(\mathbf{A} - \lambda\mathbf{I}) = -(\lambda + 3)(\lambda^2 - 2\lambda + 5) = 0$. For $\lambda_1 = -3$ we obtain

$$\mathbf{K}_1 = \begin{pmatrix} 0 \\ -2 \\ 1 \end{pmatrix}.$$

For $\lambda_2 = 1 + 2i$ we obtain

$$\mathbf{K}_2 = \begin{pmatrix} -2 - i \\ -3i \\ 2 \end{pmatrix}$$

so that

$$\mathbf{X}_2 = \begin{pmatrix} -2\cos 2t + \sin 2t \\ 3\sin 2t \\ 2\cos 2t \end{pmatrix} e^t + i \begin{pmatrix} -\cos 2t - 2\sin 2t \\ -3\cos 2t \\ 2\sin 2t \end{pmatrix} e^t.$$

Then

$$\mathbf{X} = c_1 \begin{pmatrix} 0 \\ -2 \\ 1 \end{pmatrix} e^{-3t} + c_2 \begin{pmatrix} -2\cos 2t + \sin 2t \\ 3\sin 2t \\ 2\cos 2t \end{pmatrix} e^t + c_3 \begin{pmatrix} -\cos 2t - 2\sin 2t \\ -3\cos 2t \\ 2\sin 2t \end{pmatrix} e^t.$$

41. We have $\det(\mathbf{A} - \lambda\mathbf{I}) = (1 - \lambda)(\lambda^2 - 2\lambda + 2) = 0$. For $\lambda_1 = 1$ we obtain

$$\mathbf{K}_1 = \begin{pmatrix} 0 \\ 2 \\ 1 \end{pmatrix}.$$

For $\lambda_2 = 1 + i$ we obtain

$$\mathbf{K}_2 = \begin{pmatrix} 1 \\ i \\ i \end{pmatrix}$$

so that

$$\mathbf{X}_2 = \begin{pmatrix} 1 \\ i \\ i \end{pmatrix} e^{(1+i)t} = \begin{pmatrix} \cos t \\ -\sin t \\ -\sin t \end{pmatrix} e^t + i \begin{pmatrix} \sin t \\ \cos t \\ \cos t \end{pmatrix} e^t.$$

Then

$$\mathbf{X} = c_1 \begin{pmatrix} 0 \\ 2 \\ 1 \end{pmatrix} e^t + c_2 \begin{pmatrix} \cos t \\ -\sin t \\ -\sin t \end{pmatrix} e^t + c_3 \begin{pmatrix} \sin t \\ \cos t \\ \cos t \end{pmatrix} e^t.$$

42. We have $\det(\mathbf{A} - \lambda\mathbf{I}) = -(\lambda - 6)(\lambda^2 - 8\lambda + 20) = 0$. For $\lambda_1 = 6$ we obtain

$$\mathbf{K}_1 = \begin{pmatrix} 0 \\ 1 \\ 0 \end{pmatrix}.$$

For $\lambda_2 = 4 + 2i$ we obtain

$$\mathbf{K}_2 = \begin{pmatrix} -i \\ 0 \\ 2 \end{pmatrix}$$

so that

$$\mathbf{X}_2 = \begin{pmatrix} -i \\ 0 \\ 2 \end{pmatrix} e^{(4+2i)t} = \begin{pmatrix} \sin 2t \\ 0 \\ 2\cos 2t \end{pmatrix} e^{4t} + i \begin{pmatrix} -\cos 2t \\ 0 \\ 2\sin 2t \end{pmatrix} e^{4t}.$$

Then

$$\mathbf{X} = c_1 \begin{pmatrix} 0 \\ 1 \\ 0 \end{pmatrix} e^{6t} + c_2 \begin{pmatrix} \sin 2t \\ 0 \\ 2\cos 2t \end{pmatrix} e^{4t} + c_3 \begin{pmatrix} -\cos 2t \\ 0 \\ 2\sin 2t \end{pmatrix} e^{4t}.$$

43. We have $\det(\mathbf{A} - \lambda\mathbf{I}) = (2 - \lambda)(\lambda^2 + 4\lambda + 13) = 0$. For $\lambda_1 = 2$ we obtain

$$\mathbf{K}_1 = \begin{pmatrix} 28 \\ -5 \\ 25 \end{pmatrix}.$$

For $\lambda_2 = -2 + 3i$ we obtain

$$\mathbf{K}_2 = \begin{pmatrix} 4 + 3i \\ -5 \\ 0 \end{pmatrix}$$

so that

$$\mathbf{X}_2 = \begin{pmatrix} 4 + 3i \\ -5 \\ 0 \end{pmatrix} e^{(-2+3i)t} = \begin{pmatrix} 4\cos 3t - 3\sin 3t \\ -5\cos 3t \\ 0 \end{pmatrix} e^{-2t} + i \begin{pmatrix} 4\sin 3t + 3\cos 3t \\ -5\sin 3t \\ 0 \end{pmatrix} e^{-2t}.$$

Then

$$\mathbf{X} = c_1 \begin{pmatrix} 28 \\ -5 \\ 25 \end{pmatrix} e^{2t} + c_2 \begin{pmatrix} 4\cos 3t - 3\sin 3t \\ -5\cos 3t \\ 0 \end{pmatrix} e^{-2t} + c_3 \begin{pmatrix} 4\sin 3t + 3\cos 3t \\ -5\sin 3t \\ 0 \end{pmatrix} e^{-2t}.$$

44. We have $\det(\mathbf{A} - \lambda\mathbf{I}) = -(\lambda + 2)(\lambda^2 + 4) = 0$. For $\lambda_1 = -2$ we obtain

$$\mathbf{K}_1 = \begin{pmatrix} 0 \\ -1 \\ 1 \end{pmatrix}.$$

For $\lambda_2 = 2i$ we obtain

$$\mathbf{K}_2 = \begin{pmatrix} -2 - 2i \\ 1 \\ 1 \end{pmatrix}$$

so that

$$\mathbf{X}_2 = \begin{pmatrix} -2 - 2i \\ 1 \\ 1 \end{pmatrix} e^{2it} = \begin{pmatrix} -2\cos 2t + 2\sin 2t \\ \cos 2t \\ \cos 2t \end{pmatrix} + i \begin{pmatrix} -2\cos 2t - 2\sin 2t \\ \sin 2t \\ \sin 2t \end{pmatrix}.$$

Then

$$\mathbf{X} = c_1 \begin{pmatrix} 0 \\ -1 \\ 1 \end{pmatrix} e^{-2t} + c_2 \begin{pmatrix} -2\cos 2t + 2\sin 2t \\ \cos 2t \\ \cos 2t \end{pmatrix} + c_3 \begin{pmatrix} -2\cos 2t - 2\sin 2t \\ \sin 2t \\ \sin 2t \end{pmatrix}.$$

45. We have $\det(\mathbf{A} - \lambda\mathbf{I}) = (1 - \lambda)(\lambda^2 + 25) = 0$. For $\lambda_1 = 1$ we obtain

$$\mathbf{K}_1 = \begin{pmatrix} 25 \\ -7 \\ 6 \end{pmatrix}.$$

For $\lambda_2 = 5i$ we obtain

$$\mathbf{K}_2 = \begin{pmatrix} 1 + 5i \\ 1 \\ 1 \end{pmatrix}$$

so that

$$\mathbf{X}_2 = \begin{pmatrix} 1 + 5i \\ 1 \\ 1 \end{pmatrix} e^{5it} = \begin{pmatrix} \cos 5t - 5\sin 5t \\ \cos 5t \\ \cos 5t \end{pmatrix} + i \begin{pmatrix} \sin 5t + 5\cos 5t \\ \sin 5t \\ \sin 5t \end{pmatrix}.$$

Then

$$\mathbf{X} = c_1 \begin{pmatrix} 25 \\ -7 \\ 6 \end{pmatrix} e^t + c_2 \begin{pmatrix} \cos 5t - 5\sin 5t \\ \cos 5t \\ \cos 5t \end{pmatrix} + c_3 \begin{pmatrix} \sin 5t + 5\cos 5t \\ \sin 5t \\ \sin 5t \end{pmatrix}.$$

If

$$\mathbf{X}(0) = \begin{pmatrix} 4 \\ 6 \\ -7 \end{pmatrix}$$

then $c_1 = c_2 = -1$ and $c_3 = 6$.

46. We have $\det(\mathbf{A} - \lambda\mathbf{I}) = \lambda^2 - 10\lambda + 29 = 0$. For $\lambda_1 = 5 + 2i$ we obtain

$$\mathbf{K}_1 = \begin{pmatrix} 1 \\ 1 - 2i \end{pmatrix}$$

so that

$$\mathbf{X}_1 = \begin{pmatrix} 1 \\ 1 - 2i \end{pmatrix} e^{(5+2i)t} = \begin{pmatrix} \cos 2t \\ \cos 2t + 2\sin 2t \end{pmatrix} e^{5t} + i \begin{pmatrix} \sin 2t \\ \sin 2t - 2\cos 2t \end{pmatrix} e^{5t}.$$

and

$$\mathbf{X} = c_1 \begin{pmatrix} \cos 2t \\ \cos 2t + 2\sin 2t \end{pmatrix} e^{5t} + c_3 \begin{pmatrix} \sin 2t \\ \sin 2t - 2\cos 2t \end{pmatrix} e^{5t}.$$

If $\mathbf{X}(0) = \begin{pmatrix} -2 \\ 8 \end{pmatrix}$, then $c_1 = -2$ and $c_2 = 5$.

47.

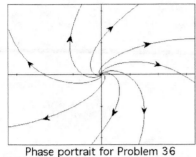

Phase portrait for Problem 36

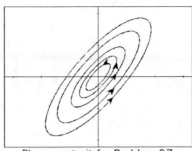

Phase portrait for Problem 37

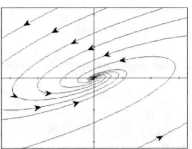

Phase portrait for Problem 38

48. (a) Letting $x_1 = y_1$, $x_1' = y_2$, $x_2 = y_3$, and $x_2' = y_4$ we have

$$y_2' = x_1'' = -10x_1 + 4x_2 = -10y_1 + 4y_3$$

$$y_4' = x_2'' = 4x_1 - 4x_2 = 4y_1 - 4y_3.$$

The corresponding linear system is

$$y_1' = y_2$$

$$y_2' = -10y_1 + 4y_3$$

$$y_3' = y_4$$

$$y_4' = 4y_1 - 4y_3$$

or

$$\mathbf{Y}' = \begin{pmatrix} 0 & 1 & 0 & 0 \\ -10 & 0 & 4 & 0 \\ 0 & 0 & 0 & 1 \\ 4 & 0 & -4 & 0 \end{pmatrix} \mathbf{Y}.$$

Using a CAS, we find eigenvalues $\pm\sqrt{2}\,i$ and $\pm 2\sqrt{3}\,i$ with corresponding eigenvectors

$$\begin{pmatrix} \mp\sqrt{2}\,i/4 \\ 1/2 \\ \mp\sqrt{2}\,i/2 \\ 1 \end{pmatrix} = \begin{pmatrix} 0 \\ 1/2 \\ 0 \\ 1 \end{pmatrix} + i \begin{pmatrix} \mp\sqrt{2}/4 \\ 0 \\ \mp\sqrt{2}/2 \\ 0 \end{pmatrix}$$

and

$$\begin{pmatrix} \pm\sqrt{3}\,i/3 \\ -2 \\ \mp\sqrt{3}\,i/6 \\ 1 \end{pmatrix} = \begin{pmatrix} 0 \\ -2 \\ 0 \\ 1 \end{pmatrix} + i \begin{pmatrix} \pm\sqrt{3}/3 \\ 0 \\ \mp\sqrt{3}/6 \\ 0 \end{pmatrix}.$$

Thus

$$
\mathbf{Y}(t) = c_1 \left[\begin{pmatrix} 0 \\ 1/2 \\ 0 \\ 1 \end{pmatrix} \cos \sqrt{2}\,t - \begin{pmatrix} -\sqrt{2}/4 \\ 0 \\ -\sqrt{2}/2 \\ 0 \end{pmatrix} \sin \sqrt{2}\,t \right]
$$

$$
+ c_2 \left[\begin{pmatrix} -\sqrt{2}/4 \\ 0 \\ -\sqrt{2}/2 \\ 0 \end{pmatrix} \cos \sqrt{2}\,t + \begin{pmatrix} 0 \\ 1/2 \\ 0 \\ 1 \end{pmatrix} \sin \sqrt{2}\,t \right]
$$

$$
+ c_3 \left[\begin{pmatrix} 0 \\ -2 \\ 0 \\ 1 \end{pmatrix} \cos 2\sqrt{3}\,t - \begin{pmatrix} \sqrt{3}/3 \\ 0 \\ -\sqrt{3}/6 \\ 0 \end{pmatrix} \sin 2\sqrt{3}\,t \right]
$$

$$
+ c_4 \left[\begin{pmatrix} \sqrt{3}/3 \\ 0 \\ -\sqrt{3}/6 \\ 0 \end{pmatrix} \cos 2\sqrt{3}\,t + \begin{pmatrix} 0 \\ -2 \\ 0 \\ 1 \end{pmatrix} \sin 2\sqrt{3}\,t \right] .
$$

The initial conditions $y_1(0) = 0$, $y_2(0) = 1$, $y_3(0) = 0$, and $y_4(0) = -1$ imply $c_1 = -\frac{2}{5}$, $c_2 = 0$, $c_3 = -\frac{3}{5}$, and $c_4 = 0$. Thus,

$$
x_1(t) = y_1(t) = -\frac{\sqrt{2}}{10} \sin \sqrt{2}\,t + \frac{\sqrt{3}}{5} \sin 2\sqrt{3}\,t
$$

$$
x_2(t) = y_3(t) = -\frac{\sqrt{2}}{5} \sin \sqrt{2}\,t - \frac{\sqrt{3}}{10} \sin 2\sqrt{3}\,t.
$$

(b) The second-order system is

$$
x_1'' = -10x_1 + 4x_2
$$

$$
x_2'' = 4x_1 - 4x_2
$$

or

$$
\mathbf{X}'' = \begin{pmatrix} -10 & 4 \\ 4 & -4 \end{pmatrix} \mathbf{X}.
$$

We assume solutions of the form $\mathbf{X} = \mathbf{V} \cos \omega t$ and $\mathbf{X} = \mathbf{V} \sin \omega t$. Since the eigenvalues are -2 and -12, $\omega_1 = \sqrt{-(-2)} = \sqrt{2}$ and $\omega_2 = \sqrt{-(-12)} = 2\sqrt{3}$. The corresponding eigenvectors are

$$
\mathbf{V}_1 = \begin{pmatrix} 1 \\ 2 \end{pmatrix} \quad \text{and} \quad \mathbf{V}_2 = \begin{pmatrix} -2 \\ 1 \end{pmatrix} .
$$

Then, the general solution of the system is

$$\mathbf{X} = c_1 \begin{pmatrix} 1 \\ 2 \end{pmatrix} \cos\sqrt{2}t + c_2 \begin{pmatrix} 1 \\ 2 \end{pmatrix} \sin\sqrt{2}t + c_3 \begin{pmatrix} -2 \\ 1 \end{pmatrix} \cos 2\sqrt{3}t + c_4 \begin{pmatrix} -2 \\ 1 \end{pmatrix} \sin 2\sqrt{3}t.$$

The initial conditions

$$\mathbf{X}(0) = \begin{pmatrix} 0 \\ 0 \end{pmatrix} \qquad \text{and} \qquad \mathbf{X}'(0) = \begin{pmatrix} 1 \\ -1 \end{pmatrix}$$

imply $c_1 = 0$, $c_2 = -\sqrt{2}/10$, $c_3 = 0$, and $c_4 = -\sqrt{3}/10$. Thus

$$x_1(t) = -\frac{\sqrt{2}}{10}\sin\sqrt{2}t + \frac{\sqrt{3}}{5}\sin 2\sqrt{3}t$$

$$x_2(t) = -\frac{\sqrt{2}}{5}\sin\sqrt{2}t - \frac{\sqrt{3}}{10}\sin 2\sqrt{3}t.$$

49. (a) From $\det(\mathbf{A} - \lambda\mathbf{I}) = \lambda(\lambda - 2) = 0$ we get $\lambda_1 = 0$ and $\lambda_2 = 2$. For $\lambda_1 = 0$ we obtain

$$\begin{pmatrix} 1 & 1 & | & 0 \\ 1 & 1 & | & 0 \end{pmatrix} \implies \begin{pmatrix} 1 & 1 & | & 0 \\ 0 & 0 & | & 0 \end{pmatrix} \quad \text{so that} \quad \mathbf{K}_1 = \begin{pmatrix} -1 \\ 1 \end{pmatrix}.$$

For $\lambda_2 = 2$ we obtain

$$\begin{pmatrix} -1 & 1 & | & 0 \\ 1 & -1 & | & 0 \end{pmatrix} \implies \begin{pmatrix} -1 & 1 & | & 0 \\ 0 & 0 & | & 0 \end{pmatrix} \quad \text{so that} \quad \mathbf{K}_2 = \begin{pmatrix} 1 \\ 1 \end{pmatrix}.$$

Then

$$\mathbf{X} = c_1 \begin{pmatrix} -1 \\ 1 \end{pmatrix} + c_2 \begin{pmatrix} 1 \\ 1 \end{pmatrix} e^{2t}.$$

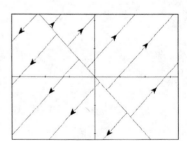

The line $y = -x$ is not a trajectory of the system.
Trajectories are $x = -c_1 + c_2 e^{2t}$, $y = c_1 + c_2 e^{2t}$ or
$y = x + 2c_1$. This is a family of lines perpendicular
to the line $y = -x$. All of the constant solutions
of the system do, however, lie on the line $y = -x$.

(b) From $\det(\mathbf{A} - \lambda\mathbf{I}) = \lambda^2 = 0$ we get $\lambda_1 = 0$ and

$$\mathbf{K} = \begin{pmatrix} -1 \\ 1 \end{pmatrix}.$$

A solution of $(\mathbf{A} - \lambda_1\mathbf{I})\mathbf{P} = \mathbf{K}$ is

$$\mathbf{P} = \begin{pmatrix} -1 \\ 0 \end{pmatrix}$$

so that

$$\mathbf{X} = c_1 \begin{pmatrix} -1 \\ 1 \end{pmatrix} + c_2 \left[\begin{pmatrix} -1 \\ 1 \end{pmatrix} t + \begin{pmatrix} -1 \\ 0 \end{pmatrix} \right].$$

All trajectories are parallel to $y = -x$, but $y = -x$ is not a trajectory. There are constant solutions of the system, however, that do lie on the line $y = -x$.

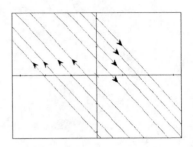

50. The system of differential equations is

$$x_1' = 2x_1 + x_2$$

$$x_2' = 2x_2$$

$$x_3' = 2x_3$$

$$x_4' = 2x_4 + x_5$$

$$x_5' = 2x_5.$$

We see immediately that $x_2 = c_2 e^{2t}$, $x_3 = c_3 e^{2t}$, and $x_5 = c_5 e^{2t}$. Then

$$x_1' = 2x_1 + c_2 e^{2t} \qquad \text{so} \qquad x_1 = c_2 t e^{2t} + c_1 e^{2t},$$

and

$$x_4' = 2x_4 + c_5 e^{2t} \qquad \text{so} \qquad x_4 = c_5 t e^{2t} + c_4 e^{2t}.$$

The general solution of the system is

$$\mathbf{X} = \begin{pmatrix} c_2 t e^{2t} + c_1 e^{2t} \\ c_2 e^{2t} \\ c_3 e^{2t} \\ c_5 t e^{2t} + c_4 e^{2t} \\ c_5 e^{2t} \end{pmatrix}$$

$$= c_1 \begin{pmatrix} 1 \\ 0 \\ 0 \\ 0 \\ 0 \end{pmatrix} e^{2t} + c_2 \left[\begin{pmatrix} 1 \\ 0 \\ 0 \\ 0 \\ 0 \end{pmatrix} t e^{2t} + \begin{pmatrix} 0 \\ 1 \\ 0 \\ 0 \\ 0 \end{pmatrix} e^{2t} \right]$$

$$+ c_3 \begin{pmatrix} 0 \\ 0 \\ 1 \\ 0 \\ 0 \end{pmatrix} e^{2t} + c_4 \begin{pmatrix} 0 \\ 0 \\ 0 \\ 1 \\ 0 \end{pmatrix} e^{2t} + c_5 \left[\begin{pmatrix} 0 \\ 0 \\ 0 \\ 1 \\ 0 \end{pmatrix} t e^{2t} + \begin{pmatrix} 0 \\ 0 \\ 0 \\ 0 \\ 1 \end{pmatrix} e^{2t} \right]$$

$$= c_1 \mathbf{K}_1 e^{2t} + c_2 \left[\mathbf{K}_1 t e^{2t} + \begin{pmatrix} 0 \\ 1 \\ 0 \\ 0 \\ 0 \end{pmatrix} e^{2t} \right]$$

$$+ c_3 \mathbf{K}_2 e^{2t} + c_4 \mathbf{K}_3 e^{2t} + c_5 \left[\mathbf{K}_3 t e^{2t} + \begin{pmatrix} 0 \\ 0 \\ 0 \\ 0 \\ 1 \end{pmatrix} e^{2t} \right].$$

There are three solutions of the form $\mathbf{X} = \mathbf{K}e^{2t}$, where $\mathbf{K}$ is an eigenvector, and two solutions of the form $\mathbf{X} = \mathbf{K}te^{2t} + \mathbf{P}e^{2t}$. See (12) in the text. From (13) and (14) in the text

$$(\mathbf{A} - 2\mathbf{I})\mathbf{K}_1 = \mathbf{0}$$

and

$$(\mathbf{A} - 2\mathbf{I})\mathbf{K}_2 = \mathbf{K}_1.$$

This implies

$$\begin{pmatrix} 0 & 1 & 0 & 0 & 0 \\ 0 & 0 & 0 & 0 & 0 \\ 0 & 0 & 0 & 0 & 0 \\ 0 & 0 & 0 & 0 & 1 \\ 0 & 0 & 0 & 0 & 0 \end{pmatrix} \begin{pmatrix} p_1 \\ p_2 \\ p_3 \\ p_4 \\ p_5 \end{pmatrix} = \begin{pmatrix} 1 \\ 0 \\ 0 \\ 0 \\ 0 \end{pmatrix},$$

so $p_2 = 1$ and $p_5 = 0$, while p_1, p_3, and p_4 are arbitrary. Choosing $p_1 = p_3 = p_4 = 0$ we have

$$P = \begin{pmatrix} 1 \\ 0 \\ 0 \\ 0 \\ 0 \end{pmatrix}.$$

Therefore a solution is

$$X = \begin{pmatrix} 1 \\ 0 \\ 0 \\ 0 \\ 0 \end{pmatrix} te^{2t} + \begin{pmatrix} 1 \\ 0 \\ 0 \\ 0 \\ 0 \end{pmatrix} e^{2t}.$$

Repeating for K_3 we find

$$P = \begin{pmatrix} 0 \\ 0 \\ 0 \\ 0 \\ 1 \end{pmatrix},$$

so another solution is

$$X = \begin{pmatrix} 0 \\ 0 \\ 0 \\ 1 \\ 0 \end{pmatrix} te^{2t} + \begin{pmatrix} 0 \\ 0 \\ 0 \\ 0 \\ 1 \end{pmatrix} e^{2t}.$$

51. From $x = 2\cos 2t - 2\sin 2t$, $y = -\cos 2t$ we find $x + 2y = -2\sin 2t$. Then

$$(x + 2y)^2 = 4\sin^2 2t = 4(1 - \cos^2 2t) = 4 - 4\cos^2 2t = 4 - 4y^2$$

and

$$x^2 + 4xy + 4y^2 = 4 - 4y^2 \qquad \text{or} \qquad x^2 + 4xy + 8y^2 = 4.$$

This is a rotated conic section and, from the discriminant $b^2 - 4ac = 16 - 32 < 0$, we see that the curve is an ellipse.

52. Suppose the eigenvalues are $\alpha \pm i\beta$, $\beta > 0$. In Problem 36 the eigenvalues are $5 \pm 3i$, in Problem 37 they are $\pm 3i$, and in Problem 38 they are $-1 \pm 2i$. From Problem 47 we deduce that the phase portrait will consist of a family of closed curves when $\alpha = 0$ and spirals when $\alpha \neq 0$. The origin will be a repellor when $\alpha > 0$, and an attractor when $\alpha < 0$.